HERBERT FEIGL and MAY BRODBECK
Editors
UNIVERSITY OF MINNESOTA

Readings in THE PHILOSOPHY OF SCIENCE

New York
APPLETON-CENTURY-CROFTS, INC.

5117-5

LIBRARY OF CONGRESS CARD
NUMBER: 53-6438

PRINTED IN THE UNITED STATES OF AMERICA

Preface

An adequate textbook in the Philosophy of the Sciences is badly needed but could hardly be written by a single scholar. The subject is vast, difficult, and undergoing rapid development. We have attempted to assemble some valuable material which, in the hands of able teachers and students, could serve as at least a "first approximation" to a good and up-to-date text. On the whole we have tried to avoid selections of either the utterly trivial or the forbiddingly difficult or too specialized kind. But between these two extremes there is a good deal of latitude. If the philosophy of science is taken seriously, then it is not to be expected that philosophical discussion of the more advanced and technical branches of a science can itself be elementary and wholly non-technical. It is true that the greater the scientific literacy of the reader, the more will he profit from these readings. As always, to him that hath shall be given. Happily, however, it is in the nature of the philosophy of science that in the course of its clarifications much purely scientific or factual material must also be presented. Therefore, in many of the essays on special branches of, say, physics, biology, or psychology, the student untrained in these fields will frequently find the minimum factual information he needs. Thus, our necessary decision to omit all purely expository scientific papers in favor of those explicitly philosophical will not, we believe, unduly handicap the reader who finds in himself gaps with regard to certain fields. Although the editors confess to a conviction that Science is on the whole a Good Thing, we have with stringent asceticism also omitted any primarily emotive and hortatory papers on this theme. Justification must, after all, wait on explanation. And the latter is what we hope our selections provide.

Sources were plentiful, as a glance at our Bibliography will testify, and principles of selection, though perhaps not as plentiful as blackberries, were plentiful enough. Our concern has been systematic rather than historical. Great Names have therefore sometimes been sacrificed in the interests of relevance to contemporary issues and a modern idiom that does not in itself present further barriers to an already difficult subject. Clarity of presentation and significance for specific, large problems and controversies in the field have been touchstones we have tried to apply in each case. In our labors of the last four years we have thoroughly combed the literature in philosophy of science; we have asked for and received valuable advice and suggestions from many expert colleagues in our field. We are indebted above all to our friend Professor Ernest Nagel for his patient and generous help and advice. Among others to whom we owe a debt of gratitude for advice and encouragement are Professors Rudolf Carnap, William H. Hay, Carl G. Hempel, and Julius R. Weinberg. Responsibility for the selections finally chosen is, of course, our own. Besides the many choices between equally desirable alternatives forced on us by limitations of space, the editors themselves were occasionally in friendly but adamant disagreement. Compromise and conciliation finally resolved, as they should, our differences. It particularly grieved us to be forced to omit some selections by authors from whom we had already obtained permission for reprinting. To these authors, we offer our very deeply felt apologies.

We have tried to provide a book of readings that will be useful on all levels of teaching. Instructors and students will be quick to pick out the more elementary selections with which a course of studies might begin. Intermediate and advanced materials provide richer food for the more robust appetite. Thus we believe that this anthology offers ample material for undergraduate courses as well as for graduate seminars in the philosophy of science.

We are grateful to the authors who permitted us to include some of their writings in this book as well as to their editors and publishers. Specific acknowledgements will be found on the first page of each selection.

Not all of the articles in this volume fall neatly and completely within the areas indicated by the headings of the eight sections of our table of contents. For example, the article by P. E. Meehl in Section VI may also well be used in connection with a discussion of laws and definitions in classical mechanics. Similarly the article by Bergmann and Spence in Section I contains much that is of interest for the methodology of psychology; and the article by Hempel and Oppenheim in Section IV has some relevance for the philosophy of biology. The article by MacCorquodale and Meehl in Section VI, while written by psychologists for psychologists, clearly bears on the question of concept formation generally, and is thus also of value to the philosophy of physics.

H. F.
M. B.

Contents

IV. THE LOGIC OF SCIENTIFIC EXPLANATION AND THEORY CONSTRUCTION

V. CAUSALITY, DETERMINISM, INDETERMINISM, AND PROBABILITY

VI. PHILOSOPHICAL PROBLEMS OF BIOLOGY AND PSYCHOLOGY

VII. PHILOSOPHY OF THE SOCIAL SCIENCES

VIII. EPILOGUE

INTRODUCTORY

The Nature and Function of the Philosophy of Science

MAY BRODBECK

IT WOULD BE hazardous to assume that all who speak of "philosophy of science" mean the same thing by it. The qualification "philosophy of" provides the initial cue that, whatever else it may be, the philosophy of science is a way of talking *about* science and is not a part of science itself, as physics, chemistry and biology are parts of science. Yet ambiguity remains, for science, either the process or the product, may be talked about in at least four different ways. Each of these reflects a different meaning of the phrase "philosophy of science". This book contains studies in the philosophy of science in only one of these meanings.

Science as an activity, like the law, the movies, the political system, is one social phenomenon among many others. The scientist's motives for doing what he does; the impact of his results on other phases of society; the converse effect of the social structure on the scientific enterprise, on its choice of problems and the conditions under which it works; all of these things can be made the subject of another investigation—the science of science. We need only set a scientist to observing his fellows. "Sociology of knowledge" and "history of ideas" are current names for this study, which is both interesting and important. It is fruitless to quarrel about words and it is true that when the layman reflects on these things, as in these times he frequently does, he thinks of himself as philosophizing about science. Yet, systematically, the science of science belongs to sociology and psychology, to the behavioral sciences. It is a way of engaging in scientific activity, rather than a way of talking about that activity. Hence, it is not a part of the philosophy of science.

Any and all cultural phenomena may be evaluated by the moralist, by the person who reflects on his or his society's value system, its implications, and the relevance of phenomena to it. Science is, of course, no exception. In fact, the growing prestige of the scientist, the increasing rôle of the scientific expert in social affairs, the strategic use by all sides in world diplomacy of the threat of new weapons, all make science of special concern to the reflective citizen and scientist. The citizen layman, feeling the force, far beyond gadgets and conveniences, of the impact of science on his life, begins to take stock of what man has wrought. The scientist, buying his prestige at the price of greater responsibility, is faced with moral problems beyond those he shares as citizen. Extolled today, he may be an object of suspicion and resentment tomorrow. In what ways and to what extent is the scientist responsible for the uses to which his knowledge is put? In what terms are the scientist and his special knowledge to be judged?

These are essentially ethical questions and as such not part of the philosophy of science itself. Yet moral evaluation of the relation of science to society must be made not only in terms of an ethical system but, if it is not to be irresponsible, also in terms of an understanding of the structure and meaning of science itself. To produce this understanding is the function of the Philosophy of Science.

The language of science, as all laymen know to their sorrow—and the specialist in one field is a layman with regard to most others—is not the same as our everyday language. Like everyone else, the scientist speaks of ordinary things, tables and chairs, clocks and rulers, minds and bodies; but in addition his language has names for entities and processes to which only he, in his probing way, has access, names which only he finds necessary in order to talk about the world, while the rest of us need never use them at all. Yet, we know, by their fruits, that these scientific words, like "electric current", "atom", "neutron", and "gene", are not mere nonsense syllables or the private language of an exclusive coterie. The entities they name in some way affect the experiences we all have and talk about in ordinary language. What is their relationship to this everyday world? What do they mean in terms of things everyone can see or hear? What is the logical, as contrasted with the practical, justification for introducing these esoteric elements into the world? The analysis of special scientific words or concepts is one large part of the task of the philosophy of science. The scientists, of course, partially do this themselves when they define their terms. But their definitions are usually of a restricted kind; a new scientific word is defined in terms of old ones. While this serves their purposes, it is still remote from common sense. It is generally the philosopher of science who exhibits the links in the chain, frequently very long, from abstract, technical words to concrete ordinary language. In particular, it is the philosopher of science who formulates the *principle* by which the chain is formed, that is, the logic of scientific concept formation.

The scientist uses in a rough and ready way notions of lawfulness, causality and probability. Concerned as he is with finding particular laws or specific causes for specific events, it is left for someone else to answer such questions as these: What exactly is meant by saying that one event is the cause of another? What precisely is the structure of a law of nature? How does such a law differ from so-called probability or statistical laws that preoccupy both physical and social scientists today? What is the nature of a scientific theory? How are concepts and laws related to it and to each other, and how are they all related to the world of experience? Science, we are told, uses now induction, now deduction; what is the nature of these methods, what is the difference between them? To answer such questions is an enterprise in logical analysis, an analysis which clarifies the basic ideas and methods of the sciences. It is thus an essential contribution to our knowledge, our knowledge about science, in contrast to knowledge within science, although much of the latter is needed before we can make this contribution. A scientist may also be a philosopher of science and sometimes he needs to be, as Einstein was and had to be when he philosophically clarified the notion of "non-local simultaneity". But, except for such "crises", when fundamental clarification is necessary before further progress can be made, the scientist works *within* his conceptual frame to formulate new truths, and does not philosophize *about* it.

Modern philosophy of science, thus construed, is a specialized part of analytical *philosophy*. Modern analytical philosophy is unlike traditional metaphysics in its rejection of the latter's implicit assumption that it is the philosopher's task to give supra-scientific descriptions and explanations of the nature of reality. On the other hand, it is continuous with classical metaphysics in its concern with the analysis and clarification of the nature of knowledge, reality, truth, and goodness. Without presupposition, it seeks to clarify what we mean when we common-sensically say that tigers exist, that chairs are real, or that honesty is good. The scientist, building on common sense, takes it for granted that his world is a real world, that other people and physical objects existing in it can be investigated by empirical methods, that knowledge is not a puzzle but a natural fact like digestion or love. Nor is it the philosopher-of-science's business to undermine or question this animal faith, since he is concerned to describe the structure of *science* itself. The task of the philosopher of science—the logical analysis of scientific concepts, laws, and theories—is not identical with that of the philosopher or epistemologist but is continuous with it. It is because of this continuity that so-called "Philosophy of Nature", the fourth meaning of "philosophy of science", is incompatible with our conception of that enterprise.

Cosmological speculations about the origin, nature, and purpose of the universe may be harmless, imaginative extrapolations from science itself. But the philosopher of nature's vaunted metaphysical explanations of the universe, allegedly cutting deeper than mere empirical scientific explanation, were so patently anthropomorphic and metaphorical as to beg all the issues that philosophers must analyze. By thus prejudging the metaphysical issues themselves they skirted rather than solved the philosophical problems. Such baldly speculative physics—all-encompassing generalizations about the universe as a whole, its "organismic" or its "dialectical" character—becomes especially preposterous when from its generalities one attempts to derive particular facts, as Schelling conjured forth the universe from A = A. Frequently, ethical conclusions are "deduced" from these imaginative constructions, as was the survival ethics of social Darwinism, or the various and mutually contradictory political conclusions drawn from the "dialectical" interpretations of natural processes. Then philosophy of nature is no longer harmless, for it provides the rationalization for a particular ethical or political ideology. Philosophy of science, as the ethically and philosophically neutral analysis, description, and clarification of the foundations of science, has thus nothing in common with philosophy of nature. It may, however, investigate the logical questions involved in that synthesis of the sciences which "philosophers of nature" sometimes attempt. Thus, of the four meanings of "philosophy of science"—the socio-psychological study of science; the moral evaluation of the scientist's rôle and knowledge; the philosophy of nature; the logical analysis of science—only the last is used here.

Most of the characteristic problems and methods of recent philosophy of science originated around the turn of the nineteenth century. Romanticism, including its "philosophy of nature", was the nineteenth century's reaction against the Enlightenment, its recoil from both reason and revolution. But the period's personality was split, for it witnessed also the strengthening of empiricist thought and the analytical temper, both spiritual descendants of the Age of Reason. At first, this second tendency was strong only in England, best represented by John Stuart Mill, whose *System of Logic* gave a systematic and comprehensive study of the logic and methods of science. But by the middle of the nineteenth century, the Continent saw a reaction away from the romantic successors of Kant, in particular from Schelling, Hegel, and their disciples. This reaction took the form of a return to the Kantian tradition of critical analysis of science, an analysis given a new turn, however, by the force of the empiricist tradition. Among those rising from either or both of these traditions, we naturally find some seminal minds in our field. After Mill, probably the most influential of these men were Hermann von Helmholtz, a German, and Ernst Mach, an Austrian. After the nineteenth-century stirrings, the turn of the century was a crucial period for the philosophy of science. It was a time of "crisis" in physics and in mathematics, and it saw the rise of the behavioral sciences.

The analysis which Helmholtz and others made of the nature of geometry, Mach's clarification of the concepts of Newtonian mechanics and, in particular, his critical analysis of the notion of absolute space were anticipations of the Einsteinian revolution. The negative results of the Michelson-Morley experiment for determining the existence of an ether reinforced Mach's critique and left physics in a state of crisis. The controversy over non-Euclidean geometries issued in a clarification of the distinction between the consistency and the applicability or truth of an axiomatic system. Henri Poincaré, a French mathematician, was one of those who emphasized that if Euclidean geometry is consistent, then so is non-Euclidean. With the advent of relativity theory, the status of non-Euclidean geometries and, more generally, the relationship between geometry and physics were no longer merely academic questions. At the beginning of the century, Planck formulated the quantum hypothesis, thus contributing to the crisis in physics and dramatically reshaping the problems of causation and probability.

One of the far-reaching results of Darwinism was to launch, at the same time the physical sciences were in ferment, the scientific study of man and society. As psychology became the science of behavior, it joined the ranks of the objective, natural sciences. Students of society also began self-conscious attempts to convert their fields into scientific disciplines. If man is made an object of scientific study, issues heretofore relevant only to inanimate matter have, of course, direct human and social impact. The rise of the behavioral sciences raises special complex problems regarding determinism and the nature of control and prediction. Given the social sciences as an accomplished fact, the senses in which we can speak of the unity of science or *the* system of the sciences can be clarified. Thus, the behavioral sciences join physics in pressing problems upon the philosopher of science.

Finally, the method and problems of recent philosophy of science were profoundly affected by the new developments in logic and mathematics. The discovery, also around the turn of the century, of paradoxes or contradictions in mathematics put it, like physics, in a state of crisis, and stimulated research into the foundations of mathematics. The new logic of Whitehead and Russell attempted to resolve this crisis and at the same time establish a foundation for mathematics in logic. With the rise of the new logic, axiomatization became a powerful tool of the philosophy of science. Although the usefulness for philosophy of the new logical techniques is still a controversial matter, many analytical philosophers consider them an indispensable tool for the resolution of philosophical puzzles. In this respect, too, philosophy of science is continuous with analytical philosophy. Because the philosophy of science is about science, it is not quite correct to speak of continuity between these two fields. Yet, because it *is* about science, new problems appear for the philosopher of science as the scientists invent new techniques and extend their knowledge. It is not strange, therefore, that in this age of science the philosophy of science is flourishing.

The Scientific Outlook: Naturalism and Humanism*

HERBERT FEIGL

An Essay on Some Issues of General Education and a Critique of Current Misconceptions Regarding Scientific Method and the Scientific Outlook in Philosophy

THE MAIN PURPOSE of this essay is to dispel certain confusions and misunderstandings which still prevent the much-needed constructive synthesis and mutual supplementation of the scientific and humanistic elements in general education. It is my contention that the philosophical foundations of both science and the humanities are widely misconceived; and that the frequently held claim of their basic incompatibilities arises out of philosophical prejudices which, owing to cultural lag, have unfortunately not as yet been completely relegated to oblivion. Science is still identified with an absurd mechanistic reductionism, but this is the caricature of science drawn by representatives of the humanities who are largely ignorant of the nature of modern science and also of the more recent scientific outlook in philosophy. The defenders of the humanities often enough increase the existing tension by holding an equally distorted view of the philosophical basis of the humanities.

The errors committed may well be characterized respectively as *reductive* and *seductive* fallacies. It is claimed that science either ignores (perhaps by its very method cannot help ignoring) or else explains away the most essential human values. Science is here charged with the reductive fallacy. Usually the same group of thinkers maintains also that there are aspects of the human mind, manifest especially in the domains of morality, religion, and the arts, which contain an irreducible spiritual element and for that reason will never be capable of explanation by the scientific method, no matter how far it advances. I call this fallacy seductive because it is usually committed by those who indulge in what William James called "tender-minded," that is, wishful and sentimental, thinking.

The impasse between seductive thesis and reductive antithesis can be overcome only by a constructive synthesis that retains and develops whatever valid suggestions or emphases we may discover underneath the

* Reprinted by kind permission of the editor from *American Quarterly*, 1, 1949.

grandiose verbiage of the first and the harsh austerities of the second. Neither a philosophy of the "Something More" nor a philosophy of the "Nothing But" will do for our time. Only an approach that is resolutely guided by the question "What is what?" will avoid reading mysteries into the facts, as well as refrain from impoverishing them by reduction to something less than experience attests them to be. Such a philosophical outlook, if not yet fully achieved, is fortunately very much in the making.

Especially in the melting pot of American thought, we find that the valuable elements of naturalism and humanism are gradually united in a new integration: the pragmatism of Peirce, James, Dewey, Mead, Otto, Kallen, and Hook; the naturalistic realism of Perry, Holt, R. W. Sellars, Drake, and Santayana; the scientific empiricism of Bridgman, Hull, Tolman, Lundberg, N. Wiener, P. Frank, C. Morris, Northrop, Carnap, Reichenbach, Nagel, and others; the liberal ("American Humanist") wing of Unitarianism. All these trends of thought and many others converge in a broad movement that one may well be tempted to regard as the twentieth-century sequel to the enlightenment of the eighteenth century.

The humanism held in common to a very large extent in these scientifically oriented philosophies is too well known to require an elaborate restatement. Suffice it to say that such human values as freedom and responsibility, rights and obligations, creative and appreciative capacities, are here disengaged from the theological and metaphysical ideologies that have traditionally pervaded their conception. Increasingly adequate and nonreductive analyses have been propounded in the last five or six decades. This reconstruction in philosophy has been and still is in the making. Under the impact of modern science philosophy is abandoning some of its earlier grandiose and overambitious claims in favor of a humbler and more useful function: the clarification of the foundations of knowledge and valuation. I shall now attempt to apply what seem to me to be the most important insights and suggestions of these currents of thought to the issues of general education.

Clearly nothing is more urgent for education today than a social philosophy that will be appropriate and workable in an age of science. Among the various prominent philosophies of education I mention first two currents which may be styled traditionalistic and which have on the whole either ignored the facts of the age of science or have tried (unsuccessfully, I think) to dispute and combat them: Neo-Thomism and Literary Humanism. Reliance on theological or metaphysical presuppositions makes these views incompatible with the modern scientific outlook. More definitely products of the modern scientific attitude are two other schools of thought: Dialectical Materialism, the official philosophy of Soviet Russia, but also fashionable in certain English scientific groups; and, scarcely worthy of being called a philosophy, the attitude of Vocationalism, quite prevalent in American education. The common element of these two views is their exclusive interest in the practical, technological applications of the natural and the social sciences. This, as well as other shortcomings, makes both points of view appear objectionable or at least badly in need of correction or supplementation. A much more acceptable position is that of Scientific Humanism. This view, at least in general outlook, is related to what is known as Progressivism or Reconstructionism in American education: a synthesis of the scientific attitude with an active interest in the whole scale of human values. Education in both the sciences *and* the humanities is the urgent need of our time. But how can these two aims properly be combined? The question reveals an uneasy feeling as to the compatibility of science and humanism.

Misunderstandings of the nature of science are primarily responsible for the appearance of incompatibility here. A proper historical and analytical perspective of the development of the scientific outlook and its distinctive traits as compared with prescientific and nonscientific attitudes helps to show that mankind achieves intellectual adulthood only with the scientific way of thinking.

Our age is still replete with remnants of and regressions to such prescientific thought patterns as magic, animism, mythology, theology, and metaphysics. The outstanding characteristics of modern scientific method are mostly absent or at best only adumbrated in those less mature phases of intellectual growth.

Criteria of the Scientific Method

What, then, are the basic characteristics of the scientific method? The often alleged difficulties of an adequate definition of science seem to me mainly a matter of terminology. We must first distinguish between pure mathematics as an exclusively formal-conceptual discipline, and the factual (or empirical, that is, the natural and the social-cultural) sciences. The certainty, complete exactitude, and necessity of pure mathematics depends precisely on its detachment from empirical fact. Mathematics as applied in the factual sciences merely lends its forms and deductive structures to the contents furnished by experience. But no matter how predominant mathematics may be in the formulations and derivations of empirical facts, factual knowledge cannot attain either the absolute precision or necessity of pure mathematics. The knowledge claimed in the natural and the social sciences is a matter of successive approximations and of increasing degrees of confirmation. Warranted assertibility or probability is all that we can conceivably secure in the sciences that deal with the facts of experience. It is empirical science, thus conceived as an unending quest (its truth-claims to be held only "until further notice"), which is under consideration here. Science in this sense differs only in degree from the knowledge accumulated throughout the ages by sound and common sense.

The aims of science are description, explanation, and prediction. The first aim is basic and indispensable, the second and third (closely related to each other) arise as the most desirable fruits of scientific labors whenever inquiry rises beyond the mere fact-gathering stage. History, often and nowadays quite fashionably declared an art, is scientific to the extent that it ascertains its facts concerning past events by a meticulous scrutiny of present evidence. Causal interpretation of these facts (in history, but similarly also in psychology, sociology, cultural anthropology, and economics) is usually much more difficult than, but in principle not logically different from, causal interpretation (that is, explanation) in the natural sciences. The aims of the pure (empirical) sciences are then essentially the same throughout the whole field. What the scientists are seeking are descriptions, explanations, and predictions which are as adequate and accurate as possible in the given context of research.

The quest for scientific knowledge is therefore regulated by certain standards or criteria which may best be formulated in the form of ideals to be approximated, but perhaps never fully attained. The most important of these regulative ideals are:

1. *Intersubjective Testability*. This is only a more adequate formulation of what is generally meant by the "objectivity" of science. What is here involved is not only the freedom from personal or cultural bias or partiality, but — even more fundamentally — the requirement that the knowledge claims of science be in principle capable of test (confirmation or disconfirmation, at the least indirectly and to some degree) on the part of any person properly equipped with intelligence and the technical devices of observation or experimentation. The term *intersubjective* stresses the social nature of the scientific enterprise. If there be any "truths" that are accessible only to privileged individuals, such as mystics or visionaries — that is, knowledge-claims which by their very nature cannot independently be checked by anyone else — then such "truths" are not of the kind that we seek in the sciences. The criterion of intersubjective testability thus delimits the scientific from the nonscientific activities of man.

Religious ecstasy, the elations of love, the inspiration of the artist, yes, even the flash of insight on the part of a scientific genius are not in themselves scientific activities. All these processes may eventually become subject matter for scientific study. But in themselves they do not validate knowledge-claims. They may, as in the case of the scientific intuition (or empathy in the psychological-cultural field) be instrumental in the generation of knowledge claims. But it is these knowledge-claims which have to be, first, formulated in an intersubjectively intelligible (or communicable) manner, and, second, subjected to the appropriate kind of tests in order to ascertain their validity. Beliefs transcending all possible tests by observation, self-observation, experiment, measurement, or statistical analysis are recognized as theological or metaphysical and therefore devoid of the type of meaning that we all associate with the knowledge-claims of common sense or factual science. From the point of view of the scientific outlook in philosophy it may be suggested that the sort of significance with which the in-principle-unconfirmable assertions of transcendent theology and metaphysics impress so many people is largely emotive. The pictorial, emotional, and motivational appeals of language, no matter how indispensable or valuable in the contexts of practical life, art, education, persuasion, and propaganda, must, however, not be confused with the cognitive meanings (purely formal- and/or factual-empirical) that are of the essence of science. Each type of significance has its function, and in most uses of language both are combined or even fused. The only point stressed here is that they must not be *con*fused, that is, mistaken for one another, if we wish to be clear as to what we are about.

2. *Reliability, or a Sufficient Degree of Confirmation.* This second criterion of scientific knowledge enables us to distinguish what is generally called "mere opinion" (or worse still, "superstition") from knowledge (well-substantiated belief). It may be considered as the delimitation of the scientific from the unscientific knowledge-claims. Clearly, in contrast to the first criterion, we face here a distinction of degree. There is no sharp line of demarcation between the well-confirmed laws, theories, or hypotheses of science, and the only poorly substantiated hunches and ideas-on-trial which may ultimately either be included in the corpus of scientific knowledge or else rejected as unconfirmed. Truth-claims which we repudiate as "superstition," and, quite generally, as judgments based upon hasty generalization or weak analogy (if they fulfill the criterion of testability), differ from what we accept as "scientific truth" in the extremely low degree of probability to which they are supported by the available evidence. Astrology or alchemy, for example, are not factually meaningless, but they are considered false to fact in that all available evidence speaks overwhelmingly against them. Modern techniques of experimentation and of statistical analysis are the most powerful tools we have in the discernment between chance and law and hence the best means of enhancing the reliability of knowledge.

3. *Definiteness and Precision.* This obvious standard of scientific method requires that the concepts used in the formulation of scientific knowledge-claims be as definitely delimited as possible. On the level of the qualitative-classificatory sciences this amounts to the attempt to reduce all border-zone vagueness to a minimum. On the level of quantitative science the exactitude of the concepts is enormously enhanced through the application of the techniques of measurement. The mensurational devices usually also increase the degree of objectivity. This is especially clear when they are contrasted with purely impressionistic ways of estimating magnitudes. Of course, there is no point in sharpening precision to a higher degree than the problem in hand requires. (You need no razor to cut butter.)

4. *Coherence or Systematic Structure.* This is what T. H. Huxley had in mind when he defined science as "organized common-sense." Not a mere collection of miscellaneous items of information, but a well-connected account of the facts is what we seek in science. On the descriptive level this results, for example, in systems of classification or division, in diagrams, sta-

tistical charts, and the like. On the explanatory levels of science sets of laws, or theoretical assumptions, are utilized. Explanation in science consists in the hypothetico-deductive procedure. The laws, theories, or hypotheses form the premises from which we derive logically, or logico-mathematically, the observed or observable facts. These facts, often belonging to heterogeneous domains, thus become integrated into a coherent, unifying structure. (Theological and metaphysical systems have, frequently enough, ambitiously tried to imitate this feature of science; but even if they succeeded in proceeding *more geometrico*, the important difference from science remains: they either lack testability or else reliability in the senses specified in our previous points.)

5. *Comprehensiveness or Scope of Knowledge.* This final point in our enumeration of criteria of science also characterizes scientific knowledge as different in degree (often enormously) from common-sense knowledge. Not only through bold and sweeping hypotheses, but especially through the ingenious devices by means of which they are tested, science acquires a reach far beyond the limits of our unaided senses. With telescopes, microscopes, spectroscopes, Geiger Counters, lie detectors, and the thousands of other contrivances of modern science we manage to amplify our senses and thus open up avenues of at least indirect access to the worlds of the very distant, the very large, the extremely small, or the disguised and concealed. The resulting increase in the completeness of our knowledge is, of course, popularly the most impressive feature of science. It must be kept in mind, however, that the scope thus achieved is a product of hard labor, and not to be confused with the sham completeness metaphysicians procure for their world pictures by verbal magic. Instead of presenting a finished account of the world, the genuine scientist keeps his unifying hypotheses open to revision and is always ready to modify or abandon them if evidence should render them doubtful. This self-corrective aspect of science has rightly been stressed as its most important characteristic and must always be kept in mind when we refer to the comprehensiveness or the unification achieved by the scientific account of the universe. It is a sign of one's maturity to be able to live with an unfinished world view.

The foregoing outline of the criteria of science has been set down in a somewhat dogmatic tone. But this was done only for the sake of brevity.[1] The spirit behind it is that of a humble account of what, I think, an impartial and elaborate study of the history of thought from magic to science would reveal. In any case, these criteria seem unquestionably the guiding ideals of present-day empirical science. They may therefore be used in a definition of science as we understand this term today. It seems rather useless to speculate about just what this term, by a change of meaning, might come to connote in the future.

It should be remembered that the criteria listed characterize the *pure*

[1] A thorough discussion of the logical, epistemological, methodological, and historical issues connected with the criteria would require a whole book, not just another essay.

factual (empirical) sciences. The aims of the *applied* sciences — the technologies, medicine, social and economic planning, and others — are practical control, production, guidance, therapy, reform, and so forth. Responsible activity in the application of science clearly presupposes information which is fairly well substantiated by the methods of the pure sciences. (These remarks intend to draw merely a logically important distinction. The obvious practical interpenetration and important mutual fertilization of the pure and the applied disciplines is of course not denied here.)

Critique of Misconceptions

Having indicated at least in broad outline the nature of scientific method we may now turn to the critique of some of the misconceptions to which it is all too commonly exposed. In what follows, a dozen typical charges against science are stated and answered consecutively.[2]

Science arises exclusively out of practical and social needs and has its only value in serving them in turn. (Dialectical Materialism and Vocationalism)

While this is important it does not tell the whole story. Science has always also been the pursuit of knowledge, the satisfaction of a deep-rooted curiosity. It should be recognized as one of the cultural values along with art, literature, and music. Better teaching of the sciences and their history can redress the balance. Fuller utilization of results and suggestions from the history and the philosophy of science would give the student a deeper appreciation of the evolution of scientific knowledge and of the scientific point of view. Through proper instruction, the student could be led to rediscover some of the important results of science. The intellectual gratification that comes with a grasp of the order of nature, with the understanding of its processes by means of laws and theories, is one of the most powerful incentives in the pursuit of pure knowledge.

Science cannot furnish a secure basis for human affairs since it is unstable. It changes its views continually. (Traditionalism)

While there is constant evolution, and occasionally a revolution, in the scientific outlook, the charge is a superficial (usually journalistic) exaggeration. The typical progress of science reveals that later views often contain much of the earlier views (to the extent that these have stood the test of repeated examination). The more radical or revolutionary changes usually amount to a revision of the conceptual frame of a scientific discipline. The criticism often also presupposes other sources of certainty which will simply not bear critical scrutiny. The quest for absolute certainty is

[2] These charges are not straw men. In more than twenty years of reading, listening, teaching, and argument I have encountered them again and again in Europe and just as frequently in this country. If space permitted and time were less valuable, I could quote many well-known writers in connection with each charge.

an immature, if not infantile, trait of thinking. The best knowledge we have can be established only by the method of trial and error. It is of the essence of science to make such knowledge as reliable as is humanly and technically possible.

Science rests on uncritical or uncriticized presuppositions. It validates its outlook by its own standards. It therefore begs the question as regards alternative approaches for settling problems of knowledge and action.

Science has been clarifying and revising its basic assumptions throughout its development. Particularly since the beginning of the modern age and still more intensively since the beginning of our century, an increasing awareness of, and critical attitude toward, the fundamental presuppositions has been most fruitfully applied in the repudiation of dogmatic prejudices and in the articulation of the conceptual frame of scientific method. It can be shown (through logical analysis) that the procedure of science is the only one we are *certain* will yield the results (reliable knowledge, that is, valid explanation and predictions) *if* such results can at all be achieved. Any alleged rival method — theology, metaphysics, mysticism, intuition, dialectics — if it made any contributions at all could not be examined and appraised on any basis other than the usual inductive criteria of science. Generally, it seems that these alleged alternatives do not even aim primarily at knowledge but, like the arts, at the enrichment of experience. They may therefore more properly be said to be *non*-scientific, rather than *un*scientific.

Science distorts the facts of reality. In its Procrustean manner it introduces discontinuities where there is continuity (and vice versa). The abstractions and idealizations used in science can never do justice to the richness and complexities of experience.

Since the task of science is to discover reliable and precise knowledge of what happens under what conditions, it always tries to approximate the facts as closely as the problem on hand requires and permits. Both continuity and discontinuity can be formulated mathematically and be given an adequate formulation only with the help of modern mathematics.

Science can deal only with the measurable and therefore tends to "explain away" that which it cannot measure.

While measurement is eminently desirable in order to enhance the precision and objectivity of knowledge, it is not indispensable in many branches of science or, at least, on their more qualitative levels of analysis. Science does not explain away the qualities of experience. It aims at, and often succeeds in, making these qualities more predictable.

Science never explains, it merely describes the phenomena of experience. The reality beyond the appearances is also beyond the reach of science.

This is partly a terminological issue and partly a result of the (traditional but most misleading and useless) metaphysical distinction between appearance and reality. In the sense in which the word *explaining* is used in common life, science *does* explain facts — it deduces them from laws or theoretical assumptions. Questions which are in principle incapable of being answered by the scientific method turn out, on closer analysis, not to be questions of knowledge. They are expressions of emotional tensions or of the wish for soothing (or exciting) experience.

Science and the scientific attitude are incompatible with religion and the religious attitude.

If by religion one refers to an explanation of the universe and a derivation of moral norms from theological premises, then indeed there is logical incompatibility with the results, methods. and general outlook of science. But if religion means an attitude of sincere devotion to human values, such as justice, peace, relief from suffering, there is not only no conflict between religion and science but rather a need for mutual supplementation.

Science is responsible for the evils and maladjustments of our civilization. It is creating ever more powerful weapons of destruction. The employment of scientific techniques in the machine age has contributed to the misery, physical and mental, of the multitudes. Moreover, the biological facts of evolution imply the negation of all morality: the law of the jungle.

These are particularly superficial charges. It is the social-political-economic structure of a society that is responsible for these various evils. Scientific knowledge itself is socially and morally neutral. But the manner in which it is applied, whether for the benefit or to the detriment of humanity, depends entirely on ourselves. Scientists are becoming increasingly aware that they, even more than the average citizen, have to work for enlightenment toward the proper use of knowledge. The facts and theories of evolution have been construed in many ways as regards their implications for ethics. Julian Huxley reads them very differently from the way his grandfather Thomas Henry did.[3] It should be easy to see that the forces active on the level of human civilization and intelligent communal life are not completely reducible to those involved in the ruthless struggle for survival.

The ethical neutrality of scientific truth and the ivory tower situation of the pure researcher is apt to generate an attitude of indifference toward the pressing problems of humanity.

Only maladjusted individuals are unable to combine the detachment

[3] Compare Julian Huxley, *Touchstone for Ethics* (Harper, 1947); but see also C. D. Broad, "Review of Julian S. Huxley's Evolutionary Ethics" (*Mind, 53,* 1944), reprinted in H. Feigl and W. Sellars, *Readings in Philosophical Analysis* (Appleton-Century-Crofts, 1949).

necessary for the pursuit of truth with an ardent interest in the improvement of the condition of humanity.

Scientific method, while eminently successful in the explanation, prediction, and control of physical phenomena, is distinctly less successful in regard to the facts of organic life and almost altogether hopeless in the mental and social realm. The methods of the physical sciences are essentially mechanistic (if not materialistic) and therefore reductionistic; they cannot do justice to the complex organismic, teleological, and emergent features of life and mind.

"Scientism" as a slogan of criticism and reproach is very fashionable these days. It is true that some scientists and especially some of the popularizers of science have indulged in reductive fallacies of various sorts. But the true scientific spirit as exemplified in some of the foremost researchers is free from that impatience and simple-mindedness that tries to finish the unfinished business of science by hasty speculation. Admittedly, there are tremendous problems yet to be solved. On the other hand what method is there but the method of science to solve them? Explanations of the mechanistic type (in *one* sense of the term) have been abandoned even in physics. But mechanistic explanation in the wider sense of a search for law (deterministic or statistical) is still the indispensable procedure of all sciences that have gone beyond the purely classificatory level. Organic wholeness, teleology, and emergence can be understood, if at all, only by causal analysis on the usual empirical basis. Purposiveness and freedom of choice, far from being incompatible with causality, presuppose causal order.

The methods of science can never replace the intuitive insight or empathic understanding of the practical psychologist, psychiatrist, cultural anthropologist, or historian. This claim is made particularly wherever the object of knowledge is the individual, the unique and unrepeatable.

It is only through the scientific method that the validity and reliability of the intuitive approach can be gauged. There is, on this ground, some doubt as to its more exaggerated claims. However, there is nothing in the principles of scientific method that would deny the occasional, or even frequent, efficacy of intuitive judgments based, as they must be, on a rich (but often not articulated) background of experience in the given field. Aside from the mere artistic contemplation of the unique and individual, knowledge, in the proper sense of the word, always means the subsumption of the specific case under general concepts or laws. This holds in the social sciences just as much as in the natural sciences.

Science cannot determine values. Since scientific knowledge can (at best) find out only what is the case, it can, by its very nature, never tell what ought to be.

This final challenge often comes from theology or metaphysics. It usually maintains that questions of aims, goals, and ideals cannot be settled by the methods of science but rather require recourse either to divine revelation, the voice of conscience, or some metaphysical a priori truths. The answer to this in a scientific age would seem to be that a mature mankind should be able to determine its own value standards on the basis of its needs, wants, and the facts of the social condition of man. But it is true that science cannot dictate value standards. It can, as in social psychology, ascertain the actual evaluations of groups and individuals, study their compatibilities and incompatibilities, and recommend (that is *applied* science!) ways and means of harmonizing conflicting evaluations. True enough, in many of the urgent issues that confront us, we do not possess enough scientific knowledge to warrant a course of action. This means that we have to act, as so often in life, on the highest probabilities available even if these probabilities be low in themselves. But such estimates of probabilities will still be made most reliable by the scientific method. Common life experience and wisdom, when freed from its adherence to prescientific thought patterns, is not fundamentally different from scientific knowledge. In both we find the procedure of self-correction, so essentially needed if knowledge is to be a guide for action. There is an important common element in mature thinking (as we find it in science) and mature social action (as we find it in democracy): progress arises out of the peaceful competition of ideas as they are put to intersubjective test. Cooperative planning on the basis of the best and fullest knowledge available is the only path left to an awakened humanity that has embarked on the adventure of science and civilization.

The scientific view of the world that we have characterized and defended against criticisms from various quarters may with historical and terminological justice be called Naturalism.[4] It differs from mechanistic materialism (too often a mere straw man put up by theologians or idealistic metaphysicians) in that it steers clear of reductive fallacies. If uninformed persons insist on viewing science as essentially materialistic and the humanities as essentially idealistic (not to say spiritualistic) the hopes of fruitful collaboration of both fields in education are slim indeed. But science, properly interpreted, is not dependent on any sort of metaphysics. It merely attempts to cover a maximum of facts by a minimum of laws. On the other side, a mature humanism requires no longer a theological or metaphysical frame either. Human nature and human history become progressively understood in the light of advancing science. It is therefore no longer justifiable to speak of science *versus* the humanities. Naturalism *and* humanism should be our maxim in philosophy and in education. A Scientific Humanism emerges as a philosophy holding considerable promise for mankind — *if* mankind will at all succeed in growing up.

[4] It should scarcely need mentioning that this meaning of naturalism has only a distant and tenuous relation to the other meaning in which it is applied to a certain type of literature.

I

THE NATURE OF SCIENTIFIC METHOD

Does Science Have Metaphysical Presuppositions? *

ARTHUR PAP

SUPPOSE AN HONORABLE citizen who prides himself of perfect soberness and rationality becomes so ecstatic over the ideal life which he thinks he lives that he decides to write an ode to soberness. Naturally, he deprecates, in that ode, the sentimental way of living. It may be expected that the sentimentalists, in reading his ode, will smile and whisper into one another's ears "isn't he sentimental about soberness and rationality, though!" Many a metaphysician of our time reacts to the positivistic worship of science, which is usually accompanied by contempt for metaphysics, somewhat the way the sentimentalists would react to that ode to soberness and rationality: the scientists themselves are metaphysicians, they say, only they are not aware of their own metaphysical presuppositions.

In evaluating this pretty bold claim, our first task will be to unfold the various meanings of the word "presupposition". Being human, one might say, presupposes the possession of two legs; or, legal marriage presupposes the attainment of a certain specified age. It is easy to see that in uses of this sort "presupposition" means "necessary condition": p presupposes $q =_{df} p$ implies q, or, which is the same, not $-q$ implies not $-p$. On the other hand, when we say "p presupposes q" we certainly do not mean that q is a sufficient condition for p. Nobody would say that having two legs presupposes being human, for we know that it is not necessary to be human for that; one might be a bird, for example. It would be mistaken, therefore, to conceive of the relation of a presupposition to those propositions which somehow rest on it as of the relation of premiss to conclusion: it is the consequence which is presupposed by the premiss, in the sense that the premiss cannot be true *unless* the consequence is true, not the other way around. Let us, now, pick out a proposition which a metaphysician might claim to be presupposed by science without nonetheless belonging to science: the principle of causality, in the simple form "every event has a cause." Could it be said that any specific causal law, such as "a deficient

* Excerpted and reprinted by kind permission of the author and the publisher from Arthur Pap, *Elements of Analytic Philosophy*, Ch. 16. The Macmillan Company, copyright 1949.

supply of vitamin B causes poor eyesight," presupposes this principle? Surely not, for "some events are uncaused" is certainly consistent with "this event has a cause." Let us try another proposition which a follower of Kant might wish to call a presupposition of empirical science: there are physical constants. Well, by an elementary rule of deductive inference, a singular statement of the form "this has the property P" entails the existential statement "there are things that have the property P." Now, physicists have discovered many physical constants: the acceleration of gravity is a constant near the surface of the earth, the atomic weight of an element is a constant, the quantity PV/T, calculated for a mol of an ideal gas, is a constant (called "the universal gas constant"), etc. Unless there were physical constants, none of these statements could be true, hence it is correct to say that they presuppose the existence of physical constants. Only, we cannot help asking why such a presupposition should be called "metaphysical"? Is any existential statement that has been verified by a singular scientific statement a metaphysical truth? Are we talking metaphysics, then, when we say "there are reptiles," "there are gases that are lighter than air," etc.? If not, how would those who believe that science is built on metaphysical foundations distinguish the metaphysical consequences of scientific propositions from those consequences that are likewise to be classified as scientific propositions?

However, there are other senses of the verb "to presuppose," maybe no less common than the one just discussed. One might say, for example, that analytical mechanics presupposes the calculus. Does this mean that the laws of mechanics would have to be abandoned if, say, the rules of integration turned out one day to be infected with a fatal inconsistency? Not quite, for it might be possible to establish the laws of mechanics without the help of the integral calculus. Thus, once the constancy of the acceleration of gravity is experimentally established, the law "$s = \frac{1}{2}gt^2$" may be derived from the definitions of acceleration and velocity as time-derivatives by merely applying the rules of integration in two successive steps. However, if the calculus should become unavailable as an instrument of deduction, the proportionality of fallen height to the square of the time of fall could still be verified by experiment. In this usage, then, the fact that *q* is presupposed by *p* does not imply that the falsity of *q* entails the falsity of *p*. What is meant is rather this: if *q* were false, then the belief in *p* would cease to be grounded, since *q* belonged to the premisses or to the rules of inference on the basis of which *p* was inferred. *q*, here, is not a necessary condition for *p*, since *p* might still be true even though *q* is false; in fact, while a belief in *p* may have been partially grounded in the assumed truth of *q*, one could still have good reasons for believing *p* to be true if *q* were false. The relationship designated by "x presupposes y" in this usage is, indeed, none other than the relation of an inferred conclusion to a part of its premisses. The fact that all men are mortal is neither a sufficient condition nor a necessary condition for the fact that, say, Jesus Christ is mortal. It is not a sufficient condition since one would moreover have to be agreed that Jesus Christ was a man, and it is not a necessary condition, since obviously the mortality of Christ would be consistent with the immortality of some men. Still, somebody might argue against the credibility of the divinity of Christ by referring to the fact that all men are bound to die, whereupon, logically speaking, two alternative rebuttals would be open to the orthodox believer: he could say "you presuppose in your argument that all men are mortal" or "you presuppose in your argument that Jesus Christ was human, which I deny, holding him to be divine."

This is also the sense in question when it is said that some sciences presuppose others. In deriving physical laws from certain selected physical axioms, the physicist uses the truths of Euclidean geometry, for example, as (for the most part unexpressed) premisses, and in this sense physics may be said to presuppose geometry. But this does not mean that the physical propositions derived with the help of geometry would necessarily be false if the propositions of geometry turned out to be false. If I calculate the magnitude of a certain force from the magnitudes of its rectangular vector components by using the Pythagorean theorem, and the latter turned out to be false, my calculation would, indeed, become unfounded. But inasmuch as the derived proposition of measurement could be verified without the use of the Pythagorean theorem, the truth of the latter is not a necessary condition for the truth of the former. It is evidently also in this sense that logic is presupposed by all the sciences: if we have no good reason for believing the principles of inference to be true, then we have no good reason for believing any proposition known by inference only to be true, no matter what subject-matter the inferred proposition may be about. To be sure, any empirical proposition presupposes the principles of logic also in the first sense of "presupposition," the sense of necessary condition: for the negation of a logical truth is a contradiction, and a contradiction entails any proposition, hence also the negation of any given empirical proposition.

Now, it is conceivable that this is the sense of "presupposition" that is intended when it is said that science makes metaphysical presuppositions. Consider such principles as "all physical magnitudes are continuous functions" or "if several laws are consistent with the data of measurement, the simplest law is the true law." The first principle—which, by the way, progressive metaphysicians, aware of the discontinuities disclosed by quantum physics, would not wish to defend any more—might be said to express a *reason* for the possibility of the graphical procedure of representing physical magnitudes by coordinates and numerical laws connecting diverse physical magnitudes by continuous curves. Obviously, if it were false—and we know nowadays that it is false, since energy can be radiated only in integral multiples of the so-called "elementary quantum of action"—all physical laws believed to be true might still be true. All we can say is that if it were not for the assumption of its truth, the scientist would be less confident in the application of the graphical method of determining numerical laws. The same is to be said of the second of the above mentioned principles. Whatever the scientist's reasons may be for believing in the simplicity of nature, this belief itself is certainly a circumstance which partially explains what he actually does—why, for example, he ascribes deviations from the simple law to errors arising from a variety of sources, and assumes unhesitatingly that we would see perfect order were we only perfect observers. However, it is important to distinguish the beliefs whose verification is the goal of scientific inquiries from the beliefs which the scientist *expresses* by his activities and which motivate his behavior as scientist. A striking example is the so-called principle of uniformity "same cause, same effect": it has been remarked that if an experiment, designed to prove a generalization "if A, B, C, then D", is repeated several times under varied conditions, it is in order to make sure that A, B, C really are the essential conditions on which the effect D depends, and that the appearance of such a dependence was not due to some "accidental" circumstance. But it would never occur to the scientist for a moment that the mere place or time of the experiment could make any difference to the effect; a law formulated as "other things being equal, then, if A, B, C then D" is to be read as "other things being equal, then for any time and for any place, if A, B, C then D." This conviction of the causal irrelevancy of mere position in space and time [1] explains why the scientist often regards one or two experiments as sufficient proof for a very general conclusion. Obviously, there would be an absurdity in the undertaking of a series of experiments for the purpose of verifying the causal irrelevancy of mere spatial and temporal position. And one might say that "same cause, same effect" is a belief, tacitly adhered to by the scientist, which explains the scientist's behavior, particularly the confidence with which he generalizes from a small number of experiments.

But here again we must ask: what additional information is conveyed, if it is said that such beliefs which the scientist manifests by what he does are "metaphysical"? Is any belief which motivates scientific procedure and which is not itself subjected to empirical test to be called "metaphysical"? Is it, then, a metaphysical belief that events are predictable, or that they obey simple laws? But that there is a simple relation, say, between the angle of incidence and the angle of reflection of a light ray, or that an inflation after a long war is predictable—these are not metaphysical beliefs? In that case a "metaphysical" belief seems to amount simply to a very *general* belief. Now, nobody would deny that men would behave differently if they changed certain general beliefs more or less unconsciously entertained; why should it be otherwise with the sort of behavior we call "scientific inquiry"? If the metaphysicians who deny that science stands on its own feet mean anything as obviously true as this, why not say so? Nobody could seriously disagree with them.

[1] See Keynes, *Treatise on Probability*, chaps. 19, 22.

Once again, the distinction between logical analysis and psychology must be emphasized. As logical analysts we are interested in clarifying the nature of scientific assertions and the methods by which scientific assertions are validated. This need not at all prevent us from being also interested in the *psychology* of scientific inquiry, the various motivating forces that impel the scientists to do what they do. However, we should not confuse these entirely different pursuits that might attract the spectator of science. It is one thing to say that the firm belief in a "deterministic universe," let us say, motivated Laplace to perfect astronomy with mathematical tools. It is different to contend that the propositions of astronomy logically depend on the validity of such sweeping beliefs.

These considerations suggest a third sense of "presupposition" which, in contrast to the other senses mentioned so far, is perhaps more psychological than logical. Assuming that a man's behavior is purposive rather than blind, we can infer from the way he behaves that he holds such and such beliefs, inasmuch as it would not be rational for him to act the way he acts unless he held those beliefs. Thus, from the mere fact that a lawyer in court cross-questions a certain witness we may infer that the lawyer believes the witness may be able to produce convincing, or at least relevant, evidence. The belief in question is a *causal condition* of the lawyer's behavior; unless the lawyer held that belief, he would behave differently. If an onlooker said "the lawyer *presupposes* that . . .", this is undoubtedly what he would mean: unless the lawyer believed . . . to be true, his actions would be pointless, irrational. Suppose, now, a philosopher made the following comment on the behavior of lawyers in court: "all lawyers presuppose the principle that convincing evidence may be produced by the procedure of cross-questioning witnesses. Unlike such propositions as 'Mr. X committed the murder' or 'Mr. X was run over by the car without premeditation' this principle is never debated in any court session; it is just taken for granted, all judicial investigations are based on it, and it is therefore a metaphysical presupposition of legal practice." If one wonders what additional information is conveyed by the grand conclusion that this proposition is a "metaphysical" presupposition, one should likewise wonder what information is conveyed by such statements as "it is a metaphysical presupposition of science that the world is predictable, that there is, for any observed coexistence of properties or sequence of events, a law which explains it, etc." For all these propositions merely express beliefs or hopes which motivate the scientist to do what he does.

The belief that physics is built on certain *a priori* principles which are a genuine source of physical knowledge and not just corollaries from definitions, is by no means original with Kant. Perhaps the most noteworthy of those alleged *a priori* principles is the so-called "principle of sufficient reason" or its counterpart, the "principle of insufficient reason." Many a rationalistically minded scientist thought that several of the established laws of physics could be proved, without experiment, solely from the principle that nothing happens without a sufficient reason. Here are two sample uses of this principle: (a) if the lever arms of two suspended weights are equal and the weights themselves are equal, then there is no reason why the lever should incline one way rather than another; hence it stands to reason that it must remain in equilibrium; (b) if no external forces act upon a body in uniform motion, then there is no reason why the body's motion should change, in magnitude or direction, in one way rather than another; hence it stands to reason that a body in uniform motion will remain in uniform motion unless acted upon by an external force. It requires little sagacity to detect the tacit *empirical* assumptions in these arguments. How do we know what sort of facts are relevant or sufficient reasons for a given effect and what sorts of facts are irrelevant or insufficient reasons? Suppose one of the equal lever arms were yellow and the other blue. This difference would be dismissed as irrelevant with regard to the question whether the lever will be in equilibrium or if not, to which side it would incline. Why? Because *experience* has taught us that such differences make no difference, while differences in weight and differences in lever arm do make a difference. Again, how do we know that the only relevant reason for an acceleration is the action of an unbalanced external force? How do we know that whether or not an acceleration occurs does not depend on the material of which the moving body is made, or on its volume, or on its density? As Hume emphasized, causal connections can be known only empirically, not by *a priori* reasoning. And the principle of sufficient reason, which Leibniz and other rationalists made so much fuss about, thus reduces to the useless truism: if experience has shown that a change in A is the only sufficient condition for a change in B, then we may expect that B will remain unchanged if A remains unchanged.

Let us, now, discuss in some detail the question whether the inductive methods by which scientific conclusions are established involve certain general assumptions about the constitution of nature which cannot, on pain of circularity, be inductively justified. In analyzing these methods frequent use will be made of the notions of necessary and sufficient condition, and it might therefore be in order to remind the reader of their definitions. A property P is a sufficient condition for a property Q, if Px implies, for every x, Qx; and R is a necessary condition for Q, if Qx implies, for every x, Rx. It follows from these definitions that if in any instance P is present while Q is absent, then P cannot be a sufficient condition for Q; and if in any instance Q is present while R is absent, then R cannot be a necessary condition for Q. It is on these corollaries from the definitions of a necessary and of a sufficient condition that the *eliminative* methods of induction are based. Suppose the problem is to discover a sufficient condition for a certain disease (here the property Q is, of course, fairly complex).[2] The first

[2] As was explained earlier in this book, the word "cause" is thoroughly ambiguous. Hence more clarity is gained if we speak of an inquiry into the sufficient conditions, or the necessary conditions, of a characteristic, instead of speaking of a "causal" inquiry.

step in the inquiry will consist in the enumeration of possible sufficient conditions: either P is a sufficient condition, or P' or P'' . . . or P^n. Obviously, if any definite conclusion is to be reached, $n-1$ alternatives must be eliminated by experimental procedures. If a situation is observed or experimentally produced in which Q is absent and P present, we may conclude that P is not a sufficient condition for Q; if in a given case Q is absent and P' is present, then, again by definition, P' cannot be a sufficient condition for Q, and so on. In this manner inductive methods enable us to reach negative conclusions. But how could a positive conclusion be reached? Showing that in a given instance, or even in several instances, the presence of Q attends the presence of P, is a far cry from establishing the law "for every x, Px implies Qx." This is the reason why a sufficient condition must be discovered indirectly by eliminating all but one of the antecedently plausible hypotheses, i.e. by finding negative instances. But suppose the class of possible sufficient conditions were infinite; in that case no positive conclusion could be reached by the eliminative method. The same considerations apply if what is to be discovered is a necessary condition for Q. Here alternative hypotheses as to R, R', . . . R^n being a necessary condition may be eliminated by verifying propositions of the form "there is an x, such that Qx and not R^ix"; and here also direct verification is impossible since no finite number of observations could establish the law "for every x, Qx implies Rx." But unless the number of alternative necessary conditions is finite and known, no demonstrative induction from the data is possible.

In actual experimental practice, of course, it is never doubted that only a small, and in fact enumerable, set of circumstances is causally *relevant* to an observed effect. In the formulation of a law the scientist often inserts the phrase "ceteris paribus" (other things being equal). If this phrase were taken literally, no law that has been confirmed by one instance could ever be applied to any new instance; for in saying there is a new instance we just imply that some of the circumstances are different. But what the scientist actually means by the phrase is "if all *relevant* circumstances are the same, then . . ." For example, consider the physical law "if a projectile is fired at such an angle and with such a momentum, then, other things being equal, it will reach such a maximum height." Here a shift of the experimental scene from the North Pole to the equator, or the breaking in of a hurricane, would be considered relevant changes, while it would be considered as an irrelevant circumstance who fired the projectile, or whether the sky at the time of the experiment was blue or partly cloudy. The distinction, then, between relevant and irrelevant circumstances, and the assumption that only a finite and knowable number of circumstances are relevant, are implicitly taken for granted by the practicing scientist. Nevertheless, the philosopher seems to be burdened with a difficult theoretical question: how, if at all, can such assumptions be justified? It is quite likely that philosophers who insist that science rests on metaphysical foundations of which the practicing scientists are no more aware than argumentative people are commonly aware of the logical principles which they constantly take for granted, mean to refer to such assumptions in terms of which inductive procedures are rationalized. And since these assumptions seem, on pain of circularity, to be themselves incapable of inductive justification, it is concluded that they are metaphysical *a priori* propositions.

A famous formulation of this principles of the finitude of relevant factors is Keynes' "principle of the limitation of independent variety." [3] Following Keynes' terminology, let us, in explaining this principle, use the concepts of the positive analogy and the negative analogy between a set of individuals. The positive analogy consists in the properties which all the individuals have (in other words, it is the class of respects in which they resemble each other), the negative analogy consists in the properties which differ from individual to individual. The positive analogy, then, is roughly what makes us regard the individuals as members of the same class, and the negative analogy is what makes us regard them as *different* members of the same class. The positive analogy, now, may be divided into two subclasses: the properties constituting the chosen basis of classification and the properties constituting the inferred analogy. For example, with regard to the generalization "all birds build nests for their young," the properties defining a bird would make up the former subclass, and the property of building nests for the young would be the inferred analogy. As Keynes conceives it, the method of observing more and more confirming instances in order to strengthen the generalization, is at bottom an eliminative method; that is, its purpose is to eliminate members of the positive analogy disregarded by the generalization as candidates to the title of properties that are relevant to the presence of the inferred analogy. For example, if the sample of birds we had observed to build nests were all inhabitants of a cold climate, we might conceivably conjecture that they build nests for protection from cold; in other words, we might suspect that nest building is a property that depends not only on the nature of a bird but also on variable circumstances such as climate. We would then endeavor to observe birds in a hot climate as well, with the result that this part of the positive analogy (living in a cold climate) is seen to be really irrelevant to the presence of the inferred analogy. Putting it into formal terms, the following seems to be involved in the procedure of strengthening a generalization by observing more instances: Suppose the generalization has the form "Fx and $F'x$ . . . F^nx implies Gx"; and suppose K, K' . . . K^m is the remaining positive analogy between the instances observed so far. If we subsequently observe an instance verifying the proposition "there is an x, such that Fx and $F'x$ . . . and F^nx and not Kx and Gx," we have established that K belongs to the negative analogy of the total class of individuals to which the generalization applies, in other words, that K was an irrelevant point of similarity; the same may be progressively shown for K' . . . K^m. If it could be shown, then one would have established that the properties men-

[3] See Keynes, *Treatise on Probability*, chap. 22.

tioned in the antecedent of the generalization are jointly sufficient for the presence of the inferred analogy. At any rate this analysis would explain why the probability of a generalization increases with the number of confirming instances only provided the negative analogy is increased by this multiplication of instances. It would also explain why the experimenter endeavors to vary the presumably unessential conditions as much as possible in repeating an experiment: at one stroke, so to speak, the negative analogy might be considerably increased, in which case the probability of finding a counter-instance to the generalization would sink rapidly. The greater the number of resemblances explicitly stated in the antecedent of the generalization, the greater the antecedent probability of the generalization (assuming, of course, the complexity of the inferred analogy remains constant). This also harmonizes with the fact that a generalization would be irrefutable if its antecedent mentioned the entire positive analogy of the instances upon which it is based; for in that case ("perfect analogy," as Keynes calls it) there could be no further instance to which the generalization is applicable, and the generalization would have no predictive content at all.

But what if the negative analogy between the members of a class were infinite? What, in other words, if the disregarded positive analogy between the members of an initially observed subclass were infinite? In that case we would never increase the probability of a generalization one bit by increasing the known negative analogy, it would be like trying to increase the value of a quotient whose denominator is infinity by increasing the value of the numerator. Hence, in order to rationalize our inductive procedures we have to make the assumption that nature is not constituted that way, that the group of (logically and causally) independent properties that vary from instance to instance of a natural kind is always limited; this is the principle of the limitation of independent variety.

Now, it seems pretty clear that the sense in which such a postulate is "presupposed" by inductive procedures—specifically the procedure by which one attempts to increase the probability of a generalization—is the psychological/pragmatic sense discussed in the first section of this chapter. That is, what scientists do would be unreasonable if they did not believe that the number of circumstances that might possibly be relevant to the production of a given phenomenon is limited. And, indeed, if the universe were so constituted that everything in it made a difference to everything else, experimental science would be a wholly unreasonable undertaking. Any purposive activity, of course, involves the belief that the means employed will lead up to the desired result; thus inductive science involves the belief that the eliminative methods employed will increase the antecedent probability [4] of a suggested hypothesis. But here again the question

[4] What postulates about the constitution of nature are required to justify the assumption that a hypothesis has a finite probability prior to its confirmation, is a further question whose discussion we omit. The reader may be referred to C. D. Broad's articles on "Probability and Induction," in *Mind*, 1918, 1920.

must be raised: what additional information is conveyed if these beliefs are characterized as "metaphysical"? Does this mean that their objects are *a priori* propositions? But they clearly are not analytic, for nothing is more easily conceived than a universe in which there are no independent, finite causal systems—in which, to pick one or two illustrations, the quantitative proportions in which chemical elements combine varied with the positions of the planets, or the acceleration of falling bodies varied with the temperature and chemical composition of the falling bodies. To be sure, in a completely chaotic universe in which no conjunction of properties and no sequence of events ever repeated itself there would be no *kinds* at all, since the concept of a kind involves the concept of similarity. Hence it might be argued that such a universe could not be described at all since our language is through and through *general,* every designative word in it referring to a *kind* of thing. Still, such a universe could be described as one which makes the application of what we call "language" impossible; since this is by no means a self-contradictory conception, the proposition that our universe admits of dissection into independent causal systems is not analytic.

But, it will be asked, how can such a proposition be justified at all if it is not capable of *a priori* demonstration? Well, the suggestion is worth considering that such a proposition is empirical if it has any specific content at all. The physicist verifies that all he needs to know in order to predict the acceleration a body will undergo in a given situation is the mass of the body and the forces acting on it; as long as these factors are constant the same acceleration is observed no matter how the other aspects of the situation vary. Hence he concludes, generalizing over all possible situations in which an acceleration might occur, that acceleration is uniquely determined by mass and force. Again, a psychologist verifies that the flow of saliva in a dog's mouth occurs whenever the dog is confronted with a stimulus which in his past experience was associated with the smell of food; hence he generalizes and asserts that the dog's response is uniquely determined by the mentioned conditions. Thus a firm belief is generated in the experimental scientist's mind that the production of any natural phenomenon depends on the values of a surveyable finite number of variables. By calling the object of this belief a "metaphysical" proposition one may intend to call attention to its great generality. As we have just seen, the confirming instances of this generalization are themselves generalizations, viz. natural laws asserting the dependence of an effect on a finite number of conditions. Whether such propositions of a high degree of generality, obtained by implicit generalization from specific inductive results but never themselves explicitly subjected to inductive test, should be called "metaphysical" is a terminological question which some may deem important, and some may not. It is moreover arbitrary whether one regards such generalizations as testable scientific propositions or as generalities which prove fascinating only to philosophers. The position would be taken that if a scientist experimentally confirms a specific causal law he indirectly also confirms the generality, discussed by philosophers outside of the laboratory, that all phenomena are subject to causal laws. On the other hand, one might argue that there can be no scientific proposition that does not belong to any specific science; in that case one will favor the denomination "metaphysical" for such generalities. But howsoever these terminological quarrels be resolved, the fact remains that such a proposition is empirical in the sense that it asserts what might conceivably not be the case and derives whatever credibility it may have from observations and inductive inferences drawn therefrom.

Finally, we should bear in mind that an inductive justification of an inductive principle is circular only if that principle has to be assumed in *every* context of inductive inquiry. Thus, if I defined an inductive argument as an argument of the form "*p;* therefore it is probable (or probable to the degree c) that *q*," I obviously could not inductively justify inductive arguments in general, if this means to offer an inductive argument which establishes it as probable that a proposition *q* is sometimes probable on some specified evidence *p*. Or again, as Hume pointed out, if by an inductive inference we mean an inference of the form "A has been accompanied by B in the past; therefore it will continue to be accompanied by B in the future," it would be circular to "justify" the implicit belief in the uniformity of nature by arguing "in the past nature has been uniform; therefore it will continue to be uniform in the future." On the other hand, it happens all the time that a principle which has been highly confirmed in past inquiries comes to function as a practically unquestioned assumption in future inquiries; and if we forget the empirical background of the principle we might be tempted to regard it as a necessary or *a priori* truth, a genuinely metaphysical presupposition of scientific procedures. To illustrate this point, let us examine a specific postulate that seems to be involved in the procedure of deriving (inductively) numerical laws or laws of functional dependence from a set of measurements.

"If C be a smallest sufficient condition of E, and if there is at least one instance in which a certain determinate value c of C is accompanied by a certain determinate value e of E, then in *every* instance in which C has the value of c, E will have the value e." This is what C. D. Broad proposes to call the "Postulate of the *Uniqueness of the Determinate Total Effect.*"[5] Suppose C were a conjunction of properties $C_1.C_2.C_3$; then it would be what Broad calls a "smallest sufficient condition" of E if neither $C_1.C_2$. nor any other part of it were a sufficient condition of E (in other words, it must involve no redundancy). To grasp the meaning of this postulate, let us substitute definite physical magnitudes for the variables "C" and "E." E might be the volume of an ideal gas and C the correlated (i.e. simultaneous) pressure and absolute temperature. According to the postulate, if we once found that the values c_1 and c_2 of pressure and absolute tempera-

[5] See "The Principles of Demonstrative Induction" (II), *Mind*, vol. 39 (1930), p. 426.

ture respectively were accompanied by the value e of the volume, and if pressure and temperature are the only variables relevant to the determination of volume, we may infer that the volume will always have the value e whenever the pressure has the value c_1 and the temperature has the value c_2. Such unique determination is then expressed by the mathematical notation "$V = f(P,T)$". Now, everybody who reflects a little on the procedures of experimental physics (or of any other experimental science in which mathematical tools are applied) will see that this postulate is, indeed, assumed. To be sure, the physicist usually takes more than one measurement of a determinate value c and the correlated determinate value e. But we know why he indulges in such repetitions: it is in order to average out accidental errors, from whichever sources these errors be estimated to arise. In other words, he takes several measurements because he is not sure that his first measurement revealed the *true* values of the magnitudes C and E at the time of measurement and under the assumed conditions. But once he is fairly certain that his data are correct, he unhesitatingly generalizes in the form of writing down a functional equation connecting the measured magnitudes in a definite mathematical way. He would not for a moment consider the possibility that with regard to the same gas at a different time, or with regard to a different gas at the same time, or with regard to a different gas at a different time, the value c should be accompanied by a different value than e.

Suppose, now, the question were raised how this postulate of unique determination is to be justified. Is there any *a priori* justification for it? Waiving the possibility that some apostles of the infallibility of intuition should rush in and claim it to be self-evident, there is only one way in which an *a priori* justification might be attempted: reduction to a definitional truth. As was mentioned before, the concept of unique determination is a defining element of the very concept of a *function*. In saying that E is a function of C, we just mean to say that to every value of C there corresponds one and only one value of E; hence it would be self-contradictory to say, on the one hand, that E is a function of C, and, on the other hand, that while at one time c was accompanied by e, at another time it was accompanied by e′. In a similar way, one might attempt to prove the more qualitative principle "same cause, same effect" from the definition of "cause": it is inconsistent to assume that A (which we may imagine to be a complex of conditions $a_1.a_2.a_3$) is the cause of B, and that A might in a given instance be attended by an effect different from B; for if the latter happened, A would *by definition* not be the cause of B, but at best a "partial cause" (for example, the total cause might be the complex $a_1.a_2.a_3.a_4$). Yet seductive as such *a priori* justifications are, they are nothing but evasions. It is true, indeed, that by the word "cause" we mean a set of conditions which uniquely determines a given effect; if we find the same set of conditions to be attended, in different instances, by different effects, we refuse application of the terms "the cause" to it; or at least we would say "it's only a partial cause." But then we merely have to rephrase the principle, thus: "if the same *conditions* will be realized again, they will be accompanied by the same effect," and the contingent character of the principle becomes obvious. What now remains in need of inductive justification is the belief that the concept of cause, defined in terms of the concept of unique determination, is *applicable:* a universe without cause-effect relations is a logically possible universe. Similarly, once we have inductively verified that $E = f(C)$, it follows, of course, analytically that c will never be accompanied by any other value than e. But what needs to be inductively justified is the belief that physical magnitudes functionally depend on each other, in other words, that the mathematical concept of functional dependence is applicable to physical magnitudes. It is logically possible as well as intuitively conceivable that there should be no regularity at all in the way physical magnitudes such as volume and pressure of a gas vary with each other, in which case we would find simply no application for the concept of functional dependence.

As it stands, Broad's postulate is, indeed, analytic. It has the logical form: if *p*, then (if *q*, then r). But the consequent of this implication really defines the antecedent. To say that C is a smallest sufficient condition is to say that if the values of $C_1 \ldots C_n$ (and no less than that) are given *at any time*, then the value of E can be calculated and will always be the same when the values of $C_1 \ldots C_n$ are the same. And to say that the values of E accompanying the same values of $C_1 \ldots C_n$ vary at different times, is the same as saying that a knowledge of the values of $C_1 \ldots C_n$ is *insufficient* to predict the value of E. But what remains synthetic, then, is the proposition that *there are* smallest sufficient conditions in the sense defined. This is the sort of *pragmatic* presupposition which was discussed above, and which is frequently called a *leading principle* of inductive inquiry.

These basic beliefs, however, can be inductively justified without circularity. Nature happens to be so constituted that its course can be described by functional equations; and it is because scientists always found nature to be constituted that way that they came to develop the mathematical language of functionally connected variables. In any experimental inquiry *now*, to be sure, they betray their belief in uniformity by the very nature of their questions: in asking, for example, "what is the period of a pendulum a function of?", the physicist evidently presupposes that the period is uniquely determined by something or other. But only a minimum of psychology should be necessary to see that these scientific habits are the product of ever repeated experiences of uniformity. And it is noteworthy that the only way Kant succeeded in proving that nature *must* be uniform was by *defining* "nature" as "the existence of things in so far as it is *determined according to universal laws*."

The Logic of Modern Physics*

P. W. BRIDGMAN

WHATEVER MAY BE one's opinion as to our permanent acceptance of the analytical details of Einstein's restricted and general theories of relativity, there can be no doubt that through these theories physics is permanently changed. It was a great shock to discover that classical concepts, accepted unquestioningly, were inadequate to meet the actual situation, and the shock of this discovery has resulted in a critical attitude toward our whole conceptual structure which must at least in part be permanent. Reflection on the situation after the event shows that it should not have needed the new experimental facts which led to relativity to convince us of the inadequacy of our previous concepts, but that a sufficiently shrewd analysis should have prepared us for at least the possibility of what Einstein did.

Looking now to the future, our ideas of what external nature is will always be subject to change as we gain new experimental knowledge, but there is a part of our attitude to nature which should not be subject to future change, namely that part which rests on the permanent basis of the character of our minds. It is precisely here, in an improved understanding of our mental relations to nature, that the permanent contribution of relativity is to be found. We should now make it our business to understand so thoroughly the character of our permanent mental relations to nature that another change in our attitude, such as that due to Einstein, shall be forever impossible. It was perhaps excusable that a revolution in mental attitude should occur once, because after all physics is a young science, and physicists have been very busy, but it would certainly be a reproach if such a revolution should ever prove necessary again.

New Kinds of Experience Always Possible

The first lesson of our recent experience with relativity is merely an intensification and emphasis of the lesson which all past experience has also taught, namely, that when experiment is pushed into new domains, we must be prepared for new facts, of an entirely different character from

* Reprinted by kind permission of the author and the publisher from P. W. Bridgman, *The Logic of Modern Physics*, pp. 1–25. The Macmillan Company, copyright 1928.

those of our former experience. This is taught not only by the discovery of those unsuspected properties of matter moving with high velocities, which inspired the theory of relativity, but also even more emphatically by the new facts in the quantum domain. To a certain extent, of course, the recognition of all this does not involve a change of former attitude; the *fact* has always been for the physicist the one ultimate thing from which there is no appeal, and in the face of which the only possible attitude is a humility almost religious. The new feature in the present situation is an intensified conviction that in reality new orders of experience do exist, and that we may expect to meet them continually. We have already encountered new phenomena in going to high velocities, and in going to small scales of magnitude: we may similarly expect to find them, for example, in dealing with relations of cosmic magnitudes, or in dealing with the properties of matter of enormous densities, such as is supposed to exist in the stars.

Implied in this recognition of the possibility of new experience beyond our present range, is the recognition that no element of a physical situation, no matter how apparently irrelevant or trivial, may be dismissed as without effect on the final result until proved to be without effect by actual experiment.

The attitude of the physicist must therefore be one of pure empiricism. He recognizes no *a priori* principles which determine or limit the possibilities of new experience. Experience is determined only by experience. This practically means that we must give up the demand that all nature be embraced in any formula, either simple or complicated. It may perhaps turn out eventually that as a matter of fact nature can be embraced in a formula, but we must so organize our thinking as not to demand it as a necessity.

The Operational Character of Concepts

Einstein's Contribution in Changing Our Attitude Toward Concepts

Recognizing the essential unpredictability of experiment beyond our present range, the physicist, if he is to escape continually revising his attitude, must use in describing and correlating nature concepts of such a character that our present experience does not exact hostages of the future. Now here it seems to me is the greatest contribution of Einstein. Although he himself does not explicitly state or emphasize it, I believe that a study of what he has done will show that he has essentially modified our view of what the concepts useful in physics are and should be. Hitherto many of the concepts of physics have been defined in terms of their properties. An excellent example is afforded by Newton's concept of absolute time. The following quotation from the Scholium in Book I of the *Principia* is illuminating:

I do not define Time, Space, Place or Motion, as being well known to all. Only I must observe that the vulgar conceive those quantities under no other notions but from the relation they bear to sensible objects. And thence arise certain prejudices, for the removing of which, it will be convenient to distinguish them into Absolute and Relative, True and Apparent, Mathematical and Common.

(1) Absolute, True, and Mathematical Time, of itself, and from its own nature flows equably without regard to anything external, and by another name is called Duration.

Now there is no assurance whatever that there exists in nature anything with properties like those assumed in the definition, and physics, when reduced to concepts of this character, becomes as purely an abstract science and as far removed from reality as the abstract geometry of the mathematicians, built on postulates. It is a task for experiment to discover whether concepts so defined correspond to anything in nature, and we must always be prepared to find that the concepts correspond to nothing or only partially correspond. In particular, if we examine the definition of absolute time in the light of experiment, we find nothing in nature with such properties.

The new attitude toward a concept is entirely different. We may illustrate by considering the concept of length: what do we mean by the length of an object? We evidently know what we mean by length if we can tell what the length of any and every object is, and for the physicist nothing more is required. To find the length of an object, we have to perform certain physical operations. The concept of length is therefore fixed when the operations by which length is measured are fixed: that is, the concept of length involves as much as and nothing more than the set of operations by which length is determined. In general, we mean by any concept nothing more than a set of operations; *the concept is synonymous with the corresponding set of operations.* If the concept is physical, as of length, the operations are actual physical operations, namely, those by which length is measured; or if the concept is mental, as of mathematical continuity, the operations are mental operations, namely those by which we determine whether a given aggregate of magnitudes is continuous. It is not intended to imply that there is a hard and fast division between physical and mental concepts, or that one kind of concept does not always contain an element of the other; this classification of concept is not important for our future considerations.

We must demand that the set of operations equivalent to any concept be a unique set, for otherwise there are possibilities of ambiguity in practical applications which we cannot admit.

Applying this idea of "concept" to absolute time, we do not understand the meaning of absolute time unless we can tell how to determine the absolute time of any concrete event, *i.e.*, unless we can measure absolute time. Now we merely have to examine any of the possible operations by which we measure time to see that all such operations are relative operations. Therefore the previous statement that absolute time does not exist is replaced by the statement that absolute time is meaningless. And in making this statement we are not saying something new about nature, but are merely bringing to light implications already contained in the physical operations used in measuring time.

It is evident that if we adopt this point of view toward concepts, namely that the proper definition of a concept is not in terms of its properties but in terms of actual operations, we need run no danger of having to revise our attitude toward nature. For if experience is always described in terms of experience, there must always be correspondence between experience and our description of it, and we need never be embarrassed, as we were in attempting to find in nature the prototype of Newton's absolute time. Furthermore, if we remember that the operations to which a physical concept are equivalent are actual physical operations, the concepts can be defined only in the range of actual experiment, and are undefined and meaningless in regions as yet untouched by experiment. It follows that strictly speaking we cannot make statements at all about regions as yet untouched, and that when we do make such statements, as we inevitably shall, we are making a conventionalized extrapolation, of the looseness of which we must be fully conscious, and the justification of which is in the experiment of the future.

There probably is no statement either in Einstein or other writers that the change described above in the use of "concept" has been self-consciously made, but that such is the case is proved, I believe, by an examination of the way concepts are now handled by Einstein and others. For of course the true meaning of a term is to be found by observing what a man does with it, not by what he says about it. We may show that this is the actual sense in which "concept" is coming to be used by examining in particular Einstein's treatment of simultaneity.

Before Einstein, the concept of simultaneity was defined in terms of properties. It was a property of two events, when described with respect to their relation in time, that one event was either before the other, or after it, or simultaneous with it. Simultaneity was a property of the two events alone and nothing else; either two events were simultaneous or they were not. The justification for using this term in this way was that it seemed to describe the behavior of actual things. But of course experience then was restricted to a narrow range. When the range of experience was broadened, as by going to high velocities, it was found that the concepts no longer applied, because there was no counterpart in experience for this absolute relation between two events. Einstein now subjected the concept of simultaneity to a critique, which consisted essentially in showing that the operations which enable two events to be described as simultaneous involve measurements on the two events made by an observer, so that "simultaneity" is, therefore, not an absolute property of the two events and nothing else, but must also involve the relation of the events to the observer. Until therefore we have experimental proof to the contrary, we must be prepared to find that the simultaneity of two events depends on their relation to the observer, and in particular on their velocity. Einstein, in thus analyzing what is involved in making a judgment of simultaneity, and in seizing on the act of the observer as the essence of the situation, is actually adopting a new point of view as to what the concepts of physics should be, namely, the operational view.

Of course Einstein actually went much further than this, and found precisely how the operations for judging simultaneity change when the observer moves, and obtained quantitative expressions for the effect of the motion of the observer on the relative time of two events. We may notice, parenthetically, that there is much freedom of choice in selecting the exact operations; those which Einstein chose were determined by convenience and simplicity with relation to light beams. Entirely apart from the precise quantitative relations of Einstein's theory, however, the important point for us is that if we had adopted the operational point of view, we would, before the discovery of the actual physical facts, have seen that simultaneity is essentially a relative concept, and would have left room in our thinking for the discovery of such effects as were later found.

Detailed Discussion of the Concept of Length

We may now gain further familiarity with the operational attitude toward a concept and some of its implications by examining from this point of view the concept of length. Our task is to find the operations by which we measure the length of any concrete physical object. We begin with objects of our commonest experience, such as a house or a house lot. What we do is sufficiently indicated by the following rough description. We start with a measuring rod, lay it on the object so that one of its ends coincides with one end of the object, mark on the object the position of the other end of the rod, then move the rod along in a straight line extension of its previous position until the first end coincides with the previous position of the second end, repeat this process as often as we can, and call the length the total number of times the rod was applied. This procedure, apparently so simple, is in practice exceedingly complicated, and doubtless a full description of all the precautions that must be taken would fill a large treatise. We must, for example, be sure that the temperature of the rod is the standard temperature at which its length is defined, or else we must make a correction for it; or we must correct for the gravitational distortion of the rod if we measure a vertical length; or we must be sure that the rod is not a magnet or is not subject to electrical forces. All these precautions would occur to every physicist. But we must also go further and specify all the details by which the rod is moved from one position to the next on the object—its precise path through space and its velocity and acceleration in getting from one position to another. Practically of course, precautions such as these are not mentioned, but the justification is in our experience that variations of procedure of this kind are without effect on the final result. But we always have to recognize that all our experience is subject to error, and that at some time in the future we may have to specify more carefully the acceleration, for example, of the rod in moving from one position to another, if experimental accuracy should be so increased as to show a measurable effect. In *principle* the operations by which length is measured should be *uniquely* specified. If we have more than one set of operations, we have more than one concept, and strictly there should be a separate name to correspond to each different set of operations.

So much for the length of a stationary object, which is complicated enough. Now suppose we have to measure a moving street car. The simplest, and what we may call the "naïve" procedure, is to board the car with our meter stick and repeat the operations we would apply to a stationary body. Notice that this procedure reduces to that already adopted in the limiting case when the velocity of the street car vanishes. But here there may be new questions of detail. How shall we jump on to the car with our stick in hand? Shall we run and jump on from behind, or shall we let it pick us up from in front? Or perhaps does now the material of which the stick is composed make a difference, although previously it did not? All these questions must be answered by experiment. We believe from present evidence that it makes no difference how we jump on to the car, or of what material the rod is made, and that the length of the car found in this way will be the same as if it were at rest. But the experiments are more difficult, and we are not so sure of our conclusions as before. Now there are very obvious limitations to the procedure just given. If the street car is going too fast, we can not board it directly, but must use devices, such as getting on from a moving automobile; and, more important still, there are limitations to the velocity that can be given to street cars or to meter sticks by any practical means in our control, so that the moving bodies which can be measured in this way are restricted to a low range of velocity. If we want to be able to measure the length of bodies moving with higher velocities such as we find existing in nature (stars or cathode particles), we must adopt another definition and other operations for measuring length, which also reduce to the operations already adopted in the static case. This is precisely what Einstein did. Since Einstein's operations were different from our operations above, *his "length" does not mean the same as our "length."* We must accordingly be prepared to find that the length of a moving body measured by the procedure of Einstein is not the same as that above; this of course is the fact, and the transformation formulas of relativity give the precise connection between the two lengths.

Einstein's procedure for measuring the length of bodies in motion was dictated not only by the consideration that it must be applicable to bodies with high velocities, but also by mathematical convenience, in that Einstein describes the world mathematically by a system of coördinate geometry, and the "length" of an object is connected simply with quantities in the analytic equations.

It is of interest to describe briefly Einstein's actual operations for measuring the length of a body in motion; it will show how operations which may be simple from a mathematical point of view may appear complicated from a physical viewpoint. The observer who is to measure the length of a moving object must first extend over his entire plane of reference (for simplicity the problem is considered two-dimensional) a system of time coördinates, *i.e.*, at each point of his plane of reference there must be a clock, and all these clocks must be synchronized. At each clock an observer must be situated. Now to find the length of the moving object at a specified instant of time (it is a subject for later investigation to find whether its length is a function of time), the two observers who happen to coincide in position with the two ends of the object at the specified time on their clocks are required to find the distance between their two positions by the procedure for measuring the length of a stationary object, and this distance is by definition the length of the moving object in the given reference system. This procedure for measuring the length of a body in motion hence involves the idea of simultaneity, through the simultaneous position of the two ends of the rod, and we have seen that the operations by which simultaneity are determined are relative, changing when the motion of the system changes. We hence are prepared to find a change in the length of a body when the velocity of the measuring system changes, and this in fact is what happens. The precise numerical dependence is worked out by Einstein, and involves other considerations, in which we are not interested at present.

The two sorts of length, the naïve one and that of Einstein, have certain features in common. In either case in the limit, as the velocity of the measuring system approaches zero, the operations approach those for measuring the length of a stationary object. This, of course, is a requirement in any good definition, imposed by considerations of convenience, and it is too obvious a matter to need elaboration. Another feature is that the operations equivalent to either concept both involve the motion of the system, so that we must recognize the possibility that the length of a moving object may be a function of its velocity. It is a matter of experiment, unpredictable until tried, that within the limits of present experimental error the naïve length is not affected by motion, and Einstein's length is.

So far, we have extended the concept of length in only one way beyond the range of ordinary experience, namely to high velocities. The extension may obviously be made in other directions. Let us inquire what are the operations by which we measure the length of a very large object. In practice we probably first meet the desirability of a change of procedure in measuring large pieces of land. Here our procedure depends on measurements with a surveyor's theodolite. This involves extending over the surface of the land a system of coördinates, starting from a base line measured with a tape in the conventional way, sighting on distant points from the extremities of the line, and measuring the angles. Now in this extension we have made one very essential change: the angles between the lines connecting distant points are now angles between beams of light. We assume that a beam of light travels in a straight line. Furthermore, we assume in extending our system of triangulation over the surface of the earth that the geometry of light beams is Euclidean. We do the best we can to check the assumptions, but at most can never get more than a partial check. Thus Gauss [1] checked whether the angles of a large terrestrial triangle add to two right angles and found agreement within experimental error. We now know from the experiments of Michelson [2] that if his measurements had been accurate enough he would not have got a check, but would have had an excess or defect according to the direction in which the beam of light travelled around the triangle with respect to the rotation of the earth. But if the geometry of light beams is Euclidean, then not only must the angles of a triangle add to two right angles, but there are definite relations between the lengths of the sides and the angles, and to check these relations the sides should be measured by the old procedure with a meter stick. Such a check on a large scale has never been attempted, and is not feasible. It seems, then, that our checks on the Euclidean character of optical space are all of restricted character. We have apparently proved that up to a certain scale of magnitude optical space is Euclidean with respect to measures of angle, but this may not necessarily involve that space is also Euclidean with respect to measures of length, so that space need not be completely Euclidean. There is a further most important restriction in that our studies of non-Euclidean geometry have shown that the *percentage* excess of the angles of a non-Euclidean triangle over 180° may depend on the magnitude of the triangle, so that it may well be that we have not detected the non-Euclidean character of space simply because our measurements have not been on a large enough scale.

We thus see that the concept of length has undergone a very essential change of character even within the range of terrestrial measurements, in that we have substituted for what I may call the tactual concept an optical concept, complicated by an assumption about the nature of our geometry. From a very direct concept we have come to a very indirect concept with a most complicated set of operations. Strictly speaking, length when measured in this way by light beams should be called by another name, since the operations are different. The practical justification for retaining the same name is that within our present experimental limits a numerical difference between the results of the two sorts of operations has not been detected.

[1] C. F. Gauss, *Gesammelte Werke*, especially vol. IV.

[2] See a discussion of the theory of this experiment by L. Silberstein, *Jour. Opt. Soc. Amer.* 5, 291–307, 1921.

We are still worse off when we make the extension to solar and stellar distances. Here space is entirely optical in character, and we never have an opportunity of even partially comparing tactual with optical space. No direct measures of length have ever been made, nor can we even measure the three angles of a triangle and so check our assumption that the use of Euclidean geometry in extending the concept of space is justified. We never have under observation more than two angles of a triangle, as when we measure the distance of the moon by observation from the two ends of the earth's diameter. To extend to still greater distance our measures of length, we have to make still further assumptions, such as that inferences from the Newtonian laws of mechanics are valid. The accuracy of our inferences about lengths from such measurements is not high. Astronomy is usually regarded as a science of extraordinarily high accuracy, but its accuracy is very restricted in character, namely to the measurement of angles. It is probably safe to say that no astronomical distance, except perhaps that of the moon, is known with an accuracy greater than 0.1%. When we push our estimates to distances beyond the confines of the solar system in which we are assisted by the laws of mechanics, we are reduced in the first place to measurements of parallax, which at best have a quite inferior accuracy, and which furthermore fail entirely outside a rather restricted range. For greater stellar distances we are driven to other and much rougher estimates, resting for instance on the extension to great distances of connections found within the range of parallax between brightness and spectral type of a star, or on such assumptions as that, because a group of stars looks as if it were all together in space and had a common origin, it actually is so. Thus at greater and greater distances not only does experimental accuracy become less, but the very nature of the operations by which length is to be determined becomes indefinite, so that the distances of the most remote stellar objects as estimated by different observers or by different methods may be very divergent. A particular consequence of the inaccuracy of the astronomical measures of great distances is that the question of whether large scale space is Euclidean or not is merely academic.

We thus see that in the extension from terrestrial to great stellar distances the concept of length has changed completely in character. To say that a certain star is 10^5 light years distant is actually and conceptually an entirely different *kind* of thing from saying that a certain goal post is 100 meters distant. Because of our conviction that the character of our experience may change when the range of phenomena changes, we feel the importance of such a question as whether the space of distances of 10^5 light years is Euclidean or not, and are correspondingly dissatisfied that at present there seems no way of giving meaning to it.

We encounter difficulties similar to those above, and are also compelled to modify our procedures, when we go to small distances. Down to the scale of microscopic dimensions a fairly straightforward extension of the ordinary measuring procedure is sufficient, as when we measure a length in a micrometer eyepiece of a microscope. This is of course a combination of tactual and optical measurements, and certain assumptions, justified as far as possible by experience, have to be made about the behavior of light beams. These assumptions are of a quite different character from those which give us concern on the astronomical scale, because here we meet difficulty from interference effects due to the finite scale of the structure of light, and are not concerned with a possible curvature of light beams in the long reaches of space. Apart from the matter of convenience, we might also measure small distances by the tactual method.

As the dimensions become smaller, certain difficulties become increasingly important that were negligible on a larger scale. In carrying out physically the operations equivalent to our concepts, there are a host of practical precautions to be taken which could be explicitly enumerated with difficulty, but of which nevertheless any practical physicist is conscious. Suppose, for example, we measure length tactually by a combination of Johanssen gauges. In piling these together, we must be sure that they are clean, and are thus in actual contact. Particles of mechanical dirt first engage our attention. Then as we go to smaller dimensions we perhaps have to pay attention to adsorbed films of moisture, then at still smaller dimensions to adsorbed films of gas, until finally we have to work in a vacuum, which must be the more nearly complete the smaller the dimensions. About the time that we discover the necessity for a complete vacuum, we discover that the gauges themselves are atomic in structure, that they have no definite boundaries, and therefore no definite length, but that the length is a hazy thing, varying rapidly in time between certain limits. We treat this situation as best we can by taking a time average of the apparent positions of the boundaries, assuming that along with the decrease of dimensions we have acquired a corresponding extravagant increase in nimbleness. But as the dimensions get smaller continually, the difficulties due to this haziness increase indefinitely in percentage effect, and we are eventually driven to give up altogether. We have made the discovery that there are *essential* physical limitations to the operations which defined the concept of length. [We perhaps do not regard the substitution of optical for tactual space on the astronomical scale as compelled by the same sort of physical necessity, because I suppose the possible eventual landing of men on the moon will always be one of the dreams of humanity.] At the same time that we have come to the end of our rope with our Johanssen gauge procedure, our companion with the microscope has been encountering difficulties due to the finite wave length of light; this difficulty he has been able to minimize by using light of progressively shorter wave lengths, but he has eventually had to stop on reaching X-rays. Of course this optical procedure with the microscope is more convenient, and is therefore adopted in practice.

Let us now see what is implied in our concept of length extended to ultramicroscopic dimensions. What, for instance, is the meaning of the statement that the distance between the planes of atoms in a certain crystal is 3×10^{-8} cm.? What we would like to mean is that $1/3 \times 10^{8}$ of these planes piled on top of each other give a thickness of 1 cm.; but of course such a meaning is not the actual one. The actual meaning may be found by examining the operations by which we arrived at the number 3×10^{-8}. As a matter of fact, 3×10^{-8} was the number obtained by solving a general equation derived from the wave theory of light, into which certain numerical data obtained by experiments with X-rays had been substituted. Thus not only has the character of the concept of length changed from tactual to optical, but we have gone much further in committing ourselves to a definite optical theory. If this were the whole story, we would be most uncomfortable with respect to this branch of physics, because we are so uncertain of the correctness of our optical theories, but actually a number of checks can be applied which greatly restore our confidence. For instance, from the density of the crystal and the grating space, the weight of the individual atoms may be computed, and these weights may then be combined with measurements of the dimensions of other sorts of crystal into which the same atoms enter to give values of the densities of these crystals, which may be checked against experiment. All such checks have succeeded within limits of accuracy which are fairly high. It is important to notice that, in spite of the checks, the character of the concept is changing, and begins to involve such things as the equations of optics and the assumption of the conservation of mass.

We are not content, however, to stop with dimensions of atomic order, but have to push on to the electron with a diameter of the order of 10^{-13} cm. What is the possible meaning of the statement that the diameter of an electron is 10^{-13} cm.? Again the only answer is found by examining the operations by which the number 10^{-13} was obtained. This number came by solving certain equations derived from the field equations of electrodynamics, into which certain numerical data obtained by experiment had been substituted. The concept of length has therefore now been so modified as to include that theory of electricity embodied in the field equations, and, most important, assumes the correctness of extending these equations from the dimensions in which they may be verified experimentally into a region in which their correctness is one of the most important and problematical of present-day questions in physics. To find whether the field equations are correct on a small scale, we must verify the relations demanded by the equations between the electric and magnetic forces and the space coördinates, to determine which involves measurement of lengths. But if these space coördinates cannot be given an independent meaning apart from the equations, not only is the attempted verification of the equations impossible, but the question itself is meaningless. If we stick to the concept of length by itself, we are landed in a vicious circle. As a matter of fact, the concept of length disappears as an independent thing, and fuses in a complicated way with other concepts, all of which are themselves altered thereby, with the result that the total number of concepts used in describing nature at this level is reduced in number. A precise analysis of the situation is difficult, and I suppose has never been attempted, but the general character of the situation is evident. Until at least a partial analysis is attempted, I do not see how any meaning can be attached to such questions as whether space is Euclidean in the small scale.

It is interesting to observe that any increased accuracy in knowledge of large scale phenomena must, as far as we now can see, arise from an increase in the accuracy of measurement of small things, that is, in the measurement of small angles or the analysis of minute differences of wave lengths in the spectra. To know the very large takes us into the same field of experiment as to know the very small, so that operationally the large and the small have features in common.

This somewhat detailed analysis of the concept of length brings out features common to all our concepts. If we deal with phenomena outside the domain in which we originally defined our concepts, we may find physical hindrances to performing the operations of the original definition, so that the original operations have to be replaced by others. These new operations are, of course, to be so chosen that they give, within experimental error, the same numerical results in the domain in which the two sets of operations may be both applied; but we must recognize in principle that in changing the operations we have really changed the concept, and that to use the same name for these different concepts over the entire range is dictated only by considerations of convenience, which may sometimes prove to have been purchased at too high a price in terms of unambiguity. We must always be prepared some day to find that an increase in experimental accuracy may show that the two different sets of operations which give the same results in the more ordinary part of the domain of experience, lead to measurably different results in the more unfamiliar parts of the domain. We must remain aware of these joints in our conceptual structure if we hope to render unnecessary the services of the unborn Einsteins.

The second feature common to all concepts brought out by the detailed discussion of length is that, as we approach the experimentally attainable limit, concepts lose their individuality, fuse together, and become fewer in number, as we have seen that at dimensions of the order of the diameter of an electron the concepts of length and the electric field vectors fuse into an amorphous whole. Not only does nature as experienced by us become different in character on its horizons, but it becomes simpler, and therefore our concepts, which are the building stones of our descriptions, become fewer in number. This seems to be an entirely natural state of affairs.

A precise analysis of our conceptual structure has never been attempted, except perhaps in very restricted domains, and it seems to me that there is room here for much important future work. It will never be possible to give a clean-cut logical analysis of the conceptual situation, for the nature of our concepts, according to our operational point of view, is the same as the nature of experimental knowledge, which is often hazy. Thus in the transition regions where nature is getting simpler and the number of operationally independent concepts changes, a certain haziness is inevitable, for the actual change in our conceptual structure in these transition regions is continuous, corresponding to the continuity of our experimental knowledge, whereas formally the number of concepts should be an integer.

Testability and Meaning *

RUDOLF CARNAP

I. Introduction

1. Our Problem: Confirmation, Testing and Meaning

Two chief problems of the theory of knowledge are the question of meaning and the question of verification. The first question asks under what conditions a sentence has meaning, in the sense of cognitive, factual meaning. The second one asks how we get to know something, how we can find out whether a given sentence is true or false. The second question presupposes the first one. Obviously we must understand a sentence, i.e. we must know its meaning, before we can try to find out whether it is true or not. But, from the point of view of empiricism, there is a still closer connection between the two problems. In a certain sense, there is only one answer to the two questions. If we knew what it would be for a given sentence to be found true then we would know what its meaning is. And if for two sentences the conditions under which we would have to take them as true are the same, then they have the same meaning. Thus the meaning of a sentence is in a certain sense identical with the way we determine its truth or falsehood; and a sentence has meaning only if such a determination is possible.

If by verification is meant a definitive and final establishment of truth, then no (synthetic) sentence is ever verifiable, as we shall see. We can only confirm a sentence more and more. Therefore we shall speak of the problem of *confirmation* rather than of the problem of verification. We distinguish the *testing* of a sentence from its confirmation, thereby understanding a procedure—e.g. the carrying out of certain experiments—which leads to a confirmation in some degree either of the sentence itself or of its negation. We shall call a sentence *testable* if we know such a method of testing for it; and we call it *confirmable* if we know under what conditions the sentence would be confirmed. As we shall see, a sentence may be confirmable without being testable; e.g. if we know that our observation of such and such a course of events would confirm the sentence, and such and such a different course would confirm its negation without knowing how to set up either this or that observation.

* Reprinted, with omissions, by kind permission of the author and the editor from *Philosophy of Science*, 3, 1936 and 4, 1937.

In what follows, the problems of confirmation, testing and meaning will be dealt with. After some preliminary discussions in this Introduction, a logical analysis of the chief concepts connected with confirmation and testing will be carried out in Chapter I, leading to the concept of reducibility. Chapter II contains an empirical analysis of confirmation and testing, leading to a definition of the terms 'confirmable' and 'testable' mentioned before. The difficulties in discussions of epistemological and methodological problems are, it seems, often due to a mixing up of logical and empirical questions; therefore it seems desirable to separate the two analyses as clearly as possible. Chapter III uses the concepts defined in the preceding chapters for the construction of an empiricist language, or rather a series of languages. Further, an attempt will be made to formulate the principle of empiricism in a more exact way, by stating a requirement of confirmability or testability as a criterion of meaning. Different requirements are discussed, corresponding to different restrictions of the language; the choice between them is a matter of practical decision.

* * *

2. Confirmation instead of Verification

If verification is understood as a complete and definitive establishment of truth then a universal sentence, e.g. a so-called law of physics or biology, can never be verified, a fact which has often been remarked. Even if each single instance of the law were supposed to be verifiable, the number of instances to which the law refers—e.g. the space-time-points—is infinite and therefore can never be exhausted by our observations which are always finite in number. We cannot verify the law, but we can test it by testing its single instances i.e. the particular sentences which we derive from the law and from other sentences established previously. If in the continued series of such testing experiments no negative instance is found but the number of positive instances increases then our confidence in the law will grow step by step. Thus, instead of verification, we may speak here of gradually increasing *confirmation* of the law.

Now a little reflection will lead us to the result that there is no fundamental difference between a universal sentence and a particular sentence with regard to verifiability but only a difference in degree. Take for instance the following sentence: "There is a white sheet of paper on this table." In order to ascertain whether this thing is paper, we may make a set of simple observations and then, if there still remains some doubt, we may make some physical and chemical experiments. Here as well as in the case of the law, we try to examine sentences which we infer from the sentence in question. These inferred sentences are predictions about future observations. The number of such predictions which we can derive from the sentence given is infinite; and therefore the sentence can never be completely verified. To be sure, in many cases we reach a practically sufficient certainty after a small number of positive instances, and then we stop experimenting.

But there is always the theoretical possibility of continuing the series of test-observations. Therefore here also *no complete verification is possible* but only a process of gradually increasing *confirmation*. We may, if we wish, call a sentence disconfirmed [1] in a certain degree if its negation is confirmed in that degree.

The impossibility of absolute verification has been pointed out and explained in detail by *Popper*.[2] In this point our present views are, it seems to me, in full accordance with *Lewis* [3] and *Nagel*.[4]

Suppose a sentence S is given, some test-observations for it have been made, and S is confirmed by them in a certain degree. Then it is a matter of practical decision whether we will consider that degree as high enough for our acceptance of S, or as low enough for our rejection of S, or as intermediate between these so that we neither accept nor reject S until further evidence will be available. Although our decision is based upon the observations made so far, nevertheless it is not uniquely determined by them. There is no general rule to determine our decision. Thus the acceptance and the rejection of a (synthetic) sentence always contains a *conventional component*. That does not mean that the decision—or, in other words, the question of truth and verification—is conventional. For, in addition to the conventional component there is always the non-conventional component—we may call it, the objective one—consisting in the observations which have been made. And it must certainly be admitted that in very many cases this objective component is present to such an overwhelming extent that the conventional component practically vanishes. For such a simple sentence as e.g. "There is a white thing on this table" the degree of confirmation, after a few observations have been made, will be so high that we practically cannot help accepting the sentence. But even in this case there remains still the theoretical possibility of denying the sentence. Thus even here it is a matter of decision or convention. . . .

II. Logical Analysis of Confirmation and Testing

3. Some Terms and Symbols of Logic

In carrying out methodological investigations especially concerning verification, confirmation, testing, etc., it is very important to distinguish clearly between logical and empirical, e.g. psychological questions. The frequent lack of such a distinction in so-called epistemological discussions has caused a great deal of ambiguity and misunderstanding. In order to make quite clear the meaning and nature of our definitions and explanations, we will separate the two kinds of definitions. In this Chapter II we are concerned with logical analysis. We shall define concepts belonging to

[1] "Erschüttert," Neurath [6].

[2] Popper [1].

[3] Lewis [2] p. 137, note 12: "No verification of the kind of knowledge commonly stated in propositions is ever absolutely complete and final."

[4] Nagel [1] p. 144f.

logic, or more precisely, to logical syntax, although the choice of the concepts to be defined and of the way in which they are defined is suggested in some respects by a consideration of empirical questions—as is often the case in laying down logical definitions. The logical concepts defined here will be applied later on, in Chapter III, in defining concepts of an empirical analysis of confirmation. These descriptive, i.e. non-logical, concepts belong to the field of biology and psychology, namely to the theory of the use of language as a special kind of human activity. [*Note*, 1950. According to present terminology, we divide the theory of language (semiotic) into three parts: pragmatics, semantics, and logical syntax. The descriptive concepts mentioned belong to pragmatics; logical analysis belongs either to semantics (if referring to meaning and interpretation) or to syntax (if formalized).]

In the following logical analysis we shall make use of some few *terms of logical syntax*, which may here be explained briefly.[5] The terms refer to a language-system, say L, which is supposed to be given by a system of rules of the following two kinds. The formative rules state how to construct sentences of L out of the symbols of L. The transformative rules state how to deduce a sentence from a class of sentences, the so-called premisses, and which sentences are to be taken as true unconditionally, i.e. without reference to premisses. The transformative rules are divided into those which have a logico-mathematical nature; they are called logical rules or L-rules (this 'L-' has nothing to do with the name 'L' of the language); and those of an empirical nature, e.g. physical or biological laws stated as postulates; they are called physical rules or P-rules.

We shall take here 'S', 'S_1', 'S_2' etc. as designations of sentences (not as abbreviations for sentences). We use '$\sim$S' as designation of the negation of S. (Thus, in this connection, '$\sim$' is not a symbol of negation but a syntactical symbol, an abbreviation for the words 'the negation of'.) If a sentence S can be deduced from the sentences of a class C according to the rules of L, S is called a *consequence* of C; and moreover an L-consequence, if the L-rules are sufficient for the deduction, otherwise a P-consequence. S_1 and S_2 are called *equipollent* (with each other) if each is a consequence of the other. If S can be shown to be true on the basis of the rules of L, S is called *valid* in L; and moreover L-valid or *analytic*, if true on the basis of the L-rules alone, otherwise P-valid. If, by application of the rules of L, S can be shown to be false, S is called *contravalid*; and L-contravalid or *contradictory*, if by L-rules alone, otherwise P-contravalid. If S is neither valid nor contravalid S is called *indeterminate*. If S is neither analytic nor contradictory, in other words, if its truth or falsehood cannot be determined by logic alone, but needs reference either to P-rules or to the facts outside of language, S is called *synthetic*. Thus the totality of the sentences of L is classified in the following way:

[5] For more exact explanations of these terms see Carnap [4]; some of them are explained also in [5].

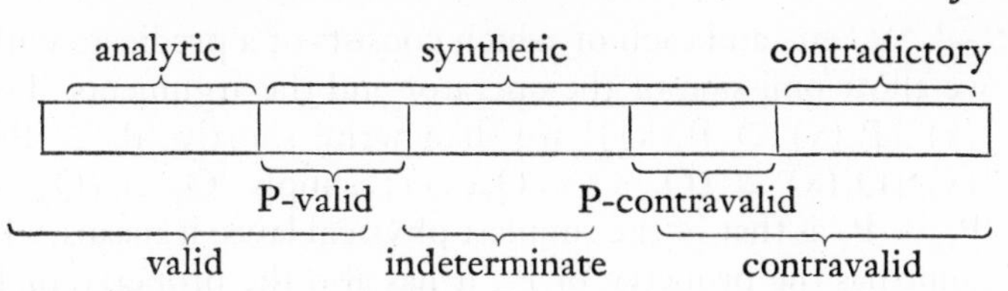

A sentence S_1 is called incompatible with S_2 (or with a class C of sentences), if the negation $\sim S_1$ is a consequence of S_2 (or of C, respectively). The sentences of a class are called mutually independent if none of them is a consequence of, or incompatible with, any other of them.

The most important kind of predicates occurring in a language of science is that of the predicates attributed to space-time-points (or to small space-time-regions). For the sake of simplicity we shall restrict the following considerations—so far as they deal with predicates—to those of this kind. The attribution of a certain value of a physical function, e.g. of temperature, to a certain space-time-point can obviously also be expressed by a predicate of this kind. The following considerations, applied here to such predicates only, can easily be extended to descriptive terms of any other kind.

In order to be able to formulate examples in a simple and exact way we will use the following symbols. We take 'a', 'b', etc. as names of space-time-points (or of small space-time-regions), i.e. as abbreviations for quadruples of space-time-coördinates; we call them *individual constants.* 'x', 'y', etc. will be used as corresponding variables; we will call them *individual variables.* We shall use 'P', 'P_1', 'P_2' etc., and 'Q', 'Q_1' etc. as *predicates*; if no other indication is given, they are supposed to be predicates of the kind described. The sentence 'Q_1(b)' is to mean: "The space-time-point b has the property Q_1." Such a sentence consisting of a predicate followed by one or several individual constants as arguments, will be called a *full sentence* of that predicate.

Connective symbols: '$\sim$' for 'not' (negation), 'V' for 'or' (disjunction), '.' for 'and' (conjunction), '$\supset$' for 'if – then' (implication), '$\equiv$' for 'if – then –, and if not – then not –' (equivalence). '$\sim$ Q(a)' is the negation of a full sentence of 'Q'; it is sometimes also called a full sentence of the predicate '$\sim$ Q'.

Operators: '(x)P(x)' is to mean: "every point has the property P" (*universal* sentence; the first '(x)' is called the universal *operator*, and the sentential function 'P(x)' its *operand*). '($\exists$x)P(x)' is to mean: "There is at least one point having the property P" (*existential* sentence; '($\exists$x)' is called the existential operator and 'P(x)' its operand). (In what follows, we shall not make use of any other operators than universal and existential operators with individual variables, as described here.) In our later examples we shall use the following abbreviated notation for universal sentences of a certain form occurring very frequently. If the sentence '(x) [– – –]' is such that '– – –' consists of several partial sentences which are connected by

'$\sim$', '$\vee$' etc. and each of which consists of a predicate with 'x' as argument, we allow omission of the operator and the arguments. Thus e.g. instead of '$(x)\ (P_1(x) \supset P_2(x))$' we shall write shortly '$P_1 \supset P_2$'; and instead of '$(x)\ [Q_1(x) \supset (Q_3(x) \equiv Q_2(x))]$' simply '$Q_1 \supset (Q_3 \equiv Q_2)$'. The form '$P_1 \supset P_2$' is that of the simplest physical laws; it means: "If any space-time-point has the property of P_1, it has also the property of P_2." . . .

4. Definitions

By an (explicit) definition of a descriptive predicate 'Q' with one argument we understand a sentence of the form

(D:) $$Q(x) \equiv \ldots x \ldots$$

where at the place of '. . . x . . . ' a sentential function – called the definiens – stands which contains 'x' as the only free variable. For several arguments the form is analogous. We will say that a definition D is based upon the class C of predicates if every descriptive symbol occurring in the definiens of D belongs to C. If the predicates of a class C are available in our language we may introduce other predicates by a chain of definitions of such a kind that each definition is based upon C and the predicates defined by previous definitions of the chain.

Definition 9. A definition is said to have atomic (or molecular, or generalized, or essentially generalized) form, if its definiens has atomic (or molecular, or generalized, or essentially generalized, respectively) form.

Theorem 5. If 'P' is defined by a definition D based upon C, 'P' is reducible to C. If D has molecular form, 'P' is completely reducible to C. If D has essentially generalized form, 'P' is incompletely reducible to C.

Proof. 'P' may be defined by '$P(x) \equiv \ldots x \ldots$'. Then, for any b, '$P(b)$' is equipollent to '. . . b . . .' and hence in the case of molecular form, according to Theorem 2, completely reducible to C, and in the other case, according to Theorems 3 and 4, reducible to C.

Let us consider the question whether the so-called *disposition-concepts* can be defined, i.e. predicates which enunciate the disposition of a point or body for reacting in such and such a way to such and such conditions, e.g. 'visible', 'smellable', 'fragile', 'tearable', 'soluble', 'indissoluble' etc. We shall see that such disposition-terms cannot be defined by means of the terms by which these conditions and reactions are described, but they can be introduced by sentences of another form. Suppose, we wish to introduce the predicate 'Q_3' meaning "soluble in water." Suppose further, that 'Q_1' and 'Q_2' are already defined in such a way that '$Q_1(x, t)$' means "the body x is placed into water at the time t," and '$Q_2(x, t)$' means "the body x dissolves at the time t." Then one might perhaps think that we could define 'soluble in water' in the following way: "x is soluble in water" is to mean "whenever x is put into water, x dissolves," in symbols:

(D:) $$Q_3(x) \equiv (t)[Q_1(x,t) \supset Q_2(x,t)].$$

But this definition would not give the intended meaning of 'Q_3'. For, suppose that c is a certain match which I completely burnt yesterday. As the match was made of wood, I can rightly assert that it was not soluble in water; hence the sentence '$Q_3(c)$' (S_1) which asserts that the match c is soluble in water, is false. But if we assume the definition D, S_1 becomes equipollent with '$(t)\ [Q_1(c, t) \supset Q_2(c, t)]$' ($S_2$). Now the match c has never been placed into water and on the hypothesis made never can be so placed. Thus any sentence of the form '$Q_1(c, t)$' is false for any value of 't'. Hence S_2 is true, and, because of D, S_1 also is true, in contradiction to the intended meaning of S_1. 'Q_3' cannot be defined by D, nor by any other definition. But we can introduce it by the following sentence:

(R:) $$(x)(t)[Q_1(x,t) \supset (Q_3(x) \equiv Q_2(x,t))],$$

in words: "if any thing x is put into water at any time t, then, if x is soluble in water, x dissolves at the time t, and if x is not soluble in water, it does not." This sentence belongs to that kind of sentences which we shall call reduction sentences.

5. Reduction Sentences

Suppose, we wish to introduce a new predicate 'Q_3' into our language and state for this purpose a pair of sentences of the following form:

(R_1) $$Q_1 \supset (Q_2 \supset Q_3)$$
(R_2) $$Q_4 \supset (Q_5 \supset \sim Q_3)$$

Here, 'Q_1' and 'Q_4' may describe experimental conditions which we have to fulfill in order to find out whether or not a certain space-time-point b has the property of Q_3, i.e. whether '$Q_3(b)$' or '$\sim Q_3(b)$' is true. 'Q_2' and 'Q_5' may describe possible results of the experiments. Then R_1 means: if we realize the experimental condition Q_1 then, if we find the result Q_2, the point has the property Q_3. By the help of R_1, from '$Q_1(b)$' and '$Q_2(b)$', '$Q_3(b)$' follows. R_2 means: if we satisfy the condition Q_4 and then find Q_5 the point has not the property Q_3. By the help of R_2, from '$Q_4(b)$' and '$Q_5(b)$', '$\sim Q_3(b)$' follows. We see that the sentences R_1 and R_2 tell us how we may determine whether or not the predicate 'Q_3' is to be attributed to a certain point, provided we are able to determine whether or not the four predicates 'Q_1', 'Q_2', 'Q_4'; and 'Q_5' are to be attributed to it. By the statement of R_1 and R_2 'Q_3' is reduced in a certain sense to those four predicates; therefore we shall call R_1 and R_2 reduction sentences for 'Q_3' and '$\sim Q_3$' respectively. Such a pair of sentences will be called a reduction pair for 'Q_3'. By R_1 the property Q_3 is attributed to the points of the class $Q_1 \cdot Q_2$, by R_2 the property $\sim Q_3$ to the points of the class $Q_4 \cdot Q_5$. If by the rules of the language – either logical rules or physical laws – we can show that no point belongs to either of these classes (in other words, if the universal sentence '$\sim [(Q_1 \cdot Q_2) \vee (Q_4 \cdot Q_5)]$' is valid) then the pair of sentences does not determine Q_3 nor $\sim Q_3$ for any point and therefore does not give a reduction for the predicate Q_3. Therefore, in the definition of 'reduction pair' to be stated, we must exclude this case.

In special cases 'Q_4' coincides with 'Q_1', and 'Q_5' with '$\sim Q_2$'. In that case the reduction pair is '$Q_1 \supset (Q_2 \supset Q_3)$' and '$Q_1 \supset (\sim Q_2 \supset \sim Q_3)$'; the latter can be transformed into '$Q_1 \supset (Q_3 \supset Q_2)$'. Here the pair can be replaced by the one sentence '$Q_1 \supset (Q_3 \equiv Q_2)$' which means: if we accomplish the condition Q_1, then the point has the property Q_3 if and only if we find the result Q_2. This sentence may serve for determining the result '$Q_3(b)$' as well as for '$\sim Q_3(b)$'; we shall call it a bilateral reduction sentence. It determines Q_3 for the points of the class $Q_1 \cdot Q_2$, and $\sim Q_3$ for those of the class $Q_1 \cdot \sim Q_2$; it does not give a determination for the points of the class $\sim Q_1$. Therefore, if '$(x)(\sim Q_1(x))$' is valid, the sentence does not give any determination at all. To give an example, let '$Q_1'(b)$' mean "the point b is both heated and not heated", and '$Q_1''(b)$': "the point b is illuminated by light-rays which have a speed of 400,000 km/sec". Here for any point c, '$Q_1'(c)$, and '$Q_1''(c)$' are contravalid – the first contradictory and the second P-contravalid; therefore, '$(x)\ (\sim Q_1'(x))$' and '$(x)\ (\sim Q_1''(x))$' are valid – the first analytic and the second P-valid; in other words, the conditions Q_1' and Q_1'' are impossible, the first logically and the second physically. In this case, a sentence of the form '$Q_1' \supset (Q_3 \equiv Q_2)$' or '$Q_1'' \supset (Q_3 \equiv Q_2)$' would not tell us anything about how to use the predicate 'Q_3' and therefore could not be taken as a reduction sentence. These considerations lead to the following definitions.

Definition 10. a. A universal sentence of the form

(R) $$Q_1 \supset (Q_2 \supset Q_3)$$

is called a *reduction sentence* for 'Q_3' provided '$\sim (Q_1 \cdot Q_2)$' is not valid.

b. A pair of sentences of the forms

(R_1) $$Q_1 \supset (Q_2 \supset Q_3)$$
(R_2) $$Q_4 \supset (Q_5 \supset \sim Q_3)$$

is called a *reduction pair* for 'Q_3' provided '$\sim [(Q_1 \cdot Q_2) \lor (Q_4 \cdot Q_5)]$' is not valid.

c. A sentence of the form

(R_b) $$Q_1 \supset (Q_3 \equiv Q_2)$$

is called a *bilateral reduction sentence* for 'Q_3' provided '$(x)(\sim Q_1(x))$' is not valid.

Every statement about reduction pairs in what follows applies also to bilateral reduction sentences, because such sentences are comprehensive formulations of a special case of a reduction pair.

If a reduction pair for 'Q_3' of the form given above is valid – i.e. either laid down in order to introduce 'Q_3' on the basis of 'Q_1', 'Q_2', 'Q_4', and 'Q_5', or consequences of physical laws stated beforehand – then for any point c '$Q_3(c)$' is a consequence of '$Q_1(c)$' and '$Q_2(c)$', and '$\sim Q_3(c)$' is a consequence of '$Q_4(c)$' and '$Q_5(c)$'. Hence 'Q_3' is completely reducible to those four predicates.

Theorem 6. If a reduction pair for 'Q' is valid, then 'Q' is completely reducible to the four (or two, respectively) other predicates occurring.

We may distinguish between logical reduction and physical reduction, dependent upon the reduction sentence being analytic or P-valid, in the latter case for instance a valid physical law. Sometimes not only the sentence '$Q_1 \supset (Q_3 \equiv Q_2)$' is valid, but also the sentence '$Q_3 \equiv Q_2$'. (This is e.g. the case if '$(x)Q_1(x)$' is valid.) Then for any b, '$Q_3(b)$' can be transformed into the equipollent sentence '$Q_2(b)$', and thus 'Q_3' can be eliminated in any sentence whatever. If '$Q_3 \equiv Q_2$' is not P-valid but analytic it may be considered as an explicit definition for 'Q_3'. Thus an *explicit definition* is a special kind of a logical bilateral reduction sentence. A logical bilateral reduction sentence which does not have this simple form, but the general form '$Q_1 \supset (Q_3 \equiv Q_2)$', may be considered as a kind of conditional definition.

If we wish to construct a language for science we have to take some descriptive (i.e. non-logical) terms as primitive terms. Further terms may then be introduced not only by explicit definitions but also by other reduction sentences. The possibility of *introduction by laws*, i.e. by physical reduction, is, as we shall see, very important for science, but so far not sufficiently noticed in the logical analysis of science. On the other hand the terms introduced in this way have the disadvantage that in general it is not possible to eliminate them, i.e. to translate a sentence containing such a term into a sentence containing previous terms only.

Let us suppose that the term 'Q_3' does not occur so far in our language, but 'Q_1', 'Q_2', 'Q_4', and 'Q_5' do occur. Suppose further that either the following reduction pair R_1, R_2 for 'Q_3':

$$(R_1) \qquad Q_1 \supset (Q_2 \supset Q_3)$$
$$(R_2) \qquad Q_4 \supset (Q_5 \supset \sim Q_3)$$

or the following bilateral reduction sentence for 'Q_3':

$$(R_b) \qquad Q_1 \supset (Q_3 \equiv Q_2)$$

is stated as valid in order to introduce 'Q_3', i.e. to give meaning to this new term of our language. Since, on the assumption made, 'Q_3' has no antecedent meaning, we do not assert anything about facts by the statement of R_b. This statement is not an assertion but a convention. In other words, the factual content of R_b is empty; in this respect, R_b is similar to a definition. On the other hand, the pair R_1, R_2 has a positive content. By stating it as valid, beside stating a convention concerning the use of the term 'Q_3', we assert something about facts that can be formulated in the following way without the use of 'Q_3'. If a point c had the property $Q_1 \cdot Q_2 \cdot Q_4 \cdot Q_5$, then both '$Q_3(c)$' and '$\sim Q_3(c)$' would follow. Since this is not possible for any point, the following universal sentence S which does not contain

'Q_3', and which in general is synthetic, is a consequence of R_1 and R_2:

(S:) $$\sim (Q_1 \cdot Q_2 \cdot Q_4 \cdot Q_5).$$

In the case of the bilateral reduction sentence R_b 'Q_4' coincides with 'Q_1' and 'Q_5' with '$\sim Q_2$'. Therefore in this case S degenerates to '$\sim (Q_1 \cdot Q_2 \cdot Q_1 \cdot \sim Q_2)$' and hence becomes analytic. Thus a bilateral reduction sentence, in contrast to a reduction pair, has no factual content.

6. Introductive Chains

For the sake of simplicity we have considered so far only the introduction of a predicate by one reduction pair or by one bilateral reduction sentence. But in most cases a predicate will be introduced by either several reduction pairs or several bilateral reduction sentences. If a property or physical magnitude can be determined by different methods then we may state one reduction pair or one bilateral reduction sentence for each method. The intensity of an electric current can be measured for instance by measuring the heat produced in the conductor, or the deviation of a magnetic needle, or the quantity of silver separated out of a solution, or the quantity of hydrogen separated out of water etc. We may state a set of bilateral reduction sentences, one corresponding to each of these methods. The factual content of this set is not null because it comprehends such sentences as e.g. "If the deviation of a magnetic needle is such and such then the quantity of silver separated in one minute is such and such, and vice versa" which do not contain the term 'intensity of electric current', and which obviously are synthetic.

If we establish one reduction pair (or one bilateral reduction sentence) as valid in order to introduce a predicate 'Q_3', the meaning of 'Q_3' is not established completely, but only for the cases in which the test condition is fulfilled. In other cases, e.g. for the match in our previous example, neither the predicate nor its negation can be attributed. We may diminish this region of indeterminateness of the predicate by adding one or several more laws which contain the predicate and connect it with other terms available in our language. These further laws may have the form of reduction sentences (as in the example of the electric current) or a different form. In the case of the predicate 'soluble in water' we may perhaps add the law stating that two bodies of the same substance are either both soluble or both not soluble. This law would help in the instance of the match; it would, in accordance with common usage, lead to the result "the match c is not soluble," because other pieces of wood are found to be insoluble on the basis of the first reduction sentence. Nevertheless, a region of indeterminateness remains, though a smaller one. If a body b consists of such a substance that for no body of this substance has the test-condition – in the above example: "being placed into water" – ever been fulfilled, then neither the predicate nor its negation can be attributed to b. This region may then be diminished still further, step by step, by stating new laws.

These laws do not have the conventional character that definitions have; rather are they discovered empirically within the region of meaning which the predicate in question received by the laws stated before. But these laws are extended by convention into a region in which the predicate had no meaning previously; in other words, we decided to use the predicate in such a way that these laws which are tested and confirmed in cases in which the predicate has a meaning, remain valid in other cases.

We have seen that a new predicate need not be introduced by a definition, but may equally well be introduced by a set of reduction pairs. (A bilateral reduction sentence may here be taken as a special form of a reduction pair.) Consequently, instead of the usual chain of definitions, we obtain a chain of sets of sentences, each set consisting either of one definition or of one or several reduction pairs. By each set a new predicate is introduced.

Definition 11. A (finite) chain of (finite) sets of sentences is called an *introductive chain* based upon the class C of predicates if the following conditions are fulfilled. Each set of the chain consists either of one definition or of one or more reduction pairs for one predicate, say 'Q'; every reduction pair is valid; every predicate occurring in the set, other than 'Q', either belongs to C or is such that one of the previous sets of the chain is either a definition for it or a set of reduction pairs for it.

Definition 12. If the last set of a given introductive chain based upon C either consists in a definition for 'Q' or in a set of reduction pairs for 'Q', 'Q' is said to be *introduced* by this chain on the basis of C.

For our purposes we will suppose that a reduction sentence always has the simple form '$Q_1 \supset (Q_2 \supset Q_3)$' and not the analogous but more complicated form '$(x)\,[---x--- \supset (\ldots x \ldots \supset Q_3(x))]$' where '$---x---$' and '$\ldots x \ldots$' indicate sentential functions of a non-atomic form. This supposition does not restrict the generality of the following considerations because a reduction sentence of the compound form indicated may always be replaced by two definitions and a reduction sentence of the simple form, namely by:

$$Q_1 \equiv ---x---$$
$$Q_2 \equiv \ldots x \ldots$$
$$Q_1 \supset (Q_2 \supset Q_3).$$

The above supposition once made, the nature of an introductive chain is chiefly dependent upon the form of the definitions occurring. Therefore we define as follows.

Definition 13. An introductive chain is said to have atomic form (or molecular form) if every definition occurring in it has atomic form (or molecular form, respectively); it is said to have generalized form (or essentially generalized form) if at least one definition of generalized form (or essentially generalized form, respectively) occurs in it.

Theorem 7. If 'P' is introduced by an introductive chain based upon

C, 'P' is reducible to C. If the chain has molecular form, 'P' is completely reducible to C; if the chain has essentially generalized form, 'P' is incompletely reducible to C. – This follows from Theorems 5 (§ 7) and 6 (§ 8).

We call *primitive symbols* those symbols of a language L which are introduced directly, i.e. without the help of other symbols. Thus there are the following kinds of symbols of L:

1) *primitive symbols* of L,
2) *indirectly introduced symbols*, i.e. those introduced by introductive chains based upon primitive symbols; here we distinguish:
   a) *defined symbols*, introduced by chains of definitions,
   b) *reduced symbols*, i.e. those introduced by introductive chains containing at least one reduction sentence; here we may further distinguish:
      α) *L-reduced symbols*, whose chains contain only L-reduction pairs,
      β) *P-reduced symbols*, whose chains contain at least one P-reduction pair.

Definition 14. a. An *introductive chain* based upon primitive predicates of a language L and having atomic (or molecular, or generalized, or essentially generalized, respectively) form is called an atomic (or molecular, or generalized, or essentially generalized, respectively) introductive chain of L.

b. A *predicate* of L is called an *atomic* (or *molecular*) predicate if it is either a primitive predicate of L or introduced by an atomic (or molecular, respectively) introductive chain of L; it is called a *generalized* (or essentially generalized) predicate if it is introduced by a generalized (or essentially generalized, respectively) introductive chain of L.

Definition 15. a. A sentence S is called an *atomic sentence* if S is a full sentence of an atomic predicate. – b. S is called a *molecular sentence* if S has molecular form and contains only molecular predicates. – c. S is called a *generalized sentence* if S contains an (unrestricted) operator or a generalized predicate. – d. S is called an essentially generalized sentence if S is a generalized sentence and is not equipollent with a molecular sentence.

It should be noticed that the term 'atomic sentence', as here defined, is not at all understood to refer to ultimate facts.[6] Our theory does not assume anything like ultimate facts. It is a matter of convention which predicates are taken as primitive predicates of a certain language L; and hence likewise, which predicates are taken as atomic predicates and which sentences as atomic sentences.

7. *Reduction and Definition*

In § 8 the fact was mentioned that in some cases, for instance in the case of a disposition-term, the reduction cannot be replaced by a definition.

[6] In contradistinction to the term 'atomic sentence' or 'elementary sentence' as used by Russell or Wittgenstein.

We now are in a position to see the situation more clearly. Suppose that we introduce a predicate 'Q' into the language of science first by a reduction pair and that, later on, step by step, we add more such pairs for 'Q' as our knowledge about 'Q' increases with further experimental investigations. In the course of this procedure the range of indeterminateness for 'Q', i.e. the class of cases for which we have not yet given a meaning to 'Q', becomes smaller and smaller. Now at each stage of this development we could lay down a definition for 'Q' corresponding to the set of reduction pairs for 'Q' established up to that stage. But, in stating the definition, we should have to make an arbitrary decision concerning the cases which are not determined by the set of reduction pairs. A definition determines the meaning of the new term once for all. We could either decide to attribute 'Q' in the cases not determined by the set, or to attribute '$\sim$ Q' in these cases. Thus for instance, if a bilateral reduction sentence R of the form '$Q_1 \supset (Q_3 \equiv Q_2)$' is stated for '$Q_3$', then the predicate '$Q_3$' is to be attributed to the points of the class $Q_1 \cdot Q_2$, and '$\sim Q_3$' to those of the class $Q_1 \cdot \sim Q_2$, while for the points of the class $\sim Q_1$ the predicate 'Q_3' has no meaning. Now we might state one of the following two definitions:

$$(D_1) \qquad Q_3 \equiv (Q_1 \cdot Q_2)$$
$$(D_2) \qquad Q_3 \equiv (\sim Q_1 \vee Q_2)$$

If *c* is a point of the undetermined class, on the basis of D_1 '$Q_3(c)$' is false, and on the basis of D_2 it is true. Although it is possible to lay down either D_1 or D_2, neither procedure is in accordance with the intention of the scientist concerning the use of the predicate 'Q_3'. The scientist wishes neither to determine all the cases of the third class positively, nor all of them negatively; he wishes to leave these questions open until the results of further investigations suggest the statement of a new reduction pair; thereby some of the cases so far undetermined become determined positively and some negatively. If we now were to state a definition, we should have to revoke it at such a new stage of the development of science, and to state a new definition, incompatible with the first one. If, on the other hand, we were now to state a reduction pair, we should merely have to add one or more reduction pairs at the new stage; and these pairs will be compatible with the first one. In this latter case we do not correct the determinations laid down in the previous stage but simply supplement them.

Thus, if we wish to introduce a new term into the language of science, we have to distinguish two cases. If the situation is such that we wish to fix the meaning of the new term once for all, then a definition is the appropriate form. On the other hand, if we wish to determine the meaning of the term at the present time for some cases only, leaving its further determination for other cases to decisions which we intend to make step by step, on the basis of empirical knowledge which we expect to obtain in the future, then the method of reduction is the appropriate one rather than that of a definition. A set of reduction pairs is a partial determination of meaning only and can therefore not be replaced by a definition. Only if we reach, by adding more and more reduction pairs, a stage in which all cases are determined, may we go over to the form of a definition.

We will examine in greater detail the situation in the case of several reduction pairs for 'Q_3':

(R_1)	$Q_1 \supset (Q_2 \supset Q_3)$
(R_2)	$Q_4 \supset (Q_5 \supset \sim Q_3)$
(R_1')	$Q_1' \supset (Q_2' \supset Q_3)$
(R_2')	$Q_4' \supset (Q_5' \supset \sim Q_3)$
etc.	

Then 'Q_3' is determined by R_1 for the points of the class $Q_1 \cdot Q_2$, by R_1' for the class $Q_1' \cdot Q_2'$, etc., and therefore, by the totality of reduction sentences for 'Q_3', for the class $(Q_1 \cdot Q_2) \vee (Q_1' \cdot Q_2') \vee \ldots$. This class may shortly be designated by '$Q_{1,2}$'. Analogously '$\sim Q_3$' is determined by the reduction sentences for '$\sim Q_3$' for the points of the class $(Q_4 \cdot Q_5) \vee (Q_4' \cdot Q_5') \vee \ldots$, which we designate by '$Q_{4,5}$'. Hence 'Q_3' is determined either positively or negatively for the class $Q_{1,2} \vee Q_{4,5}$. Therefore the universal sentence '$Q_{1,2} \vee Q_{4,5}$' means, that for every point either 'Q_3' or '$\sim Q_3$' is determined. If this sentence is true, the set of reduction sentences is complete and may be replaced by the definition '$Q_3 \equiv Q_{1,2}$'. For the points of the class $\sim (Q_{1,2} \vee Q_{4,5})$, '$Q_3$' is not determined, and hence, in the stage in question, 'Q_3' is without meaning for these points. If on the basis of either logical rules or physical laws it can be shown that all points belong to this class, in other words, if the universal sentence '$\sim (Q_{1,2} \vee Q_{4,5})$' is valid – either analytic or P-valid – then neither 'Q_3' nor '$\sim Q_3$' is determined for any point and hence the given set of reduction pairs does not even partly determine the meaning of 'Q_3' and therefore is not a suitable means of introducing this predicate.

The given set of reduction pairs asserts that a point belonging to the class $Q_{4,5}$ has the property $\sim Q_3$ and hence not the property Q_3, and therefore cannot belong to $Q_{1,2}$ because every point of this class has the property Q_3. What the set asserts can therefore be formulated by the universal sentence saying that no point belongs to both $Q_{1,2}$ and $Q_{4,5}$, i.e. the sentence '$\sim (Q_{1,2} \cdot Q_{4,5})$'. This sentence represents, so to speak, the factual content of the set. In the case of one reduction pair this representative sentence is '$\sim (Q_1 \cdot Q_2 \cdot Q_4 \cdot Q_5)$'; in the case of one bilateral reduction sentence this becomes '$\sim (Q_1 \cdot Q_2 \cdot Q_1 \cdot \sim Q_2)$' or '$(x)\ (\sim Q_1(x) \vee Q_2(x) \vee \sim Q_2(x))$', which is analytic.

The following diagram shows the tripartition of the class of all points by a reduction pair (or a bilateral reduction sentence, or a set of reduction pairs, respectively). For the first class 'Q_3' is determined, for the second class '$\sim Q_3$'. The third class lies between them and is not yet determined; but some of its points may be determined as belonging to Q_3 and some others as belonging to $\sim Q_3$ by reduction pairs to be stated in the future.

reduction pair:
bilat. reduction sentence:
set of reduction pairs:

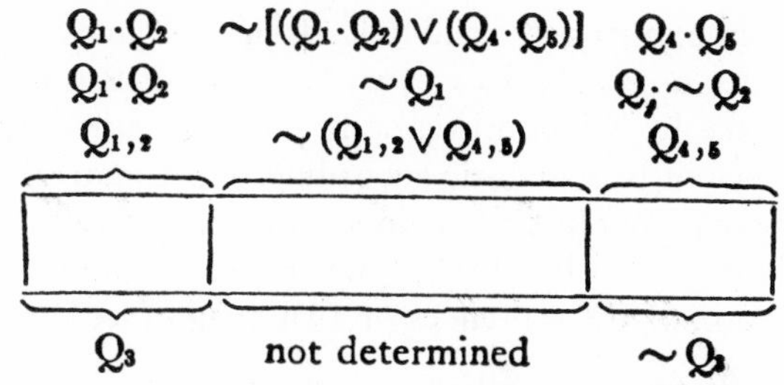

If we establish a set of *reduction pairs* as new valid sentences for the introduction of a new predicate 'Q_3', are these valid sentences *analytic* or *P-valid?* Moreover, which other sentences containing 'Q_3' are analytic? The distinction between analytic and P-valid sentences refers primarily to those sentences only in which all descriptive terms are primitive terms. In this case the criterion is as follows: [7] a valid sentence S is analytic if and only if every sentence S′ is also valid which is obtained from S when any descriptive term wherever it occurs in S is replaced by any other term whatever of the same type; otherwise it is P-valid. A sentence S containing defined terms is analytic if the sentence S′ resulting from S by the elimination of the defined terms is analytic; otherwise it is P-valid. A definition, e.g. '$Q(x) \equiv \ldots x \ldots$' is, according to this criterion, itself analytic; for, after it has been stated as a valid sentence, by the elimination of 'Q' we get from it '$\ldots x \ldots \equiv \ldots x \ldots$', which is analytic.

In the case of a new descriptive term introduced by a set of reduction pairs, the situation is not as simple as in the case of a definition because elimination is here not possible. Let us consider the question how the criterion is to be stated in this case. The introduction of a new term into a language is, strictly speaking, the construction of a new language on the basis of the original one. Suppose that we go over from the language L_1, which does not contain 'Q', to the language L_2 by introducing 'Q' by a set R of reduction pairs, whose representative sentence (in the sense explained before) may be taken to be S. Then S as not containing 'Q' is a sentence of L_1 also; its logical character within L_1 does not depend upon 'Q' and may therefore be supposed to be determined already. By stating the sentences of R as valid in L_2, S becomes also valid in L_2 because it is a consequence of R in L_2. If now S is analytic in L_1, it is also analytic in L_2; in this case R does not assert anything about facts, and we must therefore take its sentences as analytic. According to this, every bilateral reduction sentence is analytic, because its representative sentence is analytic, as we have seen before. If S is either P-valid or indeterminate in L_1, it is valid and moreover P-valid in L_2 in consequence of our stating R as valid in L_2. In this case every sentence of R is valid; it is P-valid unless it fulfills the general criterion of analyticity stated before (referring to all possible replacements of the descriptive terms, see above). If S is either P-contravalid or contradictory in L_1, it has the same property in L_2 and

[7] Carnap [4] §51.

is simultaneously valid in L_2. It may be analytic in L_2, if it fulfills the general criterion. In this case every sentence of R is both valid and contravalid, and hence L_2 is inconsistent.[8] If S is contradictory in L_1 and at least one sentence of R is analytic according to the general criterion, then L_2 is not only inconsistent but also L-inconsistent. The results of these considerations may be exhibited by the following table; column (1) gives a complete classification of the sentences of a language (see the diagram in § 3).

The representative sentence S		a reduction sentence of R (in L_2)	L_2
in L_1	in L_2		
1. analytic	analytic	analytic	consistent (if L_1 is consistent)
2. P-valid	P-valid	valid *	consistent (if L_1 is consistent)
3. indeterminate	P-valid	valid *	consistent (if L_1 is consistent)
4. P-contravalid	valid and P-contravalid	valid * and P-contravalid	inconsistent
5. contradictory	valid and contradictory	valid * and contradictory	inconsistent †

* analytic if fulfilling the general criterion (p. 61); otherwise P-valid.
† and moreover L-inconsistent if at least one sentence of R is analytic on the basis of the general criterion (p. 61).

Now the *complete criterion for 'analytic'* can be stated as follows:

Nature of S	Criterion for S being *analytic*
1. S does not contain any descriptive symbol.	S is valid.
2. All descriptive symbols of S are primitive.	Every sentence S′ which results from S when we replace any descriptive symbol at all places where it occurs in S by any symbol whatever of the same type—and hence S itself also—is valid.
3. S contains a defined descriptive symbol 'Q'.	The sentence S′ resulting from S by the elimination of 'Q' is valid.
4. S contains a descriptive symbol 'Q' introduced by a set R of reduction pairs; let L′ be the sub-language of L not containing 'Q', and S′ the representative sentence of R (comp. p. 61).	S′ is analytic in L′, and S is an L-consequence of R (e.g. one of the sentences of R); in other words, the implication sentence containing the conjunction of the sentences of R as first part and S as second part is analytic (i.e. every sentence resulting from this implication sentence where we replace 'Q' at all places by any symbol of the same type occurring in L′ is valid in L′).

[8] Compare Carnap [4] §59.

III. Empirical Analysis of Confirmation and Testing

8. Observable and Realizable Predicates

In the preceding chapter we analyzed logically the relations which subsist among sentences or among predicates if one of them may be confirmed with the help of others. We defined some concepts of a syntactical kind, based upon the concept 'consequence' as the chief concept of logical syntax. In what follows we shall deal with *empirical methodology*. Here also we are concerned with the questions of confirming and testing sentences and predicates. These considerations belong to a theory of language just as the logical ones do. But while the logical analysis belongs to an analytic theory of the formal, syntactical structure of language, here we will carry out an empirical analysis of the application of language. Our considerations belong, strictly speaking, to a biological or psychological theory of language as a kind of human behavior, and especially as a kind of reaction to observations. We shall see, however, that for our purposes we need not go into details of biological or psychological investigations. In order to make clear what is understood by empirically testing and confirming a sentence and thereby to find out what is to be required for a sentence or a predicate in a language having empirical meaning, we can restrict ourselves to using very few concepts of the field mentioned. We shall take two descriptive, i.e. non-logical, terms of this field as *basic terms* for our following considerations, namely '*observable*' and '*realizable*'. All other terms, and above all the terms 'confirmable' and 'testable', which are the chief terms of our theory, will be defined on the basis of the two basic terms mentioned; in the definitions we shall make use of the logical terms defined in the foregoing chapter. The two basic terms are of course, as basic ones, not defined within our theory. Definitions for them would have to be given within psychology, and more precisely, within the behavioristic theory of language. We do not attempt such definitions, but we shall give at least some rough explanations for the terms, which will make their meaning clear enough for our purposes.

Explanation 1. A predicate 'P' of a language L is called *observable* for an organism (e.g. a person) N, if, for suitable arguments, e.g. 'b', N is able under suitable circumstances to come to a decision with the help of few observations about a full sentence, say 'P(b)', i.e. to a confirmation of either 'P(b)' or '∼ P(b)' of such a high degree that he will either accept or reject 'P(b)'.

This explanation is necessarily vague. There is no sharp line between observable and non-observable predicates because a person will be more or less able to decide a certain sentence quickly, i.e. he will be inclined after a certain period of observation to accept the sentence. For the sake of simplicity we will here draw a sharp distinction between observable and non-observable predicates. By thus drawing an arbitrary line between observable and non-observable predicates in a field of continuous degrees of observability we partly determine in advance the possible answers to questions such as whether or not a certain predicate is observable by a given person. Nevertheless the general philosophical, i.e. methodological question about the nature of meaning and testability will, as we shall see, not be distorted by our over-simplification. Even particular questions as to whether or not a given sentence is confirmable, and whether or not it is testable by a certain person, are affected, as we shall see, at most to a very small degree by the choice of the boundary line for observable predicates.

According to the explanation given, for example the predicate 'red' is observable for a person N possessing a normal colour sense. For a suitable argument, namely a space-time-point *c* sufficiently near to N, say a spot on the table before N, N is able under suitable circumstances – namely, if there is sufficient light at *c* – to come to a decision about the full sentence "the spot *c* is red" after few observations – namely by looking at the table. On the other hand, the predicate 'red' is not observable by a colour-blind person. And the predicate 'an electric field of such and such an amount' is not observable to anybody, because, although we know how to test a full sentence of this predicate, we cannot do it directly, i.e. by a few observations; we have to apply certain instruments and hence to make a great many preliminary observations in order to find out whether the things before us are instruments of the kind required.

Explanation 2. A predicate 'P' of a language L is called '*realizable*' by N, if for a suitable argument, e.g. 'b', N is able under suitable circumstances to make the full sentence 'P(b)' true, i.e. to produce the property P at the point b.

When we use the terms 'observable', 'realizable', 'confirmable', etc. without explicit reference to anybody, it is to be understood that they are meant with respect to the people who use the language L to which the predicate in question belongs.

Examples. Let 'P_1(b)' mean: 'the space-time-point b has the temperature 100°C'. 'P_1' is realizable by us because we know how to produce that temperature at the point b, if b is accessible to us. – 'P_2(b)' may mean: 'there is iron at the point b'. 'P_2' is realizable because we are able to carry a piece of iron to the point b if b is accessible. – If 'P_3(b)' means: 'at the point b is a substance whose index of light refraction is 10', 'P_3' is not realizable by anybody at the present time, because nobody knows at present how to produce such a substance.

9. *Confirmability*

In the preceding chapter we have dealt with the concept of reducibility of a predicate 'P' to a class C of other predicates, i.e. the logical relation which subsists between 'P' and C if the confirmation of 'P' can be carried out by that of predicates of C. Now, if confirmation is to be feasible at all, this process of referring back to other predicates must terminate at some point. The reduction must finally come to predicates for which we can come to a confirmation directly, i.e. without reference to other predicates. According to Explanation 1, the observable predicates can be used as such a basis. This consideration leads us to the following definition of the concept 'confirmable'. This concept is a descriptive one, in contradistinction to the logical concept 'reducible to C' – which could be named also 'confirmable with respect to C'.

Definition 16. A *sentence* S is called *confirmable* (or completely confirmable, or incompletely confirmable) if the confirmation of S is reducible (or completely reducible, or incompletely reducible, respectively) to that of a class of observable predicates.

[*Note*, 1950. Today I should prefer to replace Def. 16 by the following definition, based on Def. 18: A *sentence* S is *confirmable* (or . . .) if every descriptive predicate occurring in S is confirmable (or . . .).]

Definition 17. A sentence S is called *bilaterally confirmable* (or bilaterally completely confirmable) if both S and ∼ S are confirmable (or completely confirmable, respectively).

Definition 18. A *predicate* 'P' is called *confirmable* (or completely confirmable, or incompletely confirmable) if 'P' is reducible (or completely reducible, or incompletely reducible, respectively) to a class of observable predicates.

Hence, if 'P' is confirmable (or completely confirmable) the full sentences of 'P' are bilaterally confirmable (or bilaterally completely confirmable, respectively).

When we call a sentence S confirmable, we do not mean that it is possible to arrive at a confirmation of S under the circumstances as they actually exist. We rather intend this possibility under some *possible circumstances*, whether they be real or not. Thus e.g. because my pencil is black and I am able to make out by visual observation that it is black and not red, I cannot come to a positive confirmation of the sentence "My pencil is red." Nevertheless we call this sentence confirmable and moreover completely confirmable for the reason that we are able to indicate the – actually non-existent, but possible – observations which would confirm that sentence. Whether the real circumstances are such that the testing of a certain sentence S leads to a positive result, i.e. to a confirmation of S, or such that it leads to a negative result, i.e. to a confirmation of ∼ S, is irrelevant for the questions of confirmability, testability and meaning of the sentence though decisive for the question of truth, i.e. sufficient confirmation.

Theorem 8. If 'P' is introduced on the basis of observable predicates, 'P' is confirmable. If the introductive chain has molecular form, 'P' is completely confirmable. – This follows from Theorem 7 (§ 9).

Theorem 9. If S is a sentence of molecular form and all predicates occurring in S are confirmable (or completely confirmable) S is bilaterally confirmable (or bilaterally completely confirmable, respectively). – From Theorem 2 (§ 6).

Theorem 10. If the sentence S is constructed out of confirmable predicates with the help of connective symbols and universal or existential operators, S is bilaterally confirmable. – From Theorems 2, 3, and 4 (§ 6).

10. Method of Testing

If 'P' is confirmable then it is not impossible that for a suitable point *b* we may find a confirmation of 'P(b)' or of '$\sim$ P(b)'. But it is not necessary that we know a method for finding such a confirmation. If such a procedure can be given – we may call it a *method of testing* – then 'P' is not only confirmable but – as we shall say later on – testable. The following considerations will deal with the question how to formulate a method of testing and thereby will lead to a definition of 'testable'.

The description of a method of testing for 'Q_3' has to contain two other predicates of the following kinds:

1) A predicate, say 'Q_1', describing a *test-condition* for 'Q_3', i.e. an experimental situation which we have to create in order to test 'Q_3' at a given point.

2) A predicate, say 'Q_2', describing a *truth-condition* for 'Q_3' with respect to 'Q_1', i.e. a possible experimental result of the test-condition Q_1 at a given point *b* of such a kind that, if this result occurs, 'Q_3' is to be attributed to *b.* Now the connection between 'Q_1', 'Q_2', and 'Q_3' is obviously as follows: if the test-condition is realized at the given point *b* then, if the truth-condition is found to be fulfilled at *b*, *b* has the property to be tested; and this holds for any point. Thus the method of testing for 'Q_3' is to be formulated by the universal sentence '$Q_1 \supset (Q_2 \supset Q_3)$', in other words, by a reduction sentence for 'Q_3'. But this sentence, beside being a reduction sentence, must fulfill the following two additional requirements:

1) 'Q_1' must be realizable because, if we did not know how to produce the test-condition, we could not say that we had a method of testing.

2) We must know beforehand how to test the truth condition Q_2; otherwise we could not test 'Q_3' although it might be confirmable. In order to satisfy the second requirement, 'Q_2' must be either observable or explicitly defined on the basis of observable predicates or a method of testing for it must have been stated. If we start from observable predicates – which, as we know, can be tested without a description of a method of testing being necessary – and then introduce other predicates by explicit definitions or by such reduction sentences as fulfill the requirements stated above and hence are descriptions of a method of testing, then we know how to test each of these predicates. Thus we are led to the following definitions.

Definition 19. An introductive chain based upon observable predicates of such a kind that in each of its reduction sentences, say '$Q_1 \supset$

$(Q_2 \supset Q_3)$' or '$Q_4 \supset (Q_5 \supset \sim Q_3)$', the first predicate – 'Q_1' or 'Q_4', respectively – is realizable, is called a *test chain*. A reduction sentence (or a reduction pair, or a bilateral reduction sentence) belonging to a test chain is called a *test sentence* (or a *test pair*, or a *bilateral test sentence*, respectively).

A test pair for 'Q', and likewise a bilateral test sentence for 'Q', describes a method of testing for both 'Q' and '$\sim$ Q'. A bilateral test sentence, e.g. '$Q_1 \supset (Q_3 \equiv Q_2)$' may be interpreted in words in the following way. "If at a space-time point x the test-condition Q_1 (consisting perhaps in a certain experimental situation, including suitable measuring instruments) is realized then we will attribute the predicate 'Q_3' to the point x if and only if we find at x the state Q_2 (which may be a certain result of the experiment, e.g. a certain position of the pointer on the scale)". To give an example, let 'Q_3(b)' mean: "The fluid at the space-time-point *b* has a temperature of 100°"; 'Q_1(b)': "A mercury thermometer is put at *b*; we wait, while stirring the liquid, until the mercury comes to a standstill"; 'Q_2(b)': "The head of the mercury column of the thermometer at *b* stands at the mark 100 of the scale." If here 'Q_3' is introduced by '$Q_1 \supset (Q_3 \equiv Q_2)$' obviously its testability is assured. . . .

11. *A Remark about Positivism and Physicalism*

One of the fundamental theses of *positivism* may perhaps be formulated in this way: every term of the whole language L of science is reducible to what we may call sense-data terms or perception terms. By a perception term we understand a predicate 'P' such that 'P(b)' means: "the person at the space-time-place *b* has a perception of the kind P". (Let us neglect here the fact that the older positivism would have referred in a perception sentence not to a space-time-place, but to an element of "consciousness"; let us here take the physicalistic formulation given above.) I think that this thesis is true if we understand the term 'reducible' in the sense in which we have defined it here. But previously reducibility was not distinguished from definability. Positivists therefore believed that every descriptive term of science could be defined by perception terms, and hence, that every sentence of the language of science could be translated into a sentence about perceptions. This opinion is also expressed in the former publications of the Vienna Circle, including mine of 1928 (Carnap [1]), but I now think that it is not entirely adequate. Reducibility can be asserted, but not unrestricted possibility of elimination and re-translation; the reason being that the method of introduction by reduction pairs is indispensable.

Because we are here concerned with an important correction of a widespread opinion let us examine in greater detail the reduction and retranslation of sentences as positivists previously regarded them. Let us take as an example a simple sentence about a physical thing:

(1) "On May 6, 1935, at 4 P.M., there is a round black table in my room."

According to the usual positivist opinion, this sentence can be translated into the conjunction of the following conditional sentences (2) about (possible) perceptions. (For the sake of simplicity we eliminate in this example only the term "table" and continue to use in these sentences some terms which are not perception terms e.g. "my room", "eye" etc., which by further reduction would have to be eliminated also.)

(2a) "If on May . . . somebody is in my room and looks in such and such direction, he has a visual perception of such and such a kind."

(2a′), (2a″), etc. Similar sentences about the other possible aspects of the table.

(2b) "If . . . somebody is in my room and stretches out his hands in such and such a direction, he has touch perceptions of such and such a kind."

(2b′), (2b″), etc. Similar sentences about the other possible touchings of the table.

(2c) etc. Similar sentences about possible perceptions of other senses.

It is obvious that no single one of these sentences (2) nor even a conjunction of some of them would suffice as a translation of (1); we have to take the whole series containing all possible perceptions of that table. Now the first difficulty of this customary positivistic reduction consists in the fact that it is not certain that the series of sentences (2) is finite. If it is not, then there exists no conjunction of them; and in this case the original sentence (1) cannot be translated into one perception sentence. But a more serious objection is the following one. Even the whole class of sentences (2) – no matter whether it be finite or infinite – is not equipollent with (1), because it may be the case that (1) is false, though every single sentence of the class (2) is true. In order to construct such a case, suppose that at the time stated there is neither a round black table in my room, nor any observer at all. (1) is then obviously false. (2a) is a universal implication sentence:

"(x) [(x is . . . in my room and looks . . .) ⊃ (x perceives . . .)]",

which we may abbreviate in this way:

(3) $$(x)[P(x) \supset Q(x)]$$

which can be transformed into

(4) $$(x)[\sim P(x) \vee Q(x)]$$

((2a) can be formulated in words in this way: "For anybody it is either not the case that he is in my room on May . . . and looks . . . or he has a visual perception of such and such a kind".) Now, according to our assumption, for every person *x* it is false that *x* is at that time in my room and looks . . . ; in symbols:

(5) $$(x)(\sim P(x)).$$

Therefore (4) is true, and hence (2a) also, and analogously every one of the other sentences of the class (2), while (1) is false. In this way the positivistic reduction in its customary form is shown to be invalid. The example dealt with is a sentence about a directly perceptible thing. If we took as examples sentences about atoms, electrons, electric field and the like, it would be even clearer that the positivistic translation into perception terms is not possible.

Let us look at the consequences which these considerations have for the construction of a scientific language on a positivistic basis, i.e. with perception terms as the only primitive terms. The most important consequence concerns the method of introduction of further terms. In introducing simple terms of perceptible things (e.g. 'table') and *a fortiori* the abstract terms of scientific physics, we must not restrict the introductive method to definitions but must also use reduction. If we do this the positivistic thesis concerning reducibility above mentioned can be shown to be true.

Let us give the name '*thing-language*' to that language which we use in every-day life in speaking about the perceptible things surrounding us. A sentence of the thing-language describes things by stating their observable properties or observable relations subsisting between them. What we have called observable predicates are predicates of the thing-language. (They have to be clearly distinguished from what we have called perception terms; if a person sees a round red spot on the table the perception term 'having a visual perception of something round and red' is attributed to the person while the observable predicate 'round and red' is attributed to the space-time point on the table.) Those predicates of the thing-language which are not observable, e.g. disposition terms, are reducible to observable predicates and hence confirmable. We have seen this in the example of the predicate 'soluble' (§ 7).

Let us give the name '*physical language*' to that language which is used in physics. It contains the thing-language and, in addition, those terms of a scientific terminology which we need for a scientific description of the processes in inorganic nature. While the terms of the thing-language for the most part serve only for a qualitative description of things, the other terms of the physical language are designed increasingly for a quantitative description. For every term of the physical language physicists know how to use it on the basis of their observations. Thus every such term is reducible to observable predicates and hence confirmable. Moreover, nearly every such term is testable, because for every term – perhaps with the exception of few terms considered as preliminary ones – physicists possess a method of testing; for the quantitative terms this is a method of measurement.

The so-called thesis of *Physicalism*[9] asserts that every term of the language of science – including beside the physical language those sub-

[9] Comp. Neurath [1], [2], [3]; Carnap [2], [8].

languages which are used in biology, in psychology, and in social science – is reducible to terms of the physical language. Here a remark analogous to that about positivism has to be made. We may assert reducibility of the terms, but not – as was done in our former publications – definability of the terms and hence translatability of the sentences.

In former explanations of physicalism we used to refer to the physical language as a basis of the whole language of science. It now seems to me that what we really had in mind as such a basis was rather the thing-language, or, even more narrowly, the observable predicates of the thing-language. In looking for a new and more correct formulation of the thesis of physicalism we have to consider the fact mentioned that the method of definition is not sufficient for the introduction of new terms. Then the question remains: can every term of the language of science be introduced on the basis of observable terms of the thing-language by using only definitions and test-sentences, or are reduction sentences necessary which are not test sentences? In other words, which of the following formulations of the thesis of physicalism is true?

1. Thesis of Physicalistic Testability: "Every descriptive predicate of the language of science is testable on the basis of observable thing-predicates."

2. Thesis of Physicalistic Confirmability: "Every descriptive predicate of the language of science is confirmable on the basis of observable thing-predicates."

If we had been asked the question at the time when we first stated physicalism, I am afraid we should perhaps have chosen the first formulation. Today I hesitate to do this, and I should prefer the weaker formulation (2). The reason is that I think scientists are justified to use and actually do use terms which are confirmable without being testable, as the example in § 14 shows.

We have sometimes formulated the thesis of physicalism in this way: "The language of the whole of science is a physicalistic language." We used to say: a language L is called a physicalistic language if it is constructed out of the physical language by introducing new terms. (The introduction was supposed to be made by definition; we know today that we must employ reduction as well.) In this definition we could replace the reference to the physical language by a reference to the thing-language or even to the observable predicates of the thing-language. And here again we have to decide whether to admit for the reduction only test-chains or other reduction chains as well; in other words, whether to define 'physicalistic language' as 'a language whose descriptive terms are testable on the basis of observable thing-predicates' or ' . . . are confirmable . . .'.

12. Sufficient Bases

A class C of descriptive predicates of a language L such that every descriptive predicate of L is reducible to C is called a *sufficient reduction basis* of L; if in the reduction only definitions are used, C is called a *sufficient definition basis.* If C is a sufficient reduction basis of L and the predicates of C – and hence all predicates of L – are confirmable, C is called a *sufficient confirmation basis* of L; and if moreover the predicates of C are completely testable, for instance observable, and every predicate of L is reducible to C by a test chain – and hence is testable – C is called a *sufficient test basis* of L.

As we have seen, positivism asserts that the class of perception-terms is a sufficient basis for the language of science; physicalism asserts the same for the class of physical terms, or, in our stronger formulation, for the class of observable thing-predicates. Whether positivism and physicalism are right or not, at any rate it is clear that there can be several and even mutually exclusive bases. The classes of terms which positivism and physicalism assert to be sufficient bases, are rather comprehensive. Nevertheless even these bases are not sufficient definition bases but only sufficient reduction bases. Hence it is obvious that, if we wish to look for narrower sufficient bases, they must be reduction bases. We shall find that there are sufficient reduction bases of the language of science which have a far narrower extension than the positivistic and the physicalistic bases.

Let L be the physical language. We will look for sufficient reduction bases of L. If physicalism is right, every such basis of L is also a basis of the total scientific language; but here we will not discuss the question of physicalism. We have seen that the class of the observable predicates is a sufficient reduction basis of L. In what follows we will consider only bases consisting of observable predicates; hence they are *confirmation bases of the physical language* L. Whether they are also test bases depends upon whether all confirmable predicates of L are also testable; this question may be left aside for the moment. The visual sense is the most important sense; and we can easily see that it is sufficient for the confirmation of any physical property. A deaf man for instance is able to determine pitch, intensity and timbre of a physical sound with the help of suitable instruments; a man without the sense of smell can determine the olfactory properties of a gas by chemical analysis; etc. That all physical functions (temperature, electric field etc.) can be determined by the visual sense alone is obvious. Thus we see that the predicates of the visual sense, i.e. the colour-predicates as functions of space-time-places, are a sufficient confirmation basis of the physical language L.

But the basis can be restricted still more. Consider a man who cannot perceive colours, but only differences of brightness. Then he is able to determine all physical properties of things or events which we can determine from photographs; and that means, all properties. Thus he determines e.g. the colour of a light with the help of a spectroscope or a spectrograph. Hence the class of predicates which state the degree of brightness at a space-time-place – or the class consisting of the one functor [10] whose

[10] Compare Carnap [4] §3.

value is the degree of brightness – is a sufficient basis of L.

Now imagine a man whose visual sense is still more restricted. He may be able to distinguish neither the different colours nor the different degree of brightness, but only the two qualities bright and dark (= not bright) with their distribution in the visual field. What he perceives corresponds to a bad phototype which shows no greys but only black and white. Even this man is able to accomplish all kinds of determinations necessary in physics. He will determine the degree of brightness of a light by an instrument whose scale and pointer form a black-white-picture. Hence the one predicate 'bright' is a sufficient basis of L.

But even a man who is completely blind and deaf, but is able to determine by touching the spatial arrangements of bodies, can determine all physical properties. He has to use instruments with palpable scale-marks and a palpable pointer (such e.g. as watches for the blind). With such a spectroscope he can determine the colour of a light; etc. Let 'Solid' be a predicate such that 'Solid(b)' means: "There is solid matter at the space-time-point b". Then this single predicate 'Solid' is a sufficient basis of L.

Thus we have found several very narrow bases which are sufficient confirmation bases for the physical language and simultaneously sufficient test bases for the testable predicates of the physical language. And, if physicalism is right, they are also sufficient for the total language of science. Some of these bases consist of one predicate only. And obviously there are many more sufficient bases of such a small extent. This result will be relevant for our further considerations. It may be noticed that this result cannot at all be anticipated *a priori*; neither the fact of the existence of so small sufficient bases nor the fact that just the predicates mentioned are sufficient, is a logical necessity. Reducibility depends upon the validity of certain universal sentences, and hence upon the system of physical laws; thus the facts mentioned are special features of the structure of that system, or – expressed in the material idiom – special features of the causal structure of the real world. Only after constructing a system of physics can we determine what bases are sufficient with respect to that system.

IV. The Construction of a Language-System

13. The Problem of a Criterion of Meaning

It is not the aim of the present essay to defend the principle of empiricism against apriorism or anti-empiricist metaphysics. Taking empiricism [11] for granted, we wish to discuss the question, what is meaningful. The word 'meaning' will here be taken in its empiricist sense; an expression of language has meaning in this sense if we know how to use it in speaking about

[11] The words 'empiricism' and 'empiricist' are here understood in their widest sense, and not in the narrower sense of traditional positivism or sensationalism or any other doctrine restricting empirical knowledge to a certain kind of experience.

empirical facts, either actual or possible ones. Now our problem is what expressions are meaningful in this sense. We may restrict this question to sentences because expressions other than sentences are meaningful if and only if they can occur in a meaningful sentence.

Empiricists generally agree, at least in general terms, in the view that the question whether a given sentence is meaningful is closely connected with the questions of the possibility of verification, confirmation or testing of that sentence. Sometimes the two questions have been regarded as identical. I believe that this identification can be accepted only as a rough first approximation. Our real problem now is to determine the precise relation between the two questions, or generally, to state the criterion of meaning in terms of verification, confirmation or testing.

I need not emphasize that here we are concerned only with the problem of meaning as it occurs in methodology, epistemology or applied logic,[12] and not with the psychological question of meaning. We shall not consider here the questions whether any images and, if so, what images are connected with a given sentence. That these questions belong to psychology and do not touch the methodological question of meaning has often been emphasized.[13]

It seems to me that the question about the criterion of meaning has to be construed and formulated in a way different from that in which it is usually done. In the first place we have to notice that this problem concerns the structure of language. (In my opinion this is true for all philosophical questions, but that is beyond our present discussion.) Hence a clear formulation of the question involves reference to a certain language; the usual formulations do not contain such a reference and hence are incomplete and cannot be answered. Such a reference once made, we must above all distinguish between two main kinds of questions about meaningfulness; to the first kind belong the questions referring to a historically given language-system, to the second kind those referring to a language-system which is yet to be constructed. These two kinds of questions have an entirely different character. A question of the first kind is a theoretical one; it asks, what is the actual state of affairs; and the answer is either true or false. The second question is a practical one; it asks, how shall we proceed; and the answer is not an assertion but a proposal or decision. We shall consider the two kinds one after the other.

A *question of the first kind* refers to a given language-system L and concerns an expression E of L (i.e. a finite series of symbols of L). The question is, whether E is meaningful or not. This question can be divided into two parts: a) "Is E a sentence of L"?, and b) "If so, does E fulfill the empiricist criterion of meaning"? Question (a) is a formal question of

[12] Our problem of meaning belongs to the field which *Tarski* [1] calls *Semantic*; this is the theory of the relations between the expressions of a language and things, properties, facts etc. described in the language.

[13] Comp. e.g. Schlick [4] p. 355.

logical syntax (comp. Chapter II); question (b) belongs to the field of methodology (comp. Chapter III). It would be advisable to avoid the terms 'meaningful' and 'meaningless' in this and in similar discussions – because these expressions involve so many rather vague philosophical associations – and to replace them by an expression of the form "a . . . sentence of L"; expressions of this form will then refer to a specified language and will contain at the place '. . .' an adjective which indicates the methodological character of the sentence, e.g. whether or not the sentence (and its negation) is verifiable or completely or incompletely confirmable or completely or incompletely testable and the like, according to what is intended by 'meaningful'.

14. The Construction of a Language-System L

A *question of the second kind* concerns a language-system L which is being proposed for construction. In this case the rules of L are not given, and the problem is how to choose them. We may construct L in whatever way we wish. There is no question of right or wrong, but only a practical question of convenience or inconvenience of a system form, i.e. of its suitability for certain purposes. In this case a theoretical discussion is possible only concerning the consequences which such and such a choice of rules would have; and obviously this discussion belongs to the first kind. The special question whether or not a given choice of rules will produce an empiricist language, will then be contained in this set of questions.

In order to make the problem more specific and thereby more simple, let us suppose that we wish to construct L as a physical language, though not as a language for all science. The problems connected with specifically biological or psychological terms, though interesting in themselves, would complicate our present discussion unnecessarily. But the main points of the philosophical discussions of meaning and testability already occur in this specialized case.

In order to formulate the rules of an intended language L, it is necessary to use a language L′ which is already available. L′ must be given at least practically and need not be stated explicitly as a language-system, i.e. by formulated rules. We may take as L′ the English language. In constructing L, L′ serves for two different purposes. First, L′ is the syntax-language [14] in which the rules of the object-language L are to be formulated. Secondly, L′ may be used as a basis for comparison for L, i.e. as a first object-language with which we compare the second object-language L, as to richness of expressions, structure and the like. Thus we may consider the question, to which sentences of the English language (L′) do we wish to construct corresponding sentences in L, and to which not. For example, in constructing the language of *Principia Mathematica*, Whitehead and Russell wished to have available translations for the English sentences of the form "There is something which has the property ψ"; they therefore constructed their

[14] Comp. Carnap [4] §1; [5], p. 39.

language-system so as to contain the sentence-form "$(\exists x) \cdot \psi x$". A difficulty occurs because the English language is not a language-system in the strict sense (i.e. a system of fixed rules) so that the concept of translation cannot be used here in its exact syntactical sense. Nevertheless this concept is sufficiently clear for our present practical purpose. The comparison of L with L′ belongs to the rather vague, preliminary considerations which lead to decisions about the system L. Subsequently the result of these decisions can be exactly formulated as rules of the system L.

It is obvious that we are not compelled to construct L so as to contain sentences corresponding to all sentences of L′. If e.g. we wish to construct a language of economics, then its sentences correspond only to a small part of the sentences of the English language L′. But even if L were to be a language adequate for all science there would be many – and I among them – who would not wish to have in L a sentence corresponding to every sentence which usually is considered as a correct English sentence and is used by learned people. We should not wish e.g. to have corresponding sentences to many or perhaps most of the sentences occurring in the books of metaphysicians. Or, to give a nonmetaphysical example, the members of our Circle did not wish in former times to include into our scientific language a sentence corresponding to the English sentence

S_1: "This stone is now thinking about Vienna."

But at present I should prefer to construct the scientific language in such a way that it contains a sentence S_2 corresponding to S_1. (Of course I should then take S_2 as false, and hence $\sim S_2$ as true.) I do not say that our former view was wrong. Our mistake was simply that we did not recognize the question as one of decision concerning the form of the language; we therefore expressed our view in the form of an assertion – as is customary among philosophers – rather than in the form of a proposal. We used to say: "S_1 is not false but meaningless"; but the careless use of the word 'meaningless' has its dangers and is the second point in which we would like at present to modify the previous formulation.

We return to the question how we are to proceed in constructing a physical language L, using as L′ the English physical language.

The following list shows the items which have to be decided in constructing a language L.

I. Formative rules (= definition of 'sentence in L').

A. Atomic sentences.

1. The form of atomic sentences.
2. The atomic predicates.
   a. Primitive predicates.
   b. Indirectly introduced atomic predicates.

B. Formative operations of the first kind: Connections; Molecular sentences.

C. Formative operations of the second kind: Operators.

1. Generalized sentences. (This is the *critical point.*)
2. Generalized predicates.

II. Transformative rules (= definition of 'consequence in L').

A. L-rules. (The rules of logical deduction.)
B. P-rules. (The physical laws stated as valid.)

In the following sections we shall consider in succession items of the kind I, i.e. the formative rules. We will choose these rules for the language L from the point of view of empiricism; and we shall try, in constructing this empiricist language L, to become clear about what is required for a sentence to have meaning.

15. Atomic Sentences: Primitive Predicates

The suitable method for stating formative rules does not consist in describing every single form of sentence which we wish to admit in L. That is impossible because the number of these forms is infinite. The best method consists in fixing

1. The forms of some sentences of a simple structure; we may call them (elementary or) *atomic sentences* (I A);
2. Certain *operations* for the formation of compound sentences (I B, C).

I A 1. Atomic sentences. As already mentioned, we will consider only predicates of that type which is most important for physical language, namely those predicates whose arguments are individual constants, i.e. designations of space-time-points. (It may be remarked that it would be possible and even convenient to admit also full sentences of physical functors as atomic sentences of L, e.g. 'te(a) = r', corresponding to the sentence of L′: "The temperature at the space-time-point *a* is *r*". For the sake of simplicity we will restrict the following considerations to predicate-sentences. The results can easily be applied to functor-sentences also.) An atomic sentence is a full sentence of an atomic predicate (Definition 15a, § 6). An atomic predicate is either primitive or introduced by an atomic chain (Definition 14b, § 6). Therefore we have to answer the following questions in order to determine the form of the atomic sentences of L:

I A 2. a) Which predicates shall we admit as primitive predicates of L?

b) Which forms of atomic introductive chains shall we admit?

I A 2a: *Primitive predicates.* Our decision concerning question (a) is obviously very important for the construction of L. It might be thought that the richness of language L depends chiefly upon how rich is the selection we make of primitive predicates. If this were the case the philosophical discussion of what sentences were to be included in L – which is usually formulated as: what sentences are meaningful? – would reduce to this question of the selection of primitive predicates. But in fact this is not the case. As we shall see, the main controversy among philosophers concerns the formation of sentences by operators (I C 1). About the selection of primitive predicates agreement can easily be attained, even among representatives of the most divergent views regarding what is meaningful and what is meaningless. This is easily understood if we remember our previous considerations about sufficient bases. If a suitable predicate is selected as the primitive predicate of L, all other physical predicates can be introduced by reduction chains.

To illustrate how the selection of primitive predicates could be carried out, let us suppose that the person N_1 who is constructing the language L trusts his sense of sight more than his other senses. That may lead him to take the colour-predicates (attributed to things or space-time-points, not to acts of perception, compare the example given on p. 69) as primitive predicates of L. Since all other physical predicates are reducible to them, N_1 will not take any other primitive predicates. It is just at this point in selecting primitive predicates, that N_1 has to face the question of observability. If N_1 possesses a normal colour sense each of the selected predicates, e.g. 'red', is observable by him in the sense explained before (§ 8). Further, if N_1 wishes to share the language L with other people – as is the case in practice – N_1 must inquire whether the predicates selected by him are also observable by them; he must investigate whether they are able to use these predicates in sufficient agreement with him, – whether it be subsequent to training by him or not. We may suppose that N_1 will come to a positive result on the basis of his experience with English-speaking people. Exact agreement, it is true, is not obtainable; but that is not demanded. Suppose however that N_1 meets a completely colour-blind man N_2. N_1 will find that he cannot get N_2 to use the colour predicates in sufficient agreement with him, in other words, that these predicates are not observable by N_2. If nevertheless N_1 wishes to have N_2 in his language-community, N_1 must change his selection of primitive predicates. Perhaps he will take the brightness-predicates which are also observable by him. But there might be a completely blind man N_3, for whom not one of the primitive predicates selected by N_1 is observable. Is N_3 now unable to take part in the total physical language of N_1? No, he is not. N_1 and N_3 might both take e.g. the predicate 'solid' as primitive predicate for their common language L. This predicate is observable both for N_3 and N_1, and it is a sufficient confirmation basis for the physical language L, as we have seen above. Or, if N_1 prefers to keep visual predicates as primitive predicates for L, he may suggest to N_3 that he take 'solid' as primitive predicate of N_3's language L_3 and then introduce the other predicates by reduction in such a way that they agree with the predicates of N_1's language L. Then L and L_3 will be completely congruent even as to the stock of predicates, though the selections of primitive predicates are different. How far N_1 will go in accepting people with restricted sensual faculties into his language-community, is a matter of practical decision. For our further considerations we shall suppose that only observable predicates are selected as primitive predicates of L. Obviously this restriction is not a necessary one. But, as empiricists, we want every predicate of our scientific language to be confirmable, and we must therefore select observable predicates as primitive ones. For the following considerations we suppose that the primitive predicates of L are observable without fixing a particular selection.

Decision 1. Every primitive descriptive predicate of L is observable.

16. The Choice of a Psychological or a Physical Basis

In selecting the primitive predicates for the physical language L we must pay attention to the question whether they are observable, i.e. whether they can be directly tested by perceptions. Nevertheless we need not demand the existence of sentences in L – either atomic or other kinds – corresponding to perception-sentences of L′ (e.g. "I am now seeing a round, red patch"). L may be a physical language constructed according to the demands of empiricism, and may nevertheless contain no perception-sentences at all.

If we choose a basis for the whole scientific language and if we decide as empiricists, to choose observable predicates, two (or three) different possibilities still remain open for specifying more completely the basis, apart from the question of taking a narrower or wider selection. For, if we take the concept 'observable' in the wide sense explained before (§ 11) we find two quite different kinds of observable predicates, namely physical and psychological ones.

1. Observable *physical predicates of the thing-language,* attributed to perceived things of any kind or to space-time-points. All examples of primitive predicates of L mentioned before belong to this kind. Examples of full sentences of such predicates: "This thing is brown," "This spot is quadrangular," "This space-time-point is warm," "At this space-time-point is a solid substance."

2. Observable *psychological predicates.* Examples: "having a feeling of anger," "having an imagination of a red triangle," "being in the state of thinking about Vienna," "remembering the city hall of Vienna." The perception predicates also belong to this kind, e.g. "having a perception (sensation) of red," ". . . of sour"; these perception predicates have to be distinguished from the corresponding thing-predicates belonging to the first kind (see p. 69). These predicates are observable in our sense in so far as a person N who is in such a state can, under normal conditions, be aware of this state and can therefore directly confirm a sentence attributing such a predicate to himself. Such an attribution is based upon that kind of observation which psychologists call introspection or self-observation, and which philosophers sometimes have called perception by the inner sense. These designations are connected with and derived from certain doctrines to which I do not subscribe and which will not be assumed in the following; but the fact referred to by these designations seems to me to be beyond discussion. Concerning these observable psychological predi-

cates we have to distinguish two interpretations or modes of use, according to which they are used either in a phenomenological or in a physicalistic language.

2a. Observable psychological predicates *in a phenomenological language*. Such a predicate is attributed to a so-called state of consciousness with a temporal reference (but without spatial determination, in contradistinction to 2b). Examples of full sentences of such predicates (the formulation varies according to the philosophy of the author): "My consciousness is now in a state of anger" (or: "I am now . . .", or simply: "Now anger"); and analogously with "such and such an imagination", ". . . remembrance", ". . . thinking", ". . . perception", etc. These predicates are here interpreted as belonging to a phenomenological language, i.e. a language about conscious phenomena as nonspatial events. However, such a language is a purely subjective one, suitable for soliloquy only, while the intersubjective thing-language is suitable for use among different subjects. For the construction of a subjective language predicates of this kind may be taken as primitive predicates. Several such subjective languages constructed by several subjects may then be combined for the construction of an intersubjective language. But the predicates of this kind cannot be taken directly as observable primitive predicates of an intersubjective language.

2b. Observable psychological predicates *in a physicalistic language*. Such a predicate is attributed to a person as a thing with spatio-temporal determination. (I believe that this is the use of psychological predicates in our language of everyday life, and that they are used or interpreted in the phenomenological way only by philosophers.) Examples of full sentences: "Charles was angry yesterday at noon," "I (i.e. this person, known as John Brown) have now a perception of red," etc. Here the psychological predicates belong to an intersubjective language. And they are intersubjectively confirmable. N_2 may succeed in confirming such a sentence as "N_1 is now thinking of Vienna" (S), as is constantly done in everyday life as well as in psychological investigations in the laboratory. However, the sentence S is confirmable by N_2 only incompletely, although it is completely confirmable by N_1. [It seems to me that there is general agreement about the fact that N_1 can confirm more directly than N_2 a sentence concerning N_1's feelings, thoughts, etc. There is disagreement only concerning the question whether this difference is a fundamental one or only a difference in degree. The majority of philosophers, including some members of our Circle in former times, hold that the difference is fundamental inasmuch as there is a certain field of events, called the consciousness of a person, which is absolutely inaccessible to any other person. But we now believe, on the basis of physicalism, that the difference, although very great and very important for practical life, is only a matter of degree and that there are predicates for which the directness of confirmation by other persons has intermediate degrees (e.g. 'sour' and 'quadrangular' or 'cold' when attributed to a piece of sugar in my mouth). But this difference in opinion need not be discussed for our present purposes.] We may formulate the fact mentioned by saying that the psychological predicates in a physicalistic language are intersubjectively confirmable but only *subjectively observable*. [As to testing, the difference is still greater. The sentence S is certainly not completely testable by N_2; and it seems doubtful whether it is at all testable by N_2, although it is certainly confirmable by N_2.] This feature of the predicates of kind 2b is a serious disadvantage and constitutes a reason against their choice as primitive predicates of an intersubjective language. Nevertheless we would have to take them as primitive predicates in a language of the whole of science if they were not reducible to predicates of the kind 1, because in such a language we require them in any case. But, if physicalism is correct they are in fact reducible and hence dispensable as primitive predicates of the whole language of science. And certainly for the physical language L under construction we need not take them as primitive.

According to these considerations, it seems to be preferable to choose the primitive predicates from the predicates of kind 1, i.e. of the observable thing-predicates. These are the only intersubjectively observable predicates. In this case, therefore, the same choice can be accepted by the different members of the language community. We formulate our decision concerning L, as a supplement to Decision 1:

Decision 2. Every primitive predicate of L is a thing predicate.

The choice of primitive predicates is meant here as the choice of a basis for possible confirmation. Thus, in order to find out whether the choice of primitive predicates of the kind 1 or 2a or 2b corresponds to the view of a certain philosopher, we have to examine what he takes as the basis for empirical knowledge, for confirmation or testing. *Mach*, by taking the sensation elements ('Empfindungselemente') as basis, can be interpreted as a representative of the standpoint 2a; and similarly other positivists, sensationalists and idealists. The views held in the first period of the Vienna Circle were very much influenced by positivists and above all by Mach, and hence also show an inclination to the view 2a. I myself took elementary experiences ('Elementarerlebnisse') as basis, (in [1]). Later on, when our Circle made the step to physicalism, we abandoned the phenomenological language recognizing its subjective limitation.[15] *Neurath* [16] requires for the basic sentences ('Protokollsätze'), i.e. those to which all confirmation and testing finally goes back, the occurrence of certain psychological terms of the kind 2b – or: of biological terms, as we may say with Neurath in order to stress the physicalistic interpretation – namely designations of actions of perception (as physicalistic terms). He does not admit in these basic sentences such a simple expression as e.g. "a black round table" which is observable in our sense but requires instead "a black round table perceived (or: seen) by Otto." This view can perhaps be interpreted as the choice of predicates of the kind 2b as primitive ones. We have seen above the disadvantages of such a choice of the basis. *Popper* [17] rejects for his basic sentences reference to mental events, whether it

[15] Comp. Carnap [2], §6.
[16] Neurath [5] and [6] p. 361.
[17] Popper [1] pp. 57ff.

be in the introspective, phenomenological form, or in physicalistic form. He characterizes his basic sentences with respect to their form as singular existential sentences and with respect to their content as describing observable events; he demands that a basic sentence must be intersubjectively testable by observation. Thus his view is in accordance with our choice of predicates of the kind 1 as primitive ones. He was, it seems to me, the first to hold this view. (The only inconvenient point in his choice of basic sentences seems to me to be the fact that the negations of his basic sentences are not basic sentences in his sense.)

I wish to emphasize the fact that I am in agreement with Neurath not only in the general outline of empiricism and physicalism but also in regard to the question what is to be required for empirical confirmation. Thus I do not deny —as neither Popper nor any other empiricist does, I believe—that a certain connection between the basic sentences and our perceptions is required. But, it seems to me, it is sufficient that the biological designations of perceptive activity occur in the formulation of the methodological requirement concerning the basic sentences – as e.g. in our formulation "The primitive descriptive predicates have to be observable," where the term "observable" is a biological term referring to perceptions – and that they need not occur in the basic sentences themselves. Also a language restricted to physics as e.g. our language L without containing any biological or perception terms may be an empiricist language provided its primitive descriptive predicates are observable; it may even fulfill the requirement of empiricism in its strictest form inasmuch as all predicates are completely testable. And this language is in its nature quite different from such a language as e.g. that of theoretical physics. The latter language – although as a part of the whole language of science, it is an empiricist language because containing only confirmable terms – does not contain observable predicates of the thing-language and hence does not include a confirmation basis. On the other hand, a physical language like L contains within itself its basis for confirmation and testing. . . .

17. Incompletely Confirmable Hypotheses in Physics

Now let us consider under what circumstances a physicist might find it necessary or desirable to state an hypothesis in a generalized form. Let us begin with one operator. The full sentences of a molecular predicate 'M_1' (i.e. '$M_1(a)$', etc.) are bilaterally completely confirmable. Suppose some of them are confirmed by observations, but not the negation of any of them so far. This fact may suggest to the physicist the sentence '$(x)M_1(x)$' of U_1 as a physical law to be adopted, i.e. a hypothesis whose negation is completely confirmable and which leads to completely confirmable predictions as consequences of it (e.g. '$M_1(b)$' etc.). If more and more such predictions are confirmed by subsequent observations, but not the negation of any of them, we may say that the hypothesis, though never confirmed completely, is confirmed in a higher and higher degree.

Considerations of this kind are very common; they are often used in order to explain that the admission of not completely confirmable ("unverifiable") universal hypotheses does not infringe the principle of empiricism. Such considerations are, I think, agreed to by all philosophers except those who demand complete confirmability ("verifiability") and thereby the limitation to a molecular language.

Now it seems to me that a completely analogous consideration applies to sentences with any number of operator sets, i.e. to sentences of U_n or E_n for any n. The following diagram may serve as an example. A *broken* arrow running from a sentence S to a class C of sentences indicates that the confirmation of S is *incompletely* reducible to that of C. S is in this case a universal sentence and C the class of its instances; each sentence of C is therefore a consequence of S, but S is not a consequence of any finite sub-class of C. A *solid* arrow running from S_1 to S_2 indicates that the confirmation of S_1 is *completely* reducible to that of S_2. In this case, S_1 is an

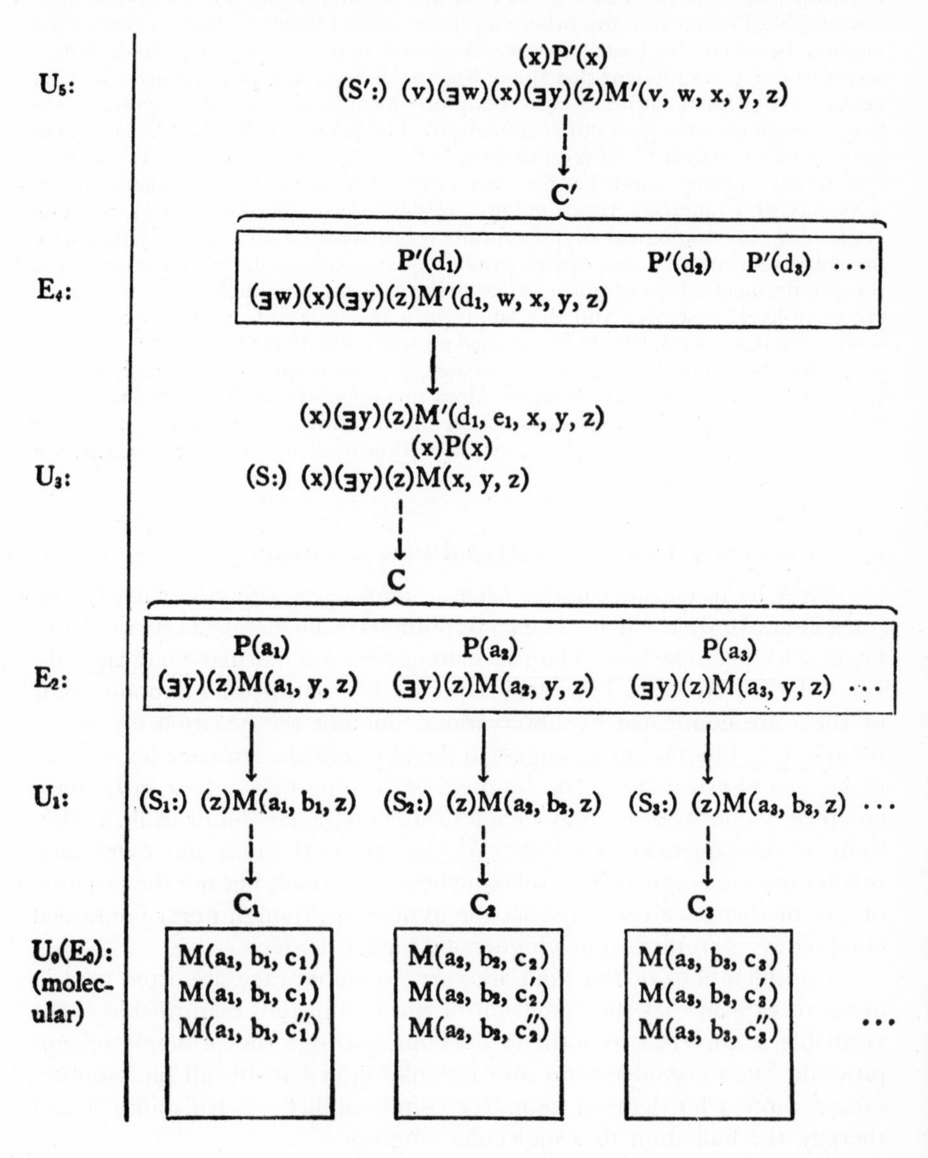

existential sentence and a consequence of S_2. At the left side are indicated the classes to which the sentences belong.

Let us start at the bottom of the diagram. The sentences of C_1 are molecular, and hence bilaterally completely testable. Let us suppose that a physicist confirms by his observations a good many of the sentences of C_1 without finding a confirmation for the negation of any sentence of C_1. According to the customary procedure described above, these experiences will suggest to him the adoption of S_1 as a well-confirmed hypothesis, which, by further confirmation of more and more sentences of C_1, may acquire an even higher degree of confirmation. Let us suppose that likewise the sentences of C_2 are confirmed by observations, further those of C_3, etc. Then the physicist will state S_2, S_3 etc. as well-confirmed hypotheses. If now sentences of the form E_2 are admitted in L, then the first sentence of C is a sentence of L, is also a consequence of S_1 and is therefore confirmed at least to the same degree as S_1. In order to make feasible the formulation of this well-confirmed hypothesis the physicist will be inclined to admit the sentences of E_2 in L. If he does so he can go one step further. He will adopt the second sentence of C as a consequence of the stated hypothesis S_2, the third one as a consequence of S_3, etc. If now the sentences of a sufficient number of classes of the series C_1, C_2, etc. are confirmed by observations, the corresponding number of sentences of the series S_1, S_2, etc. and likewise of sentences of C will be stated as well-confirmed hypotheses. If we define 'P' by '$P(x) \equiv (\exists y)(z)M(x, y, z)$', we may abbreviate the sentences of C by '$P(a_1)$', '$P(a_2)$', etc. The fact that these sentences are well-confirmed hypotheses will suggest to the physicist the sentence '$(x)P(x)$', that is S, as a hypothesis to be adopted provided he admits at all sentences of the form U_3 in L. The statement of S as confirmed by C is quite analogous to that of S_1 as confirmed by C_1. If somebody asserted that S – belonging to U_3 – is meaningless while the sentences of C – belonging to E_2 – are meaningful, he would thereby assert that it is meaningless to assume hypothetically that a certain condition which we have already assumed to subsist at several points a_1, a_2, a_3, etc. subsists at every point. Thus no reason is to be seen for prohibiting sentences of U_3, if sentences of E_2 are admitted.

This same procedure can be continued to higher and higher levels. Suppose that in the definition of 'M' two individual constants occur, say 'd_1' and 'e_1'; then we may write S in the form '$(x)(\exists y)(z)M'(d_1, e_1, x, y, z)$'. According to our previous supposition this is a hypothesis which is incompletely confirmed to a certain degree by our observations, namely by the sentences of C_1, C_2, etc. Then the first sentence of C′, being a consequence of S, is confirmed to at least the same degree. If we define 'P′' by '$P'(v) \equiv (\exists w)(x)(\exists y)(z)M'(v, w, x, y, z)$' we may abbreviate the first sentence of C′ by '$P'(d_1)$'. Now let us suppose that analogous sentences for d_2, d_3, etc. are likewise found to be confirmed by our observations.

Then by these sentences of C′ (belonging to E_4) S′ (belonging to U_5) is incompletely confirmed.

On the basis of these considerations it seems natural and convenient to make the following decisions.

Decision 5. Let S be a universal sentence (e.g. '(x)Q(x)') – which is being considered either for admission to or exclusion from L – and C be the class of the corresponding full sentences ('$Q(a_1)$', '$Q(a_2)$', etc.). Then obviously the sentences of C are consequences of S, and the confirmation of S is incompletely reducible to that of C. If the sentences of C are admitted in L we will admit the sentences of the form S, i.e. a class U_n for a certain n ($n > 0$).

Decision 6. Let S be an existential sentence (e.g. '(∃x)Q(x)') – which is being considered either for admission to or exclusion from L – and C be the class of the corresponding full sentences ('$Q(a_1)$', '$Q(a_2)$', etc.). Then obviously S is a consequence of every sentence of C, and hence the confirmation of S is completely reducible to that of C. If the sentences of C are admitted in L we will admit the sentences of the form S, i.e. a class E_n for a certain n ($n > 0$).

The acceptance of Decisions 5 and 6 leads in the first place, as shown by the example explained before, to the admission of U_1, E_2, U_3, E_4, U_5, etc. in L; and it also leads to the admission of E_1, U_2, E_3, U_4, etc. Hence the result is the choice of a language L_∞.

As an objection to our proposal of language L_∞ the remark will perhaps be made that the statement of hypotheses of a high complexity, say U_{10} or E_{10}, will never be necessary or desirable in science, and that therefore we need not choose L_∞. Our reply is, that the proposal of L_∞ by no means requires the statement of hypotheses of such a kind; it simply proposes not to prohibit their statement *a priori* by the formative rules of the language. It seems convenient to give the scientist an open field for possible formulations of hypotheses. Which of these admitted possibilities will actually be applied, must be learned from the further evolution of science, – it cannot be foreseen from general methodological considerations.

18. The Principle of Empiricism

It seems to me that it is preferable to formulate the principle of empiricism not in the form of an assertion – "all knowledge is empirical" or "all synthetic sentences that we can know are based on (or connected with) experiences" or the like – but rather in the form of a proposal or requirement. As empiricists, we require the language of science to be restricted in a certain way; we require that descriptive predicates and hence synthetic sentences are not to be admitted unless they have some connection with possible observations, a connection which has to be characterized in a suitable way. By such a formulation, it seems to me, greater clarity will be gained both for carrying on discussion between empiricists and anti-empiricists as well as for the reflections of empiricists.

We have seen that there are many different possibilities in framing an empiricist language. According to our previous considerations there are in the main four different requirements each of which may be taken as a possible formulation of empiricism; we will omit here the many intermediate positions which have been seen to consist in drawing a rather arbitrary boundary line.

RCT. Requirement of Complete Testability: "Every synthetic sentence must be completely testable". I.e. if any synthetic sentence S is given, we must know a method of testing for every descriptive predicate occurring in S so that we may determine for suitable points whether or not the predicate can be attributed to them; moreover, S must have such a form that at least certain sentences of this form can possibly be confirmed in the same degree as particular sentences about observable properties of things. This is the strongest of the four requirements. If we adopt it, we shall get a *testable molecular language* like L_0^t, i.e. a language restricted to molecular sentences and to test chains as the only introductive chains, in other words, to those reduction sentences whose first predicate is realizable.

RCC. Requirement of Complete Confirmability: "Every synthetic sentence must be completely confirmable." I.e. if any synthetic sentence S is given, there must be for every descriptive predicate occurring in S the possibility of our finding out for suitable points whether or not they have the property designated by the predicate in question; moreover, S must have a form such as is required in RCT, and hence be molecular. Thus the only difference between RCC and RCT concerns predicates. By RCC predicates are admitted which are introduced by the help of reduction sentences which are not test sentences. By the admission of the predicates of this kind the language is enlarged to a *confirmable molecular language* like L_0. It seems however that there are not very many predicates of this kind in the language of science and hence that the practical difference between RCT and RCC is not very great. But the difference in the methodological character of L_0^t and L_0 may seem important to those who wish to state RCT.

RT. Requirement of Testability: "Every synthetic sentence must be testable." RT is more liberal than RCT, but in another direction than RCC. RCC and RT are incomparable inasmuch as each of them contains predicates not admitted in the other one. RT admits incompletely testable sentences — these are chiefly universal sentences to be confirmed incompletely by their instances — and thus leads to a *testable generalized language*, like L_∞^t. Here the new sentences in comparison with L_0^t are very many; among them are the laws of science in the form of unrestricted universal sentences. Therefore the difference of RCT and RT, i.e. of L_0^t and L_∞^t, is of great practical importance. The advantages of this comprehensive enlargement have been explained in § 17.

RC. Requirement of Confirmability: "Every synthetic sentence must be confirmable". Here both restrictions are dispensed with. Predicates which are confirmable but not testable are admitted; and generalized sentences are admitted. This simultaneous enlargement in both directions leads to a *confirmable generalized language* like L_∞. L_∞ contains not only L_0^t but also L_0 and L_∞^t as proper sub-languages. RC is the most liberal of the four requirements. But it suffices to exclude all sentences of a non-empirical nature, e.g. those of transcendental metaphysics inasmuch as they are not confirmable, not even incompletely. Therefore it seems to me that RC suffices as a formulation of the principle of empiricism; in other words, if a scientist chooses any language fulfilling this requirement no objection can be raised against this choice from the point of view of empiricism. On the other hand, that does not mean that a scientist is not allowed to choose a more restricted language and to state one of the more restricting requirements for himself – though not for all scientists. There are no theoretical objections against these requirements, that is to say, objections condemning them as false or incorrect or meaningless or the like; but it seems to me that there are practical objections against them as being inconvenient for the purpose of science.

The following table shows the four requirements and their chief consequences.

Requirement	restriction to *molecular* sentences	restriction to *test* chains	language
RCT: complete testability	+	+	L_0^t
RCC: complete confirmability	+	—	L_0
RT: testability	—	+	L_∞^t
RC: confirmability	—	—	L_∞

19. Confirmability of Predictions

Let us consider the nature of a *prediction*, a sentence about a future event, from the point of view of empiricism, i.e. with respect to confirmation and testing. Modifying our previous symbolism, we will take 'c' as the name of a certain physical system, 'x' as a corresponding variable, 't' as the time-variable, 't_0' as a value of 't' designating a moment at which we have made observations about c, and 'd' as a constant designating a certain time interval, e.g. one day or one million years. Now let us consider the following sentences

$$\text{(S)} \qquad (t)[P_1(c,t) \supset P_2(c,t+d)]$$

in words: "For every instant t, if the system c has the state P_1 at the time t, then it has the state P_2 at the time t + d":

(S_1) $$P_1(c, t_0)$$

"The system c has the state P_1 at the time t_0 (of our observation)";

(S_2) $$P_2(c, t_0 + d)$$

"The system c will have the state P_2 at the time $t_0 + d$". Now let us make the following suppositions. There is a set C of laws about physical systems of that kind to which c belongs such that S can be derived from C; the predicates occurring in the laws of C, and among them 'P_1' and 'P_2', are completely testable; the laws of C have been tested very frequently and each tested instance had a positive result; S_1 is confirmed to a high degree by observations. From these suppositions it follows, that S_1 and S_2, having molecular form and containing only predicates which are completely testable, are themselves completely testable; that the laws of C are incompletely testable, but (incompletely) confirmed to a rather high degree; that S, being a consequence of C, is also confirmed to a rather high degree; that S_2, being a consequence of S and S_1, is also confirmed to a rather high degree. If we wait until the time $t_0 + d$ it may happen that we shall confirm S_2 by direct observations to a very high degree. But, as we have seen, a prediction like S_2 may have even at the present time a rather high degree of confirmation dependent upon the degree of confirmation of the laws used for the derivation of the prediction. The nature of a prediction like S_2 is, with respect to confirmation and testing, the same as that of a sentence S_3 about a past event not observed by ourselves, and the same as that of a sentence S^4 about a present event not directly observed by us, e.g. a process now going on in the interior of a machine, or a political event in China. S_3 and S_4 are, like S_2, derived from sentences based on our direct observations with the help of laws which are incompletely confirmed to some degree or other by previous observations.[18]

To give an example, let c be the planetary system, C the set of the differential equations of celestial mechanics from which S may be derived by integration, S_1 describing the present constellation of c – the positions and the velocities of the bodies – and d the interval of one million years. Let '$P_3(t)$' mean: "There are no living beings in the world at the time t," and consider the following sentence.

(S_5) $$P_3(t_0 + d) \supset P_2(c, t_0 + d)$$

meaning that, if in a million years there will be no living beings in the world then at that time the constellation of the planetary system will be P_2 (i.e. that which is to be calculated from the present constellation with the help of the laws confirmed by past observations). S_5 may be taken as

[18] *Reichenbach* ([3], p. 153) asks what position the Vienna Circle has taken concerning the methodological nature of predictions and other sentences about events not observed, after it gave up its earlier view influenced by Wittgenstein. The view explained above is that which my friends – especially Neurath and Frank – and I have held since about 1931 (compare Frank [1], Neurath [3], Carnap [2a], p. 443, 464 f.; [2b], p. 55 f., 99 f.).

a convenient formulation of the following sentence discussed by *Lewis* [19] and *Schlick*.[20] "If all minds (or: living beings) should disappear from the universe, the stars would still go on in their courses". Both Lewis and Schlick assert that this sentence is not verifiable. This is true if 'verifiable' is interpreted as 'completely confirmable'. But the sentence is confirmable and even testable, though incompletely. We have no well-confirmed predictions about the existence or non-existence of organisms at the time $t_0 + d$; but the laws C of celestial mechanics are quite independent of this question. Therefore, irrespective of its first part, S_5 is confirmed to the same degree as its second part, i.e. as S_2, and hence, as C. Thus we see that an indirect and incomplete testing and confirmation of S_2 – and thereby of S_5 – is neither logically nor physically nor even practically impossible, but has been actually carried out by astronomers. Therefore I agree with the following conclusion of Schlick concerning the sentence mentioned above (though not with his reasoning): "We are as sure of it as of the best founded physical laws that science has discovered." The sentence in question is meaningful from the point of view of empiricism, i.e. it has to be admitted in an empiricist language, provided generalized sentences are admitted at all and complete confirmability is not required. The same is true for any sentence about past, present or future events, which refers to events other than those we have actually observed, provided it is sufficiently connected with such events by confirmable laws.

The object of this essay is not to offer definitive solutions of problems treated. It aims rather to stimulate further investigation by supplying more exact definitions and formulations, and thereby to make it possible for others to state their different views more clearly for the purposes of fruitful discussion. Only in this way may we hope to develop convergent views and so approach the objective of *scientific empiricism* as a movement comprehending all related groups, – the development of an increasingly scientific philosophy.

BIBLIOGRAPHY

For the sake of shortness, the following publications are quoted by the numbers appearing in square brackets.

* Appeared after the writing of this essay.

Unnumbered items were added by Prof. Carnap in 1950.

AYER, A. J.
[1]* *Language, Truth and Logic*, London, 1936; 2nd ed., 1946.
The Foundations of Empirical Knowledge, New York, 1940.

BERGMANN, G.
"Outline of an Empiricist Philosophy of Physics", *American Journal of Physics*, 11, 1943. [Reprinted in this volume.]
"Sense Data, Linguistic Conventions, and Existence", *Philosophy of Science*, 14, 1947.

[19] Lewis [2], p. 143.
[20] Schlick [4], p. 367.

BRIDGMAN, P. W.
"Operational Analysis", *Philosophy of Science*, 5, 1938.
[1] *The Logic of Modern Physics*, New York, 1927.

CARNAP, R.
[1] *Der logische Aufbau der Welt*, Berlin, 1928.
[2a] "Die physikalische Sprache als Universalsprache der Wissenschaft", *Erkenntnis*, 2, 1932.
[2b] (Translation) *The Unity of Science*, London, 1934.
[3] "Ueber Protokollsatze", *Erkenntnis*, 3, 1932.
[4*a*] *Logische Syntax der Sprache*, Vienna, 1934.
[4*b*] (Translation:) *Logical Syntax of Language*, London, 1937.
[5] *Philosophy and Logical Syntax*, London, 1935.
[6] "Formalwissenschaft und Realwissenschaft", *Erkenntnis*, 5, 1935. (Congress [1]).
[7] "Ein Gültigkeitskriterium für die Sätze der klassischen Mathematik", *Monatsh. Math. Phys.*, 42, 1935.
[8] "Les Concepts Psychologiques et les Concepts Physiques sontils Foncièrement Différents?" *Revue de Synthese*, 10, 1935.
[9] "Wahrheit und Bewährung", in *Congress* [3].
[10] "Von der Erkenntnistheorie zur Wissenschaftslogik", in *Congress* [3].
[11] "Ueber die Einheitssprache der Wissenschaft", Logische Bemerkungen zur Enzyklopadie, in *Congress* [3].
[12] "Existe-t-il des premisses de la science qui soient incontrolables?" *Scientia*, 1936.
"Truth and Confirmation" (1936, 1945). Reprinted in Feigl and Sellars, *Readings*.
"Logical Foundations of the Unity of Science" (Vol. I, No. 1, of the *International Encyclopedia of Unified Science*), Chicago, 1938. Also reprinted in Feigl and Sellars, *Readings*.
"Foundations of Logic and Mathematics" (Vol. I, No. 3, of the *International Encyclopedia of Unified Science*), Chicago, 1939.
Introduction to Semantics, Cambridge, Mass., 1942.
Logical Foundations of Probability, Chicago, 1950.
"Empiricism, Semantics, and Ontology", *Revue Int. de Philos.*, 4, 1950.

CHISHOLM, R. M.
"The Contrary-to-Fact Conditional", *Mind*, 55, 1946. Reprinted in Feigl and Sellars, *Readings*.
"The Problem of Empiricism", *Journal of Philosophy*, 45, 1948.

CHURCH, A.
"Review of Ayer, *Language, Truth and Logic*", 2nd ed., *Journal of Symbolic Logic*, 14, 1949.
Congress [1] "Einheit der Wissenschaft. Bericht uber die Prager Vorkonferenz der Internationalen Kongresse fur Einheit der Wissenschaft, Sept. 1934," *Erkenntnis*, 5, *Heft* 1–3, 1935.
[2]* "Erster Internationaler Kongress fur Einheit der Wissenschaft" (*Congres Internat. de Philos. Scientifique*), Paris, 1935. (Report of Sessions) *Erkenntnis*, 5, *Heft* 6, 1936.
[3]* *Actes du Ier Congres Internat. de Philos. Scientifique*, Paris, 1935, 8 fasc., Paris, 1936.

DUCASSE, C. J.
[1]* "Verification, Verifiability and Meaningfulness", *Journal of Philosophy*, 33, 1936.

Feigl, H., and Sellars, W. S., eds.
Readings in Philosophical Analysis, New York, 1949.
Feigl, H.
[1]* "Sense and Nonsense in Scientific Realism", in *Congress* [3].
"Operationism and Scientific Method", *Psychological Review*, 52, 1945, reprinted in *Readings*.
"Logical Empiricism", reprinted in *Readings*.
"Existential Hypotheses; Realistic vs. Phenomenalistic Interpretations", *Philosophy of Science*, 17, 1950.
"Logical Reconstruction: Realism and Pure Semiotic", *Philosophy of Science*, 17, 1950.
"The Mind-Body Problem in the Development of Logical Empiricism", *Revue Int. de Philos.*, 4, 1950. [Reprinted in this volume.]
Frank, P.
[1] *Das Kausalgesetz und seine Grenzen*, Vienna, 1932.
Goodman, N.
"The Problem of Counterfactual Conditionals", *Journal of Philosophy*, 44, 1947.
Hempel, C. G.
[1] *Beitrage zur logischen Analyse des Wahrscheinlichkeitsbegriff*, Diss., Berlin, 1934.
[2] "Ueber den Gehalt von Wahrscheinlichkeitsaussagen", *Erkenntnis*, 5, 1935.
[3] "On the Logical Positivist's Theory of Truth", *Analysis*, 2, 1935.
[4] "Some Remarks on Empiricism", *Analysis*, 3, 1936.
"Studies in the Logic of Confirmation", *Mind*, 54, 1945.
"Problems and Changes in the Empiricist Criterion of Meaning", *Revue Int. de Philos.*, 4, 1950.
"Principles of Concept Formation in the Empirical Sciences" (forthcoming volume of the *International Encyclopedia of Unified Science*).
Hempel, C. G., and Oppenheim, P.
"Studies in the Logic of Explanation", *Philosophy of Science*, 15, 1948. [Reprinted in this volume.]
Hilbert, D., and Ackermann, W.
[1] *Grundzüge der theoretischen Logik*, Berlin, 1928.
Kaplan, A.
"Definition and Specification of Meaning", *Journal of Philosophy*, 15, 1948.
Kaufmann, F.
[1] *Das Unendliche in der Mathematik und seine Aussachaltung*, Vienna, 1930.
Methodology of the Social Sciences, New York, 1944.
Lewis, C. I.
[1] with Langford, C. H., *Symbolic Logic*, New York, 1932.
[2] "Experience and Meaning", *Philos. Review*, 43, 1934.
An Analysis of Knowledge and Valuation, La Salle, Ill., 1946.
"Prof. Chisholm and Empiricism", *Journal of Philosophy*, 45, 1948.
Margenau, H.
The Nature of Physical Reality, New York, 1950.
Mehlberg, *H.*
"Positivisme et Science", *Studia Philosophica*, 3, 1948.
Mises, R. von
Kleines Lehrbuch des Positivismus, The Hague (also Chicago), 1939.

MORRIS, C. W.
[1] "Philosophy of Science and Science of Philosophy", *Philosophy of Science*, 2, 1935.
[2] "The Concept of Meaning in Pragmatism and Logical Positivism", *Proc. 8th Internat. Congr. Philos.* (1934), Prague, 1936.
[3] "Semiotic and Scientific Empiricism", in *Congress* [3].
"Foundations of the Theory of Signs" (Vol. I, No. 2, of the *International Encyclopedia of Unified Science*), Chicago, 1938. *Signs, Language and Behavior*, New York, 1946.

NAGEL, E.
[1] "Verifiability, Truth, and Verification", *Journal of Philosophy*, 31, 1934.
[2]* "Impressions and Appraisals of Analytic Philosophy in Europe", *Journal of Philosophy*, 33, 1936.

NESS, A.
[1]* "Erkenntnis und wissenschaftliches Verhalten", *Norske Vid.-Akad. Hist.-Fil. Kl.*, No. 1, Oslo, 1936.

NEURATH, O.
[1] "Physicalism", *Monist.*, 41, 1931.
[2] "Physikalismus", *Scientia*, 50, 1931.
[3] "Soziologie im Physikalismus", *Erkenntnis*, 2, 1931.
[4] "Protokollsatze", *Erkenntnis*, 3, 1932.
[5] "Radikaler Physikalismus und 'wirkliche Welt'," *Erkenntnis*, 4, 1934.
[6] "Pseudorationalismus der Falsifikation", *Erkenntnis*, 5, 1935.
[7]* *Le Developpement du Cercle du Vienne et l'Avenir de l'Empirisme Logique*, Hermann, Paris, 1935.
[8]* "Einzelwissenschaften, Einheitswissenschaft, Pseudorationalismus", in *Congress* [3].

O'CONNOR, D. J.
"Some Consequences of Professor A. J. Ayer's Verification Principle", *Analysis*, 10, 1950.

PAP, A.
Elements of Analytic Philosophy, New York, 1949.

POPPER, K.
[1] *Logik der Forschung*, Vienna, 1935.
[2]* "Empirische Methode", in *Congress* [3].

RAMSEY, F. P.
[1] "General Propositions and Causality", 1929, published posthumously in *The Foundations of Mathematics, and Other Logical Essays*, pp. 237–255, New York, 1931.

REICHENBACH, H.
[1] *Wahrscheinlichkeitslehre*, Leyden, 1935.
[2]* "Ueber Induktion und Wahrscheinlichkeit", *Erkenntnis*, 5, 1935.
[3]* "Logistic Empiricism in Germany and the Present State of Its Problems", *Journal of Philosophy*, 33, 1936.
[4]* "L'Empirisme Logistique et la Désaggregation de l'Apriori", in *Congress* [3].
Experience and Prediction, Chicago, 1938.
Symbolic Logic, New York, 1947.

RUSSELL, B.
[1] See Whitehead.
[2] *Our Knowledge of the External World*, New York, 1914.

An Inquiry into Meaning and Truth, New York, 1940.
Human Knowledge: Its Scope and Limits, New York, 1948.

RUSSELL, L. J.
[1] "Communication and Verification", *Proc. Arist. Soc.*, Suppl. 13, 1934.

SCHLICK, M.
[1] "Die Kausalität in der gegenwartigen Physik", *Naturwiss.*, 19, 1931.
[2] "Ueber das Fundament der Erkenntnis", *Erkenntnis*, 4, 1934.
[3] "Facts and Propositions", *Analysis*, 2, 1935.
[4] "Meaning and Verification", *Philos. Review*, 45, 1936. *Gesammelte Aufsatze*, Vienna, 1938.

SELLARS, W. S.
"Realism and the New Way of Words", *Philos. and Phenom. Research*, 8, 1948. Also reprinted in Feigl and Sellars, *Readings*.
"Concepts as Involving Laws and Inconceivable Without Them", *Philosophy of Science*, 15, 1948.

STACE, W. T.
[1]* "Metaphysics and Meaning", *Mind*, 44, 1935.
"Positivism", *Mind*, 53, 1944.

STEBBING, S. L.
[1] "Communication and Verification", *Proc. Arist. Soc.*, Suppl. 13, 1934.

TARSKI, A.
[1]* "Der Wahrheitsbegriff in den formalisierten Sprachen", *Stud. Philos.*, 1, 1936.

WAISMANN, F.
[1] "Logische Analyse des Wahrscheinlichkeitsbegriffs", *Erkenntnis*, 1, 1930.
"Verifiability", *Proc. Arist. Soc.*, Suppl. 19, 1945.

WEYL, H.
[1] "Die heutige Erkenntnislage in der Mathematik", *Symposion* 1, 1925; also published separately.

WHITEHEAD, A. N., and RUSSELL, B.
[1] *Principia Mathematica*, 1910–12, 2nd ed., Cambridge, 1925–27.

WITTGENSTEIN, L.
[1] *Tractatus Logico-Philosophicus*, New York, 1922.

The Verifiability Theory of Meaning*

HANS REICHENBACH

. . . I WOULD LIKE to give a brief analysis of the verifiability theory of meaning in its present status, underlining those points about which there exists agreement among the various adherents of the theory, and setting apart those points about which there is disagreement.

(1) The verifiability theory of meaning lays down rules for the construction of meaningful expressions. These rules are conventions determining the structure of language. Being rules, they are neither true nor false, but volitional decisions. However, it is possible to make cognitive statements about the properties of the language resulting from the acceptance of these rules. These statements have the form of implications: if this convention concerning meaning is accepted, then the language thus resulting has such and such properties. It is possible to study such relations for various definitions of meaning and to compare the various languages. If finally one convention concerning meaning is accepted, it is possible to justify the decision for this set of rules in terms of a certain aim; for instance, the aim of interpreting the language of physics, or the aim of constructing a language that can be used for the purpose of human action.

On this point there is general agreement among the adherents of the verifiability theory of meaning. The problem of meaning falls under the category of what Carnap has called *explication*. A term of conversational language, so far used in a vague sense, is replaced by a precise term. The original term is called *explicandum;* for the term proposed to replace it I will use the name *explicans* (the term "explicatum" used by Carnap is misleading because of its grammatical form, which means "*what is explained*", whereas "explicans" means "what explains"). An explication can never be called true; however, it can be justified. That is, it can be shown that the explicans has properties which make the use of the term compatible with human behavior in connection with it.

(2) The verifiability theory of meaning concerns *cognitive* meaning. It therefore is not concerned with the meaning of imperatives, in which category value judgments are included, though they often do not have the grammatical form of imperatives. It is possible to correlate to impera-

* Reprinted by kind permission of the author and the editor from *Contributions to the Analysis and Synthesis of Knowledge*, Vol. 80, 1951, of the *Proceedings of the American Academy of Arts and Sciences.*

tives a cognitive statement; for instance, to the imperative "shut the door" the cognitive statement "the speaker wants the door to be shut". Imperatives may therefore be said to have a cognitive component, which is taken care of in the verifiability theory of meaning. This is not meant to say, however, that the question of the meaning of imperatives is completely settled by the transition to the cognitive component. On this point, too, there is, I think, general agreement among the adherents of the verifiability theory of meaning; the theory concerns only cognitive meaning.

(3) Cognitive meaning is defined by a step process. First, a basic class O of *observational sentences* and terms is introduced which are assumed to have *direct meaning*. We may also speak of *primitive meaning*, i.e., a meaning which is not under investigation during the analysis to be performed. Sentences and terms of the class O may also be called *direct sentences*, or *direct terms*, respectively. Second, the meaning of further terms and sentences is constructed by the help of *derivative relationships* D, which connect these new terms with the basis O. A step process of this kind is assumed in all forms of the verifiability theory of meaning. The emphasis on this step process and the analysis of the construction of indirect terms is one of the major contributions of the Vienna circle to the theory of meaning.

(4) The properties of the basic sentences O must be stated more explicitly. It is sometimes said that we must know how to verify them, and that this is the same as knowing their meaning; in other words, that for the basic sentences at least, the identity of meaning and method of verification can be assumed. But the statement "we must know how to verify them" is not very precise and open to criticism. Suppose a man is given a list of report sentences (Protokollsätze) which are not his own reports, but which he has good reasons to believe to be true. Can the man, whom I will call the reconstructor, construct the system of knowledge resulting from this list of sentences? Obviously it does not suffice him to know that the sentences are true; he must *understand* the sentences. This qualification can be made clear as follows. Suppose the report sentences are written by the use of the logical symbolism. Now if the two sentences "Peter is tall" and "John is tall" are written down in the list, it would not suffice if they are symbolized by the letters "p" and "q". They must be symbolized as "$f(x_1)$" and "$f(x_2)$", since otherwise the usual inferences, for instance, an inference of induction by enumeration, cannot be drawn. This shows that the structure of the report sentences must be known. That is, the report sentences must be symbolized, not in the calculus of propositions, but in the calculus of functions. A further distinction must be added. Even if the report sentences are given in their full structure, the reconstructor does not know to which of his own experiences the symbols "f", "x_1", etc., refer. In spite of the absence of such knowledge, he is able to follow all the inferences made for the construction of scientific theories, and indirect terms thus acquire for him a structural meaning. But what is still missing

is the relation to his own experiences. For this purpose, a final step is required. The reconstructor must be given the interpretation of the empirical constants "f", "x_1", etc.; then all terms, including the indirect ones, acquire for him an interpreted meaning. For these reasons, the formulation "the person must know how to verify the sentences of the basis *O*" is better replaced by the formulation "the person must know the meaning of the sentences of the basis *O*".[1]

For the basis *O*, the following kinds of sentences have been used:

(α) reports about the objects of our personal macroscopic environment (concreta) at a certain moment

(β) reports about the same kind of objects, but including our past observations

(γ) reports about the same kind of objects given by any human observer at any time

(δ) reports about sense data at a certain moment (or, as in β or γ, extended to include the past, or different observers)

(ϵ) reports about atomic physical occurrences, like coincidences of electrons, etc.

As to the choice of these bases, which were discussed in greater detail by Carnap and Neurath, there seems to be general agreement that the basis α has a psychological priority. The objects of the other bases then are regarded as constructed by inferences starting from the basis α. Doubts have been uttered whether the basis α is large enough; in fact, it is difficult to show how on that basis the statement that Caesar was murdered in 44 B.C. can be constructed. It seems we have to include in the basis our recollection of established laws, such as the law that looking into a suitable reference book you find reliable historical data about Caesar; but these recollections are mostly only potentially there. Who would be willing to include the unconscious in the basis α? A clarification of this point is desirable, although I believe that it involves no difficulties of principle.

(5) I will now turn to the derivative relationships *D*. There is today, finally, agreement among most of us that these relations cannot be equivalences between indirect and direct sentences. This widening of meaning is necessary in order to admit as meaningful such sentences as "the planets will go on traveling on their orbits after the death of the last human being".[2] Furthermore, it is agreed that the relations *D* cannot be merely deductive relations from the indirect to the direct sentences. The relations must transfer truth in the opposite direction: the basic sentences must confer a degree of truth-character upon the indirect sentences. This re-

[1] I think these remarks correspond to views about the verifiability theory of meaning recently presented by P. Marhenke, Presidential Address to the Pacific Division of the American Philosophical Association, Christmas 1949, to be published in *Philosophical Review*.

[2] See the discussion of such sentences in my book "Experience and Prediction", Chicago 1938, pp. 133-135.

quirement means that the indirect sentences must be so constructed as to be appropriate for the derivation of observable predictions, i.e., of future direct sentences which we have good reason to treat as true before they are directly verified. This cautious formulation will indicate that the derivative relations *D* involve inductive inferences and that such inferences cannot be proved to lead to true conclusions, or even to a large number of true conclusions.

Now we all know that the interpretation of probability and induction is highly controversial today; in fact, the derivative relations mark the point where the controversy about probability enters into the domain of the verifiability theory of meaning. My own interpretation of probability and induction is so constructed that it satisfies the above requirement; this is admitted, as far as I see, even by my opponents, with the exception of Bertrand Russell, who claims that my inductive posit "is admitted to be not intellectually justified".[3] I would like to know where he found such an admission in my writings. The objections which other writers have raised against my theory of induction and probability maintain that the frequency interpretation of probability is unsuitable for the reason that it does not express what we really mean by a probability referred to a single case, or to a scientific theory. I answer that we are concerned here with an explication, and that for an explication of probability it does not matter what a man means. The explicans given by me has the property of making a man's behavior justifiable whenever he is in a situation which, in correspondence with established usage, he describes by means of the term "probable"; or in other words, it has the property of making the use of the term "probable" compatible with human behavior in connection with the term. This is a sufficient reason to accept my explication.

If others suggest other interpretations, they would have to give a similar proof for the explicans suggested by them. As far as I see, none among the advocates of other interpretations has even tried to give such a proof. Carnap regards his interpretation of probability as justified because, as he says, it is in agreement with the beliefs which a scientist has when he makes inductive inferences.[4] I do not think that this psychological brand of justification is acceptable. Scientists often have strange beliefs, and make fallacious inferences with good results. The logician is not interested in copying the scientist's mistakes. What he wants to give is a rational reconstruction of scientific inference, and for a reconstruction of this kind, correspondence to beliefs is no criterion of adequacy.[5] The only

[3] Bertrand Russell, Logical Positivism, *Revue Internationale de Philosophie*, No. 11, 1950, p. 19.

[4] R. Carnap, On Inductive Logic, *Philosophy of Science*, vol. 12, 1945, p. 95.

[5] I would therefore say that for a fallacious argument, as a whole, there is no rational reconstruction. Such argument can be analyzed as follows: the argument contains a "jump" from one point P_1 to another point P_2. From the premises up to P_1, and from P_2 to the conclusion, we can give a rational reconstruction; but for the transition from P_1 to P_2, there is no rational reconstruction. It seems to me that even the term

way of showing that a reconstruction of scientific inference is rational is to give a proof that the explicans logically validates the inference. It would be too much to ask that the conclusion be true; the cautious formulation above given is meant to explicate the term "validate". I was glad to see that Carnap now admits that a justification of induction must be given, and that he does not share Schlick's views according to which the justification of induction concerned a pseudo problem. But I cannot regard his interpretation of probability as justified unless he gives a proof that it is advisable, in some sense, to use his probability values as a directive for action.[6] From the presentations of his theory which he has published I would infer that such a logical justification can never be given, because he introduces a probability metric *a priori*.[7] But if the scientist should have to put up with an interpretation which makes his inferences unjustifiable in the logical sense, he could as well quit working.

(6) After defining the basis *O* and the derivative relations *D*, the term "verified" can be defined as "being derived from the basis *O* in terms of the relations *D*". Now there is general agreement that the condition of meaning is not actual verification, but possible verification. This widening of meaning is necessary in order to admit as meaningful such statements as "it snowed on Manhattan Island in the year 4 A.D.". Therefore the term "possible" must now be defined.

Three kinds of possibility must be investigated: logical, physical, and technical possibility. The first means non-contradictory character; the second, non-contradictory to empirical laws; the third, being within the reach of known practical methods. That a verifiability defined in terms of technical possibility makes the definition of meaning too narrow is now generally admitted. Schlick, and with him most members of the Vienna circle, have used logical possibility. But a definition of meaning in terms of logical possibility of verification makes the definition of meaning too wide, at least, when the interpretation of physics is concerned. For instance, Einstein's principle of equivalence, according to which being in accelerated motion means the same as being in a gravitational field, presupposes a definition of verifiability based on physical possibility. For these reasons I have advocated a definition of meaning in terms of the physical possibility of verification. A suitable definition of this kind of possibility and of physical laws is given in the frame of my theory of nomological statements.[8]

Since meaning is a matter of definition, it must be kept in mind that

---

"reconstruction" cannot be defined without some criterion of validity, and that fallacious thinking cannot be reconstructed unless the reconstruction is rational at least with respect to parts of the argument.

[6] Carnap's paper, Probability as a Guide in Life, *Journ. of Philos.*, vol. 44, 1947, p. 141, does not contain any proof of this kind.

[7] I refer to the discussion in my book "The Theory of Probability", Berkeley 1949, §71 and §88.

[8] "Elements of Symbolic Logic", New York 1947, chap. VIII.

none of the three definitions resulting from the three kinds of possibility can be called "true"; moreover, none of them seems to supply the only suitable explicans of meaning. It appears that all three of them are actually used. The physicist usually assumes *physical meaning*, for which verification is physically possible. But in his discussions of physical theories which he wants to prove false, he often uses *logical meaning*, for which verification is logically possible. For instance, an absolute time can very well be defined by speaking of the logical possibility of signals faster than light; and when the physicist says that the theory of absolute time is false, he has assumed logical meaning for it. The simultaneous use of the three definitions of meaning is very expedient for the discussion of physical theories and their comparison under the viewpoint of empirical truth. We may say, however, that for the actual system of physics, physical meaning is generally assumed.[9]

(7) The conditions 1–6 together with condition 8, which I shall deal with presently, lay down conditions of meaningfulness and thus specify what I have called the first principle of the verifiability theory of meaning. The second principle, which defines sameness of meaning, must now be added.

Although equivalence was not assumed to hold between direct and indirect sentences, there can be equivalences between indirect sentences; and it is indispensable for a theory of meaning to lay down the condition that such equivalences lead to sameness of meaning. The three forms of possibility lead to a corresponding division for this category. If the equivalence is analytic, i.e., follows from the rules of logic, we have logical identity of meaning; if the equivalence is synthetic and follows from the laws of physics, we have physical identity of meaning. Technical identity of meaning is a dispensable concept. The above example of Einstein's principle of equivalence illustrates physical identity of meaning. It is an important part of physical research to discover such identities; this has been very well pointed out by Feigl,[10] who mentions the identity of light waves and electromagnetic waves, of heat and average kinetic energy of the molecules, etc., and discusses in this frame the mind-body problem.

As before, it can be useful to employ different definitions of identity of meaning in the same context; for instance, to use Frege's example, we may say that the expressions "the morning star" and "the evening star" have the same physical meaning, but not the same logical meaning. Furthermore, it appears necessary to subdivide the category of logical identity of meaning and to define synonymity by a much narrower requirement, so that, for instance, the terms "five" and "number of regular polyhedrons" are not synonymous, though they can be shown to be tautologically equiva-

[9] It is a pity, therefore, that Carnap in his enlightening book "Meaning and Necessity", Chicago 1947, does not speak at all about physical meaning and physical possibility.

[10] H. Feigl, The Mind-Body Problem, *Revue Internationale de Philosophie*, No. 11, 1950, p. 80, reprinted this volume.

lent. A definition of synonymity of this kind was recently given in a highly satisfactory form by Carnap.[11]

It is the practical significance of the second principle of the verifiability theory of meaning that it allows for the translation of expressions of emotive languages into an empirical language. Statements about mystical visions, or about "moral truth", can thus be given an empirical content, though such a translation may provoke violent opposition on the side of the advocate of superempirical meanings. Visions then acquire the status of dreams, or hallucinations, of certain persons; and "moral truths", the status of beliefs of certain persons. I refer to another publication.[12]

This discussion of identity of meaning answers the objections raised by Bertrand Russell,[13] which are based on earlier versions of the verifiability theory of meaning. He argues that, for the positivist, speaking about other persons' minds would mean the same as speaking about dreamed objects. I doubt whether this is true even for the earliest form of positivism, where the distinction between dream and waking state was already made. And it certainly is not true for a verifiability theory of meaning which allows for indirect verification, since in such a theory identity of meaning does not hold between indirect sentences and observation sentences.

(8) I now come to the discussion of a set of rules which had been overlooked in the earlier discussion of meaning and which were first introduced in my analysis of the problem of unobservables of quantum mechanics.

Going from the sentences of the basis *O* to indirect sentences is the same as going from observables to unobservables. We are all agreed that this inference is not a matter of belief in a transcendental reality; in fact, if the verifiability theory of meaning is accepted, this would be a belief in something meaningless. So, it must be a form of inductive inference; and thus arises the difficulty of how to make inductions which connect unobservables to observables. Inductions concerning a certain object must start with some properties of this object and then may add further properties to it. But since we have no knowledge of the unobservables, we have nothing to start with. We cannot say: so far the things have existed when we were not looking at them, therefore they will do the same in the future. The premise of this inference is not verified by any observation, and cannot be so verified because of the definition of the term "unobserved object".[14]

[11] R. Carnap, "Meaning and Necessity", Chicago 1947, §§ 14–15. Incidentally, it seems to me that the outcome of this book can be summarized in the following thesis: the major point is the definition of the terms "having the same extension" and "having the same intension"; interpretations of the terms "extension" and "intension" can then be added more or less arbitrarily.

[12] "Experience and Prediction", Chicago 1938, pp. 66–68.

[13] Bertrand Russell, Human Knowledge, New York 1948, p. 449.

[14] This argument was constructed by W. T. Stace, Refutation of Realism, *Mind*

This simple analysis shows that statements about unobservables cannot be introduced unless certain conventions are added to our language. In my investigation of quantum mechanics,[15] I have shown that the usual language of science includes the convention that unobservables follow the same physical laws as observables; in particular, that they satisfy the principle of causality, which for observables is an empirical law. Without such a convention, the language of unobservables is incomplete and not accessible to verification. It leads to statements of the same kind as, for instance, the statement that during the night all things, including our bodies, have become ten times larger. Such paradoxes spring from incompleteness of language, and are easily eliminated by making the language complete through suitable rules.

I will call rules of this kind *extension rules*. They extend the range of laws from observables to unobservables. They are conventions determining the structure of language. Varying the convention, we arrive at a set of *equivalent descriptions*, which are all true to the same extent. Among them, the description for which unobservables follow the same laws as observables is called the *normal system*. Yet the necessity of conventions opens up an empirical investigation: it requires an analysis whether a certain convention can be carried through, i.e., does not lead to contradictory statements about observables. Classical physics can be carried through consistently on the convention that the laws of unobservables are the same as the law of observables. Classical physics, therefore, has a normal system—which is nothing but the usual realistic language. Quantum physics does not admit of a normal system. This is a domain where the mentioned extension rule breaks down and other extension rules have to be used. We have therefore to distinguish between admissible and inadmissible conventions of language. Whether a convention is admissible, is an empirical question. If it is admissible, its use makes the resulting language not "more true" than the use of another admissible convention.

I hope these formulations will clarify a controversy which has arisen about the exposition of realism in my book "Experience and Prediction". I have introduced the term *illata* for objects that can be described only in indirect sentences.[16] This term is as legitimate as the term "indirect sentence". Certainly, illata are not determined unless the extension rules of the language are given; but this fact does not make them "less real". They share this property with all other things, since nothing can be described adequately in an incomplete language. Furthermore, in the discussion of a cubical world [17] in which bird-like shadows are visible, I have argued for a realistic language which speaks about the birds although they are un-

43, 1934. It is also discussed in my book "Philosophic Foundations of Quantum Mechanics," Berkeley 1944, p. 18. It is shown there that the solution consists, not in a refutation of realism, but in a reformulation of realism.

[15] See p. 19 of my book mentioned in the preceding footnote.

[16] "Experience and Prediction", Chicago 1938, p. 212.

[17] Ibid. §14.

observable and thus are illata. In the terminology of my analysis of quantum mechanics, I would say that in this world the realistic language constitutes the normal system, whereas the positivistic language, which speaks only about the shadows on the walls, is a restrictive interpretation. My argument therefore is that there is no reason to introduce a restrictive interpretation if a normal system exists.[18] The same would apply to quantum mechanics if, for instance, the corpuscle interpretation could be carried through without causal anomalies, even if Heisenberg's indeterminacy were to remain valid and a simultaneous ascertainment of position and momentum were impossible.

When I say that we have inductive evidence for the existence of the external world, I mean the fact that the realistic language can be carried through for the macrocosm, that there is a normal system. This is a verifiable and meaningful statement; but of course, it is so only after the language is made complete through extension rules. That the realistic hypothesis is empirical, and not a faith, or perhaps a truism, is shown by the strange results of quantum mechanics, which exclude the realistic hypothesis, in the usual sense, for the microcosm. Here we can speak about physical reality only in an indirect way, using the duality of wave and particle description; instead of the normal system, we use a set of equivalent descriptions, none of which has the directness of the normal system. A realistic language in the sense of the language of the macrocosm is here impossible; if there is any realism left, it is certainly not a "naive realism".

I should like to add the remark that the reality problem of quantum mechanics has been construed as resulting from the influence of the human observer and thus as confirming idealistic philosophies, according to which the *ego* creates the external world; in another version of such ideas, it has been argued that the line of demarcation between observer and external object cannot be clearly drawn. I do not think such a "metaphysical" interpretation of quantum mechanics is tenable. The observables of quantum mechanics are not human perceptions, but physical occurrences of a certain kind; and the quantum mechanical difficulties begin when the realm of these observables, or phenomena, is to be supplemented by a realm of unobservables, or interphenomena. It is therefore not the step from the human observer to the external object, but the step from macrophysics to microphysics which involves the difficulties. The quantum-mechanical indeterminacy is an entirely physical affair; i.e., it expresses a structural property of the physical world, which has nothing to do with the fact that this world is observed by human beings.[19] That the indeterminacy influences our system of knowledge has other reasons. Our bodies are macroscopic

[18] This answers certain objections by H. Feigl, Existential Hypotheses, *Philos. of Science*, vol. 17, 1950, p. 54, who unfortunately overlooks the exposition of the problem in my book "Philosophic Foundations of Quantum Mechanics" and bases his critique merely on my book "Experience and Prediction".

[19] See my book, "Philosophic Foundations of Quantum Mechanics", p. 15. An imaginary macroscopic analogy of quantum mechanics is described there on pp. 38–39.

organisms, and our direct observations are restricted to macroscopic objects. Our knowledge of the microcosm is acquired by way of the macrocosm, and on this transition the indeterminacy enters our statements about the microcosm.

In order to construct an adequate realistic language for quantum phenomena I have suggested to use a three-valued logic, which possesses a category of indeterminate sentences between those of true and of false sentences. Since the indeterminate sentences are neither true nor false, the objection has been raised that my interpretation of quantum mechanics contradicts the verifiability criterion of meaning.[20] This is a misunderstanding. The theory of meaning has been emancipated, for a long while, from its first dogmatic version and has assumed a moderate version, which admits of modified forms of verification. In order to include the three-valued logic of quantum mechanics, the conditions of meaningfulness, in particular, the extension rules, have to be widened so as to admit the category of indeterminate statements. Since these statements are connected by well-defined rules with the observational basis of language, they are as legitimate as any other statements exempt from direct verification. To put it briefly: a quantum-mechanical statement is meaningful if it is verifiable (in the moderate sense of probability verification) as true, false, or indeterminate.

[20] E. Nagel, *Journ. of Philosophy*, vol. 42, 1945, pp. 437–444. See also my reply, vol. 43, 1946, p. 244.

The Logic of Psychophysical Measurement*

GUSTAV BERGMANN
AND KENNETH W. SPENCE

I. Introduction

THE AIM OF this paper is to present a methodological analysis of some of the problems which arise in connection with psychophysical measurement and, incidentally, of certain allied aspects of psychology such as perception and psychological measurement in general. The discussion falls into three main parts: In the first section an attempt is made to indicate the manner in which scientific empiricism, the standpoint from which the present survey was undertaken, approaches these problems. Our exposition of this epistemological point of view must necessarily be restricted to a few very cursory remarks which have an immediate bearing on the problems at hand.[1]

The second section, which deals with physical measurement, cannot pass as a systematic exposition either. Its main purpose, again, has been to call attention to those points concerning physical measurement which must be understood in order to secure an adequate grasp of psychophysical measurement and of psychological measurement in general. Readers who find this second section difficult are referred to the elementary chapters on physical measurement which can be found in several introductory textbooks on logic and scientific method (7, 8, 9, 13). An interesting paper by Nagel (12) is on the intermediate level while the most elaborate analysis of physical measurement so far is due to Campbell (6).[2]

In the third and last part of the paper the particular problems of psychophysical measurement have been reëxamined in the light of the points previously elaborated. Also included as a necessary background for

* Reprinted from *Psychological Review*, 51, 1944, by kind permission of the authors, the *Psychological Review*, and the American Psychological Association.

[1] For a more complete and systematic account of scientific empiricism (logical positivism) the reader is referred to the writings of Carnap, Morris, and others, particularly to the monographs collected in the *International Encyclopedia of Unified Science* (21).

[2] The extent to which the methodological analysis of physical measurement has influenced psychology is best revealed in two papers, an earlier one by McGregor (11) and a recent analysis of mental tests as measuring instruments by Thomas (19).

this discussion is a sketch of the status of perception as conceived by the behavioristic psychologist.

II. The Methodological Frame of Reference

1. Scientific empiricism does not hold to the view, rightly or wrongly associated with Watson's name, that so-called mentalistic or introspectionistic terms such as 'sensation,' 'consciousness,' 'image,' etc., are *necessarily* meaningless or that their referents do not exist. But scientific empiricism does hold that it is the methodological ideal of the sciences of behavior to use such mentalistic terms only after they have been introduced by *(operational) definitions from a physicalistic meaning basis.* The meaning of the italicized portion of this statement can probably best be made clear by first giving illustrations of concepts or terms employed in science which meet this criterion. Following this we shall attempt to elucidate further by means of certain simple instances. Familiar examples of satisfactorily defined concepts are 'weight,' 'mass,' 'electric conductivity,' etc., in physics, and 'I.Q.,' 'stimulus trace' (Hull) and 'habit strength' (Hull) in psychology. The following paragraph may, for our immediate purpose, pass as an elucidation.

When mentalistic terms are introduced by (operational) definitions from a physicalistic meaning basis, then every statement which contains such terms can be tested by the *scientist's* observations (unquantified) and measurements (quantified) of physical objects. The following are three examples of sentences which express such basic observations and measurements of the scientist: 'object *A* is green,' 'the pointer of instrument *B* coincides with the point *a* of its scale,' 'the density of object *C* is 3.57.' The first of these statements is, in a certain sense, simpler than the second, because the confirmation of the latter involves the recognition of the instrument *B* and thus the confirmation of several statements like the first; again, the confirmation of the third presupposes the confirmation of such statements as the first and the second. The theory of physical measurement or, what amounts almost to the same thing, the operational analysis of physics consists in the reduction in this manner of even the most abstract of its concepts, as one also says, empirical constructs. Reduction of a concept thus involves indicating the classes of statements as "simple" as our first example, the verification of which is considered a confirmation of the statements in which the concept occurs.

2. Scientific empiricism holds to the position that all sciences, including psychology, deal with the same events, namely, the experiences or perceptions of the scientist himself. The behavior scientist who claims to study such perceptual behavior in his subjects is thus asked to start uncritically from his own perceptions; a piece of advice, the apparent circularity of which has continued to puzzle many of the more philosophically-minded psychologists. To them neither physicalism, a less sophisticated form of empiricism, which dogmatically outlaws all attempts

to clarify the puzzle of this circularity by branding them as revivals of the old mind-body metaphysics, nor solipsism the other, more traditional council of despair is acceptable. Consequently the philosophical uneasiness thus created appears to find expression in a variety of quasi-metaphysical speculations.

In the schema outlined by the scientific empiricist the experiences of the observing scientist do indeed have a privileged, even unique position. If pressed too far and without the necessary epistemological sophistication, this account of the scientist's position can very easily lead to a metaphysical thesis of the solipsistic type. The fact of the matter is that science is always epistemologically dogmatic. Scientists, *qua* scientists, are usually not interested in such matters beyond receiving the philosopher's assurance that their methodological schema does not allow for any undesirable epistemological inferences. Nevertheless, attention may be called here to the reëxamination of the mind-body issue offered by scientific empiricism (2). This reëxamination tries, on the one hand, to overcome the dogmatism of *epistemological* physicalism, and on the other, to justify the *methodological* solipsism and physicalism of science. So far as the psychologist is concerned these remarks may be expressed in a somewhat different manner. They are to the effect that the empiricist scientist should realize that his behavior, symbolic or otherwise, does not lie on the same methodological level as the responses of his subjects, and consequently that he should not in reporting the latter use any mentalistic terms which have not been introduced from a physicalistic meaning basis. This latter fact may also be expressed by saying that all his terms should be behavioristically defined.

3. In the terminology now prevailing among empiricists the last point can be stated in the following way: In studying his subjects, including their symbolic responses (object language), the behavior scientist himself uses a different language (pragmatic metalanguage). That linguistic behavior can be utilized in operational definitions, even according to the most rigorous standards, is most generally recognized today. It is important in psychology, however, to distinguish between such utilization of symbolic responses of human *subjects* on the one hand and the use of responses of human *judges* on the other. Let us consider a schematically simplified example. Assume that a scientist calls a behavior fragment of a subject aggressive if 8 out of 10 judges apply this word to the behavior in question. In doing so our scientist has made use of what might be termed the *human yardstick* in the introduction of *his* term 'aggressive.' The latter lies in the scientist's metalanguage and must, therefore, be carefully distinguished from the judges' term which belongs to the object language. The remarkable statistical refinement which has recently been brought to bear on definitions of this kind has tended to overshadow the rather fundamental methodological difference between concepts introduced with and those introduced without the use of the human yardstick. If the latter are called

strict behavioristic terms, one would have to say that the scientist of our illustration describes, in strict behavioristic terms, not the behavior of his subjects, but rather the behavior of the group composed of his subjects *and* of his judges.

Since 'behavioristic' has become an honorific label, it might be useful to add that the preceding remarks are not meant as a methodological criticism of correctly defined, but not strict behavioristic terms; they are merely a clarification of their peculiar status. The indispensability of such terms in present day clinical and social psychology is readily conceded. The clinician who applies mentalistic, not strictly introduced, terms to his patients is indeed the limiting case of the schematic situation; in this instance the single judge coincides with the observing scientist. There is, of course, no objection against calling all these procedures behavioristic, but then the word refers to nothing more precise than what is usually called the experimental attitude. And it is only fair to say that the theoretical psychologist as well as the empiricist philosopher are nowadays mainly interested in a behavior science which is behavioristic in the stricter sense (see below, IV 4 and V).

The bearing of these considerations upon some of the quantitative methods most widely used in psychology will become clear in the course of the discussion. And they raise also a question concerning psychophysical measurement proper. Does a human observer who discriminates, in one of the traditional situations, between, say, two pitches, serve as a judge or as a subject? The answer, it will be seen, depends upon which aspects of the psychophysical situation are emphasized.

III. Physical Measurement

1. Some properties of and relations between physical objects or events are accessible to further differentiation. The meaning of this statement can only be illustrated. Loudness, hotness, length can be differentiated in this sense; the property 'male' ('*X* is a male') and the relation 'to-the-left of' ('*A* is to the left of *B*') cannot. Properties of physical objects or events which are amenable to such differentiation we shall call physical *dimensions*. Physical measurement consists in the assignment of numbers to the objects or events of a physical dimension in accordance with certain rules (laws and conventions). The result is a *scale*. The distinction between a physical dimension and any of the scales which have been developed to measure it, pedantic as it might seem, is necessary in order to avoid certain confusions which have arisen. For instance in discussions on measurement a distinction has sometimes been made between intensive and extensive scales. It will be shown that intensity and extensity are properties of dimensions and should not be used with reference to scales.

2. A dimension is said to be *intensive* if the following three conditions are fulfilled. *First*, that there exist two physical relations, designated by

'$\underline{>}$' and '$\underline{=}$' respectively, so that the statements '$X \underline{>} Y$' and '$X \underline{=} Y$' are both meaningful, X and Y being any two objects or events which have the property that defines the dimension. *Second,* that these statements can be tested by the scientist's observations or *manipulations within the dimension.* The italicized clause will be explained presently (III 4). *Third,* that the two relations fulfill certain axioms, the so-called axioms of order (12, p. 315, 1–6). These axioms are empirical laws, *i.e.,* whether they hold or not for any two physical relations is entirely a question of fact. Two of these axioms, the intuitive meaning of which is obvious, are given here for the purpose of illustration.

(1) Either $X \underline{=} Y$, or $X \underline{>} Y$, or $Y \underline{>} X$.
(2) If $X \underline{>} Y$, and $Y \underline{>} Z$, then $X \underline{>} Z$,

where X, Y, Z, are arbitrary objects or events of the dimension.

If these three conditions are fulfilled, then it is (in more than one way) possible to assign to each object or event X of the dimension a number designated by $N(X)$, so that

$$N(X) > N(Y) \quad \text{if and only if} \quad X \underline{>} Y,$$
$$N(X) = N(Y) \quad \text{if and only if} \quad X \underline{=} Y.$$

Here '$>$' and '$=$' are the usual arithmetical symbols. If such a coördination has been made then a rank order scale has been constructed for the dimension.

A dimension is called *extensive* if two additional conditions are fulfilled. *Fourth,* that there is a further physical operation within the dimension, designated by '$\underline{+}$,' which is of such a nature that if performed upon any two objects or events of the dimension, it results again in an object or event of the dimension. This latter object or event is designated by '$X \underline{+} Y$.' *Fifth,* this operation, too, is supposed to fulfill certain axioms (12, p. 315, 7–12).[3] Two of them, here given for the purpose of illustration, are

(3) If $X \underline{=} X'$ and $Y \underline{=} Y'$, then $X \underline{+} Y \underline{=} X' \underline{+} Y'$.
(4) $X \underline{+} Y \underline{=} Y \underline{+} X$.

Furthermore, in an extensive dimension it is always possible to assign the numbers to the objects in such a way that

(A) $N(X \underline{+} Y) = N(X) + N(Y)$.

Again '$=$' and '$+$' are the usual arithmetical symbols and are not to be confused with '$\underline{=}$,' '$\underline{>}$,' '$\underline{+}$,' the names of physical relations and operations. A scale which has this property (A) is called *additive.* That is to say, extensive dimensions and, by the very nature of this definition, only extensive dimensions allow for the construction of additive scales.

Perhaps a simple illustration will show the value of this cumbersome

[3] It is not the purpose of this paper to examine the formal adequacy, independence, etc., of the set of axioms which Nagel takes over from the mathematician Hoelder.

terminology. Length, as is well known, is extensive and its usual scale is additive. If, however, one were to replace the numbers of our ordinary yardsticks by those of which they are the logarithms, the axioms of order and extensity would still be fulfilled, but instead of equation (A) one now has $N(X \underline{+} Y) = N(X) \cdot N(Y)$. The ordinary slide rule is another such non-additive length scale. This is one of the reasons why we distinguish between dimensions and scales, between extensity and additivity.

3. One of Campbell's and Nagel's examples (12) will be used to illustrate the next point.[4] The example deals with the density of liquids. This construct is so defined that liquid Y is said to be of greater density than liquid X if X floats on top of Y. (One of our simplifying assumptions is that the two liquids do not mix.) With this definition, density turns out to be an intensive dimension. The physical relation, '$X \underline{>} Y$,' reads in this case 'Y floats on top of X' and it will be observed that an operation '$\underline{+}$' cannot be found. Let us now attribute numbers, designated by $D(X)$, to this intensive dimension. As we know, this can be done in a great many different ways; the only requirement is that the greater ($\underline{>}$!) density gets the greater ($>$!) number. In actual practice, of course, density is not defined in this way, but as the quotient of weight (W) and volume (V). Let us designate this new 'density' of a body X by a lower case symbol: $d(X) = W(X)/V(X)$. If one says that $d(X)$ and $D(X)$ are two different measures of the "same" construct one has reference to the following empirical laws:

$$d(X) > d(Y) \quad \text{if and only if} \quad D(X) > D(Y),$$
$$d(X) = d(Y) \quad \text{if and only if} \quad D(X) = D(Y).$$

Because of these empirical laws which obtain between the three dimensions, volume, weight, and density (D), one can use $d(X)$ instead of $D(X)$ as a scale of 'density.' If, in order to scale a dimension, one thus makes use of other dimensions and of the empirical laws obtaining between them and the dimension one wants to scale, then the resulting scale is called a *derived* scale. The usual temperature scale is another familiar instance of a derived scale for an intensive dimension, the extraneous dimension involved being volume, the empirical law used that of thermic expansion. By means of derived scales one can also quantify or "measure" dimensions which are not even intensive in the sense defined above, that is to say, where no physical relations *within the dimension* that fulfill the order axioms can be found.

4. We are now in a better position to elucidate the clause 'manipulations (relations) within a dimension' to which attention was called above (III 2). Manipulations within a dimension do not involve utilization of any of the empirical laws which connect it with other dimensions. The manipulations, for instance, by which we compare the lengths of yardsticks and

[4] It must be borne in mind that all our illustrations are extremely simplified and not descriptions of practical working procedures.

build their operational sum, '$\underline{+}$,' lie entirely within the dimension of length. That is to say, the empirical laws which make length an extensive dimension are the axioms of extensity, if the symbols '$\underline{=}$,' '$\underline{>}$,' '$\underline{+}$' are read with the appropriate interpretations; *e.g.*, '$X \underline{+} Y$' reads "Take the stick Y and put one of its ends as close as possible to one end of the stick X, etc." And these laws have no reference to any other dimension.

It should be clear from the above discussion that only in the case of fundamental scales, *i.e.*, those based on operations within the dimension, is inference as to the intensity or extensity of the dimension possible. Derived scales do not allow any such inference. To say the same thing still differently: A dimension is shown to be intensive or extensive respectively, if two or three operations, '$\underline{=}$,' '$\underline{>}$,' '$\underline{+}$,' within the dimension have been found and shown to fulfill the 6 or 12 axioms.

5. Everybody agrees that the customary density scale is preferable to an arbitrary rank order; that it is more convenient to measure time in seconds than by counting the heart beats of a totem animal, to quote an illustration which Schlick was fond of using in his lectures. What, however, is the correct analysis of this situation? Is it because the one scale measures the *true* density; because any two seconds are *equal* while the intervals of a heart beat are not? Or, to mention still another expression sometimes ambiguously used in this context, is it the case that only one of the scales from which we can choose is *valid?* To the confusion surrounding these questions our attention must now be turned.

Consider the law of thermic expansion. Using the customary temperature scale this law can be formulated in the following manner: the volume of any substance is (within certain limits, approximately) a linear function of its temperature: $v_t = v_o(1 + c_x t)$. Let us call 'L' this formulation of the law. Assume now that temperature has been scaled by an arbitrary rank order (R), so that, as we know but as the users of the scale do not know, $1R = 0°$ C., $2R = 1°$ C., $3R = 4°$ C., $4R = 17°$ C., etc. Designate, furthermore, by $c(X)_{1,2}$, $c(X)_{1,3}$, $c(X)_{1,4}$, etc., the percentual increase in volume (expansion coefficient) of the substance X between the temperature levels indicated by the indices. Experiments would then lead to the formulation of the following law (L_1): the expansion coefficients of any substance stand in the following relations: $c_{1,3} = 4c_{1,2}$, $c_{1,4} = 17c_{1,2}$, etc.

L_1 is of course the form which L would take if one works with our unusual rank order. One sees that L_1 is mathematically more complicated and less intuitive than L. This observation leads to the very core of the matter under discussion. We choose our scales so that certain empirical laws receive an expression as intuitive and (or) as mathematically simple as possible. It is an inaccurate and misleading way of speaking when such choice of scales is described as an attempt to equalize the unit distances of the scale. If there is a choice as to which law should be selected, then one usually picks that which one considers more "fundamental." But one must realize that 'fundamental' is again but a figure of speech; those laws are fundamental which play or which we expect to play a prominent rôle in our everchanging theoretical structure. If this structure changes or expands, then we frequently also change our scales. In the case of temperature, for instance, the mercury scale has been replaced by the gas scale and the latter, in turn, at least for theoretical purposes, by the entropy scale. Each of these steps marked a progress in the sense that the temperature scale became more directly linked to more and more fundamental laws within an expanding theoretical structure. But it is merely another figure of speech to describe these successive steps as approximations to a true or valid scale of temperature. In itself no scale is more valid than any other. It is hunting the will-o-the-wisp to believe that such refinement as just described will ever make a scale additive. Additivity, as we have seen, cannot even be defined for nonextensive dimensions.

6. What, in general, is meant by the equality of any two units of a scale or, as one also says, by the equality of differences? An answer to this question has already been partially given in the preceding paragraphs; all that remains is to make it explicit and to supplement it by some concluding remarks. If a derived scale is built by utilizing an empirical law and if the assignment of numbers is made in a manner to give to this or another empirical law a mathematically simple expression, then the *numerical* identity of the differences between two pairs of scale points has *empirical* meaning. Sometimes, as in the case of the mercury scale for temperature or the usual time scale, this meaning is more or less intuitive, sometimes, as in the case of the entropy scale, the simplicity lies on the theoretical level. Always, however, the numerical equality of the differences between two pairs of scale points has exactly that much empirical meaning as has been put into the scale by taking account of empirical laws in attributing the numbers. There is no end to the possible refinements nor to the many quite different ways in which meaning can thus be given to a scale. But again it is very misleading if the search for such refinement, which is the search for empirical laws that could be formulated in any scale, is mistaken for the search for true or valid measurement; or, as happens to be the case in psychophysics, for the search for extensive or additive scales.

In the case of derived scales the empirical laws drawn upon are always of the form '$y = f(x)$,' where 'y' stands for the derived dimension to be scaled and 'x' for one or several extraneous dimensions already scaled. There are, however, other ways to endow a scale and, in particular, the equality of the numerical differences with empirical meaning. This time we shall illustrate by means of the usual hardness scale which, as is well known, is an arbitrary attribution of the numbers 1 to 10 in an intensive dimension. Accordingly, there is no factual meaning in the statement that the hardness differences of two pairs of minerals with the numbers 8, 7; 3, 2, respectively, are equal. But let us now assume that we have ranked, with respect to hardness, all known minerals. Assume, furthermore, that there are altogether 901 of them, and that we rescale hardness so that the softest one gets the number 1, the 101 the number 2, and 201 the number 3, and so on. If such a scale is being used, is our statement about the four minerals (8, 7; 3, 2) still devoid of all factual meaning? Obviously not, for now it means that there are exactly as many minerals the hardness of which lies between those of the first pair as there are minerals the hardness of which lies between the second pair. There is admittedly not much point to this refinement, but the example has at least the virtue of simplicity.

A very common psychological scaling technique can be shown to rest upon exactly the same principles. Assume that a property is, in a statistically stable manner, distributed over a large population and that a percentile scale has been based, in the familiar fashion, upon the area under that curve. The question then arises as to what meaning can be attributed to the numerical equality of score differences, such as, let us say, between 60 and 50, and 25 and 15 respectively. Despite the opinion current among psychologists that this numerical equality does not signify 'equality,' it does have a well defined empirical meaning, namely this: in any fair sample the number of individuals between 60 and 50 is equal to the number of individuals between 25 and 15. The situation here is, in principle, the same as in our example of hardness. In every such instance some empirical law is used to endow the numerical equality of the differences between scale points with some kind of empirical meaning. In the case of the mercury scale for temperature the law drawn upon is the expansion formula, in the case of the percentile scale it is the (assumed) stability of some statistical distribution, normal or otherwise.

In this connection it might be worthwhile to call attention to the correct analysis of what is often thought of as the equality of sigma units (*Z*-scores, *T*-scores, etc.). That a certain concept is normally distributed is a significant empirical law about that concept and for theoretical reasons psychologists are often interested in defining concepts which are thus distributed. However, the translation of raw scores into sigma units amounts, technicalities apart, to nothing but the multiplication with a constant factor. There is no methodological reason for the privileged status which many contemporary psychologists attribute to such units. On this point our analysis is in essential agreement with that of Thomas (19).

Let us close this section by a remark with which the discussion of this point often starts. In extensional dimensions and only *in extensional dimensions, a factual meaning can be given to the equality of the numerical differences without drawing upon any other empirical laws than the axioms of measurement themselves*. The fact is that wherever there is an operation '$\underline{+}$,' there is, in all known instances, also an inverse operation '$\underline{-}$,' so that the two operations stand, loosely speaking, in the same relation as the two arithmetical symbols '+' and '−.' And *if an additive scale is used,* then it is also true that

$N(X) - N(Y) = N(X') - N(Y')$ if and only if $X \underline{-} Y \underline{=} X' \underline{-} Y'$.

The "empirical equation" to the right expresses the empirical meaning of the numerical equality to the left. It is a corollary of the preceding analysis that the phrase 'the units of a scale are equal by definition' is, to say the least, not very enlightening.

IV. Psychophysical Measurement

1. Psychophysical measurement has traditionally dealt with the quantification of *attributes* (psychological dimensions). The neutral term 'quantification' instead of 'measurement' has been chosen purposely. *An attribute is not a property of physical events or objects, but is defined by means of the discriminatory responses to such objects or events on the part of observers who are different from the scientist.* Again, the term 'observer' has been chosen because of its neutrality; at the present stage of the discussion it should not be identified with either the 'subject' or the 'judge' of an earlier section (II 3). The customary definitions of attributes are all based upon the verbal discriminations of human observers or, what amounts to the same, upon their motor responses in accordance with verbal instructions. Attributes such as pitch and loudness are thus actually defined by the consistent use of one and the same adjective and its comparative forms. It is important to notice that such responses, even if they are verbal, do not belong to the (pragmatic meta-) language of the scientist, but to the (object) language of the observers. By means of their utterances such as 'equally loud' or 'louder,' the scientist introduces his empirical construct 'loudness.' To repeat the same thing in a slightly different form, one can also say that the operational basis for the introduction of an attribute includes that of the pertinent physical dimensions and, *in addition,* the observers and the procedures of eliciting their responses.[5] The situation is thus analogous to the one discussed with reference to the social psychologist's term 'aggressive,' and the observers take, in a certain sense, the place of the judges. But there is also an important difference which must not be overlooked. The observers respond to a physical dimension already scaled by physical measurement, while judges are employed where no working physical scale has yet been found.

These distinctions become particularly important if *numbers* or, rather, to adopt a convenient usage, *numerals* occur in the observer's responses, as in the method of fractionation where the observers are required to bisect or equipartition supraliminal intervals, or to adjust the variable stimulus to 'half the given pitch' (17, 18). In using such numerical estimates

[5] Attention should be called to the fact that by means of the conditioning technique attributes for nonarticulate observers can be defined.

of observers for the construction of scales one is *not* using numbers in the same sense and in the same way as one does in physical measurement.[6] One only creates confusion if he uses terms like 'additivity' or 'multiplicativity' in referring to such response scales. Furthermore, confusion is enhanced by the failure to distinguish between additivity of scales and extensionality of dimensions. There shall be occasion to return to this point (IV 5). The distinction between the use of numerical estimates by judges or observers, on the one hand, and the scientist's direct, strictly behavioristic use of numbers, on the other, applies of course also to scalings by means of equal appearing intervals outside the field of the so-called sensory discriminations.

2. If one were asked to condense into one sentence a characterization of most of the *nonphysiological* work done in psychophysics, he might venture the following formulation: By laying down the operational procedures (method of limits, constant stimuli, fractionation, etc.), psychophysics first defines the various sensory attributes and then studies the empirical laws that obtain between the responses on the one hand and the dimensions of the physical objects or events, to which these responses are made, on the other. For instance, the procedures of any of the existing methods which lead to the establishment of a j.n.d. scale contain the (operational) definition of the attribute in question. The *Weber-Fechner curve* thus obtained is one of the empirical laws of psychophysics. And there is of course no *a priori* reason why, for instance, the curve of "constant-stimuli loudness" should coincide with that of "fractionation loudness."

The adoption of the convenient term 'Weber-Fechner curve' requires two clarifications. *First*, by this curve is meant the *empirical curve* representing the relationship between the quantification of an attribute, based on j.n.d.'s or any other procedure such as fractionation, on the one hand, and the pertinent physical dimensions on the other. Thus neither the logarithmic nor any other form of this empirical relationship is assumed. It would indeed be strange to make any *a priori* assumptions of this kind. *Second*, and in view of Stevens' results (15), the expression 'curve' should be replaced by 'polydimensional surface,' for as this investigator has shown in some instances, one and the same attribute is, as a matter of fact, a function of several physical dimensions. Pitch, for instance, has been discovered to be a function of both frequency and energy. The classical view of a one-to-one correspondence between physical and psychological dimensions thus turned out to be an oversimplification. The theoretical

[6] As the terms are used in this paper, numbers belong to the scientist's metalanguage, numerals to the object language used by the subject. This clarification also leads to the correct interpretation of the so-called *ratio scales*, mentioned by Boring (5, p. 52). It might at least be mentioned that an illegitimate fusion between these two ways in which 'numbers' occur plays an important rôle in Ramsey's unsuccessful attempt to construct a theory of probability (1). See also the last paragraph of IV 5.

significance of this finding needs no emphasis. But since this refinement does not affect the present argument and since dealing with surfaces would make our formulations unnecessarily cumbersome, we shall go on speaking about the Weber-Fechner curve.

3. Assume now that by one of the psychophysical methods a Weber-Fechner curve between, let us say, pitch and frequency has been established. If this curve is monotonous, as it actually is, then one can use what we shall refer to hereafter as the *psychological* scale of j.n.d.'s or mels (17) as a scale of the physical dimension frequency. Such a procedure, though not always fruitful, is entirely legitimate and its very possibility throws an interesting light on the nature of psychological scales. As has already been pointed out, such "psychological" measurement can also be considered as a rescaling of physical dimensions by means of observer responses. The Weber-Fechner curve is the mediating empirical law.

It is realized that what is here called a psychological scale is referred to as a psychophysical scale within the traditional field of psychophysics and as a psychological scale only in such instances as the scaling of attitudes, in which no independent physical measurement exists. So far as the instructions to the participating organism and its behavior are concerned, however, there is really no difference between the two cases. Furthermore, both have in common the fact that the experimenter is not interested in the response aspects themselves but rather in the stimulus dimension involved. The difference lies entirely in the circumstance that only in the traditional psychophysical case is there an independent physical scale of the stimulus dimension. In our discussion this difference is expressed by the distinction we make between the two terms 'judge' and 'observer.'

It is also worthwhile noticing in this connection that the empirical content of the Weber-Fechner law consists in the functional connection between the physical dimension and certain response aspects within the chosen procedures such as the number of j.n.d.'s.[7] If one recalls that derived scales are established by means of mediating empirical laws between *two* independently defined *physical* dimensions, then it becomes clear that the scales of traditional psychophysics do not fall into this category. If interest lies in the stimulus aspect then they represent an additional (psychological) scaling of a (physical) dimension already scaled. When the response aspect is emphasized, then we refer to them as scaling an attribute or psychological dimension.

Within the general field of measurement the scales of psychophysics thus constitute a type of their own. Continuing our analysis with a view to describing further operational differences between these scales and physical measurement it is appropriate to elaborate once again the inapplicability to them of the two categories 'intensive' and 'extensive.' Like

[7] Accordingly, the only correct derivation of the Weber-Fechner formula is that which does not make use of differentials. Such a derivation is to be found in Woodworth's textbook (20, pp. 435–437).

'derived' these two terms apply only to physical dimensions and not to attributes.

Where indeed are the *scientist's operations upon observer responses* which would justify their use? We must confess to utter inability to think of any operation '$\underline{+}$,' which could be applied to the observers or to any of their responses which have so far been used for the introduction of attributes. Consider the case of loudness and assume even, contrary to fact (16), that the observers' judgments were 'twice as loud' if two equal sound emitters, instead of one, are put into action. In this case '$\underline{+}$' obviously means the simultaneous operation of two sound emitting devices. What is thus operated upon is the physical dimension, not the attribute or the observer; and this in spite of the occurrence of numerals (ratios) in the observer reports. The same criticism holds true for the relation (operation) '$\geq$' or intensity, even if one were to use the term 'operation' in a sense broad enough to include simple sensory discriminations. The fact would still remain that what falls, in a vague sense, into a serial order are the operations (discriminations) of the observer, not those of the scientist, and only upon those of the latter are the original definitions of intensity and extensity based. One could, of course, object that we are dealing with mere matters of definition. To this we would answer, *first*, that these definitions are not arbitrary, they formulate what actually happens in physical measurement; *second*, that the differences of actual procedure, upon which our analysis thus insists, are important matters of fact; and, *third*, that the very grasp of these operational differences has been hampered by the vague use of such terms as 'intensive,' 'extensive,' and 'additive.' It is even fair to say that understanding of the behavioristic frame of reference as a whole has suffered from this state of affairs. As was pointed out before (III 6) the failure to understand what is meant by the equality of units also contributed to the confusion.

4. If our analysis were to stop at this point, the reader would be justified in feeling that it suffers from a physicalistic bias. While it is correct that measurement in psychophysics *can* be considered simply as a regauging of physical dimensions by means of observer reactions, this is by no means the whole story of psychophysics. The psychologist is mainly, and properly so, interested in the *response aspects* of the phenomena. To this phase our attention must now turn, and it will be best to begin with some very general remarks.

Like every other scientist the psychologist is interested in discovering the empirical laws (functional connections) that obtain between the variables of his field. Unlike the physical sciences, however, behavior science at its present stage finds that its variables are divided into groups, on the one hand the so-called response variables (R) and on the other, the group of experimentally manipulated variables (S). The functional relationships the behavior scientist is looking for are typically of the form

$$R = f(S). \tag{5}$$

While this is not the place to elaborate such a schema (3, 14), a few further remarks are necessary for the understanding of our last point concerning measurement and psychophysics in general.

(*a*) Neither S nor R is necessarily a single variable. They should rather be considered as representing groups of variables, so that S really stands for $S_1, S_2, \ldots S_n$, and R for $R_1, R_2, \ldots R_m$. The need for the introduction of such groups is particularly likely to arise on the side of the manipulated variables. Indeed, this is the comprehensible content of one of the main theses of the Gestalt writers.

(*b*) Both S and R are defined operationally by the scientist. The particular purpose of the investigation determines whether one single reflex (actone) or a relatively complex series of acts (action) is to be considered as one response variable and, likewise, which features of the physical environment are to be controlled or manipulated. That is to say, the choice of the descriptive units is entirely a matter of scientific expediency.

(*c*) S (stimulus !) always stands for a feature of the physical environment, R always for a behavior segment, but the psychologist is, by the nature of his material, forced to consider certain additional variables which fall into one of these two categories only *after they have been subjected to a certain amount of analysis*. These variables, let us call them *state variables*, fall again into different groups, such as motivation (D), and training or previous experience (T). There are, moreover, the variables representing possible innate individual differences (I), which fall neither into the S nor into the R category. At the present stage of psychological knowledge equation (5) would thus have to be expanded into

$$R = f(S, T, D, I). \quad (6)$$

For our present purposes, however, equation (5) is sufficient, since it is characteristic of sensory discrimination (perception) that the response depends, within very broad limits, only upon clearly defined environmental variables (S). This feature could, indeed, be used in a behavioristic definition of what should reasonably be understood by perception. The extensive use of the term 'perception,' which the Gestalters advocate, makes it a weasel word that covers the whole of psychology only at the price of emptying it of any specific content. Historically speaking, this verbal preference is probably grounded in the intuitionistic philosophical background of the Gestalters.

(*d*) Many, and probably the theoretically most interesting, laws of contemporary psychology undoubtedly are of the forms (5) or (6) in which both stimulus and response variables occur. (The laws of physics would, in this terminology, appear as functional connections between S's only.) But there is also a body of psychological knowledge which consists primarily of response correlations that can be symbolized by either of the two formulæ

$$R_1 = f(R_2), \qquad F(R_1, R_2) = 0. \quad (7)$$

As a matter of fact any correlation between the scores on two different tests is of this type and so is much of our knowledge in the field of personality (correlation of traits). Most of the work of Lewin and his collaborators, if correctly analyzed, turns out to be concerned with $R - R$ laws and, since it lies in the field of human personality, freely uses the human yardstick (II 3). The theorizing of this group is largely a rationalization of these two features (the interest in $R - R$ laws and the use of the human yardstick) which, in themselves, are easily understood consequences of their specific research interests. Historically speaking, these preferences, too, seem to have grown out of the atmosphere which the students of Kuelpe, Meinong, and in the last analysis, Brentano created at the German universities.[8]

As a matter of historical fact we are often able to discover a response correlation $R_2 = f(R_1)$, when we do not yet know how to ascertain the corresponding stimulus-response relationships

$$(8) \qquad R_1 = f_1(S, \ldots) \quad \text{and} \quad R_2 = f_2(S, \ldots).$$

If, however, $R_1 = f_1(S)$ and $R_2 = f_2(S)$ are both known, then it is always possible to compute the response correlation. In order to do that one has but to solve one of the two equations, say the first one, and then substitute the solution into the second. Symbolically this might be indicated in the following manner:

$$(9) \qquad R_2 = f_2(f_1^{-1}(R_1)).$$

5. The last remarks lead us back to the problem at hand, namely, the response aspects of the scales of psychophysics. Assume that two pitch scales have been constructed by two different procedures, one for instance by the method of constant stimuli, the other by fractionation. As has been said before, there is no *a priori* reason to expect that any two such scales should stand in a particularly simple relationship.[9] We notice that the relationship between any two such scales is just an instance of the general relationship (9).

Consider now the empirical law, recently confirmed by Stevens and Volkmann (18), that an observer, instructed to 'bisect' the interval between two given pitches P_1 and P_2 by adjusting a third tone so that it is 'halfway between P_1 and P_2 in pitch' selects a tone P so that

$$(10) \qquad P - P_1 = P_2 - P.$$

where P, P_1 and $P_2 (P_2 > P_1)$ are the numbers of a j.n.d. scale. Obviously this law, though it is of the type (7) could be expressed by any scale whatsoever, either in frequencies or by means of still another response scale. It is

[8] Boring (5) has recently, with keen cultural sensitiveness, again called attention to these continuities.

[9] It can however be shown that any two scales obtained by the method of constant stimuli and the use of different percentage criteria are distinguished only by a multiplicative factor. This is a simple mathematical consequence of the way the j.n.d.'s are defined in this procedure (10).

true, though, that if one uses the j.n.d. scale, the mathematical form of the law takes a particularly simple form. So far the case is completely analogous to that of our earlier example concerning the specific heat of substances (III 5).

Response scales, it is true, offer further advantages in the way of stimulating certain lines of research. In the case under consideration they direct the psychologist's attention towards the relationships between thresholds and supraliminal discriminations. The shape of the functional relationship between a physical and a response scale might also suggest certain lines of physiological research or, to use Boring's (4) happy expression, help the scientist to "tap" the organism at the right place. But such expectations are, of course, purely pragmatic and have no bearing on the methodological analysis of measurement.

Another interesting result of Stevens' experimentation (16) is that what has just been said about pitch does not hold for loudness. In other words, the numbers on a j.n.d. scale for loudness are not proportional to the numbers on a scale constructed by means of the bisection procedure. The point to be made is that it is neither helpful nor enlightening to describe this state of affairs by saying that one can construct an "additive" scale for pitch, while there is no loudness scale which enjoys such mensurational excellence. Such disguise of interesting results as a search for scales cannot possibly be to the advantage of psychophysics. Furthermore, it has the drawback that it tends to blur the really important distinctions of a behavioristic analysis of measurement. In the case under consideration, for instance, the so-called "additivity" of the pitch scale is based on the use of numerals by the observer and this use is not clearly distinguished from the use of numbers by the scientist.

V. Summary and Conclusion

The results of the present discussion can be summarized into three points. *First,* it tries to discourage the use of such terms as 'intensive,' 'extensive,' and 'additive' with reference to scales in psychophysics. *Second,* it sets up measurement in psychophysics as a technique in its own right which one cannot without violence subsume under any of the customary classifications of physical measurement. Because of this methodological independence the term 'observer,' different from both 'judge' and 'subject,' has been consistently used throughout this section. So far as the response aspect of the scales is concerned, however, the observer acts really as a subject, while we have seen (IV 1) that as far as the rescaling aspect goes, his function is similar to that of a judge. *Third,* it points out the awkwardness of the fact that a field of research as significant as psychophysics has been disguised as a search for scales.

A concluding remark might help to forestall misunderstanding. No disparagement of the psychophysical scales is involved in their being set aside from physical measurement. Psychologists should indeed not rush into the use of physical terms if there is nothing else to be gained but a share in the prestige of the physical sciences. Behaviorism today is firmly enough established to make a more discriminating attitude completely compatible with our belief in the ultimate explanatory promise of the physiological level. The most fruitful expression of this belief at the present stage seems to us to emphasize the *theoretical* significance of the $S - R$ as opposed to the $R - R$ type of laws. On the other hand, it is methodologically perfectly conceivable to start the construction of science by measuring length and weight by means of observer-estimates, instead of with yardsticks and balances, provided only that the prescientific common sense level is once epistemologically secured. The actual excellence of physical measurement is entirely a matter of fact.

REFERENCES

1. Bergmann, G. The logic of probability. *Amer. J. Physics,* 1942, 9, 263–272.
2. ——. An empiricist schema of the psychophysical problem. *Phil. Sci.,* 1942, 9, 72–91.
3. ——, & Spence, K. W. Operationism and theory in psychology. *Psychol. Rev.,* 1941, 48, 1–14.
4. Boring, E. G. A psychological function is the relation of successive differentiations of events in the organism. *Psychol. Rev.,* 1937, 44, 445–461.
5. ——. *Sensation and perception in the history of experimental psychology.* New York: Appleton-Century-Crofts, 1942.
6. Campbell, N. R. *Physics: the elements.* Cambridge: Cambridge University Press, 1920.
7. ——. *What is science?* London: Methuen, 1921.
8. Carnap, R. *Physikalische Begriffsbildung.* Karlsruhe: B. Braun, 1926.
9. Cohen, R. M., & Nagel, E. *An introduction to logic and scientific method.* New York: Harcourt, Brace, 1934.
10. Egan, J. P. The measurement of sensory dimensions. Unpublished Master's Thesis, State Univ. Iowa, 1940.
11. McGregor, D. Scientific measurement and psychology. *Psychol. Rev.,* 1935, 42, 246–266.
12. Nagel, E. Measurement. *Erkenntnis,* 1930, 2, 313–333.
13. Ramsperger, A. G. *Philosophies of science.* New York: Crofts, 1942.
14. Spence, K. W. Theoretical interpretations of learning. In *Comparative psychology* (ed. F. A. Moss; rev. ed.), New York: Prentice-Hall, 1942.
15. Stevens, S. S. Volume and intensity of tones. *Amer. J. Psychol.,* 1934, 46, 397–408.
16. ——. A scale for the measurement of a psychological magnitude: loudness. *Psychol. Rev.,* 1936, 43, 405–416.
17. ——, Volkmann, J., & Newman, E. B. A scale for the measurement of the psychological magnitude pitch. *J. acoust. Soc. Amer.,* 1937, 8, 185–190.
18. ——, & Volkmann, J. The relation of pitch to frequency: a revised scale. *Amer. J. Psychol.,* 1940, 53, 329–353.
19. Thomas, L. G. Mental tests as instruments of science. *Psychol. Monogr.,* 1942, 54, No. 3.
20. Woodworth, R. S. *Experimental psychology.* New York: Henry Holt, 1938.
21. *International Encyclopedia of Unified Science* (eds. O. Neurath, R. Carnap, C. W. Morris), Chicago: University of Chicago Press, 1938–.

II

PHILOSOPHY OF THE FORMAL SCIENCES

Formal and Factual Science *

RUDOLF CARNAP

"THEORY OF SCIENCE" may be taken to cover all investigations having science itself as their subject matter. Such investigations can be undertaken from different perspectives. Accordingly, we may distinguish psychological, sociological, historical or logical analyses of science, without necessarily separating them in practice. The logical analysis of science, called for short "logic of science," as I see it may be more precisely characterized as the logical syntax of the language of science.†

As an example of a problem in the logic of science, we shall deal in what follows with the problem of the relationship between two major fields of science, namely, the *formal sciences* (logic, including mathematics) and the *factual sciences* (embracing the totality of all empirical disciplines: physics, biology, psychology, sociology, history, etc.). The problem is here taken as one in the *logic* of science: such questions as, for instance, the psychological differences between the activities of research in the two fields shall not be discussed. Only the question concerning the *logical* relations between the two fields, that is, the difference in the syntactical character of their statements and statement-systems is our concern. While in their psychological character there is only a difference of degree and not of kind between the two fields, from a logical point of view a precise and fundamental difference can be demonstrated. This is based upon the syntactical *difference between analytic and synthetic statements.*

In order to show how the delimitation of the formal from the factual sciences can be achieved, we assume that the syntactical structure of the language of science is fully established. This requires the specification of a system of syntactical rules: first, the formation rules of the language in question, that is, the rules which determine the admissible forms of statements; second, the transformation rules, that is, the rules which determine under what conditions a statement is a consequence of other statements. (There are two different possibilities for the reconstruction of the language of science: the transformation rules may be restricted to logico-mathematical rules or one may include extra-logical transformation rules.

* Translated by the editors and reprinted with kind permission of the author from *Erkenntnis*, 5, 1934.

† According to Carnap's later views, semantical analysis must supplement the purely syntactical approach. Editors' note.

We shall here, for the sake of simplicity, restrict ourselves to the first kind.) Statements, according to their syntactical character and with regard to transformation rules, may be classified in the following way: a statement of the pertinent language will be called *analytic* if it is unconditionally valid according to the transformation rules and independently of the truth or falsity of other statements. The exact definition can, however, not contain such expressions as "unconditionally valid" but only the concept of "consequence", which is defined by the transformation rules. We define: a statement is analytic if it is a consequence of the null class of statements. Further, we call a statement *inconsistent* (self-contradictory) if it is unconditionally invalid; more precisely: if every statement of the language is a consequence of it. We call a statement *determinate* if it is either analytic or inconsistent. We call a statement *synthetic* if it is neither analytic nor inconsistent.

We arrive at a different classification of statements through a classification of signs. Signs having a logico-mathematical significance as, for example, 'or', 'every', 'not', '3', we shall call *logical signs*; signs with an extra-logical significance, such as, 'large', 'house', 'anger', we shall call *descriptive signs*. This difference can also be purely syntactically defined, that is, without reference to the significance of the signs. The class of logical signs may be characterized by saying that every statement containing only signs of this class is determinate. By a *logical statement* we shall understand one containing only logical signs; by a *descriptive statement* we shall mean one which contains at least one descriptive sign. Note, however, that while all synthetic statements are descriptive, the converse does not hold. The range of descriptive sentences is wider than that of synthetic statements.

The distinction between the formal and the factual sciences consists then in this: the first contains only analytic, while the second also contains synthetic statements. These relations are shown more clearly in the adjoining table, which represents diagrammatically the division among statements. The concepts "true" and "false" are added only for the sake of elucidation. They are not logical concepts definable in a purely syntactical manner. Synthetic statements constitute the core of science. They serve in the formulation of possible states of affairs (both actual and non-actual). In addition, we have analytic statements arranged in three stages: first, the descriptive analytic statements; they are still in close relation to the factual sciences inasmuch as they contain descriptive signs, that is, signs of extra-logical entities. But they contain them in a form that permits the question as to whether such statements are true or false to be answered independently of the nature of these entities, namely, merely on the basis of the transformation rules of language. Further, there are the analytical logical statements. Among them we may distinguish those which are logical in the narrower sense of that word and the mathematical statements. There is no fundamental difference between the mathematical statements and the other

DIVISION OF STATEMENTS

(true) (false)

analytic synthetic contradictory

logical descriptive logical

mathematical | logical, in narrower sense

mathematical	logical, in narrower sense		descriptive					
2+2=4. 5 is a prime number.	F (x) or ~F (x). 'A. ~A' is a conjunction.	Chicago is on the Hudson or Chicago is not on the Hudson.	Chicago is on Lake Michigan. Lead melts at 330° C. At such and such place there is a conjunction.	Chicago is on the Hudson.	Chicago is on the Hudson and Chicago is not on the Hudson.	F (x) and ~F (x).	2+2=5.	Language L_1
	'A. ~A' is a contradictory sentence.		At such and such place there is a contradictory sentence.					Language L_2

DIVISION OF SCIENCES

Mathematics | pure syntax, Logic in narrower sense | Applied Logic | descriptive syntax

Logic in broader sense

Formal Science | Factual Science

purely logical ones; but one may for practical purposes distinguish them by the decision to call "mathematical" only those statements which contain numerals or predicates relating to numerals, etc.

Since synthetic statements are sufficient for the formulation of any particular assertion as well as of general laws, it is possible to reconstruct the language of science in such a manner that it contains only synthetic statements. This need not diminish the content of science. Given some language L_1 for the whole of science, then language L_2 can be constructed as follows: the formation rules for L_2 stipulate that all synthetic statements of L_1 and only these are admitted as statements in L_2. The transformation rules for L_2 will be established in the following way: those transformation rules of L_1 which have the form of ordinary rules of inference (i.e., transformation rules with premises) are accepted without alteration in L_2. However, the transformation rules of L_1 which have the form of axioms (i.e., transformation rules with an empty class of premises) and perhaps a few other analytic statements of L_1 are replaced by corresponding transformation rules (with premises) in L_2. For example, instead of the axiom "$P \supset (P \vee Q)$" in L_1 we adopt in L_2 the following transformation rule: "Every statement of the form $S_1 \vee S_2$ is a direct consequence of S_1." In L_2 there are then no longer any purely logical statements; what they achieve in L_1 is achieved in L_2 by corresponding rules. Similarly, "$2 + 2 = 4$" is a sentence in L_1 but not in L_2. In its place we have in L_2 the derived rule: "The expressions '$2 + 2$' and '4' are always mutually substitutable. L_2 then contains neither logic nor mathematics as statement-systems. But not only is every particular factual statement and every law of L_1 contained in L_2; also every logical deduction, including all mathematical computations and transformations, which in L_1 leads from synthetic premises to synthetic conclusions can be carried out in L_2. However, the procedure is then not as simple as in L_1; hence, the form of language L_2, while possible, is *inexpedient*. Therefore, we shall prefer the form L_1, which results from L_2 by adding to the synthetic statements certain auxiliary statements, namely, the analytic (and inconsistent) ones. These auxiliary statements have indeed no factual content or, to speak in the material idiom, they do not express any matters of fact, actual or non-actual. Rather they are, as it were, mere calculational devices, but they are so constructed that they can be subjected to the same rules as are the genuine (synthetic) statements. In this way they are an easily applicable device for operations with synthetic statements.

There is moreover the possibility of a compromise, namely, to include in a language besides the synthetic statements some but not all analytic statements contained in the present day language of science. But this procedure is probably even less expedient than that of the complete elimination of analytic statements. Once statements devoid of factual content are admitted at all, there is no cogent reason why their advantages should not be utilized to the fullest extent. The proposal to admit only the descriptive analytic statements might seem defensible. After all, they are more closely related to synthetic statements than the rest of the analytic statements: their elimination would have the unpleasant consequence that the compounding of two statements as by 'V' ("or") would not always yield a statement as, for example, the compound "S_1 or not-S_1." (This would render the formation rules indefinite, thus involve grave disadvantages.) The most inexpedient proposal, however, would be a delimitation according to which logical statements in the narrower sense are admitted in the language but the mathematical ones are excluded. (In this manner Wittgenstein, for example, drew the line of demarcation; but he formulated this formation rule not as a proposal but as an assertion about "*the* language".)

Science uses synthetic and analytic statements in the following manner. The factual sciences establish synthetic statements, e.g., singular statements for the description of observable facts or general statements which are introduced as hypotheses and used tentatively. From the statements thus established the scientists try to derive other synthetic statements, in order, for instance, to make predictions concerning the future. The analytic statements served in an auxiliary function for these inferential operations. All of logic including mathematics, considered from the point of view of the total language, is thus no more than an auxiliary calculus for dealing with synthetic statements. *Formal science* has no independent significance, but is an auxiliary component introduced for technical reasons in order to facilitate linguistic transformations in the *factual sciences*. The great importance of the formal sciences, that is, of logic and mathematics, within the total system of science is thereby not in the least denied but instead, through a characterization of this special function, emphasized. This characterization of the logical function of the formal sciences as an auxiliary calculus is not incompatible with the psychological fact that it is certainly not always, and perhaps only in infrequent cases, that the motive for research in any branch of the formal sciences is possible application in the factual sciences. The question as to whether the calculus of analytic statements, in view of the above characterization, is still to be called a science or not is a relatively unimportant terminological issue. In keeping with the customary use of terms, it may be better to designate as sciences all systems with deductive connections; hence to include therein logic and mathematics and not only systems of synthetic statements, that is, those of the factual sciences.

A remark may be added concerning the question as to where in our scheme *syntax* is to be located. The scheme represents a division of the statements of a definite language, such as S_1. Now if statements of pure syntax concerning the statement forms of this language are formulated (e.g., "A sentence of such-and-such form is analytic in S_1," "Two statements of such-and-such form are incompatible in S_1"), then this would generally be done in a second language S_2. In this case syntax lies entirely outside of our scheme, namely, in the logico-mathematical part of the language S_2. It is, however, also possible to formulate syntactical statements about statements of S_1 in S_1 itself. They then belong either to the logical statements in the narrower sense, or—if the syntax is arithmetized—to the mathematical ones. But this formulation in S_1 would not be possible for all syntactical statements; some concepts referring to S_1 (e.g., "analytic in S_1", "contradictory in S_1") cannot be defined by means of the concepts of S_1 itself but only in a richer language S_2.—What has just been said is true of pure syntax; descriptive syntax, which deals with sentences as physical objects, belongs to the factual sciences.

In adjoining the formal sciences to the factual sciences *no new area of subject matter* is introduced, despite the contrary opinion of some philosophers who believe that the "real" objects of the factual sciences must be contrasted with the "formal", "*geistig*" or "ideal" objects of the formal sciences. *The formal sciences do not have any objects at all;* they are systems of auxiliary statements without objects and without content. The emphasis on a sharp delimitation between the formal and the factual sciences therefore leaves the *unity of science* unaffected.

The Nature of a Logical or Mathematical System *

MORRIS R. COHEN AND ERNEST NAGEL

§ 1. The Function of Axioms

ALTHOUGH THE BABYLONIANS and Egyptians had much information about the eclipses of the sun and the moon, the measurement of land and the construction of buildings, the disposition of geometric figures in order to form symmetrical designs, and computation with integers and fractions, it is generally recognized that they had no *science* of these matters. The idea of a science was a contribution of the Greeks.

Information, no matter how reliable or extensive, which consists of a set of isolated propositions is not science. A telephone book, a dictionary, a cookbook, or a well-ordered catalogue of goods sold in a general store may contain accurate knowledge, organized in some convenient order, but we do not regard these as works of science. Science requires that our propositions form a logical *system*, that is, that they stand to each other in some one or other of the relations of equivalence and opposition already discussed. Therefore in the present chapter we continue our study of the nature of proof, in order to make clearer some of the generic characteristics of deductive systems. Such a study, we shall find, is identical with the study of the nature of mathematics.

Let us remember that no proposition can be *demonstrated* by any experimental method. The reader is doubtless familiar with the Pythagorean theorem that in a right triangle the square on the hypotenuse is equal to the sum of the squares on the arms. He has, no doubt, "proved" or "demonstrated" it in his school days. Nevertheless every gathering of college-trained men is likely to contain at least one member who, when asked how the theorem may be proved, will suggest protractors, carefully drawn triangles, and finely graduated rulers. In this respect, such an individual has made no essential advance upon the methods of the ancient Egyptian surveyors.

Suppose, for instance, we were to attempt to prove the Pythagorean

* From *An Introduction to Logic and Scientific Method* by Morris R. Cohen and Ernest Nagel, copyright, 1934, by Harcourt, Brace and Company, Inc., and used with their permission and that of Felix S. Cohen and Ernest Nagel.

theorem by actually drawing the squares on the three sides of a right triangle on some uniformly dense tinfoil, then cutting them out and by weighing them seeing whether the square on the hypotenuse does actually balance the other two squares. Would this constitute a proof? Obviously not, for we can never know that the tinfoil is in fact absolutely uniform in density, or that the pieces cut out are perfect squares. Hence, if in a number of experiments we should fail to find a perfect balance in the weights, we should not consider that as evidence against the view that there *would* be a perfect equilibrium *if* our lines were perfectly straight, the angles of the square were perfect right angles, and the mass of the tinfoil were absolutely uniform. A logical proof or demonstration consists in exhibiting a proposition as the necessary consequence of other propositions. The demonstration asserts nothing about the factual truth of either the premises or their logical consequences.

"But look here!" the reader may protest. "Don't we prove that the theorems in geometry are *really* true? Isn't mathematics supposed to be the most certain of the sciences, in which some property is shown to hold for all objects of a definite type, once and for all? If you examine any statement of a theorem, for example the Pythagorean, you find something asserted about 'all' triangles. Now if you admit that something is in fact proved true of all triangles, why do you refuse to admit that we are establishing the 'material' truth of such a theorem? Doesn't 'all' really mean 'all'?"

This protest, however, simply ignores that a logical proof is a "pointing-out" or "showing" of the implications between a set of propositions called axioms and a set called theorems, and that the axioms themselves are not demonstrated.

The reader may reply: "The axioms are not proved, because they need no proof. *Their truth is self-evident.* Everybody can recognize that propositions like *The whole is greater than any one of its parts* or *Through two points only one straight line may be drawn* are obviously true. They are therefore a satisfactory basis for geometry, because by their means we can establish the truth of propositions not so obvious or self-evident."

Such a reply represents a traditional view. Up to the end of the nineteenth century it was generally believed that the axioms are materially true of the physical world, and that the cogency of the demonstrations depends upon their being thus materially true. Nevertheless, this view of the axioms confuses three different issues:

1. How is the material truth of the axioms established?
2. Are the axioms materially true?
3. Are the theorems the logical consequences of the explicitly stated axioms?

We must consider these separately.

1. The answer generally given to the first question is that the axioms are self-evident truths. But this view is a rather complacent way of ignoring

real difficulties. In the first place, if by "self-evidence" is meant psychological obviousness, or an irresistible impulse to assert, or the psychological unconceivability of any contrary propositions, the history of human thought has shown how unreliable it is as a criterion of truth. Many propositions formerly regarded as self-evident, for example: *Nature abhors a vacuum; At the antipodes men walk with their heads beneath their feet; Every surface has two sides*, are now known to be false. Indeed, contradictory propositions about every variety of subject matter, thus including most debatable propositions, have each, at different times, been declared to be fundamental intuitions and therefore self-evidently true. But whether a proposition is obvious or not depends on cultural conditions and individual training, so that a proposition which is "self-evidently true" to one person or group is not so to another.

This view assumes a capacity on the part of human beings to establish universal or general propositions dealing with matter of fact simply by examining the *meaning* of a proposition. But, once more, the history of human thought, as well as the analysis of the nature of meaning, has shown that there is an enormous difference between *understanding the meaning* of a proposition and *knowing its truth*. The truth of general propositions about an indefinite number of empirical facts can never be absolutely established. The fundamental reason, therefore, for denying that the axioms of geometry or of any other branch of mathematics, are self-evidently true is that each of the axioms has at least one significant contrary.

"But doesn't the mathematician discover his axioms by observation on the behavior of matter in space and time?" the reader may ask. "And aren't they in fact more certain than the theorems?"

In order to reply, we must resort to the ancient Aristotelian distinction between the *temporal order* in which the logical dependence of propositions is discovered and the *logical order* of implications between propositions. There is no doubt that many of the axioms of mathematics are an expression of what we believe to be the truth concerning selected parts of nature, and that many advances in mathematics have been made because of the suggestions of the natural sciences. But there is also no doubt that mathematics as an *inquiry* did not historically begin with a number of axioms from which subsequently the theorems were derived. We know that many of the propositions of Euclid were known hundreds of years before he lived; they were doubtless believed to be materially true. Euclid's chief contribution did not consist in discovering additional theorems, but in exhibiting them as part of a system of connected truths. The kind of question Euclid must have asked himself was: Given the theorems about the angle sum of a triangle, about similar triangles, the Pythagorean theorem, and the rest, what are the minimum number of assumptions or axioms from which these can be inferred? As a result of his work, instead of having what were believed to be independent propositions, geometry became the first known example of a deductive system. The axioms were thus in fact *discovered later* than the theorems, although the former are *logically prior* to the latter.

It is a common prejudice to assume that the logically prior propositions are "better known" or "more certain" than the theorems, and that in general the logical priority of some propositions to others is connected in some way with their being true. Axioms are simply assumptions or hypotheses, used for the purpose of systematizing and sometimes discovering the theorems they imply. It follows that axioms *need not* be known to be true before the theorems are known, and in general the axioms of a science are much less evident psychologically than the theorems. In most sciences, as we shall see, the material truth of the theorems is not established by means of first showing the material truth of the axioms. On the contrary, the material truth of axioms is made *probable* by establishing empirically the truth or the probability of the theorems.

2. We must acknowledge, therefore, that an answer to the question, "Are the axioms materially true?" cannot be given on grounds of logic alone, and that it must be determined by the special natural science which empirically investigates the subject matter of such axioms. But it must also be admitted that the material truth or falsity of the axioms is of no concern to the logician or mathematician, who is interested only in the fact that theorems are or are not implied by the axioms. It is essential, therefore, to distinguish between *pure mathematics*, which is interested only in the facts of implication, and *applied mathematics*, or natural science, which is interested also in questions of material truth.

3. Whether the theorems are logical consequences of the axioms must, therefore, be determined by logical methods alone. This is not, however, always as easy as it appears. For many centuries Euclid's proofs were accepted as valid, although they made use of other assumptions than those he explicitly stated. There has been a steady growth in the logical rigor demanded of mathematical demonstrations, and today considerable logical maturity, as well as special technical competence, is a prerequisite for deciding questions of validity. Indeed, in certain branches of mathematics the cogency of some demonstrations has not yet been established.

We may now state summarily our first results concerning the nature of a logical system. Propositions can be demonstrated by exhibiting the relations of implication between them and other propositions. But not all propositions in the system can be demonstrated, for otherwise we would be arguing in a circle. It should, however, be noted that propositions which are axiomatic in one system may be demonstrated in another system. Also, terms that are undefined in one system may be definable in another. What we have called pure mathematics is, therefore, a *hypothetico-deductive system.* Its axioms serve as hypotheses or assumptions, which are entertained or considered for the propositions they imply. In general, the logical relation of axioms and theorems is that of a principal to its subaltern. If the whole of geometry is condensed into one proposition, the axioms are the antecedents in the hypothetical proposition so obtained. But they also characterize, as we shall see presently, the formal structure of the system in which the theorems are the elements.

§ 2. Pure Mathematics—An Illustration

The reader is probably familiar with some examples of logical systems from his study of mathematics. Consider the following propositions, which are the axioms for a special kind of geometry.

Axiom 1. If *A* and *B* are distinct points on a plane, there is at least one line containing both *A* and *B*.

Axiom 2. If *A* and *B* are distinct points on a plane, there is not more than one line containing both *A* and *B*.

Axiom 3. Any two lines on a plane have at least one point of the plane in common.

Axiom 4. There is at least one line on a plane.

Axiom 5. Every line contains at least three points of the plane.

Axiom 6. All the points of a plane do not belong to the same line.

Axiom 7. No line contains more than three points of the plane.

These axioms seem clearly to be about points and lines on a plane. In fact, if we omit the seventh one, they are the assumptions made by Veblen and Young for "projective geometry" on a plane in their standard treatise on that subject. It is unnecessary for the reader to know anything about projective geometry in order to understand the discussion that follows. But what are points, lines, and planes? The reader may think he "knows" what they are. He may "draw" points and lines with pencil and ruler, and perhaps convince himself that the axioms state truly the properties and relations of these geometric things. This is extremely doubtful, for the properties of marks on paper may diverge noticeably from those postulated. But in any case the question whether these actual marks do or do not conform is one of *applied* and not of *pure* mathematics. The axioms themselves, it should be noted, do not indicate what points, lines, and so on "really" are. For the purpose of discovering the implications of these axioms, it is unessential to know what we shall understand by points, lines, and planes. These axioms imply several theorems, not in virtue of the visual representation which the reader may give them, but in virtue of their logical form. Points, lines, and planes may be any entities whatsoever, undetermined in every way except by the relations stated in the axioms.

Let us, therefore, suppress every explicit reference to points, lines, and planes, and thereby eliminate all appeal to spatial intuition in deriving several theorems from the axioms. Suppose, then, that instead of the word "plane," we employ the letter *S;* and instead of the word "point," we use the phrase "element of S." Obviously, if the plane (*S*) is viewed as a collection of points (elements of *S*), a line may be viewed as a class of points (elements) which is a subclass of the points of the plane (*S*). We shall therefore substitute for the word "line" the expression "l-class." Our original set of axioms then reads as follows:

Axiom 1′. If *A* and *B* are distinct elements of *S*, there is at least one *l-class* containing both *A* and *B*.

Axiom 2′. If *A* and *B* are distinct elements of *S*, there is not more than one *l-class* containing both *A* and *B*.

Axiom 3′. Any two *l-classes* have at least one element of *S* in common.

Axiom 4′. There exists at least one *l-class* in *S*.

Axiom 5′. Every *l-class* contains at least three elements of *S*.

Axiom 6′. All the elements of *S* do not belong to the same *l-class*.

Axiom 7′. No *l-class* contains more than three elements of *S*.

In this set of assumptions no explicit reference is made to any specific subject matter. The only notions we require to state them are of a completely general character. The ideas of a "class," "subclass," "elements of a class," the relation of "belonging to a class" and the converse relation of a "class containing elements," the notion of "number," are part of the fundamental equipment of logic. If, therefore, we succeed in discovering the implications of these axioms, it cannot be because of the properties of space as such. As a matter of fact, none of these axioms can be regarded as propositions; none of them is in itself either true or false. For the symbols, *S*, *l-class*, *A*, *B*, and so on are *variables*. Each of the variables denotes any one of a class of possible entities, the only restriction placed upon it being that it must "satisfy," or conform to, the formal relations stated in the axioms. But until the symbols are assigned specific values the axioms are *propositional functions*, and not propositions.[1]

Our "assumptions," therefore, consist in relations considered to hold between undefined terms. But the reader will note that although no terms are *explicitly* defined, an *implicit* definition of them is made. They may denote anything whatsoever, provided that what they denote conforms to the stated relations between themselves. This procedure characterizes modern mathematical technique. In Euclid, for example, *explicit* definitions are given of points, lines, angles, and so on. In a modern treatment of geometry, these elements are defined *implicitly* through the axioms. As we shall see, this latter procedure makes it possible to give a variety of interpretations to the undefined elements, and so to exhibit an identity of structure in different concrete settings.

[1] The statement in the text is concerned with forms such as "X is a man," which does not assert anything until some definite value is assigned to the variable *X*. In this case, the truth of the proposition asserted by the sentence (obtained by substituting a determinate value of *X*) depends upon the value assigned to X. Propositions, however, of the form *X is a man implies X is mortal, for all values of X* do assert something which is true no matter what value is assigned to *X*. In this case, *X* is said to be an apparent variable, since the truth of the proposition does not depend upon the value given to X.

We shall now demonstrate six theorems, some of which may be regarded as trite consequences of our assumptions.

Theorem I. If A and B are distinct elements of S, there is one and only one *l-class* containing both A and B. It will be called the *l-class* AB.

This follows at once from Axioms 1′ and 2′.

Theorem II. Any two distinct *l-classes* have one and only one element of S in common.

This follows from Axioms 2′ and 3′.

Theorem III. There exist three elements of S which are not all in the same *l-class*.

This is an immediate consequence of Axioms 4′, 5′, and 6′.

Theorem IV. Every *l-class* in S contains just three elements of S.

This follows from Axioms 5′ and 7′.

Theorem V. Any class S which is subject to Axioms 1′ to 6′ inclusively contains at least seven elements.

Proof. For let A, B, C be three elements of S not in the same *l-class*. This is possible by Theorem III. Then there must be three distinct *l-classes*, containing AB, BC, and CA, by Theorem I. Furthermore, each of these *l-classes* must have an additional element, by Axiom 5′. And these additional elements must be distinct from each other, and from A, B, C, by Axiom 2′.

Let these additional elements be designated by D, E, and G, so that ABD, BCE, and CAG form the three distinct *l-classes* mentioned. Now AE and BG also determine *l-classes*, which must be distinct from any *l-classes* yet mentioned, by Axiom 1′. And they must have an element of S in common, by Axiom 4′, which is distinct from any element so far enumerated, by Axiom 2′. Let us call it F, so that AEF and BFG are *l-classes*.

Consequently, there are at least seven elements in S.

Theorem VI. The class S, subject to all seven assumptions, contains no more than seven elements.

Proof. Suppose there were an eighth element T. Then the *l-class* determined by AT and BFG would have to have an element in common, by Axiom 3′. But this element cannot be B, for the elements AB determine the *l-class* whose elements are ABD, so that $ABTD$ would need to belong to this very same *l-class;* which is impossible by Axiom 7′. Nor can this element be F, for then $AFTE$ would have to belong to the *l-class* AEF; nor G, for then $AGTC$ would need to belong to the *l-class* AGC; these results are impossible for the same reason (Axiom 7′).

Consequently, since the existence of an eighth element would contradict Axiom 7′, such an element cannot exist.

We have now exhibited a miniature mathematical system as a hypothetico-deductive science. The deduction makes no appeal whatsoever to experiment or observation, to any sensory elements. The reader has had a taste of pure mathematics. Whether anything in the world of existence conforms to this system requires empirical knowledge. If this be the case, that portion of the actual world must have the systematic character indicated formally in our symbolic representation. That the world does exemplify such a structure can be verified only within the limits of the errors of our experimental procedure.

§ 3. Structural Identity or Isomorphism

We want to show now that an abstract set such as the one discussed in the previous section may have more than one concrete representation, and that these different representations, though extremely unlike in material content, will be identical in logical structure.

Let us suppose there is a banking firm with seven partners. In order to assure themselves of expert information concerning various securities, they decide to form seven committees, each of which will study a special field. They agree, moreover, that each partner will act as chairman of one committee, and that every partner will serve on three and only three committees. The following is the schedule of committees and their members, the first member being chairman:

Domestic railroads	Adams,	Brown,	Smith
Municipal bonds	Brown,	Murphy,	Ellis
Federal bonds	Murphy,	Smith,	Jones
South American securities	Smith,	Ellis,	Gordon
Domestic steel industry	Ellis,	Jones,	Adams
Continental securities	Jones,	Gordon,	Brown
Public utilities	Gordon,	Adams,	Murphy

An examination of this schedule shows that it "satisfies" the seven axioms if the class S is interpreted as the banking firm, its elements as the partners, and the *l-classes* as the various committees.

We exhibit one further interpretation, which at first sight may seem to have nothing in common with those already given. In the following figure there are seven points lying by threes on seven lines, one of which is "bent." Let each point represent an element of S, and each set of three points lying on a line an *l-class*. Then all the seven assumptions are satisfied. This geometric pattern exemplifies the *same formal relations* as does the array of numbers and the schedule of the banker's committees we have already given. A third representation will be found on page 143.

Let us examine these three representations. We find, in the first place, that we can make correspond in a one-one manner every element of one interpretation with elements of the other two. And in the second place, every relation between the elements in one representation corresponds to a relation with the same logical properties between the *corresponding* elements in the other two. Thus, as an illustration, the element 0 in the numerical interpretation given below, can be placed in one-one correspondence with the point A in the geometrical interpretation, and also with Mr. Adams in the banking firm; the element 1 corresponds to point B, and also to Mr. Brown, and so on. And the three termed relation between the numbers 0, 1, 3 (page 143) in virtue of which they belong to the same group, corresponds to the relation between the points *ABD* in virtue of which they lie on the same line, and also corresponds to the relation between Messrs. Adams, Brown, and Smith in virtue of which they are on the same committee; and so on.

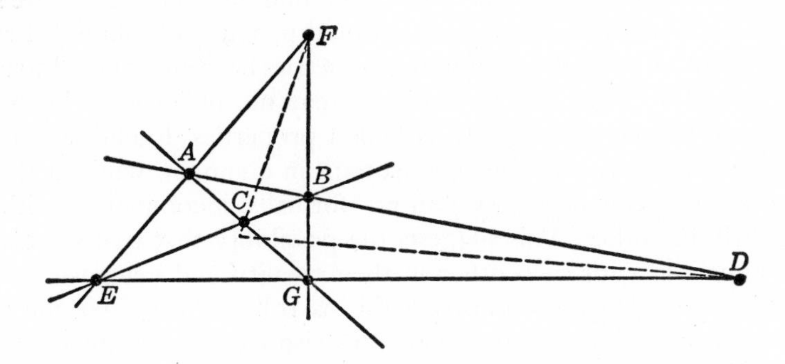

Two or more systems which are related in this manner are said to be *isomorphic* or to have an *identical structure* or *form*. We may now give a general definition of *isomorphism*. Given two classes S, with elements $a, b, c, \ldots$ and S', with elements $a', b', c', \ldots$; suppose the elements of S can be placed in one-one correspondence with those of S', so that, say, a corresponds to a', b to b', and so on. Then, if for every relation R between elements of S (so that, for example, $a\ R\ b$) there is a relation R' between the corresponding elements of S' ($a'\ R'\ b'$), the two classes are *isomorphic*.

We are now prepared to understand the great importance of the mathematical method as a tool in the natural sciences. In the first place, a hypothesis or set of assumptions may be studied for its implications without raising questions of material truth or falsity. This is essential if we are to understand *to what* a given hypothesis commits us. In the second place, a hypothesis when abstractly stated is capable of more than one concrete representation. Consequently, when we are studying pure mathematics we are studying the possible structures of many concrete situations. In this way we discover the constant or invariable factor in situations sensibly different and undergoing change. Science has been characterized as a search for system (order, constancy) amidst diversity and change. The idea of isomorphism is the clearest expression of what such a system means.

Some examples of isomorphism are well known. An ordinary map is a useful device because the relations between the points on it have a structure identical with the relations between the places in the countryside to which the map points correspond. In physics, we can see how the formula of inverse squares applies to electrical attraction and repulsion as well as to the force of gravitation. This is possible because these different subject matters have an identical formal structure with respect to the properties studied. Physics also discovers that the same set of principles is applicable to the motion of planets, the dropping of a tear, and the swinging of a pendulum. It is the isomorphism found in diverse subject matter which makes possible theoretical science as we know it today. An elementary exposition of a "dictionary" which translates theorems of Euclidean into non-Euclidean geometry the reader will find in Henri Poincaré's *The Foundations of Science*, page 59 [reprinted p. 174 this volume]. From an abstract point of view these different geometries have an identical structure.

It should be noted that two systems may not be identical in structure *throughout* and yet share many common properties. Euclidean and non-Euclidean geometries have many theorems in common, while at the same time some theorems in one system are formally incompatible with some theorems in the other. This suggests the possibility that two systems may be incompatible with each other in their totality and yet possess a common subsystem. We may illustrate this as follows. Consider the system determined by Axioms 1′ to 7′. Consider also the system obtained by replacing 7′ with the assumption 7″: *No* l-class *contains more than four elements of* S. These two systems are not isomorphic, as comparison of the representation of the first system (page 143) with that of the second system (page 144) will show. Nevertheless, all the theorems in both systems which follow from the first six axioms will be the same. The system determined by Axioms 1′ to 6′ is therefore a common subsystem of the incompatible systems determined by 1′ to 7′ on the one hand and by 1″ to 7″ on the other.

This is a very important observation. Research in the natural sciences often tempts us to believe that a theory is true because some consequence of the theory has been verified. Nevertheless, an identical consequence may be drawn from an alternative and incompatible theory. We cannot, therefore, validly affirm either theory. With care, however, we may discover those common assumptions of both theories upon which the identical consequence depends. It may then be possible to ascertain *which* of the assumptions in virtue of which the theories are *different* theories are in disagreement with experimental findings.

One further remark needs to be made about deductive systems. Every system is of necessity *abstract:* it is the structure of certain *selected* relations, and must consequently omit the structure of other relations. Thus the systems studied in physics do not include the systems explored in biology. Furthermore, as we have seen, a system is deductive not in virtue of the special meanings of its term, but in virtue of the universal relations between them. The specific quality of the things which the terms denote do not, as such, play any part in the system. Thus the theory of heat takes no account of the unique sensory qualities which heat phenomena display. A deductive system is therefore doubly abstract: it abstracts from the specific qualities of a subject matter, and it selects some relations and neglects others. It follows that there is a *plurality* of systems, each of which may be explored in isolation from the others. Such a plurality of systems may, indeed, constitute a set of subsystems of a single, comprehensive system, but we have no evidence for such a state of affairs. In any case, it is not necessary to know this comprehensive system in order to explore adequately any one of the many less inclusive systems. It appears that human knowledge of the natural world is possible only because it is capable of being studied as a set of relatively autonomous systems.

§ 4. The Equivalence of Axiom Sets

It has been pointed out that in every deductive system some propositions are indemonstrable *in that system* and some terms indefinable. We have also suggested, however, that a proposition which is an axiom in one system may be a theorem in another. We wish now to illustrate this.

Consider the following assumptions concerning a class *S;* its elements *A, B, C,* and so on; and its *l-* (or sub-) *classes a, b, c,* and so on:

Axiom 1′. If *a* and *b* are distinct *l-classes* of *S* there is at least one element of *S* in both *a* and *b*.

Axiom 2′. If *a* and *b* are distinct *l-classes* of *S* there is not more than one element of *S* in both *a* and *b*.

Axiom 3′. Any two elements of *S* are elements of some one *l-class* of *S*.

Axiom 4′. There exists at least one element in *S*.

Axiom 5′. Every element of *S* belongs to at least three *l-classes* of *S*.

Axiom 6′. There is no element of *S* belonging to all the *l-classes* of *S*.

Axiom 7′. There is no element of *S* which belongs to more than three *l-classes* of *S*.

None of these axioms are identical with any axioms of the previous set, although some of the new axioms are identical (except for verbal form) with several of the theorems we had previously demonstrated. Thus, Axiom 3′ is identical with Theorem I, Axiom 4′ with part of Theorem III. None the less, the previous set of axioms and the present set characterize the same system of relations. These two sets are *equivalent.* Two postulate sets are equivalent if, and only if, every postulate of the first is either a postulate or a theorem in the second, and every postulate of the second is either a postulate or a theorem in the first. The equivalence for the two sets above may be shown by deducing from the first set those postulates in the second set which have not already been demonstrated, and then by deducing from the second set all the postulates of the first. Thus Axiom 1′ follows at once from Axiom 3′, Axiom 5′ follows from Axioms 1′ to 5′, and so on.

It is quite important that the reader become convinced that there are no *intrinsically undemonstrable propositions.* Failure to realize this fact has been one source for the belief in "self-evidently true" propositions. It is quite easy to fall into the mistaken prejudice that because a proposition cannot be demonstrated on one set of premises, it is altogether undemonstrable. Moreover, the fact that two systems may be equivalent without being identical, axiom for axiom, throws fresh light on the question of logical priority. In a given system, one proposition is logically prior to another if the first is required as a premise, or part of the premise, for the second. In another system, however, the relation of logical priority between two propositions may be reversed.

What has been said about undemonstrated propositions is equally true for undefined terms. In the geometry the reader has studied in his youth, points were taken as fundamental and undefined, and lines, circles, defined in terms of them. That there must be undefined terms is clear from any attempt to define a term. We may try to define "equal distances" as follows: The distance between points A and B on a straight line is equal to the distance between C and D, if the segment AB can be moved *by a rigid motion of this segment* so that it coincides with the segment CD. But obviously, the phrase "a rigid motion" cannot itself be defined in terms of "equal distances," on pain of a circular definition. Nevertheless, it is a mistake to suppose that there are *intrinsically* undefinable terms. *Undemonstrability and undefinability are both relative to a system.* It is not necessary to regard points as undefinable provided we select other undefinables, such as lines, in terms of which points may themselves be defined. Thus different axiomatic foundations have been given for Euclidean geometry. Hilbert has found a set of twenty-one assumptions, requiring five primitive or undefined ideas, from which all the theorems of geometry can be deduced. Veblen, on the other hand, discovered twelve assumptions, requiring only two undefined terms, which perform the same task. We cannot pursue this topic any further, except to point out that the number of undefined terms is closely connected with the number and character of the undemonstrated propositions.

§ 5. The Independence and Consistency of Axioms

We must now consider some fundamental questions connected with a set of axioms. What are some of the essential and desirable properties which a set of axioms must possess?

1. Axioms are studied for the propositions they imply. Consequently, *fertility* is one property which axioms should possess; this means that they should imply many theorems. But there is no criterion as to whether a set of assumptions may give rise to a comprehensive set of theorems. It is very likely that fertility is not an intrinsic character of an axiom set, but reflects the ability of the human reasoner to discover their implications. Moreover, a set of assumptions is regarded as important in proportion to our ability to find *interpretations* for it in terms of investigations in the natural sciences or in other branches of mathematics. We shall return to this point.

2. A very desirable, and historically significant, property of axioms is their *independence*. A set of assumptions is *independent* if it is impossible to deduce any one of the axioms from the others. If a set of axioms is independent, it is possible to make a sharp distinction *in that system* between assumptions and theorems. And unless we know that two propositions are independent, we are unable to say whether we are entertaining different and alternate possibilities or simply the same possibility in a different form.

The question whether the axioms and postulates of Euclid are independent is historically of great interest. To the many attempts to answer it we owe some of the greatest advances that have been made in mathematics, physics, and philosophy. Mathematicians have tried for more than two thousand years to deduce the parallel postulate from the other assumptions of Euclid. The basis for their doing so was their conviction that all his assumptions except the one about parallel lines were "self-evidently true." Consequently, they believed it was a serious blemish that any non-self-evident proposition should be taken as an axiom. They did not succeed in deducing Postulate 5 from the others without assuming some other proposition not included in the original assumptions of Euclid. But what did their lack of success prove—did it prove that Postulate 5 could not be deduced from the others? It certainly did not. But it turned some inquirers' minds to search for the reason of the lack of success. It led some mathematicians to look for a proof that the parallel postulate was independent of the others.

The proof was finally discovered. We have seen that demonstrative proof consists in pointing out that certain axioms imply certain theorems. Such an alleged implication is denied if we can show that it is possible for the theorems to be false and the axioms to be true. By developing a possible system of geometry in which Euclid's parallel postulate is denied while the other axioms are retained, Lobachevsky was able to show that the parallel postulate cannot be a logical consequence of the other axioms. It will be seen that this proof illustrates the form of the logical principle we have discussed as the inconsistent triad. If a set of (consistent) propositions P imply another proposition Q, then the propositions consisting of P together with the contradictory (or contrary) of Q must be inconsistent with each other. If the inconsistency, shown by finding two contradictory propositions, appears in the set of axioms, the task is completed: Q is not independent of P. If the inconsistency does not appear in the set of axioms, then it must be possible to deduce by valid reasoning one or more theorems which contradict either some of the axioms or some other theorem validly derived. If, on the other hand, P does not imply Q, the set of propositions P together with the contradictory of Q is a consistent set, and no contradictions can ever be discovered.[2]

[2] The history of non-Euclidean geometry began when a clear perception of this simple logical principle was attained. Saccheri, an Italian mathematician of the eighteenth century, already possessed it, and by making an assumption contrary to that

Let us indicate summarily the essence of one type of non-Euclidean geometry. Euclid's Postulate 5 is equivalent to the assumption that through a point outside of a given line only one line may be drawn parallel to the given line. In the Lobachevskian geometry this is replaced by the assumption that through a point outside of a line more than one parallel may be drawn to it. From this assumption and the other assumptions of Euclid a host of theorems may be obtained, some of which are identical with the theorems of Euclid, while others are contradictories of these. Thus the propositions *The base angles of an isosceles triangle are equal* and *Two lines which are parallel to a third are parallel to each other* are common to Euclid and Lobachevsky. On the other hand, the propositions *The sum of the angles of a triangle is equal to two right angles* and *The area of a circle is* πr^2 are correct only in Euclid.

3. Here the reader may protest: "I don't yet see that the parallel postulate has been proved to be independent of the others. You have shown that by assuming a contradictory postulate a host of theorems differing from that of Euclid may be obtained. But you have not yet shown that such a new set of postulates is *consistent*. And unless you do that, you have no good reason for supposing that a non-Euclidean geometry is really possible."

This is quite right. The fact that after any finite number of theorems have been derived from a non-Euclidean set of assumptions no contradiction has turned up proves nothing about the consistency of that set. For a contradiction *may* appear after a larger number of theorems have been obtained. And the same objection can be raised no matter how large is the number of theorems deduced. The reader's protest expresses clearly how closely connected are the problems of the independence and the consistency of a set of propositions.

We may, however, be permitted to ask the reader a question in return. "You think non-Euclidean geometries have not been proved to be consistent, and that since they lack such proof their very possibility is endangered. But what basis have you for believing that Euclidean geometry is self-consistent? It is true that after thousands of years of studying it, mathematicians have not discovered any contradictions in it. But you surely will not accept *that* as a proof. The Euclidean and non-Euclidean geometries seem, in this respect, to be in the same boat."

Let us try to resolve the reader's perplexity by turning once more

---

of Euclid's parallel postulate obtained many theorems of what is now known as non-Euclidean geometry. But for some unexplained reason he came to the conclusion that such a geometry was self-contradictory—perhaps because many of the theorems he obtained were formal contradictories of the theorems of Euclid. If that was his reason for rejecting non-Euclidean geometry, he overlooked the possibility that both Euclidean and non-Euclidean geometries may be self-consistent, although the two systems are incompatible with each other. The discovery of non-Euclidean geometry must be attributed, therefore, to Lobachevsky and Bolyai, who wrote in the first half of the nineteenth century. Still another kind of non-Euclidean geometry was discovered by Riemann.

to our miniature mathematical system, and face similar problems with regard to it. Are the seven axioms independent? Are they consistent with one another?

Mathematicians have found only one way of answering the second question. The method consists in discovering a *set of entities which will embody the relations of our set of abstract axioms.* On the assumption that these entities themselves are free from contradiction and that they in fact fully embody the axioms, the latter are shown to involve no inconsistencies.

We will illustrate the use of this method. Let the integers 0 to 6 inclusive be arranged in distinct groups of three each, as follows:

0	1	2	3	4	5	6
1	2	3	4	5	6	0
3	4	5	6	0	1	2

We now regard these seven integers as the elements of the class *S.* Every column of integers will then represent an *l-class.* On this interpretation, as a little reflection shows, every one of the seven axioms in our set is verified. The axioms are therefore consistent.

It must be emphasized, however, that this method merely shifts the difficulty. For the question still remains whether the set of entities and our method of interpretation are consistent. To this question no completely satisfactory answer seems at present available. We have, however, a certain amount of confidence that since the Euclidean axioms have enabled us to deal so adequately with the properties and relations of physical bodies, Euclidean geometry as a logical system is also consistent, because we assume that nothing occupying spatial and temporal position can be self-contradictory. Since non-Euclidean geometries have been shown to correspond, element for element, to Euclidean geometry in accordance with definite transformation formulae, it follows that if a contradiction could appear in non-Euclidean geometry, a corresponding contradiction would of necessity have to occur in the geometry of Euclid.[3]

[3] The assumptions required for other branches of mathematics are shown to be consistent in a similar way. However, complications enter. Mathematics as a system of propositions has advanced much beyond the achievements of Euclid. Mathematicians have shown that all the higher branches of mathematics, such as higher algebra, analysis, geometry, and so on, may be interpreted as studying the relations between whole numbers (integers); and that they require no fundamental notions other than those employed in arithmetic. This achievement has been called the arithmetization of mathematics, and is due largely to such men as Weierstrass, Dedekind, and Hilbert. An even further step in the analysis of mathematical ideas was made when arithmetic itself was shown to require no fundamental notions except those of logic, such as "class," "member of a class," "implies," and so on. This work has been accomplished largely through the efforts of Cantor, Frege, Peano, Whitehead, and Russell, and has received its most adequate expression in the *Principia Mathematica* of the last two men. As a consequence of a century of labor many, though not all, mathematicians are convinced that mathematics can be developed in terms of the ideas of pure logic. If this thesis is sound, the consistency of every branch of mathematics is dependent upon the consistency of the principles of formal logic. The question as to the consistency of any branch of mathematics is then reduced to the question whether logical principles themselves form a consistent system.

We return once more to the problem of independence of axioms, and shall illustrate the problem by means of our miniature system. Is Axiom 7′ independent of the others? The answer is yes if the first six axioms, together with any assumption incompatible with the seventh, form a consistent set. This condition is equivalent to finding an interpretation which will satisfy the first six axioms and fail to satisfy the seventh. Such an interpretation may be given in several ways, of which the following is one:

0	1	2	3	4	5	6	7	8	9	10	11	12
1	2	3	4	5	6	7	8	9	10	11	12	0
3	4	5	6	7	8	9	10	11	12	0	1	2
9	10	11	12	0	1	2	3	4	5	6	7	8

These thirteen numbers from 0 to 12 inclusive are the members of *S*. Each column of four numbers represents an *l-class* of *S*. Examination will show that all the axioms except the seventh are satisfied. This axiom is therefore independent of the first six. In a like manner we can show that each of the other assumptions is independent of the rest.

§ 6. Mathematical Induction

"Aren't you, however, forgetting that induction takes place in mathematics?" the reader may protest. "You have been describing mathematics as a typical deductive science, in which all the theorems are necessary consequences of the axioms. But surely you are not going to overlook the method of proof known as mathematical induction?"

The reader has doubtless been ensnared by a word. There is indeed a method of *mathematical induction*, but the name is unfortunate, since it suggests some kinship with the methods of experimentation and verification of hypotheses employed in the natural sciences. But there is no such kinship, and mathematical induction is a purely demonstrative method.

Is it necessary, however, once more to caution the reader against the common error of confounding the temporal order of our discovering the propositions of a science and the order of their logical dependence? Everybody who has ever worked a problem in geometry knows that there is a preparatory "groping stage," in which we guess, speculate, draw auxiliary lines, and so on until, as the saying goes, we "hit upon" the proof. But no one will confuse that preparatory stage, however essential, with the proof finally achieved. Such an initial "groping" stage has indeed close kinship with human investigations in any field whatever. A process of tested guessing characterizes research in mathematics as well as research in the natural sciences.

The principle of mathematical induction may be stated as follows: If a property belongs to the number 1, and if when it belongs to n it can be proved to belong to $n + 1$, then it belongs to all the integers. Let us demonstrate, by its means, the theorem: For all integral values of n, $1 + 3 + 5 + 7 + \ldots (2n - 1) = n^2$.

This clearly is true for $n = 1$. Let us now show that if it holds for the integer n it holds for $(n + 1)$.

a. $1 + 3 + 5 + \ldots (2n - 1) = n^2$.

Adding $(2n - 1) + 2$ or $(2n + 1)$ to both sides, we get:

b. $1 + 3 + 5 + \ldots (2n - 1) + (2n + 1) = n^2 + (2n + 1) = (n + 1)^2$.

But *b* has the same form as *a*. Hence we have shown that if the theorem is true for the integer n it is true for $(n + 1)$. Now it is true for $n = 1$. Therefore it is true for $n = 1 + 1$ or 2; therefore it is true for $n = 2 + 1$ or 3, and so on for every integer which can be reached by successive additions of 1. The proof, therefore, is perfectly rigorous, deductive, and altogether formal. It makes no appeal to experiment. And the principle of mathematical induction, as modern researches show, is part of the very meaning of finite or "inductive" numbers.

§ 7. What Generalization Means in Mathematics

In the preceding chapter we called attention to the changes in the meaning of words by the process of *generalization*. In mathematics, too, such processes take place, and reference is often made to the "modern generalization of number." It is easy to fall into error as to the sense in which "number" has in fact been generalized. Let us examine the matter.

The word "number" was originally restricted to the *integers* 1, 2, 3, and so on. Numbers, so understood, can be added and multiplied, and in some cases subtracted and divided. The abstract nature of integers may be expressed by means of a set of propositions which indicate what operations can be made upon integers, and what the relations are in which the operations stand to one another. For example, the following are some of the abstract properties of integers:

$$a + b = b + a$$
$$(a + b) + c = a + (b + c)$$
$$a \times b = b \times a$$
$$a \times (b + c) = a \times b + a \times c$$

Now on some of the integers, the operations *inverse* to multiplication and addition can be performed. Thus, $4 \times 3 = 12$; hence there is an integer x such that $x \times 3 = 12$: such a number x is the quotient of 12 *divided by* 3. But, unless we enlarge our conception of number, the inverse operation of division cannot *always* be formed. Thus, there is no integer x such that $x \times 3 = 5$. Consequently, in order that there should be no exceptions to the possibility of division, the fractions were introduced. They were also called numbers, and so the domain of number was increased in the interest of continuity and generality.

This was the first generalization of "number." Why were the fractions designated as numbers? The answer is simple, although it has been discovered only recently. It is because operations of addition, multiplication, and even division could be performed on them; and because the *formal relations* of integers to one another with respect to these operations are the same as the formal relations of fractions. In other words, integers and fractions form isomorphic systems.

But it must be pointed out that while addition or multiplication for integers is formally the same for fractions, nevertheless the differences are not thereby denied. Thus, the sign + in $7 + 5 = 12$ and in $\frac{1}{2} + \frac{1}{3} = \frac{5}{6}$, while denoting formal properties common to the two cases, none the less denotes two distinct and different operations. The second is much more complex than the first. It is easy to confuse them because the same symbol is used to denote them both, but neither must we forget that the same symbol is applicable to the two cases because they have common elements of procedure.

Later on other "numbers" were discovered, when it was noticed that some of the previously defined numbers had square roots, cube roots, and so on, but others did not. Thus, the Pythagoreans proved that the diagonal of the square is incommensurable with its sides. In modern notation, this means that $\sqrt{2}$ cannot be expressed as the ratio of two integers. But why should the operation of extracting a root be legitimate only for some numbers (for example 4)? Why not permit the operation to be performed on every one of the previously defined numbers? Hence, in the interest of continuity of treatment and of generality, the *irrationals* were discovered, and they too were regarded as a "species of number."

Why? The answer is again simply: Because the operations upon them possess the formal properties of the operations upon integers and fractions.

Similar remarks, with only few qualifications, apply to the other "species of number" with which modern mathematics is familiar. Negative numbers, imaginary numbers, quaternions, transcendental numbers, matrices, have been introduced into the domain of number because continuity and universality of treatment demanded them. But they have been designated as "numbers" because they share certain abstract properties with the more familiar instances of mathematical entities.

Generality of treatment is thus an obvious goal of mathematics. But it is clearly a mistaken idea to suppose that the definition of "number" as applicable specifically to the cardinals 1, 2, 3, and so on, has in some sense been "extended" or "generalized" to apply to fractions, irrationals, and the rest. There is no generic definition of "number" of which the cardinals, ordinals, fractions, and so on are special instances *except in terms of the formal properties of certain "operations."* It is in virtue of the permanence or *invariance* of these formal properties that these entities are all "numbers."

This conclusion, so obvious when it is once pointed out, has been won only at the expense of tremendous labor by modern philosophers of mathematics. The source of many of the confusions in this subject is the frequent use of the same symbol to denote two essentially different ideas. Thus, the cardinal number 2 and the ratio $2/1$ are usually denoted by the same symbol 2; they denote, however, radically distinct ideas. But this danger from the symbolism of mathematics is undoubtedly outweighed by the great advantages it offers. It enables us to exhibit concisely the *structure* of mathematical propositions, and so makes possible our noting the precise analogies or isomorphisms in contexts that are in other respects very different from one another.

On the Nature of Mathematical Truth *

CARL G. HEMPEL

1. The Problem. It is a basic principle of scientific inquiry that no proposition and no theory is to be accepted without adequate grounds. In empirical science, which includes both the natural and the social sciences, the grounds for the acceptance of a theory consist in the agreement of predictions based on the theory with empirical evidence obtained either by experiment or by systematic observation. But what are the grounds which sanction the acceptance of mathematics? That is the question I propose to discuss in the present paper. For reasons which will become clear subsequently, I shall use the term "mathematics" here to refer to arithmetic, algebra, and analysis—to the exclusion, in particular, of geometry.[1]

2. Are the Propositions of Mathematics Self-evident Truths? One of the several answers which have been given to our problem asserts that the truths of mathematics, in contradistinction to the hypotheses of empirical science, require neither factual evidence nor any other justification because they are "self-evident." This view, however, which ultimately relegates decisions as to mathematical truth to a feeling of self-evidence, encounters various difficulties. First of all, many mathematical theorems are so hard to establish that even to the specialist in the particular field they appear as anything but self-evident. Secondly, it is well known that some of the most interesting results of mathematics—especially in such fields as abstract set theory and topology—run counter to deeply ingrained intuitions and the customary kind of feeling of self-evidence. Thirdly, the existence of mathematical conjectures such as those of Goldbach and of Fermat, which are quite elementary in content and yet undecided up to this day, certainly shows that not all mathematical truths can be self-evident. And finally, even if self-evidence were attributed only to the basic postulates of mathematics, from which all other mathematical propositions can be deduced, it would be pertinent to remark that judgments as to what may be considered as self-evident, are subjective; they may vary from person to person and certainly cannot constitute an adequate basis for decisions as to the objective validity of mathematical propositions.

* Reprinted by kind permission of the author and the editor from *The American Mathematical Monthly*, 52, 1945.

[1] A discussion of the status of geometry is given in my article, "Geometry and Empirical Science," *American Mathematical Monthly*, vol. 52, pp. 7–17, 1945.

3. Is Mathematics the Most General Empirical Science? According to another view, advocated especially by John Stuart Mill, mathematics is itself an empirical science which differs from the other branches such as astronomy, physics, chemistry, *etc.*, mainly in two respects: its subject matter is more general than that of any other field of scientific research, and its propositions have been tested and confirmed to a greater extent than those of even the most firmly established sections of astronomy or physics. Indeed, according to this view, the degree to which the laws of mathematics have been borne out by the past experiences of mankind is so overwhelming that—unjustifiably—we have come to think of mathematical theorems as qualitatively different from the well-confirmed hypotheses or theories of other branches of science: we consider them as certain, while other theories are thought of as at best "very probable" or very highly confirmed.

But this view, too, is open to serious objections. From a hypothesis which is empirical in character—such as, for example, Newton's law of gravitation—it is possible to derive predictions to the effect that under certain specified conditions certain specified observable phenomena will occur. The actual occurrence of these phenomena constitutes confirming evidence, their non-occurrence disconfirming evidence for the hypothesis. It follows in particular that an empirical hypothesis is theoretically disconfirmable; *i.e.*, it is possible to indicate what kind of evidence, if actually encountered, would disconfirm the hypothesis. In the light of this remark, consider now a simple "hypothesis" from arithmetic: $3 + 2 = 5$. If this is actually an empirical generalization of past experiences, then it must be possible to state what kind of evidence would oblige us to concede the hypothesis was not generally true after all. If any disconfirming evidence for the given proposition can be thought of, the following illustration might well be typical of it: We place some microbes on a slide, putting down first three of them and then another two. Afterwards we count all the microbes to test whether in this instance 3 and 2 actually added up to 5. Suppose now that we counted 6 microbes altogether. Would we consider this as an empirical disconfirmation of the given proposition, or at least as a proof that it does not apply to microbes? Clearly not; rather, we would assume we had made a mistake in counting or that one of the microbes had split in two between the first and the second count. But under no circumstances could the phenomenon just described invalidate the arithmetical proposition in question; for the latter asserts nothing whatever about the behavior of microbes; it merely states that any set consisting of $3 + 2$ objects may also be said to consist of 5 objects. And this is so because the symbols "$3 + 2$" and "5" denote the same number: they are synonymous by virtue of the fact that the symbols "2," "3," "5," and "+" are *defined* (or tacitly understood) in such a way that the above identity holds as a consequence of the meaning attached to the concepts involved in it.

4. The Analytic Character of Mathematical Propositions. The statement that $3 + 2 = 5$, then, is true for similar reasons as, say, the assertion that no sexagenarian is 45 years of age. Both are true simply by virtue of definitions or of similar stipulations which determine the meaning of the key terms involved. Statements of this kind share certain important characteristics: Their validation naturally requires no empirical evidence; they can be shown to be true by a mere analysis of the meaning attached to the terms which occur in them. In the language of logic, sentences of this kind are called analytic or true a priori, which is to indicate that their truth is logically independent of, or logically prior to, any experiential evidence.[2] And while the statements of empirical science, which are synthetic and can be validated only a posteriori, are constantly subject to revision in the light of new evidence, the truth of an analytic statement can be established definitely, once and for all. However, this characteristic "theoretical certainty" of analytic propositions has to be paid for at a high price: An analytic statement conveys no factual information. Our statement about sexagenarians, for example, asserts nothing that could possibly conflict with any factual evidence: it has no factual implications, no empirical content; and it is precisely for this reason that the statement can be validated without recourse to empirical evidence.

Let us illustrate this view of the nature of mathematical propositions by reference to another, frequently cited, example of a mathematical—or rather logical—truth, namely the proposition that whenever $a = b$ and $b = c$ then $a = c$. On what grounds can this so-called "transitivity of identity" be asserted? Is it of an empirical nature and hence at least theoretically disconfirmable by empirical evidence? Suppose, for example, that a, b, c, are certain shades of green, and that as far as we can see, $a = b$ and $b = c$, but clearly $a \neq c$. This phenomenon actually occurs under certain conditions; do we consider it as disconfirming evidence for the proposition under consideration? Undoubtedly not; we would argue that if $a \neq c$, it is impossible that $a = b$ and also $b = c$; between the terms of at least one of these latter pairs, there must obtain a difference, though perhaps only a subliminal one. And we would dismiss the possibility of empirical disconfirmation, and indeed the idea that an empirical test should be relevant here, on the grounds that identity is a transitive relation by virtue of its definition or by virtue of the basic postulates governing it.[3] Hence the principle in question is true a priori.

[2] The objection is sometimes raised that without certain types of experience, such as encountering several objects of the same kind, the integers and the arithmetical operations with them would never have been invented, and that therefore the propositions of arithmetic do have an empirical basis. This type of argument, however, involves a confusion of the logical and the psychological meaning of the term "basis." It may very well be the case that certain experiences occasion psychologically the formation of arithmetical ideas and in this sense form an empirical "basis" for them; but this point is entirely irrelevant for the logical questions as to the *grounds* on which the propositions of arithmetic may be accepted as true. The point made above is that no empirical "basis" or evidence whatever is needed to establish the truth of the propositions of arithmetic.

[3] A precise account of the definition and the essential characteristics of the identity relation may be found in A. Tarski, *Introduction to Logic*, New York, 1941, Ch. III.

5. *Mathematics as an Axiomatized Deductive System.* I have argued so far that the validity of mathematics rests neither on its alleged self-evidential character nor on any empirical basis, but derives from the stipulations which determine the meaning of the mathematical concepts, and that the propositions of mathematics are therefore essentially "true by definition." This latter statement, however, is obviously oversimplified and needs restatement and a more careful justification.

For the rigorous development of a mathematical theory proceeds not simply from a set of definitions but rather from a set of non-definitional propositions which are not proved within the theory; these are the postulates or axioms of the theory.[4] They are formulated in terms of certain basic or primitive concepts for which no definitions are provided within the theory. It is sometimes asserted that the postulates themselves represent "implicit definitions" of the primitive terms. Such a characterization of the postulates, however, is misleading. For while the postulates do limit, in a specific sense, the meanings that can possibly be ascribed to the primitives, any self-consistent postulate system admits, nevertheless, many different interpretations of the primitive terms (this will soon be illustrated), whereas a set of definitions in the strict sense of the word determines the meanings of the definienda in a unique fashion.

Once the primitive terms and the postulates have been laid down, the entire theory is completely determined; it is derivable from its postulational basis in the following sense: Every term of the theory is definable in terms of the primitives, and every proposition of the theory is logically deducible from the postulates. To be entirely precise, it is necessary also to specify the principles of logic which are to be used in the proof of the propositions, *i.e.* in their deduction from the postulates. These principles can be stated quite explicitly. They fall into two groups: Primitive sentences, or postulates, of logic (such as: If p and q is the case, then p is the case), and rules of deduction or inference (including, for example, the familiar modus ponens rule and the rules of substitution which make it possible to infer, from a general proposition, any one of its substitution instances). A more detailed discussion of the structure and content of logic would, however, lead too far afield in the context of this article.

6. *Peano's Axiom System as a Basis for Mathematics.* Let us now consider a postulate system from which the entire arithmetic of the natural numbers can be derived. This system was devised by the Italian mathematician and logician G. Peano (1858–1932). The primitives of this system are the terms "0," "number," and "successor." While, of course, no definition of these terms is given within the theory, the symbol "0" is intended to designate the number 0 in its usual meaning, while the term "number" is meant to refer to the natural numbers 0, 1, 2, 3 · · · exclusively. By the successor of a natural number n, which will sometimes

[4] For a lucid and concise account of the axiomatic method, see A. Tarski, *l.c.*, Ch. VI.

briefly be called n', is meant the natural number immediately following n in the natural order. Peano's system contains the following 5 postulates:

P1. 0 is a number

P2. The successor of any number is a number

P3. No two numbers have the same successor

P4. 0 is not the successor of any number

P5. If P is a property such that (a) 0 has the property P, and (b) whenever a number n has the property P, then the successor of n also has the property P, then every number has the property P.

The last postulate embodies the principle of mathematical induction and illustrates in a very obvious manner the enforcement of a mathematical "truth" by stipulation. The construction of elementary arithmetic on this basis begins with the definition of the various natural numbers. 1 is defined as the successor of 0, or briefly as $0'$; 2 as $1'$, 3 as $2'$, and so on. By virtue of P2, this process can be continued indefinitely; because of P3 (in combination with P5), it never leads back to one of the numbers previously defined, and in view of P4, it does not lead back to 0 either.

As the next step, we can set up a definition of addition which expresses in a precise form the idea that the addition of any natural number to some given number may be considered as a repeated addition of 1; the latter operation is readily expressible by means of the successor relation. This definition of addition runs as follows:

D1. (a) $n + o = n$; (b) $n + k' = (n + k)'$.

The two stipulations of this recursive definition completely determine the sum of any two integers. Consider, for example, the sum $3 + 2$. According to the definitions of the numbers 2 and 1, we have $3 + 2 = 3 + 1' = 3 + (0')'$; by D1 (b), $3 + (0')' = (3 + 0')' = ((3 + 0)')'$; but by D1 (a), and by the definitions of the numbers 4 and 5, $((3 + 0)')' = (3')' = 4' = 5$. This proof also renders more explicit and precise the comments made earlier in this paper on the truth of the proposition that $3 + 2 = 5$: Within the Peano system of arithmetic, its truth flows not merely from the definition of the concepts involved, but also from the postulates that govern these various concepts. (In our specific example, the postulates P1 and P2 are presupposed to guarantee that 1, 2, 3, 4, 5 are numbers in Peano's system; the general proof that D1 determines the sum of any two numbers also makes use of P5.) If we call the postulates and definitions of an axiomatized theory the "stipulations" concerning the concepts of that theory, then we may say now that the propositions of the arithmetic of the natural numbers are true by virtue of the stipulations which have been laid down initially for the arithmetical concepts. (Note, incidentally, that our proof of the formula "$3 + 2 = 5$" repeatedly made use of the transitivity of identity; the latter is accepted here as one of the rules of logic which may be used in the proof of any arithmetical theorem; it is, therefore, included among Peano's postulates no more than any other principle of logic.)

Now, the multiplication of natural numbers may be defined by means of the following recursive definition, which expresses in a rigorous form the idea that a product nk of two integers may be considered as the sum of k terms each of which equals n.

D2. (a) $n \cdot 0 = 0$; (b) $n \cdot k' = n \cdot k + n$.

It now is possible to prove the familiar general laws governing addition and multiplication, such as the commutative, associative, and distributive laws $(n + k = k + n,\ n \cdot k = k \cdot n;\ n + (k + l) = (n + k) + l,\ n \cdot (k \cdot l) = (n \cdot k) \cdot l;\ n \cdot (k + l) = (n \cdot k) + (n \cdot l))$.—In terms of addition and multiplication, the inverse operations of subtraction and division can then be defined. But it turns out that these "cannot always be performed"; *i.e.*, in contradistinction to the sum and the product, the difference and the quotient are not defined for every couple of numbers; for example, $7 - 10$ and $7 \div 10$ are undefined. This situation suggests an enlargement of the number system by the introduction of negative and of rational numbers.

It is sometimes held that in order to effect this enlargement, we have to "assume" or else to "postulate" the existence of the desired additional kinds of numbers with properties that make them fit to fill the gaps of subtraction and division. This method of simply postulating what we want has its advantages; but, as Bertrand Russell [5] puts it, they are the same as the advantages of theft over honest toil; and it is a remarkable fact that the negative as well as the rational numbers can be obtained from Peano's primitives by the honest toil of constructing explicit definitions for them, without the introduction of any new postulates or assumptions whatsoever. Every positive and negative integer—in contradistinction to a natural number which has no sign—is definable as a certain set of ordered couples of natural numbers; thus, the integer $+2$ is definable as the set of all ordered couples (m, n) of natural numbers where $m = n + 2$; the integer -2 is the set of all ordered couples (m, n) of natural numbers with $n = m + 2$. —Similarly, rational numbers are defined as classes of ordered couples of integers.—The various arithmetical operations can then be defined with reference to these new types of numbers, and the validity of all the arithmetical laws governing these operations can be proved by virtue of nothing more than Peano's postulates and the definitions of the various arithmetical concepts involved.

The much broader system thus obtained is still incomplete in the sense that not every number in it has a square root, and more generally, not every algebraic equation whose coefficients are all numbers of the system has a solution in the system. This suggests further expansions of the number system by the introduction of real and finally of complex numbers. Again, this enormous extension can be effected by mere definition, without the

[5] Bertrand Russell, *Introduction to Mathematical Philosophy*, New York and London, 1919, p. 71.

introduction of a single new postulate.[6] On the basis thus obtained, the various arithmetical and algebraic operations can be defined for the numbers of the new system, the concepts of function, of limit, of derivative and integral can be introduced, and the familiar theorems pertaining to these concepts can be proved, so that finally the huge system of mathematics as here delimited rests on the narrow basis of Peano's system: Every concept of mathematics can be defined by means of Peano's three primitives, and every proposition of mathematics can be deduced from the five postulates enriched by the definitions of the non-primitive terms.[7] These deductions can be carried out, in most cases, by means of nothing more than the principles of formal logic; the proof of some theorems concerning real numbers, however, requires one assumption which is not usually included among the latter. This is the so-called axiom of choice. It asserts that given a class of mutually exclusive classes, none of which is empty, there exists at least one class which has exactly one element in common with each of the given classes. By virtue of this principle and the rules of formal logic, the content of all of mathematics can thus be derived from Peano's modest system—a remarkable achievement in systematizing the content of mathematics and clarifying the foundations of its validity.

7. *Interpretations of Peano's Primitives.* As a consequence of this result, the whole system of mathematics might be said to be true by virtue of mere definitions (namely, of the non-primitive mathematical terms) provided that the five Peano postulates are true. However, strictly speaking, we cannot, at this juncture, refer to the Peano postulates as propositions which are either true or false, for they contain three primitive terms which have not been assigned any specific meaning. All we can assert so far is

[6] For a more detailed account of the construction of the number system on Peano's basis, *cf.* Bertrand Russell, *l.c.*, esp. Chs. I and VII.—A rigorous and concise presentation of that construction, beginning, however, with the set of all integers rather than that of the natural numbers, may be found in G. Birkhoff and S. MacLane, *A Survey of Modern Algebra*, New York, 1941, Chs. I, II, III, V.—For a general survey of the construction of the number system, *cf.* also J. W. Young, *Lectures on the Fundamental Concepts of Algebra and Geometry*, New York, 1911, esp. lectures X, XI, XII.

[7] As a result of very deep-reaching investigations carried out by K. Gödel it is known that arithmetic, and *a fortiori* mathematics, is an incomplete theory in the following sense: While all those propositions which belong to the classical systems of arithmetic, algebra, and analysis can indeed be derived, in the sense characterized above, from the Peano postulates, there exist nevertheless other propositions which can be expressed in purely arithmetical terms, and which are true, but which cannot be derived from the Peano system. And more generally: For any postulate system of arithmetic (or of mathematics for that matter) which is not self-contradictory, there exist propositions which are true, and which can be stated in purely arithmetical terms, but which cannot be derived from that postulate system. In other words, it is impossible to construct a postulate system which is not self-contradictory, and which contains among its consequences all true propositions which can be formulated within the language of arithmetic.

This fact does not, however, affect the result outlined above, namely, that it is possible to deduce, from the Peano postulates and the additional definitions of non-primitive terms, all those propositions which constitute the classical theory of arithmetic, algebra, and analysis; and it is to these propositions that I refer above and subsequently as the propositions of mathematics.

that any specific interpretation of the primitives which satisfies the five postulates—*i.e.*, turns them into true statements—will also satisfy all the theorems deduced from them. But for Peano's system, there are several—indeed, infinitely many—interpretations which will do this. For example, let us understand by 0 the origin of a half-line, by the successor of a point on that half-line the point 1 cm. behind it, counting from the origin, and by a number any point which is either the origin or can be reached from it by a finite succession of steps each of which leads from one point to its successor. It can then readily be seen that all the Peano postulates as well as the ensuing theorems turn into true propositions, although the interpretation given to the primitives is certainly not the customary one, which was mentioned earlier. More generally, it can be shown that every progression of elements of any kind provides a true interpretation, or a "model," of the Peano system. This example illustrates our earlier observation that a postulate system cannot be regarded as a set of "implicit definitions" for the primitive terms: The Peano system permits of many different interpretations, whereas in everyday as well as in scientific language, we attach one specific meaning to the concepts of arithmetic. Thus, *e.g.*, in scientific and in everyday discourse, the concept 2 is understood in such a way that from the statement "Mr. Brown as well as Mr. Cope, but no one else is in the office, and Mr. Brown is not the same person as Mr. Cope," the conclusion "Exactly two persons are in the office" may be validly inferred. But the stipulations laid down in Peano's system for the natural numbers, and for the number 2 in particular, do not enable us to draw this conclusion; they do not "implicitly determine" the customary meaning of the concept 2 or of the other arithmetical concepts. And the mathematician cannot acquiesce at this deficiency by arguing that he is not concerned with the customary meaning of the mathematical concepts; for in proving, say, that every positive real number has exactly two real square roots, he is himself using the concept 2 in its customary meaning, and his very theorem cannot be proved unless we presuppose more about the number 2 than is stipulated in the Peano system.

If therefore mathematics is to be a correct theory of the mathematical concepts in their intended meaning, it is not sufficient for its validation to have shown that the entire system is derivable from the Peano postulates plus suitable definitions; rather, we have to inquire further whether the Peano postulates are actually true when the primitives are understood in their customary meaning. This question, of course, can be answered only after the customary meaning of the terms "0," "natural number," and "successor" has been clearly defined. To this task we now turn.

8. Definition of the Customary Meaning of the Concepts of Arithmetic in Purely Logical Terms. At first blush, it might seem a hopeless undertaking to try to define these basic arithmetical concepts without presupposing other terms of arithmetic, which would involve us in a circular procedure. However, quite rigorous definitions of the desired kind can indeed be formulated, and it can be shown that for the concepts so defined, all Peano postulates turn into true statements. This important result is due to the research of the German logician G. Frege (1848–1925) and to the subsequent systematic and detailed work of the contemporary English logicians and philosophers B. Russell and A. N. Whitehead. Let us consider briefly the basic ideas underlying these definitions.[8]

A natural number—or, in Peano's term, a number—in its customary meaning can be considered as a characteristic of certain *classes* of objects. Thus, *e.g.*, the class of the apostles has the number 12, the class of the Dionne quintuplets the number 5, any couple the number 2, and so on. Let us now express precisely the meaning of the assertion that a certain class C has the number 2, or briefly, that $n(C) = 2$. Brief reflection will show that the following definiens is adequate in the sense of the customary meaning of the concept 2: There is some object x and some object y such that (1) $x \epsilon C$ (*i.e.*, x is an element of C) and $y \epsilon C$, (2) $x \neq y$, and (3) if z is any object such that $z \epsilon C$, then either $z = x$ or $z = y$. (Note that on the basis of this definition it becomes indeed possible to infer the statement "The number of persons in the office is 2" from "Mr. Brown as well as Mr. Cope, but no one else is in the office, and Mr. Brown is not identical with Mr. Cope"; C is here the class of persons in the office.) Analogously, the meaning of the statement that $n(C) = 1$ can be defined thus: There is some x such that $x \epsilon C$, and any object y such that $y \epsilon C$, is identical with x. Similarly, the customary meaning of the statement that $n(C) = 0$ is this: There is no object such that $x \epsilon C$.

The general pattern of these definitions clearly lends itself to the definition of any natural number. Let us note especially that in the definitions thus obtained, the definiens never contains any arithmetical term, but merely expressions taken from the field of formal logic, including the signs of identity and difference. So far, we have defined only the meaning of such phrases as "$n(C) = 2$," but we have given no definition for the numbers 0, 1, 2, $\cdots$ apart from this context. This desideratum can be met on the basis of the consideration that 2 is that property which is common to all couples, *i.e.*, to all classes C such that $n(C) = 2$. This common property may be conceptually represented by the class of all those classes which share this property. Thus we arrive at the definition: 2 is the class of all couples, *i.e.*, the class of all classes C for which $n(C) = 2$.—This definition is by no means circular because the concept of couple—in other words, the meaning of "$n(C) = 2$"—has been previously defined without any

[8] For a more detailed discussion, *cf.* Russell, *l.c.*, Chs. II, III, IV. A complete technical development of the idea can be found in the great standard work in mathematical logic, A. N. Whitehead and B. Russell, *Principia Mathematica*, Cambridge, England, 1910–1913.—For a very precise recent development of the theory, see W. V. O. Quine, *Mathematical Logic*, New York, 1940.—A specific discussion of the Peano system and its interpretations from the viewpoint of semantics is included in R. Carnap, *Foundations of Logic and Mathematics*, *International Encyclopedia of Unified Science*, vol. I, no. 3, Chicago, 1939; especially sections 14, 17, 18.

reference to the number 2. Analogously, 1 is the class of all unit classes, *i.e.*, the class of all classes C for which $n(C) = 1$. Finally, 0 is the class of all null classes, *i.e.*, the class of all classes without elements. And as there is only one such class, 0 is simply the class whose only element is the null class. Clearly, the customary meaning of any given natural number can be defined in this fashion.[9] In order to characterize the intended interpretation of Peano's primitives, we actually need, of all the definitions here referred to, only that of the number 0. It remains to define the terms "successor" and "integer."

The definition of "successor," whose precise formulation involves too many niceties to be stated here, is a careful expression of a simple idea which is illustrated by the following example: Consider the number 5, *i.e.*, the class of all quintuplets. Let us select an arbitrary one of these quintuplets and add to it an object which is not yet one of its members. $5'$, the successor of 5, may then be defined as the number applying to the set thus obtained (which, of course, is a sextuplet). Finally, it is possible to formulate a definition of the customary meaning of the concept of natural number; this definition, which again cannot be given here, expresses, in a rigorous form, the idea that the class of the natural numbers consists of the number 0, its successor, the successor of that successor, and so on.

If the definitions here characterized are carefully written out—this is one of the cases where the techniques of symbolic, or mathematical, logic prove indispensable—it is seen that the definiens of every one of them contains exclusively terms from the field of pure logic. In fact, it is possible to state the customary interpretation of Peano's primitives, and thus also the meaning of every concept definable by means of them—and that includes every concept of mathematics—in terms of the following 7 expressions, in addition to variables such as "x" and "C": *not, and, if—then*; *for every object x* it is the case that . . . ; *there is some object x* such that . . . ; x is an *element* of class C; *the class of all things x such that* . . . . And it is even possible to reduce the number of logical concepts needed to a mere four: The first three of the concepts just mentioned are all definable in terms of "*neither—nor*," and the fifth is definable by means of the fourth and "*neither—nor*." Thus, all the concepts of mathematics prove definable in terms of four concepts of pure logic. (The definition of one of the more complex concepts of mathematics in terms of the four primitives just mentioned may well fill hundreds or even thousands of pages; but

[9] The assertion that the definitions given above state the "customary" meaning of the arithmetical terms involved is to be understood in the logical, not the psychological sense of the term "meaning." It would obviously be absurd to claim that the above definitions express "what everybody has in mind" when talking about numbers and the various operations that can be performed with them. What is achieved by those definitions is rather a "logical reconstruction" of the concepts of arithmetic in the sense that if the definitions are accepted, then those statements in science and everyday discourse which involve arithmetical terms can be interpreted coherently and systematically in such a manner that they are capable of objective validation. The statement about the two persons in the office provides a very elementary illustration of what is meant here.

clearly this affects in no way the theoretical importance of the result just obtained; it does, however, show the great convenience and indeed practical indispensability for mathematics of having a large system of highly complex defined concepts available.)

9. The Truth of Peano's Postulates in Their Customary Interpretation. The definitions characterized in the preceding section may be said to render precise and explicit the customary meaning of the concepts of arithmetic. Moreover—and this is crucial for the question of the validity of mathematics—it can be shown that the Peano postulates all turn into true propositions if the primitives are construed in accordance with the definitions just considered.

Thus, P1 (0 is a number) is true because the class of all numbers—*i.e.*, natural numbers—was defined as consisting of 0 and all its successors. The truth of P2 (The successor of any number is a number) follows from the same definition. This is true also of P5, the principle of mathematical induction. To prove this, however, we would have to resort to the precise definition of "integer" rather than the loose description given of that definition above. P4 (0 is not the successor of any number) is seen to be true as follows: By virtue of the definition of "successor," a number which is a successor of some number can apply only to classes which contain at least one element; but the number 0, by definition, applies to a class if and only if that class is empty.—While the truth of P1, P2, P4, P5 can be inferred from the above definitions simply by means of the principles of logic, the proof of P3 (No two numbers have the same successor) presents a certain difficulty. As was mentioned in the preceding section, the definition of the successor of a number n is based on the process of adding, to a class of n elements, one element not yet contained in that class. Now if there should exist only a finite number of things altogether then this process could not be continued indefinitely, and P3, which (in conjunction with P1 and P2) implies that the integers form an infinite set, would be false. Russell's way of meeting this difficulty [10] was to introduce a special "axiom of infinity," which stipulates, in effect, the existence of infinitely many objects and thus makes P3 demonstrable. The axiom of infinity does not belong to the generally recognized laws of logic; but it is capable of expression in purely logical terms and may be treated as an additional postulate of logic.

10. Mathematics as a Branch of Logic. As was pointed out earlier, all the theorems of arithmetic, algebra, and analysis can be deduced from the Peano postulates and the definitions of those mathematical terms which are not primitives in Peano's system. This deduction requires only the principles of logic plus, in certain cases, the axiom of choice, which asserts that for any set of mutually exclusive non-empty sets $\alpha, \beta, \ldots$, there exists at least one set which contains exactly one element from each of the sets $\alpha, \beta, \ldots$, and which contains no other elements.[11] By combining

[10] *Cf.* Bertrand Russell, *l.c.*, p. 24 and Ch. XIII.

[11] This only apparently self-evident postulate is used in proving certain theorems of

this result with what has just been said about the Peano system, the following conclusion is obtained, which is also known as *the thesis of logicism concerning the nature of mathematics*:

Mathematics is a branch of logic. It can be derived from logic in the following sense:

a. All the concepts of mathematics, *i.e.* of arithmetic, algebra, and analysis, can be defined in terms of four concepts of pure logic.

b. All the theorems of mathematics can be deduced from those definitions by means of the principles of logic (including the axioms of infinity and choice).[12]

In this sense it can be said that the propositions of the system of mathematics as here delimited are true by virtue of the definitions of the mathematical concepts involved, or that they make explicit certain characteristics with which we have endowed our mathematical concepts by definition. The propositions of mathematics have, therefore, the same unquestionable certainty which is typical of such propositions as "All bachelors are unmarried," but they also share the complete lack of empirical content which is associated with that certainty: The propositions of mathematics are devoid of all factual content; they convey no information whatever on any empirical subject matter.

11. On the Applicability of Mathematics to Empirical Subject Matter. This result seems to be irreconcilable with the fact that after all mathematics has proved to be eminently applicable to empirical subject matter, and that indeed the greater part of present-day scientific knowledge has been reached only through continual reliance on and application of the propositions of mathematics.—Let us try to clarify this apparent paradox by reference to some examples.

Suppose that we are examining a certain amount of some gas, whose volume v, at a certain fixed temperature, is found to be 9 cubic feet when the pressure p is 4 atmospheres. And let us assume further that the volume of the gas for the same temperature and $p = 6$ *at.*, is predicted by means of Boyle's law. Using elementary arithmetic we reason thus: For corresponding values of v and p, $vp = c$, and $v = 9$ when $p = 4$; hence $c = 36$: Therefore, when $p = 6$, then $v = 6$. Suppose that this prediction is borne out by subsequent test. Does that show that the arithmetic used has a predictive power of its own, that its propositions have factual implications? Cer-

set theory and of real and complex analysis; for a discussion of its significance and of its problematic aspects, see Russell, *l.c.*, Ch. XII (where it is called the multiplicative axiom), and A. Fraenkel, *Einleitung in die Mengenlehre*, Dover Publications, New York, 1946, § 16, sections 7 and 8.

[12] The principles of logic developed in Quine's work and in similar modern systems of formal logic embody certain restrictions as compared with those logical rules which had been rather generally accepted as sound until about the turn of the 20th century. At that time, the discovery of the famous paradoxes of logic, especially of Russell's paradox (*cf.* Russell, *l.c.*, Ch. XIII) revealed the fact that the logical principles implicit in customary mathematical reasoning involved contradictions and therefore had to be curtailed in one manner or another.

tainly not. All the predictive power here deployed, all the empirical content exhibited stems from the initial data and from Boyle's law, which asserts that $vp = c$ for *any* two corresponding values of v and p, hence also for $v = 9$, $p = 4$, and for $p = 6$ and the corresponding value of v.[13] The function of the mathematics here applied is not predictive at all; rather, it is analytic or explicative: it renders explicit certain assumptions or assertions which are included in the content of the premises of the argument (in our case, these consist of Boyle's law plus the additional data); mathematical reasoning reveals that those premises contain—hidden in them, as it were,—an assertion about the case as yet unobserved. In accepting our premises—so arithmetic reveals—we have—knowingly or unknowingly—already accepted the implication that the p-value in question is 6. Mathematical as well as logical reasoning is a conceptual technique of making explicit what is implicitly contained in a set of premises. The conclusions to which this technique leads assert nothing that is *theoretically new* in the sense of not being contained in the content of the premises. But the results obtained may well be *psychologically new*: we may not have been aware, before using the techniques of logic and mathematics, what we committed ourselves to in accepting a certain set of assumptions or assertions.

A similar analysis is possible in all other cases of applied mathematics, including those involving, say, the calculus. Consider, for example, the hypothesis that a certain object, moving in a specified electric field, will undergo a constant acceleration of 5 feet/sec^2. For the purpose of testing this hypothesis, we might derive from it, by means of two successive integrations, the prediction that if the object is at rest at the beginning of the motion, then the distance covered by it at any time t is $\frac{5}{2}t^2$ feet. This conclusion may clearly be psychologically new to a person not acquainted with the subject, but it is not theoretically new; the content of the conclusion is already contained in that of the hypothesis about the constant acceleration. And indeed, here as well as in the case of the compression of a gas, a failure of the prediction to come true would be considered as indicative of the factual incorrectness of at least one of the premises involved (*f.ex.*, of Boyle's law in its application to the particular gas), but never as a sign that the logical and mathematical principles involved might be unsound.

Thus, in the establishment of empirical knowledge, mathematics (as well as logic) has, so to speak, the function of a theoretical juice extractor: the techniques of mathematical and logical theory can produce no more juice of factual information than is contained in the assumptions to which they are applied; but they may produce a great deal more juice of this kind than might have been anticipated upon a first intuitive inspection of those assumptions which form the raw material for the extractor.

At this point, it may be well to consider briefly the status of those mathematical disciplines which are not outgrowths of arithmetic and thus

[13] Note that we may say "hence" by virtue of the rule of substitution, which is one of the rules of logical inference.

of logic; these include in particular topology, geometry, and the various branches of abstract algebra, such as the theory of groups, lattices, fields, *etc*. Each of these disciplines can be developed as a purely deductive system on the basis of a suitable set of postulates. If P be the conjunction of the postulates for a given theory, then the proof of a proposition T of that theory consists in deducing T from P by means of the principles of formal logic. What is established by the proof is therefore not the truth of T, but rather the fact that T is true provided that the postulates are. But since both P and T contain certain primitive terms of the theory, to which no specific meaning is assigned, it is not strictly possible to speak of the truth of either P or T; it is therefore more adequate to state the point as follows: If a proposition T is logically deduced from P, then every specific interpretation of the primitives which turns all the postulates of P into true statements, will also render T a true statement.—Up to this point, the analysis is exactly analogous to that of arithmetic as based on Peano's set of postulates. In the case of arithmetic, however, it proved possible to go a step further, namely to define the customary meanings of the primitives in terms of purely logical concepts and to show that the postulates—and therefore also the theorems—of arithmetic are unconditionally true by virtue of these definitions. An analogous procedure is not applicable to those disciplines which are not outgrowths of arithmetic: The primitives of the various branches of abstract algebra have no specific "customary meaning"; and if geometry in its customary interpretation is thought of as a theory of the structure of physical space, then its primitives have to be construed as referring to certain types of physical entities, and the question of the truth of a geometrical theory in this interpretation turns into an *empirical* problem.[14] For the purpose of applying any one of these non-arithmetical disciplines to some specific field of mathematics or empirical science, it is therefore necessary first to assign to the primitives some specific meaning and then to ascertain whether in this interpretation the postulates turn into true statements. If this is the case, then we can be sure that all the theorems are true statements too, because they are logically derived from the postulates and thus simply explicate the content of the latter in the given interpretation.—In their application to empirical subject matter, therefore, these mathematical theories no less than those which grow out of arithmetic and ultimately out of pure logic, have the function of an analytic tool, which brings to light the implications of a given set of assumptions but adds nothing to their content.

But while mathematics in no case contributes anything to the content of our knowledge of empirical matters, it is entirely indispensable as an instrument for the validation and even for the linguistic expression of such knowledge: The majority of the more far-reaching theories in empirical science—including those which lend themselves most eminently to pre-

[14] For a more detailed discussion of this point, *cf*. the article mentioned in reference 1.

diction or to practical application—are stated with the help of mathematical concepts; the formulation of these theories makes use, in particular, of the number system, and of functional relationships among different metrical variables. Furthermore, the scientific test of these theories, the establishment of predictions by means of them, and finally their practical application, all require the deduction, from the general theory, of certain specific consequences; and such deduction would be entirely impossible without the techniques of mathematics which reveal what the given general theory implicitly asserts about a certain special case.

Thus, the analysis outlined on these pages exhibits the system of mathematics as a vast and ingenious conceptual structure without empirical content and yet an indispensable and powerful theoretical instrument for the scientific understanding and mastery of the world of our experience.

III

SPACE, TIME, AND RELATIVITY

Newton's Views of Time, Space, and Motion *

ERNST MACH

1. In a scholium which he appends immediately to his definitions, Newton presents his views regarding time and space which we must examine more in detail. We shall literally cite, to this end, only the passages that are absolutely necessary to the characterization of Newton's views.

"So far, my object has been to explain the senses in which certain words little known are to be used in the sequel. Time, space, place, and motion, being words well known to everybody, I do not define. Yet it is to be remarked, that the vulgar conceive these quantities only in their relation to sensible objects. And hence certain prejudices with respect to them have arisen, to remove which it will be convenient to distinguish them into absolute and relative, true and apparent, mathematical and common, respectively.

"I. Absolute, true and mathematical time, of itself, and by its own nature, flows uniformly on, without regard to anything external. It is also called *duration.*

"Relative, apparent, and common time, is some sensible and external measure of absolute time (duration), estimated by the motions of bodies, whether accurate or inequable, and is commonly employed in place of true time; as an hour, a day, a month, a year. . . .

"The natural days, which, commonly, for purpose of the measurement of time, are held as equal, are in reality unequal. Astronomers correct this inequality, in order that they may measure by a truer time the celestial motions. It may be that there is no equable motion, by which time can accurately be measured. All motions can be accelerated and retarded. But the flow of *absolute* time cannot be changed. Duration, or the persistent existence of things, is always the same, whether motions be swift or slow or null."

2. It would appear as though Newton in the remarks here cited still stood under the influence of the medieval philosophy, as though he had grown unfaithful to his resolves to investigate only actual facts. When we

* Reprinted by kind permission of the publisher from *Science of Mechanics,* translated by T. J. McCormack, The Open Court Publishing Company, Chicago 1942, pp. 271–281.

say a thing A changes with the time, we mean simply that the conditions that determine a thing A depend on the conditions that determine another thing B. The vibrations of a pendulum take place *in time* when its excursion *depends* on the position of the earth. Since, however, in the observation of the pendulum, we are not under the necessity of taking into account its dependence on the position of the earth, but may compare it with any other thing (the conditions of which of course also depend on the position of the earth), the illusory notion easily arises that *all* the things with which we compare it are unessential. Nay, we may, in attending to the motion of a pendulum, neglect entirely other external things, and find that for every position of it our thoughts and sensations are different. Time, accordingly, appears to be some particular and independent thing, on the progress of which the position of the pendulum depends, while the things that we resort to for comparison and choose at random appear to play a wholly collateral part. But we must not forget that all things in the world are connected with one another and depend on one another, and that we ourselves and all our thoughts are also a part of nature. It is utterly beyond our power to *measure* the changes of things by *time*. Quite the contrary, time is an abstraction, at which we arrive by means of the changes of things; made because we are not restricted to any one *definite* measure, all being interconnected. A motion is termed uniform in which equal increments of space described correspond to equal increments of space described by some motion with which we form a comparison, as the rotation of the earth. A motion may, with respect to another motion, be uniform. But the question whether a motion is *in itself* uniform, is senseless. With just as little justice, also, may we speak of an "absolute time"—*of a time independent of* change. This absolute time can be measured by comparison with no motion; it has therefore neither a practical nor a scientific value; and no one is justified in saying that he knows aught about it. It is an idle metaphysical conception.

It would not be difficult to show from the points of view of psychology, history, and the science of language (by the names of the chronological divisions), that we reach our ideas of time in and through the interdependence of things on one another. In these ideas the profoundest and most universal connection of things is expressed. When a motion takes place in time, it depends on the motion of the earth. This is not refuted by the fact that mechanical motions can be reversed. A number of variable quantities may be so related that one set can suffer a change without the others being affected by it. Nature behaves like a machine. The individual parts reciprocally determine one another. But while in a machine the position of one part determines the position of *all* the other parts, in nature more complicated relations obtain. These relations are best represented under the conception of a number, n, of quantities that satisfy a lesser number, n', of equations. Were $n = n'$, nature would be invariable. Were $n' = n - 1$, then with one quantity all the rest would be controlled. If this latter relation obtained in nature, time could be reversed the moment this had been accomplished with any one single motion. But the true state of things is represented by a different relation between n and n'. The quantities in question are partially determined by one another; but they retain a greater indeterminateness, or freedom, than in the case last cited. We ourselves feel that we are such a partially determined, partially undetermined element of nature. In so far as a portion only of the changes of nature depends on us and can be reversed by us, does time appear to us irreversible, and the time that is past as irrevocably gone.

We arrive at the idea of time—to express it briefly and popularly—by the connection of that which is contained in the province of our memory with that which is contained in the province of our sense-perception. When we say that time flows on in a definite direction or sense, we mean that physical events generally (and therefore also physiological events) take place only in a definite sense.[1] Differences of temperature, electrical differences, differences of level generally, if left to themselves, all grow less and not greater. If we contemplate two bodies of different temperatures, put in contact and left wholly to themselves, we shall find that it is possible only for greater differences of temperature in the field of memory to exist with lesser ones in the field of sense-perception, and not the reverse. In all this there is simply expressed a peculiar and profound connection of things. To demand at the present time a full elucidation of this matter, is to anticipate, in the manner of speculative philosophy, the results of all future special investigation, that is, a perfected physical science.

As in the study of thermal phenomena we take as our measure of temperature an *arbitrarily chosen indicator of volume*, which varies in almost parallel correspondence with our sensation of heat, and which is not liable to the uncontrollable disturbances of our organs of sensation, so, for similar reasons, we select as our measure of time an *arbitrarily chosen motion* (the angle of the earth's rotation, or path of a free body), which proceeds in almost parallel correspondence with our sensation of time. If we have once made clear to ourselves that we are concerned only with the ascertainment of the *interdependence* of phenomena, all metaphysical obscurities disappear.

I have endeavored also (*Principles of Heat*, German edition, page 51) to point out the reason for the natural tendency of man to hypostatize the concepts which have great value for him, particularly those at which he arrives instinctively, without a knowledge of their development. The considerations which I there adduced for the concept of temperature may be easily applied to the concept of time, and render the origin of Newton's concept of "absolute" time intelligible. Mention is also made there (page 338) of the connection obtaining between the concept of energy and the

[1] On the physiological nature of the sensations of time and space. Cf. *Analyse der Empfindungen*, 6th ed. [English ed. *The Analysis of Sensations* (1914)]; *Erkenntnis und Irrtum*, 2nd ed.

irreversibility of time, and the view is advanced that the entropy of the universe, if it could ever possibly be determined, would actually represent a species of absolute measure of time.

3. Views similar to those concerning time, are developed by Newton with respect to space and motion. We extract here a few passages which characterize his position.

"II. Absolute space, in its own nature and without regard to anything external, always remains similar and immovable.

"Relative space is some movable dimension or measure of absolute space, which our senses determine by its position with respect to other bodies, and which is commonly taken for immovable [absolute] space. . . .

"IV. Absolute motion is the translation of a body from one absolute place [2] to another absolute place; and relative motion, the translation from one relative place to another relative place. . . .

". . . And thus we use, in common affairs, instead of *absolute* places and motions, *relative* ones; and that without any inconvenience. But in physical disquisitions, we should abstract from the senses. For it may be that there is no body really at rest, to which the places and motions of others can be referred. . . .

"The effects by which absolute and relative motions are distinguished from one another, are centrifugal forces, or those forces in circular motion which produces a tendency of recession from the axis. For in a circular motion which is purely relative no such forces exist; but in a true and absolute circular motion they do exist, and are greater or less according to the quantity of the [absolute] motion.

"For instance. If a bucket, suspended by a long cord, is so often turned about that finally the cord is strongly twisted, then is filled with water, and held at rest together with the water; and afterwards by the action of a second force, it is suddenly set whirling about the contrary way, and continues, while the cord is untwisting itself, for some time in this motion; the surface of the water will at first be level, just as it was before the vessel began to move; but, subsequently, the vessel, by gradually communicating its motion to the water, will make it begin sensibly to rotate, and the water will recede little by little from the middle and rise up at the sides of the vessel, its surface assuming a concave form. (This experiment I have made myself.)

". . . At first, when the *relative* motion of the water in the vessel was *greatest*, that motion produced no tendency whatever of recession from the axis; the water made no endeavor to move towards the circumference, by rising at the sides of the vessel, but remained level, and for that reason its *true* circular motion had not yet begun. But afterwards, when the relative motion of the water had decreased, the rising of the water at the sides of the vessel indicated an endeavor to recede from the axis; and this en-

[2] The place, or *locus* of a body, according to Newton, is not its position, but the *part of space* which it occupies. It is either absolute or relative.—*Trans.*

deavor revealed the real motion of the water, continually increasing, till it had reached its greatest point, when *relatively* the water was at rest in the vessel. . . .

"It is indeed a matter of great difficulty to discover, and effectually to distinguish, the *true* from the apparent motions of particular bodies; for the parts of that immovable space in which bodies actually move, do not come under the observation of our senses.

"Yet the case is not altogether desperate; for there exist to guide us certain marks, abstracted partly from the apparent motions, which are the differences of the true motions, and partly from the forces that are the causes and effects of the true motions. If, for instance, two globes, kept at a fixed distance from one another by means of a cord that connects them, be revolved about their common center of gravity, one might, from the simple tension of the cord, discover the tendency of the globes to recede from the axis of their motion, and on this basis the quantity of their circular motion might be computed. And if any equal forces should be simultaneously impressed on alternate faces of the globes to augment or diminish their circular motion, we might, from the increase or decrease of the tension of the cord, deduce the increment or decrement of their motion; and it might also be found thence on what faces forces would have to be impressed, in order that the motion of the globes should be most augmented; that is, their real faces, or those which, in the circular motion, follow. But as soon as we knew which faces followed, and consequently which preceded, we should likewise know the direction of the motion. In this way we might find both the quantity and the direction of the circular motion, considered even in an immense vacuum, where there was nothing external or sensible with which the globes could be compared. . . ."

If, in a material spatial system, there are masses with different velocities, which can enter into mutual relations with one another, these masses present to us forces. We can only decide how great these forces are when we know the velocities to which those masses are to be brought. *Resting* masses too are forces if *all* the masses do not rest. Think, for example, of Newton's rotating bucket in which the water is not yet rotating. If the mass m has the velocity v_1 and it is to be brought to the velocity v_2, the force which is to be spent on it is $p = m(v_1 - v_2)/t$ or the work which is to be expended is $ps = m(v_1^2 - v_2^2)$. *All* masses and *all* velocities, and consequently *all* forces, are relative. There is no decision about relative and absolute which we can possibly meet, to which we are forced, or from which we can obtain any intellectual or other advantage. When quite modern authors let themselves be led astray by the Newtonian arguments which are derived from the bucket of water, to distinguish between relative and absolute motion, they do not reflect that the system of the world is only given *once* to us, and the Ptolemaic or Copernican view is *our* interpretation, but both are equally actual. Try to fix Newton's bucket and rotate the heaven of fixed stars and then prove the absence of centrifugal forces.

4. It is scarcely necessary to remark that in the reflections here presented Newton has again acted contrary to his expressed intention only to investigate *actual facts*. No one is competent to predicate things about absolute space and absolute motion; they are pure things of thought, pure mental constructs, that cannot be produced in experience. All our principles of mechanics are, as we have shown in detail, experimental knowledge concerning the relative positions and motions of bodies. Even in the provinces in which they are now recognized as valid, they could not, and were not, admitted without previously being subjected to experimental tests. No one is warranted in extending these principles beyond the boundaries of experience. In fact, such an extension is meaningless, as no one possesses the requisite knowledge to make use of it.

We must suppose that the change in the point of view from which the system of the world is regarded, which was initiated by Copernicus, left deep traces in the thought of Galileo and Newton. But while Galileo, in his theory of the tides, quite naively chose the sphere of the fixed stars as the basis of a new system of coordinates, we see doubts expressed by Newton as to whether a given fixed star is at rest only apparently or really (*Principia*, 1687, p. 11). This appeared to him to cause the difficulty of distinguishing between true (absolute) and apparent (relative) motion. By this he was also impelled to set up the conception of *absolute space*. By further investigations in this direction—the discussion of the experiment of the rotating spheres which are connected together by a cord and that of the rotating water-bucket (pp. 9, 11)—he believed that he could prove an absolute rotation, though he could not prove any absolute translation. By absolute rotation he understood a rotation relative to the fixed stars, and here centrifugal forces can always be found. "But how we are to collect," says Newton in the Scholium at the end of the Definitions, "the true motions from their causes, effects, and apparent differences, and *vice versa;* how from the motions, either true or apparent, we may come to the knowledge of their causes and effects, shall be explained more at large in the following Tract." The resting sphere of fixed stars seems to have made a certain impression on Newton as well. The natural system of reference is for him that which has any uniform motion or translation without rotation (relatively to the sphere of fixed stars).[3] But do not the words quoted in inverted commas give the impression that Newton was glad to be able now to pass over to less precarious questions that could be tested by experience?

[3] *Principia*, p. 19, Coroll. V: "The motions of bodies included in a given space are the same among themselves, whether that space is at rest or moves uniformly forwards in a right line without any circular motion."

Non-Euclidean Geometries and the Non-Euclidean World *

HENRI POINCARÉ

EVERY CONCLUSION supposes premises; these premises themselves either are self-evident and need no demonstration, or can be established only by relying upon other propositions, and since we can not go back thus to infinity, every deductive science, and in particular geometry, must rest on a certain number of undemonstrable axioms. All treatises on geometry begin, therefore, by the enunciation of these axioms. But among these there is a distinction to be made: Some, for example, 'Things which are equal to the same thing are equal to one another,' are not propositions of geometry, but propositions of analysis. I regard them as analytic judgments *a priori*, and shall not concern myself with them.

But I must lay stress upon other axioms which are peculiar to geometry. Most treatises enunciate three of these explicitly:

1° Through two points can pass only one straight;

2° The straight line is the shortest path from one point to another;

3° Through a given point there is not more than one parallel to a given straight.

Although generally a proof of the second of these axioms is omitted, it would be possible to deduce it from the other two and from those, much more numerous, which are implicitly admitted without enunciating them, as I shall explain further on.

It was long sought in vain to demonstrate likewise the third axiom, known as *Euclid's Postulate*. What vast effort has been wasted in this chimeric hope is truly unimaginable. Finally, in the first quarter of the nineteenth century, and almost at the same time, a Hungarian and a Russian, Bolyai and Lobachevski, established irrefutably that this demonstration is impossible; they have almost rid us of inventors of geometries 'sans postulatum'; since then the Académie des Sciences receives only about one or two new demonstrations a year.

The question was not exhausted; it soon made a great stride by the publication of Riemann's celebrated memoir entitled: *Ueber die Hypothesen welche der Geometrie zu Grunde liegen.* This paper has inspired most

* Excerpted with kind permission of the publisher from *Science and Hypothesis*, translated by G. B. Halsted, The Science Press, New York, 1905, Chs. III and V.

of the recent works of which I shall speak further on, and among which it is proper to cite those of Beltrami and of Helmholtz.

The Bolyai-Lobachevski Geometry. If it were possible to deduce Euclid's postulate from the other axioms, it is evident that in denying the postulate and admitting the other axioms, we should be led to contradictory consequences; it would therefore be impossible to base on such premises a coherent geometry.

Now this is precisely what Lobachevski did.

He assumes at the start that: *Through a given point can be drawn two parallels to a given straight.*

And he retains besides all Euclid's other axioms. From these hypotheses he deduces a series of theorems among which it is impossible to find any contradiction, and he constructs a geometry whose faultless logic is inferior in nothing to that of the Euclidean geometry.

The theorems are, of course, very different from those to which we are accustomed, and they can not fail to be at first a little disconcerting.

Thus the sum of the angles of a triangle is always less than two right angles, and the difference between this sum and two right angles is proportional to the surface of the triangle.

It is impossible to construct a figure similar to a given figure but of different dimensions.

If we divide a circumference into *n* equal parts, and draw tangents at the points of division, these *n* tangents will form a polygon if the radius of the circle is small enough; but if this radius is sufficiently great they will not meet.

It is useless to multiply these examples; Lobachevski's propositions have no relation to those of Euclid, but they are not less logically bound one to another.

Riemann's Geometry. Imagine a world uniquely peopled by beings of no thickness (height); and suppose these 'infinitely flat' animals are all in the same plane and can not get out. Admit besides that this world is sufficiently far from others to be free from their influence. While we are making hypotheses, it costs us no more to endow these beings with reason and believe them capable of creating a geometry. In that case, they will certainly attribute to space only two dimensions.

But suppose now that these imaginary animals, while remaining without thickness, have the form of a spherical, and not of a plane figure, and are all on the same sphere without power to get off. What geometry will they construct? First it is clear they will attribute to space only two dimensions; what will play for them the role of the straight line will be the shortest path from one point to another on the sphere, that is to say an arc of a great circle; in a word, their geometry will be the spherical geometry.

What they will call space will be this sphere on which they must stay, and on which happen all the phenomena they can know. Their space will therefore be *unbounded* since on a sphere one can always go forward without ever being stopped, and yet it will be *finite;* one can never find the end of it, but one can make a tour of it.

Well, Riemann's geometry is spherical geometry extended to three dimensions. To construct it, the German mathematician had to throw overboard, not only Euclid's postulate, but also the first axiom: *Only one straight can pass through two points.*

On a sphere, through two given points we can draw *in general* only one great circle (which, as we have just seen, would play the role of the straight for our imaginary beings); but there is an exception: if the two given points are diametrically opposite, an infinity of great circles can be drawn through them.

In the same way, in Riemann's geometry (at least in one of its forms), through two points will pass in general only a single straight; but there are exceptional cases where through two points an infinity of straights can pass.

There is a sort of opposition between Riemann's geometry and that of Lobachevski.

Thus the sum of the angles of a triangle is:

Equal to two right angles in Euclid's geometry;

Less than two right angles in that of Lobachevski;

Greater than two right angles in that of Riemann.

The number of straights through a given point that can be drawn coplanar to a given straight, but nowhere meeting it, is equal:

To one in Euclid's geometry;

To zero in that of Riemann;

To infinity in that of Lobachevski.

Add that Riemann's space is finite, although unbounded in the sense given above to these two words.

The Surfaces of Constant Curvature. One objection still remained possible. The theorems of Lobachevski and of Riemann present no contradiction; but however numerous the consequences these two geometers have drawn from their hypotheses, they must have stopped before exhausting them, since their number would be infinite; who can say then that if they had pushed their deductions farther they would not have eventually reached some contradiction?

This difficulty does not exist for Riemann's geometry, provided it is limited to two dimensions; in fact, as we have seen, two-dimensional Riemannian geometry does not differ from spherical geometry, which is only a branch of ordinary geometry, and consequently is beyond all discussion.

Beltrami, in correlating likewise Lobachevski's two-dimensional geometry with a branch of ordinary geometry, has equally refuted the objection so far as it is concerned.

Here is how he accomplished it. Consider any figure on a surface. Imagine this figure traced on a flexible and inextensible canvas applied over this surface in such a way that when the canvas is displaced and deformed, the various lines of this figure can change their form without changing their length. In general, this flexible and inextensible figure can not be displaced without leaving the surface; but there are certain particular surfaces for which such a movement would be possible; these are the surfaces of constant curvature.

If we resume the comparison made above and imagine beings without thickness living on one of these surfaces, they will regard as possible the motion of a figure all of whose lines remain constant in length. On the contrary, such a movement would appear absurd to animals without thickness living on a surface of variable curvature.

These surfaces of constant curvature are of two sorts: Some are *of positive curvature*, and can be deformed so as to be applied over a sphere. The geometry of these surfaces reduces itself therefore to the spherical geometry, which is that of Riemann.

The others are *of negative curvature*. Beltrami has shown that the geometry of these surfaces is none other than that of Lobachevski. The two-dimensional geometries of Riemann and Lobachevski are thus correlated to the Euclidean geometry.

Interpretation of Non-Euclidean Geometries. So vanishes the objection so far as two-dimensional geometries are concerned.

It would be easy to extend Beltrami's reasoning to three-dimensional geometries. The minds that space of four dimensions does not repel will see no difficulty in it, but they are few. I prefer therefore to proceed otherwise.

Consider a certain plane, which I shall call the fundamental plane, and construct a sort of dictionary, by making correspond each to each a double series of terms written in two columns, just as correspond in the ordinary dictionaries the words of two languages whose signification is the same:

Space: Portion of space situated above the fundamental plane.

Plane: Sphere cutting the fundamental plane orthogonally.

Straight: Circle cutting the fundamental plane orthogonally.

Sphere: Sphere.

Circle: Circle.

Angle: Angle.

Distance between two points: Logarithm of the cross ratio of these two points and the intersections of the fundamental plane with a circle passing through these two points and cutting it orthogonally.

Etc., Etc.

Now take Lobachevski's theorems and translate them with the aid of this dictionary as we translate a German text with the aid of a German-English dictionary. *We shall thus obtain theorems of the ordinary geometry*. For example, that theorem of Lobachevski: 'the sum of the angles of a triangle is less than two right angles' is translated thus: "If a curvilinear triangle has for sides circle-arcs which prolonged would cut orthogonally the fundamental plane, the sum of the angles of this curvilinear triangle will be less than two right angles." Thus, however far the consequences of Lobachevski's hypotheses are pushed, they will never lead to a contradiction. In fact, if two of Lobachevski's theorems were contradictory, it would be the same with the translations of these two theorems, made by the aid of our dictionary, but these translations are theorems of ordinary geometry and no one doubts that the ordinary geometry is free from contradiction. Whence comes this certainty and is it justified? That is a question I can not treat here because it would require to be enlarged upon, but which is very interesting and I think not insoluble.

Nothing remains then of the objection above formulated. This is not all. Lobachevski's geometry, susceptible of a concrete interpretation, ceases to be a vain logical exercise and is capable of applications; I have not the time to speak here of these applications, nor of the aid that Klein and I have gotten from them for the integration of linear differential equations.

This interpretation moreover is not unique, and several dictionaries analogous to the preceding could be constructed, which would enable us by a simple 'translation' to transform Lobachevski's theorems into theorems of ordinary geometry.

On the Nature of Axioms. Most mathematicians regard Lobachevski's geometry only as a mere logical curiosity; some of them, however, have gone farther. Since several geometries are possible, is it certain ours is the true one? Experience no doubt teaches us that the sum of the angles of a triangle is equal to two right angles; but this is because the triangles we deal with are too little; the difference, according to Lobachevski, is proportional to the surface of the triangle; will it not perhaps become sensible when we shall operate on larger triangles or when our measurements shall become more precise? The Euclidean geometry would thus be only a provisional geometry.

To discuss this opinion, we should first ask ourselves what is the nature of the geometric axioms.

Are they synthetic *a priori* judgments, as Kant said?

They would then impose themselves upon us with such force, that we could not conceive the contrary proposition, nor build upon it a theoretic edifice. There would be no non-Euclidean geometry.

To be convinced of it take a veritable synthetic *a priori* judgment, the following, for instance:

If a theorem is true for the number 1, and if it has been proved that it is true of $n + 1$ provided it is true of n, it will be true of all the positive whole numbers.

Then try to escape from that and, denying this proposition, try to found a false arithmetic analogous to non-Euclidean geometry—it can not be done; one would even be tempted at first blush to regard these judgments as analytic.

Moreover, resuming our fiction of animals without thickness, we can hardly admit that these beings, if their minds are like ours, would adopt the Euclidean geometry which would be contradicted by all their experience.

Should we therefore conclude that the axioms of geometry are experimental verities? But we do not experiment on ideal straights or circles; it can only be done on material objects. On what then could be based experiments which should serve as foundation for geometry? The answer is easy.

We have seen above that we constantly reason as if the geometric figures behaved like solids. What geometry would borrow from experience would therefore be the properties of these bodies. The properties of light and its rectilinear propagation have also given rise to some of the propositions of geometry, and in particular those of projective geometry, so that from this point of view one would be tempted to say that metric geometry is the study of solids, and projective, that of light.

But a difficulty remains, and it is insurmountable. If geometry were an experimental science, it would not be an exact science, it would be subject to a continual revision. Nay, it would from this very day be convicted of error, since we know that there is no rigorously rigid solid.

The axioms of geometry therefore are neither synthetic a priori judgments nor experimental facts.

They are *conventions;* our choice among all possible conventions is *guided* by experimental facts; but it remains *free* and is limited only by the necessity of avoiding all contradiction. Thus it is that the postulates can remain *rigorously* true even though the experimental laws which have determined their adoption are only approximative.

In other words, *the axioms of geometry* (I do not speak of those of arithmetic) *are merely disguised definitions.*

Then what are we to think of that question: Is the Euclidean geometry true?

It has no meaning.

As well ask whether the metric system is true and the old measures false; whether Cartesian coordinates are true and polar coordinates false. One geometry can not be more true than another; it can only be *more convenient.*

Now, Euclidean geometry is, and will remain, the most convenient:

1° Because it is the simplest; and it is so not only in consequence of our mental habits, or of I know not what direct intuition that we may have of Euclidean space; it is the simplest in itself, just as a polynomial of the first degree is simpler than one of the second; the formulas of spherical trigonometry are more complicated than those of plane trigonometry, and they would still appear so to an analyst ignorant of their geometric signification.

2° Because it accords sufficiently well with the properties of natural solids, those bodies which our hands and our eye compare and with which we make our instruments of measure.

The Non-Euclidean World. If geometric space were a frame imposed on *each* of our representations, considered individually, it would be impossible to represent to ourselves an image stripped of this frame, and we could change nothing of our geometry.

But this is not the case; geometry is only the résumé of the laws according to which these images succeed each other. Nothing then prevents us from imagining a series of representations, similar in all points to our ordinary representations but succeeding one another according to laws different from those to which we are accustomed.

We can conceive then that beings who received their education in an environment where these laws were thus upset might have a geometry very different from ours.

Suppose, for example, a world enclosed in a great sphere and subject to the following laws:

The temperature is not uniform; it is greatest at the center, and diminishes in proportion to the distance from the center, to sink to absolute zero when the sphere is reached in which this world is enclosed.

To specify still more precisely the law in accordance with which this temperature varies: Let R be the radius of the limiting sphere; let r be the distance of the point considered from the center of this sphere. The absolute temperature shall be proportional to $R^2 - r^2$.

I shall further suppose that, in this world, all bodies have the same coefficient of dilatation, so that the length of any rule is proportional to its absolute temperature.

Finally, I shall suppose that a body transported from one point to another of different temperature is put immediately into thermal equilibrium with its new environment.

Nothing in these hypotheses is contradictory or unimaginable.

A movable object will then become smaller and smaller in proportion as it approaches the limit-sphere.

Note first that, though this world is limited from the point of view of our ordinary geometry, it will appear infinite to its inhabitants.

In fact, when these try to approach the limit-sphere, they cool off and become smaller and smaller. Therefore the steps they take are also smaller and smaller, so that they can never reach the limiting sphere.

If, for us, geometry is only the study of the laws according to which rigid solids move, for these imaginary beings it will be the study of the laws of motion of solids *distorted by the differences of temperature* just spoken of.

No doubt, in our world, natural solids likewise undergo variations of form and volume due to warming or cooling. But we neglect these variations in laying the foundations of geometry, because, besides their being very slight, they are irregular and consequently seem to us accidental.

In our hypothetical world, this would no longer be the case, and these variations would follow regular and very simple laws.

Moreover, the various solid pieces of which the bodies of its inhabitants would be composed would undergo the same variations of form and volume.

I will make still another hypothesis; I will suppose light traverses media diversely refractive and such that the index of refraction is inversely proportional to $R^2 - r^2$. It is easy to see that, under these conditions, the rays of light would not be rectilinear, but circular.

To justify what precedes, it remains for me to show that certain changes in the position of external objects can be *corrected* by correlative movements of the sentient beings inhabiting this imaginary world, and that in such a way as to restore the primitive aggregate of impressions experienced by these sentient beings.

Suppose in fact that an object is displaced, undergoing deformation, not as a rigid solid, but as a solid subjected to unequal dilatations in exact conformity to the law of temperature above supposed. Permit me for brevity to call such a movement a *non-Euclidean displacement*.

If a sentient being happens to be in the neighborhood, his impressions will be modified by the displacement of the object, but he can reestablish them by moving in a suitable manner. It suffices if finally the aggregate of the object and the sentient being, considered as forming a single body, has undergone one of those particular displacements I have just called non-Euclidean. This is possible if it be supposed that the limbs of these beings dilate according to the same law as the other bodies of the world they inhabit.

Although from the point of view of our ordinary geometry there is a deformation of the bodies in this displacement and their various parts are no longer in the same relative position, nevertheless we shall see that the impressions of the sentient being have once more become the same.

In fact, though the mutual distances of the various parts may have varied, yet the parts originally in contact are again in contact. Therefore the tactile impressions have not changed.

On the other hand, taking into account the hypothesis made above in regard to the refraction and the curvature of the rays of light, the visual impressions will also have remained the same.

These imaginary beings will therefore like ourselves be led to classify the phenomena they witness and to distinguish among them the 'changes of position' susceptible of correction by a correlative voluntary movement.

If they construct a geometry, it will not be, as ours is, the study of the movements of our rigid solids; it will be the study of the changes of position which they will thus have distinguished and which are none other than the 'non-Euclidean displacements'; *it will be non-Euclidean geometry.*

Thus beings like ourselves, educated in such a world, would not have the same geometry as ours.

The World of Four Dimensions. We can represent to ourselves a four-dimensional world just as well as a non-Euclidean.

The sense of sight, even with a single eye, together with the muscular sensations relative to the movements of the eyeball, would suffice to teach us space of three dimensions.

The images of external objects are painted on the retina, which is a two-dimensional canvas; they are *perspectives.*

But, as eye and objects are movable, we see in succession various perspectives of the same body, taken from different points of view.

At the same time, we find that the transition from one perspective to another is often accompanied by muscular sensations.

If the transition from the perspective A to the perspective B, and that from the perspective A′ to the perspective B′ are accompanied by the same muscular sensations, we liken them one to the other as operations of the same nature.

Studying then the laws according to which these operations combine, we recognize that they form a group, which has the same structure as that of the movements of rigid solids.

Now, we have seen that it is from the properties of this group we have derived the notion of geometric space and that of three dimensions.

We understand thus how the idea of a space of three dimensions could take birth from the pageant of these perspectives, though each of them is of only two dimensions, since *they follow one another according to certain laws.*

Well, just as the perspective of a three-dimensional figure can be made on a plane, we can make that of a four-dimensional figure on a picture of three (or of two) dimensions. To a geometer this is only child's play.

We can even take of the same figure several perspectives from several different points of view.

We can easily represent to ourselves these perspectives, since they are of only three dimensions.

Imagine that the various perspectives of the same object succeed one another, and that the transition from one to the other is accompanied by muscular sensations.

We shall of course consider two of these transitions as two operations of the same nature when they are associated with the same muscular sensations.

Nothing then prevents us from imagining that these operations combine according to any law we choose, for example, so as to form a group with the same structure as that of the movements of a rigid solid of four dimensions.

Here there is nothing unpicturable, and yet these sensations are precisely those which would be felt by a being possessed of a two-dimensional retina who could move in space of four dimensions. In this sense we may say the fourth dimension is imaginable.

Conclusions. We see that experience plays an indispensable role in the genesis of geometry; but it would be an error thence to conclude that geometry is, even in part, an experimental science.

If it were experimental, it would be only approximative and provisional. And what rough approximation!

Geometry would be only the study of the movements of solids; but in reality it is not occupied with natural solids, it has for object certain ideal solids, absolutely rigid, which are only a simplified and very remote image of natural solids.

The notion of these ideal solids is drawn from all parts of our mind, and experience is only an occasion which induces us to bring it forth from them.

The object of geometry is the study of a particular 'group'; but the general group concept pre-exists, at least potentially, in our minds. It is imposed on us, not as form of our sense, but as form of our understanding.

Only, from among all the possible groups, that must be chosen which will be, so to speak, the *standard* to which we shall refer natural phenomena.

Experience guides us in this choice without forcing it upon us; it tells us not which is the truest geometry, but which is the most *convenient*.

Notice that I have been able to describe the fantastic worlds above imagined *without ceasing to employ the language of ordinary geometry*.

And, in fact, we should not have to change it if transported thither.

Beings educated there would doubtless find it more convenient to create a geometry different from ours, and better adapted to their impressions. As for us, in face of the *same* impressions, it is certain we should find it more convenient not to change our habits.

Are Natural Laws Conventions?*

MORITZ SCHLICK

EVERY DEFINITION IS an arbitrary stipulation, hence a convention. But by a "convention" in the characteristic meaning with which Poincaré introduced the word into the logic of science, we usually understand a quite especial kind of definition; namely, one which specifies that certain definite forms of propositions are to be used for the description of nature. The opposite would be, e. g., an ostensive definition, stipulating a definite word such as 'yellow' for a definite color.

As is well known, Henri Poincaré developed the procedure of convention with reference to the propositions of geometry—essentially anticipated by Helmholtz—by calling attention to the fact that those propositions in their application to the spatial properties of bodies are to be regarded as definitions. They do not assert anything about a "real space" but stipulate how the spatial relations of reality are to be described. The assertion that a triangle formed by three Euclidean straight lines has an angular sum equal to two right angles does not formulate a fact of nature, but stipulates a condition under which we will *say* of certain physical shapes that they have the properties of "Euclidean straight lines." If, following the actual custom of present-day physics, we characterize certain physical entities such as light rays, axes of rotation, etc. as "straight lines", then experience might show that they do not have the properties of "Euclidean straight lines" and hence cannot, according to the definition, be designated by that name. This, then, is an empirical fact not a geometrical proposition.

In our own manner of speaking we might express most briefly the insight into the conventional character of geometrical propositions by saying: geometry is the grammar of the language in which we describe the spatial relationships of physics.

But are the spatial—or in our modern physics, the spatial-temporal—relations exceptional as compared with other physical relations?

The language in which we speak of physical relations must after all also have its own grammar and there is no doubt that this is determined by convention. Are natural laws these conventions perhaps? Do the natural laws perhaps represent nothing else but the grammar of the natural sciences,

* Reprinted by kind permission of Mrs. Schlick from *Gesetz, Kausalität, und Wahrscheinlichkeit*, Gerold & Co., Vienna, 1948. Originally published in *Moritz Schlick, Gesammelte Aufsätze 1926–1936*, Gerold, 1938. Translated by H. F. and M. B.

i.e., in the last analysis, of physical language in general? As is well-known, this view has actually been advocated, partly by somewhat fantastic writers who do not merit mention here, but partly also by such outstanding scientists as Sir Arthur Eddington. He considered an entire class of natural laws (namely, all except the statistical ones) as mere definitions, and he must therefore be regarded as representative of an extreme "conventionalism" (if we cannot avoid this clumsy word).

I am convinced that conventionalism rests on a grave logical error which, while of great fundamental interest, can be cleared up in a few words. This clarification will be attempted briefly here.

The difference between a stipulation and a genuine proposition obviously lies in the fact that the validity of a convention is of our own making. After a stipulation has been made, we can maintain it under any circumstances. Experience might well suggest but can never compel its abandonment, for the validity of a convention remains in our power. It is well known that facts of nature can be described by means of Euclidean geometry, if we stubbornly insist upon it. However, this would involve considerable inconveniences in the description, since there are in nature, e.g., no easily producible entities that exactly correspond to straight lines as axiomatically defined in Euclidean geometry.

Turning to the formulations of natural laws, we seem to find precisely the same situation: we can, if we absolutely insist, maintain them under any circumstances, provided that we are not disturbed by highly impractical or strange formulations. If this were really possible, then the conventional character of natural laws would be demonstrated.

Before we examine the issue quite generally and in principle, let us discuss it in terms of two well-known examples.

Our first example concerns the energy principle. It has indeed, not infrequently and at a relatively early date, been maintained that the principle of the conservation of energy is a mere definition. It will be sufficient to consider the formulation customary in thermodynamics. If we transform some system from State 1 into State 2 in such a manner that a quantity of heat is imparted and an amount of work is exerted upon it, then the expression for the energy of the system in State 2 (with respect to 1) reads $E = W + Q$. Since E can be determined only through measurement of W and Q, it would seem as if this energy equation were nothing but pure definition, i.e., the introduction of a new symbol for the sum of Q and W. In that case would the energy principle be a convention? The physicist would tell us immediately that this conclusion is completely false. In point of fact the essence of the energy equation is precisely that E denotes a magnitude which depends only upon the states 1 and 2, but not upon the path by which the transformation takes place. This cannot be read out of the equation itself but must be added as a special comment. By virtue of this comment, it becomes clear that the right and the left sides of the equation are defined differently and only experience can decide whether E always assumes the same value for transformations along different paths. Thus interpreted, the energy equation amounts to an assertion which can be refuted or confirmed by the facts and is therefore not a definition. After all, the principle asserts the extremely palpable fact of the impossibility of a *perpetuum mobile*. The "conventionalists" forget that if their view were correct, then it should be possible, by suitable definitions, to become independent of the energy sources of the earth, such as coal, air, or water.

They have, nevertheless, attempted to maintain their view that the energy principle is a mere definition by saying that the constancy of the magnitude E could be guaranteed by assuming the creation and destruction of latent energies inaccessible to perception, ensuring the balance under all circumstances (Driesch). While according to this view the equation would indeed become a mere tautology, it scarcely needs to be pointed out that in this form it no longer has anything at all in common with the energy principle in physics. For this principle, it is essential that "energy" represents a magnitude that is always determinable by measurements. If, according to the conventionalists, the word "energy" is defined by the condition of constancy and the condition of observability is relinquished, then the word no longer designates what physicists or engineers mean by "energy". What we have here is a sentence which sounds like the original but means something entirely different.

Our second example concerns Galileo's law of inertia which Eddington views as a mere definition. It may be formulated as follows: A body upon which no forces act moves uniformly in a straight line. But how, asks Eddington, is a body upon which no forces act defined? And he answers: Obviously, only by the fact that it moves uniformly in a straight line. The law of inertia is therefore a tautology based upon mere stipulation.

But is the phrase "no forces acting" actually defined by rectilinear and uniform motion? It may appear so in the light of Newton's definition of force. But again, as in the preceding example, a circumstance not expressly stated is nevertheless essentially implied: In point of fact a "force" is considered a magnitude which depends upon other near-by bodies and their states. The essential point here is the empirical fact that the acceleration or curvature of trajectory of a body is related to the presence and states of other bodies. A strict definition of force therefore requires that it be a function of the total constellation of the bodies present. We thus conclude that the sentence in which Eddington formulates the law of inertia becomes a convention only by attributing to the words a meaning which they do not have in physics. Only by giving different meanings to the same words can he defend his thesis.

But, furthermore: the law of inertia speaks of "uniform motion", that is, motion in which equal distances are traversed in equal times. Eddington points out that the definition of "equal time intervals" in turn presupposes the law of inertia, which would render this law circular or tautological. It is true that equal time intervals are practically defined with the help of inertial motions (e.g., the rotation of the earth), since time intervals are considered "equal" in which equal distances (or equal angles of rotation) are traversed. Nevertheless, the charge of the purely definitional character of the principle of inertia is unjustified. In fact "equal" time intervals may be defined by means of the motion of one single body; and it is only a fact of experience that time-intervals which, according to the definition, are equal for a given moving body on which "no forces" are acting are also equal to those of any *other* arbitrary body moving under the influence of "no forces". But it is just this fact of experience which is after all to be expressed by the law of inertia.

The error here lies in disregarding the significance of the indefinite article "a" which precedes the word "body" in the law of inertia. The indefinite article here means "any arbitrary"; thus the law of inertia refers to agreement in the behavior of *all* bodies, and such agreement can only be read out of experience, not achieved by definition.

I have discussed these illustrations in order to make especially clear how the view that natural laws are conventions could come about. It is due to the formulation of the law—usually in the form of an equation—as it is written on paper, but without enough consideration given to the definitional explications through which the expression attains its meaning and which are usually not sufficiently explicitly or completely formulated. Instead, a rather willful interpretation is imputed which makes the expression in question into a tautology. One is easily misled to do just this if, for interpretation of the symbols, one uses only those aspects which are actually written down in the form of calculations. But this is the procedure of the pure mathematician and logician who quite generally cannot proceed in any other way. For in logic and mathematics the symbols have precisely the meaning which is bestowed upon them by what is expressly written down or formulated in some other fashion. Mathematics and logic do not point beyond themselves; they do not transcend their own realm of symbols; here there is no fundamental difference between theorem and definition.

The situation is very different in the natural sciences where each of the symbols used refers to definite observations and experiments which actually must be carried out, if its statements are to acquire any meaning whatsoever. After the system of physics is finished, it can of course be represented in purely mathematical form. And the mathematician amuses himself by investigating the mutual connections, derivabilities, and transformabilities of the single statements. In this kind of work the difference between definition and theorem again does not appear, since all reference to observation is disregarded. In this sort of consideration and manipulation it is immaterial whether a certain equation is interpreted as a definition or as a law of nature. There is no way of discerning whether it is the one or the other. This way of looking at things is possible only in the relatively finished and systematized field of physics, where it is no longer necessary to orient every step by recourse to experience. Thus it is most interesting to observe how Eddington, in his presentation of the theory of relativity, is seduced by the mere appearance of the Einsteinian gravitational equations to regard them as mere definitions. As remarked before, he extends this point of view to all the laws of classical physics, which indeed is characterized by that ideal closure of which the theory of relativity is the purest example.

The difference between the logico-mathematical and the experimental attitude can be made clear in its fundamental origin by reference to the distinction between "sentence" and "proposition", to which I had to refer very emphatically on an earlier occasion (*Le fondement de la connaissance*, Paris, 1935). We shall mean by "sentence" a sequence of linguistic signs with the help of which something can be asserted, such as the written sequence of letters in a written communication, or the sequence of signs in a spoken communication, or even the sequence of depressions and elevations on a phonograph record, any of which can be used for the purposes of communication. In contradistinction, we shall mean by a "proposition" such a sentence together with its *meaning*, but this meaning is not to be understood in the sense of a shadowy entity which somehow dwells in the sentence or accompanies it. But, rather, it is to be viewed simply as the set of rules which are stipulated for the actual application of the sentence, that is, for the practical use of the sentence in the representation of facts. In short, a "proposition" is a "sentence" insofar as it actually fulfills the function of communication.

The modern development of logic has shown with increasing clarity that its method, just as that of mathematics, is best characterized as *formal*. That is to say, it is a method in which the meaning of sentences and symbols is disregarded. In this manner, the actual use of the symbols is ignored and only their mutual relations to one another is given attention. The symbols have such mutual relations to one another by virtue of stipulations (syntactical rules) which form the "logical grammar" of the language in question. In other words: the logico-mathematical perspective deals with the syntactical properties and relations of sentences, but it does not deal with propositions.

However, it is essential for natural science (as quite generally for any factual science) that it never disregards meaning and significance. It is always concerned with propositions.

Natural laws are undoubtedly propositions in the sense just explained. It would certainly be absurd if one were to declare a merely written or spoken sentence, regardless of its significance, to be a natural law. One and the same sentence can of course be the vehicle of many different propositions: all that is needed would be to stipulate different rules for its use. The sentence (the sequence of words) "King remains in the background" represents quite different propositions depending upon whether "king" refers to a definite monarch, to a chess figure, or to a football player by the name of King. Also, by suitable stipulation any sentence can be made into a definition; but then it is no longer a proposition. A sentence represents a proposition by virtue of definite conventions; but a proposition is, of course, not a convention. Nor is a natural law.

Let us return to the case of geometry. One and the same physical world can be described in terms of different geometries, if only the formulation of the physical laws is each time adapted to the special geometry used. I say deliberately the *formulation* of the physical law, for it is the *sentences,* in the meaning of that word explained before, in this case the written mathematical equations, which change completely when the transition is made from one geometry to another. It is the equations consisting of mathematical symbols (and also, of course, the expressions in ordinary language which are attached to these equations) which assume a much more complex and complicated form when, for instance, in the description of gravitational phenomena we choose Euclidean instead of Riemannian geometry. But are we entitled to say that the physical laws change, i.e., a "different physics" results when the geometry is changed? Obviously not; for this would mean that mere sign sequences on paper would be honored with the name "laws", which we have already repudiated as inconsistent with our natural attitude. If at all possible, we should like to mean by "natural law" something that is invariant relative to any arbitrary mode of formulation. And this is possible. After all, we are fond of saying that natural laws are immutable and we are not tempted to say that the natural laws have changed when we introduce a new notation or even a completely new geometry. The energy principle, for example, is generally considered to express that "objective" order of facts which makes it impossible to produce work out of nothing—an impossibility which is continually impressed upon us in our daily experience and which is certainly quite independent of the manner in which we care to formulate it.

To summarize, the situation is this: neither the geometrical axioms nor the equations of physics assert anything about reality. The former are mere grammatical rules, the latter are mere "sentences". Each by itself is subject to arbitrary changes in formulation. They are therefore not what we would call natural laws. Only both together can form genuine propositions. The proper content of a natural law may be seen in the fact that to certain grammatical rules (for instance, of a geometry) some quite definite propositions correspond as true descriptions of reality. And this fact is completely invariant with respect to any arbitrary changes in notation.

What is arbitrary are, first, the rules which determine the mutual relations of the symbols used, the mathematical axioms, and the explicit definitions of the derived concepts of natural science and, secondly, the ostensive definitions by means of which, in the last analysis, the meanings of the fundamental concepts of natural science are determined. These rules in their totality form the grammar of the scientific language, i.e., the complete inventory of rules according to which the symbols (letters, words, sentences, etc.) are to be used in the description of facts. All these "grammatical" rules, and these alone, together determine the meaning of the propositions of science. For the meaning of a sentence is indicated if and only if it is precisely stated how the sentence is to be used: and that is precisely what these rules do. *They* are the only conventions, not the natural laws. It is those rules which turn mere sentences into genuine propositions, for they determine their significance.

Once the rules are fixed, i.e., once agreement is reached concerning the grammar of the scientific language, then there is no longer any choice about how to formulate any facts of nature. After this there is only one possibility, only one way of formulating the sentence which will fulfill the purpose. A natural law can then be represented in only one quite definite form and not in any other.[1]

It is of course very easy to change the grammar, that is, to introduce new rules for the use of our symbols. However, as soon as we do that we must, in order to describe the same regularity of nature as before, now use a different sentence or sequence of signs. If a natural law is represented by the sentence S_1 in the grammar G_1, then it will have to be formulated in grammar G_2 by the sentence S_2. The law now *reads* differently. But, actually, it is only the signs that have been changed, the meaning remains the same. The sentences S_1 and S_2 are indeed different sign-sequences but both represent the same proposition, very much in the way in which "le roi est mort" and "the king is dead" are different sentences but the same proposition. Which proposition corresponds to which sentence depends upon the grammar that is presupposed, for only the grammar gives meaning to the signs. In the present case the grammar G_1 gives the sentence S_1 the same meaning which grammar G_2 gives the sentence S_2. In both cases, therefore, the same proposition is expressed.

Thus we see that all genuine propositions, as for instance natural laws, are something objective, something invariant with respect to the manner of representation, and not dependent in any way upon convention. What is conventional and, hence, arbitrary, is only the form of expression, the symbols, the sentences, thus only something external or superficial which is immaterial to the empirical scientist. In science, as in knowledge gen-

[1] When Carnap (*The Logical Syntax of Language*, 1949 printing, pp. 180 f.) explains that one can construct a language with "extra-logical" transformation rules by, for instance, including natural laws among the principles (i.e., they are considered as grammatical rules), then this way of putting things seems to me misleading in the same sense as is the thesis of conventionalism. It is true that a sentence (a sign sequence) which, under the presuppositions of customary grammar, expresses a natural law can be made into a principle of language simply by stipulating it as a syntactical rule. But precisely by this device one changes the grammar and, consequently, interprets the sentence in an entirely new sense, or, rather, one deprives the sentence of its original sense. It is then not a natural law any more at all; it is not even a proposition, but merely a rule for the manipulation of signs. This whole reinterpretation appears therefore trivial and useless.—Any interpretation which blurs such fundamental distinctions is extremely dangerous.

erally, we search for nothing but the truth. However, only propositions are true or false, not sentences. Sentences, indeed, are subject to arbitrary modification, but this does not concern anyone whose goal is the knowledge of facts. With the help of the rules for the use of the symbols (the grammar which, of course, he must know, because without it the sentences would be meaningless for him) he can always penetrate to the genuine propositions whose truth does not depend upon anybody's predilections.

The insight that conventions play an important rôle in the formulation of knowledge claims must therefore not be misunderstood to mean that these claims are therefore lacking in objective validity, as if truth were somehow subjective, or natural laws merely a product of our preferences. Wherever conventionalism asserts anything of this sort, it is guilty of confusing sentences and propositions. It mistakes the garment for the essence.

That the garment is purely conventional is indeed a trivial insight, for nobody doubts that a symbol can acquire its significance only through a stipulation; nevertheless, it is an important insight just because it enables us to reflect upon the difference between essence and garment, between kernel and husk: a genuinely philosophical task.

In sum, the theory of conventions, as the historical facts prove, contains the danger of grave misunderstandings. But it is a valuable instrument for separating that which pertains to knowledge itself from that which pertains merely to its formulation. Many a confusion still dominant in the logic of science can thereby be overcome.

Geometry and Experience*

ALBERT EINSTEIN

ONE REASON WHY mathematics enjoys special esteem, above all other sciences, is that its laws are absolutely certain and indisputable, while those of all other sciences are to some extent debatable and in constant danger of being overthrown by newly discovered facts. In spite of this, the investigator in another department of science would not need to envy the mathematician if the laws of mathematics referred to objects of our mere imagination, and not to objects of reality. For it cannot occasion surprise that different persons should arrive at the same logical conclusions when they have already agreed upon the fundamental laws (axioms), as well as the methods by which other laws are to be deduced therefrom. But there is another reason for the high repute of mathematics, in that it is mathematics which affords the exact natural sciences a certain measure of security, to which without mathematics they could not attain.

At this point an enigma presents itself which in all ages has agitated inquiring minds. How can it be that mathematics, being after all a product of human thought which is independent of experience, is so admirably appropriate to the objects of reality? Is human reason, then, without experience, merely by taking thought, able to fathom the properties of real things?

In my opinion the answer to this question is, briefly, this:—As far as the laws of mathematics refer to reality, they are not certain; and as far as they are certain, they do not refer to reality. It seems to me that complete clearness as to this state of things first became common property through that new departure in mathematics which is known by the name of mathematical logic or "Axiomatics." The progress achieved by axiomatics consists in its having neatly separated the logical-formal from its objective or intuitive content; according to axiomatics the logical-formal alone forms the subject-matter of mathematics, which is not concerned with the intuitive or other content associated with the logical-formal.

Let us for a moment consider from this point of view any axiom of geometry, for instance, the following:—Through two points in space there always passes one and only one straight line. How is this axiom to be interpreted in the older sense and in the more modern sense?

* Reprinted by kind permission of the author and the publisher from Albert Einstein, *Sidelights of Relativity*, E. P. Dutton & Co., Inc., New York 1923, pp. 27–45.

The older interpretation:—Every one knows what a straight line is, and what a point is. Whether this knowledge springs from an ability of the human mind or from experience, from some collaboration of the two or from some other source, is not for the mathematician to decide. He leaves the question to the philosopher. Being based upon this knowledge, which precedes all mathematics, the axiom stated above is, like all other axioms, self-evident, that is, it is the expression of a part of this *a priori* knowledge.

The more modern interpretation:—Geometry treats of entities which are denoted by the words straight line, point, etc. These entities do not take for granted any knowledge or intuition whatever, but they presuppose only the validity of the axioms, such as the one stated above, which are to be taken in a purely formal sense, i.e. as void of all content of intuition or experience. These axioms are free creations of the human mind. All other propositions of geometry are logical inferences from the axioms (which are to be taken in the nominalistic sense only). The matter of which geometry treats is first defined by the axioms. Schlick in his book on epistemology has therefore characterized axioms very aptly as "implicit definitions."

This view of axioms, advocated by modern axiomatics, purges mathematics of all extraneous elements, and thus dispels the mystic obscurity which formerly surrounded the principles of mathematics. But a presentation of its principles thus clarified makes it also evident that mathematics as such cannot predicate anything about perceptual objects or real objects. In axiomatic geometry the words "point," "straight line," etc., stand only for empty conceptual schemata. That which gives them substance is not relevant to mathematics.

Yet on the other hand it is certain that mathematics generally, and particularly geometry, owes its existence to the need which was felt of learning something about the relations of real things to one another. The very word geometry, which, of course, means earth-measuring, proves this. For earth-measuring has to do with the possibilities of the disposition of certain natural objects with respect to one another, namely, with parts of the earth, measuring-lines, measuring-wands, etc. It is clear that the system of concepts of axiomatic geometry alone cannot make any assertions as to the relations of real objects of this kind, which we will call practically-rigid bodies. To be able to make such assertions, geometry must be stripped of its merely logical-formal character by the co-ordination of real objects of experience with the empty conceptual frame-work of axiomatic geometry. To accomplish this we need only add the proposition:—Solid bodies are related, with respect to their possible dispositions, as are bodies in Euclidean geometry of three dimensions. Then the propositions of Euclid contain affirmations as to the relations of practically-rigid bodies.

Geometry thus completed is evidently a natural science; we may in fact regard it as the most ancient branch of physics. Its affirmations rest essentially on induction from experience, but not on logical inferences only. We will call this completed geometry "practical geometry," and shall distinguish it in what follows from "purely axiomatic geometry." The question whether the practical geometry of the universe is Euclidean or not has a clear meaning, and its answer can only be furnished by experience. All linear measurement in physics is practical geometry in this sense, so too is geodetic and astronomical linear measurement, if we call to our help the law of experience that light is propagated in a straight line, and indeed in a straight line in the sense of practical geometry.

I attach special importance to the view of geometry which I have just set forth, because without it I should have been unable to formulate the theory of relativity. Without it the following reflection would have been impossible:—In a system of reference rotating relatively to an inert system, the laws of disposition of rigid bodies do not correspond to the rules of Euclidean geometry on account of the Lorentz contraction; thus if we admit non-inert systems we must abandon Euclidean geometry. The decisive step in the transition to general co-variant equations would certainly not have been taken if the above interpretation had not served as a stepping-stone. If we deny the relation between the body of axiomatic Euclidean geometry and the practically-rigid body of reality, we readily arrive at the following view, which was entertained by that acute and profound thinker, H. Poincaré:—Euclidean geometry is distinguished above all other imaginable axiomatic geometries by its simplicity. Now since axiomatic geometry by itself contains no assertions as to the reality which can be experienced, but can do so only in combination with physical laws, it should be possible and reasonable—whatever may be the nature of reality—to retain Euclidean geometry. For if contradictions between theory and experience manifest themselves, we should rather decide to change physical laws than to change axiomatic Euclidean geometry. If we deny the relation between the practically-rigid body and geometry, we shall indeed not easily free ourselves from the convention that Euclidean geometry is to be retained as the simplest. Why is the equivalence of the practically-rigid body and the body of geometry—which suggests itself so readily—denied by Poincaré and other investigators? Simply because under closer inspection the real solid bodies in nature are not rigid, because their geometrical behaviour, that is, their possibilities of relative disposition, depend upon temperature, external forces, etc. Thus the original, immediate relation between geometry and physical reality appears destroyed, and we feel impelled toward the following more general view, which characterizes Poincaré's standpoint. Geometry (G) predicates nothing about the relations of real things, but only geometry together with the purport (P) of physical laws can do so. Using symbols, we may say that only the sum of (G) + (P) is subject to the control of experience. Thus (G) may be chosen arbitrarily, and also parts of (P); all these laws are conventions. All that is necessary to avoid contradictions is to choose the remainder of (P) so that (G) and the whole of (P) are together in accord with experience. Envisaged in this way, axiomatic geometry and the part of natural law which has been given a conventional status appear as epistemologically equivalent.

Sub specie aeterni Poincaré, in my opinion, is right. The idea of the measuring-rod and the idea of the clock co-ordinated with it in the theory of relativity do not find their exact correspondence in the real world. It is also clear that the solid body and the clock do not in the conceptual edifice of physics play the part of irreducible elements, but that of composite structures, which may not play any independent part in theoretical physics. But it is my conviction that in the present stage of development of theoretical physics these ideas must still be employed as independent ideas; for we are still far from possessing such certain knowledge of theoretical principles as to be able to give exact theoretical constructions of solid bodies and clocks.

Further, as to the objection that there are no really rigid bodies in nature, and that therefore the properties predicated of rigid bodies do not apply to physical reality,—this objection is by no means so radical as might appear from a hasty examination. For it is not a difficult task to determine the physical state of a measuring-rod so accurately that its behaviour relatively to other measuring-bodies shall be sufficiently free from ambiguity to allow it to be substituted for the "rigid" body. It is to measuring-bodies of this kind that statements as to rigid bodies must be referred.

All practical geometry is based upon a principle which is accessible to experience, and which we will now try to realise. We will call that which is enclosed between two boundaries, marked upon a practically-rigid body, a tract. We imagine two practically-rigid bodies, each with a tract marked out on it. These two tracts are said to be "equal to one another" if the boundaries of the one tract can be brought to coincide permanently with the boundaries of the other. We now assume that:

If two tracts are found to be equal once and anywhere, they are equal always and everywhere.

Not only the practical geometry of Euclid, but also its nearest generalisation, the practical geometry of Riemann, and therewith the general theory of relativity, rest upon this assumption. Of the experimental reasons which warrant this assumption I will mention only one. The phenomenon of the propagation of light in empty space assigns a tract, namely, the appropriate path of light, to each interval of local time, and conversely. Thence it follows that the above assumption for tracts must also hold good for intervals of clock-time in the theory of relativity. Consequently it may be formulated as follows:—If two ideal clocks are going at the same rate at any time and at any place (being then in immediate proximity to each other), they will always go at the same rate, no matter where and when they are again compared with each other at one place.—If this law were not valid for real clocks, the proper frequencies for the separate atoms of the same chemical element would not be in such exact agreement as experience demonstrates. The existence of sharp spectral lines is a convincing experimental proof of the above-mentioned principle of practical geometry. This is the ultimate foundation in fact which enables us to speak with meaning of the mensuration, in Riemann's sense of the word, of the four-dimensional continuum of space-time.

The question whether the structure of this continuum is Euclidean, or in accordance with Riemann's general scheme, or otherwise, is, according to the view which is here being advocated, properly speaking a physical question which must be answered by experience, and not a question of a mere convention to be selected on practical grounds. Riemann's geometry will be the right thing if the laws of disposition of practically-rigid bodies are transformable into those of the bodies of Euclid's geometry with an exactitude which increases in proportion as the dimensions of the part of space-time under consideration are diminished.

It is true that this proposed physical interpretation of geometry breaks down when applied immediately to spaces of sub-molecular order of magnitude. But nevertheless, even in questions as to the constitution of elementary particles, it retains part of its importance. For even when it is a question of describing the electrical elementary particles constituting matter, the attempt may still be made to ascribe physical importance to those ideas of fields which have been physically defined for the purpose of describing the geometrical behaviour of bodies which are large as compared with the molecule. Success alone can decide as to the justification of such an attempt, which postulates physical reality for the fundamental principles of Riemann's geometry outside of the domain of their physical definitions. It might possibly turn out that this extrapolation has no better warrant than the extrapolation of the idea of temperature to parts of a body of molecular order of magnitude.

It appears less problematical to extend the ideas of practical geometry to spaces of cosmic order of magnitude. It might, of course, be objected that a construction composed of solid rods departs more and more from ideal rigidity in proportion as its spatial extent becomes greater. But it will hardly be possible, I think, to assign fundamental significance to this objection. Therefore the question whether the universe is spatially finite or not seems to me decidedly a pregnant question in the sense of practical geometry. I do not even consider it impossible that this question will be answered before long by astronomy. Let us call to mind what the general theory of relativity teaches in this respect. It offers two possibilities:—

1. The universe is spatially infinite. This can be so only if the average spatial density of the matter in universal space, concentrated in the stars, vanishes, i.e. if the ratio of the total mass of the stars to the magnitude of the space through which they are scattered approximates indefinitely to the value zero when the spaces taken into consideration are constantly greater and greater.

2. The universe is spatially finite. This must be so, if there is a mean density of the ponderable matter in universal space differing from zero. The smaller that mean density, the greater is the volume of universal space.

I must not fail to mention that a theoretical argument can be adduced in favour of the hypothesis of a finite universe. The general theory of relativity teaches that the inertia of a given body is greater as there are more ponderable masses in proximity to it; thus it seems very natural to reduce the total effect of inertia of a body to action and reaction between it and the other bodies in the universe, as indeed, ever since Newton's time, gravity has been completely reduced to action and reaction between bodies. From the equations of the general theory of relativity it can be deduced that this total reduction of inertia to reciprocal action between masses—as required by E. Mach, for example—is possible only if the universe is spatially finite.

On many physicists and astronomers this argument makes no impression. Experience alone can finally decide which of the two possibilities is realised in nature. How can experience furnish an answer? At first it might seem possible to determine the mean density of matter by observation of that part of the universe which is accessible to our perception. This hope is illusory. The distribution of the visible stars is extremely irregular, so that we on no account may venture to set down the mean density of star-matter in the universe as equal, let us say, to the mean density in the Milky Way. In any case, however great the space examined may be, we could not feel convinced that there were no more stars beyond that space. So it seems impossible to estimate the mean density.

But there is another road, which seems to me more practicable, although it also presents great difficulties. For if we inquire into the deviations shown by the consequences of the general theory of relativity which are accessible to experience, when these are compared with the consequences of the Newtonian theory, we first of all find a deviation which shows itself in close proximity to gravitating mass, and has been confirmed in the case of the planet Mercury. But if the universe is spatially finite there is a second deviation from the Newtonian theory, which, in the language of the Newtonian theory, may be expressed thus:—The gravitational field is in its nature such as if it were produced, not only by the ponderable masses, but also by a mass-density of negative sign, distributed uniformly throughout space. Since this factitious mass-density would have to be enormously small, it could make its presence felt only in gravitating systems of very great extent.

Assuming that we know, let us say, the statistical distribution of the stars in the Milky Way, as well as their masses, then by Newton's law we can calculate the gravitational field and the mean velocities which the stars must have, so that the Milky Way should not collapse under the mutual attraction of its stars, but should maintain its actual extent. Now if the actual velocities of the stars, which can, of course, be measured, were smaller than the calculated velocities, we should have a proof that the actual attractions at great distances are smaller than by Newton's law. From such a deviation it could be proved indirectly that the universe is finite. It would even be possible to estimate its spatial magnitude.

The Philosophical Significance of the Theory of Relativity *

HANS REICHENBACH

I

THE PHILOSOPHICAL SIGNIFICANCE of the theory of relativity has been the subject of contradictory opinions. Whereas many writers have emphasized the philosophical implications of the theory and have even tried to interpret it as a sort of philosophical system, others have denied the existence of such implications and have voiced the opinion that Einstein's theory is merely a physical matter, of interest only to the mathematical physicist. These critics believe that philosophical views are constructed by other means than the methods of the scientist and are independent of the results of physics.

Now it is true that what has been called the philosophy of relativity represents, to a great extent, the fruit of misunderstandings of the theory rather than of its physical content. Philosophers who regard it as an ultimate wisdom that everything is relative are mistaken when they believe that Einstein's theory supplies evidence for such a sweeping generalization; and their error is even deeper when they transfer such a relativity to the field of ethics, when they claim that Einstein's theory implies a relativism of men's duties and rights. The theory of relativity is restricted to the cognitive field. That moral conceptions vary with the social class and the structure of civilization is a fact which is not derivable from Einstein's theory; the parallelism between the relativity of ethics and that of space and time is nothing more than a superficial analogy, which blurs the essential logical differences between the fields of volition and cognition. It appears understandable that those who were trained in the precision of mathematico-physical methods wish to divorce physics from such blossoms of philosophizing.

Yet it would be another mistake to believe that Einstein's theory is not a philosophical theory. This discovery of a physicist has radical consequences for the theory of knowledge. It compels us to revise certain traditional conceptions that have played an important part in the history of philosophy, and it offers solutions for certain questions which are as old as

* Reprinted by kind permission of the author and the publisher from P. A. Schilpp, ed., *Albert Einstein: Philosopher-Scientist*, Essay 10, copyright, 1949, by The Library of Living Philosophers, Inc.

the history of philosophy and which could not be answered earlier. Plato's attempt to solve the problems of geometry by a theory of ideas, Kant's attempt to account for the nature of space and time by a "*reine Anschauung*" and by a transcendental philosophy, these represent answers to the very questions to which Einstein's theory has given a different answer at a later time. If Plato's and Kant's doctrines are philosophical theories, then Einstein's theory of relativity is a philosophical and not a merely physical matter. And the questions referred to are not of a secondary nature but of primary import for philosophy; that much is evident from the central position they occupy in the systems of Plato and Kant. These systems are untenable if Einstein's answer is put in the place of the answers given to the same questions by their authors; their foundations are shaken when space and time are not the revelations of an insight into a world of ideas, or of a vision grown from pure reason, which a philosophical apriorism claimed to have established. The analysis of knowledge has always been the basic issue of philosophy; and if knowledge in so fundamental a domain as that of space and time is subject to revision, the implications of such criticism will involve the whole of philosophy.

To advocate the philosophical significance of Einstein's theory, however, does not mean to make Einstein a philosopher; or, at least, it does not mean that Einstein is a philosopher of primary intent. Einstein's primary objectives were all in the realm of physics. But he saw that certain physical problems could not be solved unless the solutions were preceded by a logical analysis of the fundamentals of space and time, and he saw that this analysis, in turn, presupposed a philosophic readjustment of certain familiar conceptions of knowledge. The physicist who wanted to understand the Michelson experiment had to commit himself to a philosophy for which the meaning of a statement is reducible to its verifiability, that is, he had to adopt the verifiability theory of meaning if he wanted to escape a maze of ambiguous questions and gratuitous complications. It is this positivist, or let me rather say, empiricist commitment which determines the philosophical position of Einstein. It was not necessary for him to elaborate on it to any great extent; he merely had to join a trend of development characterized, within the generation of physicists before him, by such names as Kirchhoff, Hertz, Mach, and to carry through to its ultimate consequences a philosophical evolution documented at earlier stages in such principles as Occam's razor and Leibnitz' identity of indiscernibles.

Einstein has referred to this conception of meaning in various remarks, though he has never felt it necessary to enter into a discussion of its grounds or into an analysis of its philosophical position. The exposition and substantiation of a philosophical theory is nowhere to be found in his writings. In fact, Einstein's philosophy is not so much a philosophical system as a philosophical attitude; apart from occasional remarks, he left it to others to say what philosophy his equations entail and thus remained a philosopher by implication, so to speak. That is both his strength and his weakness; his strength, because it made his physics so conclusive; his weakness, because it left his theory open to misunderstandings and erroneous interpretations.

It seems to be a general law that the making of a new physics precedes a new philosophy of physics. Philosophic analysis is more easily achieved when it is applied to concrete purposes, when it is done within the pursuit of research aimed at an interpretation of observational data. The philosophic results of the procedure are often recognized at a later stage; they are the fruit of reflection about the methods employed in the solution of the concrete problem. But those who make the new physics usually do not have the leisure, or do not regard it as their objective, to expound and elaborate the philosophy implicit in their constructions. Occasionally, in popular presentations, a physicist attempts to explain the logical background of his theories; thus many a physicist has been misled into believing that philosophy of physics is the same as a popularization of physics. Einstein himself does not belong to this group of writers who do not realize that what they achieve is as much a popularization of philosophy as it is one of physics, and that the philosophy of physics is as technical and intricate as is physics itself. Nevertheless, Einstein is not a philosopher in the technical sense either. It appears to be practically impossible that the man who is looking for new physical laws should also concentrate on the analysis of his method; he will perform this second task only when such analysis is indispensable for the finding of physical results. The division of labor between the physicist and the philosopher seems to be an inescapable consequence of the organization of the human mind.

It is not only a limitation of human capacities which calls for a division of labor between the physicist and the philosopher. The discovery of general relations that lend themselves to empirical verification requires a mentality different from that of the philosopher, whose methods are analytic and critical rather than predictive. The physicist who is looking for new discoveries must not be too critical; in the initial stages he is dependent on guessing, and he will find his way only if he is carried along by a certain faith which serves as a directive for his guesses. When I, on a certain occasion, asked Professor Einstein how he found his theory of relativity, he answered that he found it because he was so strongly convinced of the harmony of the universe. No doubt his theory supplies a most successful demonstration of the usefulness of such a conviction. But a creed is not a philosophy; it carries this name only in the popular interpretation of the term. The philosopher of science is not much interested in the thought processes which lead to scientific discoveries; he looks for a logical analysis of the completed theory, including the relationships establishing its validity. That is, he is not interested in the context of discovery, but in the context of justification. But the critical attitude may make a man incapable of discovery; and, as long as he is successful, the creative physicist may very well prefer his creed to the logic of the analytic philosopher.

The philosopher has no objections to a physicist's beliefs, so long as they are not advanced in the form of a philosophy. He knows that a personal faith is justified as an instrument of finding a physical theory, that it is but a primitive form of guessing, which is eventually replaced by the elaborate theory, and that it is ultimately subject to the same empirical tests as the theory. The philosophy of physics, on the other hand, is not a product of creed but of analysis. It incorporates the physicist's beliefs into the psychology of discovery; it endeavors to clarify the meanings of physical theories, independently of the interpretation by their authors, and is concerned with logical relationships alone.

Seen from this viewpoint it appears amazing to what extent the logical analysis of relativity coincides with the original interpretation by its author, as far as it can be constructed from the scanty remarks in Einstein's publications. In contradistinction to some developments in quantum theory, the logical schema of the theory of relativity corresponds surprisingly with the program which controlled its discovery. His philosophic clarity distinguishes Einstein from many a physicist whose work became the source of a philosophy different from the interpretation given by the author. In the following pages I shall attempt to outline the philosophical results of Einstein's theory, hoping to find a friendly comment by the man who was the first to see all these relations, even though he did not always formulate them explicitly. And the gratitude of the philosopher goes to this great physicist whose work includes more implicit philosophy than is contained in many a philosophical system.

II

The logical basis of the theory of relativity is the discovery that many statements, which were regarded as capable of demonstrable truth or falsity, are mere definitions.

This formulation sounds like the statement of an insignificant technical discovery and does not reveal the far-reaching implications which make up the philosophical significance of the theory. Nonetheless it is a complete formulation of the *logical* part of the theory.

Consider, for instance, the problem of geometry. That the unit of measurement is a matter of definition is a familiar fact; everybody knows that it does not make any difference whether we measure distances in feet or meters or light-years. However, that the comparison of distances is also a matter of definition is known only to the expert of relativity. This result can also be formulated as the definitional character of congruence. That a certain distance is congruent to another distance situated at a different place can never be proved to be true; it can only be maintained in the sense of a definition. More precisely speaking, it can be maintained as true only after a definition of congruence is given; it therefore depends on an original comparison of distances which is a matter of definition. A comparison of distances by means of the transport of solid bodies is but one definition of congruence. Another definition would result if we regarded a rod, once it had been transported to another location, as twice as long, thrice transported as three times as long, and so on. A further illustration refers to time: that the simultaneity of events occurring at distant places is a matter of definition was not known before Einstein based his special theory of relativity on this logical discovery.

The definitions employed for the construction of space and time are of a particular kind: they are co-ordinative definitions. That is, they are given by the co-ordination of a physical object, or process, to some fundamental concept. For instance, the concept "equal length" is defined by reference to a physical object, a solid rod, whose transport lays down equal distances. The concept "simultaneous" is defined by the use of light-rays which move over equal distances. The definitions of the theory of relativity are all of this type; they are co-ordinative definitions.

In the expositions of the theory of relativity the use of different definitions is often illustrated by a reference to different observers. This kind of presentation has led to the erroneous conception that the relativity of space-time measurements is connected with the subjectivity of the observer, that the privacy of the world of sense perception is the origin of the relativity maintained by Einstein. Such Protagorean interpretation of Einstein's relativity is utterly mistaken. The definitional character of simultaneity, for instance, has nothing to do with the perspective variations resulting for observers located in different frames of reference. That we co-ordinate different definitions of simultaneity to different observers merely serves as a simplification of the presentation of logical relationships. We could as well interchange the co-ordination and let the observer located in the "moving" system employ the time definition of the observer located in the system "at rest," and vice versa; or we could even let both employ the same time definition, for instance that of the system "at rest." Such variations would lead to different transformations; for instance, the last mentioned definition would lead, not to the Lorentz transformation, but to the classical transformation from a system at rest to a moving system. It is convenient to identify one definitional system with one observer; to speak of different observers is merely a mode of speech expressing the plurality of definitional systems. In a logical exposition of the theory of relativity the observer can be completely eliminated.

Definitions are arbitrary; and it is a consequence of the definitional character of fundamental concepts that with the change of the definitions various descriptional systems arise. But these systems are equivalent to each other, and it is possible to go from each system to another one by a suitable transformation. Thus the definitional character of fundamental concepts leads to a plurality of equivalent descriptions. A familiar illustration is given by the various descriptions of motion resulting when the system regarded as being at rest is varied. Another illustration is presented by the various geometries resulting, for the same physical space, through changes in the definition of congruence. All these descriptions represent different languages saying the same thing; equivalent descriptions, therefore, express the same physical content. The theory of equivalent descriptions is also applicable to other fields of physics; but the domain of space and time has become the model case of this theory.

The word "relativity" should be interpreted as meaning "relative to a certain definitional system." That relativity implies plurality follows because the variation of definitions leads to the plurality of equivalent descriptions. But we see that the plurality implied is not a plurality of different views, or of systems of contradictory content; it is merely a plurality of equivalent languages and thus of forms of expression which do not contradict each other but have the same content. Relativity does not mean an abandonment of truth; it only means that truth can be formulated in various ways.

I should like to make this point quite clear. The two statements "the room is 21 feet long" and "the room is 7 yards long" are equivalent descriptions; they state the same fact. That the simple truth they express can be formulated in these two ways does not eliminate the concept of truth; it merely illustrates the fact that the number characterizing a length is relative to the unit of measurement. All relativities of Einstein's theory are of this type. For instance, the Lorentz transformation connects different descriptions of space-time relations which are equivalent in the same sense as the statements about a length of 21 feet and a length of 7 yards.

Some confusion has arisen from considerations referring to the property of simplicity. One descriptional system can be simpler than another; but that fact does not make it "truer" than the other. The decimal system is simpler than the yard-foot-inch system; but an architect's plan drawn in feet and inches is as true a description of a house as a plan drawn in the decimal system. A simplicity of this kind, for which I have used the name of *descriptive simplicity*, is not a criterion of truth. Only within the frame of inductive considerations can simplicity be a criterion of truth; for instance, the simplest curve between observational data plotted in a diagram is regarded as "truer," i.e., more probable, than other connecting curves. This *inductive simplicity*, however, refers to non-equivalent descriptions and does not play a part in the theory of relativity, in which only equivalent descriptions are compared. The simplicity of descriptions used in Einstein's theory is therefore always a descriptive simplicity. For instance, the fact that non-Euclidean geometry often supplies a simpler description of physical space than does Euclidean geometry does not make the non-Euclidean description "truer."

Another confusion must be ascribed to the theory of conventionalism, which goes back to Poincaré. According to this theory, geometry is a matter of convention, and no empirical meaning can be assigned to a statement about the geometry of physical space. Now it is true that physical space can be described by both a Euclidean and a non-Euclidean geometry; but it is an erroneous interpretation of this relativity of geometry to call a statement about the geometrical structure of physical space meaningless. The choice of a geometry is arbitrary only so long as no definition of congruence is specified. Once this definition is set up, it becomes an empirical question *which* geometry holds for a physical space. For instance, it is an empirical fact that, when we use solid bodies for the definition of congruence, our physical space is practically Euclidean within terrestrial dimensions. If, in a different part of the universe, the same definition of congruence were to lead to a non-Euclidean geometry, that part of universal space would have a geometrical structure different from that of our world. It is true that a Euclidean geometry could also be introduced for that part of the universe; but then the definition of congruence would no longer be given by solid bodies.[1] The combination of a statement about a geometry with a statement of the co-ordinative definition of congruence employed is subject to empirical test and thus expresses a property of the physical world. The conventionalist overlooks the fact that only the incomplete statement of a geometry, in which a reference to the definition of congruence is omitted, is arbitrary; if the statement is made complete by the addition of a reference to the definition of congruence, it becomes empirically verifiable and thus has physical content.

Instead of speaking of conventionalism, therefore, we should speak of the relativity of geometry. Geometry is relative in precisely the same sense as other relative concepts. We might call it a convention to say that Chicago is to the left of New York; but we should not forget that this conventional statement can be made objectively true as soon as the point of reference is included in the statement. It is not a convention but a physical fact that Chicago is to the left of New York, seen, for instance, from Washington, D.C. The relativity of simple concepts, such as left and right, is well known. That the fundamental concepts of space and time are of the same type is the essence of the theory of relativity.

The relativity of geometry is a consequence of the fact that different geometries can be represented on one another by a one-to-one correspondence. For certain geometrical systems, however, the representation will not be continuous throughout, and there will result singularities in individual points or lines. For instance, a sphere cannot be projected on a plane without a singularity in at least one point; in the usual projections, the North Pole of the sphere corresponds to the infinity of the plane. This peculiarity involves certain limitations for the relativity of geometry. Assume that in one geometrical description, say, by a spherical space, we have a normal causality for all physical occurrences; then a transformation to certain other geometries, including the Euclidean geometry, leads to viola-

[1] Poincaré believed that the definition of a solid body could not be given without reference to a geometry. That this conception is mistaken, is shown in the present author's *Philosophie der Raum-Zeit-Lehre* (Berlin, 1928) §5.

tions of the principle of causality, to *causal anomalies.* A light signal going from a point A by way of the North Pole to a point B in a finite time will be so represented within a Euclidean interpretation of this space, that it moves from A in one direction towards infinity and returns from the other side towards B, thus passing through an infinite distance in a finite time. Still more complicated causal anomalies result for other transformations.[2] If the principle of normal causality, i.e., a continuous spreading from cause to effect in a finite time, or *action by contact*, is set up as a necessary prerequisite of the description of nature, certain worlds cannot be interpreted by certain geometries. It may well happen that the geometry thus excluded is the Euclidean one; if Einstein's hypothesis of a closed universe is correct, a Euclidean description of the universe would be excluded for all adherents of a normal causality.

It is this fact which I regard as the strongest refutation of the Kantian conception of space. The relativity of geometry has been used by Neo-Kantians as a back door through which the apriorism of Euclidean geometry was introduced into Einstein's theory: if it is always possible to select a Euclidean geometry for the description of the universe, then the Kantian insists that it be this description which should be used, because Euclidean geometry, for a Kantian, is the only one that can be visualized. We see that this rule may lead to violations of the principle of causality; and since causality, for a Kantian, is as much an *a priori* principle as Euclidean geometry, his rule may compel the Kantian to jump from the frying pan into the fire. There is no defense of Kantianism, if the statement of the geometry of the physical world is worded in a complete form, including all its physical implications; because in this form the statement is empirically verifiable and depends for its truth on the nature of the physical world.[3]

It should be clear from this analysis that the plurality of equivalent descriptions does not rule out the possibility of true empirical statements. The empirical content of statements about space and time is only stated in a more complicated way.

III

Though we now possess, in Einstein's theory, a complete statement of the relativity of space and time, we should not forget that this is the result of a long historical development. I mentioned above Occam's razor and Leibnitz' identity of indiscernibles in connection with the verifiability theory of meaning. It is a matter of fact that Leibnitz applied his prin-

[2] Cf. the author's *Philosophie der Raum-Zeit-Lehre* (Berlin, 1928), §12. It has turned out that within the plurality of descriptions applicable to quantum mechanics the problem of causal anomalies plays an even more important part, since we have there a case where no description exists which avoids causal anomalies. (Cf. also the author's *Philosophic Foundations of Quantum Mechanics*, Berkeley, 1944), §§5–7, §26.

[3] This refutation of Kantianism was presented in the author's *Relativitätstheorie und Erkenntnis A priori* (Berlin, 1920).

ciple successfully to the problem of motion and that he arrived at a relativity of motion on logical grounds. The famous correspondence between Leibnitz and Clarke,—the latter a contemporary defender of Newton's absolutism,—presents us with the same type of discussion which is familiar from the modern discussions of relativity and reads as though Leibnitz had taken his arguments from expositions of Einstein's theory. Leibnitz even went so far as to recognize the relationship between causal order and time order.[4] This conception of relativity was carried on at a later time by Ernst Mach, who contributed to the discussion the important idea that a relativity of rotational motion requires an extension of relativism to the concept of inertial force. Einstein has always acknowledged Mach as a forerunner of his theory.

Another line of development, which likewise found its completion through Einstein's theory, is presented by the history of geometry. The discovery of non-Euclidean geometries by Gauss, Bolyai, and Lobachewski was associated with the idea that physical geometry might be non-Euclidean; and it is known that Gauss tried to test the Euclidean character of terrestrial geometry by triangular measurements from mountain tops. But the man to whom we owe the philosophical clarification of the problem of geometry is Helmholtz. He saw that physical geometry is dependent on the definition of congruence by means of the solid body and thus arrived at a clear statement of the nature of physical geometry, superior in logical insight to Poincaré's conventionalism developed several decades later. It was Helmholtz, too, who clarified the problem of a visual presentation of non-Euclidean geometry by the discovery that visualization is a fruit of experiences with solid bodies and light-rays. We find in Helmholtz' writings the famous statement that imagining something visually means depicting the series of sense perceptions which one would have if one lived in such a world. That Helmholtz did not succeed in dissuading contemporary philosophers from a Kantian apriorism of space and time is not his fault. His philosophical views were known only among a small group of experts. When, with Einstein's theory, the public interest turned toward these problems, philosophers began to give in and to depart from Kant's apriorism. Let us hope that this development will continue and eventually include even those philosophers who in our day still defend an apriorist philosophy against the attacks of the mathematical physicist.

Although there exists a historical evolution of the concepts of space and motion, this line of development finds no analogue in the concept of time. The first to speak of a relativity of the measure of time, i.e., of what is called the uniform flow of time, was Mach. However, Einstein's idea of a relativity of simultaneity has no forerunners. It appears that this discovery could not be made before the perfection of experimental methods of physics. Einstein's relativity of simultaneity is closely associated with the

[4] For an analysis of Leibnitz' views see the author's "Die Bewegungslehre bei Newton, Leibnitz und Huyghens," *Kantstudien* [vol. 29, 1924], 416.

assumption that light is the fastest signal, an idea which could not be conceived before the negative outcome of such experiments as that by Michelson.

It was the combination of the relativity of time and of motion which made Einstein's theory so successful and led to results far beyond the reach of earlier theories. The discovery of the special theory of relativity, which none of Einstein's forerunners had thought of, thus became the key to a general theory of space and time, which included all the ideas of Leibnitz, Gauss, Riemann, Helmholtz, and Mach, and which added to them certain fundamental discoveries which could not have been anticipated at an earlier stage. In particular, I refer to Einstein's conception according to which the geometry of physical space is a function of the distribution of masses, an idea entirely new in the history of geometry.

This short account shows that the evolution of philosophical ideas is guided by the evolution of physical theories. The philosophy of space and time is not the work of the ivory tower philosopher. It was constructed by men who attempted to combine observational data with mathematical analysis. The great synthesis of the various lines of development, which we owe to Einstein, bears witness to the fact that philosophy of science has taken over a function which philosophical systems could not perform.

IV

The question of what is space and time has fascinated the authors of philosophical systems over and again. Plato answered it by inventing a world of "higher" reality, the world of ideas, which includes space and time among its ideal objects and reveals their relations to the mathematician who is able to perform the necessary act of vision. For Spinoza space was an attribute of God. Kant, on the other hand, denied the reality of space and time and regarded these two conceptual systems as forms of visualization, i.e., as constructions of the human mind, by means of which the human observer combines his perceptions so as to collect them into an orderly system.

The answer we can give to the question on the basis of Einstein's theory is very different from the answers of these philosophers. The theory of relativity shows that space and time are neither ideal objects nor forms of order necessary for the human mind. They constitute a relational system expressing certain general features of physical objects and thus are descriptive of the physical world. Let us make this fact quite clear.

It is true that, like all concepts, space and time are inventions of the human mind. But not all inventions of the human mind are fit to describe the physical world. By the latter phrase we mean that the concepts refer to certain physical objects and differentiate them from others. For instance, the concept "centaur" is empty, whereas the concept "bear" refers to certain physical objects and distinguishes them from others. The concept "thing," on the other hand, though not empty, is so general that it does not differentiate between objects. Our examples concern one-place predicates, but the same distinction applies to two-place predicates. The relation "telepathy" is empty, whereas the relation "father" is not. When we say that non-empty one-place predicates like "bear" describe real objects, we must also say that non-empty many-place predicates like "father" describe real relations.

It is in this sense that the theory of relativity maintains the reality of space and time. These conceptual systems describe relations holding between physical objects, namely, solid bodies, light-rays, and watches. In addition, these relations formulate physical laws of great generality, determining some fundamental features of the physical world. Space and time have as much reality as, say, the relation "father" or the Newtonian forces of attraction.

The following consideration may serve as a further explanation why geometry is descriptive of physical reality. As long as only one geometry, the Euclidean geometry, was known, the fact that this geometry could be used for a description of the physical world represented a problem for the philosopher; and Kant's philosophy must be understood as an attempt to explain why a structural system derived from the human mind can account for observational relations. With the discovery of a plurality of geometries the situation changed completely. The human mind was shown to be capable of inventing all kinds of geometrical systems, and the question, which of the systems is suitable for the description of physical reality, was turned into an empirical question, i.e., its answer was ultimately left to empirical data. Concerning the empirical nature of this answer we refer the reader to our considerations in Section II; it is the combined statement of geometry and co-ordinative definitions which is empirical. But, if the statement about the geometry of the physical world is empirical, geometry describes a property of the physical world in the same sense, say, as temperature or weight describe properties of physical objects. When we speak of the reality of physical space we mean this very fact.

As mentioned above, the objects whose general relationship is expressed in the spatio-temporal order are solid bodies, light-rays, and natural watches, i.e., closed periodic systems, like revolving atoms or revolving planets. The important part which light-rays play in the theory of relativity derives from the fact that light is the fastest signal, i.e., represents the fastest form of a causal chain. The concept of causal chain can be shown to be the basic concept in terms of which the structure of space and time is built up. The spatio-temporal order thus must be regarded as the expression of the causal order of the physical world. The close connection between space and time on the one hand and causality on the other hand is perhaps the most prominent feature of Einstein's theory, although this feature has not always been recognized in its significance. Time order, the order of *earlier* and *later*, is reducible to causal order; the cause is always earlier than the effect, a relation which cannot be reversed. That Einstein's theory admits of a reversal of time order for certain events, a result known from the relativity of simultaneity, is merely a consequence of this fundamental fact. Since the speed of causal transmission is limited, there exist events of such a kind that neither of them can be the cause or the effect of the other. For events of this kind a time order is not defined, and either of them can be called earlier or later than the other.

Ultimately even spatial order is reducible to causal order; a space point *B* is called closer to *A* than a space point *C*, if a direct light-signal, i.e., a fastest causal chain, from *A* to *C* passes by *B*. For a construction of geometry in terms of light-rays and mass-points, i.e., a light-geometry, I refer to another publication.[5]

The connection between time order and causal order leads to the question of the direction of time. I should like to add some remarks about this problem which has often been discussed, but which has not always been stated clearly enough. The relation between cause and effect is an asymmetrical relation; if *P* is the cause of *Q*, then *Q* is not the cause of *P*. This fundamental fact is essential for temporal order, because it makes time a serial relation. By a serial relation we understand a relation that orders its elements in a linear arrangement; such a relation is always asymmetrical and transitive, like the relation "smaller than." The time of Einstein's theory has these properties; that is necessary, because otherwise it could not be used for the construction of a serial order.

But what we call the direction of time must be distinguished from the asymmetrical character of the concepts "earlier" and "later." A relation can be asymmetrical and transitive without distinguishing one direction from the opposite one. For instance, the points of a straight line are ordered by a serial relation which we may express by the words "before" and "after." If *A* is before *B*, then *B* is not before *A*, and if *A* is before *B* and *B* is before *C*, then *A* is before *C*. But which direction of the line we should call "before" and which one "after" is not indicated by the nature of the line; this definition can only be set up by an arbitrary choice, for instance, by pointing into one direction and calling it the direction of "before." In other words, the relations "before" and "after" are structurally indistinguishable and therefore interchangeable; whether we say that point *A* is before point *B* or after point *B* is a matter of arbitrary definition. It is different with the relation "smaller than" among real numbers. This relation is also a serial relation and thus asymmetrical and transitive; but in addition, it is structurally different from its converse, the relation "larger than," a fact expressible through the difference of positive and negative numbers. The square of a positive number is a positive number, and the square of a negative number is also a positive number. This peculiarity enables us to define the relation "smaller than:" a number which cannot be the square of another number is smaller than a number which is the square of another number. The series of real numbers possesses therefore a direction: the di-

[5] H. Reichenbach, *Philosophie der Raum-Zeit-Lehre* (Berlin, 1928), §27.

rection "smaller than" is not interchangeable with the direction "larger than;" these relations are therefore not only asymmetrical but also *unidirectional.*

The problem of the time relation is whether it is unidirectional. The relation "earlier than" which we use in everyday life is structurally different from the relation "later than." For instance, we may make up our mind to go to the theatre tomorrow; but it would be nonsensical to make up our mind to go to the theatre yesterday. The physicist formulates this distinction as the *irreversibility of time:* time flows in one direction, and the flow of time cannot be reversed. We see that, in the language of the theory of relations, the question of the irreversibility of time is expressed, not by the question of whether time is an asymmetrical relation, but by the question of whether it is a unidirectional relation.

For the theory of relativity, time is certainly an asymmetrical relation, since otherwise the time relation would not establish a serial order; but it is not unidirectional. In other words, the irreversibility of time does not find an expression in the theory of relativity. We must not conclude that that is the ultimate word which the physicist has to say about time. All we can say is that, as far as the theory of relativity is concerned, we need not make a qualitative distinction between the two directions of time, between the "earlier" and "later." A physical theory may very well abstract from certain properties of the physical world; that does not mean that these properties do not exist. The irreversibility of time has so far been dealt with only in thermodynamics, where it is conceived as being merely of a statistical nature, not applicable to elementary processes. This answer is none too satisfactory; particularly in view of the fact that it has led to certain paradoxes. Quantum physics so far, however, has no better answer. I would like to say that I regard this problem as at present unsolved and do not agree with those who believe that there is no genuine problem of the direction of time.

It is an amazing fact that the mathematico-physical treatment of the concept of time formulated in Einstein's theory has led to a clarification which philosophical analysis could not achieve. For the philosopher such concepts as time order and simultaneity were primitive notions inaccessible to further analysis. But the claim that a concept is exempt from analysis often merely springs from an inability to understand its meaning. With his reduction of the time concept to that of causality and his generalization of time order toward a relativity of simultaneity, Einstein has not only changed our conceptions of time; he has also clarified the meaning of the classical time concept which preceded his discoveries. In other words, we know better today what absolute time means than any one of the adherents of the classical time conceptions. Absolute simultaneity would hold in a world in which there exists no upper limit for the speed of signals, i.e., for causal transmission. A world of this type is as well imaginable as Einstein's world. It is an empirical question to which type our world belongs.

Experiment has decided in favor of Einstein's conception. As in the case of geometry, the human mind is capable of constructing various forms of a temporal schema; the question which of these schemes fits the physical world, i.e., is true, can only be answered by reference to observational data. What the human mind contributes to the problem of time is not one definite time order, but a plurality of possible time orders, and the selection of one time order as the real one is left to empirical observation. Time is the order of causal chains; that is the outstanding result of Einstein's discoveries. The only philosopher who anticipated this result was Leibnitz; though, of course, in his day it was impossible to conceive of a relativity of simultaneity. And Leibnitz was a mathematician as well as a philosopher. It appears that the solution of the problem of time and space is reserved to philosophers who, like Leibnitz, are mathematicians, or to mathematicians who, like Einstein, are philosophers.

V

From the time of Kant, the history of philosophy shows a growing rift between philosophical systems and the philosophy of science. The system of Kant was constructed with the intention of proving that knowledge is the resultant of two components, a mental and an observational one; the mental component was assumed to be given by the laws of pure reason and conceived as a synthetic element different from the merely analytic operations of logic. The concept of a *synthetic a priori* formulates the Kantian position: there is a *synthetic a priori* part of knowledge, i.e., there are non-empty statements which are absolutely necessary. Among these principles of knowledge Kant includes the laws of Euclidean geometry, of absolute time, of causality and of the conservation of mass. His followers in the 19th century took over this conception, adding many variations.

The development of science, on the other hand, has led away from Kantian metaphysics. The principles which Kant regarded as *synthetic a priori* were recognized as being of a questionable truth; principles contradictory to them were developed and employed for the construction of knowledge. These new principles were not advanced with a claim to absolute truth but in the form of attempts to find a description of nature fitting the observational material. Among the plurality of possible systems, the one corresponding to physical reality could be singled out only by observation and experiment. In other words, the synthetic principles of knowledge which Kant had regarded as *a priori* were recognized as *a posteriori*, as verifiable through experience only and as valid in the restricted sense of empirical hypotheses.

It is this process of a dissolution of the *synthetic a priori* into which we must incorporate the theory of relativity, when we desire to judge it from the viewpoint of the history of philosophy. A line which began with the invention of non-Euclidean geometries 20 years after Kant's death runs uninterruptedly right up and into Einstein's theory of space and time. The laws of geometry, for 2000 years regarded as laws of reason, were recognized as empirical laws, which fit the world of our environment to a high degree of precision; but they must be abandoned for astronomic dimensions. The apparent self-evidence of these laws, which made them seem to be inescapable presuppositions of all knowledge, turned out to be the product of habit; through their suitability to all experiences of everyday life these laws had acquired a degree of reliability which erroneously was taken for absolute certainty. Helmholtz was the first to advocate the idea that human beings, living in a non-Euclidean world, would develop an ability of visualization which would make them regard the laws of non-Euclidean geometry as necessary and self-evident, in the same fashion as the laws of Euclidean geometry appear self-evident to us. Transferring this idea to Einstein's conception of time, we would say that human beings, in whose daily experiences the effects of the speed of light would be noticeably different from those of an infinite velocity, would become accustomed to the relativity of simultaneity and regard the rules of the Lorentz-transformation as necessary and self-evident, just as we regard the classical rules of motion and simultaneity self-evident. For instance, if a telephone connection with the planet Mars were established, and we would have to wait a quarter of an hour for the answer to our questions, the relativity of simultaneity would become as trivial a matter as the time difference between the standard times of different time zones is today. What philosophers had regarded as laws of reason turned out to be a conditioning through the physical laws of our environment; we have ground to assume that in a different environment a corresponding conditioning would lead to another adaptation of the mind.

The process of the dissolution of the *synthetic a priori* is one of the significant features of the philosophy of our time. We should not commit the mistake of considering it a breakdown of human abilities, if conceptions which we regarded as absolutely true are shown to be of limited validity and have to be abandoned in certain fields of knowledge. On the contrary, the fact that we are able to overcome these conceptions and to replace them by better ones reveals unexpected abilities of the human mind, a versatility vastly superior to the dogmatism of a pure reason which dictates its laws to the scientist.

Kant believed himself to possess a proof for his assertion that his *synthetic a priori* principles were necessary truths: According to him these principles were necessary conditions of knowledge. He overlooked the fact that such a proof can demonstrate the truth of the principles only if it is taken for granted that knowledge within the frame of these principles will always be possible. What has happened, then, in Einstein's theory is a proof that knowledge within the framework of Kantian principles is not possible. For a Kantian, such a result could only signify a breakdown of science. It is a fortunate fact that the scientist was not a Kantian and, instead of abandoning his attempts of constructing knowledge, looked for ways of changing the so-called *a priori* principles. Through his ability of dealing with space-time relations essentially different from the traditional frame of knowledge, Einstein has shown the way to a philosophy superior to the philosophy of the *synthetic a priori.*

It is the philosophy of empiricism, therefore, into which Einstein's relativity belongs. It is true, Einstein's empiricism is not the one of Bacon and Mill, who believed that all laws of nature can be found by simple inductive generalizations. Einstein's empiricism is that of modern theoretical physics, the empiricism of mathematical construction, which is so devised that it connects observational data by deductive operations and enables us to predict new observational data. Mathematical physics will always remain empiricist as long as it leaves the ultimate criterion of truth to sense perception. The enormous amount of deductive method in such a physics can be accounted for in terms of analytic operations alone. In addition to deductive operations there is, of course, an inductive element included in the physics of mathematical hypotheses; but even the principle of induction, by far the most difficult obstacle to a radical empiricism, can be shown today to be justifiable without a belief in a *synthetic a priori.* The method of modern science can be completely accounted for in terms of an empiricism which recognizes only sense perception and the analytic principles of logic as sources of knowledge. In spite of the enormous mathematical apparatus, Einstein's theory of space and time is the triumph of such a radical empiricism in a field which had always been regarded as a reservation for the discoveries of pure reason.

The process of the dissolution of the *synthetic a priori* is going on. To the abandonment of absolute space and time quantum physics has added that of causality; furthermore, it has abandoned the classical concept of material substance and has shown that the constituents of matter, the atomic particles, do not possess the unambiguous nature of the solid bodies of the macroscopic world. If we understand by metaphysics the belief in principles that are non-analytic, yet derive their validity from reason alone, modern science is anti-metaphysical. It has refused to recognize the authority of the philosopher who claims to know the truth from intuition, from insight into a world of ideas or into the nature of reason or the principles of being, or from whatever super-empirical source. There is no separate entrance to truth for philosophers. The path of the philosopher is indicated by that of the scientist: all the philosopher can do is to analyze the results of science, to construe their meanings and stake out their validity. Theory of knowledge is analysis of science.

I said above that Einstein is a philosopher by implication. That means that making the philosophic implications of Einstein's theory explicit is the task of the philosopher. Let us not forget that it is implications of an enormous reach which are derivable from the theory of relativity, and let us realize that it must be an eminently philosophical physics that lends itself to such implications. It does not happen very often that physical systems of such philosophical significance are presented to us; Einstein's predecessor was Newton. It is the privilege of our generation that we have among us a physicist whose work occupies the same rank as that of the man who determined the philosophy of space and time for two centuries. If physicists present us with implicational philosophies of such excellence, it is a pleasure to be a philosopher. The lasting fame of the philosophy of modern physics will justly go to the man who made the physics rather than to those who have been at work deriving the implications of his work and who are pointing out its position in the history of philosophy. There are many who have contributed to the philosophy of Einstein's theory, but there is only one Einstein.

Philosophical Interpretations and Misinterpretations of the Theory Of Relativity *

PHILIPP FRANK

Introduction

THROUGHOUT THE PERIOD of the unquestioned rule of mechanistic physics, philosophical interpretations played a comparatively modest rôle. Discussions of this kind existed only on the borderlands of science, between physics and biology, between natural science and religion, and so on. Within actual physical discourse so-called philosophical matters were considered only on solemn occasions, such as the seventieth birthday of a famous physicist or the centennial of a scientific society. This state of affairs has changed considerably since the theory of relativity came into being and received increasing recognition. Not only did the theory of relativity give rise to a series of strange speculations within the fields of psychology, metaphysics, politics, ethics, and last but not least, race theory, but philosophical interpretations even found their way into the scientific journals on physics.

It is hardly possible to open a textbook on the theory of relativity — even if written by an otherwise competent physicist — without coming upon sentences of an entirely metaphysical character. Such sentences, wholly meaningless in physics, stand side by side with obviously physical sentences. It is therefore not amazing that great confusion occurred among young physicists and also in wider circles of educated people, and that the opinion arose that the theory of relativity is of an entirely different character from all previous physical theories: that it is constructed less logically and contains many contradictions. One cannot blame the philosophers who sought enlightenment in the writings of physicists for believing that all statements in these papers were the outcome of physical research. But in spite of their sincere desire for scientific enlightenment, they assimilated from those papers on physics a host of purely metaphysical sentences. As previously mentioned, such sentences may be found in the publications

* Reprinted by kind permission of the author from *Interpretations and Misinterpretations of Modern Physics*, Hermann Cie, Paris, 1938.

of very important and competent physicists. In the first two sections of this paper we will deal with philosophical sentences and interpretations of the kind which sometimes appear in the writings of physicists on the subject of the theory of relativity. But there are also physicists who are so much under the influence of traditional philosophy that they actually develop a coherent philosophical interpretation of the theory of relativity. Such systematic philosophical interpretations are then employed to support all sorts of metaphysical systems, now the Hegelian philosophy, now fatalism, and so on. With interpretations of this kind we shall deal in the last section.

1. In the Theory of Relativity the Observing Subject Plays a Greater Part than in Classical Physics

An attempt is often made to characterize the difference between the relativity mechanics of Einstein and the classical mechanics of Newton in the following fashion: While in Newton's mechanics there occur only sentences treating of objective facts, the sentences of Einstein's relativity mechanics also contain statements about the observing subject. Thus, in Newtonian physics, sentences such as the following occur: "This iron rod has a length of three feet." There is no mention of an observer. "Length" is considered an objective property of the rod. In relativity mechanics, the place of such sentences is taken by sentences of this kind: "This rod has a length of three feet for an observer who is at rest with respect to the rigid system S." In this case the sentences of physics mention the observer quite explicitly.

This mode of expression, however, is not very adequate. For it leads to great confusion in the opinions concerning the logical structure of the theory of relativity. It promotes the view that there is an essential difference between the sentences of classical Newtonian physics and those of the theory of relativity as to the manner in which references to physical object and observer occur.

The illusion of such a difference arises because the observer is explicitly mentioned in the sentences of the theory of relativity, but not in those of classical physics. This illusion vanishes at once, however, when one tries to cast the sentences of both theories into a form in which they are verifiable by direct experiments. For then we obtain in each of the two theories a sentence of the following syntactical form: "If, with respect to the iron rod, a certain quite concretely described measuring procedure is carried out, then any arbitrary observer reads its length as three feet on the measuring stick used." The measuring procedure applied in the case of the theory of relativity is, however, a more special one than that applied in classical physics. Roughly speaking, measurement consists in laying a rigid measuring stick along the iron rod to be measured. In classical physics it is irrelevant in this connection whether the iron rod and the measuring stick are in relative rest or motion. The magnitude of the length read off the scale of the measuring stick is entirely independent of this relative velocity. In relativity physics on the other hand, the statement of this velocity is part of the description of the measuring procedure. To different velocities there correspond different measuring procedures and therefore possibly different readings on the scale. But the rôle of the observer is exactly the same as in classical physics. He has nothing to do but to read the scale, or, more precisely, to find out which marks on the scale coincide at a certain moment with the ends of the iron rod to be measured. How the observer moves is entirely irrelevant. Nothing is said of this in the description of the measuring procedure.

The difference between the two theories consists in the fact that in the classical description of how to measure lengths the term "velocity" does not occur at all, while in relativity mechanics the statement of the velocity of the measuring stick relative to the body to be measured constitutes an essential part of the description. The designation of the result of the measurement must therefore also contain a reference to this velocity. In order to indicate this, the magnitude defined by the measuring procedure is designated as the "length of the iron rod in a certain frame of reference S", namely, in the frame of reference in which the measured rod has the velocity v.

These are, so far, only differences in definitions, or, more precisely, in the correlations by means of which the measuring procedures are brought into correspondence with physical quantities that bear certain names. The difference between the physical theories themselves we cannot determine until we know whether the magnitudes of length obtained with various velocities v of the measuring rod are really different, or whether they only bear different names. Only experiment can show which is the case. And the theory of relativity sets up hypotheses from which it follows that, with respect to different frames of reference, or, to put it differently, in the case of different velocities, the lengths of an iron rod turn out to be different on experimental examination; while according to the hypotheses of classical physics, all these quantities turn out to be equal.

Thus relativity physics differs from classical physics in precisely the same way as distinct physical theories differ from one another in general, namely, in making different assertions about the results of experiments carried out under quite concretely described circumstances. In the case in question they assert something different about the results of measurements of lengths that are carried out with differently moved measuring sticks.

In order to formulate different physical theories it is often convenient to avail oneself of different modes of expression. Using a terminology introduced by Wittgenstein and employed very frequently and fruitfully by Carnap, any physical theory may be stated most simply if formulated in a grammar — or, more exactly, a syntax — especially suited to it and to the sentential forms occurring in it. In other words, in every theory there are different rules (formation rules) in accordance with which it is to be decided whether or not a certain combination of words constitutes a meaningful sentence. On the basis of this view it may be said that classical and relativity physics differ in the fact that, with respect to them, different syntactical — and, in particular, formation — rules are valid for sentences containing expressions such as "length of an iron rod" or "duration of the vibration of a pendulum".

But in order not to precipitate logical confusion, it is necessary to differentiate clearly between the physical content of a theory, i. e. the statements it makes about experimentally verifiable facts, and the syntactical form in which the sentences of the theory are formulated. It is quite possible by means of sentences of the same syntactical form to express different physical facts, and vice versa.

According to the syntactical formation rules of classical physics, the sentence "this iron rod has a length of three feet" has a definite sense, but according to the syntax of the theory of relativity that is not the case. The words "this iron rod is three feet long" do not form a significant sentence, but a meaningless combination of words. The word-combination "this iron rod has a length of three feet with respect to the system S", on the other hand, is a significant sentence in the syntax of the theory of relativity, while it is a meaningless combination of words in the syntax of classical physics.

In themselves the formative rules of the two syntaxes are, of course, entirely arbitrary. It is, for instance, quite possible to express the physical content of relativity mechanics in sentences which are formed according to the formation rules of the syntax of classical physics. Thus we may start out from the fact that the contraction of bodies through motion belongs to the physical facts asserted by the theory of relativity. This may be expressed in the linguistic form of classical physics as follows: "an iron rod having a length of three feet in the state of rest, has a length of only two feet if moved sufficiently fast". Here, by "state of rest" we may understand "rest with respect to the ether".

But if one considers the physical content of the theory of relativity to be correct, then there is no correlation by means of which the expression "an iron rod three feet in length" can be brought into correspondence with observable facts. For "velocity of a certain rod with respect to the ether" does not occur in any sentence which asserts a fact verifiable by observation, or — still more logically expressed — in any verifiable sentence. But the expression "length of an iron rod" always occurs in sentences which can only be verified by using at the same time the velocity of the rod with respect to the ether. Therefore all the sentences in which something is stated about the "length of a rod" are completely isolated from those sentences which assert something about facts verifiable by experience. The former constitute a system of sentences which is coherent and isolated from the verifiable sentences. One usually calls these isolated sentences "metaphysical" sentences which state something about a real world. Being nonverifiable sentences they are meaningless as far as science is concerned. If therefore one wants to express the physical content of the theory of relativity with the help of sentences which comply with the syntactical rules of classical physics, it is possible to express all physically true sentences, but one also introduces whole systems of meaningless sentences.

If, on the other hand, one wants to formulate classical electrodynamics, say the theory of the motionless ether according to which bodies are contracted by motion through the ether, then it is perfectly legitimate to retain the syntax of classical physics. For it is possible to determine by experiments the velocity of a rod relative to the ether. Consequently, sentences speaking of the length of an iron rod are verifiable sentences, and hence meaningful.

But the relativity hypothesis creates a state of "splendid isolation" for sentences about the length of a rod, and makes it impossible to reduce them to verifiable sentences. Philosophers often expand these isolated sentences into a large system of sentences all logically connected with one another, but from which there is no bridge leading to the scientifically verifiable sentences. The danger of such large isolated systems of sentences consists in the fact that their existence and logical consistency readily leads to the belief that they are systems of statements about a realm of things. This belief constitutes the foundation of the philosophical misinterpretations of physical theories, and makes it possible to look upon modern physics as a confirmation of the traditional idealistic philosophy.

2. The Theory of Relativity Explains Phenomena, Not by Means of a Physical Hypothesis, but by Introducing a New Conception of Space and Time

The contraction of bodies in their motion through the ether was explained before Einstein in approximately the following way. All bodies are made up of electrically charged particles which attract and repel each other in accordance with Coulomb's law. In the state of rest relative to the ether, every body has a definite length resulting from the fact that the particles, at a certain relative distance, exert electrostatic forces upon one another which just balance. When the body is moved through the ether, then the moved charges have the effect of electrical currents, and in addition to the electrical forces, there arise magnetic forces analogous to those exerted by electrical currents upon one another. The equilibrium is disturbed. The particles which constitute the body have to assume new relative distances such that the electrical forces, augmented by the magnetic ones, just balance each other. Thus the motion brings about a new equilibrium-shape of the body, namely, a shape flattened in the direction of motion; there results what is called the Lorentz contraction, which changes every sphere into an ellipsoid of revolution flattened in the direction of motion. The contraction is thus explained by a physical theory, namely, by the additional magnetic forces arising on account of the motion. From these forces the new equilibrium may be calculated.

Einstein's theory of relativity, many authors tell us, no longer explains the contraction by a physical hypothesis, but uses instead a new conception of space and time. In those textbooks of physics which are thought through more carefully, one no longer finds the assertion that the theory of relativity has replaced a physical hypothesis by something totally different, but one will hardly find a textbook of this kind in which it is not maintained that the theory of relativity has introduced a new conception of space and time, or that it no longer recognizes the old conceptions of space and time. This mode of expression is, however, a very dangerous one. For the words "conception of space and time" always create the impression that through the theory of relativity a novelty is introduced into psychology, since a "conception of space and time" obviously belongs in psychology. These words may, of course, be construed quite differently, and this the physicist always does instinctively, as long as he deals with physics. For the philosopher, however, who reads books on physics, expressions like these always occasion misinterpretations. It is therefore expedient, as we shall see, not to speak at all of a "change in the conception of space and time", but to choose a mode of expression which is not open to misinterpretation even in the boundary domains of physics.

In order to determine how far this juxtaposition of "physical hypothesis" and "change in the conceptions of space and time" is justified, one need only try to express both views in such sentences as are verifiable by experiments, that is, in sentences which are reducible to verifiable sentences.

The explanation of the contraction on the basis of the ether hypothesis starts out from the classical Maxwell-Lorentzian theory of electromagnetic phenomena. When we formulate a suitable hypothesis as to the way in which bodies are built up of electrical charges, then we can deduce from the fundamental equations of the electromagnetic field that every body, when moved through the ether, must alter its shape and thus contract itself. Or, stated more exactly, the contraction is a logical consequence of several simultaneous hypotheses, namely, the validity of the electromagnetic field-equations and laws of force, and the hypothesis that all bodies are built up of electrical charges.

Now, Einstein's theory of relativity rests on two hypotheses of a much more general character. According to the first of these, there is a rigid system S having the property that, relatively to S, light is propagated through the vacuum in all directions with the same velocity, and moreover, independently of the velocity relative to S of the source of light (hypothesis of the constancy of the velocity of light). The second hypothesis states that if a rigid system S′ moves relatively to S in a straight line and uniformly with the velocity v, then all processes can be calculated with respect to S′ from their initial conditions with respect to S′ according to certain laws which do not contain the relative velocity v of S′ with respect to S (hypothesis of relativity). Or, briefly expressed, all processes can be described with reference to S′ by the same set of formulas as with reference to S, if the formulas contain merely the calculation of later states on the basis of the initial ones.

When we try to formulate these two hypotheses in such a way as to render them reducible to verifiable sentences, then it is easily seen that they are hypotheses concerning the behavior of so-called measuring rods and clocks, i. e. of rigid bodies in motion, in relation to the propagation of light. The hypotheses set up by the ether theory for the sake of explaining the contraction are then of the same kind, provided that we express them also by experimentally verifiable sentences. They say something about the behavior of rigid bodies in relation to electromagnetic processes.

The difference consists only in this: The hypotheses of the theory of relativity are *very general* assertions about the behavior of rigid bodies, about uniform revolution and electromagnetic radiation. In this connection, terms like "rigid body", "uniform revolution", and so on, occurring in these assertions, are defined by indication of concrete examples, say, of an iron rod as "rigid body" of a pocket watch as a "uniformly revolving body", and so on.

Classical dynamics, on the other hand (and in particular those sentences which lead to an explanation of the Lorentz contraction), consists of more special assumptions concerning the connection between electrical field strengths and electrical charges, e. g. Maxwell's field equations, and of assumptions concerning the construction of solid bodies out of electrical charges. If the theory of relativity is right, then no special sentence of electrodynamics can be contradictory to the fundamental hypotheses of the theory of relativity. It happens to be one of the greatest advantages of the theory of relativity that from its fundamental assumptions (constancy of velocity of light and principle of relativity) a great deal can be deduced about the behavior of bodies in an electromagnetic field without ever using the Maxwell equations themselves. Similarly, a great deal can be deduced and predicted concerning the behavior of rigid bodies in the case of motion without using any particular assumption about the construction of bodies out of electrical charges. Thus, for example, the contraction of bodies through motion can be predicted without bringing in the alteration of the electrical forces due to the motion.

For anyone who is somewhat familiar with nineteenth-century physics, understanding of the logical structure of the theory of relativity will be facilitated by way of an analogy. Precisely speaking, it is a question of the logical structure of the system consisting of the following sentences: the relativity hypothesis, the electromagnetic field-equations, the description of the atomic structure of bodies, and those verifiable sentences which are deducible from these fundamental assumptions.

The same rôle as is played by the relativity hypothesis today was played in the nineteenth-century theory of heat by the first and second laws of thermodynamics, if we direct our attention towards the logical structure of the theories. From these general hypotheses (which are essentially those of the impossibility of a *perpetuum mobile* of the first and second kind), it was possible to deduce sentences which are experimentally verifiable. These same sentences, however, were also capable of being deduced from a set of special hypotheses consisting of the following assumptions: the theorems of Newtonian mechanics in conjunction with some statistical hypotheses, and the hypotheses concerning the molecular structure of bodies.

Here, again, no contradiction can arise between the consequences of the general thermodynamic hypotheses and the special mechanical theories. This is true because the main theorems of thermodynamics, those asserting the impossibility of a *perpetuum mobile* of the first or second kind, mean in more exact language this: "All special theories concerning the motion and the molecular structure of bodies ought to be qualified in such a way as to fit into the framework prescribed by the two principles of thermodynamics; that is to say, it must not be the case that from a correct molecular theory a sentence can be inferred that contradicts those general principles."

In just the same way Einstein's principle of relativity prescribed a framework into which all special theories concerning the electromagnetic field and the construction of bodies out of electrical charges have to fit. If the Einsteinian theory is correct, then any law about the construction of bodies out of charges that may ever be discovered must not lead to sentences which contradict the hypothesis of relativity. The value of this hypothesis consists in the fact that it permits the formulation of laws about the behavior of bodies without setting up definite hypotheses about the construction of bodies out of electrons and about the laws of the field effects. But, in this connection, we must keep in mind that Einstein's hypotheses, if formulated in a language reducible to verifiable sentences, are also hypotheses concerning the behavior of rigid bodies in relation to the propagation of electromagnetic waves. Now, Einstein's theory of relativity is usually formulated in a language in which the terms "length of an iron rod", "temporal distance of two events", "simultaneity of two events", and such like, are combined in a manner different from that customary in the language of every-day life or (what here amounts to the same thing) in the language of classical mechanics.

If, as often happens, Einstein's theory is said to bring with it new conceptions of space and time, then one ought to consider the following fact. When the velocities of bodies are small as compared to the velocity of light, then the Einsteinian theory coincides with the Newtonian, and everything can be described within the language of classical physics, that is, with the space and time concepts of every-day life; or, more exactly, words like "length of a rod", and so on, are combined according to the rules of ordinary syntax. If, now, one wants to grasp the terms "conception of space", "conception of time", and so on, in their real sense, i. e. as they occur in sentences about verifiable facts, one has to take them in the psychological sense. It should then be said that on the basis of Einstein's theory we are in a position to make statements about our psychological space and time conceptions different from those made on the grounds of classical physics. It would thus follow that the theory of relativity has also brought us progress in psychology.

We ought to be able therefore to indicate psychological experiments which, according to the theory of relativity, should turn out otherwise than would be expected on the basis of classical physics. If we exclude so-called introspection as a method of scientific psychology, because its results can never be expressed in an intersubjective language which is generally and unambiguously comprehensible, then all psychological experiments depend on the observation of the behavior of test-persons, i. e. ultimately on physical observations. It can here only be a question of observing how a person reacts to changes in the spatial and temporal relations of the world. In the case of an experiment that we reckon as psychological, we never have to do with the motions of bodies whose velocity is great enough to approach the velocity of light. All psychological experiments are concerned with what are called "small velocities" in this sense. But in this range there is no difference at all between the laws of classical and of relativity physics. Thus the theory of relativity cannot lead to any new theorems of psychology, or of the field of space and time "conceptions", if this word is taken in its psychological sense.

The whole mode of expression which implies that the theory of relativity has introduced new conceptions of space and time is therefore quite misleading if applied outside the most narrow realm of physics. If it is desired to formulate what happens in the physical theory of relativity in a manner that is really logically correct, this can be done without giving rise to confusions in neighboring domains. As we have already indicated in the first section, we should say: "For the description of motions with large velocities, it is expedient to carry out the construction of sentences out of the terms "length of an iron rod", "simultaneity of two events", and so on, in accordance with syntactical rules other than those used in every-day life and in classical physics." These two sets of syntactical formation rules for sentences are certainly not compatible with one another. But it leads to gross misunderstandings if this state of affairs in the domain of logical syntax is expressed in an apparently psychological language as follows: "the conception of space and time of the theory of relativity is incompatible with that of classical physics". For this would mean that there are psychological experiments which according to Einstein should yield results different from what had been expected earlier. Of course, one might think up such experiments, but there is at present none which even approximately falls within the limits of so-called psychological experiments, i. e. experiments concerning the behavior of human beings.

If, however, we wish to express the difference between the theory of relativity and classical physics not merely as a fact of *logical* syntax (according to which we may only state that we are confronted with two mutually contradictory sets of formation rules), then we may formulate the difference between the two theories as two different hypotheses about the actual world of sense-experiences. That is, we may say: The syntactical rules (formation rules) according to which the words "length of an iron rod", and so on, were combined into sentences before Einstein, have always been employed to describe the processes of motion with which we have to do in every-day life. These rules have proved to be practical in this field, and even in the more general application which Newton gave them in his mechanics. But this syntax turned out to be unsuitable for the representation of experiences involving very rapid motions. As we have shown in the first section, these formation rules permit the importation of many meaningless sentences into physics. For this reason Einstein proposed new formation rules to represent these rapid motions.

The achievements of the theory of relativity which are new as contrasted with the older physics may therefore be divided from the standpoint of the logic of science into two kinds: Firstly, new general hypotheses have been established concerning the behavior of rigid bodies and light waves. Only experimentation can show whether these lead to results which contradict experience. They can only be rejected if such contradictions show up, or if — as compared with the old hypothesis — they do not bring to light any new facts. Secondly, however, as previously mentioned, a new syntax concerning the usage of such terms as "length of an iron rod", "simultaneity of two events" has been proposed by Einstein. This is a proposal and not an assertion. It can therefore never be declared correct or false, but in the course of application it has to be determined whether or not the new proposal is more expedient than the old one. There can be no refutation by referring to spatio-temporal sense-experiences, because nothing is therein asserted about psychological facts.

On the basis of all these considerations we see very clearly the point of importance for the physicist in the doctrines of logical syntax and of the logic of science. They do not help him to find something new in physics itself. One can go even further and say that only rarely will they help him to arrive at clearer formulations in physics itself. For that which appears obscure to the non-physicist is often perfectly comprehensible to the physicist, since he constantly sees — so to speak — how these concepts are being employed, since — to use logical terms — he has always before his eyes the "correlating definitions" of which the non-physicist is not aware at all while reading physical treatises, because they are written "between the lines". On the other hand, logical syntax is an invaluable instrument for the physicist when he wants to establish the connection between his sentences and those of neighboring sciences, e. g. psychology, and with sentences of the general theory of science. And if he does not establish this connection in a scientific manner, then it will inevitably be established by traditional philosophy and metaphysics, thus turning physics from an enlightening science into a source of confusion and sometimes even of infection of the whole intellectual life.

3. The Theory of Relativity Can Be Employed for the Proof of Metaphysical Sentences

As I have already remarked in the foregoing sections, the lack of logical clarity in the formulation of the theory of relativity does not show its dangerous character for clear thinking very distinctly until we consider its consequences outside the special field of physics. And, as everybody knows, we have only too often occasion to observe such consequences. It can be said without exaggeration that there is no philosophical congress, no philosophical textbook, not even an issue of a philosophical journal, where we do not encounter examples of attempts to draw arguments in favor of metaphysical opinions from the statements of the theory of relativity. And in all these cases it can be shown that the source of all such arguments lies in the fact that the "physical" sentences from which they started were themselves formulated not in a scientifically physical manner, but in a metaphysical manner resulting from a distortion of the correct logical mode of expression.

One of the most wide-spread metaphysical interpretations of the theory of relativity, to the consideration of which we will confine ourselves here, is that which undertakes to prove the fatalistic conception of the world, that is to say, the view that everything that happens is determined from all eternity, and that there is no development and nothing really new in the world.

In order to find a formulation of this opinion by a philosopher, we may turn at random to any collection of utterances of philosophers about questions of the day, for instance, to the proceedings of the Eighth International Congress of Philosophy (Prague, 1934). There we find the following passage from a lecture by F. Lipsius (Leipzig): "The question arises whether, thereby, space has lost its independence of time altogether. The theory of relativity and Minkowski's sentence, "Henceforth, space by itself and time by itself are doomed to fade away into mere shadows and only a kind of union of the two will preserve an independent reality" [1] suggest this view. The question remains whether the mathematico-formalistic theory which desires to make time the fourth dimension of space, can be maintained, although this consideration reintroduces into philosophy the doctrine of the unreality of change and declares all development to be illusion."

I do not intend to argue about this quotation. I have cited it only as an example of the views which likewise occur in hundreds of other philosophical writers. What I should like to show here is rather the fact that these metaphysical interpretations of the theory of relativity have their

[1] Translation from *The Principle of Relativity*, by A. Einstein and others, p. 75.

origin in the insufficiently clear formulations which can be found in treatises of physics themselves, and which we discussed in the preceding sections. Thus, analogously to the statements mentioned in Section One in which it is said that an iron rod may have different lengths "for two observers", we find similar modes of expression concerning the simultaneity of events. For instance, it is frequently said that two events E and F happen at the same time for the observer B_1, while for the observer B_2, F occurs later than E. Everybody will have read sentences of this kind in textbooks on physics. As I have shown at the end of the preceding section, no great misfortune will follow from this, for the physicists, among themselves, know very well that although one speaks of two observers B_1 and B_2, one does not employ two observers in the actual application of this mode of expression but two kinds of measurements, and that speaking of two observers is merely a form of expression which is somehow believed to be particularly clear and interesting and attractive to the non-physicist. The irony of the matter lies in the fact that it is just the non-physicist and the philosopher, for whose sake this mode of expression is introduced, that are misled, while for the physicist himself it is comparatively irrelevant whether this or that expression is chosen.

This subjective formulation of the theory of relativity, which speaks of two observers B_1 and B_2, has given rise to consequences which belong to the field of moral philosophy and contain advice on human conduct. From this subjective formulation arose that utilization of the theory of relativity as an argument in favor of fatalism of which I spoke at the beginning of this section. I fear that some readers will accuse me of exaggeration in this connection. I will therefore confess immediately that it was not only the philosophers who misunderstood this subjective mode of expression, but that some of the physicists have done so themselves. Often the philosophers have not misinterpreted the formulations of the physicists, but have simply taken over the formulations together with their misinterpretations ready for use.

As an example I will therefore not quote a philosopher but the well known physicist and astronomer Sir James Jeans who, in his Sir Halley Stewart Lecture of 1935, "Man and the Universe", also refers to the theory of relativity as an argument in favor of fatalism. Jeans starts out from the fact that, according to this theory, two events E and F may happen simultaneously for an observer B_1, and yet one after the other for a different observer B_2. But then obviously the following many occur. For the observer B_1, events E and F both happen in the present, but for the other observer B_2, F happens in the present, while E happened earlier, that is, in the past. Thus one and the same event E, which B_1 only expects to occur, may already have happened and be over for the observer B_2. This, to cite Jeans literally, is formulated as follows: "It is meaningless to speak of the facts which are apt to come . . . and it is futile to speak of trying to alter them, because, although they may be yet to come for us, they may already have come for others." And he at once draws conclusions from this for human behavior. He says in fact: "Such a view reduces living beings to automata." And he describes in poetical style how man has changed from a participant into a mere spectator in the world theatre.

To see quite clearly through this kind of argument, let us illustrate it in terms of a concrete example. Suppose the event F occurs for both observers B_1 and B_2 at the same time, say the present; let it consist in a watch showing the time of ten o'clock on its face. Let the event E be the collision of two motor-cars. For B_1, this happens simultaneously with the event F, that is to say, the watch shows ten o'clock. But for B_2, according to what has been said before, the event E occurs *before* the event F, i. e. the collision *before* ten o'clock, say at one minute to ten. Immediately before ten o'clock (say, just one second before) the impact has not yet occurred as far as B_1 is concerned, while, for B_2 it has already taken place, namely at 9.59. Therefore, so Jeans argues, the observer B_1 cannot prevent the motor-cars from colliding, although, for him, they have as yet not collided. There is no use in making any effort, since for his fellow observer B_2 the accident has already happened at one minute to ten. In this way, the ancient fatalistic belief of the Mussulmans is justified with the help of the newest physics of the 20th century.

But however evident this argument may appear to many, and however often and in however many variations it may be used by philosophers of our time, it is in reality void of any logical justification. It can even be safely said that with a correct logical formulation of the theory of relativity it dissolves into thin air.

A sentence of the form "the collision of these motor-cars will take place at 10 o'clock for the observer B_1, but has already taken place at one minute to 10 for the observer B_2" is certainly a sentence conforming to the customary formation rules of relativistic syntax, and thus significant. But we have yet to examine which statement about empirically verifiable facts is meant by this sentence according to the language of the theory of relativity. If this sentence is formulated in this way, then the two observers, as men of flesh and blood, no longer occur, and the sentence referred to has the meaning: "at the time of the collision of the motor-cars a certain watch shows exactly ten o'clock, while another watch, which moves relatively to the first with a certain velocity v, only shows one minute to ten". Here the three events, collision of the motor-cars, position of the hands on the first watch at ten, and position of the hands on the second watch at one minute to ten, coincide spatially and temporally.

If this mode of expression is chosen, it becomes at once perfectly obvious that in relativity as well as in classical mechanics only one collision of motor-cars takes place, and that two different watches moving with different velocities merely show different times at the moment of impact. These different time data result in the following way from the theory of relativity: in every rigid system of reference, the watches are regulated at any of its points synchronously "with respect to this system". Here, in every system, the position of the hands of one single watch at a certain time point is still arbitrarily choosable. Let us choose the watch at the origin of the coördinates. If, say, S_1 and S_2 are the two systems of reference in respect to which the observers B_1 and B_2 mentioned above and the watches by which we replaced them are at rest, then we will assume of the watches at the origins of S_1 and S_2 that they show the same time while passing one another, in which case S_2 may have the velocity v with respect to S_1. If then x denotes the projection of the distance of a certain watch from the origin of the system S_1 in which it rests, e. g., of the watch showing ten o'clock at the moment of the motor-car accident, then — as shown first by Einstein — at the coincidence of both watches, the position of the hands of the first watch differs from the watch resting in S_2 by $\frac{xv}{c^2}$, on account of the synchronous regulation with respect to two different systems (namely, S_1 and S_2). And that is the one minute which the watch in S_2 (in inexact terms: for the observer B_2) lacks of ten o'clock.

But in this formulation it is quite impossible to express the following assertion: "the observer B_1 cannot prevent the automobile accident, although for him it has not yet happened, because it has already happened for B_2". This sentence can only be made expressible by introducing the observing subject in an incorrect manner into the language of the theory of relativity. The real rôle of the observer is here, just as in classical physics (as we have shown in the first section), only that of reading off a scale the number with which the pointer coincides. But as already mentioned, there is no objection against one and the same observer reading both watches. Then, in the above case, he will simply find that, at the moment of the automobile collision, one of the two watches coinciding with the impact, namely, the one resting in S_1, shows ten o'clock, while the one resting in S_2 shows one minute to ten. But in that case it will be difficult to formulate the assertion that the impact which is only going to happen, has yet, in a different sense, already taken place. There exists no such moment when the watch in S_1 does not yet show ten o'clock (but, say, just one second before ten) while the watch resting in S_2 shows only one minute to ten, because, at the place of the impact, there is no time interval between those two time points where the one watch shows ten o'clock and the other one minute to ten, since both time points coincide at that place.

This argument leading to fatalism is usually formulated in a manner more general and abstract and even more congenial to metaphysical misinterpretation. It contemplates all events which ever happened or ever will happen as being already contained in Minkowski's spatio-temporal world. Every present is merely a three-dimensional cross-section through this four dimensional world. Moreover, this section is arbitrary, inasmuch as it is laid through all time points which are simultaneous with respect to an arbitrary system S of reference. This system of reference may be chosen at liberty. That which we call development is therefore nothing but a wandering through the eternally existing four-dimensional continuum. And this wandering may be carried out in many ways. We may start out from an arbitrary three-dimensional plane section, as we have seen. Then the development of the world merely consists in a parallel translation of this section vertically to itself. But nothing new can arise. Everything has existed forever.

This argument is found in variant forms in innumerable philosophical writings. But even physicists apply it occasionally. Again, I will quote only a few passages from the lecture by Jeans already mentioned: "Then the theory of relativity came and taught that there is no clear cut distinction between space and time; time is so interwoven with space that it is impossible to divide it up into past, present, and future in any absolute manner. This being so, the tapestry cannot consistently be divided into those parts which are already woven and those which are still to be woven. Such a distinction can have no objective reality behind it. . . ." And now we get to the point. Jeans next proceeds to make a hypothesis, an assumption, which is intended to provide a suitable *explanation* of this state of affairs, namely, of the relativity of the subdivision into past and future. He says literally: "The shortest cut to logical consistency was to suppose that the tapestry is already woven throughout its full extent, both in space and time, so that the whole picture exists, although we only become conscious of it bit by bit — like separate flies crawling over a tapestry."

This assumption is already of such a kind as to be untranslatable into a scientific language; it is irreducible to verifiable sentences. Words are here combined according to formation rules contradicting the syntax of every scientific language. The jump into metaphysics has been made. This can easily be shown. For what, in Jeans' sentence, do the words "already woven" mean? In ordinary syntax, the word "already" means in such a context the same as "at an earlier time". But here it is applied to the four-dimensional continuum, and with reference to this continuum a time-point means merely a three-dimensional cross-section. "The four-dimensional continuum subsists at a certain time point" is a meaningless word combination, if considered from the standpoint of customary syntax. And "already woven in space and time" is only another formulation of this meaningless word combination. But this meaningless sentence only serves to pave the way for another meaningless sentence, namely, that "the whole picture exists". Thereby the transition has been made to a kind of metaphysical sentences particularly dear to philosophers, namely, to sentences containing the word "exists" in a manner that precludes any reduction to verifiable sentences.

People talk as if the four-dimensional world continuum might "exist" in the same way as a real empirical body exists. They go so far as to say: "the really existing is not the three-dimensional world of bodies but the four-dimensional space-time world". If a real body, say, the table at which

I am sitting, "does not exist", but a four-dimensional continuum does, then the word "exists" is deprived of its reducibility to verifiable sentences. For the testing of the sentence "P exists" always happens in such a way that I can convince myself of the existence of P in just the same manner as I do of the existence of the table at which I am sitting.

If one wants to attach a sense to the sentence "the four-dimensional space-time continuum exists", then the word "exists" must here be taken in an entirely different sense, namely, in the sense in which it is said of a mathematical formula: "a formula exists by means of which the area of a plane figure is calculable", or "there exists a solution for a certain type of differential equations". This second meaning can be thought of as being reduced to the first, if the formula is imagined as something corporeal, say an accumulation of ink marks on paper. It may then be said that this formula, namely, this accumulation of ink, exists and supplies us with an instrument for solving a problem, just as an axe exists and supplies us with an instrument for splitting wood. Then the "existence of the four-dimensional continuum" is tantamount to the existence of a formula for the calculation of the future state of the world from the present one. And the predetermination of the future, which is supposed to be supported by this view, is the same as was already implied in classical mechanics and symbolized in the Laplacean mind: the future is calculable in advance with the help of mechanics.

If we wish to employ this mode of expression, that everything which is calculable beforehand is really already there and does not yield anything "new", then one ought also to say with respect to classical mechanics that there is no such thing as development. For in relativity mechanics we also know the four-dimensional continuum only by virtue of a calculation from an initial state by means of the equations of motion. "Existence of this continuum" means just this calculability.

The only difference consists in the fact that relativity mechanics permits us to establish an additional connection which classical physics does not mention. There are formulas by which we can calculate the various three-dimensional cross-sections from one another. In the simplest case this is afforded by the Lorentz transformation. But with this nothing is gained as far as predetermination is concerned, for not until we know the whole four-dimensional continuum are we in a position to lay cross-sections through it. Just as in classical mechanics, we derive our knowledge of the four-dimensional world only from an integration of the equations of motion. Relativity theory merely teaches us that these equations must have certain invariant properties. The illusion of the reality of the four-dimensional continuum arises only from the metaphysical employment of the word "exists", which, in turn, as we have shown, has been prepared for by the metaphysical employment of the word "already".

How strong the suggestive power of the metaphysical language is may best be seen from the way in which Jeans, in his already mentioned lecture, subordinates his interpretation of the theory of relativity to a history, especially constructed for this purpose, of the human acquisition of knowledge of nature. After explaining how deeply human self-consciousness has suffered through Copernicus' discovery of the earth being but one body like any other among millions of bodies, and how, through Darwin's theory, man lost his exceptional position among the animals and became an animal like any other, he continues: "It is difficult to imagine human importance being rated lower than this; yet many thought that the physical theory of relativity, which Einstein advanced in 1905, exhibited human life in a still more ignoble light. Hitherto, the scientist and the plain man had been at one in thinking that events came to maturity with the passage of time, somewhat as the pattern of a tapestry is woven out of a loom. . . . The pattern of the yet unwoven part of the picture may be inevitably determined by the way in which the loom is set, or it may not; at any rate, this part of the picture is not yet in existence. And so long as the weaving is not yet an accomplished fact, it is at least conceivable that something may still happen to modify it. The operator who works the loom can still alter the setting of the loom, and so, within limits, modify those parts of the tapestry which are still to come, according to his choice. In the same way, it seemed possible that humanity, and life in general, might be able to exercise some influence, however slight, on events that had not yet emerged from the womb of time."

As opposed to this view, in the opinion of Jeans, through his and many other philosophers' interpretation of the theory of relativity, a fundamental change has taken place. The future is not merely predetermined by the present initial states and the mechanical laws, i. e. by the "setting of the loom"; the whole four-dimensional continuum, and thus the future too, is already there. From this juxtaposition it can be seen quite clearly that here the physicist Jeans has in mind exactly that metaphysical formulation of the theory of relativity which, as we have shown, is in no way reducible to verifiable sentences, and thus has no scientifically formulable content. That Jeans considers this metaphysical interpretation a real explanation can be gathered from the fact that he has retained a certain doubt concerning it. He says: "I do not think that such a view is absolutely forced upon us in any compelling manner by the facts of physics. At one time it seemed plausible because it gave a simple explanation of these facts, but no one would maintain that it is the unique explanation."

Thus the confusion of metaphysics and science comes to such a pass that Jeans treats the metaphysical interpretation as if it were a physical hypothesis, which is capable of being confirmed or disconfirmed by scientific progress. In reality, the metaphysical statements are not verifiable through any observational sentences, and hence they can neither be confirmed by physical or any other research, nor, likewise, can they be refuted. According to Jeans, however, it is a fortunate fact for a mankind discouraged by fatalism, that the progress of physics, or, more precisely of astronomy, has, after all, proved that the hypothesis of the eternal existence of the entire space-time world was mistaken. "If the theory of relativity", Jeans continues, "was to be enlarged so as to cover the facts of astronomy, then the symmetry between space and time which had hitherto prevailed must be discarded. Thus time regained a real objective existence, although only on the astronomical scale, and with reference to astronomical phenomena". By this is meant that the four-dimensional line element representing in cosmic dimensions the gravitational field of the mass distribution in the universe is not symmetrical with respect to the spatial and temporal coördinates, as shown by Einstein and De Sitter. Of this asymmetry Jeans goes on to say: "This gives us every justification for reverting to our old intuitional belief that past, present, and future have real objective meanings, and are not mere hallucinations of our individual minds — in brief we are free to believe that time is real."

We have seen that even in the special theory of relativity, that is, in space free from gravitational forces, the symmetry of the line element which does then obtain in respect of space and time could not be construed in favor of the eternal existence of the future. And therefore the asymmetry involved in the gravitational field is not required in order to refute this fatalistic belief. Jeans, however, not satisfied with this, pursues still further the history of confirmations and refutations of that sentence which in any case is meaningless within science. Although this sentence is not even formulable in any scientific language, Jeans thinks that it has now been completely refuted by quantum mechanics, and that the belief of mankind in a future which may bring us something really new and which has not been existing for ever may be revived.

And thus the metaphysical misinterpretation of the theory of relativity is harmoniously joined by the metaphysical misinterpretation of the quantum theory. Since the quantum theory does not provide any laws by means of which, from observations of the present time, future observations may be uniquely predicted (since only statistical laws are available concerning the subtlest processes), the future cannot be already existing but must be freely disposable. Thus room is gained for free decisions of the will which had been excluded according to the theory of relativity.

We dealt with the metaphysical interpretation of quantum mechanics in Part I. We can only state here that also on the basis of quantum mechanics the existence of the future in the metaphysical sense inferred from the theory of relativity by Jeans and others cannot be refuted, because it is not a verifiable fact, and consequently does not even require a refutation.

A certain contradiction sometimes spoken of between quantum mechanics and the theory of relativity consists in the fact that in the equations of quantum mechanics the spatial coördinates, but not the temporal coördinate, are replaced by matrices, a circumstance which is incompatible with the symmetry demanded by the theory of relativity. Or, to put it in physical terms, the equations and laws of quantum mechanics do not contain the values for the coördinates of a material particle, but merely the probability that the measuring of the coördinate of a particle will give a certain value; time, however, still occurs in the laws. The requirement of symmetry demands the erection of a more general quantum theory in which there occurs also the probability of a measurement leading to a certain value of the time coördinate. But in order to combat fatalism this is unnecessary, since, anyway, it has nothing to do with the theory of relativity. What is in conflict with the statistical character of the fundamental laws of quantum mechanics is merely the deterministic character which the theory of relativity still has in common with classical mechanics. The fatalism which in the opinion of some philosophers is present in addition is, as we have seen, not scientifically formulable at all and can therefore not contradict quantum mechanics, if the latter is formulated in scientific and not in metaphysical terms.

All that can be said is this: The metaphysical formulation of the theory of relativity contradicts the metaphysical formulation of the quantum theory. The sentences "the future already exists" and "the future is yet to arise" or "the future is still free" do formally contradict each other, since A and not-A are contradictory, whether A is a meaningless or a meaningful assertion.

The metaphysician, however, looks upon the history of science as a struggle for or against his particular metaphysical theses. But this struggle has nothing to do with the development of science itself; it is merely a fight as to how human beings can express their private or collective wishes in such terms as also occur in the sentences of contemporary science. In this struggle the words may be combined into sentences according to rules incompatible with those of real scientific syntax. And thus Jeans solemnizes the scientific achievements of the last centuries as follows: "Reviewing the history of the problem as a whole, we have seen that until early in the present century scientific knowledge was continually compelling man to lower his estimate of his importance and of his position in the universe. . . . But to me, at least, it seems that within the last few years the tide has begun to turn. In the light of recent knowledge gained from the theory of relativity [here the author means the general theory of relativity and of gravitation] and quanta we seem entitled to take a more hopeful view of our position than Victorian science had been willing to concede. The plain average man . . . believed, among other things, that he was free to chose between good and evil, between progress and decadence. To many, Victorian science seemed to challenge all such beliefs . . . it knew only of a vast machine, which ran on automatically. . . . We now begin to think that this challenge was a mistaken one, that the universe may be more like the untutored man's commonsense conception of it than had seemed possible a generation ago. . . ."

As in almost any utterance of traditional philosophy, we find here again the idea suggested that the more advanced it is, the more science corresponds to what man had always known without benefit of science. The special theory of relativity was still in contradiction to the self-consciousness of the ordinary man, but the general theory of relativity and of gravitation, and, to an even greater degree, the quantum theory, have finally come to agree again with the view of the man in the street.

I have analyzed all these metaphysical interpretations of Jeans in some detail, not because I hold that they are thought out in a particularly artificial way, but, on the contrary, because they seem to me to represent very well the typical attitude of the philosopher and the philosophically orientated physicist towards modern physics. These views are of great significance for the whole of our intellectual and social life; for, through the agency of the popular presentations of modern physics — of which Jeans himself is so great a master — they create for the large educated public the picture which this public forms of modern science. For although the physical textbooks for specialists and students sometimes succeed to a certain degree in refraining from metaphysical formulations, almost all popularizations of modern physics are full of metaphysical and unscientific sentences; and if one wants to be honest, one has to admit that the popularity which these modern theories like the theories of relativity and quanta enjoy among the general public is due mainly to just these unscientific metaphysical formulations.

But if we want to see to it that these theories really promote the cause of scientific enlightenment and not intellectual confusion, we must risk presenting them to the public in a form in which they may possibly be less appealing. This risk has to be taken as a safeguard against the possibility that popularized presentations of modern physics serve intellectual, and hence social, reaction and supply it with arms.

IV

THE LOGIC OF SCIENTIFIC EXPLANATION AND THEORY CONSTRUCTION

Physical Theory and Experiment *

PIERRE DUHEM

1. *The experimental test of a theory does not have the same logical simplicity in Physics as it has in Physiology.*

The sole aim of physical theory is to provide a representation and classification of experimental laws; the only test permitting us to judge a physical theory and pronounce it good or bad, is the comparison between the consequences of this theory and the experimental laws it has to represent and classify. Now that we have minutely analyzed the characters of a physical experiment and of a physical law, we can establish the principles that should govern the comparison between experiment and theory; we can tell how we shall recognize whether a theory is confirmed or weakened by facts.

When many philosophers talk about experimental sciences, they think only of sciences still close to their origins, e.g., Physiology or certain branches of Chemistry in which the experimenter reasons directly on the facts by a method which is only common sense brought to greater attentiveness but where mathematical theory has not yet introduced its symbolic representations. In such sciences the comparison between the deductions of a theory and the facts of experiment is subject to very simple rules; these rules have been formulated in a particularly forceful manner by Claude Bernard who would condense them into a single principle,[1] as follows:

"The experimenter should suspect and stay away from fixed ideas and always preserve his freedom of mind.

"The first condition that has to be fulfilled by a scientist who is devoted to the investigation of natural phenomena is to preserve a complete freedom of mind based on philosophical doubt."

If a theory suggests experiments to be done, so much the better: "we can follow our judgment and our thought, give free rein to our imagination provided that all our ideas are only pretexts for instituting new experiments that may furnish us probative facts or unexpected and fruitful

* Excerpted from Pierre Duhem, *Aim and Structure of Physical Theory*, translated by Philip P. Wiener, Princeton University Press, 1953, Ch. VI. By kind permission of Professor Wiener and the publisher.

1 Claude Bernard, *Introduction à la Médecine expérimentale*, Paris, 1865, p. 63.

ones." [2] Once the experiment is done and the results clearly established, if a theory takes them over in order to generalize them, coordinate them, and draw from them new subjects for experiment, so much the better still: "if one is imbued with the principles of experimental method, there is nothing to fear; for so long as the idea is a right one, it will go on being developed: when it is an erroneous idea, experiment is there to correct it." [3] But so long as the experiment lasts, the theory should remain waiting, under strict orders to stay outside the door of the laboratory; it should keep silent and leave the scientist without disturbing him while he faces the facts directly; the latter must be observed without a preconceived idea and gathered with the same scrupulous impartiality, whether they confirm or contradict the predictions of the theory; the report that the observer will give us of his experiment should be a faithful and scrupulously exact reproduction of the phenomena, and should not let us even guess what system the scientist places his confidence in or distrusts.[4]

"Men who have an excessive faith in their theories or in their ideas are not only poorly disposed to make discoveries but they also make very poor observations. They necessarily observe with a preconceived idea and, when they have begun an experiment, they want to see in its results only a confirmation of their theory. Thus they distort observation and often neglect very important facts because they do not race to their goal. That is what made us say elsewhere that we must never do experiments in order to confirm our ideas but merely to check them. . . . But it quite naturally happens that those who believe too much in their own theories do not sufficiently believe in the theories of others. Then the dominant idea of these condemners of others is to find fault with the theories of the latter and to seek to contradict them. The setback for science remains the same. They are doing experiments only in order to destroy a theory instead of doing them in order to look for the truth. They also make poor observations because they take into the results of their experiments only what fits their purpose, by neglecting what is unrelated to it, and by very carefully avoiding whatever might go in the direction of the idea they wish to combat. Thus one is led by two parallel paths to the same result, that is to say, to falsifying science and the facts.

"The conclusion of all this is that it is necessary to obliterate one's opinions, as well as that of others, when facing the decisions of the experiment; . . . that we must accept the results of experiment just as they present themselves with all that is unforeseen and accidental in them."

Here, for example, is a physiologist who admits that the anterior roots of the spinal nerve contain the motor nerve-fibers and the posterior roots the sensory fibers; the theory he accepts leads him to imagine an experiment: if he cuts a certain anterior root, he ought to be suppressing the

[2] Claude Bernard, *op. cit.*, p. 64.
[3] *Ibid.*, p. 70.
[4] Claude Bernard, *op. cit.*, p. 67.

mobility of a certain part of the body without destroying its sensibility; after making the section of this root, when he observes the consequences of his operation and when he makes a report of it, he must put aside all his ideas concerning the physiology of the spinal nerve; his report must be a raw description of the facts; he is not permitted to overlook and fail to mention any movement or quiver contrary to his predictions or to attribute it to some secondary cause unless some special experiment has given evidence of this cause; he must, if he does not wish to be accused of bad scientific faith, establish an absolute separation or water-tight compartment between the consequences of his theoretical deductions and the establishing of the facts shown by his experiments.

Such a rule is not by any means easily followed; it requires of the scientist an absolute detachment from his own thought and a complete absence of animosity when confronted with the opinion of another person; neither vanity nor envy ought to be countenanced by him; as Bacon put it, he should never show "eyes lustrous with human passions." Freedom of mind which constitutes the sole principle of experimental method, according to Claude Bernard, does not depend merely on intellectual conditions, but also on moral conditions making its practice rarer and more meritorious.

But if experimental method as just described is difficult to practice the logical analysis of it is very simple. This is no longer the case when the theory to be subjected to test by the facts is not a theory of Physiology but a theory of Physics. In the latter case, in fact, it is impossible to leave outside the laboratory door the theory that we wish to test, for without theory it is impossible to regulate a single instrument or to interpret a single reading; we have seen that in the mind of the physicist there are constantly present two sorts of apparatus; one is the concrete apparatus in glass and metal, manipulated by him, the other is the schematic and abstract apparatus which theory substitutes for the concrete apparatus and on which the physicist does his reasoning; both of these ideas are indissolubly connected in his intelligence, each necessarily calls on the other; the physicist can no sooner conceive the concrete apparatus without associating with it the idea of the schematic apparatus than a Frenchman can conceive an idea without associating it with the French word expressing it. This radical impossibility, preventing one from dissociating physical theories from the experimental procedures appropriate for testing these theories, complicates this test in a singular way, and obliges us to examine the logical meaning of it carefully.

Of course, the physicist is not the only one who appeals to theories at the very time he is experimenting or reporting the results of his experiments; the chemist and the physiologist when they make use of physical instruments, e.g., the thermometer, the manometer, the calorimeter, the galvanometer, saccharimeter, implicitly admit the accuracy of the theories justifying the use of these pieces of apparatus as well as of the theories giving meaning to the abstract ideas of temperature, pressure, quantity of heat, intensity of current, of polarized light, by means of which the concrete indications of these instruments are translated. But the theories used as well as the instruments employed belong to the domain of Physics; by accepting with these instruments the theories without which their readings would be devoid of meaning, the chemist and the physiologist show their confidence in the physicist whom they suppose to be infallible. The physicist on the other hand is obliged to trust his own theoretical ideas or those of his fellow physicists. From the standpoint of logic, the difference is of little importance; for the physiologist and chemist as well as for the physicist, the statement of the result of an experiment implies in general an act of faith in a whole group of theories.

* * *

2. *That an experiment in Physics can never condemn an isolated hypothesis but only a whole theoretical group.*

The physicist who carries out an experiment, or gives a report of one, implicitly recognizes the accuracy of a whole group of theories. Let us accept this principle and see what consequences we may deduce from it when we seek to estimate the rôle and logical import of a physical experiment.

In order to avoid any confusion we shall distinguish two sorts of experiments; experiments of application, which we shall just mention first, and experiments of *testing*, which will be our chief concern.

You are confronted with a problem in Physics to be solved practically; in order to produce a certain effect you need to make use of knowledge acquired by physicists; you wish to light an incandescent bulb; accepted theories indicate to you the means for solving the problem; but to make use of these means you have to secure certain information; you ought, I suppose, determine the electromotive force of the battery of generators at your disposal; you measure this electromotive force; that is what I call an *experiment of application;* this experiment does not aim at recognizing whether accepted theories are accurate or not; it merely intends to draw on these theories; in order to carry it out, you make use of instruments that these same theories legitimize; there is nothing shocking to logic in this procedure.

But experiments of application are not the only ones the physicist has to perform; only with their aid can science help practice, but it is not through them that science creates and develops itself; besides experiments of application, we have *experiments of testing*.

A physicist disputes a certain law; he calls into doubt a certain theoretical point; how will he justify these doubts? How will he demonstrate the inaccuracy of the law? From the proposition under indictment he will derive the prediction of an experimental fact; he will bring into existence the conditions under which this fact should be produced; if the predicted fact is not produced, the proposition which served as the basis of the prediction will be irremediably condemned.

* * *

Such a mode of demonstration seems as convincing and as irrefutable as the proof by reduction to absurdity customary among geometers; moreover, this demonstration is copied from the reduction to absurdity, experimental contradiction playing the same rôle in one as logical contradiction plays in the other.

Indeed, the demonstrative value of the experimental method is far from being so rigorous or absolute; the conditions under which it functions are much more complicated than is supposed in what we have just said; the evaluation of results is much more delicate and subject to caution.

A physicist decides to demonstrate the inaccuracy of a proposition; in order to deduce from this proposition the prediction of a phenomenon and institute the experiment which is to show whether this phenomenon is or is not produced, in order to interpret the results of this experiment and establish that the predicted phenomenon was not produced, he does not confine himself to making use of the proposition in question; he makes use also of a whole group of theories accepted by him as beyond dispute; the prediction of the phenomenon whose nonproduction is to cut off debate, does not derive from the proposition challenged if taken by itself, but from the proposition at issue joined by that whole group of theories; if the predicted phenomenon is not produced, not only is the proposition questioned at fault, but so is the whole theoretical scaffolding used by the physicist; the only thing the experiment teaches us is that among the propositions used to predict the phenomenon and to establish whether it would be produced, there is at least one error; but where this error lies is just what it does not tell us. The physicist may declare that this error is contained exactly in the proposition he wished to refute, but is he sure it is not in another proposition? If he is, he accepts implicitly the accuracy of all the other propositions he has used, and the validity of his conclusion is as great as the validity of his confidence.

* * *

We know that Newton imagined an emission theory for optical phenomena. The emission theory supposes light formed of extremely thin projectiles, thrown out with very great speed by the sun and other sources of light; these projectiles penetrate all transparent bodies; on account of the various parts of the media through which they move, they undergo attractions and repulsions; when the distance separating the acting particles is very small these actions are very powerful, and vanish when the masses between which they act are appreciably far from each other. These essential hypotheses joined to several others, which we pass over without mention, lead to the formulation of a complete theory of reflection and refraction of light; in particular, they imply the following consequence: The index of refraction of light passing from one medium into another is equal to the velocity of the light projectile within the medium it penetrates, divided by the velocity of the same projectile in the medium it leaves behind.

This is the consequence that Arago chose in order to show the theory of emission in contradiction with the facts. From this proposition a second follows: light travels faster in water than in air. Now Arago had indicated an appropriate procedure for comparing the velocity of light in air with the velocity of light in water; the procedure, it is true, was inapplicable, but Foucault modified the experiment in such a way that it could be carried out; he found that the light was propagated less rapidly in water than in air; we may conclude from this, with Foucault, that the system of emission is incompatible with the facts.

I say the *system* of emission and not the *hypothesis* of emission; in fact, what the experiment declares stained with error is the whole group of propositions accepted by Newton, and after him by Laplace and Biot, that is the whole theory from which we deduce the relation between the index of refraction and the velocity of light in various media; but in condemning this system as a whole by declaring it stained with error, the experiment does not tell us where the error lies; is it in the fundamental hypothesis that light consists in projectiles thrown out with great speed by luminous bodies? Is it in some other assumption concerning the actions experienced by light corpuscles due to the media through which they move? We know nothing about that. It would be rash to believe, as Arago seems to have thought, that Foucault's experiment condemns once and for all the very hypothesis of emission, i.e., the assimilation of a ray of light to a swarm of projectiles; if physicists had attached some value to this task, they might have succeeded undoubtedly in founding on this assumption a system of optics that would agree with Foucault's experiment.

In sum, the physicist can never subject an isolated hypothesis to experimental test, but only a whole group of hypotheses; when the experiment is in disagreement with his predictions, what he learns is that at least one of the hypotheses constituting this group is unacceptable and ought to be modified; but the experiment does not designate which one should be changed.

We have gone a long way from the conception of the experimental method held arbitrarily by persons unfamiliar with its actual functioning. People generally think that each one of the hypotheses employed in Physics can be taken in isolation, checked by experiment, then when many varied tests have established its validity, given a definitive place in the system of Physics. In reality, this is not the case. Physics is not a machine which lets itself be taken apart; we cannot try each piece in isolation, and in order to adjust it, wait until its solidity has been carefully checked; physical science is a system that must be taken as a whole; it is an organism in which one part cannot be made to function without the parts that are most remote from it being called into play, some more so than others, but all to some degree. If something goes wrong, if some discomfort is felt in the functioning of the organism, the physicist will have to ferret out through its effect on the entire system which organ needs to be remedied or modified without the possibility of isolating this organ and examining it apart. The watchmaker to whom you give a watch that has stopped separates all the wheelworks and examines them one by one until he finds the part that is defective or broken; the doctor to whom a patient appears cannot dissect him in order to establish his diagnosis; he has to guess the seat and cause of the ailment solely by inspecting disorders affecting the whole body. Now, the physicist concerned with remedying a limping theory resembles the doctor and not the watchmaker.

3. *A "crucial experiment" is impossible in Physics.*

Let us press this point further, for we are touching on one of the essential features of experimental method, as it is employed in Physics.

Reduction to absurdity seems to be merely a means of refutation, but it may become a method of demonstration; in order to demonstrate the truth of a proposition it suffices to corner anyone who would admit the contradictory of the given proposition into admitting an absurd consequence; we know to what extent the Greek geometers drew heavily on this mode of demonstration.

Those who assimilate experimental contradiction to reduction to absurdity imagine that in Physics we may use a line of argument similar to the one Euclid employed so frequently in Geometry. Do you wish to obtain from a group of phenomena a theoretically certain and indisputable explanation? Enumerate all the hypotheses that can be made to account for this group of phenomena; then, by experimental contradiction eliminate them all except one; the latter will no longer be a hypothesis, but will become a certainty.

Suppose, for instance, we are confronted with only two hypotheses; seek experimental conditions such that one of the hypotheses forecasts the production of a phenomenon and the other the production of quite a different effect; bring these conditions into being and observe what happens; depending on whether you observe the first or the second of the predicted phenomena, you will condemn the second or the first hypothesis; the hypothesis not condemned will be henceforth indisputable; debate will be cut off, and a new truth will be acquired by science. Such is the experimental test that the author of the *Novum Organum* has called "*fact of the cross*, borrowing this expression from the crosses which at an intersection indicate the various roads."

We are confronted with two hypotheses concerning the nature of light; for Newton, Laplace, or Biot light consists of projectiles hurled with extreme speed, but for Huygens, Young, or Fresnel light consists of vibrations whose waves are propagated within an ether; these are the only two possible hypotheses envisaged; either the motion is carried by the body it excites and remains attached to it, or else it passes from one body to another.

Let us pursue the first hypothesis; it declares that light travels more quickly in water than in air; but if we follow the second, it declares that light travels more quickly in air than in water. Let us set up Foucault's apparatus; we set into motion the turning mirror; we see before us two luminous spots formed, one colorless, the other greenish. If the greenish band is to the left of the colorless one, it means that light travels faster in water than in air, and that the hypothesis of vibrating waves is false. If, on the contrary, the greenish band is to the right of the colorless one, that means that light travels faster in air than in water, and that the hypothesis of emissions is condemned. We look through the magnifying glass used to examine the two luminous spots, and we notice that the greenish spot is to the right of the colorless one; the debate is over; light is not a body, but a vibratory wave motion propagated by the ether; the emission hypothesis has had its day; the wave hypothesis has been put beyond doubt, and the crucial experiment has made it a new article of the scientific *Credo.*

What we have said in the foregoing paragraph shows how mistaken we should be to attribute to Foucault's experiment so simple a meaning and so decisive an importance; for it is not between two hypotheses, the emission and wave hypotheses, that Foucault's experiment judges trenchantly; it decides rather between two theoretical sets each of which has to be taken as a whole, i.e., between two entire systems, viz., Newton's Optics and Huygens' Optics. But let us admit for a moment that in each of these systems everything is determined or necessitated by strict logic except a single hypothesis; consequently, let us admit that the facts in condemning one of the two systems condemn once for all the single doubtful assumption it contains. Does it follow that we can find in the "crucial experiment" an irrefutable procedure for transforming one of the two hypotheses before us into a demonstrated truth? Between two contradictory theorems of Geometry there is no room for a third judgment, if one is false, the other is necessarily true. Do two hypotheses in Physics ever constitute such a strict dilemma? Shall we ever dare to assert that no other hypothesis is imaginable? Light may be a swarm of projectiles, or it may be a vibratory motion whose waves are propagated in a medium; is it forbidden to be anything else at all? Arago undoubtedly thought so when he formulated this incisive alternative: Does light move more quickly in water than in air? "Light is a body. If the contrary is the case, then light is a wave." But it would be difficult for us to take such a decisive stand; Maxwell, in fact, has shown that we might just as well attribute light to a periodical electrical disturbance that would be propagated within a dielectric medium.

Unlike the reduction to absurdity employed by geometers, experimental contradiction does not have the power to transform a physical hypothesis into an indisputable truth; in order to confer this power on it, it would be necessary to enumerate completely the various hypotheses which may cover a determinate group of phenomena; now the physicist is never sure he has exhausted all the imaginable assumptions; the truth of a physical theory is not decided by heads or tails.

4. *Criticism of the Newtonian method.—First Example: Celestial Mechanics.*

It is illusory to seek to construct by means of experimental contradiction a line of argument in imitation of the reduction to absurdity; but Geometry is acquainted with other methods for attaining certainty than the method of reducing to an absurdity; the direct demonstration in which the truth of a proposition is established by itself and not by the refutation of the contradictory proposition seems to him the most perfect of arguments. Perhaps, physical theory would be more fortunate in its attempts if it sought to imitate direct demonstration. The hypotheses from which it starts and develops its conclusions would then be tested one by one; none would have to be accepted until it presented all the certainty that experimental method can confer on an abstract and general proposition; that is to say, each would necessarily be either a law drawn from observation by the sole use of these two intellectual operations called induction and generalization, or else a corollary mathematically deduced from such laws; a theory based on such hypotheses would not present then anything arbitrary or doubtful; it would deserve all the confidence merited by the faculties which serve us in formulating natural laws.

It was this sort of physical theory that Newton had in mind when, in the General Scholium which crowns his *Principles*, he rejected so vigorously as outside of Natural Philosophy any hypothesis that induction did not extract from experiment; when he asserted that in a sound Physics every proposition should be drawn from phenomena and generalized by induction.

The ideal method we have just described therefore deserves to be named the Newtonian method. Besides, did not Newton follow this method when he established the system of universal attraction, thus adding to his precepts the most magnificent of examples? Is not his theory of gravitation derived entirely from the laws which were revealed to Kepler by observation, laws which problematic reasoning transforms and whose consequences induction generalizes?

This first law of Kepler's: "The radial vector from the sun to a planet sweeps out an area proportional to the time during which the planet's motion is observed" did, in fact, teach Newton that each planet is constantly subjected to a force directed towards the sun.

The second law of Kepler's: "The orbit of each planet is an ellipse having the sun at one focus" taught him that the force attracting a given planet varies with the distance of this planet from the sun, and that it is in an inverse ratio to the square of this distance.

The third law of Kepler's: "The squares of the periods of revolution of the various planets are proportional to the cubes of the major axes of their orbits" showed him that different planets would, if they were brought to the same distance from the sun, undergo in relation to it attractions proportional to their respective masses.

The experimental laws established by Kepler and transformed by geometric reasoning yield all the characters present in the action exerted by the sun on a planet; by induction Newton generalizes the result obtained; he allows this result to express the law according to which any portion of matter acts on any other portion whatsoever, and he formulates this great principle: "Any two bodies whatsoever attract each other mutually with a force which is proportional to the product of their masses and in inverse ratio to the square of the distance between them." The principle of universal gravitation is found, and it has been obtained, without any use having been made of any fictive hypothesis, by the inductive method the plan of which Newton outlined.

Let us again examine this application of the Newtonian method more closely; let us see if a somewhat strict logical analysis will leave intact the appearance of rigor and simplicity that this very summary exposition attributes to it.

In order to assure this discussion of all the clarity it needs, let us begin by recalling the following principle, familiar to all those who deal with Mechanics: We cannot speak of the force which attracts a body in given circumstances before we have designated the supposedly fixed term of reference to which we relate the motion of all bodies; when we change this point of reference or term of comparison, the force representing the effect produced on the observed body by the other bodies surrounding it changes in direction and magnitude according to the rules stated by Mechanics with precision.

That posited, let us follow Newton's reasoning.

Newton first takes the sun as the fixed term of reference; he considers the motions affecting the different planets by reference to this term; he admits Kepler's laws as governing these motions, and derives the following proposition: If the sun is the term of reference in relation to which all forces are compared, each planet is subjected to a force directed towards the sun, proportional to the mass of the planet and to the inverse square of its distance from the sun. Since the latter is taken as the reference-term, it is not subject to any force.

In an analogous manner Newton studies the motion of the satellites and for each of these he chooses as a fixed reference-term the planet which the satellite accompanies, the Earth in the case of the Moon, Jupiter in the case of the masses moving around Jupiter. Laws just like Kepler's are taken as governing these motions, from which it follows that we can formulate the following proposition: If we take as a fixed reference-term the planet accompanied by a satellite, this satellite is subject to a force directed towards the planet inversely with the square of the distance. If, as happens with Jupiter, the same planet possesses several planets, these satellites, were they at the same distance from the planet, would be acted on by the latter with forces proportional to their respective masses. The planet is itself not acted on by the satellite.

Such are the propositions in very precise form which Kepler's laws of planetary motion and the extension of these laws to the motions of satellites authorize us to formulate. For these propositions Newton substituted another which may be stated as follows: Any two celestial bodies whatsoever exert on each other a force of attraction in the direction of the straight line joining them, proportional to the product of their masses and to the inverse square of the distance between them; this statement presupposes all motions and forces related to the same reference-term; the latter is an ideal standard of reference which may well be conceived by the geometer but which does not characterize in an exact and concrete manner the position in the sky of any body.

Is this principle of universal gravitation merely a generalization of the two statements provided by Kepler's laws and their extension to the motion of satellites? Can induction derive from these two statements? Not at all. In fact, not only is it more general than these two statements and heterogeneous to them, but it contradicts them. The student of Mechanics who accepts the principle of universal attraction can calculate the magnitude and direction of the forces between the various planets and the sun when the latter is taken as the reference-term, and he finds that these forces are not what our first statement would require. He can determine the magnitude and direction of each of the forces between Jupiter and its satellites when we refer all the motions to the planet, assumed to be fixed, and he notices that these forces are not what our second statement would require.

The principle of universal gravity, very far from being derivable by generalization and induction from the observational laws of Kepler, formally contradicts these laws. If Newton's theory is correct, Kepler's laws are necessarily false.

Kepler's laws based on the observation of celestial motions do not transfer their immediate experimental certainty to the principle of universal weight, since if, on the contrary, we admit the absolute exactness of Kepler's laws, we should be compelled to reject the proposition on which Newton bases his celestial mechanics. Far from adhering to Kepler's laws, the physicist who claims to justify the theory of universal gravitation finds that he has, first of all, to resolve a difficulty in these laws; he has to prove that his theory, incompatible with the exactness of Kepler's laws, subjects the motions of the planets and satellites to other laws scarcely different enough from the first laws for Tycho Brahe, Kepler, and their contemporaries to have been able to discern the deviations between the Keplerian and Newtonian orbits; this proof derives from the circumstances that the sun's mass is very large in relation to the masses of the various planets and the mass of a planet is very large in relation to the masses of its satellites.

Therefore, if the certainty of Newton's theory does not emanate from the certainty of Kepler's laws, how will this theory prove its validity? It will calculate with all the high degree of approximation that the constantly perfected methods of algebra involve, the *perturbations* which at each instant remove every heavenly body from the orbit assigned to it by Kepler's laws; then it will compare the calculated perturbations with the perturbations observed by means of the most precise instruments and the most scrupulous methods. Such a comparison will not only bear on this or that part of the Newtonian principle, but will involve all its parts at the same time; with that it will also involve all the principles of Dynamics; besides, it will call in the aid of all the propositions of Optics, the Statics of gases, the theory of heat, which are necessary to justify the properties of telescopes in their construction, regulation, and correction, and in the elimination of the errors caused by diurnal or annual aberration and by atmospheric refraction. It is no longer a matter of taking one by one laws justified by observation, and raising each of them by induction and generalization to the rank of a principle; it is a matter of comparing the corollaries of a whole group of hypotheses to a whole group of facts.

Now, if we seek out the causes which have made the Newtonian method fail in this case for which it had been imagined and which seemed to be the most perfect application for it, we shall find them in that double character of any law made use of by theoretical Physics: This law is symbolic and approximate.

Undoubtedly, Kepler's laws bear very directly on the very objects of astronomical observation; they are as little symbolic as possible. But in this purely experimental form they remain inappropriate for suggesting the principle of universal gravitation; in order to acquire this fecundity they must be transformed and must yield the characters of the forces by which the sun attracts the various planets.

Now this new form of Kepler's laws is a symbolic form; only Dynamics gives a meaning to the words *force* and *mass* which serve to state it, and only Dynamics permits us to substitute the new symbolic formulas for the old realistic formulas, to substitute statements relative to forces and masses for laws relative to orbits. The legitimacy of such a substitution implies full confidence in the laws of Dynamics.

And in order to justify this confidence let us not proceed to claim that the laws of Dynamics were beyond doubt at the time Newton made use of them in translating symbolically Kepler's laws; that they had received enough empirical confirmation to warrant the support of reason. In fact, the laws of Dynamics had been subjected up to that time to only very limited and very crude tests; even their enunciations had remained very vague and involved; only in the book of Newton's *Principles* had they been for the first time formulated in a precise manner; it was in the agreement of the facts with the celestial mechanics which Newton's labors gave birth to, that they received their first convincing verification.

Thus the translation of Kepler's laws into symbolic laws, the only kind useful for a theory, presupposed the prior adherence of the physicist to a whole group of hypotheses. But, in addition, Kepler's laws being only approximate laws, Dynamics permitted giving them an infinity of different symbolic translations. Among these various forms, infinite in number, there is one and only one which agrees with Newton's principle. The observations of Tycho Brahe, so felicitously reduced to laws by Kepler, permit the theorist to choose this form, but they do not constrain him to do so, for there are an infinity of others they permit him to choose.

The theorist cannot, therefore, be content to invoke Kepler's laws in order to justify his choice. If he wishes to prove that the principle he has adopted is truly a principle of natural classification for celestial motions, he must show that the observed perturbations are in agreement with those which had been calculated in advance; he has to show how from the course of Uranus he can deduce the existence and position of a new planet, and find Neptune in an assigned direction at the end of his telescope.

* * *

8. *Are certain postulates of physical theory incapable of being refuted by experiment?*

We recognize a correct principle by the facility with which it straightens out the complicated difficulties into which the use of erroneous principles brought us.

If, therefore, the idea we have put forth is correct, namely, that comparison is established necessarily between the *whole* of theory and the *whole* of experimental facts, we ought in the light of this principle see the disappearance of the obscurities in which we would be lost by thinking we subject each isolated theoretical hypothesis to the test of facts.

Foremost among the assertions in which we shall aim at eliminating the appearance of a paradox, we shall place one that has recently been often formulated and discussed. Stated at first by Mr. G. Milhaud [5] in connection with the *pure bodies* of Chemistry, it has been developed at length and forcefully by Mr. H. Poincaré [6] with regard to principles of Mechanics; Mr. Edouard Le Roy has also formulated it with great clarity.[7]

That assertion is as follows:

Certain fundamental hypotheses of physical theory cannot be contradicted by any experiment, because they constitute in reality *definitions*, and because certain expressions in the physicist's usage take their meaning only through them.

Let us take one of the examples cited by Mr. Le Roy:

When a heavy body falls freely, the acceleration of its fall is constant.

[5] G. Milhaud, "La Science rationnelle," *Revue de Métaphysique et de Morale* IV (1896), p. 280.—*Le Rationnel* (Paris, 1898), p. 45.

[6] H. Poincaré, "Sur les Principes de la Mécanique," *Bibliothèque du Congrès International de Philosophie*. III. Logique et Histoire des Sciences, *Revue de Metaphysique et de Morale* X (1902), p. 263.—*La Science et l'Hypothèse*, p. 110.

[7] E. Le Roy, "Un positivisme nouveau," *Revue de Métaphysique et de Morale* IX (1901), pp. 143–144.

Can such a law be contradicted by experiment? No, for it constitutes the very definition of what is meant by *falling freely*. If while studying the fall of a heavy body we found that this body does not fall with uniform acceleration, we should conclude not that the stated law is false, but that the body does not fall freely, that some cause obstructs its motion, and that the deviations of the observed facts from the law as stated would serve to discover this cause and to analyze its effects.

Thus, Mr. Le Roy concludes, "laws are not verifiable, taking things strictly . . . , because they constitute the very criterion by which we judge appearances as well as the methods that it would be necessary to utilize in order to submit them to an inquiry whose precision is capable of exceeding any assignable limit."

Let us study again in greater detail, in the light of the principles previously set down, what this comparison is between the law of falling bodies and experiment.

Our daily observations have made us acquainted with a whole category of motions which we have brought together under the name of motions of heavy bodies; among these motions is the falling of a heavy body when it is not hindered by an obstacle. The result of this is that the words "free fall of a heavy body" have a meaning for the man who appeals only to the knowledge of common sense and who has no notion of physical theories.

On the other hand, in order to classify the laws of motion in question the physicist has created a theory, the theory of weight, an important application of Rational Mechanics; in that theory, intended to furnish a symbolic representation of reality, there is also the question of "free fall of a heavy body," and as a consequence of the hypotheses supporting this whole scheme free fall must necessarily by a uniformly accelerated motion.

The words "free fall of a heavy body" now have two distinct meanings. For the man ignorant of physical theories, they have their *real* meaning, and they mean what common sense means in pronouncing them; for the physicist they have a *symbolic* meaning, and mean "uniformly accelerated motion." Theory would not have realized its aim if the second meaning were not the sign of the first, if a fall regarded as free by common sense were not also regarded as a uniformly accelerated fall, or *nearly* uniformly, since common-sense observations are essentially devoid of precision, as we have already said.

This agreement, without which the theory would have been rejected without further examination, is finally arrived at; a fall declared by common sense to be nearly free is also a fall whose acceleration is nearly constant. But noticing this crudely approximate agreement does not satisfy us; we wish to push on and surpass the degree of precision which common sense can claim. With the aid of the theory that we have imagined, we put together apparatus enabling us to recognize with sensitive accuracy whether the fall of a body is or is not uniformly accelerated; this apparatus shows us that a certain fall regarded by common sense as a free fall has a slightly variable acceleration. The proposition which in our theory gives its symbolic meaning to the word "free fall" does not represent with sufficient accuracy the properties of the real and concrete fall that we have observed.

Two alternatives are then open to us.

In the first place, we can declare that we were right in regarding the fall studied as a free fall and to require that the theoretical definition of these words agree with our observations; in this case since our theoretical definition does not satisfy this requirement, it must be rejected; we must construct another Mechanics on new hypotheses, a Mechanics in which the words "free fall" would no longer signify "uniformly accelerated motion," but "fall whose acceleration varies according to a certain law."

In the second alternative, we may declare that we were wrong in establishing a connection between the concrete fall we have observed and the symbolic free fall defined by our theory, that the latter was too simplified a scheme of the former, that in order to represent suitably the fall as our experiments have reported it the theorist should give up imagining a weight falling freely and think in terms of a weight hindered by certain obstacles like the resistance of the air, that in picturing the action of these obstacles by means of appropriate hypotheses he will compose a more complicated scheme than a free weight but one more apt to reproduce the details of the experiment; in short, in accord with the language we have previously established (ch. IV, sec. 3), we may seek to eliminate by means of suitable *corrections* the *causes of error*, such as air-resistance, which influenced our experiment.

Mr. Le Roy asserts that we will prefer the second to the first alternative, and he is surely right in this. The reasons dictating this choice are easy to perceive. By taking the first alternative we should be obliged to destroy from top to bottom a very vast theoretical system which represents in a most satisfactory manner a very extensive and complex set of experimental laws. The second alternative, on the other hand, does not make us lose anything of the terrain already conquered by physical theory; in addition, it has succeeded in so large a number of cases that we can count on a new success. But in this confidence accorded the law of fall of weights, we see nothing analogous to the certainty that a mathematical definition draws from its very essence, that is, to the kind of certainty we have when it would be foolish to doubt that the various points on a circumference are all equidistant from the center.

We have here nothing more than a particular application of the principle set down in section 2. A disagreement between the concrete facts constituting an experiment and the symbolic representation which theory substitutes for this experiment proves that some part of this symbol is to be rejected. But which part? This the experiment does not tell us, but leaves to our sagacity the burden of guessing. Now among the theoretical elements entering into the composition of this symbol there is always a certain number which the physicists of a certain epoch agree in accepting without test and which they regard as beyond dispute. Whence, the physicist who wishes to modify his symbol will surely bring his modification to bear on elements other than those just mentioned.

But what impels the physicist to act thus is *not* logical necessity; it would be awkward and ill inspired for him to do otherwise, but it would not be doing something logically absurd; he would not, for all that, be walking in the footsteps of the mathematician foolish enough to contradict his own definitions. More than this, perhaps some day by acting differently, by refusing to invoke causes of error and take recourse to corrections in order to reestablish agreement between the theoretical scheme and the fact, and by resolutely carrying out a reform among the propositions declared untouchable by common consent, he will accomplish the work of a genius who opens a new career for a theory.

Indeed, we must guard against believing forever warranted those hypotheses which have become universally adopted conventions, and whose certainty seems to beat down experimental contradiction by throwing the latter back to more doubtful assumptions. The history of Physics shows us that very often the human mind has been led to overthrow such principles completely, though regarded by common consent for centuries as inviolable axioms, and to rebuild its physical theories on new hypotheses.

Was there, for instance, a clearer or more certain principle for thousands of years than this one: In a homogeneous medium, light is propagated in a straight line? Not only did this hypothesis carry all former Optics, Catoptrics, and Dioptrics whose elegant geometric deductions represented at will an enormous number of facts, but it had become, so to speak, the physical definition of a straight line. It is to this hypothesis that any man wishing to make a straight line appeals, the carpenter who verifies the straightness of a piece of wood, the surveyor who lines up his sights, the geodetic surveyor who obtains a direction with the help of the pinholes of his alidade, the astronomer who defines the position of stars by the optical axis of his telescope. However, the day came when physicists tired of attributing to some cause of error the diffraction effects observed by Grimaldi, when they resolved to reject the law of the rectilinear propagation of light and to give Optics entirely new foundations; and this bold resolution was the signal of remarkable progress for physical theory.

* * *

10. *Good sense is judge of hypotheses which ought to be abandoned.*

When certain consequences of a theory are upset by experimental contradiction, we learn that this theory should be modified but we are not told by the experiment what must be changed. It leaves to the physicist the task of finding out the weak spot that impairs the whole system. No absolute principle directs this inquiry which different physicists may conduct in very different ways without having the right to accuse one another of illogicality. For instance, one may be obliged to safeguard certain fundamental hypotheses while he tries to reestablish harmony between the consequences of the theory and the facts by complicating the schematism in which these hypotheses are applied, by invoking various causes of error, and by multiplying corrections. The next physicist, disdainful of these complicated artificial procedures, may decide to change some one of the essential assumptions supporting the entire system. The first physicist does not have the right to condemn in advance the boldness of the second one, nor does the latter have the right to treat the timidity of the first physicist as absurd. The methods they follow are justifiable only by experiment, and if they both succeed in satisfying the requirements of experiment, each is logically permitted to declare himself content with the work that he has accomplished.

That does not mean that we cannot very properly prefer the work of one of the two to that of the other: pure logic is not the only rule for our judgments; certain opinions which do not fall under the hammer of the principle of contradiction are in any case perfectly unreasonable; these motives which do not proceed from logic and yet direct our choices, these "reasons which reason does not know" and which speak to the ample "mind of finesse" but not to the "geometric mind," constitute what is appropriately called *good sense*.

Now, it may be *good sense* that permits us to decide between two physicists. It may be that we do not approve of the haste with which the second one upsets the principles of a vast and harmoniously constructed theory whereas a modification of detail, a slight correction, would have sufficed to put these theories in accord with the facts. On the other hand, it may be that we find it childish and unreasonable for the first physicist to maintain obstinately at any cost, at the price of continual repairs and many tangled up stays, the worm eaten columns of a building tottering in every part, whereas by razing these columns, it would be possible to construct a simple, elegant, and solid system.

But these reasons of good sense do not impose themselves with the same implacable rigor that the prescriptions of logic do; there is something vague and uncertain about them; they do not reveal themselves at the same time with the same degree of clarity to all minds. Whence, the possibility of lengthy quarrels between the adherents of an old system and the partisans of a new doctrine, each camp claiming to have good sense on its side, each party finding the reasons of the adversary inadequate. The history of Physics would furnish us with innumerable illustrations of these quarrels at all times and in all domains. Let us confine ourselves to the tenacity and ingenuity with which Biot by a continual bestowal of corrections and accessory hypotheses maintained the emissionist doctrine in Optics, while Fresnel opposed this doctrine constantly with new experiments favoring the wave theory.

In any event this state of indecision does not last forever. The day arrives when good sense comes out so clearly in favor of one of the two sides that the other side gives up the struggle even though pure logic would not forbid its continuation. After Foucault's experiment had shown that light traveled faster in air than in water, Biot gave up supporting the emission hypothesis; strictly, pure logic would not have compelled him to give it up, for Foucault's experiment was *not* the *crucial experiment* that Arago thought he saw in it, but by resisting wave Optics for a longer time Biot would have been *lacking in good sense.*

Since logic does not determine with strict precision the time when an inadequate hypothesis should give way to a more fruitful assumption, and since recognizing this moment belongs to good sense, physicists may hasten this judgment and increase the rapidity of scientific progress by trying consciously to make good sense within themselves more lucid and more vigilant. Now nothing contributes more to entangle good sense and to disturb its insight than passions and interests. Therefore, nothing will delay the decision which should determine a fortunate reform in a physical theory more than the vanity which makes a physicist too indulgent towards his own system and too severe towards the system of another. We are thus led to the conclusion so clearly expressed by Claude Bernard: The sound experimental criticism of a hypothesis is subordinated to certain moral conditions; in order to estimate correctly the agreement of a physical theory with the facts, it is not enough to be a good mathematician and skillful experimenter; one must also be an impartial and faithful judge.

The Fundaments of Theoretical Physics *

ALBERT EINSTEIN

SCIENCE IS THE ATTEMPT to make the chaotic diversity of our sense-experience correspond to a logically uniform system of thought. In this system single experiences must be correlated with the theoretic structure in such a way that the resulting coordination is unique and convincing.

The sense-experiences are the given subject-matter. But the theory that shall interpret them is man-made. It is the result of an extremely laborious process of adaptation: hypothetical, never completely final, always subject to question and doubt.

The scientific way of forming concepts differs from that which we use in our daily life, not basically, but merely in the more precise definition of concepts and conclusions; more painstaking and systematic choice of experimental material; and greater logical economy. By this last we mean the effort to reduce all concepts and correlations to as few as possible logically independent basic concepts and axioms.

What we call physics comprises that group of natural sciences which base their concepts on measurements; and whose concepts and propositions lend themselves to mathematical formulation. Its realm is accordingly defined as that part of the sum total of our knowledge which is capable of being expressed in mathematical terms. With the progress of science, the realm of physics has so expanded that it seems to be limited only by the limitations of the method itself.

The larger part of physical research is devoted to the development of the various branches of physics, in each of which the object is the theoretical understanding of more or less restricted fields of experience, and in each of which the laws and concepts remain as closely as possible related to experience. It is this department of science, with its ever-growing specialization, which has revolutionized practical life in the last centuries, and given birth to the possibility that man may at last be freed from the burden of physical toil.

On the other hand, from the very beginning there has always been present the attempt to find a unifying theoretical basis for all these single sciences, consisting of a minimum of concepts and fundamental relationships, from which all the concepts and relationships of the single disciplines

* Reprinted by kind permission of the author and the editor from *Science*, 91, 1940.

might be derived by logical process. This is what we mean by the search for a foundation of the whole of physics. The confident belief that this ultimate goal may be reached is the chief source of the passionate devotion which has always animated the researcher. It is in this sense that the following observations are devoted to the foundations of physics.

From what has been said it is clear that the word foundations in this connection does not mean something analogous in all respects to the foundations of a building. Logically considered, of course, the various single laws of physics rest upon this foundation. But whereas a building may be seriously damaged by a heavy storm or spring flood, yet its foundations remain intact, in science the logical foundation is always in greater peril from new experiences or new knowledge than are the branch disciplines with their closer experimental contacts. In the connection of the foundation with all the single parts lies its great significance, but likewise its greatest danger in face of any new factor. When we realize this, we are led to wonder why the so-called revolutionary epochs of the science of physics have not more often and more completely changed its foundation than has actually been the case.

The first attempt to lay a uniform theoretical foundation was the work of Newton. In his system everything is reduced to the following concepts: (1) Mass points with invariable mass; (2) action at a distance between any pair of mass points; (3) law of motion for the mass point. There was not, strictly speaking, any all-embracing foundation, because an explicit law was formulated only for the actions-at-a-distance of gravitation; while for other actions-at-a-distance nothing was established *a priori* except the law of equality of *actio* and *reactio*. Moreover, Newton himself fully realized that time and space were essential elements, as physically effective factors, of his system, if only by implication.

This Newtonian basis proved eminently fruitful and was regarded as final up to the end of the nineteenth century. It not only gave results for the movements of the heavenly bodies, down to the most minute details, but also furnished a theory of the mechanics of discrete and continuous masses, a simple explanation of the principle of the conservation of energy and a complete and brilliant theory of heat. The explanation of the facts of electrodynamics within the Newtonian system was more forced; least convincing of all, from the very beginning, was the theory of light.

It is not surprising that Newton would not listen to a wave theory of light; for such a theory was most unsuited to his theoretical foundation. The assumption that space was filled with a medium consisting of material points that propagated light waves without exhibiting any other mechanical properties must have seemed to him quite artificial. The strongest empirical arguments for the wave nature of light, fixed speeds of propagation, interference, diffraction, polarization, were either unknown or else not known in any well-ordered synthesis. He was justified in sticking to his corpuscular theory of light.

During the nineteenth century the dispute was settled in favor of the wave theory. Yet no serious doubt of the mechanical foundation of physics arose, in the first place because nobody knew where to find a foundation of another sort. Only slowly, under the irresistible pressure of facts, there developed a new foundation of physics, field-physics.

From Newton's time on, the theory of action-at-a-distance was constantly found artificial. Efforts were not lacking to explain gravitation by a kinetic theory, that is, on the basis of collision forces of hypothetical mass particles. But the attempts were superficial and bore no fruit. The strange part played by space (or the inertial system) within the mechanical foundation was also clearly recognized, and criticized with especial clarity by Ernst Mach.

The great change was brought about by Faraday, Maxwell and Hertz —as a matter of fact half-unconsciously and against their will. All three of them, throughout their lives, considered themselves adherents of the mechanical theory. Hertz had found the simplest form of the equations of the electromagnetic field, and declared that any theory leading to these equations was Maxwellian theory. Yet toward the end of his short life he wrote a paper in which he presented as the foundation of physics a mechanical theory freed from the force-concept.

For us, who took in Faraday's ideas so to speak with our mother's milk, it is hard to appreciate their greatness and audacity. Faraday must have grasped with unerring instinct the artificial nature of all attempts to refer electromagnetic phenomena to actions-at-a-distance between electric particles reacting on each other. How was each single iron filing among a lot scattered on a piece of paper to know of the single electric particles running round in a nearby conductor? All these electric particles together seemed to create in the surrounding space a condition which in turn produced a certain order in the filings. These spatial states, to-day called fields, if their geometrical structure and interdependent action were once rightly grasped, would, he was convinced, furnish the clue to the mysterious electromagnetic interactions. He conceived these fields as states of mechanical stress in a space-filling medium, similar to the states of stress in an elastically distended body. For at that time this was the only way one could conceive of states that were apparently continuously distributed in space. The peculiar type of mechanical interpretation of these fields remained in the background—a sort of placation of the scientific conscience in view of the mechanical tradition of Faraday's time. With the help of these new field concepts Faraday succeeded in forming a qualitative concept of the whole complex of electromagnetic effects discovered by him and his predecessors. The precise formulation of the time-space laws of those fields was the work of Maxwell. Imagine his feelings when the differential equations he had formulated proved to him that electromagnetic fields spread in the form of polarized waves and with the speed of light! To few men in the world has such an experience been vouchsafed. At that thrilling moment he surely never guessed that the riddling nature of light, apparently so completely solved, would continue to baffle succeeding generations. Meantime, it took physicists some decades to grasp the full significance of Maxwell's discovery, so bold was the leap that his genius forced upon the conceptions of his fellow-workers. Only after Hertz had demonstrated experimentally the existence of Maxwell's electromagnetic waves, did resistance to the new theory break down.

But if the electromagnetic field could exist as a wave independent of the material source, then the electrostatic interaction could no longer be explained as action-at-a-distance. And what was true for electrical action could not be denied for gravitation. Everywhere Newton's actions-at-a-distance gave way to fields spreading with finite velocity.

Of Newton's foundation there now remained only the material mass points subject to the law of motion. But J. J. Thomson pointed out that an electrically charged body in motion must, according to Maxwell's theory, possess a magnetic field whose energy acted precisely as does an increase of kinetic energy to the body. If, then, a part of kinetic energy consists of field energy, might that not then be true of the whole of the kinetic energy? Perhaps the basic property of matter, its inertia, could be explained within the field theory? The question led to the problem of an interpretation of matter in terms of field theory, the solution of which would furnish an explanation of the atomic structure of matter. It was soon realized that Maxwell's theory could not accomplish such a program. Since then many scientists have zealously sought to complete the field theory by some generalization that should comprise a theory of matter; but so far such efforts have not been crowned with success. In order to construct a theory, it is not enough to have a clear conception of the goal. One must also have a formal point of view which will sufficiently restrict the unlimited variety of possibilities. So far this has not been found; accordingly the field theory has not succeeded in furnishing a foundation for the whole of physics.

For several decades most physicists clung to the conviction that a mechanical substructure would be found for Maxwell's theory. But the unsatisfactory results of their efforts led to gradual acceptance of the new field concepts as irreducible fundamentals—in other words, physicists resigned themselves to giving up the idea of a mechanical foundation.

Thus physicists held to a field-theory program. But it could not be called a foundation, since nobody could tell whether a consistent field theory could ever explain on the one hand gravitation, on the other hand the elementary components of matter. In this state of affairs it was necessary to think of material particles as mass points subject to Newton's laws of motion. This was the procedure of Lorentz in creating his electron theory and the theory of the electromagnetic phenomena of moving bodies.

Such was the point at which fundamental conceptions had arrived at the turn of the century. Immense progress was made in the theoretical penetration and understanding of whole groups of new phenomena; but the establishment of a unified foundation for physics seemed remote indeed. And this state of things has even been aggravated by subsequent developments. The development during the present century is characterized by two theoretical systems essentially independent of each other: the theory of relativity and the quantum theory. The two systems do not directly contradict each other; but they seem little adapted to fusion into one unified theory. We must briefly discuss the basic idea of these two systems.

The theory of relativity arose out of efforts to improve, with reference to logical economy, the foundation of physics as it existed at the turn of the century. The so-called special or restricted relativity theory is based on the fact that Maxwell's equations (and thus the law of propagation of light in empty space) are converted into equations of the same form, when they undergo Lorentz transformation. This formal property of the Maxwell equations is supplemented by our fairly secure empirical knowledge that the laws of physics are the same with respect to all inertial systems. This leads to the result that the Lorentz transformation—applied to space and time coordinates—must govern the transition from one inertial system to any other. The content of the restricted relativity theory can accordingly be summarized in one sentence: all natural laws must be so conditioned that they are covariant with respect to Lorentz transformations. From this it follows that the simultaneity of two distant events is not an invariant concept and that the dimensions of rigid bodies and the speed of clocks depend upon their state of motion. A further consequence was a modification of Newton's law of motion in cases where the speed of a given body was not small compared with the speed of light. There followed also the principle of the equivalence of mass and energy, with the laws of conservation of mass and energy becoming one and the same. Once it was shown that simultaneity was relative and depended on the frame of reference, every possibility of retaining actions-at-a-distance within the foundation of physics disappeared, since that concept presupposed the absolute character of simultaneity (it must be possible to state the location of the two interacting mass points "at the same time").

The general theory of relativity owes its origin to the attempt to explain a fact known since Galileo's and Newton's time but hitherto eluding all theoretical interpretation: the inertia and the weight of a body, in themselves two entirely distinct things, are measured by one and the same constant, the mass. From this correspondence it follows that it is impossible to discover by experiment whether a given system of coordinates is accelerated, or whether its motion is straight and uniform and the observed effects are due to a gravitational field (this is the equivalence principle of the general relativity theory). It shatters the concepts of the inertial system, as soon as gravitation enters in. It may be remarked here that the inertial system is a weak point of the Galilean-Newtonian mechanics. For there is presupposed a mysterious property of physical space, conditioning the kind of coordinate systems for which the law of inertia and the Newtonian law of motion hold good.

These difficulties can be avoided by the following postulate: natural laws are to be formulated in such a way that their form is identical for coordinate systems of any kind of states of motion. To accomplish this is the task of the general theory of relativity. On the other hand, we deduce from the restricted theory the existence of a Riemannian metric within the time-space continuum, which, according to the equivalence principle, describes both the gravitational field and the metric properties of space. Assuming that the field equations of gravitation are of the second differential order, the field law is clearly determined.

Aside from this result, the theory frees field physics from the disability it suffered from, in common with the Newtonian mechanics, of ascribing to space those independent physical properties which heretofore had been concealed by the use of an inertial system. But it can not be claimed that those parts of the general relativity theory which can to-day be regarded as final have furnished physics with a complete and satisfactory foundation. In the first place, the total field appears in it to be composed of two logically unconnected parts, the gravitational and the electromagnetic. And in the second place, this theory, like the earlier field theories, has not up till now supplied an explanation of the atomistic structure of matter. This failure has probably some connection with the fact that so far it has contributed nothing to the understanding of quantum phenomena. To take in these phenomena, physicists have been driven to the adoption of entirely new methods, the basic characteristics of which we shall now discuss.

In the year nineteen hundred, in the course of a purely theoretic investigation, Max Planck made a very remarkable discovery: the law of radiation of bodies as a function of temperature could not be derived solely from the laws of Maxwellian electrodynamics. To arrive at results consistent with the relevant experiments, radiation of a given frequency had to be treated as though it consisted of energy atoms of the individual energy *h.v.*, where *h* is Planck's universal constant. During the years following it was shown that light was everywhere produced and absorbed in such energy quanta. In particular Niels Bohr was able largely to understand the structure of the atom, on the assumption that atoms can have only discrete energy values, and that the discontinuous transitions between them are connected with the emission or absorption of such an energy quantum. This threw some light on the fact that in their gaseous state elements and their compounds radiate and absorb only light of certain sharply defined frequencies. All this was quite inexplicable within the frame of the hitherto existing theories. It was clear that at least in the field of atomistic phenomena the character of everything that happens is determined by discrete states and by apparently discontinuous transitions between them, Planck's constant *h* playing a decisive role.

The next step was taken by De Broglie. He asked himself how the discrete states could be understood by the aid of the current concepts, and hit on a parallel with stationary waves, as for instance in the case of the proper frequencies of organ pipes and strings in acoustics. True, wave actions of the kind here required were unknown; but they could be constructed, and their mathematical laws formulated, employing Planck's constant *h*. De Broglie conceived an electron revolving about the atomic nucleus as being connected with such a hypothetical wave train, and made intelligible to some extent the discrete character of Bohr's "permitted" paths by the stationary character of the corresponding waves.

Now in mechanics the motion of material points is determined by the forces or fields of force acting upon them. Hence it was to be expected that those fields of force would also influence De Broglie's wave fields in an analogous way. Erwin Schroedinger showed how this influence was to be taken into account, re-interpreting by an ingenious method certain formulations of classical mechanics. He even succeeded in expanding the wave mechanical theory to a point where without the introduction of any additional hypotheses, it became applicable to any mechanical system consisting of an arbitrary number of mass points, that is to say possessing an arbitrary number of degrees of freedom. This was possible because a mechanical system consisting of *n* mass points is mathematically equivalent to a considerable degree, to one single mass point moving in a space of 3 *n* dimensions.

On the basis of this theory there was obtained a surprisingly good representation of an immense variety of facts which otherwise appeared entirely incomprehensible. But on one point, curiously enough, there was failure: it proved impossible to associate with these Schroedinger waves definite motions of the mass points—and that, after all, had been the original purpose of the whole construction.

The difficulty appeared insurmountable, until it was overcome by Born in a way as simple as it was unexpected. The De Broglie-Schroedinger wave fields were not to be interpreted as a mathematical description of how an event actually takes place in time and space, though, of course, they have reference to such an event. Rather they are a mathematical description of what we can actually know about the system. They serve only to make statistical statements and predictions of the results of all measurements which we can carry out upon the system.

Let me illustrate these general features of quantum mechanics by means of a simple example: we shall consider a mass point kept inside a restricted region G by forces of finite strength. If the kinetic energy of the mass point is below a certain limit, then the mass point, according to classical mechanics, can never leave the region G. But according to quantum mechanics, the mass point, after a period not immediately predictable, is able to leave the region G, in an unpredictable direction, and escape into surrounding space. This case, according to Gamow, is a simplified model of radioactive disintegration.

The quantum theoretical treatment of this case is as follows: at the time t_0 we have a Schroedinger wave system entirely inside G. But from the time t_0 onwards, the waves leave the interior of G in all directions, in such a way that the amplitude of the outgoing wave is small compared to the initial amplitude of the wave system inside G. The further these outside waves spread, the more the amplitude of the waves inside G diminishes, and correspondingly the intensity of the later waves issuing from G. Only after infinite time has passed is the wave supply inside G exhausted, while the outside wave has spread over an ever-increasing space.

But what has this wave process to do with the first object of our interest, the particle originally enclosed in G? To answer this question, we must imagine some arrangement which will permit us to carry out measurements on the particle. For instance, let us imagine somewhere in the surrounding space a screen so made that the particle sticks to it on coming into contact with it. Then from the intensity of the waves hitting the screen at some point, we draw conclusions as to the probability of the particle hitting the screen there at that time. As soon as the particle has hit any particular point of the screen, the whole wave field loses all its physical meaning; its only purpose was to make probability predictions as to the place and time of the particle hitting the screen (or, for instance, its momentum at the time when it hits the screen).

All other cases are analogous. The aim of the theory is to determine the probability of the results of measurement upon a system at a given time. On the other hand, it makes no attempt to give a mathematical representation of what is actually present or goes on in space and time. On this point the quantum theory of to-day differs fundamentally from all previous theories of physics, mechanistic as well as field theories. Instead of a model description of actual space-time events, it gives the probability distributions for possible measurements as functions of time.

It must be admitted that the new theoretical conception owes its origin not to any flight of fancy but to the compelling force of the facts of experience. All attempts to represent the particle and wave features displayed in the phenomena of light and matter, by direct course to a space-time model, have so far ended in failure. And Heisenberg has convincingly shown, from an empirical point of view, any decision as to a rigorously deterministic structure of nature is definitely ruled out, because of the atomistic structure of our experimental apparatus. Thus it is probably out of the question that any future knowledge can compel physics again to relinquish our present statistical theoretical foundation in favor of a deterministic one which would deal directly with physical reality. Logically the problem seems to offer two possibilities, between which we are in principle given a choice. In the end the choice will be made according to which kind of description yields the formulation of the simplest foundation, logically speaking. At the present, we are quite without any deterministic theory directly describing the events themselves and in consonance with the facts.

For the time being, we have to admit that we do not possess any general theoretical basis for physics, which can be regarded as its logical foundation. The field theory, so far, has failed in the molecular sphere. It is agreed on all hands that the only principle which could serve as the basis of quantum theory would be one that constituted a translation of the field theory into the scheme of quantum statistics. Whether this will actually come about in a satisfactory manner, nobody can venture to say.

Some physicists, among them myself, can not believe that we must abandon, actually and forever, the idea of direct representation of physical reality in space and time; or that we must accept the view that events in nature are analogous to a game of chance. It is open to every man to choose the direction of his striving; and also every man may draw comfort from Lessing's fine saying, that the search for truth is more precious than its possession.

Outline of an Empiricist Philosophy of Physics *

GUSTAV BERGMANN

I. Logic, Epistemology and the Philosophy of Science

This is not a technical paper in philosophy. It merely tries to provide, from the standpoint of *scientific empiricism*, or *logical positivism*, a survey of that interrelated cluster of clarifications which is now usually referred to as the philosophy of physical science.[1] Thus it is comparable in character to an earlier paper in this journal which undertook a similarly informal exposition of the problems that arise in connection with the concept of probability.[2] Since this latter article has been mentioned by Kemble and Margenau, it might not be inappropriate to add that I shall, at least in part, go over the ground covered in these and Margenau's earlier publications.[3] I shall, however, omit specific references since my intention is not polemical and little claim is laid to originality except, possibly, that modicum which is implied in any attempt to fit earlier and often specialized contributions to the latest stage of a philosophy which shows as vigorous a development as contemporary empiricism.

It is paradoxical indeed that a philosopher who presents to a scientific public his views on such a topic as probability, finds the philosophical scientist willing to furnish the epistemological or, if you please, metaphysical foundations upon which any such analysis ultimately rests, but which the philosopher himself thought wise to pass in silence. Some light should be shed, by way of introduction, upon this truly perplexing intellectual situation. But even here, I think, the easiest approach leads through the consideration of an instance that lies relatively near to the everyday interests of the physicist, rather than through a systematic discussion of the task of

* Reprinted by kind permission of the author and the editor from *American Journal of Physics*, 11, 1943.

[1] Concerning application to psychology and the behavior sciences in general see G. Bergmann and K. W. Spence, *Psychol. Rev.* 48, 1 (1941) and the following two articles which will appear in *Psychol. Rev.* 51 (1944): K. W. Spence, "The nature of theory construction in contemporary psychology"; G. Bergmann and K. W. Spence, "The logic of psychophysical measurement."

[2] *Am. J. Phys.* 9, 263 (1941).

[3] E. Kemble, *Am. J. Phys.* 10, 6 (1942); H. Margenau, *Am. J. Phys.* 10, 224 (1942); *Rev. Mod. Phys.* 13, 176 (1941); *Phil. Sci.* 2, 48 (1935); *Phil. Sci.* 2, 164 (1935).

epistemology and its relation to science. As such an example I shall choose the problem of time and space; it will be well, though, to bear in mind that what immediately follows is not a popular exposition of the topic with which it deals. Generally speaking, this whole first section is more condensed and more "philosophical," in the sense which, to put it mildly, does not particularly interest scientists, than any of the following ones. But it seems that at least a brief statement of this sort is called for.

Many of us still remember the imprint, comparable to that of a heel on an ant hill, which the relativistic analysis left upon the philosophy of time and space. All that could survive, so it seemed at the moment, was a careful operational analysis, on the one hand, and an axiomatization, on the other, of the clock and yardstick basis. This was, roughly speaking, also the thesis of modern empiricism in its physicalistic phase. Much indeed has been stamped out by that heel never to return again into the forefront of the intellectual process, including the very stronghold of the Kantian form of intuitionism (rationalism); philosophers who, without changing their basic frame of reference, insisted upon a dialectical distinction between philosophical time and space on the one hand, and physical or metric space-time on the other, did a poor service to their cause. But there is a kernel of truth in all their defensive arguments; there are some things that go beyond the clock-yardstick analysis. This latter type of analysis in its more sophisticated form, which includes the distinction between pure and applied geometry, is representative of the philosophy of science; what goes beyond it is epistemology proper. That there is an epistemology in this technical sense is fully realized by empiricism in its present, redintegrative phase; but it is also realized that this core cannot be made explicit by regression to any of the traditional philosophical positions. I shall turn presently to the difficulties which this situation implies. Let me first try to make my point more concrete by at least a fleeting glimpse at the philosophy, in this stricter sense, of time and space.

Clocks and yardsticks are material objects, *things* in the common-sense meaning of the term, and it is indeed of the highest significance that the whole structure of science, including its space and time frame, rests, in a manner still to be discussed, upon some very few immediately observable properties of and relations among material things. Local simultaneity—spatio-temporal coincidence—is, as we all know, one of these basic or undefined relations. But are not, so the traditionalist would argue, simultaneity or coincidence themselves spatio-temporal concepts, so that in a final manner nothing has really been said about the "nature" of time and space? Do we not, by calling them undefined, dogmatically preclude inquiry into the manner in which they are given and what their givenness presupposes and implies? One answer to this objection is simple enough; it insists that the 'given' or 'immediately observed' is investigated by the experimental science of psychology, not through the introspections and rationalizations of the man in the armchair. This answer is most pertinent as well as very necessary, since one of the most important steps which must be taken in the construction of an empiricist theory of knowledge consists in the disentanglement of its historical connection with psychology. Yet such an answer is not final in a philosophical sense, for either it leads to circularity or else psychology —which, as a science, must itself start from the given or immediately observable—is in turn left without a foundation. The pragmatist's phrase about inquiry as an ongoing concern, offers a fortunate label rather than an analysis of this bedeviling situation. At this point, I trust, physicists feel strongly that the evasion of such predicaments may be left to the epistemologist, since they cannot possibly be relevant to those still very general, though in a sense less fundamental, clarifications which we call the methodology, or philosophy, of science. This is exactly the point I am trying to make, so I shall leave the issue there and turn from these negative remarks to the positive case for a philosophy of time and space.

No matter how we *technically* escape mistaking armchair psychology for epistemology, there must be a level—we now call it that of verification or the verification basis [4]—on which we cannot learn verbally but only, as the classical phrase has it, by experience. This is the sense in which a person who was born blind cannot understand the meaning of "this is green" or "that is bright." The point is that not only qualities of, but also some relations among particulars, such as "this is earlier than that" or "this is between that and that," are basic or undefined in the same sense. Therefore, no matter in how sophisticated or Pickwickian a fashion one conceives of the reality of the external world, time and space or, rather, the spatio-temporal relations, are as real as the things or events among which they obtain. Let us, with this in mind, remember the emphasis with which it was said, in the empiricist camp, that time and space are merely a system of coordinates, entirely arbitrary and external to what they describe. As a reaction against Newton's conceptions such emphasis is sound enough, but when it becomes exclusive it contains at least the danger of what philosophers would call an extreme nominalism. For only the rules by which numbers are assigned to the events during the metrical elaboration of the clock-yardstick basis are arbitrary and external to the events. Thus the following is plausible: irrespective of whether "perceptual data" or the more complex level of common-sense material things is chosen as the verification basis, and irrespective of the fact that logical analysis is able to penetrate, in a manner I can here not specify, to a level which is even more elementary than any imaginable verification basis, it seems that any account of the world in which we live must, on its ground floor, contain an undefined relational nucleus of both time and space.

[4] Within the trichotomy, syntax, semantics, and pragmatics, which are so characteristic of the positivistic epistemology, verification falls into the domain of pragmatics, that is, it can be dealt with either axiomatically (pure pragmatics) or scientifically (applied pragmatics), but not "metaphysically." The distinction between semantical truth and verification also takes care of one of the roots of the realism issue. See also Carnap's *Introduction to semantics* (Harvard Univ. Press, 1942).

I am well aware how strange all this must sound to the physicist, and would even if it were not as condensed as it necessarily is.[5] I certainly have not proved my point, and it is even a very difficult problem to decide what could possibly be meant by proof on this level of analysis. But my purpose was, after all, merely to present a sample of epistemological subject matter and, if possible, an idea of the special technics, hardly comparable to traditional philosophies or any of their well-meant "scientific" dilutions, with which empiricists try to approach it. Concerning these technics, or at least concerning the most potent and, in many ways, most bewildering and forbidding of them, another brief statement is in order. I refer, of course, to the so-called formalistic or linguistic turn which the empiricist epistemology has recently taken.

Some people, it seems, honestly believe that all that logical positivists are interested in is formal logic, words and languages. I, for one, am willing to concede that some statements which were either incautious or simply makeshifts during a rapid development, are at least partly responsible for so patent a misunderstanding. Furthermore, it is true that the purely formal study of symbolic structures occupies an ever more important part in the technical writings of the empiricists.[6] Historically speaking this trend originated in fields that are very relevant to the physical sciences, namely, in the foundations of mathematics and in geometrical axiomatics. One of the results of this study which is better known in our semantics-conscious age is the realization of how imperfect and inconsistent as tools are colloquial English and, in many instances, even the terminology of science. But this is still not the whole story. For it is rather obvious that *one speaks about facts and not just about language if one points out features that would be common to every strict and consistent calculus capable of describing our experiences.* Why then, so runs the next objection, go about one's main business, the description of those facts, in such a devious and complicated manner that it is almost bound to create misunderstanding? The direction at least of the answer to this objection can easily be indicated. It is this very formalistic technic that enables the modern empiricist to avoid the snares of the traditional metaphysical issues such as the realism problem and the psychological predicament which have been mentioned. If epistemological analysis has thus become a highly specialized enterprise, then it is rather fortunate that one of its main results can be stated in the following manner. Even for an exhaustive treatment of the topics of the philosophy of science, such as operationism, the nature of scientific explanation, of laws and theories including the status of atomic conceptions, relativity and quantum axiomatics, causality, probability, statistics, and so forth, it is not necessary

[5] It would be particularly desirable to clarify the expression 'undefined.' In axiomatics, terms which occupy a somewhat similar position are often referred to as 'implicitly defined.' However, any further discussion would require too much of an epistemological and logical apparatus. See also G. Bergmann, *Phil. Sci.* 9, 283 (1942).

[6] The classic in this field is the *Principia mathematica*, by Russell and Whitehead (3 vols., 1910, 1912, 1913).

to delve into epistemology proper or, what amounts to the same thing, to penetrate beneath the verification basis of common sense. To put it differently, in an empiricist philosophy of science there is neither need nor room for a discussion of perception [7] or the nature of the given or the reality of the external world. Still differently, statements such as "this is a material thing (physical object, external body)" or "this is a real lake, not a mirage" refer to states of affairs in terms of which all scientific statements can be analyzed, while the meaning and the modes of verification of these statements themselves do not stand in need of any further clarification for the purposes of the philosophy of science. But even one who accepts this thesis for the sake of discussion might still ask for a "definition" of this level of verification. As an intuitive characterization of it, Carnap's expressions, 'thing level' and, correspondingly, 'thing language,' seem to me rather well chosen, but a definition in any stricter sense cannot, of course, be given. All one could do is to draw up lists of basic words—names of "immediately observable" properties and relations—in terms of which the "construction" of science can be achieved; it is rather interesting, though, that, as a matter of fact, such a list could be amazingly short. It will also be noticed that in the last sentences I have spoken about words. This has been done mainly for the purpose of illustration; in the main part of this paper I hope to express myself in a less involved manner and, after the danger of metaphysical blind alleys has once been pointed out, speak about facts.

Let us, in summarizing this introduction, see what light it throws on what has been called a truly perplexing intellectual situation, namely, that the empiricist philosopher seems sometimes less philosophical than scientists who are sensitive to epistemological issues. Three factors which together might be able to account for this paradox have indeed emerged. There is, first, the technical difficulty and relative abstruseness of the empiricist epistemology. Second, reasons have been given why empiricists frequently do not discuss epistemology proper in their writings on the philosophy of science. Third, there are certain false impressions or distorted emphases which linger on from earlier phases of the empiricist thought movement. One such phase which I, for one, would like to consider closed, is that of physicalism. Physicalism dogmatically asserts that nothing can be said or need be said which cannot be said in terms of the thing level. Since this is true for science, this overemphasis, though wrong, can at least be understood as a consequence of the now classical successes of the empiricist philosophy of science—relativity axiomatics, operationism, probability, behaviorism in psychology. Another phase now closed is the syntactical. The main formal achievements of this period were in the field of pure logic rather than in the field of language application; thus, the impression of an empty formalism could arise. Such misunderstandings, however, or so at

[7] Except of course insofar as the scientific concept of perception, which belongs to psychology, must be operationally defined and freed from its pseudoepistemological connotations. See also footnote 1 and G. Bergmann, *Phil. Sci.* 9, 72 (1942).

least it seems to me, are due to the technical character of the subject matter rather than to an occasional overemphasis on the part of the investigators.

II. Empirical Constructs

The discussion of scientific method falls into three main parts dealing with concept formation, the nature of empirical laws, and theory structure, respectively. The division, however, is not a hard and fast one; it will soon appear that the subject matter under the first heading, for instance, cannot be treated without many references to the second. The following two remarks should serve as orienting sign posts for the material of this section. *First,* the study of concept formation is the proper and, as will soon be seen, the main concern of that kind of analysis which is also referred to as operational, or operationism. The section is thus a restatement of the essence of the first two chapters of Bridgman's classical *Logic of Modern Physics.* I shall therefore be very brief on many noncontroversial points and make it my main task to circumscribe the scope of operationism as precisely as possible. This is not done with any critical or restrictive intent but rather in order to forestall that kind of criticism which is apt to follow too literal as well as too sweeping interpretations. *Second,* within the operational analysis the term 'concept' is understood in that narrower sense which is synonymous with 'empirical construct;' in other words, "theoretical" entities such as electrons, atoms or the ether are not considered at this stage of the discussion, while the operational analysis does claim to apply to all scientific concepts that do not contain the theoretical entities just mentioned. This, however, is in a certain sense not an exclusive classification. What makes the difference depends in many cases on how a concept is construed. Take for instance, gas pressure and the Loschmidt number. If the latter is considered as explicitly defined through the measured variables which serve for its actual computation, then it is as empirical as pressure—though, as we shall say, a more abstract construct. Within the kinetic theory, on the other hand, both are defined in terms that exclude them from direct location within the hierarchy of empirical constructs. To these matters we shall return in the section on theory.

Let us start from the familiar first-approximation definition of length in terms of rules for the manipulation of yardsticks.[8] Such rules are now referred to as the operational definition of the concept in question, and then one usually goes on to say that such a set of defining operations is the meaning of the concept. If meant to be exhaustive, such use of 'meaning' is undoubtedly very restrictive, as can easily be seen if one considers what he would then have to accept as the whole meaning of the Loschmidt number. To this point I shall attend later. Here it will merely be pointed out that formulations like those just given lay themselves open to all kinds of super-

[8] Concerning the logic of measurement see the selective bibliography given in the last reference of footnote 1.

ficial misunderstanding simply because they do not clearly distinguish the symbols from their referents. This must at least be pointed out. But it will be found that in order to avoid verbosity the customary ambiguous usage has been followed at many places in this paper. Briefly and figuratively speaking, the operational definition of 'length' stands in the same relation to length as the recipe for a pie to the pie itself. For definitions are really a purely verbal affair, a technic for the introduction of new terms, which are in principle dispensable and serve merely as abbreviations for unwieldy, frequently recurring expressions. As is well known, definitions are therefore neither true nor false and cannot be criticized on any formal grounds as long as they fulfill certain logical requirements which, by the way, are in some cases not quite as obvious as, for instance, the rule that one must avoid circularity in explicit definitions. Psychologically and pragmatically, we could not handle our language effectively without introducing appropriate definitions. This, however, is entirely irrelevant for our purposes since the *philosophy of science is neither its history and sociology nor the psychology of the scientist*. Empiricists understand by philosophy or methodology of science only its logical analysis, not the socio-psychological analysis of the processes of discovery, which is in principle itself a natural science. This distinction can hardly be overemphasized, particularly in view of the fact that failure to grasp its entirely nonevaluational character has been responsible for much adverse criticism of the allegedly onesided, static and reductive nature of the positivistic analysis. Cabbages ought not to be blamed for not being carrots. We should, of course, have a balanced diet, but then it seems to me that the empiricist methodology, with its systematic and epistemological emphasis, is rather making up for a deficiency caused by the traditional confusion between psychology and the theory of knowledge. These remarks apply not only to "operational" definitions but also, as we shall see, to their nonlinguistic counterparts. The requirements, in particular, which an operationally defined concept must fulfill in order to be a useful scientific concept cannot be specified in any *a priori* or prescriptive manner. All one can do is to point out which conditions (empirical laws) are fulfilled and which must be fulfilled in order to make certain concepts pragmatically successful. To introduce here a familiar illustration: Even in a rubber world, as one might call the topological universe which is used to explain the axiomatics of rigid bodies, one could still define length by means of a distinguished object. Psychologically, though, the thought is not likely to occur to a rubber-world physicist nor would his definition, in case it did occur to him, be likely to prove a useful one. But all this is really anticipating the discussion of the relation between laws and concepts. Let us first see what can be said about the empirical constructs themselves and, first of all, what can be said about them in a purely formal manner. In other words, what can we say about the recipe, not about the pie itself or its nutritional value?

In speaking of definitions one usually thinks of their simplest type: so-called explicit definition as it occurs, for instance, in pure geometry, in the definition of the volume of a rectangular prism as the product of its three extensions. So-called operational definitions are not that simple. Even in the elementary case of length the definitional sentence has the following relatively complex structure: "Rod A has the length x if and only if $(\cdot\cdot\cdot A\cdot\cdot\cdot x\cdot\cdot\cdot.)$" The blank is to be filled with a description of the yardstick procedure *which is itself an if-then clause.* The letters 'A' and 'x' have been inserted into the blank in order to indicate that the omitted clause makes reference to the object A and to the count of the successive layings-off of the standard.[9] The operational definition of the volume of a prismatic object (applied or physical geometry!) contains a compound of three definitions of length and, in addition, the prescription to carry out the computation which we have already encountered, in the form of an explicit definition, in pure geometry. So one sees that an operational definition is the verbal account not only of certain manipulations, but also of computations. As a rule the amount of computation involved has something to do with what we shall presently call the degree of abstractness of the construct. Furthermore, operational definitions, as can be seen even from this sketch, do have a rather complicated logical form. The most elaborate study of their linguistic structure, which proved to be very enlightening, not only in a formal sense, has been undertaken by Carnap in his essay on "Testability and Meaning." [10]

It could, of course, be said that in the definitional schema just outlined the word 'prism' or 'orthogonal prism' stands itself in need of definition or, to practice our philosophical vocabulary, is not simple enough to be included in the verification basis. This we would readily concede and continue the reduction until a basis we have agreed upon is reached. But we understand already how operational definitions come by their name. In a way, though, the qualification "operational" is a mere matter of emphasis. Operational definitions are, linguistically considered, just definitions or, rather, chains of definitions of a complex form, interspersed with explicit definitions and rules for computations. Typically they contain *if-then* clauses where the antecedent phrase after the 'if' describes manipulations and the consequent phrase after the 'then' records observations such as pointer readings or the result of a counting procedure. The decisive points are these. *First,* since such definitional chains can be provided for all empirical constructs, operational reduction amounts to a procedure of successive elimination of all terms not belonging to that very restricted vocabulary which we have called a sufficient verification basis on the thing level. This is the

[9] In case x is not an integer the definition undergoes considerable complication, since counting is the only primary way in which numbers enter into empirical statements. All further use of them in (extensional) measurement is a definitional structure which rests upon this basis. But numbers can also be used as *names* of intensity levels or as proper names (coordinates). In point of fact, all working coordinate systems are based on rules and there the numbers assigned are, in the last analysis, always determined by counting.

[10] *Phil. Sci.* 3, 420 (1936); 4, 1 (1937).

perfectly good sense in which science can be said to deal with common-sense objects and with common-sense objects only. Both the significance and the truth of such a formulation of the operationalistic thesis are too well recognized to require any further comment. I shall therefore rather point out how essential it is that the verification basis contain relation words, for instance 'moving,' since the description of manipulations is really a description of relational events on the thing level; *the agency of the experimenter, though pragmatically of the greatest importance, is systematically quite incidental. Second,* the definition of an empirical construct—for instance, 'electric field'—always provides the instructions, in terms of the thing level, for testing, that is, for determining the truth or falsehood of statements in which the construct occurs, for example, "there is an electric field in the neighborhood of object *B*." [11] In this sense, and only in this sense, it can be said that the operational definition of a construct *is* its meaning. This, however, is only one of the two main meanings in which the term 'meaning' is used by scientists.

Attention should here be called to two points where I have tried to forestall oversimplification. Sometimes it is said, and significantly enough just by such rationalistic writers as Eddington, that operationism reduces physics to pointer readings. Point-pointer coincidence is itself relational, and even this basis is therefore not quite as primitive as it is sometimes made to appear; but, in spite of that, this formulation has for me a rather invidious overreductionistic flavor. Less abstractly speaking, the physicist must also be able to recognize the apparatus whose pointer positions he reads and, furthermore, to identify the experimental set-up. There is no evident reason why the construction of the vocabulary which is required for this account could not be achieved from a basis as narrow as that of a space-time axiomatics based on coincidence. On the other hand, there is little doubt that relationships different from the point-pointer coincidence would have to be shown to be reducible to this nucleus in order to substantiate its claim as a sufficient verification basis. Taken as it stands, the pointer-reading formula is therefore somewhat misleading. Furthermore, the definitions of empirical constructs do contain calculational or, as one vaguely says, theoretical elements. Theory in any specific sense of the term can therefore not be identified with symbolic elaboration and still less be set in opposition to an operationism thus narrowly conceived. That operational analysis is not the complete story of science has been said before and is implicit in the whole organization of the present outline. Confusions of this sort, however, have played a major rôle so far only in the discussion which has been provoked by the impact of the operational thesis on psychology and the social sciences.

[11] Carnap's finer distinctions among *testability*, *confirmability* and *verifiability* are here neglected. Generally speaking, the inductive or hypothetical character of all scientific knowledge is simply taken for granted throughout this paper. In what sense this can be said to apply to the verification basis is again a question for technical epistemology. Concerning this problem see the reference given in footnote 5.

When one considers the stepwise way in which the operational analysis reduces concepts, it is not hard to understand what is meant by saying that it arranges the empirical constructs in some sort of a hierarchy which rests upon the verification basis. In this hierarchy the direction from the verification basis upward might be visualized vertically and spoken of as one of degree of abstractness. One must realize, though, that such language expresses broad structural insights rather than precise and quantifiable notions. At any rate, the term 'abstract' seems preferable to 'theoretical.' The former goes well with the idea of degree, and this agrees with the fact that no methodological reason can be given for any "horizontal cut" within the empirical hierarchy, so that the terms above such an arbitrary line would be theoretical in a sense in which those below it are not. There is an opportunity here for a remark which, though on the science level, is epistemological in nature. We leave it to the epistemologist to decide with what safeguards, Pickwickian or sophisticated, he wants to surround the common-sense truth that physical things—chairs, tables and laboratory equipment—are real. The point is this: If the hierarchy of the empirical constructs is the unitary and gapless structure that it appears to be in the operational analysis, then constructs such as forces, fields and energies are as real as tables and chairs. For how indeed can one, within the hierarchy, draw the line where reality ceases and where fiction or, in a vicious sense of the term, "construction" begins. To put it briefly, for science as well as for common sense, the referents of empirical constructs are as real as material things.

One of the first difficulties every attempt to visualize the hierarchy is likely to encounter is this: One and the same concept can often be defined in several different ways. In the case of 'electric current,' for instance, there are as many different operational definitions as there are methods of measuring current. Sometimes one will find that two such definitions do not even lie on approximately the same level of the hierarchy, whatever that might mean, since this very fact makes it again doubtful how much significance there is in this idea of an orderly hierarchy. At this point the empirical laws which obtain between the referents of the empirical constructs enter the picture. Systematically, 'current as measured by the deviation of a magnetic needle,' 'current as measured by "*its*" thermic effects,' and 'current as measured by sedimentation out of an electrolytic solution' are indeed three different constructs.[12] We "identify" them, use the same term, 'electric current,' and speak about its alternative "effects" for the sole reason that these effects are, as a matter of empirical law, concomitant and found to be in a constant quantitative relation. A goodly portion of the empirical laws of physics are of this cross-wise identification type. So one can still, in an illustrative manner, speak about levels within the hierarchy.

[12] This is the point Bridgman makes in distinguishing yardstick length and surveyor's length on the one hand and the length of astronomy and that of atomic physics on the other. The empirical laws which mediate between the first two of these definitions are of course the various theorems of (applied) geometry.

Whether the following remarks concerning empirical constructs should still be made in this section or rather under the next heading of empirical laws is largely a matter of the convenience of presentation. It is merely for such external reasons that the second of these alternatives has here been chosen.

III. Empirical Laws

Let us return to the physicist of the imaginary rubber universe who insists on defining length by means of an arbitrarily selected yardstick, but otherwise in the same way in which we do it. Several alternatives are possible. His topological universe might oscillate at such a rate that the measuring procedure cannot be repeated with the same result at all. Again, the elastic trend of his world might be slow relative to the time required for the manipulations involved. In the latter case, at least a restricted check, as we usually say, of length measurements would be possible. But it is well to realize, first, that one would have to provide length with a time index, and, second, and even more important, that our very ideas of test and experiment break down to the extent that such a world is genuinely "historical." Yet such a strange length is not only correctly defined, it could also fulfill the pragmatic criterion of usefulness. To see that, one merely has to suppose that our physicist were able to plot, to extrapolate successfully and to intercorrelate in a "theory" the variable length ratios of his universe. This is not only conceivable, but almost within the reach of our imagination. What are the implications of this illustration?

The following are no doubt two very basic factual features of the world in which we live. *First*, we can successfully apply to it empirical constructs that, under specifiable conditions, remain constant in time, which means that they fulfill empirical laws of a very special form. There comes to mind, on the prescientific thing level, the relative spatio-temporal constancy of solid bodies which pragmatically and psychologically molds and restrains our anticipations. *Second*, with respect to constructs that do not show such *constancy*, we have been extremely successful in connecting them with temporal invariants by empirical laws into which, as one usually says, time as such does not enter. All these comments are also part of the groundwork for the remarks on causality which will be found at the end of this section. For the time being their purpose is merely to help us differentiate between temporal constancy, which amounts always to a *law* about constructs, on the one hand, and, on the other, to that definiteness or specificity which their operational definitions supposedly must possess. Whatever such definiteness or specificity might mean, the illustration shows that it has not necessarily anything to do with temporal constancy. The reason why that is not always readily seen is this: No definition is specific in the sense that it either controls all the possibly relevant variables or that it *completely* specifies the manipulations themselves.[13] The operational definition of length, for instance, does not mention the color of the yardstick and neither prescribes nor forbids its being twirled around between successive layings-off. We never think of all the unmentioned possibilities as long as we actually reach our aim, namely, the discovery of empirical laws of the type we have come to expect. Conversely, when we define a new construct and then discover that it is neither itself temporally constant nor tied to such invariants in a lawful manner, we feel "that we have not defined or measured anything" and proceed to modify our definitions until we arrive at constructs which fulfill our expectations of lawfulness. As a matter of fact, but as a matter of fact only, this procedure has been extremely successful. Our imaginary example shows that science is possible even in a world which in this respect is radically different from ours. It is therefore rather confusing to bring some unprecise ideas of constancy into the discussion of operational definitions. Constancy, in any meaningful sense, is either temporal constancy and then it is really a matter of laws, or it refers to the recurrence of situations in which constructs are applicable. If the word 'constancy' must be used, the latter feature could be described as the temporal constancy of the verification basis.[14] Still another use of this weasel word connotes simply the existence of laws, no matter of what type, including those that would obtain in the lawfully pulsating rubber world.[15] So, we see, there is no additional methodological requirement of constancy, specificity or definiteness which a correctly defined empirical construct must fulfill. What such expressions refer to is a pragmatic set of expectations, a frame of reference, concerning the general character of laws about the constructs.

Since all this is so abstract I shall elaborate it by a few very unsystematic remarks, not in order to add anything new, but merely to make more explicit what has already been said. Consider, for instance, the example of the

[13] That this is so reflects another, still more basic, feature of our experience. Our perceptual universe is spatially continuous, it does not tick in time, colors shade into each other, and so forth.

[14] This, too, is not necessarily so; but to break down, in a radical manner, this feature of our experience would probably affect the very structure of consciousness. Here one has reached the level that can be dealt with only by the formalistic technics of the empiricist epistemology which are, in this sense, the contemporary equivalent of the traditional categorial analysis. The tendency, in particular, to deal with general features of the actually obtaining *law*fulness in the analysis of *concept* formation is an unmistakable vestige of the transcendental deduction attempted by Kant and, as our discussion of constancy shows, doomed to failure. A specimen, on the science level, of what takes its place is the connotational analysis described in the passages on causality at the end of this section.

[15] The progress from the Aristotelian to the Galileo-Newtonian conception of science marks, among other things, the transition from a frame of reference which requires a law, in order to be philosophically acceptable, to exhibit constancy on or near the thing level, to a frame of reference which is satisfied with constancy in the sense that the laws do not contain *time as such*. Again our "historical" rubber world violates this frame of reference even more radically than does the abandonment of its deterministic and mechanistic features which has recently occurred. This remark, too, is relevant to the discussion of causality.

electric current. Previously we have referred to the well-known facts of the case as an "identification" of different empirical constructs on the basis of laws. The same situation could also be accounted for by saying that after the discovery of the pertinent laws one changes one's language, discards the old constructs and defines a new one by means of a broader class of alternative procedures. Again, we usually say that we modify a definition if we decide that the construct we want to define requires the control of an additional variable. In this case, too, one adds to the class of operations, though in a manner that is different from the case of the electric current. And there is still another type of modification which one might describe as a narrowing down of the class of operations; this modification has something to do with what has been called the unspecificity of any operational definition. I am thinking of the case where one decides that the yardstick should not be twirled around after all, or, less whimsically, that it should not be made of certain materials nor be put into certain solutions between successive layings-off. Such amplifications of the operational definition really narrow down the indefinite number of possible ways in which any prescription, which is necessarily couched in general terms, can be carried out. And let it be said again, at the risk of being repetitious, that when I just spoke about the concepts one wants to define, this merely means that one is searching for a construct that lies in the approximate region of one's previous attempts and that fulfills certain laws which one expects, either for theoretical or for intuitive reasons, to obtain in this area. For, no matter how important psychologically and pragmatically the definition of the "right" concepts might be, systematically the scientist has, by defining them, merely laid out the tools for the main phase of his work, which consists in the discovery of the empirical laws that obtain among these constructs. Since the actual usefulness of concepts in this sense depends at least in part upon the laws obtaining among the less abstract concepts which enter into their definition, it can be seen that empirical laws, too, fall into a hierarchy of abstractness which is, figuratively speaking, induced by the hierarchy of the constructs. It is plausible, for instance, that density would probably not be a useful concept, if it were not for those laws which make for the approximate constancy of volume and mass of solid bodies. These, however, are plausibility considerations which are, strictly speaking, neither here nor there. Let me therefore conclude this string of unsystematic comments by a brief examination of two other expressions that have just been used. If one considers the successive stages in the definitions and (or) measuring technics of, let us say, length or temperature, it is natural enough to speak about successive *refinements* and about *approximation* to the true length or the true temperature. It should be clear by now that some of the comprehensible connotations of such expressions belong to the history and psychology of science. Systematically, any modification of a definition is a new definition; if we call one a refinement of another, this is but an expression of satisfaction (usually for theoretical reasons) with the newly discovered laws. And it is only the empirical laws that tend, at least in the intervals not obtained by extrapolation, to converge in a crude and not quantifiable manner towards a curve which they may thus be said to approximate.

It is now possible to characterize very succinctly the second scientific meaning of 'meaning' which has already been mentioned when it was pointed out in what sense the operational definition of a construct can be said to be its meaning. Every worthwhile empirical construct occurs actually in several, and potentially in an indefinite number, of empirical laws which connect it with other constructs. In disciplines as highly quantified as physics these laws take the form of a set of equations with one term occurring in all of them. It is not difficult to see that this *set of laws in which the construct occurs* has something to do with meaning. For one stays undoubtedly within the limits of common usage if he says that a person who knows how to determine the mass, let us say, of a stone, still does not know what it means as long as he does not realize that mass is (in Newtonian mechanics) a constant in the well-known sense in which weight is not. And we have also seen that such an assertion of constancy is an empirical law, and no doubt a very significant one, in which the concept of mass occurs. Clearly, one is here dealing with a second meaning of 'meaning,' and its relation to the common-sense notion of significance is similar to that of its first meaning to the idea of verification. If one wants to imitate the current formulation, according to which meaning_1 is the operational definition of the term, one might even say that meaning_2 *is* the set of the empirical laws in which the term occurs. There is finally a further scientific connotation of meaning. To become aware of it, one merely has to consider such a constant as the Loschmidt number, which reveals its full "meaning" only within the theoretical model. But we shall not spend any more time on the connotations of a term which, after all, does not belong to physical science itself.

If this were a textbook of the philosophy of science, much would have to be said about the nature of empirical laws or, to use the traditional terms, about causality and induction. As far as induction is concerned, hardly anything needs to be said in a selective outline like this. The inductive character of all empirical knowledge is taken for granted, and it is also taken for granted that the so-called principle of induction is essentially a pragmatic rule of conduct.[16] A similar omission is justified as to those questions concerning laws which traditional metaphysics tries to formulate under the heading of causality. To the scientist it is obvious that there is no point in ontological speculation about lawfulness, that is, in discussing laws irrespective of their being known and, in many cases, even irrespective of their being knowable. To the empiricist it is likewise obvious that nothing can be said in an *a priori* manner about the structure or form of the laws already known or still to be discovered. Again, it seems safe to trust the specialist with the dissolution of the traditional intuitionistic (rationalistic) and real-

[16] Compare parts of the reference given in footnote 2 and H. Feigl, *Phil. Sci.* 1, 20 (1934).

istic (ontological) arguments according to the rules of the epistemological chess game. There are, however, certain very interesting problems that occupy, in the philosophy of science, the traditional place of causality and induction. To the problem of induction correspond the attempts to arrive at a measure, within the calculus of probabilities or at least in a similar manner, of the reliability of an inductive generalization. This is a very special line of research, and moreover, in the opinion of many analysts, of rather doubtful promise, so that nothing more needs to be said about it in this outline. What empiricism offers instead of the old causality metaphysics is of much greater general interest. The most complete presentation of this group of clarifications is due to Ph. Frank,[17] and the material is so comprehensive that I can but try to give an idea of its general character. Nontechnically speaking, a law is a statement of the form "Whenever *A* then *B*" and in a certain sense this is all that can be said about it on the formal level. Traditional causality metaphysics attempted to do two different things. First it tried to equate the degree of certainty, or whatever technical expression one prefers, of such statements to the infallibility characteristic of mathematical identities and of logical inference.[18] But it also tried to determine, by intuition or transcendental deduction in the Kantian vein, structural features which the laws of nature must or must not exhibit. Such features are, for instance, those customarily referred to as action over distance, homogeneity with respect to time and space, ineffectiveness of time as such, no action over distance in time without mediating traces, and so on. Some of these principles would be violated in the world which has been given as an imaginary example at the beginning of this section.

It is hardly necessary to emphasize that there is no room, within an empiricist philosophy of science, for a speculative "explanation" of such very general factual features of our world, but it is likewise clear that descriptively a connotational analysis of them proves very clarifying. The term 'connotational' has been chosen because what one does is to separate from the formal idea of law the connotations that it has acquired at any time by virtue of the features which some, many or maybe even all of the laws then known actually possess. It is commonly accepted, for instance, that the better part of the Kantian philosophy of nature is but a rationalization of the various connotations which can be abstracted from Newton's equations. This Kant-Newtonian frame of reference has still interesting terminological after effects in the inclination of many writers, including some empiricists, to reserve the expression 'causal law' for process laws of the Newtonian type which "deterministically" connect successive temporal cross sections or states of a closed system, while the distinguishing epithet

[17] *Das Kausalgesetz und seine Grenzen* (Vienna, 1932). A new English edition or even a translation of this work seems to me highly desirable. It contains, among many other interesting points, the most detailed empiricist analysis of the vitalism issue of which I know.

[18] This is indeed one of the traditional points which have been mentioned before as not relevant for our purpose.

'causal' is being withheld from statistical laws or from laws that connect the state variables of an equilibrium, such as Ohm's law or the general formula for ideal gases. It is well known, finally, how glibly and confusingly people recently spoke and wrote about a breakdown of causality and a *philosophical* crisis when what actually happened was, within *physics*, the breakdown of some connotations of causality which, through dint of time and success, had become rather deeply rooted thought habits. This is the more amazing because whatever breakdown occurred of the mechanistic and deterministic features took place within the theoretical model and not within the realm of the empirical laws. But to appreciate this point we must gain some insight into the methodological status of theories.

IV. Theories

Even an outline as selective and nontechnical as this must at some place indicate the role which logic and mathematics play within the methodological schema of science.[19] The sharp dichotomy between logical and mathematical knowledge on the one hand and factual knowledge on the other is one of the cornerstones of any empiricist philosophy. 'Formal' and 'empirical' are simply two other names for the same pair of opposites. It is fair to say that the tremendous sophistication with which ever more precise formulations of this distinction have been elaborated constitutes one of the main achievements of the empiricist thought movement; it is mainly because of the services which it can render there that formal logic has become so essential for the new theory of knowledge.[20] Even the most complex chains of deductive reasoning, mathematical or otherwise, are as empty of factual content, and therefore as certain, as '2 = 2.' They are all in the same boat with the old standby, 'If (all men are mortal) and if (Socrates is a man) then (Socrates is mortal).' Clearly the three statements in parentheses are

[19] In order to emphasize these remarks they have been placed at the beginning of a section. Otherwise, it will soon be noted, the transition is as gradual as that between the two preceding sections [*Am. J. Phys.* 11, 248 (1943)]. A relatively nontechnical presentation of the main problems will be found in Carnap's *Foundations of logic and mathematics* (monograph I, 3 of the International Encyclopedia of Unified Science). The standard works for everybody whose main interest is not the formalism itself are Carnap's *Logical syntax of language* (1934, 1937) and his *Introduction to semantics* (1942).

[20] In Sec. I, I mentioned the syntactical phase of empiricism. This can now be somewhat elucidated. The first, most important, and most difficult achievement was the recognition of logic and mathematics as an essentially unified formal structure without factual content or, as one also says, as *syntactical* truth, tautological and thus *a priori.* There was therefore a tendency to press every statement which was rightly felt to be nonfactual into the Procrustean bed of syntax. With the newer methods, however, one can also elucidate the formal elements in the relations among languages, their referents and their users (semantics and pragmatics). The concept 'formal' is therefore, in a certain sense, broader than the concept 'syntactical'; and this broadened frame of reference allows for a much more sophisticated dissolution and transformation of the old metaphysical issues without, however, diluting the essential thesis that all knowledge which is not empirical in the common-sense meaning of the term belongs to the linguistic structure and is, like the camera, never part of what it depicts.

empirical, since their truth or falsehood depends upon facts; the compound statement, however, is true no matter what the facts are, and its truth is therefore formal. This is so because, *first,* the conclusion merely states (part of) what is stated in the premises, and, *second,* the compound statement as a whole asserts merely that the conclusion is true *if* the premises are true. It might help to avoid misunderstanding if it is emphasized that only mathematical identities are formal truths in this sense. The functional connection asserted in a physical formula—for instance, in the Newtonian gravitational formula, is not a mathematical identity, but the partial expression [21] of a quantified empirical law. It is, therefore, on the same level with 'All men are mortal.' If one wants to carry the analogy further, one might compare any set of initial conditions (state) of the planetary system with 'Socrates is a man' and, finally, Kepler's laws or, for that matter, any astronomical prediction within the planetary system with 'Socrates is mortal.'

All this is pitifully primitive and inaccurate, but my purpose is merely to recall certain general ideas which, on the one hand, are presumed to be known in some manner and, on the other, cannot possibly be presented here with even a small part of the sophistication to which they are amenable. The obvious and important point is that mathematical deduction merely makes explicit what is already contained in the premises and that any attempt to derive empirical laws from pure mathematics is, therefore, hopeless. But even a remark as plain and obvious as this does not set up straw men, for the group-theoretical speculations in Eddington's most recent book are in the last analysis nothing but the latest product of those age-old Platonistic tendencies which try to derive factual from formal knowledge.[22] It seems significant to me that the same writer, in an earlier stage of his thought, was given to overphysicalistic formulations. This has been pointed out before.

We are now prepared to understand the basic connotation of the term 'theory.' Consider, for instance, the three formulas connected with the description of a free falling body:

$$s = \tfrac{1}{2}gt^2, \qquad v = gt, \qquad a = g.$$

They contain one parameter, g, and, besides, four operationally defined constructs, s, t, v, a, that are not independent of one another. First, these constructs rest upon the same operational basis; this almost self-explanatory expression signifies that the situations to which they apply are either the same or contain at least many common elements. Second, their definitions themselves contain, in a certain order, each other; in less simple cases they contain common clauses. The point now is this: Obviously none of the three

[21] The other part consists of the operational definitions of the constructs which occur in the law. Concerning the way in which the quantification is achieved, see footnote 9.

[22] For a remarkable analysis of Eddington's *The philosophy of physical science* see Braithwaite's review in *Mind* 49, 455 (1940).

empirical laws can be deduced from the definitions. This would be as absurd as trying to derive them from mathematics.[23] However, experimental evidence for any one of the three laws is *ipso facto* also evidence for the other two since they are logico-mathematical consequences of one another *and* of the definitions that interrelate the variables. (I neglect the refinement necessitated by the constants of integration, which is both obvious and irrelevant for our purposes.) Thus a deductive connection has been established among several empirical laws. Such organization of empirical laws into deductive systems is the distinguishing characteristic of scientific theories. There are, as we shall see, different technics which lead to deductive integration; but if one had to be selected as the prototype for all of them, I should choose the case where the deduction of empirical laws from other empirical laws is achieved by using, as additional premises, those relations among the occurring variables that are given in their definitions. This is indeed the case that our elementary example illustrates. Another deductive technic, the derivation of new laws by elimination (in our example, $v^2 = 2\,sg$) is methodologically rather trivial.

In order to avoid misunderstanding, it must be said that the isolation of such types of theory structure is essentially a descriptive job, not dissimilar in character to connotational analysis, and that actual scientific theories must therefore not be expected to be true to such pure types. But it seems to me that there are, besides the two elementary ones just mentioned, only two more relatively clear-cut deductive technics. These are represented by the electromagnetic theory of light and by atomic (model) theories, respectively. Since their analysis is less obvious, I shall, in the next two paragraphs, preface it by a few elementary comments and a survey of some of the more superficial connotations of the term 'theory.' But first of all I should like to express a terminological preference. It seems to me that communication is simplified if the term 'theory' is introduced as late as possible into a methodological discussion of the kind in which we are engaged. As long as one stays unambiguously within the realm of empirical laws and constructs, it might be as well to say so. I, for one, should therefore prefer to speak of systems of empirical laws, or of scientific systems, and reserve the word 'theory' for existential models (for example, atomic theories), since it is only this latter most sophisticated device for deductive organization that requires an additional methodological clarification. However, this proposal deviates from the common usage which is well established.

Theories are said to *explain* rather than merely to *describe;* to *unify* science; and to produce *understanding*. While it would be worth while to devote a monograph to a complete connotational analysis of these and similar terms, we shall here content ourselves with a few hints. In what sense, for instance, have Kepler's laws been unified by Newtonian mechanics, so

[23] This similarity reflects itself in an older formulation according to which formal truth is "truth by definition." The phrase is still current, but one had better avoid it since it leads easily to confusion.

that the latter explains what the former merely describe? Let us assume that Kepler had found the exponents in his third law to be 1 and 2, instead of 2 and 3, respectively. This result would not have disturbed him at all; as a matter of fact it might have pleased him even more, since he was still under the influence of Pythagorean-Platonic number mysticism and might have thought the smaller integers to be more beautiful. The success of Newton's inverse-square hypothesis, on the other hand, was predicated upon these constants being what they actually are. Elaboration of these elementary points seems superfluous. Let me emphasize, instead, that what has just been called Newton's hypothesis was a candidate for a position as an empirical law even at the time he formulated it. This status of a statement does not depend upon the practical possibility and the directness of its verification, but merely upon its form, namely, that only empirical constructs occur in it. In this sense the attraction formula is, at least for terrestrial bodies, undoubtedly an empirical law. So one sees how the attempt at deductive organization might even lead to the formulation of empirical laws that are basic in the prospective system, or, as one usually says, theory. If, on the other hand, a deductive organization has been achieved, then it is as a rule possible to derive from it and subject to experimental test further empirical laws which stand in exactly the same relation to the basic laws of the theory as do the theorems of geometry to its axioms. However, if the terms 'basic' or 'axiomatic' are used with reference to empirical laws, it must always be understood that these characteristics refer to their position within a deductive schema. In itself no empirical law is more basic or fundamental than any other. Summarizing these remarks one might say that 'explanation' and 'description' are relative terms which refer to the positions of laws (and individual facts) within a deductive system. Another rather neat way of putting things is to say that while laws predict individual facts, theories enable us to predict laws. But this formulation is certainly over-simplified and as vague as the customary use of the word 'theory' itself. For a set of theoretically unrelated empirical laws or even a single empirical law might very well exhibit a predictive power which leads to its being dubbed with the honorific label of theory. The root of such predictive or explanatory power lies typically in the fact that the law or laws in question contain parameters which allow for their application to a variety of situations of widely diverging appearance and outcome.

Concerning the term 'unification,' it should be clear without further comment in what sense Newtonian mechanics has unified astronomy, but it is also commonly accepted that one of its most outstanding achievements lies in the unification which it has brought about between the two hitherto unrelated areas of mechanics and astronomy. Again, we leave it to an elementary textbook to show in what way and within which limits the word 'area' can be given a precise meaning. Obviously the concept of operational basis which we have introduced before will play an important role in any such attempt. As far as unification is concerned, there is no doubt that whenever it has been achieved between two or several previously unconnected fields or areas, understanding is felt to have made progress of prime importance.

Some doubt may have arisen as to how the deductive character of theories, which I have so strongly emphasized, can be reconciled with the patent fact that theories are daily being subjected to experimental verification, that it is even the common fate of theories to undergo modification and to be ultimately discarded because of the unsatisfactory outcome of such tests. So strongly have scientists been impressed with this very feature that some of them like to say theories are neither true nor false, but merely convenient fictions, or at least still one more step further removed from conclusive verification than empirical laws. This is, after all, the so-called instrumental character of theories which pragmatists are so inclined to stress. How does this viewpoint agree with our insistence on theories being deductive, that is, as one might think, true *a priori*, independent of fact? As far as the idea of convenient fictions is concerned, its analysis will have to wait until we discuss existential models. For the rest, however, the apparent contradiction is merely verbal; the whole thing has been brought up not as a real issue but merely as a pretext for the last one in this string of preliminary remarks about the nature of theory in general. Take the typical case where an empirical law, previously unknown or unnoticed, has first been deduced from a theory and then not been borne out by subsequent systematic experimentation. What we do in this case is, again typically, either try another theoretical organization, or redefine our constructs, or, more frequently, both. The typology of the situation is somewhat similar to, and as difficult to treat exhaustively as that which has been sketched with respect to the modification of empirical constructs; we shall therefore not enter into a detailed discussion of it. The deductive aspect of the schema, however, remains always the same; what it amounts to, in the last analysis, is always that if Socrates is not mortal, either he is not human or the general premise is false. The difference is, of course, that in a theory the steps of the argument are not as simple as this and concern whole groups of empirical laws. What one does if the structure has to be mended is to redefine variables, take additional ones into account (the color of the yardstick might matter after all!), change one's assumptions as to indirectly tested empirical laws, and, if one has used any models, modify or discard them. Another noteworthy feature, finally, is that the successive theoretical organizations of a particular field which are proposed as time passes might very radically differ. For instance, an empirical law that has once been taken as basic might turn out to be not only a rather imperfect approximation, but also a remote and theoretically not very interesting consequence of the set of axioms which now proves more "convenient." This kind of discontinuity becomes particularly apparent when, as happened in our generation, atomic models are either radically modified or entirely discarded. Here, by the way, is another point where one can, at least in a descriptive manner, distinguish between empirical laws and theories. It will be remembered from Sec. III in what sense empirical laws can be said to be successive approximations. No such convergence, no matter how crudely and informally conceived, needs to connect successive theories, though, as a matter of fact, a general theoretical frame of reference might survive for a long time, as the mechanistic-deterministic frame of classical atomistics actually did. This discontinuity of theory is compatible, not only with the fact that empirical laws occurring at different places within the successive schemata are frequently successive approximations, but also with the circumstance that a whole theory can sometimes be said to be a limiting case of another. The existence of such a limiting process does not affect the radical theoretical or, if you please, structural discontinuity I have in mind. This discontinuity of theory construction is, to my mind, one of the strongest arguments in favor of an epistemological approach that insists on what is vaguely referred to as the fictitious or imaginary character of the theoretical particles, such as atoms and electrons.

Let us turn, now, to the electromagnetic theory of light in the form it had when originally put forth. It has already been implied that even this outstanding "theoretical" achievement lies entirely within the realm of the empirical constructs. If one should raise the objection that actually it was tied up with the idea of the theoretical medium, ether, and that it might not even have been proposed otherwise, I should use the opportunity to reassert the distinction between logical and socio-psychological (historical) analysis. In methodology we are primarily interested, not in the process of discovery, but in the fact that the theory in question can be accounted for in a certain manner. Such methodological analysis will then reveal that the electromagnetic theory of light shows considerable similarity with the case of the "three" electric currents (Sec. III) which were identified on the basis of empirical laws. But there are also differences between the two situations; to understand those we make use again of the notion of operational basis. In the case of the various definitions of the current the three experimental lay-outs contain common elements; indeed, except for the measuring instruments, they are the same. When the theoretical identification of optical and electromagnetic phenomena was proposed, their respective operational bases were still sufficiently different from each other to justify their being spoken about as belonging to two different areas. The operational basis for the one was, roughly speaking, light sources, screens, mirrors, prisms, and so forth, while the basis for the other consisted, among other things, of batteries, magnets, induction coils and condensers. The decisive feature they had in common was merely the mathematical structure of a very abstract empirical law which regulated the propagation of excitations and was rather fundamental in both fields. And, lest there be any misunderstanding, only the form of the two equations was the same; the operational definitions, within the two fields, of the two constructs which gave their meaning (meaning_1) to corresponding variables were, and for that matter still are, radically different. And there were also, within each system, equations that hitherto had not been interpreted as empirical laws by substituting the operational definitions of the other area—as for instance, the laws of reflection. Accordingly, a good deal of the testing and development of the theory consisted of the translating and testing of such "parallel" constructs and laws. Such was obviously the purpose of Hertz' classical experiments. All this is, of course, merely a methodological schema which claims neither historical nor scientific accuracy. In particular, any worth-while identification theory is likely to lead to an expansion and, finally, to a certain overlapping of the two operational bases. Development in this direction could almost be considered as the criterion for the ultimate success of this type of theory construction. Be that as it may, the point I am trying to make is merely that such theories can be accounted for within the realm of the empirical constructs. In a certain sense the electromagnetic theory of light is but a much more sophisticated instance of the technic that one applies to the three definitions of the current. Taking up a terminological suggestion that has been made before, one might say that all the constructs in question —currents, electric and optical fields, and so forth—have real referents, but that all of them refer to non-things, not to material objects. Theoretical or existential constructs, on the other hand, are fictitious or, as I should prefer to say, calculational things. What that means will be explained presently. But before we turn to the type of theory in which these theoretical or existential constructs occur, a few remarks on axiomatics are in order.

The mathematician who studies the deductive connections between formulas is not concerned with the operations which yield the substitution values for his variables, nor is he interested in the actual truth or falsehood of the empirical laws which his formulas express when the symbols are thus taken to represent empirical constructs of one kind or another. For the mathematician the wave equation, whether optically or electromagnetically interpreted, *is* the same; whatever identification takes place does not occur in his bailiwick. Generally speaking, one can develop the deductive consequences of any set of so-called axioms without ever asking whether there are any empirical constructs and laws which can be considered as their *interpretation*. Such a linguistic structure we call a deductive or axiomatic system, a scientific calculus, or, briefly, a calculus. Any pure or axiomatic geometry is a scientific calculus; analytic mechanics is another well-developed example which, by the way, if it is to be complete, must include an axiomatic geometry. Such calculi are sometimes called *formal*, but this must not be understood to mean that their axioms and theorems constitute logical or mathematical truths. Formal in this latter sense is only the deductive connection between axioms and theorems, and this, as we know, holds true of any deductive connection between statements. Therefore, if the term 'formal' is applied to scientific calculi, it merely signifies that in order to give them any empirical meaning at all, rules must be laid down which coordinate at least some of their terms to terms either of the empirical hierarchy or of the verification basis itself. Following a proposal by Reichenbach, one often speaks of these rules as *coordinating definitions.*

Like any elaborate linguistic structure, scientific calculi do contain defined terms; 'circle,' for instance, is a defined term in the usual axiomatizations of geometry. But each calculus must also contain a set of specific, undefined or basic terms, such as 'point' or 'straight line' in the axioms of projective geometry, or 'point mass' in analytic mechanics. If the basic terms of a calculus are coordinated to the terms of the empirical hierarchy, interpretations are automatically secured for the defined terms of the calculus, too. In order to find them one has merely to retrace the definitional structure of the calculus within the empirical hierarchy. It would therefore not be possible to choose coordinations arbitrarily for more than a limited set among all the terms of a scientific calculus, even if no attention were paid to empirical laws. What actually decides the acceptance of a calculus is again a feature connected with the laws: The formulas which, by virtue of the axioms, obtain between the terms of the calculus must be structurally identical with the mathematical expressions of the empirical laws which, as a matter of fact, connect the empirical constructs to which they are coordinated.[24] Loosely speaking, the two sets of formulas must be the same in the sense in which the wave equation is always the same.

There is little or no point in all this as long as coordinations are given for the basic terms of the scientific calculus, since in this case the latter is merely the replica of a system of empirical laws, obtained by simply disregarding the operational definitions of the variables. Forcing oneself to think thus "formally" might be a good way to become aware of deductive connections among empirical laws, but the whole thing is really without any particular methodological significance. A new methodological problem does present itself when coordination is provided not for the basis, but only for certain more or less highly defined terms of the calculus. This is, of course, the schema of theories of the *atomic*, or *model*, type. Visualizing the terms of a calculus as a hierarchy analogous to, but different from, the hierarchy of the empirical constructs, one could say that in this case only terms above a certain level are coordinated to empirical constructs. The classical kinetic theory is the prototype of all such partially coordinated calculi. The point is that in order to achieve deductive unification between the fields of mechanics and thermodynamics it was necessary to resort to the partial coordination technic. The difficulties which this particular at-

[24] What decides the applicability of a calculus is thus a syntactical feature, namely, an isomorphism between the formulas of the uninterpreted calculus on the one hand and the meaningful formulas of our empirical language on the other. But the meaning or interpretation of the empirical constructs does not necessarily enter the picture. *Coordinating definitions* must therefore not be confused with the semantic concept of *designation,* which formalizes, in a different manner, the relation between a term and its extralinguistic referents. For elaboration of this point see G. Bergmann, "Pure semantics, sentences, and propositions," *Mind* 53 (1944).

tempt encountered when it came to grips with the ergodic hypothesis are here none of our concern, and the tremendous deductive power of atomic theories and the role they play in modern physics are too well known to require any further comment. It is likewise obvious that I am using 'atom' and 'atomic' in a generic sense, meant to comprise molecules, atoms, electrons, the various kinds of nuclear particles and even the macroscopic continuous ether; methodologically they are all in the same category and so we are impartially interested in all of them, whether or not they happen to be now current. Characteristic of these calculi is, first, that they are but partially coordinated and that, second, their basic uncoordinated terms have certain features in common. The second point will be taken up presently. But it can already be seen that this situation faces us with the task of clarifying what a traditional philosopher might be tempted to call the ontological status of those uncoordinated calculational entities. It was mainly for the purpose of such analysis or, if you please, terminological clarification, that the distinction between a calculus and a set of empirical laws has been introduced into the present outline.

What are those features which all theoretical constructs were said to have in common? Consider, in analytic mechanics, the basic term 'point mass.' The most marked traits with which it is axiomatically endowed are, it seems to me, localization, persistence, and continuous motion along orbits. The very general character of these traits indicates that what their enumeration amounts to is really a *connotational analysis of the thing concept* and, like all such analyses, it is necessarily vague and hardly ever exhaustive. It is well to realize, for instance, that the connection between the mathematical concept of continuity on the one hand and the intuitive idea of the continuous motion of physical objects on the other is by no means simple and, moreover, is in a certain sense arbitrary. Again, it is a far cry from the relative stability of physical objects to the conservation of mass in Newtonian mechanics. Yet it seems safe to say that whenever the basic terms of a calculus do not possess some formal equivalents of these three connotations of thinghood, we do not consider the interpreted calculus as a model and are, accordingly, not faced with the "philosophical" question in what sense its elements can be said to be real or to exist.[25] This question, as we can now formulate it, concerns the status of the theoretical or existential constructs, that is, of those *uncoordinated basic terms of a partially interpreted calculus which exhibit the characteristics of formal thinghood.* Interpreted calculi of this kind we call atomic, or model, theories. It should be obvious by now

[25] One could speculate that whatever the history of mechanics might have been, a stuff theory of mechanical energy could never have been proposed. For, though a conservation principle holds, mechanical energy is not localized and does not move along orbits, but resides, at least in its potential form, in the configuration as a whole. What models have actually been proposed is a subjective or historical matter; objective, however, are those features of the empirical laws which account for the possibility of a model. It is well known, for instance, how much Carnot could achieve with a stuff theory whose empirical basis was essentially the conservation principle expressed in the thermometric equation.

why and in what sense this technic of theory construction has been said to be the only one that transcends the realm of empirical laws and constructs.[26]

The two notions of formal thinghood and of a partially coordinated calculus are the tools necessary to clarify the status of the atoms, a question that has not come to rest ever since Mach, Ostwald and certain French analysts reopened the age-old issue. As to the question itself the scientific empiricist will be inclined to consider it largely as a terminological matter, but let it be clearly understood that the analysis of model theories which has just been sketched is itself no verbal affair. A question of terminology is merely, how in the light of this analysis we are going to use, within the philosophy of science, such words as reality and existence. The reason it is so difficult for any terminological decision on this point to find general acceptance is that the unanalyzed notion of reality contains, among other things, at least the two ideas of being a member of the empirical hierarchy and of having formal thinghood. These two connotations are not coextensive. Many, indeed most of the empirical constructs, including some properties and all the relations of the verification basis itself, do not possess formal thinghood. On the other hand, formal thinghood is a purely structural notion and can therefore be attributed to calculational entities which need not have any connection whatever with the empirical hierarchy. The suggestion has already been made much earlier in this paper that 'real' be used, at least in the philosophy of science, as equivalent to 'belonging to the empirical hierarchy.' Then atoms are not real by definition. The reason for this suggestion is that all the essential epistemological questions which are tied in with the realism issue revolve around the status of the empirical hierarchy (always, of course, including the verification basis itself). The opinion that the status of the atoms is more closely connected with the realism issue than is any other problem of the philosophy of science is simply a sign of philosophical dilettantism.

There is one more point to be considered. One might wonder whether an existential construct of today might not be coordinated to an empirical construct tomorrow so that the whole issue is still less important than it has been made out to be. This is no doubt a very sound argument at a moment when even the layman knows that in the Wilson cloud chamber and in the Geiger counter we have almost put our finger on the individual particle. Individualization of this kind is no doubt one of the vaguer connotations of thinghood. It is certainly conceivable that one can define empirical constructs which possess many criteria of formal thinghood and can be coordinated to the basic particles of a theory. All I would insist on is that this very statement which I have just written down is a clearer account of

[26] The set of values of empirical constructs which characterizes the *state* of a physical system is, of course, not an existential construct. The concept of a state and its indices is closely related to the idea of a closed system which, in turn, is clarified under the heading of empirical laws.

the situation than any possible assertion about the existence or reality of the particles. And I should further insist on the obvious fact that even such a construct with formal thing-features would be derived *from*, but could never occur *on*, the verification basis of the common sense things.[27] However, the situation is even more dialectical than that. While on the one hand we have been able to put our finger on the particle, this very particle has, within the model, lost more and more of the connotations of formal thinghood. This is after all but another way of referring to what is usually called the breakdown of the mechanistic-deterministic model, so that today it even appears doubtful whether we are still making use of a model at all, and many physicists prefer what they call, rather loosely, the positivistic interpretation of their theories. What this section offers is merely the positivistic analysis, in a little more technical sense, of the terms in which physicists speak about their theories.

With this I shall rest the case which I have made, in the form of a methodological and terminological analysis, for the thesis that there are no atoms. But it is only fair to point out that if this analysis is strictly adhered to, even stars and microscopic objects are not physical things in a literal sense, but merely by courtesy of language and pictorial imagination. This might seem awkward. But when I look through a microscope or a telescope, all I see is a patch of color which creeps through the field like a shadow over a wall. And a shadow, though real, is certainly not a physical thing. Whether such literal-mindedness is philosophical clarity or merely the extreme of positivistic indoctrination is not for me to decide.

[27] The fact that empirical correlates of particles would have to be *defined* constructs while the particles themselves are *basic* terms of their calculus accounts for the choice of the alternative expression 'existential construct.' For in a certain sense one cannot strictly speak about the *existence* of basic terms or particulars. In the methodological discussions at the beginning of this century these entities were referred to as *nonphenomenological*.

The Structure of Theories*

NORMAN R. CAMPBELL

What I Do Not Mean by a Theory. It will be well to start by explaining in some detail exactly what meaning I propose to attach to the term "theory". I shall not assume at the outset that my use of the word coincides with that generally adopted; indeed, since I shall urge that the general use covers propositions of widely different form and significance, I can expressly disclaim that assumption. When the meaning is defined the question will have to be put which, if any, of the propositions of science, whether generally termed theories or not, are theories according to my definition? And since the word, being adopted from common discourse, has already attached to it many connotations, it will be convenient at the outset to free it from these associations, and to state carefully what is *not* meant by the word.

In common usage "theory" is always contrasted with "practice", and the contrast is justified by etymology. Theory, in its origin, is the state of contemplation as distinct from the state of action, and it is perfectly correct to term "theoretical" discussions which can have no influence in active life. The same distinction justifies the division of treatises or examination papers into "theoretical" and "practical", so long as the latter are confined strictly to the manipulative details of laboratory experiments and the former to a consideration of all the intellectual processes and results to which such experiments may give rise. For in this original sense of the word all propositions are necessarily theoretical, since they concern thought and not action; and in this sense all science, in so far as consists of propositions, is theoretical.

A slight and obvious extension, however, leads to the use of the contrasted terms to distinguish propositions which need much thought for their establishment from those which need little. In this sense the same proposition may be theoretical or practical according to the evidence on which it is based. The statement that an unsupported stone will fall to the ground is "practical" so long as it is asserted as the result of common experience; it is theoretical if asserted as the consequence of the "law" of gravitation. Thus theory is a question of degree, and science becomes progressively more theoretical as we pass from its elementary and fundamental judgements to the various ranks of propositions derived from them.

* Reprinted by kind permission of the publisher from Norman R. Campbell, *Physics: The Elements*, Cambridge University Press, 1920, pp. 120–140.

This use of the term has certainly played some part in determining that certain propositions in actual science are termed theories; they are so termed because they are complicated. This meaning will not be attached to the word here; some of the propositions termed theories are extremely simple. On the other hand they are all removed from the fundamental propositions further than are laws, and involve another step in the development of ideas.

Another association arises directly from the use of the word "theoretical" to denote propositions which require much consideration for their establishment. All thought and all reasoning processes are liable to introduce error, and though, in one sense, a proposition is more likely to be true the greater is the consideration that has been given to it, in another sense it is more likely to be false; the longer and more complicated the process of reasoning involved in the attainment of a conclusion, the greater is the chance that error has crept in. And so it has come about that the word "theory" has become associated with a feeling of uncertainty; the view is prevalent that the more "theoretical" is a proposition, the less should be the conviction of its truth; conversely propositions are apt to be termed theories simply because their truth is not certain.

There is no need to insist on the fallacy of this opinion in its cruder forms. The desire of many half-educated persons to rely on "practical conclusions" rather than on the reasoning of the "theorist" is founded merely on ignorance and on an inability to differentiate between the kinds of thought likely to lead to truth and those which may be associated with error. It is certainly true that, if a conclusion can be obtained by a brief and simple train of reasoning, to seek to attain it by complicated argument is to court the introduction of error. But the attempt to avoid complex reasoning often results only in the concealment of it. The views of "practical men" are usually derived from assumptions and arguments no less complex than those on which theory is based; they are more and not less liable to error because they are less openly expressed. The idea that there are propositions "true in theory, but false in practice" has its foundation only in the incompetence of the uninitiated to understand theory, and in their habit of applying propositions to circumstances entirely foreign to the theory. To those who have not the power to think, theory will always be dangerous.

But the association of the word theory with a feeling of uncertainty extends to those who are quite free from such vulgar errors, and it is of the greatest importance for our present purpose to break that association at the outset. It is connected both as cause and as effect with the failure to recognise the true nature and even the distinctive characteristics of the class of propositions which we are about to consider. It is the cause of that failure, since the observation that these propositions are distinguished from others by a lesser certainty has obscured the fact that they are distinguished by other features as well; it is the effect of that failure, since the confusion in a single class of propositions essentially different in their nature has led directly to error which would have been avoided if that difference had been appreciated. It may turn out that the propositions which it is proposed to call theories can never attain to the same certainty as laws, but this result must follow on an examination of the nature of the propositions; for since laws are also not wholly free from the possibility of error, the difference can never serve to distinguish them from laws.

Closely connected with "theory" is another word, "hypothesis". In fact the two terms are often regarded, especially in the older literature, as synonymous; Laplace's Nebular Theory and Nebular Hypothesis are used indifferently. An hypothesis is, strictly speaking, a proposition which is put forward for consideration, and concerning the truth or falsity of which nothing is asserted until the consideration is completed. It is thus necessarily associated with doubt, but with doubt of a negative rather than of a positive kind, with the doubt which consists of a suspense of judgement rather than with the doubt which consists of an inclination to disbelieve. In current usage, however, the word, especially in the adjectival form, almost always connotes doubt of the second kind; to term a view hypothetical is practically equivalent to expressing dissent from it. From this connotation I want also to be free. The word will be given a special sense which is justified by its origin to this extent that an hypothesis will always be a proposition which cannot be judged to be either true or false unless there are added to it certain other propositions, although it has a distinct significance apart from these other propositions. Hypothesis and hypothetical must be taken to imply doubt of the first kind and never doubt of the second.

What I Do Mean by a Theory. I have now stated what I do not mean by a theory and an hypothesis; it remains to state what I do mean.

A theory is a connected set of propositions which are divided into two groups. One group consists of statements about some collection of ideas which are characteristic of the theory; the other group consists of statements of the relation between these ideas and some other ideas of a different nature. The first group will be termed collectively the "hypothesis" of the theory; the second group the "dictionary". The hypothesis is so called, in accordance with the sense that has just been stated, because the propositions composing it are incapable of proof or of disproof by themselves; they must be significant, but, taken apart from the dictionary, they appear arbitrary assumptions. They may be considered accordingly as providing a "definition by postulate" of the ideas which are characteristic of the hypothesis. The ideas which are related by means of the dictionary to the ideas of the hypothesis are, on the other hand, such that something is known about them apart from the theory. It must be possible to determine, apart from all knowledge of the theory, whether certain propositions involving these ideas are true or false. The dictionary relates some of these propositions of which the truth or falsity is known to certain propositions involving the hypothetical ideas by stating that if the first set of propositions is true then the second set is true and vice versa; this relation may be expressed by the statement that the first set implies the second.

In scientific theories (for it seems that there may be sets of propositions having exactly the same features in departments of knowledge other than science) the ideas connected by means of the dictionary to the hypothetical ideas are always concepts, that is collections of fundamental judgements related in laws by uniform association; and the propositions involving these ideas, of which the truth or falsity is known, are always laws. Accordingly those ideas involved in a theory which are not hypothetical ideas will be termed concepts; it must be remembered that this term is used in a very special sense; concepts depend for their validity on laws, and any proposition in which concepts are related to concepts is again a law. Whether there is any necessary limitation on the nature of the ideas which can be admitted as hypothetical ideas is a question which requires much consideration; but one limitation is obviously imposed at the outset by the proviso that propositions concerning them are arbitrary, namely that they must not be concepts. As a matter of fact the hypothetical ideas of most of the important theories of physics, but not of other sciences, are mathematical constants and variables. (Except when the distinction is important, the term "variable" will be used in this chapter to include constants.)

The theory is said to be true if propositions concerning the hypothetical ideas, deduced from the hypothesis, are found, according to the dictionary, to imply propositions concerning the concepts which are true, that is to imply laws; for all true propositions concerning concepts are laws. And the theory is said to explain certain laws if it is these laws which are implied by the propositions concerning the hypothetical ideas.

An illustration will make the matter clearer. To spare the feelings of the scientific reader and to save myself from his indignation, I will explain at the outset that the example is wholly fantastic, and that a theory of this nature would not be of the slightest importance in science. But when it has been considered we shall be in a better position to understand why it is so utterly unimportant, and in what respects it differs from valuable scientific theories.

The hypothesis consists of the following mathematical propositions:

(1) $u, v, w, \ldots$ are independent variables.

(2) a is a constant for all values of these variables.

(3) b is a constant for all values of these variables.

(4) $c = d$, where c and d are dependent variables.

The dictionary consists of the following propositions:

(1) The assertion that $(c^2 + d^2)a = R$, where R is a positive and rational number, implies the assertion that the resistance of some definite piece of pure metal is R.

(2) The assertion that $cd/b = T$ implies the assertion that the temperature of the same piece of pure metal is T.

From the hypothesis we deduce

$$(c^2 + d^2)a / \frac{cd}{b} = 2ab = \text{constant}.$$

Interpreting this proposition by means of the dictionary we arrive at the following law:

The ratio of the resistance of a piece of pure metal to its absolute temperature is constant.

This proposition is a true law (or for our purpose may be taken as such). The theory is therefore true and explains the law.

This example, absurd though it may seem, will serve to illustrate some of the features which are of importance in actual theories. In the first place, we may observe the nature of the propositions, involving respectively the hypothetical ideas and the concepts, which are stated by the dictionary to imply each other. When the hypothetical ideas are mathematical variables, the concepts are measurable concepts (an idea of which much will be said hereafter), and the propositions related by mutual implication connect the variables, or some function of them, to the same number as these measurable concepts. When such a relation is stated by the dictionary it will be said for brevity that the function of the hypothetical ideas "is" the measurable concept; thus, we shall say that $(c^2 + d^2)a$ and cd/b "are" respectively the resistance and temperature. But it must be insisted that this nomenclature is adopted only for brevity; it is not meant that in any other sense of that extremely versatile word "is" $(c^2 + d^2)a$ is the resistance; for there are some senses of that word in which a function of variables can no more "be" a measurable concept than a railway engine can "be" the year represented by the same number.

If an hypothetical idea is directly stated by the dictionary to be some measurable concept, that idea is completely determined and every proposition about its value can be tested by experiment. But in the example which has been taken this condition is not fulfilled. It is only functions of the hypothetical ideas which are measurable concepts. Moreover since only two functions, which involve four mathematical variables and between which one relation is stated by the hypothesis, are stated to be measurable concepts, it is impossible by a determination of those concepts to assign definitely numerical values to them. If some third function of them had been stated to be some third measurable concept, then it would have been possible to assign to all of them numerical values in an unique manner. If further some fourth function has been similarly involved in the dictionary, the question would have arisen whether the values determined from one set of three functions is consistent with those determined from another set of three.

These distinctions are important. There is obviously a great difference between a theory in which some proposition based on experiment can be asserted about each of the hypothetical ideas, and one in which nothing can be said about these ideas separately, but only about combinations of them. There is also a difference between those in which several statements about those ideas can be definitely shown to be consistent and those in which such statements are merely known not to be inconsistent. In these respects actual theories differ in almost all possible degrees; it very often happens that some of the hypothetical ideas can be directly determined by experiment while others cannot; and in such cases there is an important difference between the two classes of ideas. Those which can be directly determined are often confused with the concepts to which they are directly related, while those which cannot are recognised as distinctly theoretical. But it must be noticed that a distinction of this nature has no foundation. The ideas of the hypothesis are never actually concepts; they are related to concepts only by means of the dictionary. Whatever the nature of the dictionary, all theories have this in common that no proposition based on experimental evidence can be asserted concerning the hypothetical ideas except on the assumption that the propositions of the theory are true. This is a most important matter which must be carefully borne in mind in all our discussions.

It will be observed that in our example there are no propositions in the dictionary relating any of the independent variables of the hypothesis to measurable concepts. This feature is characteristic of such theories. The nature of the connection between the independent variables and the concepts is clear from the use made, in the deduction of the laws, of the fact that a and b are constants, not varying with the independent variables. The conclusion that the electrical resistance is proportional to the absolute temperature would not follow unless $(c^2 + d^2)a$ were the resistance in the same state of the system as that in which cd/b is the temperature; and on the other hand it would not follow if a and b were not the same constants in all the propositions of the dictionary. Accordingly the assertion that a or b is a constant must imply that it is the same so long as the state of the system to which the concepts refer is the same; the independent variables on the contrary may change without a corresponding change in the state of the system. If therefore there is to be in the dictionary a proposition introducing the independent variables, it must state that a change in the independent variables does *not* imply a change in the state of the system; the omission of these variables from the dictionary must be taken to mean a definite negative statement. On the other hand, the independent variables may bear some relation to measurable concepts, so long as these concepts are not properties of the system. Thus, in almost all theories of this type, one of the independent variables is called the "time", and the use of this name indicates that it is related in some manner to the physically measurable "time" since some agreed datum. It is to be noted that a relation between one of the independent variables and physically measured time is not inconsistent with the statement that a change in this variable does not imply any change in the state of the system; for it is one of the essential properties of a system that its state should be, in a certain degree and within certain limits, independent of the time.

In some theories again, there are dependent variables which are not mentioned in the dictionary. But in such cases the absence of mention is not to be taken as involving the definite assertion that there is no relation between these variables and the concepts. It must always be regarded as possible that a further development of the theory may lead to their introduction into the dictionary.

An Example of Physical Theories. The fantastic example on which this discussion has been based was introduced in order that, in defining a theory and examining some features of its formal constitution, we might be free from associated ideas which would be sure to arise if the example were taken from any actual theory. It is easier thus to realise the difference between the hypothesis of the theory and the dictionary, and between the nature of the ideas which are characteristic of those two parts of the theory, or to recognise that numerical values can be attributed by experiment to the hypothetical ideas only in virtue of the propositions of the theory. But now we have to consider whether there are any actual scientific propositions which have this formal constitution, and, if there are, whether the application of the term theory to them accords with the usual practice; further we have to decide, if we answer these questions in the affirmative, what it is that gives them a value so very much greater than that of the absurd example which has been used so far. For this purpose an actual scientific proposition will be taken which is generally considered to have considerable value and is always called a theory; and it will be shown that it has the formal constitution which has just been explained. It will thus appear that in one instance at least our definition accords with ordinary usage.

The theory which will be selected is the dynamical theory of gases. We shall start with it in its very simplest form, in which it explains only the laws of Boyle and Gay-Lussac. For such explanation no account need be taken of collisions between the molecules, which may therefore be supposed to be of infinitely small size. Though the theory in this form is known now not to be true, it will be admitted that it is as much a theory in this form as in its more complex modern form. By starting with the simplest form we shall abbreviate our original discussion and at the same time permit the interesting process of the development of a theory to be traced. And when the development of the theory is mentioned, it should be explained that the development traced will not be that which has actually occurred but that which might have occurred; no attention is paid to merely historical considerations. One further word of warning should be given at the outset. Objections have at times been raised to this theory, and to all of similar type, by those who would admit theories of a somewhat different nature. By taking the dynamical theory of gases as an example I am not overlooking these objections or assuming in any way that all scientific theories are essentially the same in nature as the example; we shall discuss these matters later.

Let us then attempt to express the theory in the form which has been explained. The hypothesis of the theory may be stated as follows:

(1) There is a single independent variable t.

(2) There are three constants, m, v, and l, independent of t.

(3) There are $3n$ dependent variables (x_s, y_s, z_s) $(s = 1 \text{ to } n)$ which

are continuous functions of t. They form a continuous three-dimensional series and are such that $(x_s^2 + y_s^2 + z_s^2)$ is invariant for all linear transformations of the type $x' = ax + by + cz$. (This last sentence is merely a way of saying that (x, y, z) are related like rectangular coordinates; but since any definitely spatial notions might give the idea that the properties of the (x, y, z) were somehow determined by experiment, they have been avoided.)

(4) $\frac{d}{dt}(x_s, y_s, z_s)$ is constant, except when (x_s, y_s, z_s) is 0 or l; when it attains either of these values it changes sign.

(5) $\frac{1}{n}\sum_{1}^{n}\left(\frac{dx_s}{dt}\right)^2 = v^2$, and similar propositions for y_s and z_s.

The dictionary contains the following propositions:

(1) l is the length of the side of a cubical vessel in which a "perfect" gas is contained.

(2) nm is the mass of the gas, M.

(3) $\frac{1}{\alpha}mv^2$ is T, the absolute temperature of the gas, where α is some number which will vary with the arbitrary choice of the degree of temperature.[1]

(4) Let $\Delta m\frac{dx_s}{dt}$ be the change in $m\frac{dx_s}{dt}$ which occurs when x_s attains the value l; let $\Sigma_\gamma \Delta m\frac{dx_s}{dt}$ be the sum of all values of $\Delta m\frac{dx_s}{dt}$ for which t lies between t and $t + \gamma$; let

$$(p_a, p_b, p_c) = \mathrm{Lt}_{n\to\infty,\gamma\to\infty} \sum_{s=1}^{s=n} \frac{1}{\gamma}\Sigma_\gamma \Delta m\frac{d(x_s, y_s, z_s)}{dt},$$

then pa, pb, pc are the pressures P_a, P_b, P_c on three mutually perpendicular walls of the cubical containing vessel.

From the propositions of the hypothesis it is possible to prove that

$$p_a = p_b = p_c = \frac{1}{3l^3}nmv^2.$$

But l^3 is V, the volume of the gas. If we interpret this proposition according to the dictionary we find

[1] The occurrence of α needs some remark. Is it a hypothetical idea or a measurable concept? It is neither. We shall consider its nature when we deal with temperature, but it may be stated here briefly why a number of this kind occurs in this entry in the dictionary and not in the others. The reason is this. Experiment shows that pv is proportional to T. For various reasons, which we shall discuss, we desire that the factor of proportionality shall *not* change if the unit of mass or the unit of pressure is changed; but we do not object to its changing when the degree of temperature changes. If we gave the factor a definite value once and for all, the degree of temperature would have to change when the units of mass and pressure changed; we wish to avoid this necessity and do so by changing the value of α when we change the degree. The value of α is therefore as purely arbitrary as the choice of a unit in any system of measurement.

$$P_a = P_b = P_c = \frac{T}{V} \cdot \frac{an}{3},$$

which is the expression of Boyle's and Gay-Lussac's Laws, since $\frac{an}{3}$ is constant.

The theory is here expressed in a form exactly similar to that of our original example, and it will now be seen that this form is not wholly artificial, but has a real significance. In explaining the laws by the theory, we do actually deduce propositions from the hypothesis and interpret them in experimental terms by means of the dictionary. Moreover the distinction between the various kinds of variable in respect of their connection with measurable concepts is apparent. l is directly connected by the dictionary to a measurable concept, and the attribution to it of a numerical value requires nothing but a knowledge of the dictionary; the hypothesis is not involved. At the other extreme, the variables or constants n, m, x_s, y_s, z_s cannot be given numerical values by experiment even with help of the hypothesis; only functions of these variables and not the variables separately can be determined. Between these two extremes lies the constant v. We have deduced from the hypothesis that $v^2 = \frac{3l^3 p_a}{nm}$. The right-hand side of this equation can be given by experiment a numerical value, namely $\frac{3VP_a}{M}$, by means of the dictionary, so that v can also be evaluated. But this evaluation depends wholly on the acceptance of the propositions of the hypothesis; apart from those propositions a statement that v has a certain numerical value does not assert anything which can be proved by experiment.

Having thus shown that the dynamical theory of gases is a theory in our sense, we must now ask what is the difference between this valuable theory and the trivial example with which we began? It lies, of course, in the fact that the propositions of the hypothesis of the dynamical theory of gases display an analogy which the corresponding propositions of the other theory do not display. The propositions of the hypothesis are very similar in form to the laws which would describe the motion of a large number of infinitely small and highly elastic bodies contained in a cubical box. If we had such a number of particles, each of mass m, occupying points in a box of side l represented by the coordinates (x_s, y_s, z_s), and initially in motion, then their momentum would change sign at each impact on the walls of the box. $l^2(p_a, p_b, p_c)$ would be the rate of change of momentum at the walls of the box and would, accordingly, be the average force exerted upon those walls. And so on; it is unnecessary to state the analogy down to its smallest details. All these symbols, m, l, t, x, y, z, . . . would denote the numerical values of actually measurable physical concepts, and it would be a law that they were related in the way described; if they were actually measured and the resulting numerical values inserted in the equations stated those equations would be satisfied.

Further the propositions of the dictionary are suggested by the analogy displayed by the propositions of the hypothesis. p is called the "pressure", and the pressure of the gas P is specially related to the variable p, because p, in the law to which the hypothesis is analogous, would be the average pressure on the walls of the box actually observed. Similar considerations suggested the establishment of the relation between nm and the total mass of the gas, and between l^3 and its volume. The basis of the relation established between T and mv^2 is rather more complex, and its full consideration must be left till we deal in detail with the theory as a part of actual physics; but again it lies in an analogy. Speaking roughly, we may say that the relation is made because, in the law of the elastic particles, mv^2 would be a magnitude which would be found to remain constant so long as the box containing the particles was isolated from all exterior interference, while in the case of the gas the temperature is found so to remain constant during complete isolation.

The Importance of the Analogy. We see then that the class of physical theories of which the theory of gases is a type has two characteristics. First they are of the form which has been described, consisting of an hypothesis and a dictionary; if they are to be true, they must be such that laws which are actually found to be true by observation can be deduced from the hypothesis by means of logical reasoning combined with translation through the dictionary. But in order that a theory may be valuable it must have a second characteristic; it must display an analogy. The propositions of the hypothesis must be analogous to some known laws.

This manner of expressing the formal constitution of a theory is probably not familiar to most readers, but there is nothing new in the suggestion that analogy with laws plays an important part in the development of theories. No systematic writer on the principles of science is in the least inclined to overlook the intimate connection between analogy and theories or hypotheses. Nevertheless it seems to me that most of them have seriously misunderstood the position. They speak of analogies as "aids" to the formations of hypotheses (by which they usually mean what I have termed theories) and to the general progress of science. But in the view which is urged here analogies are not "aids" to the establishment of theories; they are an utterly essential part of theories, without which theories would be completely valueless and unworthy of the name. It is often suggested that the analogy leads to the formulation of the theory, but that once the theory is formulated the analogy has served its purpose and may be removed and forgotten. Such a suggestion is absolutely false and perniciously misleading. If physical science were a purely logical science, if its object were to establish a set of propositions all true and all logically connected but characterised by no other feature, then possibly this view might be correct. Once the theory was established and shown to lead by purely logical deduction to the laws to be explained, then certainly the analogy might be abandoned as having no further significance. But, if this were true, there would never have been any need for the analogy to be introduced. Any fool can invent a logically satisfactory theory to explain any law. There is as a matter of fact no satisfactory physical theory which explains the variation of the resistance of a metal with the temperature. It took me about a quarter of an hour to elaborate the theory given on p. 291; and yet it is, I maintain, formally as satisfactory as any theory in physics. If nothing but this were required we should never lack theories to explain our laws; a schoolboy in a day's work could solve the problems at which generations have laboured in vain by the most trivial process of trial and error. What is wrong with the theory of p. 291, what makes it absurd and unworthy of a single moment's consideration, is that it does not display any analogy; it is just because an analogy has not been used in its development that it is so completely valueless.

Analogy, so far from being a help to the establishment of theories, is the greatest hindrance. It is never difficult to find a theory which will explain the laws logically; what is difficult is to find one which will explain them logically and at the same time display the requisite analogy. Nor is it true that, once the theory is developed, the analogy becomes unimportant. If it were found that the analogy was false it would at once lose its value; if it were presented to someone unable to appreciate it, for him the theory would have little value. To regard analogy as an aid to the invention of theories is as absurd as to regard melody as an aid to the composition of sonatas. If the satisfaction of the laws of harmony and the formal principles of development were all that were required of music, we could all be great composers; it is the absence of the melodic sense which prevents us all attaining musical eminence by the simple process of purchasing a text-book.

The reason why the perverse view that analogies are merely an incidental help to the discovery of theories has ever gained credence lies, I believe, in a false opinion as to the nature of theories. I said just now that it was a commonplace that analogies were important in the framing of hypotheses, and that the name "hypotheses" was usually given in this connection to the propositions (or sets of propositions) which are here termed theories. This statement is perfectly true, but it is not generally recognised by such writers that the "hypotheses" of which they speak are a distinct class of propositions, and especially that they are wholly different from the class of laws; there is a tendency to regard an "hypothesis" merely as a law of which full proof is not yet forthcoming.

If this view were correct, it might be true that the analogy was a mere auxiliary to the discovery of laws and of little further use when the law was discovered. For once the law had been proposed the method of ascertaining whether or no it were true would depend in no way on the analogy; if the "hypothesis" were a law, its truth would be tested like that of any other law by examining whether the observations asserted to be connected by the relation of uniformity were or were not so connected. According as the test succeeded or failed, the law would be judged true or false; the analogy would have nothing to do with the matter. If the test succeeded, the law would remain true, even if it subsequently appeared that the analogy which suggested it was false; and if the test failed, it would remain untrue, however complete and satisfactory the analogy appeared to be.

A Theory Is Not a Law. But a theory is not a law; it cannot be proved, as a law can, by direct experiment; and the method by which it was suggested is not unimportant. For a theory may often be accepted without the performance of any additional experiments at all; so far as it is based on experiments, those experiments are often made and known before the theory is suggested. Boyle's Law and Gay-Lussac's Law were known before the dynamical theory of gases was framed; and the theory was accepted, or partially accepted, before any other experimental laws which can be deduced from it were known. The theory was an addition to scientific knowledge which followed on no increase of experimental knowledge and on the establishment of no new laws; it cannot therefore have required for its proof new experimental knowledge. The reasons why it was accepted as providing something valuable which was not contained in Boyle's and Gay-Lussac's Laws were not experimental. The reason for which it was accepted was based directly on the analogy by which it was suggested; with a failure of the analogy, all reason for accepting it would have disappeared.

The conclusion that a theory is not a law is most obvious when it is such that there are hypothetical ideas contained in it which are not completely determined by experiment, such ideas for example as the m, n, x, y, z in the dynamical theory of gases in its simple form. For in this case the theory states something, namely propositions about these ideas separately, which cannot be either proved or disproved by experiment; it states something, that is, which cannot possibly be a law, for all laws, though they may not always be capable of being proved by experiment, are always capable of being disproved by it. It may be suggested that it is only because the theory which has been taken as an example is of this type that it has been possible to maintain that it is not a law. In the other extreme, when all the hypothetical ideas are directly stated by the dictionary to "be" measurable concepts, the conclusion is much less obvious; for then a statement can be made about each of the hypothetical ideas which, if it is not actually a law, can be proved and disproved by experiment. This condition is attained only in theories of a special, though a very important type, which will receive attention presently.

The case which demands further consideration immediately is that in which the dictionary relates functions of some, but not all, of the hypothetical ideas to measurable concepts, and yet these functions are sufficiently numerous to determine all the hypothetical ideas. In this case it is true that propositions can be stated about each of the hypothetical ideas which can be proved or disproved by experiment. Thus, in our example, if one litre of gas has a volume mass of 0.09 gm. when the pressure is a million dynes per cm.^{2} then, in virtue of this experimental knowledge, it can be stated that v is 1.8×10^5 cm./sec. A definite statement can be made about the hypothetical idea v on purely experimental grounds. If the dictionary mentioned sufficient functions of the other ideas, similar definite experimental statements might be made about them. If the theory can thus be reduced to a series of definite statements on experimental grounds, ought it not to be regarded as a law, or at least as a proposition as definitely experimental as a law?

I maintain not. A proposition or set of propositions is not the same thing as another set to which they are logically equivalent and which are implied by them. They may differ in meaning. By the meaning of a proposition I mean (the repetition of the word is useful) the ideas which are called to mind when it is asserted. A theory may be logically equivalent to a set of experimental statements, but it means something perfectly different; and it is its meaning which is important rather than its logical equivalence. If logical equivalence were all that mattered, the absurd theory of p. 291 would be as important as any other; it is absurd because it means nothing, evokes no ideas, apart from the laws which it explains. A theory is valuable, and is a theory in any sense important for science, only if it evokes ideas which are not contained in the laws which it explains. The evocation of these ideas is even more valuable than the logical equivalence to the laws. Theories are often accepted and valued greatly, by part of the scientific world at least, even if it is known that they are not quite true and are not strictly equivalent to any experimental laws, simply because the ideas which they bring to mind are intrinsically valuable. It is because men differ about intrinsic values that it has been necessary to insert the proviso, "by part of the scientific world at least"; for ideas which may be intrinsically valuable to some people may not be so to others. It is here that theories differ fundamentally from laws. Laws mean nothing but what they assert. They assert that certain judgements of the external world are related by uniformity, and they mean nothing more; if it is shown that there may be a case in which these judgements are not so related, then what the law asserts is false, and, since nothing remains of the law but this false assertion, the law has no further value. We can get agreement concerning this relation and we can therefore get agreement as to the value of laws.

The Development of Theories. The distinction between what a theory means and what it asserts is of the utmost importance for the comprehension of all physical science. And it is in order to insist on this distinction that the case has been considered when all the hypothetical ideas can be determined by experiment, although not all of them are stated by the dictionary to "be" concepts. As a matter of fact I do not think this case ever occurs, though we cannot be certain of that conclusion until all physics has been examined in detail. There is always, or almost always, some hypothetical idea propositions concerning which cannot be proved or disproved by experiment; and a theory always asserts, as well as means, something which cannot be interpreted in terms of experiment. Nevertheless it is true that a theory is the more satisfactory the more completely the hypothetical ideas in it can be experimentally determined; those ideas may be valuable even if nothing can be stated definitely about them, but they are still more valuable, if something can be stated definitely. Thus, in our example, the theory is valuable even though we cannot determine m or n; but it will be more valuable if they can be determined. Accordingly when a theory containing such undetermined ideas is presented and appears to be true, efforts are always directed to determine as many as possible of the undetermined ideas still remaining in it.

The determination of the hypothetical ideas is effected, as we have noticed before, by the addition of new propositions to the hypothesis or to the dictionary, stating new relations of the hypothetical ideas to each other or to the concepts. The process demands some attention because it is intimately connected with a very important property of theories, namely their power to predict laws in much the same way as laws predict events. In passing it may be noted that a failure to distinguish a law from an event and a consequent confusion of two perfectly distinct kinds of prediction has also tended to obscure the difference between a theory and a law.

There is an important difference between the addition of new propositions to the hypothesis and to the dictionary. The hypothesis gives the real meaning of the theory and involves the analogy which confers on it its value; the dictionary uses the analogy, and the propositions contained in it are usually suggested by the analogy, but it adds nothing to it. Accordingly a change in the hypothesis involves to some extent a change in the essence of a theory and makes it in some degree a new theory; an addition to the dictionary does not involve such a change. If, then, a new law can be deduced by the theory by a simple addition to the dictionary, that law has been in the fullest and most complete sense predicted by the theory; for it is a result obtained by no alteration of the essence of the theory whatever. On the other hand if, in order to explain some new law or in order to predict a new one, a change in the hypothesis is necessary, it is shown that the original theory was not quite complete and satisfactory. The explanation of a new law and the determination of one more hypothetical idea by addition to the dictionary is thus a very powerful and convincing confirmation of the theory; a similar result by an addition to the hypothesis is, in general, rather evidence against its original form.

But the degree in which the necessity for an alteration in the hypothesis militates against the acceptance of the theory depends largely on the nature of the alteration. If it arises directly and immediately out of the analogy on which the hypothesis is based, it scarcely is an alteration. Thus, in the theory of gases in the form in which it has been stated so far, the only dynamical proposition (or more accurately the only proposition analogous to a dynamical law) which has been introduced is that the momentum is reversed in sign at an impact with the wall, while its magnitude is unchanged. But in dynamical systems this condition is fulfilled only if the systems are conservative; it is natural therefore to extend the hypothesis and to include in it any other propositions concerning the hypothetical ideas which are analogous to other laws [2] of a conservative system. Such an extension involves no essential alteration of the theory, but it permits the explanation of additional laws and thus provides arguments for rather than against the theory. For example, if the extension is made (the new propositions are so complex if they are stated in a full analytical form that space need not be wasted in stating them) the effect on the behaviour of the gas of the motion of the walls of the vessel can be deduced and the laws of adiabatic expansion predicted. Here no addition is made to the dictionary; only the hypothesis is altered. But if the dictionary is altered, the establishment of a complete analogy between the hypothesis and the laws of a conservative system leads immediately to the view that $\frac{1}{2}nmv^2$ is the energy of the gas and to the explanation of all the laws, involving specific heats, which follow directly from Boyle's and Gay-Lussac's laws combined with the doctrine of energy and with the proposition that quantity of heat is energy. All these ideas are essentially contained in the original theory which can hardly be said to be altered by explicit statement of them. As a matter of fact they seem to have been stated in the earliest forms of the dynamical theory, although they were not necessary to explain the laws of Boyle and Gay-Lussac.

However further inquiry shows that a more important alteration is necessary. So long as we are considering only perfect gases (and it must be insisted that some gases over certain ranges are experimentally perfect) and no measurable concepts other than pressure, volume, temperature, and quantity of heat, the theory in its original form, with all its natural implications, explains all the experimental laws. The only objection to it is that the constants m, n, x, y, z remain undetermined. But if we attempt to explain the laws of viscosity or conduction of heat, we meet with new objections. The dynamical analogy leads immediately to an entry in the dictionary relating viscosity to the hypothetical ideas; for viscosity consists experimentally in the transfer of momentum from one to the other of two parallel planes in relative motion. But in the system of elastic particles there would also be such a transfer of momentum if the sides of the box in which they were contained were moving relatively to each other, and the known laws of such a system show that there is a relation between this transfer of momentum and the masses and velocities of the particles together with the distance and relative velocity of the sides; the transfer of momentum is a function of these magnitudes. Accordingly it is suggested that a similar

[2] The "laws" of a conservative system are not really laws, but for the present they may pass as such.

function of the corresponding variables of the hypothesis should be related by means of the dictionary to the viscosity of the gas.

We can now deduce the relation which should exist according to the theory between the pressure, density, and temperature of the gas and its viscosity. The relation predicted does not accord with that determined experimentally; in particular it is found that the theory predicts that the coefficient of viscosity will be determined by the size and shape of the containing vessel, whereas experiment shows that it depends, in a given gas, only on the density and temperature.[3] Here the addition of an entry to the dictionary has led to a new law, but a law which is false. The theory is not true; it must be altered; and it can only be altered by changing the hypothesis. The change which is made is, of course, the introduction of a new hypothetical idea, a mathematical constant σ, and a consequent modification of the equations relating the variables and constants. The hypothesis thus modified is analogous to the laws of a system of elastic particles which are spheres of finite size, and the part which σ plays in those equations is the same as that of the diameter of the spheres in those laws. With this modification, and with such change in the dictionary as necessarily accompanies it, the relation between the coefficient of viscosity and the density and temperature predicted by the theory becomes in accordance with that experimentally determined.[4] The theory is once more satisfactory; and though in its earlier form the theory must be rejected, we do not regard the whole theory as false, because the new ideas introduced into the hypothesis are such an extremely natural extension of the old. If the analogy is based on the behaviour of elastic bodies, it is extremely natural to attribute to them finite dimensions.

Thermal conductivity is related to transfer of energy as the coefficient of viscosity is to transfer of momentum. The addition of an entry in the dictionary to introduce thermal conductivity is therefore suggested in just the same manner as the entry to introduce viscosity, for in the system of elastic particles which provides the analogy of the hypothesis energy as well as momentum would be transferred between the walls. No addition to the hypothesis is necessary to deduce the relation between thermal conduc-

[3] The theory which neglects the size of the molecules leads to the familiar result

$$\eta = \tfrac{1}{3}\,\rho\nu\lambda,$$

but λ, the mean free path, will be the distance that the molecules travel between the walls of the vessel, and will depend on its size and shape instead of simply on the properties of the gas, as it will if the free path is between successive collisions with molecules.

[4] Of course this statement is not true, so far as the temperature is concerned. Agreement between theory and experiment in respect of the variation of viscosity with temperature can be obtained, if at all, only by giving to the molecules some form more complex than spheres, and by introducing forces between the molecules when not in contact. It is not my object here to expound the dynamical theory, but only to use it as an example; that use is not affected by supposing things to turn out more simply than they actually do. The further statements which will be made presently and are equally untrue will not be specifically noticed. The instructed reader will not require the notice; the uninstructed will be merely confused by it.

tivity, density and temperature; the relation predicted turns out to accord with experiment. Here an addition to the dictionary alone has predicted a true law, and the theory is correspondingly strengthened.

But in spite of these alterations the objection still remains that n, m, x, y, z are undetermined; indeed an additional undetermined idea, σ, has been introduced. This addition does not, however, make matters worse, for in the original theory n and m were so connected that the determination of one would involve the determination of the other; whereas now n, m, σ are found to be so connected that a determination of one would determine all three. The determination is effected by the application of the theory to gases which are not perfect. The introduction of σ alters somewhat the laws predicted by the theory for the relation between pressure, volume and temperature; they are no longer exactly those of Boyle and Gay-Lussac. It is found experimentally that these laws are not actually experimentally true; by comparing the deviations found experimentally with those, involving σ, predicted by the theory a new relation between n, m, σ and experimentally determined magnitudes is established. These relations, in addition to those arising from viscosity or thermal conductivity, enable each of these three hypothetical ideas to be determined. Here we have (or should have, if the statements made were correct) the most powerful confirmation of the theory; not only is a new law predicted without addition to the hypothesis and confirmed by experiment, but undetermined ideas in the hypothesis are determined. If no further discrepancies between theory and experiment were found, when yet other propositions were introduced into the dictionary, for the completion and final establishment of the theory only the determination of x, y, z would be necessary.

But in this case, and in some others similar to it, special considerations make the determination of these variables less important than usual. In order to determine them completely it is necessary to know their values and the values of their first differential coefficients with respect to t for some value of t; their values for all other t's can then be deduced. But it can be shown that this knowledge is not required if it is required to determine only the limit to which some function of these variables tends as n tends to infinity.

Whatever values of (x, y, z) and $\frac{d}{dt}(x, y, z)$ are associated with the value $t = t_o$, consistent with the relation between $\frac{d}{dt}(x, y, z)$ and v which is asserted by the hypothesis, then the value for $t = T + t_o$ of

$$\mathrm{Lt}_{n \to \infty} \sum_{1}^{n} f\left(x_s, y_s, z_s, \frac{dx_s}{dt}, \frac{dy_s}{dt}, \frac{dz_s}{dt}\right),$$

where f is any function, will tend to the same limit as T tends to infinity.[5]

[5] Certain very exceptional values of the variables and certain exceptional functions should strictly be excepted from this statement.

Or, expressing the matter in terms of the analogy, the properties of any infinite collection of the particles will be the same whatever were the positions of the particles and their velocities at a previous period infinitely distant. Now all the propositions of the dictionary which involve (x, y, z) at all, involve them in the form of the limit of some function as n tends to infinity. So long as we can imagine that the values which should be attributed to them, when experiments on the gas are made, correspond to a value t_o such that the state of the system is unchanged for all values of t between t_o and $t_o - T$, where T may be greater than any assigned quantity, then the laws predicted by the theory will be the same whatever values are assumed to correspond to $t_o - T$. For various reasons into which we need not inquire for the moment, we are prepared to make the assumption contained in the last sentence. Accordingly though we cannot determine the variables we can, by assigning any "initial" value to them that we please (i.e. values at $t_o - T$), find values for them in the conditions of experiment which are indistinguishable by any experiment that we can perform from the values resulting from the assumption of any other initial values. That is to say, even if we could determine the variables, the deductions which could be made from the theory would be precisely the same as the deductions made from the theory with the assumed initial values; for if the values could be determined, these values would be associated with some initial values, and these initial values would lead to the same result as those which have been assumed.

We are therefore reconciled to the impossibility of determining these variables because we know that, if we could determine them, it would not make the slightest difference to the theory. Nevertheless, it causes us, I think, some slight mental discomfort; we feel that the theory would be even more satisfactory if they could be determined. Now the determination is impossible only so long as all the propositions in the dictionary introduce only the limits of functions when n is infinite; it would not be impossible if an entry in the dictionary could be made which introduced a function for a finite value of n. In recent years such an entry has been made in connection with the phenomenon known as Brownian motion; and the entry, without additions to the hypothesis, leads to the explanation of new laws and enables the determination of the variables to be made for certain systems. It was felt that the importance of the theory was thereby increased; and M. Perrin, on whose work the advance largely depended, wrote a book describing it entitled *Brownian motion and Molecular Reality*. He felt that his researches had made molecules real in a way that they had not been real before.

A Digression on the Use of Certain Words. It may have been noticed that, until the end of the discussion, care was taken not to use the term "molecule" which is so intimately associated with the dynamical theory. A molecule, it may be said, is what corresponds in the analogy to an elastic particle. But strictly speaking, there is nothing said in the hypothesis or the dictionary about molecules. The analogy suggests that we should call v the "mean velocity of the molecules", (x_s, y_s, z_s) the "position", and $\frac{d}{dt}(x_s, y_s, z_s)$ the "velocity" of the molecule s. Accordingly when we say that the velocity of the molecule s is so-and-so, or that the mean velocity of the molecules is so-and-so, we are asserting something which is asserted by the theory and has a very definite meaning according to the theory; further, since v can be determined by experiment through the dictionary, the second statement means something that can be interpreted in terms of observation and proved true or false by experiment. And if we say that the molecule s has a certain velocity, then again our statement will have a clear and definite meaning, so long as it is simply equivalent to the statement that the "velocity-of-the-molecule-s" is so-and-so. But it must be remembered that the hyphened words, though grammatically divisible, form a single indivisible idea. If we take out the grammatically separate words "molecule" and "velocity" and, in stating the proposition in the alternative form, allow ourselves to imply that there is a molecule which has a velocity and a velocity which the molecule has, then, the statement may perhaps be correct, but we are implying something entirely foreign to the theory. We may land ourselves in even greater difficulties if we say "there are molecules", because the analogy permits the statement "there are elastic particles", and imply that the two statements are of the same kind, supported by similar evidence. The latter statement asserts a uniform association, which is a law and defines the properties of a system. The former statement is not one of the propositions of the hypothesis; and it is very difficult to give to it any precise meaning at all. Does it state any kind of uniform association? I cannot see what form, unless it be simply that $\frac{dx_s}{dt}$ is the differential coefficient of x_s and not of some other x, or that (x_s, y_s, z_s) is a single term of the 3-dimensional series. But these are not very important propositions, or, perhaps it would be more accurate to say, they are so important that they are inextricably involved in the meaning of all mathematical symbols. In either case they do not require or admit of separate expression.

I am far from urging that we should never make the statement that there are molecules. It is a very useful and compact way of calling to our minds all the assertions and implications of the dynamical theory of gases. But it has this use only because we know all about that theory and are intimately familiar with it. To anyone not familiar with the theory it would not evoke the ideas which we associate with it; and such a person, in his endeavour to find some meaning for the phrase, would be almost certain to find a perfectly wrong meaning. If there is anyone who thinks it in the least important that science should not be misunderstood by the laity, and is at all concerned to attempt the hopeless task of preserving them from egregious error, he will be careful how he uses such a phrase. But he will be very sanguine; for however careful we are in the form of our statements, the delusion concerning the relation between grammatical form and logical content will probably be too strong for him.

A second word connected with theories which deserves special attention was purposely introduced at the end of the last section. It was said that researches on Brownian motion had proved the "reality" of molecules.

It is most important to observe this use of the word "real." No word has been productive of more confusion of thought and more futile controversy, but it is here used in a sense to which a very clear and definite meaning can be attached. When scientific men say that something is *real*, that something *really* happens or that the *real* truth about a matter is so-and-so, they are very often referring to a theory which has been proved to be true. The something that is *real* is an idea of the hypothesis of the true theory,[6] the event *really* happens if the proposition asserting it is analogous to the assertion of some event according to the laws which provide the analogy for that hypothesis, and the *real* truth about the matter is the theory which explains it. It is difficult to prove this assertion without collecting and analysing numerous examples of the use of "real" in scientific writings. That would be a very interesting but very lengthy task. It will perhaps be a better method to use in future the term real whenever it occurs naturally, and sometimes to interrupt the argument for a moment to show that what its use implies is that which has just been stated.

Lastly it will be convenient to notice another ambiguous word. The word "cause" is often used to denote the connection between a theory and the laws which it explains. Thus, it might be said that the impacts of the molecules on the walls are the "cause" of the pressure on them.

This use of the word has occasioned much confusion, for among those who believe that laws assert causal relations, it has naturally led to the fallacy that what is stated by such theories is a law. It is true that the theory asserts some kind of uniformity between the impacts and the pressure, but this relation must be carefully distinguished from that discussed in the chapter on laws; the uniformity is not something observed and determined by direct judgements of the external world; it is a consequence of intellectual processes, and is something characteristic of internal judgements. The test of universal assent may be applied. Many persons have actually asserted that they do not believe in the dynamical theory of gases and do not believe in the uniform association of impacts and pressure; and those who do believe have discovered no way of converting them or of showing that they do believe, for action will always be determined by a belief in the laws which the theory explains and not in the theory which explains them.

Yet the use of "cause" in this sense is sometimes directly related to that in the sense in which causes may be asserted by laws. For, in the sys-

[6] The statement that the "something is . . ." must be interpreted in the sense just discussed in connection with molecules.

tem of material elastic particles which provide the analogy of the theory of gases, the impact of the particles would be the cause of the pressure, at least in a psychological sense; at any rate it would be uniformly associated with it in the manner characteristic of a law, and it would be the cause if we could accept the view that laws always assert cause and effect. But in other cases the relation is not so direct, and all that is meant is that the ideas which are said to be the cause are contained in the hypothesis of the theory which explains laws in which the effect is a concept; in fact the relation of cause and effect is almost exactly that of the hypothetical ideas and the concepts in the dictionary. In yet other cases it is only meant that the concepts which are stated to be cause and effect are explained by the same theory; for instance, when it is said that the high reflecting power of silver is the effect of its high electrical conductivity, and when more is implied than that the two properties are merely associated.

It would be troublesome and superfluous to analyse all the senses in which cause and effect are occasionally used; so long as we recognise that they are used in different senses and that one of these senses implies a theoretical connection which is wholly different from the connection asserted by laws, then we are not likely to be led into error.

The Interpretation of Physics *

RUDOLF CARNAP

Physical Calculi and Their Interpretations

THE METHOD DESCRIBED with respect to geometry can be applied likewise to any other part of physics: we can first construct a calculus and then lay down the interpretation intended in the form of semantical rules, yielding a physical theory as an interpreted system with factual content. The customary formulation of a physical calculus is such that it presupposes a logico-mathematical calculus as its basis, e.g., a calculus of real numbers. To this basic calculus are added the specific primitive signs and the axioms, i.e., specific primitive sentences, of the physical calculus in question.

Thus, for instance, a calculus of mechanics of mass points can be constructed. Some predicates and functors (i.e., signs for functions) are taken as specific primitive signs, and the fundamental laws of mechanics as axioms. Then semantical rules are laid down stating that the primitive signs designate, say, the class of material particles, the three spatial coordinates of a particle x at the time t, the mass of a particle x, the class of forces acting on a particle x or at a space point s at the time t. (As we shall see later [p. 314], the interpretation can also be given indirectly, i.e., by semantical rules, not for the primitive signs, but for certain defined signs of the calculus. This procedure must be chosen if the semantical rules are to refer only to observable properties.) By the interpretation, the theorems of the calculus of mechanics become physical laws, i.e., universal statements describing certain features of events; they constitute physical mechanics as a theory with factual content which can be tested by observations. The relation of this theory to the calculus of mechanics is entirely analogous to the relation of physical to mathematical geometry. The customary division into theoretical and experimental physics corresponds roughly to the distinction between calculus and interpreted system. The work in theoretical physics consists mainly in constructing calculi and carrying out deductions

* Reprinted by kind permission of the author and publisher from *Foundations of Logic and Mathematics*, pp. 56–69, Vol. I, No. 3 of the *International Encyclopedia of Unified Science*, University of Chicago Press, 1939.

within them; this is essentially mathematical work. In experimental physics interpretations are made and theories are tested by experiments.

In order to show by an example how a deduction is carried out with the help of a physical calculus, we will discuss a calculus which can be interpreted as a theory of thermic expansion. To the primitive signs may belong the predicates 'Sol' and 'Fe', and the functors 'lg', 'te', and 'th'. Among the axioms may be A 1 and A 2. (Here, 'x', 'β' and the letters with subscripts are real number variables; the parentheses are used as in algebra and for the arguments of functors.)

A 1. For every $x, t_1, t_2, l_1, l_2, T_1, T_2, \beta$ [if [x is a Sol and $\mathrm{lg}(x,t_1) = l_1$ and $\mathrm{lg}(x,t_2) = l_2$ and $\mathrm{te}(x,t_1) = T_1$ and $\mathrm{te}(x,t_2) = T_2$ and $\mathrm{th}(x) = \beta$] then $l_2 = l_1 \times (1 + \beta \times (T_2 - T_1))$].

A 2. For every x, if [x is a Sol and x is a Fe] then $\mathrm{th}(x) = 0.000012$.

The *customary interpretation*, i.e., that for whose sake the calculus is constructed, is given by the following semantical rules. '$\mathrm{lg}(x,t)$' designates the length in centimeters of the body x at the time t (defined by the statement of a method of measurement); '$\mathrm{te}(x,t)$' designates the absolute temperature in centigrades of x at the time t (likewise defined by a method of measurement); '$\mathrm{th}(x)$' designates the coefficient of thermic expansion for the body x; 'Sol' designates the class of solid bodies; 'Fe' the class of iron bodies. By this interpretation, A 1 and A 2 become physical laws. A 1 is the law of thermic expansion in quantitative form, A 2 the statement of the coefficient of thermic expansion for iron. As A 2 shows, a statement of a physical constant for a certain substance is also a universal sentence. Further, we add semantical rules for two signs occurring in the subsequent example: the name 'c' designates the thing at such and such a place in our laboratory; the numerical variable 't' as time coordinate designates the time-point t seconds after August 17, 1938, 10:00 A.M.

Now we will analyze an example of a derivation within the calculus indicated. This derivation D_2 is, when interpreted by the rules mentioned, the deduction of a prediction from premisses giving the results of observations. The construction of the derivation D_2, however, is entirely independent of any interpretation. It makes use only of the rules of the calculus, namely, the physical calculus indicated together with a calculus of real numbers as basic calculus. We have discussed, but not written down, a similar derivation D_1, which, however, made use only of the mathematical calculus. Therefore the physical laws used had to be taken in D_1 as premisses. But here in D_2 they belong to the axioms of the calculus (A 1 and A 2, occurring as [6] and [10]). Any axiom or theorem proved in a physical calculus may be used within any derivation in that calculus without belonging to the premisses of the derivation, in exactly the same way in which a proved theorem is used within a derivation in a logical or mathematical calculus. Therefore only singular sentences (not containing variables) occur as premisses in D_2.

Derivation D_2:

Premisses	1. c is a Sol. 2. c is a Fe. 3. $\mathrm{te}(c,0) = 300$. 4. $\mathrm{te}(c,600) = 350$. 5. $\mathrm{lg}(c,0) = 1{,}000$.
Axiom A 1	6. For every $x, t_1, t_2, l_1, l_2, T_1, T_2, \beta$ [if [x is a Sol and $\mathrm{lg}(x,t_1) = l_1$ and $\mathrm{lg}(x,t_2) = l_2$ and $\mathrm{te}(x,t_1) = T_1$ and $\mathrm{te}(x,t_2) = T_2$ and $\mathrm{th}(x) = \beta$] then $l_2 = l_1 \times (1 + \beta \times (T_2 - T_1))$].
Proved mathem. theorem:	7. For every $l_1, l_2, T_1, T_2, \beta$ [$l_2 - l_1 = l_1 \times \beta \times (T_2 - T_1)$ if and only if $l_2 = l_1 \times (1 + \beta \times (T_2 - T_1))$].
(6)(7)	8. For every $x, t_1, \ldots$ (as in [6]) . . . [if [- - -] then $l_2 - l_1 = l_1 \times \beta \times (T_2 - T_1)$].
(1)(3)(4)(8)	9. For every l_1, l_2, β [if [$\mathrm{th}(c) = \beta$ and $\mathrm{lg}(c, 0) = l_1$ and $\mathrm{lg}(c,600) = l_2$] then $l_2 - l_1 = l_1 \times \beta \times (350 - 300)$].
Axiom A 2	10. For every x, if [x is a Sol and x is a Fe] then $\mathrm{th}(x) = 0.000012$.
(1)(2)(10)	11. $\mathrm{th}(c) = 0.000012$.
(9)(11)(5)	12. For every l_1, l_2 [if [$\mathrm{lg}(c,0) = l_1$ and $\mathrm{lg}(c,600) = l_2$] then $l_2 - l_1 = 1{,}000 \times 0.000012 \times (350 - 300)$].
Proved mathem. theorem:	13. $1{,}000 \times 0.000012 \times (350 - 300) = 0.6$.
(12)(13) *Conclusion:*	14. $\mathrm{lg}(c,600) - \mathrm{lg}(c,0) = 0.6$.

On the basis of the interpretation given before, the premisses are singular sentences concerning the body c. They say that c is a solid body made of iron, that the temperature of c was at 10:00 A.M. 300° abs., and at 10:10 A.M. 350° abs., and that the length of c at 10:00 A.M. was 1,000 cm. The conclusion says that the increase in the length of c from 10:00 to 10:10 A.M. is 0.6 cm. Let us suppose that our measurements have confirmed the premisses. Then the derivation yields the conclusion as a prediction which may be tested by another measurement.

Any physical theory, and likewise the whole of physics, can in this way be presented in the form of an interpreted system, consisting of a specific calculus (axiom system) and a system of semantical rules for its interpretation; the axiom system is, tacitly or explicitly, based upon a logico-mathematical calculus with customary interpretation. It is, of course, logically possible to apply the same method to any other branch of science as well. But practically the situation is such that most of them seem at the present time to be not yet developed to a degree which would suggest this strict form of presentation. There is an interesting and successful attempt of an axiomatization of certain parts of biology, especially genetics, by Woodger (Vol. I, No. 10). Other scientific fields which we may expect to be soon accessible to this method are perhaps chemistry, economics,, and some elementary parts of psychology and social science.

Within a physical calculus the mathematical and the physical theorems, i.e., C-true formulas, are treated on a par. But there is a fundamental difference between the corresponding *mathematical* and the *physical propositions* of the physical theory, i.e., the system with customary interpretation. This difference is often overlooked. That physical theorems are sometimes mistaken to be of the same nature as mathematical theorems is perhaps due to several factors, among them the fact that they contain mathematical symbols and numerical expressions and that they are often formulated incompletely in the form of a mathematical equation (e.g., A 1 simply in the form of the last equation occurring in it). A mathematical proposition may contain only logical signs, e.g., 'for every m, n, $m + n = n + m$', or descriptive signs also, if the mathematical calculus is applied in a descriptive system. In the latter case the proposition, although it contains signs not belonging to the mathematical calculus, may still be provable in this calculus, e.g., '$\mathrm{lg}(c) + \mathrm{lg}(d) = \mathrm{lg}(d) + \mathrm{lg}(c)$' ('lg' designates length as before). A physical proposition always contains descriptive signs, because otherwise it could not have factual content; in addition, it usually contains also logical signs. Thus the difference between mathematical theorems and physical theorems in the interpreted system does not depend upon the kinds of signs occurring but rather on the kind of truth of the theorems. The truth of a mathematical theorem, even if it contains descriptive signs, is not dependent upon any facts concerning the designata of these signs. We can determine its truth if we know only the semantical rules; hence it is L-true. (In the example of the theorem just mentioned, we need not know the length of the body c.) The truth of a physical theorem, on the other hand, depends upon the properties of the designata of the descriptive signs occurring. In order to determine its truth, we have to make observations concerning these designata; the knowledge of the semantical rules is not sufficient. (In the case of A 2, e.g., we have to carry out experiments with solid iron bodies.) Therefore, a physical theorem, in contradistinction to a mathematical theorem, has factual content.

Elementary and Abstract Terms

We find among the concepts of physics—and likewise among those of the whole of empirical science—differences of abstractness. Some are more elementary than others, in the sense that we can apply them in concrete cases on the basis of observations in a more direct way than others. The others are more abstract; in order to find out whether they hold in a certain case, we have to carry out a more complex procedure, which, however, also finally rests on observations. Between quite elementary concepts and those of high abstraction there are many intermediate levels. We shall not try to give an exact definition for 'degree of abstractness'; what is meant will become sufficiently clear by the following series of sets of concepts, proceeding from elementary to abstract concepts: bright, dark, red, blue, warm, cold, sour, sweet, hard, soft (all concepts of this first set are meant as properties of things, not as sense-data); coincidence; length; length of time; mass, velocity, acceleration, density, pressure; temperature, quantity of heat; electric charge, electric current, electric field; electric potential, electric resistance, coefficient of induction, frequency of oscillation; wave function.

Suppose that we intend to construct an interpreted system of physics —or of the whole of science. We shall first lay down a calculus. Then we have to state semantical rules for the specific signs, i.e., for the physical terms. Since the physical terms form a system, i.e., are connected with one another, obviously we need not state a semantical rule for each of them. For which terms, then, must we give rules, for the elementary or for the abstract ones? We can, of course, state a rule for any term, no matter what its degree of abstractness, in a form like this: 'the term 'te' designates temperature', provided the metalanguage used contains a corresponding expression (here the word 'temperature') to specify the designatum of the term in question. But suppose we have in mind the following purpose for our syntactical and semantical description of the system of physics: the description of the system shall teach a layman to understand it, i.e., to enable him to apply it to his observations in order to arrive at explanations and predictions. A layman is meant as one who does not know physics but has normal senses and understands a language in which observable properties of things can be described (e.g., a suitable part of everyday nonscientific English). A rule like 'the sign '*P*' designates the property of being blue' will do for the purpose indicated; but a rule like 'the sign '*Q*' designates the property of being electrically charged' will not do. In order to fulfil the purpose, we have to give semantical rules for elementary terms only, connecting them with observable properties of things. For our further discussion we suppose the system to consist of rules of this kind, as indicated in the following diagram.

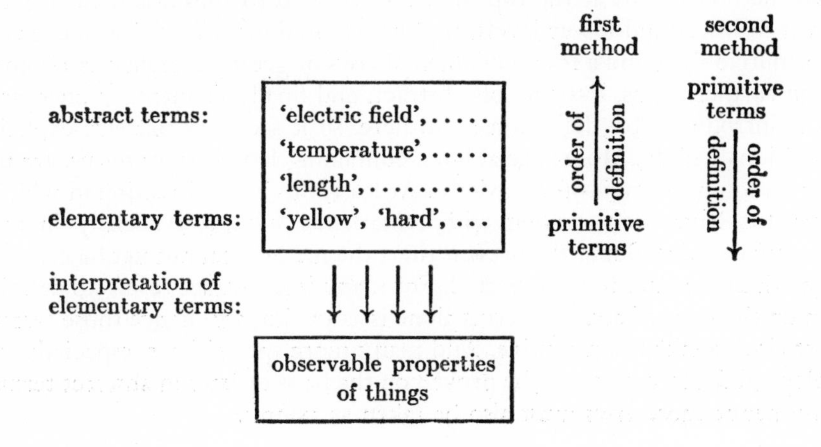

Now let us go back to the construction of the calculus. We have first to decide at which end of the series of terms to start the construction. Should we take elementary terms as primitive signs, or abstract terms? Our decision to lay down the semantical rules for the elementary terms does not decide this question. Either procedure is still possible and seems to have some reasons in its favor, depending on the point of view taken. The *first method* consists in taking elementary terms as primitive and then introducing on their basis further terms step by step, up to those of highest abstraction. In carrying out this procedure, we find that the introduction of further terms cannot always take the form of explicit definitions; conditional definitions must also be used (so-called reduction sentences [see Vol. I, No. 1, p. 50]). They describe a method of testing for a more abstract term, i.e., a procedure for finding out whether the term is applicable in particular cases, by referring to less abstract terms. The first method has the advantage of exhibiting clearly the connection between the system and observation and of making it easier to examine whether and how a given term is empirically founded. However, when we shift our attention from the terms of the system and the methods of empirical confirmation to the laws, i.e., the universal theorems, of the system, we get a different perspective. Would it be possible to formulate all laws of physics in elementary terms, admitting more abstract terms only as abbreviations? If so, we would have that ideal of a science in sensationalistic form which Goethe in his polemic against Newton, as well as some positivists, seems to have had in mind. But it turns out—this is an empirical fact, not a logical necessity—that it is not possible to arrive in this way at a powerful and efficacious system of laws. To be sure, historically, science started with laws formulated in terms of a low level of abstractness. But for any law of this kind, one nearly always later found some exceptions and thus had to confine it to a narrower realm of validity. The higher the physicists went in the scale of terms, the better did they succeed in formulating laws applying to a wide range of phenomena. Hence we understand that they are inclined to choose the *second method.* This method begins at the top of the system, so to speak, and then goes down to lower and lower levels. It consists in taking a few abstract terms as primitive signs and a few fundamental laws of great generality as axioms. Then further terms, less and less abstract, and finally elementary ones, are to be introduced by definitions; and here, so it seems at present, explicit definitions will do. More special laws, containing less abstract terms, are to be proved on the basis of the axioms. At least, this is the direction in which physicists have been striving with remarkable success, especially in the past few decades. But at the present time, the method cannot yet be carried through in the pure form indicated. For many less abstract terms no definition on the basis of abstract terms alone is as yet known; hence those terms must also be taken as primitive. And many more special laws, especially in biological fields, cannot yet be proved on the basis of laws in abstract terms only; hence those laws must also be taken as axioms.

Now let us examine the result of the interpretation if the first or the second method for the construction of the calculus is chosen. In both cases the semantical rules concern the elementary signs. In the first method these signs are taken as primitive. Hence, the semantical rules give a complete interpretation for these signs and those explicitly defined on their basis. There are, however, many signs, especially on the higher levels of abstraction, which can be introduced not by an explicit definition but only by a conditional one. The interpretation which the rules give for these signs is in a certain sense incomplete. This is due not to a defect in the semantical rules but to the method by which these signs are introduced; and this method is not arbitrary but corresponds to the way in which we really obtain knowledge about physical states by our observations.

If, on the other hand, abstract terms are taken as primitive—according to the second method, the one used in scientific physics—then the semantical rules have no direct relation to the primitive terms of the system but refer to terms introduced by long chains of definitions. The calculus is first constructed floating in the air, so to speak; the construction begins at the top and then adds lower and lower levels. Finally, by the semantical rules, the lowest level is anchored at the solid ground of the observable facts. The laws, whether general or special, are not directly interpreted, but only the singular sentences. For the more abstract terms, the rules determine only an *indirect interpretation*, which is—here as well as in the first method—incomplete in a certain sense. Suppose '*B*' is defined on the basis of '*A*'; then, if '*A*' is directly interpreted, '*B*' is, although indirectly, also interpreted completely; if, however, '*B*' is directly interpreted, '*A*' is not necessarily also interpreted completely (but only if 'A' is also definable by '*B*').

To give an example, let us imagine a calculus of physics constructed, according to the second method, on the basis of primitive specific signs like 'electromagnetic field', 'gravitational field', 'electron', 'proton', etc. The system of definitions will then lead to elementary terms, e.g., to 'Fe', defined as a class of regions in which the configuration of particles fulfils certain conditions, and 'Na-yellow' as a class of space-time regions in which the temporal distribution of the electromagnetic field fulfils certain conditions. Then semantical rules are laid down stating that 'Fe' designates iron and 'Na-yellow' designates a specified yellow color. (If 'iron' is not accepted as sufficiently elementary, the rules can be stated for more elementary terms.) In this way the connection between the calculus and the realm of nature, to which it is to be applied, is made for terms of the calculus which are far remote from the primitive terms.

Let us examine, on the basis of these discussions, the example of a derivation D_2 (p. 311). The premisses and the conclusion of D_2 are singular sentences, but most of the other sentences are not. Hence the premisses and the conclusion of this as of all other derivations of the same type can be directly interpreted, understood, and confronted with the results of observations. More of an interpretation is not necessary for a practical application of a derivation. If, in confronting the interpreted premisses with our observations, we find them confirmed as true, then we accept the conclusion as a prediction and we may base a decision upon it. The sentences occurring in the derivation between premisses and conclusion are also interpreted, at least indirectly. But we need not make their interpretation explicit in order to be able to construct the derivation and to apply it. All that is necessary for its construction are the formal rules of the calculus. This is the advantage of the method of formalization, i.e., of the separation of the calculus as a formal system from the interpretation. If some persons want to come to an agreement about the formal correctness of a given derivation, they may leave aside all differences of opinion on material questions or questions of interpretation. They simply have to examine whether or not the given series of formulas fulfils the formal rules of the calculus. Here again, the function of calculi in empirical science becomes clear as instruments for transforming the expression of what we know or assume.

Against the view that for the application of a physical calculus we need an interpretation only for singular sentences, the following objection will perhaps be raised. Before we accept a derivation and believe its conclusion we must have accepted the physical calculus which furnishes the derivation; and how can we decide whether or not to accept a physical calculus for application without interpreting and understanding its axioms? To be sure, in order to pass judgment about the applicability of a given physical calculus we have to confront it in some way or other with observation, and for this purpose an interpretation is necessary. But we need no explicit interpretation of the axioms, nor even of any theorems. The empirical examination of a physical theory given in the form of a calculus with rules of interpretation is not made by interpreting and understanding the axioms and then considering whether they are true on the basis of our factual knowledge. Rather, the examination is carried out by the same procedure as that explained before for obtaining a prediction. We construct derivations in the calculus with premisses which are singular sentences describing the results of our observations, and with singular sentences which we can test by observations as conclusions. The physical theory is indirectly confirmed to a higher and higher degree if more and more of these predictions are confirmed and none of them is disconfirmed by observations. Only singular sentences with elementary terms can be directly tested; therefore, we need an explicit interpretation only for these sentences.

"Understanding" in Physics

The development of physics in recent centuries, and especially in the past few decades, has more and more led to that method in the construction, testing, and application of physical theories which we call *formalization*, i.e., the construction of a calculus supplemented by an interpretation.

It was the progress of knowledge and the particular structure of the subject matter that suggested and made practically possible this increasing formalization. In consequence it became more and more possible to forego an "intuitive understanding" of the abstract terms and axioms and theorems formulated with their help. The possibility and even necessity of abandoning the search for an understanding of that kind was not realized for a long time. When abstract, nonintuitive formulas, as, e.g., Maxwell's equations of electromagnetism, were proposed as new axioms, physicists endeavored to make them "intuitive" by constructing a "model", i.e., a way of representing electromagnetic micro-processes by an analogy to known macro-processes, e.g., movements of visible things. Many attempts have been made in this direction, but without satisfactory results. It is important to realize that the discovery of a model has no more than an aesthetic or didactic or at best a heuristic value, but is not at all essential for a successful application of the physical theory. The demand for an intuitive understanding of the axioms was less and less fulfilled when the development led to the general theory of relativity and then to quantum mechanics, involving the wave function. Many people, including physicists, have a feeling of regret and disappointment about this. Some, especially philosophers, go so far as even to contend that these modern theories, since they are not intuitively understandable, are not at all theories about nature but "mere formalistic constructions", "mere calculi". But this is a fundamental misunderstanding of the function of a physical theory. It is true a theory must not be a "mere calculus" but possess an interpretation, on the basis of which it can be applied to facts of nature. But it is sufficient, as we have seen, to make this interpretation explicit for elementary terms; the interpretation of the other terms is then indirectly determined by the formulas of the calculus, either definitions or laws, connecting them with the elementary terms. If we demand from the modern physicist an answer to the question what he means by the symbol 'ψ' of his calculus, and are astonished that he cannot give an answer, we ought to realize that the situation was already the same in classical physics. There the physicist could not tell us what he meant by the symbol '*E*' in Maxwell's equations. Perhaps, in order not to refuse an answer, he would tell us that '*E*' designates the electric field vector. To be sure, this statement has the form of a semantical rule, but it would not help us a bit to understand the theory. It simply refers from a symbol in a symbolic calculus to a corresponding word expression in a calculus of words. We are right in demanding an interpretation for '*E*', but that will be given indirectly by semantical rules referring to elementary signs together with the formulas connecting them with '*E*'. This interpretation enables us to use the laws containing '*E*' for the derivation of predictions. Thus we understand '*E*', if "understanding" of an expression, a sentence, or a theory means capability of its use for the description of known facts or the prediction of new facts. An "intuitive understanding" or a direct translation of '*E*' into terms referring to observable properties is neither necessary nor possible. The situation of the modern physicist is not essentially different. He knows how to use the symbol 'ψ' in the calculus in order to derive predictions which we can test by observations. (If they have the form of probability statements, they are tested by statistical results of observations.) Thus the physicist, although he cannot give us a translation into everyday language, understands the symbol 'ψ' and the laws of quantum mechanics. He possesses that kind of understanding which alone is essential in the field of knowledge and science.

The Logic of Explanation *

CARL G. HEMPEL AND
PAUL OPPENHEIM [1]

§1. Introduction

To EXPLAIN THE PHENOMENA in the world of our experience, to answer the question "why?" rather than only the question "what?", is one of the foremost objectives of all rational inquiry; and especially, scientific research in its various branches strives to go beyond a mere description of its subject matter by providing an explanation of the phenomena it investigates. While there is rather general agreement about this chief objective of science, there exists considerable difference of opinion as to the function and the essential characteristics of scientific explanation. In the present essay, an attempt will be made to shed some light on these issues by means of an elementary survey of the basic pattern of scientific explanation and a subsequent more rigorous analysis of the concept of law and of the logical structure of explanatory arguments.

The elementary survey is presented in Part I of this article; Part II contains an analysis of the concept of emergence; in Part III, an attempt is made to exhibit and to clarify in a more rigorous manner some of the peculiar and perplexing logical problems to which the familiar elementary analysis of explanation gives rise.

* Reprinted by kind permission of the authors and the editor from *Philosophy of Science*, 15, 1948.

[1] This paper represents the outcome of a series of discussions among the authors; their individual contributions cannot be separated in detail. The technical developments contained in Part IV, however, are due to the first author, who also put the article into its final form. [Part IV omitted in this reprinting.]

Some of the ideas presented in Part II were suggested by our common friend, Kurt Grelling, who, together with his wife, became a victim of Nazi terror during the war. Those ideas were developed by Grelling in a discussion, by correspondence with the present authors, of emergence and related concepts. By including at least some of that material, which is indicated in the text, in the present paper, we feel that we are realizing the hope expressed by Grelling that his contributions might not entirely fall into oblivion.

We wish to express our thanks to Dr. Rudolf Carnap, Dr. Herbert Feigl, Dr. Nelson Goodman, and Dr. W. V. Quine for stimulating discussions and constructive criticism.

Part I. Elementary Survey of Scientific Explanation

§2. *Some Illustrations*

A mercury thermometer is rapidly immersed in hot water; there occurs a temporary drop of the mercury column, which is then followed by a swift rise. How is this phenomenon to be explained? The increase in temperature affects at first only the glass tube of the thermometer; it expands and thus provides a larger space for the mercury inside, whose surface therefore drops. As soon as by heat conduction the rise in temperature reaches the mercury, however, the latter expands, and as its coefficient of expansion is considerably larger than that of glass, a rise of the mercury level results.—This account consists of statements of two kinds. Those of the first kind indicate certain conditions which are realized prior to, or at the same time as, the phenomenon to be explained; we shall refer to them briefly as antecedent conditions. In our illustration, the antecedent conditions include, among others, the fact that the thermometer consists of a glass tube which is partly filled with mercury, and that it is immersed into hot water. The statements of the second kind express certain general laws; in our case, these include the laws of the thermic expansion of mercury and of glass, and a statement about the small thermic conductivity of glass. The two sets of statements, if adequately and completely formulated, explain the phenomenon under consideration: They entail the consequence that the mercury will first drop, then rise. Thus, the event under discussion is explained by subsuming it under general laws, i.e., by showing that it occurred in accordance with those laws, by virtue of the realization of certain specified antecedent conditions.

Consider another illustration. To an observer in a row boat, that part of an oar which is under water appears to be bent upwards. The phenomenon is explained by means of general laws—mainly the law of refraction and the law that water is an optically denser medium than air—and by reference to certain antecedent conditions—especially the facts that part of the oar is in the water, part in the air, and that the oar is practically a straight piece of wood.—Thus, here again, the question "*Why* does the phenomenon happen?" is construed as meaning "according to what general laws, and by virtue of what antecedent conditions does the phenomenon occur?"

So far, we have considered exclusively the explanation of particular events occurring at a certain time and place. But the question "Why?" may be raised also in regard to general laws. Thus, in our last illustration, the question might be asked: Why does the propagation of light conform to the law of refraction? Classical physics answers in terms of the undulatory theory of light, i.e. by stating that the propagation of light is a wave phenomenon of a certain general type, and that all wave phenomena of that type satisfy the law of refraction. Thus, the explanation of a general regularity consists in subsuming it under another, more comprehensive regularity, under a more general law.—Similarly, the validity of Galileo's law for the free fall of bodies near the earth's surface can be explained by deducing it from a more comprehensive set of laws, namely Newton's laws of motion and his law of gravitation, together with some statements about particular facts, namely the mass and the radius of the earth.

§3. *The Basic Pattern of Scientific Explanation*

From the preceding sample cases let us now abstract some general characteristics of scientific explanation. We divide an explanation into two major constituents, the explanandum and the explanans.[2] By the explanandum, we understand the sentence describing the phenomenon to be explained (not that phenomenon itself); by the explanans, the class of those sentences which are adduced to account for the phenomenon. As was noted before, the explanans falls into two subclasses; one of these contains certain sentences $C_1, C_2, \cdots, C_k$ which state specific antecedent conditions; the other is a set of sentences $L_1, L_2, \cdots L_r$ which represent general laws.

If a proposed explanation is to be sound, its constituents have to satisfy certain conditions of adequacy, which may be divided into logical and empirical conditions. For the following discussion, it will be sufficient to formulate these requirements in a slightly vague manner; in Part III, a more rigorous analysis and a more precise restatement of these criteria will be presented.

I. *Logical conditions of adequacy*

(R1) The explanandum must be a logical consequence of the explanans; in other words, the explanandum must be logically deducible from the information contained in the explanans, for otherwise, the explanans would not constitute adequate grounds for the explanandum.

(R2) The explanans must contain general laws, and these must actually be required for the derivation of the explanandum.—We shall not make it a necessary condition for a sound explanation, however, that the explanans must contain at least one statement which is not a law; for, to mention just one reason, we would surely want to consider as an explanation the derivation of the general regularities governing the motion of double stars from the laws of celestial mechanics, even though all the statements in the explanans are general laws.

(R3) The explanans must have empirical content; i.e., it must be capable, at least in principle, of test by experiment or observa-

[2] These two expressions, derived from the Latin *explanare*, were adopted in preference to the perhaps more customary terms "explicandum" and "explicans" in order to reserve the latter for use in the context of explication of meaning, or analysis. On explication in this sense, cf. Carnap [Concepts], p. 513.—Abbreviated titles in brackets refer to the bibliography at the end of this article.

tion.—This condition is implicit in (R1); for since the explanandum is assumed to describe some empirical phenomenon, it follows from (R1) that the explanans entails at least one consequence of empirical character, and this fact confers upon it testability and empirical content. But the point deserves special mention because, as will be seen in §4, certain arguments which have been offered as explanations in the natural and in the social sciences violate this requirement.

II. *Empirical condition of adequacy*

(R4) The sentences constituting the explanans must be true.

That in a sound explanation, the statements constituting the explanans have to satisfy some condition of factual correctness is obvious. But it might seem more appropriate to stipulate that the explanans has to be highly confirmed by all the relevant evidence available rather than that it should be true. This stipulation however, leads to awkward consequences. Suppose that a certain phenomenon was explained at an earlier stage of science, by means of an explanans which was well supported by the evidence then at hand, but which had been highly disconfirmed by more recent empirical findings. In such a case, we would have to say that originally the explanatory account was a correct explanation, but that it ceased to be one later, when unfavorable evidence was discovered. This does not appear to accord with sound common usage, which directs us to say that on the basis of the limited initial evidence, the truth of the explanans, and thus the soundness of the explanation, had been quite probable, but that the ampler evidence now available made it highly probable that the explanans was not true, and hence that the account in question was not—and had never been—a correct explanation. (A similar point will be made and illustrated, with respect to the requirement of truth for laws, in the beginning of §6.)

Some of the characteristics of an explanation which have been indicated so far may be summarized in the following schema:

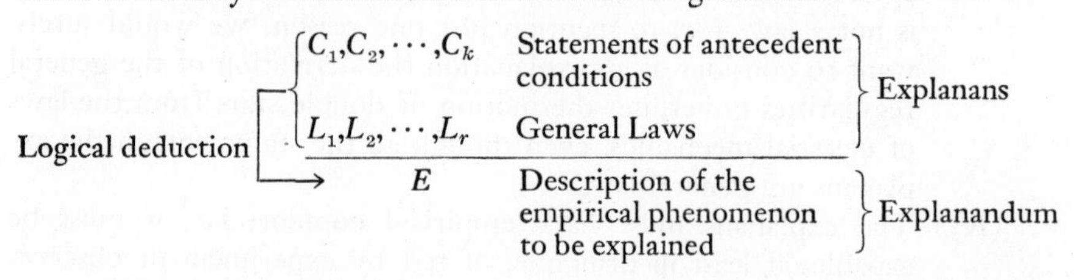

Let us note here that the same formal analysis, including the four necessary conditions, applies to scientific prediction as well as to explanation. The difference between the two is of a pragmatic character. If E is given, i.e. if we know that the phenomenon described by E has occurred, and a suitable set of statements $C_1, C_2, \cdots, C_k, L_1, L_2, \cdots, L_r$ is provided afterwards, we speak of an explanation of the phenomenon in question. If the latter statements are given and E is derived prior to the occurrence of the phenomenon it describes, we speak of a prediction. It may be said, therefore, that an explanation is not fully adequate unless its explanans, if taken account of in time, could have served as a basis for predicting the phenomenon under consideration.[2a]—Consequently, whatever will be said in this article concerning the logical characteristics of explanation or prediction will be applicable to either, even if only one of them should be mentioned.

It is this potential predictive force which gives scientific explanation its importance: only to the extent that we are able to explain empirical facts can we attain the major objective of scientific research, namely not merely to record the phenomena of our experience, but to learn from them, by basing upon them theoretical generalizations which enable us to anticipate new occurrences and to control, at least to some extent, the changes in our environment.

Many explanations which are customarily offered, especially in prescientific discourse, lack this predictive character, however. Thus, it may be explained that a car turned over on the road "because" one of its tires blew out while the car was travelling at high speed. Clearly, on the basis of just this information, the accident could not have been predicted, for the explanans provides no explicit general laws by means of which the prediction might be effected, nor does it state adequately the antecedent conditions which would be needed for the prediction.—The same point may be illustrated by reference to W. S. Jevons's view that every explanation consists in pointing out a resemblance between facts, and that in some cases this process may require no reference to laws at all and "may involve nothing more than a single identity, as when we explain the appearance of shooting stars by showing that they are identical with portions of a comet".[3] But clearly, this identity does not provide an explanation of the phenomenon of shooting stars unless we presuppose the laws governing the development of heat and light as the effect of friction. The observation of similarities has explanatory value only if it involves at least tacit reference to general laws.

In some cases, incomplete explanatory arguments of the kind here illustrated suppress parts of the explanans simply as "obvious"; in other cases, they seem to involve the assumption that while the missing parts are not obvious, the incomplete explanans could at least, with appropriate effort, be so supplemented as to make a strict derivation of the explanandum possible. This assumption may be justifiable in some cases, as when we say

[2a] The logical similarity of explanation and prediction, and the fact that one is directed towards past occurrences, the other towards future ones, is well expressed in the terms "postdictability" and "predictability" used by Reichenbach in [Quantum Mechanics], p. 13.

[3] [Principles], p. 533.

that a lump of sugar disappeared "because" it was put into hot tea, but it is surely not satisfied in many other cases. Thus, when certain peculiarities in the work of an artist are explained as outgrowths of a specific type of neurosis, this observation may contain significant clues, but in general it does not afford a sufficient basis for a potential prediction of those peculiarities. In cases of this kind, an incomplete explanation may at best be considered as indicating some positive correlation between the antecedent conditions adduced and the type of phenomenon to be explained, and as pointing out a direction in which further research might be carried on in order to complete the explanatory account.

The type of explanation which has been considered here so far is often referred to as causal explanation. If E describes a particular event, then the antecedent circumstances described in the sentences $C_1, C_2, \cdots, C_k$ may be said jointly to "cause" that event, in the sense that there are certain empirical regularities, expressed by the laws $L_1, L_2, \cdots, L_r$, which imply that whenever conditions of the kind indicated by $C_1, C_2, \cdots, C_k$ occur, an event of the kind described in E will take place. Statements such as $L_1, L_2, \cdots, L_r$, which assert general and unexceptional connections between specified characteristics of events, are customarily called causal, or deterministic laws. They are to be distinguished from the so-called statistical laws which assert that in the long run, an explicitly stated percentage of all cases satisfying a given set of conditions are accompanied by an event of a certain specified kind. Certain cases of scientific explanation involve "subsumption" of the explanandum under a set of laws of which at least some are statistical in character. Analysis of the peculiar logical structure of that type of subsumption involves difficult special problems. The present essay will be restricted to an examination of the causal type of explanation, which has retained its significance in large segments of contemporary science, and even in some areas where a more adequate account calls for reference to statistical laws.[4]

[4] The account given above of the general characteristics of explanation and prediction in science is by no means novel; it merely summarizes and states explicitly some fundamental points which have been recognized by many scientists and methodologists.

Thus, e.g., Mill says: "An individual fact is said to be explained by pointing out its cause, that is, by stating the law or laws of causation of which its production is an instance", and "a law of uniformity in nature is said to be explained when another law or laws are pointed out, of which that law itself is but a case, and from which it could be deduced." ([Logic], Book III, Chapter XII, section 1.) Similarly, Jevons, whose general characterization of explanation was critically discussed above, stresses that "the most important process of explanation consists in showing that an observed fact is one case of a general law or tendency." ([Principles], p. 533.) Ducasse states the same point as follows: "Explanation essentially consists in the offering of a hypothesis of fact, standing to the fact to be explained as case of antecedent to case of consequent of some already known law of connection." ([Explanation], pp. 150-51.) A lucid analysis of the fundamental structure of explanation and prediction was given by Popper in [Forschung], section 12, and, in an improved version, in his work [Society], especially in Chapter 25 and in note 7 referring to that chapter.—For a recent characterization of explanation as subsumption under general theories, cf., for example, Hull's concise discussion in [Principles], chapter I. A clear elementary examination of certain aspects of

§4. *Explanation in the Non-Physical Sciences. Motivational and Teleological Approaches*

Our characterization of scientific explanation is so far based on a study of cases taken from the physical sciences. But the general principles thus obtained apply also outside this area.[5] Thus, various types of behavior in laboratory animals and in human subjects are explained in psychology by subsumption under laws or even general theories of learning or conditioning; and while frequently, the regularities invoked cannot be stated with the same generality and precision as in physics or chemistry, it is clear, at least, that the general character of those explanations conforms to our earlier characterization.

Let us now consider an illustration involving sociological and economic factors. In the fall of 1946, there occurred at the cotton exchanges of the United States a price drop which was so severe that the exchanges in New York, New Orleans, and Chicago had to suspend their activities temporarily. In an attempt to explain this occurrence, newspapers traced it back to a large-scale speculator in New Orleans who had feared his holdings were too large and had therefore begun to liquidate his stocks; smaller speculators had then followed his example in a panic and had thus touched off the critical decline. Without attempting to assess the merits of the argument, let us note that the explanation here suggested again involves statements about antecedent conditions and the assumption of general regularities. The former include the facts that the first speculator had large stocks of cotton, that there were smaller speculators with considerable holdings, that there existed the institution of the cotton exchanges with their specific mode of operation, etc. The general regularities referred to are—as often in semi-popular explanations—not explicitly mentioned; but there is obviously implied some form of the law of supply and demand to account for the drop in cotton prices in terms of the greatly increased supply under conditions of practically unchanged demand; besides, reliance is necessary on certain regularities in the behavior of individuals who are trying to preserve or improve their economic position. Such laws cannot be formulated at present with satisfactory precision and generality, and therefore, the suggested explanation is surely incomplete, but its intention is unmistakably to account for the phenomenon by integrating it into a general pattern of economic and socio-psychological regularities.

We turn to an explanatory argument taken from the field of linguistics.[6] In Northern France, there exist a large variety of words synonymous

explanation is given in Hospers [Explanation], and a concise survey of many of the essentials of scientific explanation which are considered in the first two parts of the present study may be found in Feigl [Operationism], pp. 284 ff.

[5] On the subject of explanation in the social sciences, especially in history, cf. also the following publications, which may serve to supplement and amplify the brief discussion to be presented here: Hempel [Laws]; Popper [Society]; White [Explanation]; and the articles *Cause* and *Understanding* in Beard and Hook [Terminology].

[6] The illustration is taken from Bonfante [Semantics], section 3.

with the English "bee," whereas in Southern France, essentially only one such word is in existence. For this discrepancy, the explanation has been suggested that in the Latin epoch, the South of France used the word "apicula", the North the word "apis". The latter, because of a process of phonologic decay in Northern France, became the monosyllabic word "é"; and monosyllables tend to be eliminated, especially if they contain few consonantic elements, for they are apt to give rise to misunderstandings. Thus, to avoid confusion, other words were selected. But "apicula", which was reduced to "abelho", remained clear enough and was retained, and finally it even entered into the standard language, in the form "abbeille". While the explanation here described is incomplete in the sense characterized in the previous section, it clearly exhibits reference to specific antecedent conditions as well as to general laws.[7]

While illustrations of this kind tend to support the view that explanation in biology, psychology, and the social sciences has the same structure as in the physical sciences, the opinion is rather widely held that in many instances, the causal type of explanation is essentially inadequate in fields other than physics and chemistry, and especially in the study of purposive behavior. Let us examine briefly some of the reasons which have been adduced in support of this view.

One of the most familiar among them is the idea that events involving the activities of humans singly or in groups have a peculiar uniqueness and irrepeatability which makes them inaccessible to causal explanation because the latter,—with its reliance upon uniformities, presupposes repeatability of the phenomena under consideration. This argument which, incidentally, has also been used in support of the contention that the experimental method is inapplicable in psychology and the social sciences, involves a misunderstanding of the logical character of causal explanation. Every individual event, in the physical sciences no less than in psychology or the social sciences, is unique in the sense that it, with all its peculiar characteristics, does not repeat itself. Nevertheless, individual events may conform to, and thus be explainable by means of, general laws of the causal type. For all that a causal law asserts is that any event of a specified kind, i.e. any event having certain specified characteristics, is accompanied by another event which in turn has certain specified characteristics; for example, that in any event involving friction, heat is developed. And all that is needed for the testability and applicability of such laws is the recurrence of events with the antecedent characteristics, i.e. the repetition of those characteris-

[7] While in each of the last two illustrations, certain regularities are unquestionably relied upon in the explanatory argument, it is not possible to argue convincingly that the intended laws, which at present cannot all be stated explicitly, are of a causal rather than a statistical character. It is quite possible that most or all of the regularities which will be discovered as sociology develops will be of a statistical type. Cf., on this point, the suggestive observations by Zilsel in [Empiricism] section 8, and [Laws]. This issue does not affect, however, the main point we wish to make here, namely that in the social no less than in the physical sciences, subsumption under general regularities is indispensable for the explanation and the theoretical understanding of any phenomenon.

tics, but not of their individual instances. Thus, the argument is inconclusive. It gives occasion, however, to emphasize an important point concerning our earlier analysis: When we spoke of the explanation of a single event, the term "event" referred to the occurrence of some more or less complex characteristic in a specific spatio-temporal location or in a certain individual object, and not to *all* the characteristics of that object, or to all that goes on in that space-time region.

A second argument that should be mentioned here[8] contends that the establishment of scientific generalizations—and thus of explanatory principles—for human behavior is impossible because the reactions of an individual in a given situation depend not only upon that situation, but also upon the previous history of the individual.—But surely, there is no *a priori* reason why generalizations should not be attainable which take into account this dependence of behavior on the past history of the agent. That indeed the given argument "proves" too much, and is therefore a *non sequitur*, is made evident by the existence of certain physical phenomena, such as magnetic hysteresis and elastic fatigue, in which the magnitude of a specific physical effect depends upon the past history of the system involved, and for which nevertheless certain general regularities have been established.

A third argument insists that the explanation of any phenomenon involving purposive behavior calls for reference to motivations and thus for teleological rather than causal analysis. Thus, for example, a fuller statement of the suggested explanation for the break in the cotton prices would have to indicate the large-scale speculator's motivations as one of the factors determining the event in question. Thus, we have to refer to goals sought, and this, so the argument runs, introduces a type of explanation alien to the physical sciences. Unquestionably, many of the—frequently incomplete—explanations which are offered for human actions involve reference to goals and motives; but does this make them essentially different from the causal explanations of physics and chemistry? One difference which suggests itself lies in the circumstance that in motivated behavior, the future appears to affect the present in a manner which is not found in the causal explanations of the physical sciences. But clearly, when the action of a person is motivated, say, by the desire to reach a certain objective, then it is not the as yet unrealized future event of attaining that goal which can be said to determine his present behavior, for indeed the goal may never be actually reached; rather—to put it in crude terms—it is (a) his desire, present before the action, to attain that particular objective, and (b) his belief, likewise present before the action, that such and such a course of action is most likely to have the desired effect. The determining motives and beliefs, therefore, have to be classified among the antecedent

[8] Cf., for example, F. H. Knight's presentation of this argument in [Limitations], pp. 251–52.

conditions of a motivational explanation, and there is no formal difference on this account between motivational and causal explanation.

Neither does the fact that motives are not accessible to direct observation by an outside observer constitute an essential difference between the two kinds of explanation; for also the determining factors adduced in physical explanations are very frequently inaccessible to direct observation. This is the case, for instance, when opposite electric charges are adduced in explanation of the mutual attraction of two metal spheres. The presence of those charges, while eluding all direct observation, can be ascertained by various kinds of indirect test, and that is sufficient to guarantee the empirical character of the explanatory statement. Similarly, the presence of certain motivations may be ascertainable only by indirect methods, which may include reference to linguistic utterances of the subject in question, slips of the pen or of the tongue, etc.; but as long as these methods are "operationally determined" with reasonable clarity and precision, there is no essential difference in this respect between motivational explanation and causal explanation in physics.

A potential danger of explanation by motives lies in the fact that the method lends itself to the facile construction of ex-post-facto accounts without predictive force. It is a widespread tendency to "explain" an action by ascribing it to motives conjectured only after the action has taken place. While this procedure is not in itself objectionable, its soundness requires that (1) the motivational assumptions in question be capable of test, and (2) that suitable general laws be available to lend explanatory power to the assumed motives. Disregard of these requirements frequently deprives alleged motivational explanations of their cognitive significance.

The explanation of an action in terms of the motives of the agent is sometimes considered as a special kind of teleological explanation. As was pointed out above, motivational explanation, if adequately formulated, conforms to the conditions for causal explanation, so that the term "teleological" is a misnomer if it is meant to imply either a non-causal character of the explanation or a peculiar determination of the present by the future. If this is borne in mind, however, the term "teleological" may be viewed, in this context, as referring to causal explanations in which some of the antecedent conditions are motives of the agent whose actions are to be explained.[9]

[9] For a detailed logical analysis of the character and the function of the motivation concept in psychological theory, see Koch [Motivation].—A stimulating discussion of teleological behavior from the standpoint of contemporary physics and biology is contained in the article [Teleology] by Rosenblueth, Wiener and Bigelow. The authors propose an interpretation of the concept of purpose which is free from metaphysical connotations, and they stress the importance of the concept thus obtained for a behavioristic analysis of machines and living organisms. While our formulations above intentionally use the crude terminology frequently applied in philosophical arguments concerning the applicability of causal explanation to purposive behavior, the analysis presented in the article referred to is couched in behavioristic terms and avoids reference to "motives" and the like.

Teleological explanations of this kind have to be distinguished from a much more sweeping type, which has been claimed by certain schools of thought to be indispensable especially in biology. It consists in explaining characteristics of an organism by reference to certain ends or purposes which the characteristics are said to serve. In contradistinction to the cases examined before, the ends are not assumed here to be consciously or subconsciously pursued by the organism in question. Thus, for the phenomenon of mimicry, the explanation is sometimes offered that it serves the purpose of protecting the animals endowed with it from detection by its pursuers and thus tends to preserve the species.—Before teleological hypotheses of this kind can be appraised as to their potential explanatory power, their meaning has to be clarified. If they are intended somehow to express the idea that the purposes they refer to are inherent in the design of the universe, then clearly they are not capable of empirical test and thus violate the requirement (R3) stated in §3. In certain cases, however, assertions about the purposes of biological characteristics may be translatable into statements in non-teleological terminology which assert that those characteristics function in a specific manner which is essential to keeping the organism alive or to preserving the species.[10] An attempt to state precisely what is meant by this latter assertion—or by the similar one that without those characteristics, and other things being equal, the organism or the species would not survive—encounters considerable difficulties. But these need not be discussed here. For even if we assume that biological statements in teleological form can be adequately translated into descriptive statements about the life-preserving function of certain biological characteristics, it is clear that (1) the use of the concept of purpose is not essential in these contexts, since the term "purpose" can be completely eliminated from the statements in question, and (2) teleological assumptions, while now endowed with empirical content, cannot serve as explanatory principles in the customary contexts. Thus, e.g., the fact that a given species of butterflies displays a particular kind of coloring cannot be inferred from—and therefore cannot be explained by means of—the statement that this type of coloring has the effect of protecting the butterflies from detection by pursuing birds, nor can the presence of red corpuscles in the human blood be inferred from the statement that those corpuscles have a specific function in assimilating oxygen and that this function is essential for the maintenance of life.

One of the reasons for the perseverance of teleological considerations in biology probably lies in the fruitfulness of the teleological approach as a heuristic device: Biological research which was psychologically motivated by a teleological orientation, by an interest in purposes in nature, has frequently led to important results which can be stated in non-teleological

[10] An analysis of teleological statements in biology along these lines may be found in Woodger [Principles], especially pp. 432 ff.; essentially the same interpretation is advocated by Kaufmann in [Methodology], chapter 8.

terminology and which increase our scientific knowledge of the causal connections between biological phenomena.

Another aspect that lends appeal to teleological considerations is their anthropomorphic character. A teleological explanation tends to make us feel that we really "understand" the phenomenon in question, because it is accounted for in terms of purposes, with which we are familiar from our own experience of purposive behavior. But it is important to distinguish here understanding in the psychological sense of a feeling of empathic familiarity from understanding in the theoretical, or cognitive, sense of exhibiting the phenomenon to be explained as a special case of some general regularity. The frequent insistence that explanation means the reduction of something unfamiliar to ideas or experiences already familiar to us is indeed misleading. For while some scientific explanations do have this psychological effect, it is by no means universal: The free fall of a physical body may well be said to be a more familiar phenomenon than the law of gravitation, by means of which it can be explained; and surely the basic ideas of the theory of relativity will appear to many to be far less familiar than the phenomena for which the theory accounts.

"Familiarity" of the explicans is not only not necessary for a sound explanation—as we have just tried to show—, but it is not sufficient either. This is shown by the many cases in which a proposed explicans sounds suggestively familiar, but upon closer inspection proves to be a mere metaphor, or an account lacking testability, or a set of statements which includes no general laws and therefore lacks explanatory power. A case in point is the neovitalistic attempt to explain biological phenomena by reference to an entelechy or vital force. The crucial point here is not—as it is sometimes made out to be—that entelechies cannot be seen or otherwise directly observed; for that is true also of gravitational fields, and yet, reference to such fields is essential in the explanation of various physical phenomena. The decisive difference between the two cases is that the physical explanation provides (1) methods of testing, albeit indirectly, assertions about gravitational fields, and (2) general laws concerning the strength of gravitational fields, and the behavior of objects moving in them. Explanations by entelechies satisfy the analogue of neither of these two conditions. Failure to satisfy the first condition represents a violation of (R3); it renders all statements about entelechies inaccessible to empirical test and thus devoid of empirical meaning. Failure to comply with the second condition involves a violation of (R2). It deprives the concept of entelechy of all explanatory import; for explanatory power never resides in a concept, but always in the general laws in which it functions. Therefore, notwithstanding the flavor of familiarity of the metaphor it invokes, the neovitalistic approach cannot provide theoretical understanding.

The preceding observations about familiarity and understanding can be applied, in a similar manner, to the view held by some scholars that the explanation, or the understanding, of human actions requires an empathic understanding of the personalities of the agents.[11] This understanding of another person in terms of one's own psychological functioning may prove a useful heuristic device in the search for general psychological principles which might provide a theoretical explanation; but the existence of empathy on the part of the scientist is neither a necessary nor a sufficient condition for the explanation, or the scientific understanding, of any human action. It is not necessary, for the behavior of psychotics or of people belonging to a culture very different from that of the scientist may sometimes be explainable and predictable in terms of general principles even though the scientist who establishes or applies those principles may not be able to understand his subjects empathically. And empathy is not sufficient to guarantee a sound explanation, for a strong feeling of empathy may exist even in cases where we completely misjudge a given personality. Moreover, as the late Dr. Zilsel has pointed out, empathy leads with ease to incompatible results; thus, when the population of a town has long been subjected to heavy bombing attacks, we can understand, in the empathic sense, that its morale should have broken down completely, but we can understand with the same ease also that it should have developed a defiant spirit of resistance. Arguments of this kind often appear quite convincing; but they are of an *ex post facto* character and lack cognitive significance unless they are supplemented by testable explanatory principles in the form of laws or theories.

Familiarity of the explanans, therefore, no matter whether it is achieved through the use of teleological terminology, through neovitalistic metaphors, or through other means, is no indication of the cognitive import and the predictive force of a proposed explanation. Besides, the extent to which an idea will be considered as familiar varies from person to person and from time to time, and a psychological factor of this kind certainly cannot serve as a standard in assessing the worth of a proposed explanation. The decisive requirement for every sound explanation remains that it subsume the explanandum under general laws.

Part II. On the Idea of Emergence

§5. *Levels of Explanation. Analysis of Emergence*

As has been shown above, a phenomenon may often be explained by sets of laws of different degrees of generality. The changing positions of a planet, for example, may be explained by subsumption under Kepler's laws, or by derivation from the far more comprehensive general law of gravitation in combination with the laws of motion, or finally by deduction from the general theory of relativity, which explains—and slightly modifies—the preceding set of laws. Similarly, the expansion of a gas with rising

[11] For a more detailed discussion of this view on the basis of the general principles outlined above, cf. Zilsel [Empiricism], sections 7 and 8, and Hempel [Laws], section 6.

temperature at constant pressure may be explained by means of the Gas Law or by the more comprehensive kinetic theory of heat. The latter explains the Gas Law, and thus indirectly the phenomenon just mentioned, by means of (1) certain assumptions concerning the micro-behavior of gases (more specifically, the distributions of locations and speeds of the gas molecules) and (2) certain macro-micro principles, which connect such macro-characteristics of a gas as its temperature, pressure and volume with the micro-characteristics just mentioned.

In the sense of these illustrations, a distinction is frequently made between various levels of explanation.[12] Subsumption of a phenomenon under a general law directly connecting observable characteristics represents the first level; higher levels require the use of more or less abstract theoretical constructs which function in the context of some comprehensive theory. As the preceding illustrations show, the concept of higher-level explanation covers procedures of rather different character; one of the most important among them consists in explaining a class of phenomena by means of a theory concerning their micro-structure. The kinetic theory of heat, the atomic theory of matter, the electromagnetic as well as the quantum theory of light, and the gene theory of heredity are examples of this method. It is often felt that only the discovery of a micro-theory affords real scientific understanding of any type of phenomenon, because only it gives us insight into the inner mechanism of the phenomenon, so to speak. Consequently, classes of events for which no micro-theory was available have frequently been viewed as not actually understood; and concern with the theoretical status of phenomena which are unexplained in this sense may be considered as a theoretical root of the doctrine of emergence.

Generally speaking, the concept of emergence has been used to characterize certain phenomena as "novel", and this not merely in the psychological sense of being unexpected,[13] but in the theoretical sense of being unexplainable, or unpredictable, on the basis of information concerning the spatial parts or other constituents of the systems in which the phenomena occur, and which in this context are often referred to as wholes. Thus, e.g., such characteristics of water as its transparence and liquidity at room temperature and atmospheric pressure, or its ability to quench thirst have been considered as emergent on the ground that they could not possibly have been predicted from a knowledge of the properties of its chemical constituents, hydrogen and oxygen. The weight of the compound, on the contrary, has been said not to be emergent because it is a mere "resultant" of its components and could have been predicted by simple addition even before the compound had been formed. The conceptions of explanation and prediction which underly this idea of emergence call for various critical observations, and for corresponding changes in the concept of emergence.

[12] For a lucid brief exposition of this idea, see Feigl [Operationism], pp. 284–288.

[13] Concerning the concept of novelty in its logical and psychological meanings, see also Stace [Novelty].

(1) First, the question whether a given characteristic of a "whole", *w*, is emergent or not cannot be significantly raised until it has been stated what is to be understood by the parts or constituents of *w*. The volume of a brick wall, for example, may be inferable by addition from the volumes of its parts if the latter are understood to be the component bricks, but it is not so inferable from the volumes of the molecular components of the wall. Before we can significantly ask whether a characteristic *W* of an object *w* is emergent, we shall therefore have to state the intended meaning of the term "part of". This can be done by defining a specific relation *Pt* and stipulating that those and only those objects which stand in *Pt* to *w* count as parts or constituents of *w*. '*Pt*' might be defined as meaning "constituent brick of" (with respect to buildings), or "molecule contained in" (for any physical object), or "chemical element contained in" (with respect to chemical compounds, or with respect to any material object), or "cell of" (with respect to organisms), etc. The term "whole" will be used here without any of its various connotations, merely as referring to any object *w* to which others stand in the specified relation *Pt*. In order to emphasize the dependence of the concept of part upon the definition of the relation *Pt* in each case, we shall sometimes speak of *Pt*-parts, to refer to parts as determined by the particular relation *Pt* under consideration.

(2) We turn to a second point of criticism. If a characteristic of a whole is to be qualified as emergent only if its occurrence cannot be inferred from a knowledge of all the properties of its parts, then, as Grelling has pointed out, no whole can have any emergent characteristics. Thus, to illustrate by reference to our earlier example, the properties of hydrogen include that of forming, if suitably combined with oxygen, a compound which is liquid, transparent, etc. Hence the liquidity, transparence, etc. of water can be inferred from certain properties of its chemical constituents. If the concept of emergence is not to be vacuous, therefore, it will be necessary to specify in every case a class *G* of attributes and to call a characteristic *W* of an object *w* emergent relatively to *G* and *Pt* if the occurrence of *W* in *w* cannot be inferred from a complete characterization of all the *Pt*-parts with respect to the attributes contained in G, i.e. from a statement which indicates, for every attribute in *G*, to which of the parts of *w* it applies.—Evidently, the occurrence of a characteristic may be emergent with respect to one class of attributes and not emergent with respect to another. The classes of attributes which the emergentists have in mind, and which are usually not explicitly indicated, will have to be construed as non-trivial, i.e. as not logically entailing the property of each constituent of forming, together with the other constituents, a whole with the characteristics under investigations.—Some fairly simple cases of emergence in the sense so far specified arise when the class *G* is restricted to certain simple properties of the parts, to the exclusion of spatial or other relations among them. Thus, the electromotive force of a system of several electric batteries cannot be inferred from the electromotive forces of its

constituents alone without a description, in terms of relational concepts, of the way in which the batteries are connected with each other.[14]

(3) Finally, the predictability of a given characteristic of an object on the basis of specified information concerning its parts will obviously depend on what general laws or theories are available.[15] Thus, the flow of an electric current in a wire connecting a piece of copper and a piece of zinc which are partly immersed in sulfuric acid is unexplainable, on the basis of information concerning any nontrivial set of attributes of copper, zinc and sulfuric acid, and the particular structure of the system under consideration, unless the theory available contains certain general laws concerning the functioning of batteries, or even more comprehensive principles of physical chemistry. If the theory includes such laws, on the other hand, then the occurrence of the current is predictable. Another illustration, which at the same time provides a good example for the point made under (2) above, is afforded by the optical activity of certain substances. The optical activity of sarco-lactic acid, for example, i.e. the fact that in solution it rotates the plane of polarization of plane-polarized light, cannot be predicted on the basis of the chemical characteristics of its constituent elements; rather, certain facts about the relations of the atoms constituting a molecule of sarco-lactic acid have to be known. The essential point is that the molecule in question contains an asymmetric carbon atom, i.e. one that holds four different atoms or groups, and if this piece of relational information is provided, the optical activity of the solution can be predicted provided that furthermore the theory available for the purpose embodies the law that the presence of one asymmetric carbon atom in a molecule implies optical activity of the solution; if the theory does not include this micro-macro law, then the phenomenon is emergent with respect to that theory.

An argument is sometimes advanced to the effect that phenomena such

[14] This observation connects the present discussion with a basic issue in Gestalt theory. Thus, e.g., the insistence that "a whole is more than the sum of its parts" may be construed as referring to characteristics of wholes whose prediction requires knowledge of certain structural relations among the parts. For a further examination of this point, see Grelling and Oppenheim [Gestaltbegriff] and [Functional Whole].

[15] Logical analyses of emergence which make reference to the theories available have been propounded by Grelling and recently, in a very explicit form, by Henle in [Emergence]. In effect, Henle's definition characterizes a phenomenon as emergent if it cannot be predicted, by means of the theories accepted at the time, on the basis of the data available before its occurrence. In this interpretation of emergence, no reference is made to characteristics of parts or constituents. Henle's concept of predictability differs from the one implicit in our discussion (and made explicit in Part III of this article) in that it implies derivability from the "simplest" hypothesis which can be formed on the basis of the data and theories available at the time. A number of suggestive observations on the idea of emergence and on Henle's analysis of it are contained in Bergmann's article [Emergence].—The idea that the concept of emergence, at least in some of its applications, is meant to refer to unpredictability by means of "simple" laws was advanced also by Grelling in the correspondence mentioned in note (1). Reliance on the notion of simplicity of hypotheses, however, involves considerable difficulties; in fact, no satisfactory definition of that concept is available at present.

as the flow of the current, or the optical activity, in our last examples, are absolutely emergent at least in the sense that they could not possibly have been predicted before they had been observed for the first time; in other words, that the laws requisite for their prediction could not have been arrived at on the basis of information available before their first observed occurrence.[16] This view is untenable, however. On the strength of data available at a given time, science often establishes generalizations by means of which it can forecast the occurrence of events the like of which have never before been encountered. Thus, generalizations based upon periodicities exhibited by the characteristics of chemical elements then known, enabled Mendeleeff in 1871 to predict the existence of a certain new element and to state correctly various properties of that element as well as of several of its compounds; the element in question, germanium, was not discovered until 1886.—A more recent illustration of the same point is provided by the development of the atomic bomb and the prediction, based on theoretical principles established prior to the event, of its explosion under specified conditions, and of its devastating release of energy.

As Grelling has stressed, the observation that the predictability of the occurrence of any characteristic depends upon the theoretical knowledge available, applies even to those cases in which, in the language of some emergentists, the characteristic of the whole is a mere resultant of the corresponding characteristics of the parts and can be obtained from the latter by addition. Thus, even the weight of a water molecule cannot be derived from the weights of its atomic constituents without the aid of a law which expresses the former as some specific mathematical function of the latter. That this function should be the sum is by no means self-evident; it is an empirical generalization, and at that not a strictly correct one, as relativistic physics has shown.

Failure to realize that the question of the predictability of a phenomenon cannot be significantly raised unless the theories available for the prediction have been specified has encouraged the misconception that certain phenomena have a mysterious quality of absolute unexplainability, and that their emergent status has to be accepted with "natural piety", as F. L. Morgan put it. The observations presented in the preceding discussion strip the idea of emergence of these unfounded connotations: emergence

[16] C. D. Broad, who in chapter 2 of his book [Mind] gives a clear presentation and critical discussion of the essentials of emergentism, emphasizes the importance of "laws of composition" in predicting the characteristics of a whole on the basis of those of its parts. (cf. [Mind], pp. 61 ff.); but he subscribes to the view characterized above and illustrates it specifically by the assertion that "if we want to know the chemical (and many of the physical) properties of a chemical compound, such as silver-chloride, it is absolutely necessary to study samples of *that particular compound*. . . . The essential point is that it would also be useless to study chemical compounds in general and to compare their properties with those of their elements in the hope of discovering a *general* law of composition by which the properties of *any* chemical compound could be foretold when the properties of its separate elements were known." (Ibid., p. 64)—That an achievement of precisely this sort has been possible on the basis of the periodic system of the elements is pointed out above.

of a characteristic is not an ontological trait inherent in some phenomena; rather it is indicative of the scope of our knowledge at a given time; thus it has no absolute, but a relative character; and what is emergent with respect to the theories available today may lose its emergent status tomorrow.

The preceding considerations suggest the following redefinition of emergence: The occurrence of a characteristic W in an object w is emergent relatively to a theory T, a part relation Pt, and a class G of attributes if that occurrence cannot be deduced by means of T from a characterization of the Pt-parts of w with respect to all the attributes in G.

This formulation explicates the meaning of emergence with respect to *events* of a certain kind, namely the occurrence of some characteristic W in an object w. Frequently, emergence is attributed to *characteristics* rather than to events; this use of the concept of emergence may be interpreted as follows: A characteristic W is emergent relatively to T, Pt, and G if its occurrence in *any* object is emergent in the sense just indicated.

As far as its cognitive content is concerned, the emergentist assertion that the phenomena of life are emergent may now be construed, roughly, as an elliptic formulation of the following statement: Certain specifiable biological phenomena cannot be explained, by means of contemporary physico-chemical theories, on the basis of data concerning the physical and chemical characteristics of the atomic and molecular constituents of organisms. Similarly, the so-called emergent status of mind reduces to the assertion that present-day physical, chemical and biological theories do not suffice to explain all psychological phenomena on the basis of data concerning the physical, chemical, and biological characteristics of the cells or of the molecules or atoms constituting the organisms in question. But in this interpretation, the emergent character of biological and psychological phenomena becomes trivial; for the description of various biological phenomena requires terms which are not contained in the vocabulary of present day physics and chemistry; hence we cannot expect that all specifically biological phenomena are explainable, i.e. deductively inferable, by means of present day physico-chemical theories on the basis of initial conditions which themselves are described in exclusively physico-chemical terms. In order to obtain a less trivial interpretation of the assertion that the phenomena of life are emergent, we have therefore to include in the explanatory theory all those laws known at present which connect the physico-chemical with the biological "level", i.e., which contain, on the one hand, certain physical and chemical terms, including those required for the description of molecular structures, and on the other hand, certain concepts of biology. An analogous observation applies to the case of psychology. If the assertion that life and mind have an emergent status is interpreted in this sense, then its import can be summarized approximately by the statement that no explanation, in terms of micro-structure theories, is available at present for large classes of phenomena studied in biology and psychology.[17]

Assertions of this type, then, appear to represent the rational core of the doctrine of emergence. In its revised form, the idea of emergence no longer carries with it the connotation of absolute unpredictability—a notion which is objectionable not only because it involves and perpetuates certain logical misunderstandings, but also because, not unlike the ideas of neo-vitalism, it encourages an attitude of resignation which is stifling for scientific research. No doubt it is this characteristic, together with its theoretical sterility, which accounts for the rejection, by the majority of contemporary scientists, of the classical absolutistic doctrine of emergence.[18]

PART III. LOGICAL ANALYSIS OF LAW AND EXPLANATION

§6. *Problems of the Concept of General Law*

From our general survey of the characteristics of scientific explanation, we now turn to a closer examination of its logical structure. The explanation of a phenomenon, we noted, consists in its subsumption under laws or under a theory. But what is a law, what is a theory? While the meaning of these concepts seems intuitively clear, an attempt to construct adequate explicit definitions for them encounters considerable difficulties. In the present section, some basic problems of the concept of law will be described and analyzed; in the next section, we intend to propose, on the basis of the suggestions thus obtained, definitions of law and of explanation for a formalized model language of a simple logical structure.

The concept of law will be construed here so as to apply to true statements only. The apparently plausible alternative procedure of requiring high confirmation rather than truth of a law seems to be inadequate: It would lead to a relativized concept of law, which would be expressed by the phrase "sentence *S* is a law relatively to the evidence *E*". This does not seem to accord with the meaning customarily assigned to the concept of law in science and in methodological inquiry. Thus, for example, we would not say that Bode's general formula for the distance of the planets from the sun was a law relatively to the astronomical evidence available in the 1770s, when Bode propounded it, and that it ceased to be a law after the discovery

[17] The following passage from Tolman [Behavior] may serve to support this interpretation: ". . . 'behavior-acts', though no doubt in complete one-to-one correspondence with the underlying molecular facts of physics and physiology, have, as 'molar' wholes, certain emergent properties of their own. . . . Further, these molar properties of behavior-acts cannot in the present state of our knowledge, i.e., prior to the working-out of many empirical correlations between behavior and its physiological correlates, be known even inferentially from a mere knowledge of the underlying, molecular, facts of physics and physiology." (l. c., pp. 7–8).—In a similar manner, Hull uses the distinction between molar and molecular theories and points out that theories of the latter type are not at present available in psychology. Cf. [Principles], pp. 19 ff.; [Variables], p. 275.

[18] This attitude of the scientist is voiced, for example, by Hull in [Principles], pp. 24–28.

of Neptune and the determination of its distance from the sun; rather, we would say that the limited original evidence had given a high probability to the assumption that the formula was a law, whereas more recent additional information reduced that probability so much as to make it practically certain that Bode's formula is not generally true, and hence not a law.[18a]

Apart from being true, a law will have to satisfy a number of additional conditions. These can be studied independently of the factual requirement of truth, for they refer, as it were, to all logically possible laws, no matter whether factually true or false. Adopting a convenient term proposed by Goodman,[19] we will say that a sentence is lawlike if it has all the characteristics of a general law, with the possible exception of truth. Hence, every law is a lawlike sentence, but not conversely.

Our problem of analyzing the concept of law thus reduces to that of explicating the meaning of "lawlike sentence". We shall construe the class of lawlike sentences as including analytic general statements, such as "A rose is a rose", as well as the lawlike sentences of empirical science, which have empirical content.[20] It will not be necessary to require that each lawlike sentence permissible in explanatory contexts be of the second kind; rather, our definition of explanation will be so constructed as to guarantee the factual character of the totality of the laws—though not of every single one of them—which function in an explanation of an empirical fact.

What are the characteristics of lawlike sentences? First of all, lawlike sentences are statements of universal form, such as "All robins' eggs are greenish-blue", "All metals are conductors of electricity", "At constant pressure, any gas expands with increasing temperature". As these examples illustrate, a lawlike sentence usually is not only of universal, but also of conditional form; it makes an assertion to the effect that universally, if a certain set of conditions, C, is realized, then another specified set of conditions, E, is realized as well. The standard form for the symbolic expression of a lawlike sentence is therefore the universal conditional. However, since any conditional statement can be transformed into a non-conditional one, conditional form will not be considered as essential for a lawlike sentence, while universal character will be held indispensable.

But the requirement of universal form is not sufficient to characterize lawlike sentences. Suppose, for example, that a certain basket, b, contains

[18a] The requirement of truth for laws has the consequence that a given empirical statement S can never be definitely known to be a law; for the sentence affirming the truth of S is logically equivalent with S and is therefore capable only of acquiring a more or less high probability, or degree of confirmation, relatively to the experimental evidence available at any given time. On this point, cf. Carnap [Remarks].—For an excellent non-technical exposition of the semantical concept of truth, which is here applied, the reader is referred to Tarski [Truth].

[19] [Counterfactuals]. p. 125.

[20] This procedure was suggested by Goodman's approach in [Counterfactuals].—Reichenbach, in a detailed examination of the concept of law, similarly construes his concept of nomological statement as including both analytic and synthetic sentences; cf. [Logic], chapter VIII.

at a certain time t a number of red apples and nothing else.[21] Then the statement

(S_1) Every apple in basket b at time t is red

is both true and of universal form. Yet the sentence does not qualify as a law; we would refuse, for example, to explain by subsumption under it the fact that a particular apple chosen at random from the basket is red. What distinguishes S_1 from a lawlike sentence? Two points suggest themselves, which will be considered in turn, namely, finite scope, and reference to a specified object.

First, the sentence S_1 makes, in effect, an assertion about a finite number of objects only, and this seems irreconcilable with the claim to universality which is commonly associated with the notion of law.[22] But are not Kepler's laws considered as lawlike although they refer to a finite set of planets only? And might we not even be willing to consider as lawlike a sentence such as the following?

(S_2) All the sixteen ice cubes in the freezing tray of this refrigerator have a temperature of less than 10 degrees centigrade.

This point might well be granted; but there is an essential difference between S_1 on the one hand and Kepler's laws as well as S_2 on the other: The latter, while finite in scope, are known to be consequences of more comprehensive laws whose scope is not limited, while for S_1 this is not the case.

Adopting a procedure recently suggested by Reichenbach,[23] we will therefore distinguish between fundamental and derivative laws. A statement will be called a derivative law if it is of universal character and follows from some fundamental laws. The concept of fundamental law requires further clarification; so far, we may say that fundamental laws, and similarly fundamental lawlike sentences, should satisfy a certain condition of non-limitation of scope.

It would be excessive, however, to deny the status of fundamental lawlike sentence to all statements which, in effect, make an assertion about a finite class of objects only, for that would rule out also a sentence such as "All robins' eggs are greenish-blue", since presumably the class of all

21 The difficulty illustrated by this example was stated concisely by Langford ([Review]), who referred to it as the problem of distinguishing between universals of fact and causal universals. For further discussion and illustration of this point, see also Chisholm [Conditional], especially pp. 301f.—A systematic analysis of the problem was given by Goodman in [Counterfactuals], especially part III.—While not concerned with the specific point under discussion, the detailed examination of counterfactual conditionals and their relation to laws of nature, in Chapter VIII of Lewis's work [Analysis], contains important observations on several of the issues raised in the present section.

22 The view that laws should be construed as not being limited to a finite domain has been expressed, among others, by Popper ([Forschung], section 13) and by Reichenbach ([Logic], p. 369).

23 [Logic], p. 361.—Our terminology as well as the definitions to be proposed later for the two types of law do not coincide with Reichenbach's, however.

robins' eggs—past, present, and future—is finite. But again, there is an essential difference between this sentence and, say, S_1. It requires empirical knowledge to establish the finiteness of the class of robins' eggs, whereas, when the sentence S_1 is construed in a manner which renders it intuitively unlawlike, the terms "basket *b*" and "apple" are understood so as to imply finiteness of the class of apples in the basket at time *t*. Thus, so to speak, the meaning of its constitutive terms alone—without additional factual information—entails that S_1 has a finite scope.—Fundamental laws, then, will have to be construed so as to satisfy what we have called a condition of non-limited scope; our formulation of that condition however, which refers to what is entailed by "the meaning" of certain expressions, is too vague and will have to be revised later. Let us note in passing that the stipulation here envisaged would bar from the class of fundamental lawlike sentences also such undesirable candidates as "All uranic objects are spherical", where "uranic" means the property of being the planet Uranus; indeed, while this sentence has universal form, it fails to satisfy the condition of non-limited scope.

In our search for a general characterization of lawlike sentences, we now turn to a second clue which is provided by the sentence S_1. In addition to violating the condition of non-limited scope, this sentence has the peculiarity of making reference to a particular object, the basket *b*; and this, too, seems to violate the universal character of a law.[24] The restriction which seems indicated here, should however again be applied to fundamental lawlike sentences only; for a true general statement about the free fall of physical bodies on the moon, while referring to a particular object, would still constitute a law, albeit a derivative one.

It seems reasonable to stipulate, therefore, that a fundamental lawlike sentence must be of universal form and must contain no essential—i.e., uneliminable—occurrences of designations for particular objects. But this is not sufficient; indeed, just at this point, a particularly serious difficulty presents itself. Consider the sentence

(S_3) Everything that is either an apple in basket *b* at time *t* or a sample of ferric oxide is red.

If we use a special expression, say "*x* is ferple", as synonymous with "*x* is either an apple in *b* at *t* or a sample of ferric oxide", then the content of S_3 can be expressed in the form

(S_4) Everything that is ferple is red.

The statement thus obtained is of universal form and contains no designations of particular objects, and it also satisfies the condition of non-limited

[24] In physics, the idea that a law should not refer to any particular object has found its expression in the maxim that the general laws of physics should contain no reference to specific space-time points, and that spatio-temporal coordinates should occur in them only in the form of differences or differentials.

scope; yet clearly, S_4 can qualify as a fundamental lawlike sentence no more than can S_3.

As long as "ferple" is a defined term of our language, the difficulty can readily be met by stipulating that after elimination of defined terms, a fundamental lawlike sentence must not contain essential occurrences of designations for particular objects. But this way out is of no avail when "ferple", or another term of the kind illustrated by it, is a primitive predicate of the language under consideration. This reflection indicates that certain restrictions have to be imposed upon those predicates—i.e., terms for properties or relations,—which may occur in fundamental lawlike sentences.[25]

More specifically, the idea suggests itself of permitting a predicate in a fundamental lawlike sentence only if it is purely universal, or, as we shall say, purely qualitative, in character; in other words, if a statement of its meaning does not require reference to any one particular object or spatio-temporal location. Thus, the terms "soft", "green", "warmer than", "as long as", "liquid", "electrically charged", "female", "father of" are purely qualitative predicates, while "taller than the Eiffel Tower", "medieval", "lunar", "arctic", "Ming" are not.[26]

Exclusion from fundamental lawlike sentences of predicates which are not purely qualitative would at the same time ensure satisfaction of the condition of non-limited scope; for the meaning of a purely qualitative predicate does not require a finite extension; and indeed, all the sentences considered above which violate the condition of non-limited scope make explicit or implicit reference to specific objects.

The stipulation just proposed suffers, however, from the vagueness of

[25] The point illustrated by the sentences S_3 and S_4 above was made by Goodman, who has also emphasized the need to impose certain restrictions upon the predicates whose occurrence is to be permissible in lawlike sentences. These predicates are essentially the same as those which Goodman calls projectible. Goodman has suggested that the problems of establishing precise criteria for projectibility, of interpreting counterfactual conditionals, and of defining the concept of law are so intimately related as to be virtually aspects of a single problem. (Cf. his articles [Query] and [Counterfactuals].) One suggestion for an analysis of projectibility has recently been made by Carnap in [Application]. Goodman's note [Infirmities] contains critical observations on Carnap's proposals.

[26] That laws, in addition to being of universal form, must contain only purely universal predicates was clearly argued by Popper ([Forschung], sections 14, 15).—Our alternative expression "purely qualitative predicate" was chosen in analogy to Carnap's term "purely qualitative property" (cf. [Application]).—The above characterization of purely universal predicates seems preferable to a simpler and perhaps more customary one, to the effect that a statement of the meaning of the predicate must require no reference to particular objects. For this formulation might be too exclusive since it could be argued that stating the meaning of such purely qualitative terms as "blue" or "hot" requires illustrative reference to some particular object which has the quality in question. The essential point is that no one specific object has to be chosen; any one in the logically unlimited set of blue or of hot objects will do. In explicating the meaning of "taller than the Eiffel Tower", "being an apple in basket b at the time t", "medieval", etc., however, reference has to be made to one specific object or to some one in a limited set of objects.

the concept of purely qualitative predicate. The question whether indication of the meaning of a given predicate in English does or does not require reference to some one specific object does not always permit an unequivocal answer since English as a natural language does not provide explicit definitions or other clear explications of meaning for its terms. It seems therefore reasonable to attempt definition of the concept of law not with respect to English or any other natural language, but rather with respect to a formalized language—let us call it a model language, *L*,—which is governed by a well-determined system of logical rules, and in which every term either is characterized as primitive or is introduced by an explicit definition in terms of the primitives.

This reference to a well-determined system is customary in logical research and is indeed quite natural in the context of any attempt to develop precise criteria for certain logical distinctions. But it does not by itself suffice to overcome the specific difficulty under discussion. For while it is now readily possible to characterize as not purely qualitative all those among the defined predicates in *L* whose definiens contains an essential occurrence of some individual name, our problem remains open for the primitives of the language, whose meanings are not determined by definitions within the language, but rather by semantical rules of interpretation. For we want to permit the interpretation of the primitives of *L* by means of such attributes as blue, hard, solid, warmer, but not by the properties of being a descendant of Napoleon, or an arctic animal, or a Greek statue; and the difficulty is precisely that of stating rigorous criteria for the distinction between the permissible and the non-permissible interpretations. Thus the problem of setting up an adequate definition for purely qualitative attributes now arises again; namely for the concepts of the metalanguage in which the semantical interpretation of the primitives is formulated. We may postpone an encounter with the difficulty by presupposing formalization of the semantical meta-language, the meta-meta-language, and so forth; but somewhere, we will have to stop at a non-formalized meta-language, and for it a characterization of purely qualitative predicates will be needed and will present much the same problems as non-formalized English, with which we began. The characterization of a purely qualitative predicate as one whose meaning can be made explicit without reference to any one particular object points to the intended meaning but does not explicate it precisely, and the problem of an adequate definition of purely qualitative predicates remains open.

There can be little doubt, however, that there exists a large number of property and relation terms which would be rather generally recognized as purely qualitative in the sense here pointed out, and as permissible in the formulation of fundamental lawlike sentences; some examples have been given above, and the list could be readily enlarged. When we speak of purely qualitative predicates, we shall henceforth have in mind predicates of this kind.

In the following section, a model language L of a rather simple logical structure will be described, whose primitives will be assumed to be qualitative in the sense just indicated. For this language, the concepts of law and explanation will then be defined in a manner which takes into account the general observations set forth in the present section.

§7. *Definition of Law and Explanation for a Model Language*

Concerning the syntax of our model language L, we make the following assumptions:

L has the syntactical structure of the lower functional calculus without identity sign. In addition to the signs of alternation (disjunction), conjunction, and implication (conditional), and the symbols of universal and existential quantification with respect to individual variables, the vocabulary of L contains individual constants ('a', 'b', · · ·), individual variables ('x', 'y', · · ·), and predicates of any desired finite degree; the latter may include, in particular, predicates of degree 1 ('P', 'Q', · · ·), which express properties of individuals, and predicates of degree 2 ('R', 'S', · · ·), which express dyadic relations among individuals.

For simplicity, we assume that all predicates are primitive, i.e., undefined in L, or else that before the criteria subsequently to be developed are applied to a sentence, all defined predicates which it contains are eliminated in favor of primitives.

The syntactical rules for the formation of sentences and for logical inference in L are those of the lower functional calculus. No sentence may contain free variables, so that generality is always expressed by universal quantification.

For later reference, we now define, in purely syntactical terms, a number of auxiliary concepts. In the following definitions, S is always understood to be a sentence in L.

(*7.1a*) S is formally true (formally false) in L if S (the denial of S) can be proved in L, i.e. by means of the formal rules of logical inference for L. If two sentences are mutually derivable from each other in L, they will be called equivalent.

(*7.1b*) S is said to be a singular, or alternatively, a molecular sentence if S contains no variables. A singular sentence which contains no statement connectives is also called atomic. Illustrations: The sentences '$R(a, b) \supset (P(a) \cdot \sim Q(a))$', '$\sim Q(a)$', '$(R(a, b)$', '$P(a)$' are all singular, or molecular; the last two are atomic.

(*7.1c*) S is said to be a generalized sentence if it consists of one or more quantifiers followed by an expression which contains no quantifiers. S is said to be of universal form if it is a generalized sentence and all the quantifiers occurring in it are universal. S is called purely generalized (purely universal) if S is a generalized sentence (is of universal form) and contains no individual constants. S is said to be essentially universal if it is of universal form and not equivalent to a singular sentence. S is called essentially generalized if it is not equivalent to a singular sentence.

Illustrations: '$(x)(P(x) \supset Q(x))$', '$(x)R(a, x)$', '$(x)(P(x) \vee P(a))$', '$(x)(P(x) \vee \sim P(x))$', '$(Ex)(P(x) \cdot \sim Q(x))$', '$(Ex)(y)(R(a, x) \cdot S(a, y))$' are all generalized sentences; the first four are of universal form, the first and fourth are purely universal; the first and second are essentially universal, the third being equivalent to the singular sentence '$P(a)$', and the fourth to '$P(a) \vee \sim P(a)$'. All sentences except the third and fourth are essentially generalized.

Concerning the semantical interpretation of L, we lay down the following two stipulations:

(7.2*a*) The primitive predicates of L are all purely qualitative.
(7.2*b*) The universe of discourse of L, i.e., the domain of objects covered by the quantifiers, consists of all physical objects, or of all spatio-temporal locations.

A linguistic framework of the kind here characterized is not sufficient for the formulation of scientific theories since it contains no functors and does not provide the means for dealing with real numbers. Besides, the question is open at present whether a constitution system can be constructed in which all of the concepts of empirical science are reduced, by chains of explicit definitions, to a basis of primitives of a purely qualitative character. Nevertheless, we consider it worthwhile to study the problems at hand for the simplified type of language just described because the analysis of law and explanation is far from trivial even for our model language L, and because that analysis sheds light on the logical character of the concepts under investigation also in their application to more complex contexts.

In accordance with the considerations developed in section 6, we now define:

(7.3*a*) S is a fundamental lawlike sentence in L if S is purely universal; S is a fundamental law in L if S is purely universal and true.
(7.3*b*) S is a derivative law in L if (1) S is essentially, but not purely, universal and (2) there exists a set of fundamental laws in L which has S as a consequence.
(7.3*c*) S is a law in L if it is a fundamental or a derivative law in L.

The fundamental laws as here defined obviously include, besides general statements of empirical character, all those statements of purely universal form which are true on purely logical grounds; i.e. those which are formally true in L, such as '$(x)(P(x) \vee \sim P(x))$', and those whose truth derives exclusively from the interpretation given to its constituents, as is the case with '$(x)(P(x) \supset Q(x))$', if 'P' is interpreted as meaning the property of being a father, and '*Q*' that of being male.—The derivative laws, on the other hand, include neither of these categories; indeed, no fundamental law is also a derivative one.

As the primitives of *L* are purely qualitative, all the statements of universal form in *L* also satisfy the requirement of non-limited scope, and thus it is readily seen that the concept of law as defined above satisfies all the conditions suggested in section 6.[27]

The explanation of a phenomenon may involve generalized sentences which are not of universal form. We shall use the term "theory" to refer to such sentences, and we define this term by the following chain of definitions:

(7.4*a*) *S* is a fundamental theory if *S* is purely generalized and true.
(7.4*b*) *S* is a derivative theory in *L* if (1) *S* is essentially, but not purely, generalized and (2) there exists a set of fundamental theories in *L* which has *S* as a consequence.
(7.4*c*) *S* is a theory in *L* if it is a fundamental or a derivative theory in *L*.

By virtue of the above definitions, every law is also a theory, and every theory is true.

With the help of the concepts thus defined, we will now reformulate more precisely our earlier characterization of scientific explanation with specific reference to our model language *L*. It will be convenient to state our criteria for a sound explanation in the form of a definition for the expression "the ordered couple of sentences, (*T*, *C*), constitutes an explanans for the sentence *E*." Our analysis will be restricted to the explanation of particular events, i.e., to the case where the explanandum, *E*, is a singular sentence.[28]

In analogy to the concept of lawlike sentence, which need not satisfy a requirement of truth, we will first introduce an auxiliary concept of potential explanans, which is not subject to a requirement of truth; the notion

[27] As defined above, fundamental laws include universal conditional statements with vacuous antecedents, such as "All mermaids are brunettes". This point does not appear to lead to undesirable consequences in the definition of the explanation to be proposed later.—For an illuminating analysis of universal conditionals with vacuous antecedents, see Chapter VIII in Reichenbach's [Logic].

[28] This is not a matter of free choice: The precise rational reconstruction of explanation as applied to general regularities presents peculiar problems for which we can offer no solution at present. The core of the difficulty can be indicated briefly by reference to an example: Kepler's laws, *K*, may be conjoined with Boyle's law, *B*, to a stronger law *K.B;* but derivation of *K* from the latter would not be considered as an explanation of the regularities stated in Kepler's laws; rather, it would be viewed as representing, in effect, a pointless "explanation" of Kepler's laws by themselves. The derivation of Kepler's laws from Newton's laws of motion and of gravitation, on the other hand, would be recognized as a genuine explanation in terms of more comprehensive regularities, or so-called higher-level laws. The problem therefore arises of setting up clear-cut criteria for the distinction of levels of explanation or for a comparison of generalized sentences as to their comprehensiveness. The establishment of adequate criteria for this purpose is as yet an open problem.

of explanans will then be defined with the help of this auxiliary concept.—The considerations presented in Part I suggest the following initial stipulations:

(7.5) An ordered couple of sentences, (T, C), constitutes a potential explanans for a singular sentence E only if
   (1) T is essentially generalized and C is singular
   (2) E is derivable in L from T and C jointly, but not from C alone.

(7.6) An ordered couple of sentences, (T, C), constitutes an explanans for a singular sentence E if and only if
   (1) (T, C) is a potential explanans for E
   (2) T is a theory and C is true.

(7.6) is an explicit definition of explanation in terms of the concept of potential explanation.[29] On the other hand, (7.5) is not suggested as a definition, but as a statement of necessary conditions of potential explanation. These conditions will presently be shown not to be sufficient, and additional requirements will be discussed by which (7.5) has to be supplemented in order to provide a definition of potential explanation.

Before we turn to this point, some remarks are called for concerning the formulation of (7.5). The analysis presented in Part I suggests that an explanans for a singular sentence consists of a class of generalized sentences and a class of singular ones. In (7.5), the elements of each of these classes separately are assumed to be conjoined to one sentence. This provision will simplify our formulations, and in the case of generalized sentences, it serves an additional purpose: A class of essentially generalized sentences may be equivalent to a singular sentence; thus, the class {'$P(a) \vee (x)Q(x)$', '$P(a) \vee \sim (x)Q(x)$'} is equivalent with the sentence '$P(a)$'. Since scientific explanation makes essential use of generalized sentences, sets of laws of this kind have to be ruled out; this is achieved above by combining all the generalized sentences in the explanans into one conjunction, T, and stipulating that T has to be essentially generalized.—Again, since scientific explanation makes essential use of generalized sentences, E must not be a consequence of C alone: The law of gravitation, combined with the singular sentence "Mary is blonde and blue-eyed" does not constitute an explanans for "Mary is blonde". The last stipulation in (7.5) introduces the requisite restriction and thus prohibits complete self-explanation of the explanandum, i.e., the derivation of E from some singular sentence which has E as a consequence.—The same restriction also dispenses with the need for a special requirement to the effect that T has to have factual content if (T, C) is to be a potential explanans for an

[29] It is necessary to stipulate, in (7.6) (2), that T be a theory rather than merely that T be true, for as was shown in section 6, the generalized sentences occurring in an explanans have to constitute a theory, and not every essentially generalized sentence which is true is actually a theory, i.e., a consequence of a set of purely generalized true sentences.

empirical sentence E. For if E is factual, then, since E is a consequence of T and C jointly, but not of C alone, T must be factual, too.

Our stipulations in (7.5) do not preclude, however, what might be termed partial self-explanation of the explanandum. Consider the sentences $T_1 =$ '$P(a) \cdot (x)(P(x) \supset Q(x))$', $C_1 =$ '$R(a, b) \cdot U(b)$', $E_1 =$ '$Q(a) \cdot R(a, b)$'. They satisfy all the requirements laid down in (7.5), but it seems counter-intuitive to say that (T_1, C_1) potentially explains E_1, because the occurrence of the component '$R(a, b)$' of C_1 in the sentence E_1 amounts to a partial explanation of the explanandum by itself. Is it not possible to rule out, by an additional stipulation, all those cases in which E shares part of its content with C, i.e. where C and E have a common consequence which is not formally true in L? This stipulation would be tantamount to the requirement that C and E have to be exhaustive alternatives in the sense that their alternation is formally true, for the content which any two sentences have in common is expressed by their alternation. The proposed restriction, however, would be very severe. For if E does not share even part of its content with C, then C is altogether unnecessary for the derivation of E from T and C, i.e., E can be inferred from T alone. Therefore, in every potential explanation in which the singular component of the explanans is not dispensable, the explanandum is partly explained by itself. Take, for example, the potential explanation of $E_2 =$ '$Q(a)$' by $T_2 =$ '$(x)(P(x) \supset Q(x))$' and $C_2 =$ '$P(a)$', which satisfies (7.5), and which surely is intuitively unobjectionable. Its three components may be equivalently expressed by the following sentences: $T_2' =$ '$(x)(\sim P(x) \vee Q(x))$'; $C_2' =$ '$(P(a) \vee Q(a)) \cdot (P(a) \vee \sim Q(a))$'; $E_2' =$ '$(P(a) \vee Q(a)) \cdot (\sim P(a) \vee Q(a))$'. This reformulation shows that part of the content of the explanandum is contained in the content of the singular component of the explanans and is, in this sense, explained by itself.

Our analysis has reached a point here where the customary intuitive idea of explanation becomes too vague to provide further guidance for rational reconstruction. Indeed, the last illustration strongly suggests that there may be no sharp boundary line which separates the intuitively permissible from the counterintuitive types of partial self-explanation; for even the potential explanation just considered, which is acceptable in its original formulation, might be judged unacceptable on intuitive grounds when transformed into the equivalent version given above.

The point illustrated by the last example is stated more explicitly in the following theorem, which we formulate here without proof.

(7.7) *Theorem.* Let (T, C) be a potential explanans for the singular sentence E. Then there exist three singular sentences, E_1, E_2, and C_1 in L such that E is equivalent to the conjunction $E_1 \cdot E_2$, C is equivalent to the conjunction $C_1 \cdot E_1$, and E_2 can be derived in L from T alone.[30]

[30] In the formulation of the above theorem and subsequently, statement connective symbols are used not only as signs *in* L, but also autonomously in speaking *about* com-

In more intuitive terms, this means that if we represent the deductive structure of the given potential explanation by the schema $\{T, C\} \rightarrow E$, then this schema can be restated in the form $\{T, C_1 \cdot E_1\} \rightarrow E_1 \cdot E_2$, where E_2 follows from T alone, so that C_1 is entirely unnecessary as a premise; hence, the deductive schema under consideration can be reduced to $\{T, E_1\} \rightarrow E_1 \cdot E_2$, which can be decomposed into the two deductive schemata $\{T\} \rightarrow E_2$ and $\{E_1\} \rightarrow E_1$. The former of these might be called a purely theoretical explanation of E_2 by T, the latter a complete self-explanation of E_1. Theorem (7.7) shows, in other words, that every explanation whose explanandum is a singular sentence can be decomposed into a purely theoretical explanation and a complete self-explanation; and any explanation of this kind in which the singular constituent of the explanans is not completely unnecessary involves a partial self-explanation of the explanandum.[31]

To prohibit partial self-explanation altogether would therefore mean limitation of explanation to purely theoretical explanation. This measure seems too severely restrictive. On the other hand, an attempt to delimit, by some special rule, the permissible degree of self-explanation does not appear to be warranted because, as we saw, customary usage provides no guidance for such a delimitation, and because no systematic advantage seems to be gained by drawing some arbitrary dividing line. For these reasons, we refrain from laying down stipulations prohibiting partial self-explanation.

The conditions laid down in (7.5) fail to preclude yet another unacceptable type of explanatory argument, which is closely related to complete self-explanation, and which will have to be ruled out by an additional stipulation. The point is, briefly, that if we were to accept (7.5) as a definition, rather than merely as a statement of necessary conditions, for potential explanation, then, as a consequence of (7.6), any given particular fact could be explained by means of any true lawlike sentence whatsoever. More explicitly, if E is a true singular sentence—say, "Mt. Everest is snowcapped",—and T is a law—say, "All metals are good con-

pound expressions of L. Thus, when 'S' and 'T' are names or name variables for sentences in L, their conjunction and disjunction will be designated by '$S.T$' and '$S \vee T$', respectively; the conditional which has S as antecedent and T as consequent will be designated by '$S \supset T$', and the denial of S by '$\sim S$'. (Incidentally, this convention has already been used, tacitly, at one place in note 28).

[31] The characteristic here referred to as partial self-explanation has to be distinguished from what is sometimes called the circularity of scientific explanation. The latter phrase has been used to cover two entirely different ideas. (a) One of these is the contention that the explanatory principles adduced in accounting for a specific phenomenon are inferred from that phenomenon, so that the entire explanatory process is circular. This belief is false, since general laws cannot be inferred from singular sentences. (b) It has also been argued that in a sound explanation the content of the explanandum is contained in that of the explanans. That is correct since the explanandum is a logical consequence of the explanans; but this peculiarity does not make scientific explanation trivially circular since the general laws occurring in the explanans go far beyond the content of the specific explanandum. For a fuller discussion of the circularity objection, see Feigl, [Operationism], pp. 286 ff., where this issue is dealt with very clearly.

ductors of heat",—then there exists always a true singular sentence C such that E is derivable from T and C, but not from C alone; in other words, such that (7.5) is satisfied. Indeed, let T_s be some arbitrarily chosen particular instance of T, such as "If the Eiffel Tower is metal, it is a good conductor of heat". Now since E is true, so is the conditional $T_s \supset E$, and if the latter is chosen as the sentence C, then T, C, E satisfy the conditions laid down in (7.5).

In order to isolate the distinctive characteristic of this specious type of explanation, let us examine an especially simple case of the objectionable kind. Let $T_1 =$ '$(x)P(x)$' and $E_1 =$ '$R(a, b)$'; then the sentence $C_1 =$ '$P(a) \supset R(a, b)$' is formed in accordance with the preceding instructions, and T_1, C_1, E_1 satisfy the conditions (7.5). Yet, as the preceding example illustrates, we would not say that (T_1, C_1) constitutes a potential explanans for E_1. The rationale for the verdict may be stated as follows: If the theory T_1 on which the explanation rests, is actually true, then the sentence C_1, which can also be put into the form '$\sim P(a) \vee R(a, b)$', can be verified, or shown to be true, only by verifying '$R(a, b)$', i.e., E_1. In this broader sense, E_1 is here explained by itself. And indeed, the peculiarity just pointed out clearly deprives the proposed potential explanation for E_1 of the predictive import which, as was noted in Part I, is essential for scientific explanation: E_1 could not possibly be predicted on the basis of T_1 and C_1 since the truth of C^1 cannot be ascertained in any manner which does not include verification of E_1. (7.5) should therefore be supplemented by a stipulation to the effect that if (T, C) is to be a potential explanans for E, then the assumption that T is true must not imply that verification of C necessitates verification of E.[32]

How can this idea be stated more precisely? Study of an illustration will suggest a definition of verification for molecular sentences. The sentence $M =$ '$(\sim P(a) \cdot Q(a)) \vee R(a, b)$' may be verified in two different ways, either by ascertaining the truth of the two sentences '$\sim P(a)$' and '$Q(a)$', which jointly have M as a consequence, or by establishing the truth of the sentence '$R(a, b)$', which, again, has M as a consequence. Let us say that S is a basic sentence in L if S is either an atomic sentence or the denial of an atomic sentence in L. Verification of a molecular sentence S may then be defined generally as establishment of the truth of some class of basic sentences which has S as a consequence. Hence, the intended additional stipulation may be restated: The assumption that T is true must not imply that every class of true basic sentences which has C as a consequence also has E as a consequence.

As brief reflection shows, this stipulation may be expressed in the following form, which avoids reference to truth: T must be compatible in

[32] It is important to distinguish clearly between the following two cases: (a) If T is true then C cannot be true without E being true; and (b) If T is true, C cannot be verified without E being verified.—Condition (a) must be satisfied by any potential explanation; the much more restrictive condition (b) must not be satisfied if (T,C) is to be a potential explanans for E.

L with at least one class of basic sentences which has C but not E as a consequence; or, equivalently: There must exist at least one class of basic sentences which has C, but neither $\sim T$ nor E as a consequence in L.

If this requirement is met, then surely E cannot be a consequence of C, for otherwise there could be no class of basic sentences which has C but not E as a consequence; hence, supplementation of (7.5) by the new condition renders the second stipulation in (7.5) (2) superfluous.—We now define potential explanation as follows:

(7.8) An ordered couple of sentences (T, C), constitutes a potential explanans for a singular sentence E if and only if the following conditions are satisfied:

(1) T is essentially generalized and C is singular
(2) E is derivable in L from T and C jointly
(3) T is compatible with at least one class of basic sentences which has C but not E as a consequence.

The definition of the concept of explanans by means of that of potential explanans as formulated in (7.6) remains unchanged.

In terms of our concept of explanans, we can give the following interpretation to the frequently used phrase "this fact is explainable by means of that theory":

(7.9) A singular sentence E is explainable by a theory T if there exists a singular sentence C such that (T, C) constitutes an explanans for E.

The concept of causal explanation, which has been examined here, is capable of various generalizations. One of these consists in permitting T to include statistical laws. This requires, however, a previous strengthening of the means of expression available in L, or the use of a complex theoretical apparatus in the metalanguage.—On the other hand, and independently of the admission of statistical laws among the explanatory principles, we may replace the strictly deductive requirement that E has to be a consequence of T and C jointly by the more liberal inductive one that E has to have a high degree of confirmation relatively to the conjunction of T and C. Both of these extensions of the concept of explanation open important prospects and raise a variety of new problems. In the present essay, however, these issues will not be further pursued.

BIBLIOGRAPHY

Throughout the article, the abbreviated titles in brackets are used for reference.

Beard, Charles A., and Hook, Sidney. [Terminology] Problems of terminology in historical writing. Chapter IV of Theory and practice in historical study: A report of the Committee on Historiography. Social Science Research Council, New York, 1946.

Bergmann, Gustav. [Emergence] Holism, historicism, and emergence. *Philosophy of science*, vol. 11 (1944), pp. 209–221.

Bonfante, G. [Semantics] Semantics, language. An article in P. L. Harriman, ed., The encyclopedia of psychology. Philosophical Library, New York, 1946.

Broad, C. D. [Mind] The mind and its place in nature. New York, 1925.

Carnap, Rudolf. [Semantics] Introduction to semantics. Harvard University Press, 1942.

———. [Inductive Logic] On inductive logic. *Philosophy of science*, vol. 12 (1945), pp. 72–97.

———. [Concepts] The two concepts of probability. *Philosophy and phenomenological research*, vol. 5 (1945), pp. 513–532.

———. [Remarks] Remarks on induction and truth. *Philosophy and phenomenological research*, vol. 6 (1946), pp. 590–602.

———. [Application] On the application of inductive logic. *Philosophy and phenomenological research*, vol. 8 (1947), pp. 133–147.

Chisholm, Roderick M. [Conditional] The contrary-to-fact conditional. *Mind*, vol. 55 (1946), pp. 289–307.

Church, Alonzo. [Logic] Logic, formal. An article in Dagobert D. Runes, ed. The dictionary of philosophy. Philosophical Library, New York, 1942.

Ducasse, C. J. [Explanation] Explanation, mechanism, and teleology. *The journal of philosophy*, vol. 22 (1925), pp. 150–155.

Feigl, Hebert. [Operationism] Operationism and scientific method. *Psychological review*, vol. 52 (1945), pp. 250–259 and 284–288.

Goodman, Nelson. [Query] A query on confirmation. *The journal of philosophy*, vol. 43 (1946), pp. 383–385.

———. [Counterfactuals]. The problem of counterfactual conditionals. *The journal of philosophy*, vol. 44 (1947), pp. 113–128.

———. [Infirmities] On infirmities of confirmation theory. *Philosophy and phenomenological research*, vol. 8 (1947), pp. 149–151.

Grelling, Kurt and Oppenheim, Paul. [Gestaltbegriff] Der Gestaltbegriff im Lichte der neuen Logik. *Erkenntnis*, vol. 7 (1937–38), pp. 211–225 and 357–359.

Grelling, Kurt and Oppenheim, Paul. [Functional Whole] Logical Analysis of "Gestalt" as "Functional whole". Preprinted for distribution at Fifth Internat. Congress for the Unity of Science, Cambridge, Mass., 1939.

Helmer, Olaf and Oppenheim, Paul. [Probability] A syntactical definition of probability and of degree of confirmation. *The journal of symbolic logic*, vol. 10 (1945), pp. 25–60.

Hempel, Carl G. [Laws] The function of general laws in history. *The journal of philosophy*, vol. 39 (1942), pp. 35–48.

———. [Studies] Studies in the logic of confirmation. *Mind*, vol. 54 (1945); Part I: pp. 1–26, Part II: pp. 97–121.

Hempel, Carl G. and Oppenheim, Paul. [Degree] A definition of "degree of confirmation". *Philosophy of science*, vol. 12 (1945), pp. 98–115.

Henle, Paul. [Emergence] The status of emergence. *The journal of philosophy*, vol. 39 (1942), pp. 486–493.

Hospers, John. [Explanation] On explanation. *The journal of philosophy*, vol. 43 (1946), pp. 337–356.

Hull, Clark L. [Variables] The problem of intervening variables in molar behavior theory. *Psychological review*, vol. 50 (1943), pp. 273–291.

———. [Principles] Principles of behavior. New York, 1943.

Jevons, W. Stanley. [Principles] The principles of science. London, 1924. (1st ed. 1874.)

Kaufmann, Felix. [Methodology] Methodology of the social sciences. New York, 1944.

Knight, Frank H. [Limitations] The limitations of scientific method in eco-

nomics. In Tugwell, R., ed., The trend of economics. New York, 1924.
Koch, Sigmund. [Motivation] The logical character of the motivation concept. *Psychological review*, vol. 48 (1941). Part I: pp. 15–38, Part II: pp. 127–154.
Langford, C. H. [Review] Review in *The journal of symbolic logic*, vol. 6 (1941), pp. 67–68.
Lewis, C. I. [Analysis] An analysis of knowledge and valuation. La Salle, Ill., 1946.
McKinsey, J. C. C. [Review] Review of Helmer and Oppenheim [Probability]. *Mathematical reviews*, vol. 7 (1946), p. 45.
Mill, John Stuart. [Logic] A system of logic.
Morgan, C. Lloyd. Emergent evolution. New York, 1923.
———. The emergence of novelty. New York, 1933.
Popper, Karl. [Forschung] Logik der Forschung. Wien, 1935.
———. [Society] The open society and its enemies. London, 1945.
Reichenbach, Hans. [Logic] Elements of symbolic logic. New York, 1947.
———. [Quantum mechanics] Philosophic foundations of quantum mechanics. University of California Press, 1944.
Rosenblueth, A., Wiener, N., and Bigelow, J. [Teleology] Behavior, Purpose, and Teleology. *Philosophy of science*, vol. 10 (1943), pp. 18–24.
Stace, W. T. [Novelty] Novelty, indeterminism and emergence. *Philosophical review*, vol. 48 (1939), pp. 296–310.
Tarski, Alfred. [Truth] The semantical conception of truth, and the foundations of semantics. *Philosophy and phenomenological research*, vol. 4 (1944), pp. 341–376.
Tolman, Edward Chase. [Behavior] Purposive behavior in animals and men. New York, 1932.
White, Morton G. [Explanation] Historical explanation. *Mind*, vol. 52 (1943), pp. 212–229.
Woodger, J. H. [Principles] Biological principles. New York, 1929.
Zilsel, Edgar. [Empiricism] Problems of empiricism. In *International encyclopedia of unified science*, vol. II, no. 8. The University of Chicago Press, 1941.
———. [Laws] Physics and the problem of historico-sociological laws. *Philosophy of science*, vol. 8 (1941), pp. 567–579.

Induction, Explanation, and Transcendent Hypotheses *

WILLIAM KNEALE

Nature of Transcendent Hypotheses

When we explain laws by showing that they are logically entailed by other laws, the propositions which serve as postulates in our system are of the same kind as those they explain, and they can be established by the same means, namely, by direct induction from experience. In physics, however, attempts have been made to explain laws by deriving them from postulates of a different kind. The oldest suggestion of this sort is the atomic theory. This was first put forward by Democritus in the fifth century B.C., but did not receive general approval from scientists until the beginning of the last century, when Dalton showed that it would provide an explanation of some simple laws about the constant combining weights of chemical substances. In its modern form it explains a host of empirical generalizations, and everyone engaged in physical science assumes that with further specification it will explain still more. The novelty of the theory is that it explains laws by means of postulates which are not themselves established by direct induction from experience and cannot, indeed, be tested directly in any way. These postulates are hypotheses about the existence of objects which must, from the nature of the case, be imperceptible. Another physical theory of the same type is the undulatory theory of light, first suggested by Huyghens in the seventeenth century and later developed by Clerk-Maxwell into the general theory of electro-magnetism. This is obviously not the place in which to try to expound either of these theories in detail, but it is important for our purpose to make clear the peculiar nature of the hypotheses on which they are based.

The peculiarity of the objects and processes assumed by physical scientists in the formulation of these theories is not merely that they are small in relation to the sticks and stones about which we talk in common speech. Indeed, according to later developments of the undulatory theory electromagnetic waves may be of very large dimensions, and it is sometimes argued that in a certain sense each electron occupies the whole of space. The essen-

* Reprinted by kind permission of the author and the publisher from William Kneale, *Probability and Induction*, The Clarendon Press, Oxford, 1949, pp. 92–110.

tial point is rather that the physical world as described in such theories cannot, from the nature of the case, be observed as sticks and stones are observed. I can see a wave passing over the surface of a pond, but it is merely senseless to speak of seeing or observing in any other way an electromagnetic wave.[1] It is even impossible to imagine these things, for if we try to imagine them we must attribute to them qualities such as colour or perceptible hardness which they cannot possess. I propose to call hypotheses about things of this kind *transcendent*, because I think it is necessary to indicate quite clearly that they are concerned with things which are not observable even in principle. This is a difficult doctrine, and two questions about it come to mind immediately.

In the first place, if all our ideas are derived from experience, as it seems plausible to say with Locke and the empirical school of philosophers, how can we even suppose the existence of things which are in principle unobservable? The answer is that in these hypotheses we suppose only the existence of a set of things having a certain structure which can be expressed in the language of mathematics. The sense in which the word 'structure' is used here can best be understood from an example. A tune which is heard and a musical score which is seen may be said to have the same logical structure although they are sensibly very different. That structure might conceivably be expounded to a person who had neither hearing nor sight but only touch. Structure cannot, of course, exist without content, and, when I say that in transcendent hypotheses we suppose only the existence of a set of things having a certain structure, I do not mean that we suppose the existence of a set of things having only a certain structure, for that would be absurd. What I mean is that, although we cannot even conjecture what the content is that embodies the structure, we can reasonably suppose that there is a set of things of that structure, just as a man deaf from birth can suppose that there are complex objects called tunes which embody the structures about which he reads in books on music. That transcendent hypotheses are concerned only with structure has often been overlooked in the past, because scientists and philosophers have mistakenly allowed themselves to slip some imaginative elements, such as perceptible hardness, into their conceptions of the objects mentioned in the hypotheses. Berkeley pointed out quite correctly that the hypothetical entities of the physicists were unimaginable, but he concluded wrongly that because they were unimaginable they were inconceivable.[2]

Secondly, how can hypotheses of this kind explain laws about observable things? If the hypotheses contained no reference to the world of common sense it would, of course, be impossible to explain laws about observables by their help. The hypotheses are, however, doubly gen-

[1] We say, of course, that we observe light, but by 'light' we mean in this context a perceptual object.

[2] Locke's distinction of primary and secondary qualities, which Berkeley derided, was an attempt to deal with the notion of structure. The distinction was first suggested by Democritus.

eral propositions (universal and existential) of such forms as: 'Wherever light of such-and-such a colour (i.e. a perceptual object) occurs, there is a wave process of such-and-such a wave-length, and vice versa.' They are introduced for the purpose of explaining laws, and, however abstruse they may become in the course of development, they must always remain attached in this way to the world of perceptual objects if they are to achieve their purpose.

The making of transcendent hypotheses involves the introduction of a new terminology, and it is important to realize how this is related to the sensum terminology and the perceptual object terminology. There is no direct connexion between transcendent object terminology and the sensum terminology, for the physical scientist is not concerned as such with sensa. His aim in formulating transcendent hypotheses is to explain laws about perceptual objects (not sensa), and his new terminology therefore has direct connexion only with perceptual object terminology. In relation to this latter it appears as a more comprehensive language. That is to say, the new terminology of the physicist would, if complete, provide an expression corresponding to every expression of the perceptual object terminology, e.g. 'copper', 'lightning', 'freezing', &c., but contain also expressions, e.g. 'electron', to which there is nothing corresponding in the perceptual object terminology. Natural laws which have been formulated originally in the perceptual object terminology can therefore be translated into the transcendent object terminology. When so translated they naturally appear more complex, because the new terminology is, so to say, of finer grain. Instead of a comparatively simple statement about the melting-point of a chemical substance we have a statement about the average velocity of molecules of such-and-such internal constitution at the time when the attractive forces between them no longer suffice to keep them in a rigid formation. But the greater complexity of the expressions for laws in the new terminology is intended to exhibit the necessity of the laws, and the price paid is small if the new terminology does indeed make it possible to explain the laws within a comprehensive theory.

I have spoken of correspondence between expressions of the perceptual object terminology and expressions of the transcendent object terminology, and I have said that statements of the first can be translated into statements of the second, although the converse is not always true. This way of speaking is not common among scientists, but I wish to indicate that the transcendent object terminology is really a quite new language and not a mere supplement to the perceptual object terminology. We may fall into serious confusion if we try to mix expressions from the two terminologies. Although it is quite correct to translate the word 'table' in certain contexts by the expression 'set of molecules', it is absurd to say that I now perceive a set of molecules. A famous example of confusion of this kind is to be found in the first sentence of Sir Arthur Eddington's *Nature of the Physical World.* Instead of talking of two terminologies to be kept distinct, he speaks there of two tables, one a perceptual object which is solid, and the other a scientific object which is full of empty spaces, since it consists of molecules whose volume is small in relation to the total volume within which they move. The mystery disappears as soon as we recognize that when the table is said in perceptual object terminology to be solid, the word 'solid' is to be understood in the appropriate way, i.e. as a word of the perceptual object terminology. There is then no inconsistency between the assertion of the plain man and the assertion of the physicist. On the contrary, the sentence 'The table is solid' can quite well be translated as a whole into the terminology of physics. It would be very strange if it could not, for the terminology of physics is designed to explain among other things why some perceptual objects are solid and others not. When we say that tables and pennies consist of molecules with certain forces between them, we suppose the molecules and the forces to be such that pennies cannot drop through tables.

When first introduced a transcendent hypothesis may be extremely vague, provided only that it entails the laws which it is intended to explain. When Huyghens tried to explain the diffraction and the interference of light by means of his undulatory theory, he had no clear idea of the nature of the waves he supposed to occur, but the wave-motion seemed to render some laws of optics intelligible and there was no rival suggestion which could do as much. The theory therefore began to win acceptance among scientists and was gradually developed by greater definition of all the necessary details. As it developed, it became capable of explaining other known laws of optics and also some laws which had not been established before by direct induction but which were verified after they had been deduced from the hypothesis. For when such a hypothesis has some degree of success, it immediately begins to dominate the interest of scientific researchers. At first they try to devise additional tests, that is, to discover more and more consequences which they can verify. Admittedly, verification of these consequences can never amount to demonstration of the hypothesis, just as the confirmation of a law of nature in many instances can never amount to demonstration of the law. But when several uniformities foretold by the theory, that is to say, deduced from the hypothesis, have been confirmed by direct induction, scientists soon cease to debate whether the hypothesis is acceptable in principle. Their interest now is to devise tests by which to decide between alternative developments of the theory in those parts or aspects that have hitherto been left indefinite.

In the earlier stages of its development a transcendent hypothesis may contain assumptions about unobservable objects which are similar to the laws of nature we formulate about observable objects in that they cannot be seen to be necessary. Thus Dalton assumed that the atoms of different elements could combine only in certain fixed ratios. This seemed to explain some laws which had been discovered by chemists, but it was itself something requiring explanation, and hypotheses about valency are still being developed in our own time for the improvement of the general theory. It is felt as an imperfection of a theory that it should assume any laws which cannot be seen to be intrinsically necessary, and attempts are therefore made to specify the hypothetical entities of the system in such a way that any connexions between them required for the purposes of the theory are intrinsically necessary. This does not mean, however, that we can hope to derive laws of nature some day from self-evident truths alone. Although the connexions *within* the world of transcendent entities posited by a theory may all be self-evident, the relations *between* this world and the world of perceptual objects remain opaque to the intellect, and it is only by assuming these relations that we can explain our laws about observables.

Criticism and Defence of Transcendent Hypotheses

Transcendent hypotheses of the kind we have been considering were first introduced into physics by the Greek atomists, but they were of little use for many centuries, because they were very vaguely formulated at the beginning and the philosophers who propounded them were unable to derive from them any new consequences which could be tested in experience. Greek atomism was a programme for the making of a theory rather than a theory, and it was not until the seventeenth century that transcendent hypotheses were employed in a genuinely scientific manner. Huyghens was the first great physicist to attempt this method of explaining natural laws with full consciousness of what he was about.[3] In the preface to his *Treatise on Light* of 1690 we find the following passage:

> 'There is to be found here a kind of demonstration which does not produce a certainty as great as that of geometry and is, indeed, very different from that used by geometers, since they prove their propositions by certain and incontestable principles, whereas here principles are tested by the consequences derived from them. The nature of the subject permits no other treatment. It is possible nevertheless to attain in this way a degree of probability which is little short of complete certainty. This happens when the consequences of our assumed principles agree perfectly with the observed phenomena, and especially when such verifications are numerous, but above all when we conceive in advance new phenomena which should follow from the hypotheses we employ and then find our expectations fulfilled. If in the following treatise all these evidences of probability are to be found together, as I think they are, the success of my enquiry is strongly confirmed and it is scarcely possible that things should not be almost exactly as I have represented them. I venture to hope, therefore, that those who enjoy finding out causes and can appreciate the wonders of light will be interested in these varied speculations about it.'

From that time onwards there have always been scientists and philosophers to defend the method. Of all who have written about scientific method

[3] Leibniz had stated the programme of explanation by hypotheses as early as 1678 in a letter to Conring (see L. Couturat, *La Logique de Leibniz*, p. 268), but that does not detract from the merit claimed here for Huyghens. Leibniz often compared scientific hypotheses with suggestions for the solution of cryptograms (cf. *Nouveaux Essais*, IV. xii. 13).

Whewell is perhaps the most vigorous in his championship of the use of hypotheses. There have been criticisms, however, and to these we must now turn.

In a celebrated General Scholium at the end of his *Principia* Newton writes:

> So far I have explained the phenomena of the heavens and of the sea by the force of gravity, but I have not yet assigned the cause of gravity. . . . I have not yet been able to deduce from the phenomena the reasons for these properties of gravity and I invent no hypotheses (*hypotheses non fingo*). For everything which is not deduced from the phenomena should be called an hypothesis, and hypotheses, whether metaphysical or physical, whether of occult qualities or mechanical, have no place in experimental philosophy. In this philosophy propositions are deduced from phenomena and rendered general by induction. It is thus we have come to know the impenetrability, the mobility, the *impetus* of bodies and the laws of motion and of gravity. It is enough that gravity really exists, that it acts according to the laws we have set out and that it suffices for all the movements of the heavenly bodies and of the sea.

This is a strange passage and has given rise to much debate. It will be noticed that Newton speaks in a very curious way of *deducing* propositions from phenomena. This expression occurs in other places, and we must assume that Newton used it deliberately; but it obviously cannot mean what is ordinarily called deduction, and I can only conclude that Newton meant that the propositions which interested him were derived from observations in a very strict way. Apart, however, from the peculiarity of its phraseology, the passage is fairly clear. Newton seems to be saying in effect that he thinks it should be possible to find an explanation for gravitation but that this must be discovered by ordinary induction from facts found in experience, because no other method is admissible in natural science. His phrase *hypotheses non fingo* has been used as a slogan by those who distrust transcendent hypotheses.

Newton's doctrine in this passage and in other places where he talks of scientific method is very puzzling, because it does not square with his own practice. He was obviously inclined to favour the atomic hypothesis about matter and the corpuscular theory of light, and he allowed himself occasionally (e.g. at the end of his *Optics*) to make speculations of a transcendent character about the explanation of gravitation. But more remarkable still, his establishment of the theory of motion and of the principle of universal gravitation, which he cites as an example of direct induction from phenomena, is in truth a very notable achievement of the hypothetical method. The so-called law of gravitation is that every body attracts every other body with a force which is proportional to its own mass but varying inversely as the square of its distance from that other. This is indeed a universal proposition, but not one which could conceivably be established by the discovery in experience of instances falling under it. We do not perceive forces of attraction between the bodies we can observe, and we never shall, because forces are objects of a sort we cannot hope to perceive. What we do observe are movements of perceptual objects such as stones, but these give no direct confirmation of the law of gravitation. My chair and my table, for example, are not, so far as I can see, moving towards each other at present; indeed, the law of gravitation does not require that they should, for it deals only with forces, not with actual movements. Even the famous apple did not furnish an instance which directly confirmed the law. For, as Newton himself would insist, the movement of the apple was not determined solely by the attraction of the earth; the resistance of the air and the attraction of the distant heavenly bodies all had some part in determining the course of events. Newton's law of gravitation was, of course, established by an argument from experience, but not by ordinary induction. The true account of the matter seems to be that Newton offered a general theory of mechanics and that the so-called law of gravitation was one of the transcendent hypotheses in this theory. The fundamental principles of his theory are given in his laws of motion:

> '(1) Every body continues in its state of rest or uniform motion, except in so far as it is compelled by a force to change that state. (2) Change of motion is proportional to the force and takes place in the direction of the straight line in which the force acts. (3) To any action there is always an equal and contrary reaction, or the mutual actions of any two bodies are always equal and oppositely directed along the same straight line.'

These propositions are not laws in any ordinary sense, but rather postulates which define the idea of force by relating it to that of motion. Given these postulates and hypotheses concerning forces of various kinds such as gravitation, the motions to be expected of bodies in various kinds of situation can be deduced. When these consequences, themselves general in form, are confirmed by observation, as they are, the whole theory is said to be confirmed; but none of the propositions which go to make up the theory has been or can be tested directly. For an explanation of the paths of the heavenly bodies in the solar system Newton had to consider not only the force of gravitation, but also centrifugal force (or inertia). His hypotheses provided together a very satisfactory theory and were therefore accepted, but none of them could have been established separately.

Newton's authority, therefore, should not prejudice us against the use of transcendent hypotheses. His remarks should be taken rather as a somewhat confused protest against the unscientific use of hypotheses. In the past many philosophers, e.g. Descartes, had undoubtedly tried to explain phenomena in a grand manner by the use of hypotheses which they were either unwilling or unable to submit to detailed testing, and I think that for Newton the word 'hypothesis' probably had some of the unfortunate associations which the word 'speculation' now has for natural scientists. The value of an hypothesis is to be judged, however, by its explanatory power and the agreement of its consequences with all the known facts. Hypotheses which survive these tests obviously deserve more respect than dogmas about which their supporters will allow no question or idle fancies which cannot be put to the test because they are consistent with any facts whatsoever. If he were alive to-day, Newton would probably admit without hesitation that hypotheses like that which Huyghens put forward have been amply justified, and that it is inconceivable that physical science should now try to dispense with them.

In more recent times opposition to the use of transcendent hypotheses has come mostly from philosophers and scientists who are influenced by phenomenalism. Berkeley did not discuss the question explicitly, but it is clear from his general attitude to physical science that he did not think it necessary or even possible to find a place anywhere in his theory of knowledge for the atomic hypothesis or anything similar. Since his day the successes of the hypothetical method have been so great that no one would now propose to reject it entirely. The aim of phenomenalists in our time is, therefore, rather to explain away the appearance of transcendence which they find in physical theories. Some of them content themselves with saying that any statement which appears to be about transcendent objects can be replaced in principle by a series of hypothetical statements about sensa. I have never seen any detailed attempt to carry out this programme, but I am quite confident that any such attempt would fail. Since, as we have seen, statements about perceptual objects cannot be replaced by statements about sensa, there is no reason at all to suppose that statements about atoms and electrons can be eliminated in this way. On the contrary, a direct transition from the terminology of physical theory to the sensum terminology is clearly impossible. Other modern phenomenalists argue that to find the meaning of such an assertion as that there are electrons we must consider the method by which it is tested and then identify that method with the meaning. This suggestion is equally unplausible. There is no single method by which such an hypothesis is tested, for it has been introduced precisely in order to co-ordinate a multitude of laws about perceptual objects, and the evidence for the hypothesis is all the evidence for those laws. The observation of X-ray shadows or of vapour trails in Wilson chambers may perhaps seem to bring us nearer to the transcendent objects of which the physicist speaks than any experiment with familiar perceptual objects, but this is mere illusion. The physical theories were formulated before these particular techniques were developed and do not stand or fall by the results obtained from them rather than by the results of any other physical experiments.

These are comparatively crude attempts to explain away the need for supposing the existence of transcendent objects. A more subtle attempt has been made by some philosophers who belong to the phenomenalist tradition although they might disclaim the title of phenomenalist. In the previous section I spoke of the introduction of a new terminology for the formulation of transcendent hypotheses in physics. The philosophers to whom I have just referred argue that all the novelty of those physical theories which appear to be transcendent lies in their terminology. According to their view the physicist is mistaken if he thinks that he has introduced new existential hypotheses in talking of atoms and electrons. He has merely found a new and more convenient way of talking about observables. The new way is more convenient because it makes for what Mach called economy of thought. For expressions of the perceptual object terminology, which are comparatively simple but yield only mutually independent propositions, there are substituted more complex expressions which enable us to present natural laws as consequences of some small number of postulates. This is just a matter of definition. Nothing is asserted about the world in the new terminology which was not asserted in the perceptual object terminology, but what is said is given in a form more convenient for calculation.

This account of the innovation seems to me wholly unsatisfactory. In the first place the new terminology allows the formulation of statements to which there is nothing corresponding in the perceptual object terminology, e.g. statements about what takes place inside a single atom. For the philosophers just mentioned such statements must be very mysterious. They cannot be translated into the perceptual object terminology and therefore apparently say nothing; but they cannot be disregarded because they are framed in accordance with the rules of the new terminology and are even necessary for the development of the theory. Are we to say that they are merely scraps of symbolism with no independent meaning, and that they are related to statements which have counterparts in the perceptual object terminology much as single letters are related to the words in which they appear? This is a very strange doctrine. It is only by allowing for the construction of these new statements that a physical theory can provide any explanation of established laws, and all the development of a theory consists in the attempt to make these new statements more precise in order that the theory may be submitted to new tests and applied in new ways. This brings us to a second point. If the novelty of a new theory lay solely in the new terminology it used for the expression of established laws, it would be quite inexplicable that a theory should make possible the prediction of laws not hitherto established by direct induction. For, according to the view we are now examining, the making of theory is only the introduction of a new terminology and the terminology is chosen freely by human beings for their own convenience in the formulation of laws already assumed. There seems to be no reason why anyone should expect to derive from consideration of such terminology information about anything other than (*a*) the laws for the expression of which it was designed, and (*b*) the characteristics of the minds which devised it. Yet all notable hypotheses have in fact provided explanations of some laws other than those for the explanation of which they were originally put forward, and it is now regarded by scientists as obvious that a good hypothesis may be expected to yield interesting new consequences.

I conclude, then, that the statements made by physical scientists in the formulation of transcendent hypotheses are to be taken at their face value, namely, as assertions of the existence of imperceptible objects with certain specified structures. No other account seems to me to do justice to the facts; and I think that, when philosophers and scientists feel difficulty in admitting that transcendent hypotheses are what they seem to be, that is only because, like Berkeley, they have adopted an unduly narrow view of the possibilities of thinking.

The Relation Between Induction and the Hypothetical Method

We must now ask whether we should apply the term 'induction' to the kind of reasoning by which transcendent hypotheses are established. This is a verbal question to be settled according to our own convenience; but it has some importance, because in trying to decide what is the most convenient usage to adopt we are led to remark similarities and dissimilarities which might otherwise be overlooked.

If we understand by 'induction' reasoning in which universal propositions are established by consideration of instances falling under them, we cannot apply the term to the reasoning which establishes transcendent hypotheses. For the essential feature of such an hypothesis is that it relates observables of certain kind to some other things which are not observable. The hypothesis is indeed a universal proposition (e.g. about all light), but it is of such a character that cases falling under it cannot be verified by observation. It can be confirmed only indirectly by the testing of its more remote consequences. If any one of these consequences is a universal proposition about observables which is falsified by experience, the hypothesis must be rejected. If, however, all the consequences we can test are universal propositions confirmed by experience, that is to say, propositions established by direct ampliative induction either before or after being deduced from the hypothesis, all the evidence in favour of the consequences is evidence in favour of the hypothesis, although the latter is still in principle capable of being falsified through the falsification of one of its consequences. The best convention is perhaps to extend the use of the word 'induction' to cover the hypothetical method but at the same time to distinguish this new application of the term by adding the adjective 'secondary'. If we refused to call such reasoning inductive, we should ignore the obvious continuity of interest between it and primary or direct induction and make it more difficult to discuss what they have in common, whereas if we omitted to add any qualification when describing the hypothetical method as a form of induction we should slur over an important distinction.

Some logicians have been so impressed by the importance of hypotheses in what we commonly call the inductive sciences that they have confused together the notions of induction and hypothetical method, supposing all induction to be an application of the hypothetical method and every use of hypotheses an instance of induction. We even find the word 'induction' applied sometimes to the use of hypotheses by historians in the tentative reconstruction of the course of past events. This seems to me an unprofitable and even dangerous widening of the meaning of the term, but I think it is interesting to see what has suggested it.

A universal proposition of natural science which is established by induction may reasonably be called an hypothesis, although, of course, not a transcendent hypothesis. The particular cases falling under it are its consequences and the verification of them can be said to confirm the hypothesis but never to prove it conclusively. It is, indeed, precisely because such a proposition can be no more than a well-confirmed hypothesis that I have called the sort of induction which establishes it ampliative. It is natural, then, that logicians should try to treat of induction together with other attempts to establish hypotheses by consideration of their consequences. But the suggestion that every use of hypotheses is a variety of induction is based on a failure to distinguish different kinds of hypotheses. Apart from laws concerning perceptual objects and postulates introduced to explain such laws, natural scientists have sometimes put forward hypotheses which are, strictly speaking, historical in character. Thus the nebular hypothesis about the origin of the solar system is not a universal proposition about the behaviour of all things of a certain kind, but rather a suggestion for the explanation of the special order found among a number of particular things. It resembles an hypothesis put forward by an archaeologist to explain the origin of Stonehenge. In each case we can do no more than look for evidence which will confirm or refute the hypothesis by verifying or falsifying some of its consequences, but in each case the hypothesis is a proposition of the same kind as those we can claim to establish conclusively by observation, differing from them only in that it is about the past. We can conceive the possibility of receiving wireless messages from astronomers in some other part of the universe to the effect that records made by their predecessors over many millions of years confirmed the nebular hypothesis, just as we can conceive the possibility of finding a contemporary inscription about the building of Stonehenge. If such additional evidence were forthcoming, it would have to be treated according to the ordinary methods of historical criticism.

A specially interesting example of the making of historical hypotheses in natural science is to be found in what is usually called the theory of the evolution of species. Many empirical generalizations have been made about the organisms of various species, e.g. that lions are carnivorous, that frogs grow out of tadpoles, that wheat grains contain vitamin B. It is now assumed that these laws are to be explained by biologists in the sense of being deduced from the constitution of the organisms and the general laws of physiology. In so far as biologists are able to carry out this programme they make their study systematic or theoretical in the original sense of that word. There is, however, a further question which they may ask, namely, how there came to be organisms of these various constitutions. There are obvious similarities between species which have led natural historians long since to classify them in genera and families. But species appear to be genetically distinct, that is to say, the individuals of a species reproduce organisms of their own kind only. And so, in spite of the suggestions contained in such words as 'genus' and 'family', natural historians of earlier times felt compelled to assume that species had been established separately at some remote date in the past. The doctrine of the separate creation of species was not an invention of priests, designed to buttress a system of theology, but the best guess that could be given at the time. The theory put forward by Darwin and his successors is simply an hypothesis to the effect that what we call specific differences have come about through the accumulation of many small differences between individuals of successive generations. The laws of genetics show what can be accomplished by selective breeding. Whether, and, if so, by what stages, the organisms we know have been evolved from organisms of simpler types is a question of historical fact. It is extremely unlikely that biologists will ever be able to trace all the steps by which all the known species have been established, but they have apparently found enough to convince themselves that the general hypothesis of evolution is as probable as an historical hypothesis of that kind can be.

It seems unwise to extend the use of the word 'induction' to cover the establishment of historical hypotheses like those we have just considered and those which are put forward in social and literary studies. Historical hypotheses are quite different in logical character from the transcendent hypotheses of physics and also from the laws which are established by primary induction, for the former purport to be matters of fact, the latter to be truths of principle, and we cannot safely assume that the probability we ascribe to historical hypotheses is the same as that we ascribe to the results of induction, whether primary or secondary. I think this point worth making because it has not been realized by many otherwise estimable writers on the theory of induction, e.g. Whewell.

The Consilience of Primary Inductions

Having decided that we may reasonably call the establishment of transcendent hypotheses secondary induction, we must now consider how the results of secondary induction compare with the results of primary induction in reliability. This is a subject on which there has been much confusion. Some writers who recognize a distinction between different stages of induction have supposed that secondary induction, being dependent on the results of primary induction, must inevitably give results which are less reliable than those of primary induction. I think this view is mistaken and that it arises from a misunderstanding of the relation between the two stages. These writers apparently think of secondary induction as the application of induction to the results of induction and assume that, since the results of any ampliative induction must obviously be less certain than the premisses from which it starts, secondary induction will give less certainty than primary induction. A more satisfactory account of the matter was given by Whewell, who laid great emphasis on what he called the *consilience* of inductions. What I have to say is suggested by his work *Novum Organum Renovatum* but is adapted to the phraseology I have used hitherto.

In order to understand what happens when a law is explained it is best to start by considering the explanation of laws by other laws which are also established by primary induction. We have seen that we can sometimes explain empirical generalizations in biology by showing that they follow from certain physical and chemical laws which are already accepted. When such an explanation has been given, the probability of the biological generalization may very well be greater than it was before. For the biological generalization cannot now be less probable than the physical and chemical laws from which it is seen to follow, and, since these laws, being of great generality, have presumably been confirmed in many more instances than those which provide evidence for the biological generalization, it is reasonable to suppose that their probability may be greater than that which the biological generalization had attained before the explanation. This is a very common situation. It often happens that we make a tentative generalization in some field of study without reposing much confidence in the result of our induction but discover later that what we have conjectured is entailed by some well-established laws and immediately regard our generalization as itself established beyond reasonable doubt. Something similar happens when laws are explained by transcendent hypotheses, but the situation is then more complicated.

If a transcendent hypothesis was put forward to explain a single supposed law, it could clearly have no greater probability than the supposed law which it explained, and might be thought to have less, since it could only explain the supposed law by being in some way more comprehensive, and this greater comprehensiveness would lay it open to greater danger of refutation. No transcendent hypothesis, however, is put forward to explain a single law. When we look for explanations we want to coordinate and simplify. We must therefore assume that we have a number of supposed laws, say L_1, L_2, and L_3, which are all shown to be consequences of an hypothesis H. Each of these supposed laws has its own evidence, consisting of a number of instances from which it was originally established by primary induction. How does the probability of H compare with the probability of L_1, L_2, and L_3? Clearly H cannot be more probable than L_1, L_2, and L_3 are *after they have been explained*, for it entails them and therefore communicates to them whatever probability it possesses, but it may be more probable than L_1, L_2, *and* L_3 were *before they were explained.*

For the evidence in favour of *H* is all the evidence in favour of all the consequences that follow from it, and in relation to this mass of evidence *H* may well attain a higher degree of probability than any one of its consequences, L_1, L_2, and L_3, had in relation to its own special range of evidence before it was explained. After the explanation L_1, L_2, and L_3 may therefore be more probable than they were before, because each of them derives support indirectly from the evidence in favour of each of the others. This is the consilience of inductions which fit together into a theory, and I think it is a consideration which has great weight with scientists when they estimate the value of theories. Only in this way can we explain the undoubted fact that the supposed laws of physics and chemistry seem to scientists better established now than they were a century ago. The mere accumulation of new instances confirming special laws will not explain the increase of probability. For the number of new instances is comparatively insignificant in relation to the number which had been observed already a century ago, and no one supposes that the long-continued accumulation of similar instances adds much to the probability of a generalization. Those philosophers who advocate a coherence theory of truth may perhaps have in mind something like the notion of consilience, but, if so, they are guilty of misusing it. For the notion of consilience belongs properly to the theory of that kind of probability which attaches to inductive conclusions, not to the theory of truth.

So far I have made no mention of a feature of some transcendent hypotheses to which Huyghens drew special attention in the passage I have quoted from his *Treatise on Light*, namely, their entailment of laws not hitherto established by primary induction. Although this is a very striking merit of transcendent hypotheses, it should not be confused with the considerations which determine the probability of an hypothesis in relation to the evidence of experience and the laws which have already been derived from that evidence by primary induction. It cannot affect the probability of an hypothesis whether the laws it entails were established by primary induction before or after the suggestion of the hypothesis. The confirmation of a hitherto unsuspected law which is deduced from an hypothesis must, of course, raise the probability of the hypothesis, but it cannot raise the probability beyond the degree which it would have reached if that law had already been accepted before the suggestion of the hypothesis. The power of prediction is impressive and important rather because it convinces us that the hypothesis is more than a mere rewording of the laws it was introduced to explain. It gives us the assurance that we are not merely playing with symbols but saying something new and interesting about the world. This can be seen from the fact that we are as much impressed by the power of an hypothesis to explain a law which was indeed already established when the hypothesis was first formulated but not then considered as a law to be explained by the hypothesis. In either case the hypothesis must be taken seriously, because it obviously offers a hope of real simplification, without which there can be no explanation worth the name and no increase of probability according to the principles explained in the previous paragraph. If an hypothesis H were equivalent to a mere conjunction of the laws L_1, L_2, and L_3 which it was supposed to explain, there would be no consilience of inductions and the evidence for L_1 would not help in any way to confirm L_2 or L_3. The conjunctive proposition would indeed be only as probable in relation to our total evidence as the least probable of the conjoined propositions, and would have no special interest for us. When, however, a law L_4 is derived from an hypothesis H which was originally intended to explain L_1, L_2, and L_3, it can no longer be supposed that H is merely a rewording of the three first laws.

It may sometimes occur at a certain stage of development in a science that two rival hypotheses appear to explain equally well all the accepted laws of the field to which they apply. It is then of the greatest importance that scientists should try to find some testable proposition which follows from one but is incompatible with the other; for this is the way to make what Bacon called an *experimentum crucis*. In the circumstances I have indicated the proposition by which they decide must obviously be some suggestion of law not hitherto established by primary induction. If, however, they are unable to find any such proposition, and so cannot devise an *experimentum crucis*, they begin to suspect that the two rival hypotheses differ only in their symbolic formulation, and try to prove this by logical analysis. In recent years, for example, Heisenberg's version of the quantum theory and that of Schrödinger have been shown to be equivalent. In any case the uncomfortable situation to which I have referred rarely lasts for more than a comparatively short period.

Constructions and Inferred Entities*

LEWIS WHITE BECK

1. *Terminological Considerations.* Since Russell enunciated the principle, "Wherever possible logical constructions are to be substituted for inferred entities," or "Wherever possible, substitute constructions out of known entities for inferences to unknown entities," [1] the terminological situation has become confused. Russell defined neither "construction" [2] nor "inferred entity." "Construct" soon came to be used for "construction," perhaps to avoid the ambiguity whereby the latter term was used to refer to both a process and a result. But many writers now use "construction" or "construct" to refer to what Russell called the "inferred entity." This sometimes seems to be the usage of Margenau,[3] Ramsperger,[4] Benjamin,[5] Bures,[6] and many others. Again, some of the same writers in other places (e.g. Benjamin [7]) remain closer to Russell's usage. And I find it difficult to determine exactly the relation of the usage of some writers to that of Russell because of the differences between their contexts and Russell's. I experience this difficulty in reading, for instance, both Miss Stebbing [8] and

* Reprinted by kind permission of the author and the editor from *Philosophy of Science*, 17, 1950.

1 "The Relation of Sense-Data to Physics," in *Mysticism and Logic* (New York, 1918), p. 155; "Logical Atomism," in *Contemporary British Philosophy* (London, 1924), I, p. 363.

2 An explicit definition of logical construction is given by Ernest Nagel, "Russell's Philosophy of Science," in *The Philosophy of Bertrand Russell* (Library of Living Philosophers, V, 319–49), p. 324.

3 H. Margenau, "Metaphysical Elements in Physics," *Reviews of Modern Physics*, XIII (1941), 176–89; "Phenomenology and Physics," *Philosophy and Phenomenological Research*, V (1944), 269–80. "Construct" seems generally for Margenau, to be almost synonymous with Kant's "object."

4 A. G. Ramsperger, *Philosophies of Science* (New York, 1942), p. 128.

5 A. C. Benjamin, "Science and Vagueness," *Philosophy of Science*, VI (1939), 422–31.

6 C. E. Bures, "Operationism, Construction, and Inference," *Journal of Philosophy*, XXXVII (1940), 393–401.

7 "On the Formation of Constructions," *The Monist*, XXXVIII (1928), 402–12.

8 L. S. Stebbing, "Constructions," *Proceedings of the Aristotelian Society* (1933–34), 1–30. Miss Stebbing compares the usage of Russell, Stace, Eddington, Price, and Carnap. She speaks of "unificatory" and "existential" constructions, but holds that the latter have only "constructive existence." Elsewhere ("Logical Constructions and Knowledge through Description," *Proceedings of the Seventh International Congress of Philosophy*, 1930, 117–22) she objects to the alleged exhaustiveness of the disjunction between inferred entities and constructions. For her a pen is a construction in the

Werkmeister.[9] The terminological difficulties have been evaded by some other writers who have formulated new terms to refer to Russell's inferred entities. Thus Northrop [10] speaks of the "theoretic component" and Miller [11] has coined the word, "interphenomena." The terms reflecting Russell's rule in psychology have become so confused that a set of explicit definitions has recently been proposed.[12]

In view of this disarray, it seems well either to employ entirely new terms with explicit definitions, as do Northrop and Miller, or to return to Russell's terms and provide them with explicit definitions. In this paper I shall follow the latter alternative, and attempt to make the definitions conform as far as possible to Russell's prior usage of them.

Before defining these words, however, we need to define several others. The first is *substantive hypothesis*. A substantive hypothesis is an hypothesis to be tested. If it is confirmed, we are justified in asserting the existence of that which it is about. To the extent that the hypothesis is confirmed, to that extent we are justified in asserting the existence in question. Thus, "If there are free hydrogen ions present in this solution, it will give a reading on a pH-meter," is a substantive hypothetical proposition. If a reading is made, if all other consequences previously drawn from the hypothesis have been confirmed, if some consequences of rival hypotheses have been disconfirmed, and if there are no other hypotheses with the same consequences and the same or higher degree of fruitfulness and simplicity, the chemist infers the existence of hydrogen ions.

Next we must define two modes of existence. *Systemic existence* is the mode of existence of an entity all descriptions of which are analytic within a system of propositions. *Real existence* is the mode of existence attributed to an entity if there is any true synthetic proposition that can be made about it. To return to our previous illustration, the chemist would normally attribute real existence to the hydrogen ions because he thinks he may later discover (i.e., really *add* to his knowledge) something about them not included in their definition. But he might, on the contrary, say that "the existence of hydrogen ions" is *equivalent* to "the reading on the pH-meter and the other relevant data we possess." In the former instance, he attributes real existence, in the latter systemic existence, to the ion.

We are now prepared to define inferred entity and construct. An

---

sense that it cannot be referred to by a demonstrative symbol (i.e., it is not an object of knowledge by acquaintance), but this does not imply to her that it is a construction in Russell's sense (which to her is equivalent to fiction) or an inferred entity.

[9] W. H. Werkmeister, *The Basis and Structure of Knowledge* (New York, 1948), p. 105. My difficulty in interpreting Werkmeister is due to no indefiniteness on his part, but to the difficulty in translating from a Kantian to a Russellian language.

[10] F. S. C. Northrup, *The Meeting of East and West* (New York, 1946), ch. viii.

[11] D. L. Miller, "Metaphysics in Physics," *Philosophy of Science*, XIII (1946), 281–6; "Explanation vs. Description," *Philosophical Review*, LVI (1947), 301–12.

[12] Cf. Kenneth MacCorquodale and P. E. Meehl, "On a Distinction between Hypothetical Constructs and Intervening Variables," *Psychological Review*, LV (1948), 95–107. [Reprinted in this volume.]

inferred entity is the supposed real existent whose existence is inferred if and only if a given substantive hypothetical proposition about it is confirmed. Or: an inferred entity is the supposedly real existent corresponding to the antecedent of a substantive hypothetical proposition. "Supposed real existence" is not a mode of real existence *per se*, like Miss Stebbing's "constructive existence" or our "systemic existence," but intimates the element of doubt as to real existence; and no hypothesis is ever confirmed "beyond a shadow of doubt." In this sense we shall say that the hydrogen ion is an inferred entity whose real existence is supposed by non-positivists if and only if the hypotheses about it are confirmed.

A *construct* (we prefer this term to *construction* when referring to an entity instead of a logical process) is that entity whose systemic existence is affirmed by the confirmation of the relevant hypothesis. In Russell's language, a construction is "nothing but a certain grouping of certain sensibilia," [13] i.e., it is nothing but the class of appearances which have been grouped as appearances of a single thing—after the thing has been evaporated out. Thus for the positivist, the hydrogen ion is not an entity inferred to have real existence about which he might later make more discoveries (new synthetic propositions). It is the organization of data used in such an inference when the inference is forbidden by Russell's rule.

2. *The Metaphysical and Methodological Questions.* With one caveat, we shall turn to an evaluation of the ways in which constructs and inferred entities function in scientific work. The caveat is this:—In this paper we shall avoid the issue of phenomenalism vs. realism, and consider only the methodological usefulness of constructs and inferred entities in physics. The infinitely complex epistemological issue has frequently obscured the fact that it is primarily a methodology and not a metaphysics that is at stake in Russell's precept. We are encouraged in this restriction of our topic of discussion by Russell's example as much as by his words; for Russell at various times in his career has taken various points of view towards phenomenalism, neutral monism, and scientific realism, while presumably remaining faithful to his methodological preferences for construction over inference. His arguments for scientific realism, for instance, have been based on his causal theory of perception and not at all on any alleged weakness of the theory of construction. We are further encouraged in this course by Max Black's argument [14] which has shown that the theory of constructions has two independent premises, namely, the theory of description, and the theory of meaning as acquaintance. It is the latter premise, not the former, that would imply that the inferred entity is a mere fiction, as Russell often calls it; the theory of description and of constructions as descriptions does not have any metaphysical implication concerning the status of the objects of the construction. Nor does the success of science in

[13] *Mysticism and Logic*, p. 169.

[14] "Russell's Theory of Language," in *The Philosophy of Bertrand Russell*, pp. 229–55, at p. 246.

the explanation of data in terms of inferred entities directly contribute to the solution of the metaphysical and epistemological issue, since it is always possible, at least *post facto*, to interpret the results of science solely in terms of Russell's constructions. If there is any a priori probability of the existence of inferred entities, the success of science with their use might be regarded as raising this probability almost to certainty; but in this paper we shall not be concerned either with such a priori probability or the metaphysical conclusions which might be based upon it if it does exist. Therefore our conclusions concerning the importance of inferred entities will remain irrelevant to the *metaphysical* question of their alleged mode of existence.

Our problem, therefore, is exclusively methodological, a question of scientific tactics. Because real existence is at most supposed, whereas systemic existence is apodictically certain, Russell's rule of method is not only a consequence of Occam's razor but also a corollary of the "quest for certainty" in science. If constructs will perform all the desirable functions of inferred entities and avoid the uncertainties implicit in the notion of supposed existence, then we shall conclude that Russell's rule is sound.

The inferred entity serves three purposes in science. (i) It "summarizes" the observed facts. (ii) It is an ideal object for search, i.e., it provides a goal for the improvement of observations so that what was formerly unobserved may, if real, become an object of observation. (iii) It is a basis of predictions of further facts and "explains" them. We shall consider these three functions in some detail.

3. *The Summarizing Function of Inferred Entities.* The inferred entity summarizes the observed facts. It is an object of thought not of the senses, but it is devised or formulated in the light of the observations. The old empirical thesis, "There is nothing in the intellect not first in the senses," must be given up, but for it we can substitute the rule that in the hypothesis which allegedly refers to the inferred entity, there shall be nothing except that which is necessary and sufficient for the entailment of observable consequents. Inasmuch as the antecedent of the hypothetical proposition allegedly refers to the inferred entity, and by definition does so if the hypothesis is true, we can formulate the rule to read: There is nothing in the inferred entity except what is necessary and sufficient to support the data in the consequent which are interpreted as evidence for the existence of the inferred entity. (The precise sense of the word "support" will be examined later.) Thus we attribute position, velocity, and charge to the electron, but not color or odor or taste. To do so would infringe on the rule that the inferred entity contain only the necessary and sufficient conditions, for the rule of parsimony means that the condition shall be *just*-sufficient.

Constructs, in Russell's sense, will meet this requirement and serve this purpose. Definitions containing only demonstrative symbols are purely empirical and insure that this function of inferred entities is fulfilled by constructs. Nevertheless, it seems to be a "natural" state of mind (which

Russell calls a prejudice) [15] to attribute this function to inferred entities. This prejudice can be avoided, but it seldom is avoided in the heat of scientific research: when it is absent, it has usually been translated out of existence in the study when the work in the laboratory is finished.

4. *The Inferred Entity as Object of Search.* The inferred entity is an object of search, and its existence seems to be proved if it can be observed as a fact, i.e., if its status is changed by new observations. For instance, imagine a chemical compound which does not exhibit the features we expect from it; we infer the existence of an impurity, and through a series of analytical steps we isolate the inferred impurity and examine it as a fact.

Again, however, the procedure just described is explicable in terms of constructs. For when the isolation and observation have been effected, we have in Russell's language only more sense-data to be synthesized with the sense-data we organized as the construct we called the original compound. In other words, we may not have projected our knowledge into a world of unobservables, but merely broadened the world of sense-data to include something not previously in it. And that need not imply that the something now observed was previously existent outside the world of observation. To be sure, we ordinarily interpret the observations in such a way that we can extrapolate the impurity we have found back into the compound prior to the analysis, but we need not do so, and again Russell could say it is only a prejudice which allows us to do so. Hence the second function of inferred entities can be fulfilled by constructs.

5. *The Predictive Function of the Inferred Entity.* When we turn to the third function of inferred entities, however, and see how they provide a foundation for predictions, we find a somewhat different situation, from which they cannot be so easily dismissed as unemployed metaphysics. Specifically, we can ask how the transition from the first to the second function of either constructs or inferred entities is effected. More generally, what does any observation suggest about further observations? In the language of constructs, the answer to this question is, "Nothing." The function of constructs is to preserve and summarize; their virtue is metaphysical chastity, not scientific pregnancy. Exactness and precision are the virtues of constructs in the role they play as summaries, for there is nothing in the construct which may not be in the senses. But we are not content with mere summary; we need at least prediction of what is to come, and at most an explanation of what has happened. If we speak only of what has occurred, no legerdemain[16] will extract from it what will occur or even what may have occurred though not actually observed (Russell's sensibilia). A construct is a summary, and if the things summarized are all that exist

[15] *Our Knowledge of the External World* (Chicago, 1914), p. 105.

[16] Cf. A. Lowinger, *The Methodology of Pierre Duhem* (New York, 1941). Duhem is inconsistent on the role of prediction and the service rendered by inferred entities, as Lowinger points out (pp. 41, 44 and n., 53n., 69). For "legerdemain" Duhem offers intuition and "good sense." A sounder view, in my opinion, is provided by Lowinger in his criticisms; cf. ch. x.

(by hypothesis), the summary cannot have any prospective reference. The events summarized in the construct are unique and irrepeatable, and without some additional assumptions (e.g., that they are representative of some lasting condition, i.e., an inferred entity, or are a sample of observations which *could* have been made, i.e., sensibilia), predictiveness simply does not obtain. What predictions we make when we possess constructs are made not by virtue of them, but in spite of them. The predictions must be accepted with natural piety; that any prediction works has something of the character of a miracle in a world of summary constructs. Natural piety is all very good in its way, but if miracles occur over and over again, it wears thin, and they cease to be regarded as miracles because we seek explanations of them.

In the name of supreme simplicity, the proponents of the adequacy of constructs in effect give up plausibility. They use one rule of simplicity (a generic metaphysical simplicity) at the expense of an existential intelligibility, in the light of which data might be expected to "hang together" and "make sense." Even so, they do not achieve complete generic simplicity, for if inferred physical entities are eliminated, they assume unperceived sensibilia, which are another and peculiar kind of inferred entities. The resulting picture of the world is no simpler with its alternative series of sensa and sensibilia than the world of inferred physical entities with only potentially alternative families of observations.

Simplicity is by no means a simple notion, and what is simplest in one sense may not be simplest in another; there is no single and unique ideal of simplicity. In reply to John Laird's[17] criticism of Russell's logical atomism, in which Laird had argued that Russell's theory is unparsimonious for the reasons just given, A. E. Heath wrote[18]

> To condemn logical atomism as inconsistent with the principle of parsimony is to confuse the latter . . . with Mach's principle of 'economy.' For the economy contemplated by Mach was economy of description, and that is attained by an immense multiplication of entities—atoms, electrons, and the like. On the other hand, the 'principle of parsimony' seeks economy in the kind of entity assumed, accepting the resulting complexity of description with unconcern.

The quest of scientific methodology, therefore, cannot be for some absolute and undefined simplicity, and need not be for metaphysical simplicity of genera of existences. It must be for the methodologically just-sufficient set of assumptions necessary for the on-going of science, and the goal may be quite different at different stages of science. Now it seems obvious that Russell's constructs, though metaphysically rather simple, do not provide a sufficient reason for one prediction as against another, and are therefore methodologically insufficient.

[17] John Laird, "The Law of Parsimony," *The Monist*, XXIX (1919), 321–44.

[18] A. E. Heath, *ibid.*, XXX (1920), 309. I have dealt with this and other meanings of "simplicity" in "The Principle of Parsimony in Empirical Science," *Journal of Philosophy*, XL (1943), 617–33.

This has been succinctly argued by two writers. A. D. Ritchie[19] contrasted the "mythologists," who appeal to inferred entities, with "rationalists," who use only constructs, and gave the victory to the latter only with respect to the summarizing function of inferred entities, but granted the superiority of "mythology" in the predicting function. He writes, ". . . The mythological school have usually made more discoveries than the strict rationalists, but the rationalist criticism has cleared away absurdities." Benjamin,[20] even more trenchantly, says

> If a construct is strictly a construct, and is operationally definable in terms of past events, it has no future reference at all and no predictions could be made from it.
>
> It seems not unlikely that [the] inferred element which Russell is so anxious to avoid is precisely the factor that must be added to every construct to give it predictive value.

6. *Four Stages of Scientific Work.* Whereas we concluded with respect to the first two functions of inferred entities that their job could be done by constructs if we preferred a generic metaphysical simplicity of data to descriptive simplicity (in Heath's sense), it seems unlikely that constructs can carry the burden of method in which prediction is one of the chief functions of hypothesis. If this conclusion is justified, it remains to show more specifically how inferred entities do function in rationalizing the predictive function of science. We shall distinguish four stages in scientific work and show the role of inferred entities in more detail. These four steps are: (a) description, (b) establishment of symptom-relations, (c) elaboration of the structure of inferred entities, and (d) verification.

(a) *Description.* In describing a series of events, we distinguish between the causal and the functional accounts. In the causal account will appear such statements as these: "The temperature was increased by a certain amount, and . . . ;" "I increased the pressure, and the volume changed." These statements are genetic accounts of how certain effects were brought about or how certain phenomena were observed. They are generally understood, in the technical situation in which they arise, to express an efficient causation. Wherever in a sequence of events within which one event is subject much more readily to operational control than the others, we call the readily operable event the cause, and the subsequent event the effect, the cause being the event at which, under the present conditions of technique, "a major redistribution of energy [seems] to have taken place." [21]

We attempt to go beyond this level of description for several reasons. First, with a causal account one-to-one relations between causes and effects can not usually be established. The cause is not determined solely by the objective situation but by the temporary technical limits of control.

[19] A. D. Ritchie, *Scientific Method* (London, 1923), p. 166.
[20] "Science and Vagueness," 426, 428.
[21] H. A. Larrabee, *Reliable Knowledge* (Boston, 1945), p. 291.

Second, in such formulations the operator is stated or implied to be one of the causes, yet the heterogeneity between his (psychological or historical) causation and the data is so great that simplicity of formulation is sacrificed. Third, such expressions usually, though not always, take the form of all-or-none causation, and the collateral conditions which are necessary to the event are neglected. Finally, in the causal account there is at least a "ghost of modality," which should, if possible, be eliminated from what purports to be description.

The functional level of description is reached when (i) operational control can be exerted on more than one variable, (ii) each variable can be measured, and (iii) variables are discovered between which correlations or mathematical functions can be established. In these cases, we have reciprocal relations between events, and scientific inference can go in either direction. That is, we have one-to-one correlations such that we can make either predictions or retrodictions.

(b) *Establishment of symptom-relations*. Our next task is to relate the described data to an inferred entity. We postulate an unobserved relation between a single datum and an unobserved but inferred entity which is said to "support" it. This relation has been called by Northrop[22] the "epistemic correlation" and by Margenau a "rule of correspondence." We shall call it the "symptom-relation." Though it is a causal or a functional relation, it is used as evidence when, in a given case of scientific work, it does not constitute a problem for investigation. Thus the height of a mercury column is a symptom of an infection in the body, the causal connection between the two having been previously established as a general rule of evidence. In many cases, however, the inferred entity has not ever been observed. Thus gas pressure is taken as a symptom of the change of the momentum of the molecules, though the molecules and their momentum have never been observed.

We then make the following methodological rule: Each component of the inferred entity must be symptomized by some datum, actual or available, and each relevant datum must be regarded as a symptom of some component in the inferred entity. This rule prevents the assumption of both "hidden qualities" and "floating data."

Not all data, of course, are at any time regarded as symptoms of a specific inferred entity. For instance, in gathering data for the kinetic theory of gases we ignore the color of the gas used. In the choice of data for description, we see a good illustration of the interplay between observation and hypothesis, in which a perhaps vague hypothesis functions as a criterion of relevance, and success in establishing a unique symptom-relation both defines, and prepares the way for confirming the existence of, the inferred entity.

(c) *Elaboration of inferred entity*. We must relate the components

[22] F. S. C. Northrop, *The Logic of the Sciences and the Humanities* (New York, 1947), p. 117, etc.; and *loc. cit.*

or aspects of the inferred entity to each other, or one inferred entity to another. We shall do so in such a way that every functional relation among relevant data has its counterpart in an inferred relation among inferred entities of which they are symptoms. We always have alternative possibilities for both the interpretation of the symptom relation and for the isomorphism which is to be inferred within the inferred entities. We choose among these alternatives by a number of considerations, among which the following are the most important.

(i) The principle of parsimony requires that the inferential route from one datum to another be as short as possible. We do not consider all events in a single causal chain or functional relation but use isolated systems with a small number of variables. The inferred relations among inferred entities or their components should therefore be logically as simple as possible.

(ii) The same principle, taken in high generality as a principle of continuity or homogeneity of successive explanations within any science, requires that the diverse relationships of a single inferred entity to several others shall be homogeneous.

(iii) The principle of sufficient reason requires that there be no relevant data—and, ultimately, no data at all—that are not regarded as symptoms of the homogeneous body of inferred entities. It requires, furthermore, that the differentiations inferred to exist among the inferred entities must be *at least* as highly articulated as the discriminations possible among the data, while the principle of parsimony prevents us from attributing articulations and differentiations to the inferred entity which do not correspond to discriminations possible among the data. Where discriminations among the data are quantitative, the differentiations among the inferred entities must be quantitative; ideally, where discriminations are qualitative, inferred differentiations should still be quantitative.

(iv) If the inferred entity is to serve as a basis of prediction, its concept should refer at least hypothetically to components which can be symptomized by data not yet obtained, or at least by data not actually used in establishing the symptom relations and the definition of the entity. Otherwise all propositions about the inferred entity will be analytical. If they are analytical, inference to entities certainly multiplies entities beyond necessity and merely duplicates the world of data in a world of otiose metaphysical "reality". In brief, if the inferred entity is to be of any value, it must be possible to predict the result of "soundings" which have not yet been made and the results of which are accidental from the standpoint of the *present* definition of the entity.

In another place[23] I have argued that a distinctive trait of real in contrast to systemic existence (the mode of existence of a construct) is the possession by the former of accidental properties. If all the properties of an entity are essential, all that we can legitimately conclude is that it has

[23] "Potentiality, Property, and Accident," *Philosophical Review*, LVI (1947), 613–30.

systemic existence as defined in a set of postulates and definitions internally consistent but claiming no independent status.

What was there stated as a general metaphysical doctrine has its methodological corollary in this consideration of the ways in which constructs are distinguished from inferred entities. This corollary is that the inferred entity must be more than it is defined to be, for otherwise it cannot support predictions.

(v) Finally, there is the role of analogy and intelligibility.[24] Other things being equal, and in view of the fact that the inferred entity may later be observed, we prefer that the internal organization of the inferred entity be analogous to something in the world of direct experience.[25] This role of analogy or of models is not a strict rule of method, and in fact modern quantum theory, which has shown a certain bravado in disregarding this consideration, has succeeded where it has been most daring. But the consideration is nonetheless psychologically important, in determining to a large extent which alternative but equally adequate hypotheses will be rejected, and, even more, which ones will probably never even occur to the mind of the investigator.

(d) *Verification.* Finally, there is the stage of verification.[26] Since an inferred entity cannot as such be observed, and since it corresponds to the antecedent of a substantive hypothetical proposition, verification can not be effected by *modus ponens.* Confirmation can come only from the disconfirmation of all alternative hypotheses through the evidential denial of at least one consequent of each alternative and the absence of denial of any consequent common both to any alternative and to the hypothesis in question.

The only *modus ponens* which can be effected is that of an operational hypothesis, viz., "If I do so and so, such and such will occur." But as we have seen above, the operational antecedent does not belong to the corpus of a science, and even if it did the operational hypothesis alone shows no intelligible connection between what is done and what is observed. But the operational hypothetical proposition is an elliptical expression for a full hypothetical proposition, containing collateral hypotheses, which are assumed as postulates, and the substantive hypothesis we are interested in testing as a candidate for the corpus of the science. The full hypothetical proposition would read: "Granting such and such conditions, if the in-

[24] Cf. Agnes Arber, "Analogy in the History of Science," in *Studies and Essays in the History of Science and Learning Offered in Homage to George Sarton* (New York, 1944), pp. 219–35; W. Rosenblueth and N. Wiener, "The Role of Models in Science," *Philosophy of Science*, XII (1945), 316–22.

[25] Russell follows this principle in choosing among possible inferred entities when some inference is necessary. He says, ". . . The inferred entities should, whenever this can be done, be similar to those whose existence is given . . ." (*Mysticism and Logic*, p. 157). Thus he is led to posit sensibilia and the minds of other persons as inferred entities instead of matter. A similar argument for his spiritualism is used by Berkeley.

[26] The three following paragraphs are a summary of my paper, "The Distinctive Traits of an Empirical Method," *Journal of Philosophy*, XLIV (1947), 337–44.

ferred entity exists, and if then I do this and this, such and such data will occur." The transition from the observable fact of what I do to the data I obtain is made not on the level of the data, but on the level of the elaboration of the inferred entity as this has been carried out in the development of the collateral and substantive hypotheses, their inter-relations, and their symptom-relations to the data I possess. Hence if the data are as predicted, we still have not affirmed the existence of the inferred entity unless we know that no other inferred entity could serve as a basis for the observations obtained. This we do not usually know, except in the very limited sense that the collateral hypotheses may be assumed as incorrigible postulates, and then the number of possible substantive hypotheses may be small. If we can find differentiating consequents to each full hypothesis, and disconfirm all save one, then within the universe of discourse established by our collateral hypotheses we can infer the existence of the entity corresponding to the substantive hypothesis which has not been eliminated. But we affirm the existence of a single inferred entity only in the light of the family of hypotheses which have served in its elaboration and implication of still other components or aspects which may be symptomized by the data predicted in our operational hypothesis.

This means that the inferred entity can never be assumed dogmatically to exist; but it also means that we never have reason even for a tentative assumption of existence unless some symptom-relations which did not go into its original definition can be posited for the interpretation of the data resulting from the manipulations described in the operational hypothesis. In other words, inference to the existence of the object of the substantive antecedent is justified only if there are alternative routes to its symptomization, i.e., only if it does more than fulfill the operational definitions or constructs which provide for its original definition. Hence the fourth factor in the choice of alternative inferred entities, i.e., its predictiveness beyond the implications of its definition, is absolutely basic to the assertion of the existence of *any* inferred entity.

7. *Illustration from the Kinetic Theory*. Let us now illustrate these notions by reference to an example. We take part of the kinetic theory of gases. We begin with two observations which undoubtedly began as causal accounts and ended as functional relations. Boyle's law tells us that the pressure and volume of a gas vary inversely. Charles's law states that if the temperature of a gas increases, its volume will increase so long as the pressure is constant, and the pressure will increase if the volume is constant. With these two observations, and under the assumption of certain collateral hypotheses, especially Newton's laws of motion and the definitions of force and momentum, we can formulate the symptom-relations and elaborate the inferred entity, viz., the motion of the molecules comprising the gas. The definitions we need are: force $=$ change of momentum/time, and momentum $=$ mass $\times$ velocity.

We now formulate a substantive hypothetical proposition about molecules and posit certain symptom-relations. We follow the rules given above, with special attention to the requirement that if the antecedent of an operational hypothetical proposition, such as "If I raise this temperature . . .", is affirmed, certain observed results described by Charles could have been expected to occur even if the experiment had never been done. The full substantive hypothesis is lengthy, and I shall give only a few parts of it, but it is important to notice the role that analogy played in its formulation. We assume that there are molecules, that their number is constant in any confined gas, that they are perfectly elastic, that they are moving with high velocity, that their contact times are short in comparison to their time of free-movement, and that the free space through which they move is large compared with the volume the molecules occupy.

We then posit two symptom-relations. First, we state that there is a symptom-relation between the datum of temperature and the unobserved velocities of the molecules. Second, there is a symptom-relation between the observed pressure and the force with which the molecules hit the surface where the pressure is measured.

The collateral hypothesis provides a basis for the relation between two of the component aspects of the inferred entity (velocity with force, through the definition of force), and these two aspects are symptomized by the observable variables of temperature and pressure. As momentum increases with velocity (by definition), and velocity increases with temperature (by the symptom-relation), so also pressure should increase with temperature, as found by Charles. Moreover, if the volume of the gas is reduced, the ratio of empty to filled space will become smaller; this implies that the intervals between successive hits will become shorter if the velocity (temperature) is constant; but as pressure is the symptom of the sum of changes of momenta of all the particles hitting the surface in any given interval, then the pressure will increase as the volume is diminished. This was already known to be the case.

Thus far our inferred entity "works", and our substantive hypothesis has been confirmed. (It is, to be sure, an indirect confirmation through the elimination of other hypotheses, such as that of caloric fluid; but for lack of space we shall not go through a description of their elimination.) But have we not perhaps multiplied entities beyond necessity? After all, we knew Boyle's law and Charles's law before this hypothesis was confirmed. Do we know any more with this hypothesis than we did without it? If not, the law of parsimony would require that our inferred entity be replaced by a construct with no "surplus existential" significance.

But the rule that an inferred entity must support predictions which are not mere tautologous consequences of definition justifies us not only in choosing among specific entities, but justifies *in general* the use of inferred entities in preference to constructs wherever predictiveness is considered in the establishment of hypotheses. That rule states that there should be in any inferred entity certain components which are not symptomized by present data or by data used in its definition, but which can be symptomized by data not yet available and not *prima facie* relevant to the definition of the inferred entity. This rule is not only a rule of preference for inferred entities over constructs, or a rule of choice of good (vs. poor) inferred entities, but it is also a condition of the empirical verification of any entity after it has been chosen on any grounds.

Now from Boyle's and Charles's laws or from a construct summarizing them, I do not see any way in which we could predict, for instance, the observations which were later formulated as Graham's law of diffusion. The history of science shows that it was not done. But from the inferred entity which summarized the work of Boyle and Charles and contained a "surplus existential" meaning, this prediction could be made. The surplus meaning involved the assumption that the entity really existed and therefore had some characteristics in addition to those operationally defined as summaries (logical constructs) of the observations made by Boyle and Charles. Thus not only is Graham's work an interesting additional confirmation of the kinetic theory, but also its discovery is a revealing example of the predictive function of inferred entities, a function completely lacking in constructs.

Let us see how the inferred entity functioned in this case. We have not said anything directly about the mass of molecules,[27] for we did not need this factor in our summaries of Boyle's and Charles's observations. Nevertheless, if molecules exist, then they have mass because they have momentum. And if they have mass we might expect to find some other variable, *not included in the observations of Boyle and Charles*, which would symptomize this mass. Furthermore, our collateral hypothesis would relate the mass to other characteristics of the entity, and experimental observation would relate the symptom of the mass to the symptoms of the other characteristics. (In order to establish these relations, we make another collateral assumption that the mass is unaffected by the velocity of the particles, though, of course, at the time of Graham's work there was no need to make this assumption explicit.)

On this assumption, which was indeed self-evident in the nineteenth century, the mass of the molecules will not vary with temperature, and if we posit a symptom-relation between their mass and the density of the gas (a symptom-relation justified by the collateral hypothesis of Avogadro), we have an observed fact of nature, viz., that temperature variations do not affect the total mass of a gas.

Now let us posit, with Graham, another symptom-relation, namely, that velocity will be symptomized by the rate of diffusion of the gas through a porous membrane. We then *predict* that the rate of diffusion

[27] In symptomizing momentum, we have indeed used the concept of mass, but we did not symptomize it through any observed variable which would distinguish between the mass-component and the velocity-component; and as the work was done without varying the mass of the gas used, the only effect of mass would be on the proportionality constant that would appear in the final equations.

of a given gas will vary directly as the temperature. This was confirmed by Graham.

From the work of Boyle and Charles, it was found that pressure is a function of the number of molecules, their momentum (momentum = mass × velocity), and their velocity (more specifically, $p = \frac{1}{3} NmV^2$—I omit the derivation which can be found in any textbook). But as N, the number of molecules, is constant, it follows that the velocity V will vary as $m^{-1/2}$, and $V = km^{-1/2}$, where m is the mass of the molecule and k is the constant of proportionality. Thus we predict what Graham actually observed, viz., that the rate of diffusion R (a symptom of V) varies directly as the temperature t (a symptom of V), and inversely as the square root of the density d of the gas (a symptom of m). Hence Graham's law

$$R = ktd^{-1/2}.$$

The important thing to notice is that this law is not an analytical consequence of the general gas laws which relate p, v, and t.

What Graham's law thus illustrates concerning the predictive power of an inferred entity might equally well be exemplified by citing the work of van der Waals on deviations from Boyle's law, for in it the attraction of the molecules is added to the other components of the inferred entity by virtue of still other collateral hypotheses taken from electromagnetic theory. Or we might cite the work of Gay-Lussac on combining volumes, for there chemical reactions are interpreted in the same context.

Positivism and constructionalism therefore seem to me to be useful in scientific work at only one stage: in clipping the wings of speculation and dogmatism after experimental discoveries have been made. Positivism and the preference for constructs too early in the scientific enterprise neither reflect the actual thinking of scientists nor promote the rationalization of present experience in the light of what is yet to come.

Unity of Science and Unitary Science *

HERBERT FEIGL

IN ORDER TO clear up much current confusion *three* meanings of the term "unity of science" (and of "physicalism") should be distinguished.

The *first* meaning, adopted by Carnap, Neurath, and others is the *unity of the language of science* which is also the basic idea of the Encyclopedia of Unified Science. This idea can be considered as a logically revised and refined formulation of the essential thesis of empiricism and operationism (on an inter-subjective basis).

The *second* meaning is the thesis of *naturalism.* It is hardly possible to give even a moderately definite and precise formulation of this so frequently debated but so poorly defined point of view. Approximately it seems to amount to the belief (or, in a more adequate formulation, the heuristic program) according to which the explanatory constructs of all sciences will not need to go beyond the spatio-temporal-causal frame. This program excludes not only metaphysical entities ("absolutes", "entelechies", etc.) — as does the weaker first thesis of empiricism — but rules out also certain logically conceivable and empirically meaningful forms of hypotheses. Only certain "normal" forms of spatio-temporal frames and causal (or statistical) laws are considered necessary for an explanation of the observed phenomena. One somewhat vague aspect of this naturalistic doctrine lies in certain (implicit) postulates concerning the continuity of causal influences. Naturalism of this form leaves open, but does not positively affirm, the reducibility of biological, psychological, and sociological laws to physical laws. Even if irreducibility is assumed (emergentist), naturalism would still differ from vitalistic and animistic doctrines which assert this irreducibility on entirely different grounds.

The thesis which I wish to clarify and whose present value I wish to appraise is the *third* one: *physicalism in the strict sense,* postulating the potential derivability of *all* scientific laws from the laws of physics. This is the most radical and therefore also the most problematic of the three theses. As it is an open question as to whether biology, psychology, and the social sciences are ultimately reducible to physical theory, we cannot afford to be dogmatic — one way or the other. It is also expressly admitted

* Paper sent in for the fifth International Congress for the Unity of Science (Cambridge, Mass. U.S.A. 1939).

that speculation in the direction of this sort of unification may in many fields be premature and therefore possibly harmful to scientific progress. The success of biological, psychological, and sociological theories formulated in their own specific terms indicates that a temporary disregard for farther reaching reductions can be of great heuristic value. It will, however, always be of paramount logical and general scientific interest to determine whether the facts as known and scientific method, being what it it at a given stage of development, exclude, leave open, or even make plausible the thesis (prognosis) of radical physicalism.

The main motivation of the following defense of this thesis lies in the need to refute the more and more frequent misconceptions concerning it — exemplified in their extreme form by the confusion of physicalism with "mechanistic materialism". This designation spreads generally a rather repellent odor and is used by many writers as a weapon of aggression and disparagement even against scientific trends which are completely free from the metaphysical nonsense in traditional materialism and the factual inadequacies of the mechanistic world view. But if we bring up to date that which, scientifically and methodologically, was always valuable in materialism, we merely pursue the program of the unity of science (in the first, second, and as far as possible, in the third sense).

There is a good deal of historical, experimental, and theoretical evidence in favor of strict physicalism. A parallel study of the *levels of explanation* (i.e., of the levels of description, empirical laws, and theories of two or three orders) in the various branches of science reveals an impressive *convergence of theories toward a unitary scheme*. Mechanics, astronomy, acoustics, thermodynamics, optics, electricity, magnetics, and chemistry are integratively united (at least to an astounding extent) in the theories of relativity and quanta. Biology, through biophysics and biochemistry, psychology, through neuro-physiology, seem to follow in the same direction.

The notoriously most recalcitrant problems for such a radical reduction are the explanation of "*purposiveness*" in all organic life and the facts of "*consciousness*", "*meaning*", "*freedom*", "*value*", and "*creativity*" in mental life. The central difficulty here, as well as in the reduction of the social sciences seems to lie in a clear definition of "*emergence*" and in the problem of the predictability of emergent wholes and their features. Logical analysis of these difficulties seems to indicate that the customary philosophical arguments against physicalistic reducibility are either logically faulty (metaphysically confused) or rest on a deficient understanding of the meaning and methods of modern physical science. Constructively, it can be shown that the empirical translations (first thesis) of the "recalcitrant" facts make it at least plausible that physical explanations (third thesis) are not logically inconceivable — much as the enormous technical difficulties must be admitted.

There is an empirical formulation of purposiveness as a characteristic of certain types of dynamic systems; there is the behavioristic analysis of consciousness and the logical demonstration of the pseudo-character of the traditional mind-body difficulty (i.e., the dualism is of linguistic, not of factual nature); the semiotic meaning-relation can be accounted for on the basis of rule-controlled symbolic behavior. Similarly the terms "right" and "wrong" — whether they refer to formal or factual truth, to esthetic, ethical, or legal objects of evaluation — indicate conformity or non-conformity to accepted standards or rules whose origin, acceptance, evaluation, modification, or abolition in turn can be subjected to scientific study. There is the account of freedom as a special form of causation (i.e., the situation in which the person as a whole, more than the momentary environment, is the condition of action) and there are behavioristic, gestaltist, psychoanalytic approaches to the problems of cognitive and artistic creativity. Finally, an analysis of the concept "emergent novelty" does away with the ontological mysteries and enables us to define its empirical nucleus as a special form of configurational order, not necessarily beyond the possibility of prediction on the basis of more elementary laws. In view of the ever-changing theoretical structure of physics it must be admitted that "radical physicalism" also does not have any very precise meaning. It seems that only through fairly arbitrary decision can "physical" laws be delimited from "non-physical" ones. A more definite meaning may be suggested by formulating the thesis of physicalism in the following way: The set of physical laws which enables us to deduce the facts of chemistry will also be sufficient for biology and psychology.

A presentation such as this is likely to evoke the suspicion that it aims impatiently at a solution of the "riddles of the universe". I hope, however, that it is sufficiently clear that I have tried only to survey some major issues in order to analyze and assess the logical possibility of physicalism and thus to counteract a certain philosophical defeatism now again greatly in fashion. I also do not in the least wish to belittle scientific theorizing on its given autonomous levels of research. Only such actual scientific work will finally show either that the physicalistic synthesis is hopeless or that (and how) it can be achieved.

V

CAUSALITY, DETERMINISM, INDETERMINISM, AND PROBABILITY

On the Notion of Cause, with Applications to the Free-Will Problem*

BERTRAND RUSSELL

IN THE FOLLOWING paper I wish, first, to maintain that the word "cause" is so inextricably bound up with misleading associations as to make its complete extrusion from the philosophical vocabulary desirable; secondly, to inquire what principle, if any, is employed in science in place of the supposed "law of causality" which philosophers imagine to be employed; thirdly, to exhibit certain confusions, especially in regard to teleology and determinism, which appear to me to be connected with erroneous notions as to causality.

All philosophers, of every school, imagine that causation is one of the fundamental axioms or postulates of science, yet, oddly enough, in advanced sciences such as gravitational astronomy, the word "cause" never occurs. Dr. James Ward, in his *Naturalism and Agnosticism*, makes this a ground of complaint against physics: the business of those who wish to ascertain the ultimate truth about the world, he apparently thinks, should be the discovery of causes, yet physics never even seeks them. To me it seems that philosophy ought not to assume such legislative functions, and that the reason why physics has ceased to look for causes is that, in fact, there are no such things. The law of causality, I believe, like much that passes muster among philosophers, is a relic of a bygone age, surviving, like the monarchy, only because it is erroneously supposed to do no harm.

In order to find out what philosophers commonly understand by "cause," I consulted Baldwin's *Dictionary*, and was rewarded beyond my expectations, for I found the following three mutually incompatible definitions:—

"CAUSALITY. (1) The necessary connection of events in the time-series. . . .

"CAUSE (notion of). Whatever may be included in the thought or perception of a process as taking place in consequence of another process. . . .

* Reprinted by kind permission of the author and the publishers from Bertrand Russell, *Mysticism and Logic* (George Allen & Unwin, Ltd.), pp. 180–205, and his *Our Knowledge of the External World* (W. W. Norton & Co., London, 1929, New York, 1929), pp. 247–256.

"CAUSE AND EFFECT. (1) Cause and effect . . . are correlative terms denoting any two distinguishable things, phases, or aspects of reality, which are so related to each other that whenever the first ceases to exist the second comes into existence immediately after, and whenever the second comes into existence the first has ceased to exist immediately before."

Let us consider these three definitions in turn. The first, obviously, is unintelligible without a definition of "necessary." Under this head, Baldwin's *Dictionary* gives the following:—

"NECESSARY. That is necessary which not only is true, but would be true under all circumstances. Something more than brute compulsion is, therefore, involved in the conception; there is a general law under which the thing takes place."

The notion of cause is so intimately connected with that of necessity that it will be no digression to linger over the above definition, with a view to discovering, if possible, *some* meaning of which it is capable; for, as it stands, it is very far from having any definite signification.

The first point to notice is that, if any meaning is to be given to the phrase "would be true under all circumstances," the subject of it must be a propositional function, not a proposition.[1] A proposition is simply true or false, and that ends the matter: there can be no question of "circumstances." "Charles I's head was cut off" is just as true in summer as in winter, on Sundays as on Mondays. Thus when it is worth saying that something "would be true under all circumstances," the something in question must be a propositional function, i.e. an expression containing a variable, and becoming a proposition when a value is assigned to the variable; the varying "circumstances" alluded to are then the different values of which the variable is capable. Thus if "necessary" means "what is true under all circumstances," then "if x is a man, x is mortal" is necessary, because it is true for any possible value of x. Thus we should be led to the following definition:—

"NECESSARY is a predicate of a propositional function, meaning that it is true for all possible values of its argument or arguments."

Unfortunately, however, the definition in Baldwin's *Dictionary* says that what is necessary is not only "true under all circumstances" but is also "true." Now these two are incompatible. Only propositions can be "true," and only propositional functions can be "true under all circumstances." Hence the definition as it stands is nonsense. What is meant seems to be this: "A proposition as necessary when it is a value of a propositional function which is true under all circumstances, i.e. for all values of its argument or arguments." But if we adopt this definition, the same prop-

[1] A propositional function is an expression containing a variable, or undetermined constituent, and becoming a proposition as soon as a definite value is assigned to the variable. Examples are: "A is A," "x is a number." The variable is called the *argument* of the function.

osition will be necessary or contingent according as we choose one or other of its terms as the argument to our propositional function. For example, "if Socrates is a man, Socrates is mortal," is necessary if Socrates is chosen as argument, but not if *man* or *mortal* is chosen. Again, "if Socrates is a man, Plato is mortal," will be necessary if either Socrates or *man* is chosen as argument, but not if Plato or *mortal* is chosen. However, this difficulty can be overcome by specifying the constituent which is to be regarded as argument, and we thus arrive at the following definition:

"A proposition is *necessary* with respect to a given constituent if it remains true when that constituent is altered in any way compatible with the proposition remaining significant."

We may now apply this definition to the definition of causality quoted above. It is obvious that the argument must be the time at which the earlier event occurs. Thus an instance of causality will be such as: "If the event e_1 occurs at the time t_1, it will be followed by the event e_2." This proposition is intended to be necessary with respect to t_1, i.e. to remain true however t_1 may be viewed. Causality, as a universal law, will then be the following: "Given any event e_1, there is an event e_2 such that, whenever e_1 occurs, e_2 occurs later." But before this can be considered precise, we must specify how much later e_2 is to occur. Thus the principle becomes:—

"Given any event, e_1, there is an event e_2 and a time interval τ such that, whenever e_1 occurs, e_2 follows after an interval τ."

I am not concerned as yet to consider whether this law is true or false. For the present, I am merely concerned to discover what the law of causality is supposed to be. I pass, therefore, to the other definitions quoted above.

The second definition need not detain us long, for two reasons. First, because it is psychological: not the "thought or perception" of a process, but the process itself, must be what concerns us in considering causality. Secondly, because it is circular: in speaking of a process as "taking place in consequence of" another process, it introduces the very notion of cause which was to be defined.

The third definition is by far the most precise; indeed as regards clearness it leaves nothing to be desired. But a great difficulty is caused by the temporal contiguity of cause and effect which the definition asserts. No two instants are contiguous, since the time-series is compact; hence either the cause or the effect or both must, if the definition is correct, endure for a finite time; indeed, by the wording of the definition it is plain that both are assumed to endure for a finite time. But then we are faced with a dilemma: if the cause is a process involving change within itself, we shall require (if causality is universal) causal relations between its earlier and later parts; moreover, it would seem that only the later parts can be relevant to the effect, since the earlier parts are not contiguous to the effect, and therefore (by the definition) cannot influence the effect. Thus we shall be led to diminish the duration of the cause without limit, and however much we may diminish it, there will still remain an earlier part which might be altered without altering the effect, so that the true cause, as defined, will not have been reached, for it will be observed that the definition excludes plurality of causes. If, on the other hand, the cause is purely static, involving no change within itself, then, in the first place, no such cause is to be found in nature, and in the second place, it seems strange —too strange to be accepted, in spite of bare logical possibility—that the cause, after existing placidly for some time, should suddenly explode into the effect, when it might just as well have done so at any earlier time, or have gone on unchanged without producing its effect. This dilemma, therefore, is fatal to the view that cause and effect can be contiguous in time; if there are causes and effects, they must be separated by a finite time-interval τ, as was assumed in the above interpretation of the first definition.

What is essentially the same statement of the law of causality as the one elicited above from the first of Baldwin's definitions is given by other philosophers. Thus John Stuart Mill says:—

"The Law of Causation, the recognition of which is the main pillar of inductive science, is but the familiar truth, that invariability of succession is found by observation to obtain between every fact in nature and some other fact which has preceded it." [2]

And Bergson, who has rightly perceived that the law as stated by philosophers is worthless, nevertheless continues to suppose that it is used in science. Thus he says:—

"Now, it is argued, this law [the law of causality] means that every phenomenon is determined by its conditions, or, in other words, that the same causes produce the same effects." [3]

And again:—

"We perceive physical phenomena, and these phenomena obey laws. This means: (1) That phenomena *a, b, c, d,* previously perceived, can occur again in the same shape; (2) that a certain phenomenon P, which appeared after the conditions *a, b, c, d,* and after these conditions only, will not fail to recur as soon as the same conditions are again present." [4]

A great part of Bergson's attack on science rests on the assumption that it employs this principle. In fact, it employs no such principle, but philosophers—even Bergson—are too apt to take their views on science from each other, not from science. As to what the principle is, there is a fair consensus among philosophers of different schools. There are, however, a number of difficulties which at once arise. I omit the question of plurality of causes for the present, since other graver questions have to be considered. Two of these, which are forced on our attention by the above statement of the law, are the following:—

[2] *Logic*, Bk. III, Chap. V, §2.
[3] *Time and Free Will*, p. 199.
[4] *Time and Free Will*, p. 202.

(1) What is meant by an "event"?

(2) How long may the time-interval be between cause and effect?

(1) An "*event,*" in the statement of the law, is obviously intended to be something that is likely to recur, since otherwise the law becomes trivial. It follows that an "event" is not a particular, but some universal of which there may be many instances. It follows also that an "event" must be something short of the whole state of the universe, since it is highly improbable that this will recur. What is meant by an "event" is something like striking a match, or dropping a penny into the slot of an automatic machine. If such an event is to recur, it must not be defined too narrowly: we must not state with what degree of force the match is to be struck, nor what is to be the temperature of the penny. For if such considerations were relevant, our "event" would occur at most once, and the law would cease to give information. An "event," then, is a universal defined sufficiently widely to admit of many particular occurrences in time being instances of it.

(2) The next question concerns the time-interval. Philosophers, no doubt, think of cause and effect as contiguous in time, but this, for reasons already given, is impossible. Hence, since there are no infinitesimal time-intervals, there must be some finite lapse of time τ between cause and effect. This, however, at once raises insuperable difficulties. However short we make the interval τ, something may happen during this interval which prevents the expected result. I put my penny in the slot, but before I can draw out my ticket there is an earthquake which upsets the machine and my calculations. In order to be sure of the expected effect, we must know that there is nothing in the environment to interfere with it. But this means that the supposed cause is not, by itself, adequate to insure the effect. And as soon as we include the environment, the probability of repetition is diminished, until at last, when the whole environment is included, the probability of repetition becomes almost *nil.*

In spite of these difficulties, it must, of course, be admitted that many fairly dependable regularities of sequence occur in daily life. It is these regularities that have suggested the supposed law of causality; where they are found to fail, it is thought that a better formulation could have been found which would have never failed. I am far from denying that there may be such sequences which in fact never do fail. It may be that there will never be an exception to the rule that when a stone of more than a certain mass, moving with more than a certain velocity, comes in contact with a pane of glass of less than a certain thickness, the glass breaks. I also do not deny that the observation of such regularities, even when they are not without exceptions, is useful in the infancy of a science: the observation that unsupported bodies in air usually fall was a stage on the way to the law of gravitation. What I deny is that science assumes the existence of invariable uniformities of sequence of this kind, or that it aims at discovering them. All such uniformities, as we saw, depend upon a certain vagueness in the definition of the "events." That bodies fall is a vague qualitative statement; science wishes to know how fast they fall. This depends upon the shape of the bodies and the density of the air. It is true that there is more nearly uniformity when they fall in a vacuum; so far as Galileo could observe, the uniformity is then complete. But later it appeared that even there the latitude made a difference, and the altitude. Theoretically, the position of the sun and moon must make a difference. In short, every advance in a science takes us farther away from the crude uniformities which are first observed, into greater differentiation of antecedent and consequent, and into a continually wider circle of antecedents recognised as relevant.

The principle "same cause, same effect," which philosophers imagine to be vital to science, is therefore utterly otiose. As soon as the antecedents have been given sufficiently fully to enable the consequent to be calculated with some exactitude, the antecedents have become so complicated that it is very unlikely they will ever recur. Hence, if this were the principle involved, science would remain utterly sterile.

The importance of these considerations lies partly in the fact that they lead to a more correct account of scientific procedure, partly in the fact that they remove the analogy with human volition which makes the conception of cause such a fruitful source of fallacies. The latter point will become clearer by the help of some illustrations. For this purpose I shall consider a few maxims which have played a great part in the history of philosophy.

(1) "Cause and effect must more or less resemble each other." This principle was prominent in the philosophy of occasionalism, and is still by no means extinct. It is still often thought, for example, that mind could not have grown up in a universe which previously contained nothing mental, and one ground for this belief is that matter is too dissimilar from mind to have been able to cause it. Or, more particularly, what are termed the nobler parts of our nature are supposed to be inexplicable, unless the universe always contained something at least equally noble which could cause them. All such views seem to depend upon assuming some unduly simplified law of causality; for, in any legitimate sense of "cause" and "effect," science seems to show that they are usually very widely dissimilar, the "cause" being, in fact, two states of the whole universe, and the "effect" some particular event.

(2) "Cause is analogous to volition, since there must be an intelligible *nexus* between cause and effect." This maxim is, I think, often unconsciously in the imaginations of philosophers who would reject it when explicitly stated. It is probably operative in the view we have just been considering, that mind could not have resulted from a purely material world. I do not profess to know what is meant by "intelligible"; it seems to mean "familiar to imagination." Nothing is less "intelligible," in any other sense, than the connection between an act of will and its fulfilment. But

obviously the sort of nexus desired between cause and effect is such as could only hold between the "events" which the supposed law of causality contemplates; the laws which replace causality in such a science as physics leave no room for any two events between which a nexus could be sought.

(3) "The cause *compels* the effect in some sense in which the effect does not compel the cause." This belief seems largely operative in the dislike of determinism; but, as a matter of fact, it is connected with our second maxim, and falls as soon as that is abandoned. We may define "compulsion" as follows: "Any set of circumstances is said to compel A when A desires to do something which the circumstances prevent, or to abstain from something which the circumstances cause." This presupposes that some meaning has been found for the word "cause"—a point to which I shall return later. What I want to make clear at present is that compulsion is a very complex notion, involving thwarted desire. So long as a person does what he wishes to do, there is no compulsion, however much his wishes may be calculable by the help of earlier events. And where desire does not come in, there can be no question of compulsion. Hence it is, in general, misleading to regard the cause as compelling the effect.

A vaguer form of the same maxim substitutes the word "determine" for the word "compel"; we are told that the cause *determines* the effect in a sense in which the effect does not *determine* the cause. It is not quite clear what is meant by "determining"; the only precise sense, so far as I know, is that of a function or one-many relation. If we admit plurality of causes, but not of effects, that is, if we suppose that, given the cause, the effect must be such and such, but, given the effect, the cause may have been one of many alternatives, then we may say that the cause determines the effect, but not the effect the cause. Plurality of causes, however, results only from conceiving the effect vaguely and narrowly and the cause precisely and widely. Many antecedents may "cause" a man's death, because his death is vague and narrow. But if we adopt the opposite course, taking as the "cause" the drinking of a dose of arsenic, and as the "effect" the whole state of the world five minutes later, we shall have plurality of effects instead of plurality of causes. Thus the supposed lack of symmetry between "cause" and "effect" is illusory.

(4) "A cause cannot operate when it has ceased to exist, because what has ceased to exist is nothing." This is a common maxim, and a still more common unexpressed prejudice. It has, I fancy, a good deal to do with the attractiveness of Bergson's "*durée*": since the past has effects now, it must still exist in some sense. The mistake in this maxim consists in the supposition that causes "operate" at all. A volition "operates" when what it wills takes place; but nothing can operate except a volition. The belief that causes "operate" results from assimilating them, consciously or unconsciously, to volitions. We have already seen that, if there are causes at all, they must be separated by a finite interval of time from their effects and thus cause their effects after they have ceased to exist.

It may be objected to the above definition of a volition "operating" that it only operates when it "causes" what it wills, not when it merely happens to be followed by what it wills. This certainly represents the usual view of what is meant by a volition "operating," but as it involves the very view of causation which we are engaged in combating, it is not open to us as a definition. We may say that a volition "operates" when there is some law in virtue of which a similar volition in rather similar circumstances will usually be followed by what it wills. But this is a vague conception, and introduces ideas which we have not yet considered. What is chiefly important to notice is that the usual notion of "operating" is not open to us if we reject, as I contend that we should, the usual notion of causation.

(5) "A cause cannot operate except where it is." This maxim is very widespread; it was urged against Newton, and has remained a source of prejudice against "action at a distance." In philosophy it has led to a denial of transient action, and thence to monism or Leibnizian monadism. Like the analogous maxim concerning temporal contiguity, it rests upon the assumption that causes "operate," i.e. that they are in some obscure way analogous to volitions. And, as in the case of temporal contiguity, the inferences drawn from this maxim are wholly groundless.

I return now to the question, What law or laws can be found to take the place of the supposed law of causality?

First, without passing beyond such uniformities of sequence as are contemplated by the traditional law, we may admit that, if any such sequence has been observed in a great many cases, and has never been found to fail, there is an inductive probability that it will be found to hold in future cases. If stones have hitherto been found to break windows, it is probable that they will continue to do so. This, of course, assumes the inductive principle, of which the truth may reasonably be questioned; but as this principle is not our present concern, I shall in this discussion treat it as indubitable. We may then say, in the case of any such frequently observed sequence, that the earlier event is the *cause* and the later event the *effect*.

Several considerations, however, make such special sequences very different from the traditional relation of cause and effect. In the first place, the sequence, in any hitherto unobserved instance, is no more than probable, whereas the relation of cause and effect was supposed to be necessary. I do not mean by this merely that we are not sure of having discovered a true case of cause and effect; I mean that, even when we have a case of cause and effect in our present sense, all that is meant is that on grounds of observation, it is probable that when one occurs the other will also occur. Thus in our present sense, A may be the cause of B even if there actually are cases where B does not follow A. Striking a match will be the cause of its igniting, in spite of the fact that some matches are damp and fail to ignite.

In the second place, it will not be assumed that *every* event has some antecedent which is its cause in this sense; we shall only believe in causal sequences where we find them, without any presumption that they always are to be found.

In the third place, *any* case of sufficiently frequent sequence will be causal in our present sense; for example, we shall not refuse to say that night is the cause of day. Our repugnance to saying this arises from the ease with which we can imagine the sequence to fail, but owing to the fact that cause and effect must be separated by a finite interval of time, *any* such sequence *might* fail through the interposition of other circumstances in the interval. Mill, discussing this instance of night and day, says:—

"It is necessary to our using the word cause, that we should believe not only that the antecedent always *has* been followed by the consequent, but that as long as the present constitution of things endures, it always *will* be so." [5]

In this sense, we shall have to give up the hope of finding causal laws such as Mill contemplated; any causal sequence which we have observed may at any moment be falsified without a falsification of any laws of the kind that the more advanced sciences aim at establishing.

In the fourth place, such laws of probable sequence, though useful in daily life and in the infancy of a science, tend to be displaced by quite different laws as soon as a science is successful. The law of gravitation will illustrate what occurs in any advanced science. In the motions of mutually gravitating bodies, there is nothing that can be called a cause, and nothing that can be called an effect; there is merely a formula. Certain differential equations can be found, which hold at every instant for every particle of the system, and which, given the configuration and velocities at one instant, or the configurations at two instants, render the configuration at any other earlier or later instant theoretically calculable. That is to say, the configuration at any instant is a function of that instant and the configurations at two given instants. This statement holds throughout physics, and not only in the special case of gravitation. But there is nothing that could be properly called "cause" and nothing that could be properly called "effect" in such a system.

No doubt the reason why the old "law of causality" has so long continued to pervade the books of philosophers is simply that the idea of a function is unfamiliar to most of them, and therefore they seek an unduly simplified statement. There is no question of repetitions of the "same" cause producing the "same" effect; it is not in any sameness of causes and effects that the constancy of scientific law consists, but in sameness of relations. And even "sameness of relations" is too simple a phrase; "sameness of differential equations" is the only correct phrase. It is impossible to state this accurately in non-mathematical language; the nearest approach would be as follows: "There is a constant relation between the state of the

[5] *Loc. cit.*, §6.

universe at any instant and the rate of change in the rate at which any part of the universe is changing at that instant, and this relation is many-one, i.e. such that the rate of change in the rate of change is determinate when the state of the universe is given." If the "law of causality" is to be something actually discoverable in the practice of science, the above proposition has a better right to the name than any "law of causality" to be found in the books of philosophers.

In regard to the above principle, several observations must be made—

(1) No one can pretend that the above principle is *a priori* or self-evident or a "necessity of thought." Nor is it, in any sense, a premiss of science: it is an empirical generalisation from a number of laws which are themselves empirical generalisations.

(2) The law makes no difference between past and future: the future "determines" the past in exactly the same sense in which the past "determines" the future. The word "determine," here, has a purely logical significance: a certain number of variables "determine" another variable if that other variable is a function of them.

(3) The law will not be empirically verifiable unless the course of events within some sufficiently small volume will be approximately the same in any two states of the universe which only differ in regard to what is at a considerable distance from the small volume in question. For example, motions of planets in the solar system must be approximately the same however the fixed stars may be distributed, provided that all the fixed stars are very much farther from the sun than the planets are. If gravitation varied directly as the distance, so that the most remote stars made the most difference to the motions of the planets, the world might be just as regular and just as much subject to mathematical laws as it is at present, but we could never discover the fact.

(4) Although the old "law of causality" is not assumed by science, something which we may call the "uniformity of nature" is assumed, or rather is accepted on inductive grounds. The uniformity of nature does not assert the trivial principle "same cause, same effect," but the principle of the permanence of laws. That is to say, when a law exhibiting, e.g. an acceleration as a function of the configuration has been found to hold throughout the observable past, it is expected that it will continue to hold in the future, or that, if it does not itself hold, there is some other law, agreeing with the supposed law as regards the past, which will hold for the future. The ground of this principle is simply the inductive ground that it has been found to be true in very many instances; hence the principle cannot be considered certain, but only probable to a degree which cannot be accurately estimated.

The uniformity of nature, in the above sense, although it is assumed in the practice of science, must not, in its generality, be regarded as a kind of major premiss, without which all scientific reasoning would be in error. The assumption that *all* laws of nature are permanent has, of course, less probability than the assumption that this or that particular law is permanent; and the assumption that a particular law is permanent for all time has less probability than the assumption that it will be valid up to such and such a date. Science, in any given case, will assume what the case requires, but no more. In constructing the *Nautical Almanac* for 1915 it will assume that the law of gravitation will remain true up to the end of that year; but it will make no assumption as to 1916 until it comes to the next volume of the almanac. This procedure is, of course, dictated by the fact that the uniformity of nature is not known *a priori*, but is an empirical generalisation, like "all men are mortal." In all such cases, it is better to argue immediately from the given particular instances to the new instance, than to argue by way of a major premiss; the conclusion is only probable in either case, but acquires a higher probability by the former method than by the latter.

In all science we have to distinguish two sorts of laws: first, those that are empirically verifiable but probably only approximate; secondly, those that are not verifiable, but may be exact. The law of gravitation, for example, in its applications to the solar system, is only empirically verifiable when it is assumed that matter outside the solar system may be ignored for such purposes; we believe this to be only approximately true, but we cannot empirically verify the law of universal gravitation which we believe to be exact. This point is very important in connection with what we may call "relatively isolated systems." These may be defined as follows:—

A system relatively isolated during a given period is one which, within some assignable margin of error, will behave in the same way throughout that period, however the rest of the universe may be constituted.

A system may be called "practically isolated" during a given period if, although there *might* be states of the rest of the universe which would produce more than the assigned margin of error, there is reason to believe that such states do not in fact occur.

Strictly speaking, we ought to specify the respect in which the system is relatively isolated. For example, the earth is relatively isolated as regards falling bodies, but not as regards tides; it is *practically* isolated as regards economic phenomena, although, if Jevons' sunspot theory of commercial crises had been true, it would not have been even practically isolated in this respect.

It will be observed that we cannot prove in advance that a system is isolated. This will be inferred from the observed fact that approximate uniformities can be stated for this system alone. If the complete laws for the whole universe were known, the isolation of a system could be deduced from them; assuming, for example, the law of universal gravitation, the practical isolation of the solar system in this respect can be deduced by the help of the fact that there is very little matter in its neighbourhood. But it should be observed that isolated systems are only important as providing a possibility of *discovering* scientific laws; they have no theoretical importance in the finished structure of a science.

The case where one event A is said to "cause" another event B, which philosophers take as fundamental, is really only the most simplified instance of a practically isolated system. It may happen that, as a result of general scientific laws, whenever A occurs throughout a certain period, it is followed by B; in that case, A and B form a system which is practically isolated throughout that period. It is, however, to be regarded as a piece of good fortune if this occurs; it will always be due to special circumstances, and would not have been true if the rest of the universe had been different though subject to the same laws.

The essential function which causality has been supposed to perform is the possibility of inferring the future from the past, or, more generally, events at any time from events at certain assigned times. Any system in which such inference is possible may be called a "deterministic" system. We may define a deterministic system as follows:—

A system is said to be "deterministic" when, given certain data, $e_1, e_2, \ldots, e_n$, at times $t_1, t_2, \ldots, t_n$ respectively, concerning this system, if E_t is the state of the system at any time t, there is a functional relation of the form

$$E_t = f(e_1, t_1, e_2, t_2, \ldots, e_n, t_n, t). \tag{A}$$

The system will be "deterministic throughout a given period" if t, in the above formula, may be any time within that period, though outside that period the formula may be no longer true. If the universe, as a whole, is such a system, determinism is true of the universe; if not, not. A system which is part of a deterministic system I shall call "determined"; one which is not part of any such system I shall call "capricious."

The events $e_1, e_2, \ldots, e_n$ I shall call "determinants" of the system. It is to be observed that a system which has one set of determinants will in general have many. In the case of the motions of the planets, for example, the configurations of the solar system at any two given times will be determinants.

We may take another illustration from the hypothesis of psycho-physical parallelism. Let us assume, for the purposes of this illustration, that to a given state of brain a given state of mind always corresponds, and vice versa, i.e. that there is a one-one relation between them, so that each is a function of the other. We may also assume, what is practically certain, that to a given state of a certain brain a given state of the whole material universe corresponds, since it is highly improbable that a given brain is ever twice in exactly the same state. Hence there will be a one-one relation between the state of a given person's mind and the state of the whole material universe. It follows that, if n states of the material universe are determinants of the material universe, then n states of a given man's mind are determinants of the whole material and mental universe—assuming, that is to say, that psycho-physical parallelism is true.

The above illustration is important in connection with a certain confusion which seems to have beset those who have philosophised on the relation of mind and matter. It is often thought that, if the state of the mind is determinate when the state of the brain is given, and if the material world forms a deterministic system, then mind is "subject" to matter in some sense in which matter is not "subject" to mind. But if the state of the brain is also determinate when the state of the mind is given, it must be exactly as true to regard matter as subject to mind as it would be to regard mind as subject to matter. We could, theoretically, work out the history of mind without ever mentioning matter, and then, at the end, deduce that matter must meanwhile have gone through the corresponding history. It is true that if the relation of brain to mind were many-one, not one-one, there would be a one-sided dependence of mind on brain, while conversely, if the relation were one-many, as Bergson supposes, there would be a one-sided dependence of brain on mind. But the dependence involved is, in any case, only logical; it does not mean that we shall be compelled to do things we desire not to do, which is what people instinctively imagine it to mean.

As another illustration we may take the case of mechanism and teleology. A system may be defined as "mechanical" when it has a set of determinants that are purely material, such as the positions of certain pieces of matter at certain times. It is an open question whether the world of mind and matter, as we know it, is a mechanical system or not; let us suppose, for the sake of argument, that it is a mechanical system. This supposition—so I contend—throws no light whatever on the question whether the universe is or is not a "teleological" system. It is difficult to define accurately what is meant by a "teleological" system, but the argument is not much affected by the particular definition we adopt. Broadly, a teleological system is one in which purposes are realised, i.e. in which certain desires—those that are deeper or nobler or more fundamental or more universal or what not—are followed by their realisation. Now the fact—if it be a fact—that the universe is mechanical has no bearing whatever on the question whether it is teleological in the above sense. There might be a mechanical system in which all wishes were realised, and there might be one in which all wishes were thwarted. The question whether, or how far, our actual world is teleological, cannot, therefore, be settled by proving that it is mechanical, and the desire that it should be teleological is no ground for wishing it to be not mechanical.

There is, in all these questions, a very great difficulty in avoiding confusion between what we can infer and what is in fact determined. Let us consider, for a moment, the various senses in which the future may be "determined." There is one sense—and a very important one—in which it is determined quite independently of scientific laws, namely, the sense that it will be what it will be. We all regard the past as determined simply by the fact that it has happened; but for the accident that memory works backward and not forward, we should regard the future as equally determined by the fact that it will happen. "But," we are told, "you cannot alter the past, while you can to some extent alter the future." This view seems to me to rest upon just those errors in regard to causation which it has been my object to remove. You cannot make the past other than it was—true, but this is a mere application of the law of contradiction. If you already know what the past was, obviously it is useless to wish it different. But also you cannot make the future other than it will be; this again is an application of the law of contradiction. And if you happen to know the future—e.g. in the case of a forthcoming eclipse—it is just as useless to wish it different as to wish the past different. "But," it will be rejoined, "our wishes can *cause* the future, sometimes, to be different from what it would be if they did not exist, and they can have no such effect upon the past." This, again, is a mere tautology. An effect being *defined* as something subsequent to its cause, obviously we can have no *effect* upon the past. But that does not mean that the past would not have been different if our present wishes had been different. Obviously, our present wishes are conditioned by the past, and therefore could not have been different unless the past had been different; therefore, if our present wishes were different, the past would be different. Of course, the past cannot be different from what it was, but no more can our present wishes be different from what they are; this again is merely the law of contradiction. The facts seem to be merely (1) that wishing generally depends upon ignorance, and is therefore commoner in regard to the future than in regard to the past; (2) that where a wish concerns the future, it and its realisation very often form a "practically independent system," i.e. many wishes regarding the future are realised. But there seems no doubt that the main difference in our feelings arises from the accidental fact that the past but not the future can be known by memory.

Although the sense of "determined" in which the future is determined by the mere fact that it will be what it will be is sufficient (at least so it seems to me) to refute some opponents of determinism, notably M. Bergson and the pragmatists, yet it is not what most people have in mind when they speak of the future as determined. What they have in mind is a formula by means of which the future can be exhibited, and at least theoretically calculated, as a function of the past. But at this point we meet with a great difficulty, which besets what has been said above about deterministic systems, as well as what is said by others.

If formulæ of any degree of complexity, however great, are admitted, it would seem that any system, whose state at a given moment is a function of certain measurable quantities, *must* be a deterministic system. Let us consider, in illustration, a single material particle, whose co-ordinates at time t are x_t, y_t, z_t. Then, however the particle moves, there must be, theoretically, functions f_1, f_2, f_3, such that

$$x_t = f_1(t), \qquad y_t = f_2(t), \qquad z_t = f_3(t).$$

It follows that, theoretically, the whole state of the material universe at time t must be capable of being exhibited as a function of t. Hence our universe will be deterministic in the sense defined above. But if this be true, no information is conveyed about the universe in stating that it is deterministic. It is true that the formulæ involved may be of strictly infinite complexity, and therefore not practically capable of being written down or apprehended. But except from the point of view of our knowledge, this might seem to be a detail: in itself, if the above considerations are sound, the material universe *must* be deterministic, *must* be subject to laws.

This, however, is plainly not what was intended. The difference between this view and the view intended may be seen as follows. Given some formula which fits the facts hitherto—say the law of gravitation—there will be an infinite number of other formulæ not empirically distinguishable from it in the past, but diverging from it more and more in the future. Hence, even assuming that there are persistent laws, we shall have no reason for assuming that the law of the inverse square will hold in future; it may be some other hitherto indistinguishable law that will hold. We cannot say that *every* law which has held hitherto must hold in the future, because past facts which obey one law will also obey others, hitherto indistinguishable but diverging in future. Hence there must, at every moment, be laws hitherto unbroken which are now broken for the first time. What science does, in fact, is to select the *simplest* formula that will fit the facts. But this, quite obviously, is merely a methodological precept, not a law of Nature. If the simplest formula ceases, after a time, to be applicable, the simplest formula that remains applicable is selected, and science has no sense that an axiom has been falsified. We are thus left with the brute fact that, in many departments of science, quite simple laws have hitherto been found to hold. This fact cannot be regarded as having any *a priori* ground, nor can it be used to support inductively the opinion that the same laws will continue; for at every moment laws hitherto true are being falsified, though in the advanced sciences these laws are less simple than those that have remained true. Moreover it would be fallacious to argue inductively from the state of the advanced sciences to the future state of the others, for it may well be that the advanced sciences are advanced simply because, hitherto, their subject-matter has obeyed simple and easily ascertainable laws, while the subject-matter of other sciences has not done so.

The difficulty we have been considering seems to be met partly, if not wholly, by the principle that the *time* must not enter explicitly into our formulæ. All mechanical laws exhibit acceleration as a function of configuration, not of configuration and time jointly; and this principle of the irrelevance of the time may be extended to all scientific laws. In fact we might interpret the "uniformity of nature" as meaning just this, that no scientific law involves the time as an argument, unless, of course, it is given in an integrated form, in which case *lapse* of time, though not absolute time, may appear in our formulæ. Whether this consideration suffices to overcome our difficulty completely, I do not know; but in any case it does much to diminish it.

It will serve to illustrate what has been said if we apply it to the question of free will.

The problem of free will * is so intimately bound up with the analysis of causation that, old as it is, we need not despair of obtaining new light on it by the help of new views on the notion of cause. The free-will problem has, at one time or another, stirred men's passions profoundly, and the fear that the will might not be free has been to some men a source of great unhappiness. I believe that, under the influence of a cool analysis, the doubtful questions involved will be found to have no such emotional importance as is sometimes thought, since the disagreeable consequences supposed to flow from a denial of free will do not flow from this denial in any form in which there is reason to make it. It is not, however, on this account chiefly that I wish to discuss this problem, but rather because it affords a good example of the clarifying effect of analysis and of the interminable controversies which may result from its neglect.

Let us first try to discover what it is we really desire when we desire free will. Some of our reasons for desiring free will are profound, some trivial. To begin with the former: we do not wish to feel ourselves in the hands of fate, so that, however much we may desire to will one thing, we may nevertheless be compelled by an outside force to will another. We do not wish to think that, however much we may desire to act well, heredity and surroundings may force us into acting ill. We wish to feel that, in cases of doubt, our choice is momentous and lies within our power. Besides these desires, which are worthy of all respect, we have, however, others not so respectable, which equally make us desire free will. We do not like to think that other people, if they knew enough, could predict our actions, though we know that we can often predict those of other people, especially if they are elderly. Much as we esteem the old gentleman who is our neighbour in the country, we know that when grouse are mentioned he will tell the story of the grouse in the gun-room. But we ourselves are not so mechanical: we never tell an anecdote to the same person twice, or even once unless he is sure to enjoy it; although we once met (say) Bismarck, we are quite capable of hearing him mentioned without relating the occasion when we met him. In this sense, everybody thinks that he himself has free will, though he knows that no one else has. The desire for this kind of free will seems to be no better than a form of vanity. I do not believe that this desire can be gratified with any certainty; but the other, more respectable desires are, I believe, not inconsistent with any tenable form of determinism.

We have thus two questions to consider: (1) Are human actions

* The remainder of this selection is reprinted from pp. 247–56 of *Our Knowledge of the External World*, by Bertrand Russell by permission of W. W. Norton & Company, Inc.

theoretically predictable from a sufficient number of antecedents? (2) Are human actions subject to an external compulsion? The two questions, as I shall try to show, are entirely distinct, and we may answer the first in the affirmative without therefore being forced to give an affirmative answer to the second.

(1) *Are human actions theoretically predictable from a sufficient number of antecedents?* Let us first endeavour to give precision to this question. We may state the question thus: Is there some constant relation between an act and a certain number of earlier events, such that, when the earlier events are given, only one act, or at most only acts with some well-marked character, can have this relation to the earlier events? If this is the case, then, as soon as the earlier events are known, it is theoretically possible to predict either the precise act, or at least the character necessary to its fulfilling the constant relation.

To this question, a negative answer has been given by Bergson, in a form which calls in question the general applicability of the law of causation. He maintains that every event, and more particularly every mental event, embodies so much of the past that it could not possibly have occurred at any earlier time, and is therefore necessarily quite different from all previous and subsequent events. If, for example, I read a certain poem many times, my experience on each occasion is modified by the previous readings, and my emotions are never repeated exactly. The principle of causation, according to him, asserts that the same cause, if repeated, will produce the same effect. But owing to memory, he contends, this principle does not apply to mental events. What is apparently the same cause, if repeated is modified by the mere fact of repetition, and cannot produce the same effect. He infers that every mental event is a genuine novelty, not predictable from the past, because the past contains nothing exactly like it by which we could imagine it. And on this ground he regards the freedom of the will as unassailable.

Bergson's contention has undoubtedly a great deal of truth, and I have no wish to deny its importance. But I do not think its consequences are quite what he believes them to be. It is not necessary for the determinist to maintain that he can foresee the whole particularity of the act which will be performed. If he could foresee that A was going to murder B, his foresight would not be invalidated by the fact that he could not know all the infinite complexity of A's state of mind in committing the murder, nor whether the murder was to be performed with a knife or with a revolver. If the *kind* of act which will be performed can be foreseen within narrow limits, it is of little practical interest that there are fine shades which cannot be foreseen. No doubt every time the story of the grouse in the gun-room is told, there will be slight differences due to increasing habitualness, but they do not invalidate the prediction that the story will be told. And there is nothing in Bergson's argument to show that we can never predict what *kind* of act will be performed.

Again, his statement of the law of causation is inadequate. The law does not state merely that, if the *same* cause is repeated, the *same* effect will result. It states rather that there is a constant relation between causes of certain kinds and effects of certain kinds. For example, if a body falls freely, there is a constant relation between the height through which it falls and the time it takes in falling. It is not necessary to have a body fall through the *same* height which has been previously observed, in order to be able to foretell the length of time occupied in falling. If this were necessary, no prediction would be possible, since it would be impossible to make the height exactly the same on two occasions. Similarly, the attraction which the sun will exert on the earth is not only known at distances for which it has been observed, but at all distances, because it is known to vary as the inverse square of the distance. In fact, what is found to be repeated is always the *relation* of cause and effect, not the cause itself; all that is necessary as regards the cause is that it should be of the same *kind* (in the relevant respect) as earlier causes whose effects have been observed.

Another respect in which Bergson's statement of causation is inadequate is in its assumption that the cause must be *one* event, whereas it may be two or more events, or even some continuous process. The substantive question at issue is whether mental events are determined by the past. Now in such a case as the repeated reading of a poem, it is obvious that our feelings in reading the poem are most emphatically dependent upon the past, but not upon one single event in the past. All our previous readings of the poem must be included in the cause. But we easily perceive a certain law according to which the effect varies as the previous readings increase in number, and in fact Bergson himself tacitly assumes such a law. We decide at last not to read the poem again, because we know that this time the effect would be boredom. We may not know all the niceties and shades of the boredom we should feel, but we know enough to guide our decision, and the prophecy of boredom is none the less true for being more or less general. Thus the kind of cases upon which Bergson relies are insufficient to show the impossibility of prediction in the only sense in which prediction has practical or emotional interest. We may therefore leave the consideration of his arguments and address ourselves to the problem directly.

The law of causation, according to which later events can theoretically be predicted by means of earlier events, has often been held to be *a priori*, a necessity of thought, a category without which science would be impossible. These claims seem to me excessive. In certain directions the law has been verified empirically, and in other directions there is no positive evidence against it. But science can use it where it has been found to be true, without being forced into any assumption as to its truth in other fields. We cannot, therefore, feel any *a priori* certainty that causation must apply to human volitions.

The question how far human volitions are subject to causal laws is a purely empirical one. Empirically it seems plain that the great majority of our volitions have causes, but it cannot, on this account, be held necessarily certain that all have causes. There are, however, precisely the same kinds of reasons for regarding it as probable that they all have causes as there are in the case of physical events.

We may suppose—though this is doubtful—that there are laws of correlation of the mental and the physical, in virtue of which, given the state of all the matter in the world, and therefore of all the brains and living organisms, the state of all the minds in the world could be inferred, while conversely the state of all the matter in the world could be inferred if the state of all the minds were given. It is obvious that there is *some* degree of correlation between brain and mind, and it is impossible to say how complete it may be. This, however, is not the point which I wish to elicit. What I wish to urge is that, even if we admit the most extreme claims of determinism and of correlation of mind and brain, still the consequences inimical to what is worth preserving in free will do not follow. The belief that they follow results, I think, entirely from the assimilation of causes to volitions, and from the notion that causes *compel* their effects in some sense analogous to that in which a human authority can compel a man to do what he would rather not do. This assimilation, as soon as the true nature of scientific causal laws is realised, is seen to be a sheer mistake. But this brings us to the second of the two questions which we raised in regard to free will, namely, whether, assuming determinism, our actions can be in any proper sense regarded as compelled by outside forces.

(2) *Are human actions subject to an external compulsion?* We have, in deliberation, a subjective sense of freedom, which is sometimes alleged against the view that volitions have causes. This sense of freedom, however, is only a sense that we can choose which we please of a number of alternatives: it does not show us that there is no causal connection between what we please to choose and our previous history. The supposed inconsistency of these two springs from the habit of conceiving causes as analogous to volitions—a habit which often survives unconsciously in those who intend to conceive causes in a more scientific manner. If a cause is analogous to a volition, outside causes will be analogous to an alien will, and acts predictable from outside causes will be subject to compulsion. But this view of cause is one to which science lends no countenance. Causes, we have seen, do not *compel* their effects, any more than effects *compel* their causes. There is a mutual relation, so that either can be inferred from the other. When the geologist infers the past state of the earth from its present state, we should not say that the present state *compels* the past state to have been what it was; yet it renders it necessary as a consequence of the data, in the only sense in which effects are rendered necessary by their causes. The difference which we *feel*, in this respect, between causes and effects is a mere confusion due to the fact that we remember past events but do not happen to have memory of the future.

The apparent indeterminateness of the future, upon which some advocates of free will rely, is merely a result of our ignorance. It is plain that no desirable kind of free will can be dependent simply upon our ignorance; for if that were the case, animals would be more free than men, and savages than civilised people. Free will in any valuable sense must be compatible with the fullest knowledge. Now, quite apart from any assumption as to causality, it is obvious that complete knowledge would embrace the future as well as the past. Our knowledge of the past is not wholly based upon causal inferences, but is partly derived from memory. It is a mere accident that we have no memory of the future. We might—as in the pretended visions of seers—see future events immediately, in the way in which we see past events. They certainly will be what they will be, and are in this sense just as determined as the past. If we saw future events in the same immediate way in which we see past events, what kind of free will would still be possible? Such a kind would be wholly independent of determinism: it could not be contrary to even the most entirely universal reign of causality. And such a kind must contain whatever is worth having in free will, since it is impossible to believe that mere ignorance can be the essential conditon of any good thing. Let us therefore imagine a set of beings who know the whole future with absolute certainty, and let us ask ourselves whether they could have anything that we should call free will.

Such beings as we are imagining would not have to wait for the event in order to know what decision they were going to adopt on some future occasion. They would know now what their volitions were going to be. But would they have any reason to regret this knowledge? Surely not, unless the foreseen volitions were in themselves regrettable. And it is less likely that the foreseen volitions would be regrettable if the steps which would lead to them were also foreseen. It is difficult not to suppose that what is foreseen is fated, and must happen however much it may be dreaded. But human actions are the outcome of desire, and no foreseeing can be true unless it takes account of desire. A foreseen volition will have to be one which does not become odious through being foreseen. The beings we are imagining would easily come to know the causal connections of volitions, and therefore their volitions would be better calculated to satisfy their desires than ours are. Since volitions are the outcome of desires, a prevision of volitions contrary to desires could not be a true one. It must be remembered that the supposed prevision would not create the future any more than memory creates the past. We do not think we were necessarily not free in the past, merely because we can now remember our past volitions. Similarly, we might be free in the future, even if we could now see what our future volitions were going to be. Freedom, in short, in any valuable sense, demands only that our volitions shall be, as they are, the result of our own desires, not of an outside force compelling us to will what we would rather not will. Everything else is confusion of thought, due to the feeling that knowledge *compels* the happening of what it knows when this is future, though it is at once obvious that knowledge has no such power in regard to the past. Free will, therefore, is true in the only form which is important; and the desire for other forms is a mere effect of insufficient analysis.

Notes on Causality*

HERBERT FEIGL

The clarified (purified) concept of causation is defined in terms of *predictability according to a law* (or, more adequately, according to a set of laws).

The purification referred to was most emphatically initiated by Galileo and completed by Hume. It consisted in the elimination of (as we might put it today) metaphysical, i.e., in principle unconfirmable, connotations that had traditionally obscured, if not eclipsed, the only meaning of causation that is logically tenable and methodologically adequate and fruitful. These *disturbing* or *interfering connotations* are:

1. The *teleological* conception (final causes), eliminated from physics by Galileo, but still surviving in various disguises in the thinking of some biologists, psychologists and social scientists (especially historians), — not to mention philosophers.

2. The *animistic* conception, according to which there is an internal (but unconfirmable) compulsion (conceived anthropomorphically in analogy to coercion as experienced on the human level when forced against our own impulses), which supposedly accounts for the invariable connection of causes with their effects. One fallacious inference from this conception is the doctrine of *fatalism.*

3. The *rationalistic* conception which identifies (I should say, confuses) the causal relation with the logical relation of implication (or entailment). This, as well as the preceding connotations, were repudiated once and for all by Hume. The Kantian attempt at a resuscitation of causal necessity in terms of an a priori cognizable presupposition for the possibility of knowledge in general boils down to an explication of what we customarily mean by "Knowledge", i.e., the ascertainment of lawful relationships. (Kant thus did not effectively advance our conception of causality beyond that of Hume. And he was not able to carry out his intention of demonstrating the certainty of *any* causal law.) Other attempts to assimilate causation to logical entailment (Meyerson, Ewing, Cohen, Blanshard) may be said to have failed (for diverse reasons, such as mistaken conceptions of logical identity or necessity, mistaken conceptions of the meaning of the conservation laws, etc.).[1]

* This article was written with the purpose of summarizing succinctly some results of the logical and methodological analyses of the concept of causation. Special attention was given to aspects not sufficiently covered in other related articles included in this volume. I am indebted to many other writers on the subject. Among the more recent ones, I mention especially B. Russell, M. Schlick, E. Zilsel, and H. Reichenbach.

[1] Trenchant criticisms of these misconceptions may be found in: M. Schlick, "Causality in Everyday Life and in Recent Science", Univ. of California *Publications in*

Once this "purge" is accomplished, a more detailed definiton of *causation* may proceed by attending to the *types and forms of laws* and the *domains and levels of their application.*

It will be helpful to distinguish classes of laws under the following rubrics:

Types:

1. Deterministic
   I.e., strict and precise predictability of individual events or of some of their aspects.
2. Statistical
   I.e., predictability on the basis of stable frequency-ratios or according to strict laws governing frequency distributions.

Forms:

1. *Qualitative*
   E.g., friction produces heat; hydrogen and chlorine combine into hydrochloric acid; thick layers of lead are not penetrated by X-rays; etc.
2. *Semi-quantitative* (*topological*)
   E.g., the higher the temperature the greater the speed of chemical reactions; the greater the distance, the smaller the force. Only the relations of "equal" and "greater than" are here defined.
3. *Fully quantitative* (*metrical*)
   E.g., $F = G \frac{M_1 M_2}{r^2}$
   $E = I \cdot R$; $p v = RT$; etc.
   Here we express functional relationships between magnitudes defined in terms of equality of intervals, zero-point and units (in addition to the topological ordering which is presupposed).

Domains:

1. *Temporal* (*sequential*)
   This is the most common form of scientific law; most regularities of our world pertain to temporal succession.
2. *Coexistential* (*simultaneous*)
   The regular co-presence of certain characteristics, such as of electric and thermal conductivity; generally, of various physical and chemical properties of substances, organisms, etc. or regular concomitances in changes of such properties, e.g., of gravitational and inertial mass.

Levels:

1. Macro ("molar")
2. Micro ("molecular")
   This is a *relative* distinction; there may be as many levels as it is methodologically fruitful to distinguish. Classical thermodynamics with its concepts of temperature, pressure, energy, entropy, etc., is *molar* in contradistinction to statistical (molecular) thermodynamics. Once the language of the micro-science (or of the micro-model) is introduced, the concepts of the corresponding macro-laws become explicitly definable in terms of the micro-concepts. Thus the ordinary concept of (macro) temperature of a gas, may be defined in terms of the average velocities of the molecules

---

Philosophy, 15, 1932 (reprinted in Feigl and Sellars, *Readings in Philosophical Analysis*). Hobart, R. E., "Hume without Scepticism," *Mind*, 1930. Miller, D. S., "An Event in Philosophy", *Phil. Rev.*, 54, 1945. Nagel, E., "Sovereign Reason", in *Freedom and Experience*, Cornell Univ. Press, 1948.

composing the gas. Analogously, the macro-concept of the intensity of an electric current may be defined in terms of the number of electrons that pass through a wire per unit of time. Empirical laws in sociology are formulated in typical macro-concepts. In a descending scale toward increasingly "molecular" (micro) levels, we may then distinguish the concepts of behavioristic psychology (dealing, e.g., with dispositions, motivations, learning-processes) of individuals; the neuro-physiological processes "underlying" the behavior; and ultimately at least two levels of physico-chemical conceptualizations, i.e. again in terms of classical thermodynamics, molecular and finally atomic, quantum, and subatomic theories.

Another distinction: "atomistic" (additive, summative, mechanistic) and "holistic" (organic, emergent, telic, gestalt-like-configurational) while not necessarily without merit, is fraught with the dangers of metaphysical confusion.

Most combinations of each case in one rubric with some one in the other rubrics yield important further classes of laws, actually exemplified in various fields of knowledge.

The terms "cause" and "effect" of ordinary language need not be rejected if proper caution is employed in their application. In most of the practically significant applications we must remember that it is an entire *set* of conditions that represents "the" cause of an event. Otherwise we should have to identify the "cause" with the eliciting event or the differential factor, which—given the total set of conditions—is sufficient to produce the effect in question. Since all concept-formation is abstractive we must also remember that what is designated as "cause" or "effect" in a complex situation is usually only some factor, aspect, magnitude, etc., that we select from a more complex (and possibly inexhaustible) welter of factual details.

"A causes B" or (what is tantamount) "A is the cause of B" means that wherever and whenever A occurs it is followed (or attended) by B. Since a precise repetition of A may not be feasible (or discoverable), a less stringent formulation would use something like a mathematical limit process: The more the actual condition A′ approximates the conceived (ideal) condition A, the more the actual effect B′ will approximate the (ideal) effect B.

In the case of unrepeatable (unique) events, as described in the historical disciplines (as in the history of the inorganic, organic, mental, social, cultural or individual-biographical occurrences), the assertion of causal relations (as in statements regarding who or what influenced events to what degree and in which direction) is often methodologically precarious, i.e., only very weakly confirmable. But it is not meaningless. Just as in considerations of contrary-to-fact conditionals ("iffy" questions) we must here fall back upon a system of laws only indirectly and incompletely confirmed but nonetheless the basis of prediction, explanation, and of answers to "iffy" questions.

On the whole, the ordinary cause-effect terminology fits best the qualitative macro-level; thus it is part and parcel of the language of common sense and of those levels of science which deal with gross behavior and have not as yet introduced quantitative (metrical) concepts. Once measurement is introduced, the gross cause-effect relation gives way to a mathematical formulation in terms of a functional relationship. (Simple functional equations between one or more independent variables and one dependent variable; or sets of such equations; differential and integral equations wherever we relate rates of change, or gradients, with other variables, or where certain integral aspects of functions are related to other variables.

Common observation and especially the successes of the physical sciences (until about 1900) have tended to establish the following connotations of "*causality*": [2]

1. *Determinism* (i.e., ideally complete and precise predictability, given the momentary conditions, the pertinent laws, and the required mathematical techniques). The best-known formulation of this idea is contained in a famous passage of Laplace's *Essai philosophique sur les probabilités.* The possibility of a world-formula (and consequently of a complete world calendar of events—past, present and future) must however not be identified with the concept of determinism. Aside from the obviously utopian character of the idea of a world-formula which, to put it mildly, renders it a practical impossibility, there are difficulties in principle: the application of deterministic laws to a spatially infinite universe can yield definite results only under highly artificial, restrictive conditions. The case for a finite (unbounded) universe is in principle much more favorable since it resembles the case of closed systems. But even if we restrict ourselves to closed systems (or what is tantamount, initial and boundary conditions) there remains the question [3] as to whether a predictor (human or mechanical) can conceivably ascertain *all* the relevant initial conditions, especially as regards his own momentary state. It would seem, however, that these difficulties concern merely the (physical) possibility of accurate prediction and not the idea of determinism as such.

Even according to classical, i.e., nineteenth century molecular, physics, there are insurmountable limitations to the exactness of measurement. The heat motion (Brownian motion) of the molecules in every measuring device makes it physically impossible to ascertain absolutely precise values of the variables constituting initial conditions. Nevertheless, here as every-

[2] The basic meaning, of course, remains *lawfulness* or *predictability* (extrapolatability, interpolatability). This conception is not readily defined with precision. But it seems possible to give at least an approximate explication in logical and mathematical terms. (In the problem of interpolation a definition of the *formally simplest* curve that most smoothly connects the points representing results of actual measurements can be stated by means of a minimum principle: the minimum integral over the curvature of the total curve.) If the formally simplest function (in the sense just indicated) holds for a sufficiently large sample of points and lends itself without serious modification to successful interpolation and extrapolation from here on out, then we consider the phenomenon thus diagrammed as one of a specifiable degree of *lawfulness.*

[3] Discussed in a very thought-provoking article "Indeterminism in Quantum Physics" (containing also a discussion of the problem for classical physics), by K. R. Popper in the *British Journal of Philosophy of Science,* 2, 1951.

where else in pre-quantum physics the assumption of strict lawfulness of molecular motion was at least compatible with the (then) available evidence. The principle of determinism may therefore be interpreted as a—to be sure, very bold and hence extremely problematic—hypothesis concerning the order of nature and falls thus under the jurisdiction of inductive evidence. (The principle of induction itself must then be interpreted not as an hypothesis regarding the universe, but as a regulative maxim of generalizing inference, or as a definition of "inductive probability" or of "degree of confirmation".) The kind of evidence that the experiments of quantum physics (since 1900, and in any case since 1923) have furnished, points very decisively to an indeterminism, at least on the level of those physical variables and magnitudes which are at present accessible to measurement.

2. *Homogeneity and Isotropy of Space, and Homogeneity of Time.* This principle, clearly formulated by Maxwell,[4] states the irrelevance of absolute space or time co-ordinates, and in this sense the purely relational character of space and time as seen already by Leibniz and re-emphasized in Einstein's theory of relativity. The place and the time at which events occur do not by themselves have any modifying effect on these events. Mathematically this may be expressed by saying that the space and time variables do not enter *explicitly* into the functions representing natural laws. The same sort of irrelevance applies to *direction* in space, as in the case of the propagation of forces. "Same causes, same effects" makes sense only if there is such a neutral medium as space-time which thus is no more than a *principium individuationis*. Differences in effects must always be accounted for in terms of differences in the *conditions*, not in terms of purely spatio-temporal location. The empirical-factual, and hence ultimately non-necessary, character of this principle of homogeneity becomes clear through a consideration of its denial: this would be equivalent to asserting the absolute character of space and (or) time. Some of the basic physical "constants" would then be really variable in space and/or time; and these variations would (under our supposition) not be accountable by functional relations to any other physical variables, except those of space or time. In such a "queer" world determinism need not be invalid. The functions (monotonic, periodic, or what not) might well be capable of successful extrapolation.

3. *Contiguity or "Nearby Action"*. This principle which established itself firmly in the minds of the nineteenth-century physicists, mainly owing to the field theories of Faraday and Maxwell, displaced all previous notions of "action at a distance". The propagation of electric or magnetic fields, even when the ether hypothesis had been relinquished, was conceived as a process that spreads "continuously from point to point" in space. One must ask what precisely is asserted by this rather pictorial phrase. As far as empirically confirmable content is concerned, it seems to

[4] *Matter and Motion.*

assert no more than that: (*a*) there is an upper limit to the propagation speed of causal influences. This limit, according to the theory of relativity, is approximately 186,000 miles/second, i.e., the speed of light, or of electromagnetic waves generally, in the vacuum; (*b*) the propagation is spatially continuous, in the sense that in all regions of space that lie between the source of energy and any recipient (absorber), other recipients introduced there in between would also be affected. An analogous principle holds for time, in that modifications of behavior (be it inorganic or organic) seem to be based on modification of structure and function which extend continuously through time; (*c*) the diminution of effects with increasing distance—in Euclidean space generally according to an inverse square function. These three components of the meaning of "contiguity" may serve to explicate the commonsense phrase "A cause acts only where it is."

More significant philosophically is the insight that the finite upper limit of physical velocities involves again certain limitations on predictability. Messages and influences coming from the depths of astronomical space may bring news of cosmic events (e.g., of the explosion of a star as in the case of super-novae) which could not have been anticipated on the basis of previous evidence. For the same reason prediction of the behavior of local systems is limited by ignorance concerning incoming influences traveling with the speed of light. No advance notice of such influence is physically possible. But again, this does not abrogate determinism, it merely restricts predictability. The principle of determinism can still be formulated in terms of initial and boundary conditions. In Minkowski's representation this means that *if* we know the base and the mantle (without the upper surface) of a four-dimensional cylinder (its axis representing the dimension of time and the other three dimensions, of course, space) in terms of the distribution of physical magnitudes then, with the help of the laws of physics, we are able to compute the total content of the cylinder, i.e., the processes occurring in that spatial region for a chosen interval of time.

4. *The Continuity of the Functions* (and usually also of their first and second derivatives) that represent the metrical relations between measurable or hypothetically inferred magnitudes. This may be taken as an explication of Leibniz' "lex continui" (*natura non facit saltus*). Obviously even in classical physics there was not (and there could not have been) any conclusive evidence for this bold principle. Any apparently discontinuous change (like the increase in pressure in the case of an explosion) can always be described as a rapid but continuous change. The idea of continuity, especially in nineteenth-century field physics, simply comes down to this: Most, if not all, of the basic laws of nature can be *conveniently* represented by means of mathematical functions that are strictly continuous. The utilization of the mathematical continuum (of real numbers) is no more than an expedient device for elegant mathematical for-

mulation and computation. A rather small subset of the rational numbers would in principle suffice for representing the actually measurable values of physical magnitudes and their functional relations. There is, however, an empirical core in the continuity principle: In many types of phenomena described in classical mechanics and electromagnetics there is no striking evidence for abrupt changes of state. Nevertheless, the atomic structure of matter and certain singularities in the solution of the differential equations even of field physics involve discontinuities which are not easily "explained away".

5. *Practical Irreversibility* (temporal asymmetry) and *Theoretical Reversibility* (symmetry) *of the Cause-Effect Relation.* The macro-processes of everyday life are without exception marked by their temporal irreversibility. A movie (or better still, a talkie) seen in reverse order illustrates this point vividly. "Time's arrow", as Eddington called it, finds its classical formulation in the second law of thermodynamics, i.e., the law of increasing entropy, or of the dissipation of energy. It seems very plausible that the irreversibility of biological, psychological, and social process is ultimately also reducible to the entropy principle. But, as is well known, in the molecular-statistical explanations of irreversibility as given by Gibbs and Boltzmann, the strict reversibility of molecular processes is assumed. Macro-irreversibility therefore is a mass-phenomenon and hence holds only with probability. The probability of reversions for processes involving large numbers of molecules is however so small that, for all practical purposes, it may be safely neglected. Only in phenomena (such as the Brownian motion) where a relatively small number of molecules is involved have actual "reversions" been experimentally demonstrated. While the issues concerned are by no means completely settled, the prevalent opinion accounts for Time's Arrow in Boltzmann's terms: the probabilities for a transition from a more highly ordered state to one of lower order (greater disorder) are always higher than those for the process in the opposite direction. Our immediate experience of temporal unidirectional passage may ultimately be explained on the basis of the very same physical principles. It is clear, in any case, that all processes which produce traces (which may serve as evidence for earlier events) are entropic in character. This is obvious in such processes as writing, engraving, etc., and may apply also to the production of memory-traces in nervous systems or brains. Since the basic laws of classical mechanics and electrodynamics as well as those of modern quantum mechanics are temporally symmetrical, it would seem that the direction of causality may indeed be reducible to Boltzmann's explanation. Once this is assumed, such statements as "earlier actions can influence later events but not vice versa" are recognized as sheer tautologies, derivable from the definition of the relation "influencing" in terms of "cause" and "effect"—the latter concepts in turn defined by their temporal succession as based on the entropy-principle.

6. *Conservation of Basic Quantities.* The mediaeval slogan "*causa*

aequat effectum" is of course almost useless for scientific purposes. But one very charitable interpretation may accept such conservation principles as those of energy, action or momentum as a modern explication of the old idea. It is essentially the *trigger phenomena* which generally arouse a puzzlement resolvable only if we can justifiably point to the source of the energies which are released in trigger action. Some philosophers of science, notably Emile Meyerson, felt that a scientific explanation is really worth while or gets down to fundamentals only if it points out a basic identity of cause and effect. The term "identity" is however replete with ambiguities. Modern science surely has demonstrated that highly adequate causal explanations can be given without the idea of *things* remaining identical in the flux of events. By no stretch of the imagination can the modern physical concept of energy be understood in terms of a thing or substance that undergoes all sorts of transformations. The meaning of the conservation laws quite generally amounts to no more than asserting the constancy of certain numerical relationships between directly or indirectly measurable magnitudes. The only concepts of identity that are relevant here are then, first, the identity of the law by means of which we explain and predict a variety of phenomena and the identity of numerical constants (i.e., the constancy of certain numerical values).

The list of six connotations of classical causality may be incomplete; but it is a list of some such aspects as these that the scientific methodologist may present when challenged by the question: Is causality nothing more than predictability (i.e., regularity of succession, Hume's "constant conjunction")? Hume himself had stressed contiguity and spatio-temporal homogeneity among the characteristics of the causal relation.

Lately there has been a resurgence of dissatisfaction with Hume's analysis of causality. It is true that even a longer list of subsidiary characteristics will not provide the element of *necessity* that seems, to more rationalistically inclined philosophers, to be missing. Empiricists have traditionally identified necessity with logical deducibility or, more generally, with analyticity. Given a scientific law (of deterministic type) and given a description of the antecedent condition in the law, it is of course always possible to deduce the description of the effect with logical necessity. An analogous situation holds even more impressively for the derivation of experimental laws from higher order theoretical postulates. The intellectual satisfaction that attends the explanation of, e.g., the laws of chemistry by those of atomic physics, no doubt stems from the logical necessity with which the former are entailed by the latter. But the theoretical postulates are not themselves *logically* necessary. To the empiricist way of thinking they can be held valid only "until further notice"—such notice being given when the derived conclusions do not match sufficiently accurately the facts of observation.

The only way in which a conception of necessity may be introduced in the explication of the causal relation is to consider fundamental natural laws as implicit definitions of the concepts by means of which they are formulated. In this sense, and in this sense only, are natural laws true by virtue of the meaning of the terms they contain. But this does not render them analytic in the customary sense of this term. Analytic propositions are true by virtue of meanings stipulated by explicit definitions. Analytic propositions like "A yard is equal to three feet", or "a degree Fahrenheit equals five-ninths of a degree in the centigrade scale" give no information regarding matters of physical fact; they are consequences of in principle completely arbitrary definitions. But the relations expressed, e.g., in Maxwell's equations between electric and magnetic field vectors may be regarded as establishing the meaning of the concepts of electric and magnetic forces within the network of the postulates of Maxwell's theory, but also as a characterization of lawful relations between physical matters of fact. Some such conception of natural laws (possibly formulated in syntactical and semantical terms) seems indispensable if one wishes to give a plausible account of the meaning of subjunctive conditionals, and especially of contrary-to-fact conditionals. For example, a physicist would consider the following a true statement: "If there were an electric current flowing through this wire (a condition which at the given time may not be fulfilled) then there would be a magnetic field surrounding that wire, etc., etc". The application of natural laws to "iffy" questions of this sort requires conceptual tools that are not contained explicitly in extensional logic or in Hume's somewhat too psychologistic empiricism. Nevertheless, the basic tenets of a logical empiricism are thereby not called into question. Natural laws remain synthetic and a posteriori, only their logical structure and epistemic role may require a fresh analysis.[5]

Returning after this excursion to the list of component meanings of causality it must be stressed that every one of these six connotations has been seriously doubted at one occasion or another in twentieth-century physics (relativity and especially in the recent developments of the quantum theory). Most of the younger-generation physicists have definitely abandoned (1); and (4) and (3) are at present under strong suspicion. It looks as though none of the classical (e.g., Kantian)"a priori" requirements of causality could be endorsed with any assurance—except, of course, a rather diluted conception of lawfulness (predictability, functional relationship) in the *statistical* sense. These radical departures from classical determinism are, however, by and large negligible on the macrophysical level. (Heisenberg's formula: $\Delta p . \Delta q \geqq h$ clearly indicates this

[5] For important discussions of this controversial issue *cf:* R. Chisholm, "The Contrary-to-Fact Conditional", *Mind,* 55, 1946. Reprinted in Feigl and Sellars, *Readings.* N. Goodman, "The Problem of Counterfactual Conditionals", *Jl. of Phil.*, 44, 1947. Reprinted in Linsky, *Semantics.* K. R. Popper, "A note on natural laws and so-called contrary-to-fact conditionals", *Mind,* 58, 1949. W. S. Sellars, "Inference and Meaning", *Mind,* 62, 1953 and "Is there a Synthetic *A Priori?*", *Philosophy of Science,* 20, 1953. W. Kneale, *Probability and Induction,* Clarendon Press, Oxford, 1949.

inverse dependence of the uncertainties in momentum and co-ordinates upon the mass of the bodies concerned.)

On the macro-level we deal with many regularities (that are usually styled "causal relations" which are not fundamental, but dependent upon the presence of certain structures. Old Faithful Geyser, e.g., behaves in a highly predictable fashion, but the very pattern displayed depends on the relative constancy of the underground situation (cavern, water-supply, heat-flux, etc.) The stimulus-response laws of psychology are similarly dependent upon the (anatomical) structure and the (physiological) functioning of the organism; and on the level of sociological and economic analysis many of the regularities (trends, correlations, influences, etc.) depend upon institutional structures, cultural traditions, etc., etc.

The crude concepts of cause and effect connote of course the generally accepted definition in terms of the temporal precedence of *cause*. But an equally well established usage seems to prevail even if the two events (factors, processes) are contemporaneous. Since the purely mathematical concept of the "independent variable" is obviously arbitrary (to every function there is its inverse), the empirical meaning of "independent" and "dependent" variable must lie somewhere else. Perhaps what we mean here by "cause" (independent variable) and "effect" (dependent variable) simply hinges upon which of the variables are open to active control, accessible to intervention. We can control the temperature or the concentrations at which some chemical process takes place and thereby influence the speed of the reaction. But we have no direct control over that speed by itself. Or, to take an example from social psychology, we can change the environment of a given individual, but have no direct access to his personality traits.

The identification of causes (or causal factors) proceeds most reliably by the experimental and statistical methods. The canons of experimental inquiry as formulated by J. S. Mill (while never sufficient as definitive *proofs* of causation, may establish at least some inductive probabilities) can be generalized and refined for the field of statistical regularities (correlation-theory and factor-analysis). The usual difficulties encountered here are the "plurality of causes", the "ignored concomitant causal conditions", etc. These difficulties make up *the* major concern of causal (etiological, prognosticative) research in the empirical sciences. But, granting a certain measure of determinism on some level of the investigated phenomena, these difficulties, important (and often exasperating) as they may be, are only practical-technical ones; they have nothing to do with the meaning of "causation". These difficulties can, in principle, be overcome by shrewd techniques of experimentation or statistical analyses.

Prediction may be analyzed as a form of deductive inference from inductive premises (laws, hypotheses, theories) with the help of descriptions or existential hypotheses. The logic of prediction (and of post-diction, i.e., of the reconstruction of past events) is thus precisely the same as that of explanation.

The one remarkable feature in which social-science predictions differ from those in the natural sciences is the well-known fact that once these predictions have been divulged, their very existence (i.e., their being taken cognizance of) may upset the original prediction. It seems at present problematic as to whether it is possible to devise something like a method of convergent successive approximations, in order to take account of the effect of divulged predictions and thus to obviate the notorious difficulty.

This means that on the human level (in addition to the mnemic macrocausality on the animal level in general) we have to take account of goal-directed behavior and of docility. Drives and learning; ingenuity, language, critical reflection and creative novelty are features of the bio-psycho-social realm which have as yet only been sketchily incorporated in the (still-to-be-developed) causal explanations of organic, mental and social phenomena.

The Causal Character of Modern Physical Theory*

ERNEST NAGEL

RECENT DEVELOPMENTS in physical science have made evident the limitations of the theories of classical physics as universally adequate systems of explanation. These developments have also brought under critical scrutiny the validity of many time-honored principles of scientific inquiry. Chief among these is the classical view that the aim of science is the discovery of the causal orders in which the events of nature occur. It is frequently maintained, on the strength of contemporary innovations in physical theory, that the assumption of such orders is no longer warranted, and that the ideal of a universal science of physics whose laws and theories possess a strictly deterministic form must be relinquished as inherently unrealizable. It is with some of the issues involved in these claims that the present paper is concerned.

The problem which the advance of physics has made acute is not the traditional one, much discussed by philosophers, concerning the correct analysis of the meaning of "cause," as this word is employed in familiar practical affairs. Whether the causal relations encountered in these latter contexts are further analyzable, whether at bottom they indicate some kind of necessity or identity, or whether they can be rendered in terms of regular though contingent sequences of events, are alternative views that are irrelevant to the debate stimulated by quantum physics. The current problem is generated by the successes of a comprehensive physical theory which is apparently non-deterministic in its structure, and which is allegedly incompatible with the assumption of an underlying causal pattern for the interactions of the elementary processes postulated by it. In consequence, the questions that require answers are the precise sense in which classical physics is deterministic while current subatomic physics is supposedly not, and the import of recent theoretical innovations for an adequate view of the nature and aims of science.

Accordingly, since classical mechanics is the generally acknowledged paradigm of a deterministic theory, and since the language of current dis-

* Reprinted by kind permission of the author and the publisher from *Freedom and Reason,* pp. 244–268, The Free Press, Glencoe, Ill., 1951.

cussions of determinism is heavily indebted to mechanics for many of its distinctions, I shall first offer a brief account of the nature of determinism in this branch of physics. I shall next generalize a technical notion occurring in mechanics, so as to provide a tool for analyzing the structure of other theories in physics. And finally, I shall argue that though quantum mechanics does indeed exhibit important differences from classical physics, the former is indeterministic only in a somewhat Pickwickian sense, and that the present situation in physics does not necessitate the wholesale rejection of the category of causal determinism.

I

Viewed formally, the theory of mechanics is a set of equations which formulate the dependence of certain traits of bodies in motion on other physical properties. The equations of motion in their Newtonian form assert the dependence of the time-rate of change of the momentum of each "mass-point" belonging to a given physical system—*i.e.*, of each body whose spatial dimensions can be neglected—upon a definite set of other factors, such as the distance of the body from other bodies, their relative masses, and the like. The equations are often said to express causal laws, even though the word "cause" does not occur in them, because they assert that the time-rate of change of a certain magnitude (the momentum of a mass-point) is a definite though generally unspecified function of various other physical properties of mass-points. And for similar reasons a similar locution is frequently employed in other branches of physical science.

A closer examination of the fundamental laws of motion shows them to be linear differential equations which in their general formulation contain an unspecified function, the so-called "force-function." Two important consequences directly follow from this. Before the equations can be applied to a concrete physical problem, the force-function must be specified for the case at hand; that is, a specific assumption must be made concerning the detailed form of the dependence between the time-rate of change in the momentum of a body and other parameters of the physical system to which it belongs. And secondly, since the equations can be used in concrete contexts only in their mathematically integrated form, the values of the constants of integration—two for each body, namely its initial position and initial momentum—must also be assigned. It is a truism that neither the specific form of the force function nor the values of these constants can be deduced from the general theory of motion, and that in principle they must be obtained on the basis of an independent experimental study of the physical system under consideration. Each concrete use of the fundamental theoretical equations of motion thus requires two supplementary assumptions.

Some brief remarks on each of these is now in order. In general, the form of the force-function will vary from case to case, though it is possible to classify these cases into comprehensive types and to prescribe a force-function for each type. For example, the Newtonian theory of gravitation consists in the assumption that the change in the momentum of a body belonging to a system of bodies is a function only of the masses and the mutual distances between members of the system. In point of fact, the force-function employed in many of the familiar applications of the equations of motion is specified in a manner analogous to the Newtonian hypothesis, in so far as it does not contain the time-variable explicitly. Indeed, though there are numerous cases for which the time-variable enters explicitly into the force-function (as in the case of damped vibrations), it is commonly assumed that the explicit presence of the time-variable can in principle be eliminated if the initial system of interacting bodies is suitably enlarged by including other bodies into it. For reasons that will be presently apparent, what is called the "principle of causality" (as distinguished from special causal laws) is in fact usually construed in classical physics as the maxim that should the force-function for a given physical system contain the time-variable explicitly, the system is to be enlarged in such a manner as to allow a specification of the force-function in which the time-variable does not appear.[1] And it is a matter of historical fact that in the main the search for such enlarged systems that do not coincide with the entire cosmos has been successful.

A physical system satisfying the condition that the force-function does not contain the time-variable explicitly possesses the important characteristic that its total mechanical energy is constant in time. But such a system has an even more arresting feature, namely, that what is called its "mechanical state" at one time completely determines its mechanical state at any other time. By the mechanical state of a mass-point at a given time we must understand its position and momentum at that time, where the position and momentum of a particle are said to be the coordinates of mechanical state or the mechanical state-variables. Analogously, the mechanical state of a system consisting of *n* mass-points is the set of values of the coordinates of state of each constituent particle. The mechanical state of a system of bodies whose dimensions cannot be ignored and which, in addition to translatory motions, may exhibit rotations, is defined in a similar manner.

The notion of mechanical state is an important one, and its significance can be conveyed with the help of an idealized example. Suppose S is a system of bodies completely isolated from all other systems. Members of S exhibit various traits (such as mass, distribution in space, motions, etc.) which can be described with the help of a fixed and finite set of predicates "P," "Q," "R," etc. If the specific form of these traits for each member of S were known at a given time t_0, we could say that the state of S is known for that time. Suppose then that at time t_0, S is in a state describable as P_0, Q_0, R_0, etc., that the state of S changes with time, and that at time t_1 S is in a state describable as P_1, Q_1, R_1, etc. Next imagine that S is brought back into the state it originally possessed at time t_0, that it is then permitted to change of its own accord, and that after an interval $t_1 - t_0$ it once more ex-

[1] *Cf.* Silberstein, Ludwik, *Causality*, p. 69 ff.

hibits the state describable as P_1, Q_1, R_1, that is, its state is once more what it was at time t_1. A system which always behaved in this manner would be one in which its state at one time uniquely determined its state at any other time.

Let us now complicate this abstract example. Suppose that in addition to the preceding it is possible to establish a set of general laws L which enable us, given the state of the system S at one time, to deduce the formulation of the state at any other time. It would then be theoretically possible to predict the state of the system at any time, given the state of the system at some initial time. On the other hand, if the number of predicates needed to characterize the state of S were very large, it would not be feasible practically to formulate the state or to discover the laws L. Let us therefore assume that there is a small subset in the total set of predicates required to characterize the state of S completely—for example, the subset consisting of the two predicates "P" and "Q"—which is a sufficient basis for defining the remaining predicates or for formulating general laws connecting the predicates in the subset and all the others. On this assumption, a knowledge of the specific nature of the traits expressed by the predicates in the subset enables us to conclude to the specific nature of the remaining traits of members of S, and therefore to the state of S. Accordingly, the laws L need only formulate the connections between the traits in the subset at one time and these traits at any other time, in order to enable us to infer the state of S at any time, given the traits in the subset at some initial time. Under the circumstances, therefore, it will be useful to amend slightly the original meaning of "the state of the system S," and to stipulate that the relatively small number of predicates in the subset will characterize the state of S.

The relevance of this abstract example for the analysis of mechanics is perhaps obvious. Physical bodies exhibit various properties which are the special concern of the science of mechanics and which may therefore be called "mechanical properties." Moreover, all the mechanical properties of a system at a given time are in effect specified, if for that time the properties formulated by the mechanical coordinates of state are known; for example, if the position and momentum of a mass-point is given, its kinetic energy can be readily calculated. Accordingly, given the laws of motion and the specific form of the force-function, together with the mechanical state of the system for some specified initial instant, the mechanical state of the system for any other time—and therefore the full complexion of its mechanical properties—is uniquely determined.

It is this feature of the laws of classical mechanics which is the basis for characterizing the theory of mechanics as "deterministic." Certainly it is this feature that Laplace had in mind when he declared in a well-known passage that for an intelligence acquainted with the positions of all material particles and with the forces acting between them "the future as well as the past would be present to its eyes." For Laplace as well as for most of his 19th century successors, a satisfactory physical theory was one which conformed to the norm exhibited by analytical mechanics. Their ideal for physics was a theory which is deterministic in the sense that it employs a definition of physical state quite like that of classical mechanics, and that it makes possible, given an initial state of a system, the calculation of a unique state for any other time.

II

Some further comments must now be added to this brief account of mechanics, so that the notion of physical state, thus far developed only for this science, may be extended to other branches of classical physics.

(1) It requires only passing mention that classical mechanics like any branch of inquiry is concerned only with a limited set of physical properties. The laws of mechanics can in fact explicitly deal only with those changes in physical systems which are expressible in terms of the mechanical coordinates of state in the manner indicated previously. At the same time, it is worth stressing that though classical mechanics is a deterministic theory, it is deterministic specifically and exclusively with respect to the mechanical states of system. Thus, given only the initial positions of a set of bodies, or given only the initial kinetic energy of such a system, mechanics does not enable us to calculate the positions or the kinetic energy for any other time. Again, the laws of mechanics assert nothing about electro-magnetic properties, and cannot be used to calculate variations in the magnitudes of such properties, however much may be known concerning the initial mechanical state of a system of bodies or concerning the forces operating between them. Quite clearly, then, a non-sequitur is involved in Laplace's dictum that "nothing would be uncertain" for an intelligence possessing a requisite knowledge of mechanical states and forces. His claim can be regarded as warranted only if it is understood to mean that a sufficiently vast intelligence, knowing the mechanical state of the universe at one time, would be able to calculate the *mechanical state* of the universe at any other time. In brief, the determinism of classical mechanics is relative to physical states specified in terms of the mechanical coordinates of state.

(2) It is also important not to overlook the simple yet frequently ignored point that mechanics as a physical theory is not a descriptive account, whether partial or complete, of the actual course of events. For not only is that theory relevant only to certain selected phases of things—all discourse is selective in this sense. That theory expresses only a framework of abstract relations, and it is formulated with the help of notions that are defined as ideal limits of hypothetical observations rather than in terms of anything that is experimentally identifiable. For as already noted, the fundamental laws of mechanics must be supplemented by two distinct types of information before they can be put to actual use: by a special assumption concerning the forces involved in a given system, and by information concerning the initial mechanical state of the system. Moreover, and this is of

particular importance for the present theme, classical mechanics is formulated as a set of differential equations, so that in consequence it is the "instantaneous" coordinates of mechanical state that are required to be known in the application of the theory. However, instantaneous positions and momenta are never experimental data, for actual observation can ascertain the positions and momenta of bodies only during some non-vanishing interval of time.

The determinism characterizing mechanics must therefore be understood as holding only relative to the *theoretical* specification of mechanical state, according to which the coordinates of state are *instantaneous* positions and momenta. It is quite a different issue, not capable of being settled merely by analyzing the formal structure of mechanical theory, whether initial positions and momenta of bodies *as measured experimentally* uniquely determine positions and momenta *similarly* measured at any other time.

This last point requires some expansion. The classical coordinates of mechanical state are instantaneous individual coordinates: each individual mass-point is assumed to possess an instantaneous position and momentum, and the predication of such positions and momenta does not in principle rest upon any statistical assumption or procedure. On the other hand, in experimental practice one never encounters anything that *literally* satisfies the conditions defining a mass-point, even if in the interest of applying theoretical analysis one may treat as "points" bodies whose dimensions are small when compared to the distances separating them. Again, the positions and momenta assigned to bodies on the basis of actual measurement are obtained by studying the behavior of bodies over some non-vanishing interval of time; and in consequence, experimentally evaluated positions and momenta are never instantaneous. Indeed, from the standpoint of the *theoretical* requirements for the coordinates of mechanical state, the values obtained for these coordinates by experiment are *average* values which involve some *statistical* assumptions. Thus, if the velocity of a body is ascertained by measuring the distance it moves during one second, from the standpoint of theory the value so obtained is simply a mean of the "instantaneous" velocities the body possesses during that second. Classical physics tacitly assumes that the temporal interval involved in measuring the coordinates of state may, in principle, be progressively diminished without limit. Nevertheless, this assumption is clearly not fully congruous with the facts of experimental procedure; for however refined techniques of measurement may become, they cannot yield instantaneous values but only what, from the perspective of theory, are merely statistically defined functions of such values. To be sure, there is a well-known procedure for bringing into concordance the theoretical definition of mechanical state with the magnitudes for coordinates of state obtained by overt measurement. But this procedure is based on the theory of experimental errors, and involves the adoption of statistical hypotheses concerning the frequencies with which various experimentally ascertained magnitudes occur. In any event, the fact remains that the relations of dependence which mechanical theory asserts can be ascertained to hold between properties whose experimentally determined magnitudes, from the standpoint of theory, are statistical coefficients.

It is sometimes concluded from considerations such as these that even classical mechanics is not a deterministic theory and is only approximately one. It has been maintained, for example, that if the mechanical state of a system is specified in "observational terms," the laws of mechanics assert no more than relations of probability or statistical correlation between states at different times. On this view, the formulation of the laws of mechanics as strictly universal statements represents simply an idealization, an idealization justified because the coefficients of probability are close to the maximum value of 1, so that the discrepancy between the true value of the probability and this maximum can be neglected in practice.

But this conception of the matter is based on the assumption that all theories, and the theory of mechanics in particular, are simply generalized descriptive formulations of the actual sequences of events encountered in experience; and some reasons have already been stated for questioning such an assumption. Moreover, and for the present paper this is the central point, the view under consideration appears to confound two issues which need to be kept distinct: the question as to what is the *logical structure* of a given theory, and the question as to the relevance of an abstract theory to observational data and the degree of agreement between the theory and experiment. It is hardly more than a truism to maintain that classical mechanics is "indeterministic" or statistical in nature, if the claim rests on no other grounds than that the experimental confirmation of classical mechanics involves the use of statistical procedures and that experiment confirms it only approximately. For any quantitatively formulated theory viewed from this standpoint is "indeterministic" and statistical: the experimental measurement of physical magnitudes such as velocity always yields a "spread" of values, and no law asserting a relation of dependence between continuous variables is in absolutely precise agreement with data of observation. Nonetheless, when a theory is analyzed for its logical structure, it may possess features that can be properly labelled as "deterministic" with respect to some *theoretical* definition of physical state. And if classical mechanics is so analyzed it is without question a deterministic theory relative to the theoretical definition of mechanical state.

(3) But it is time to remind ourselves that mechanics is not the only branch of classical physics, and that mechanics is not the only physical theory with a deterministic structure. Moreover, even a cursory survey of other branches of physical science provides evidence for the conclusion that there are other ways of defining the state of a physical system than that employed in mechanics. However, the task of exhibiting these alternative ways requires attention to much technical detail, and it will not be attempted here. Instead, a short list will be constructed which will present in a schematic way definitions of physical state alternative to the one adopted

in mechanics. The list does not pretend to be exhaustive, and it undoubtedly suffers from oversimplification. But in spite of its faults it may make clear the existence of genuine alternatives to the mechanical definition of physical state, and thus provide a helpful perspective for viewing current discussions of the causal character of a quantum theory.

Let us note once more that the mechanical state of a system is defined in terms of the instantaneous values of two coordinates for each mass-point belonging to the system, each coordinate being the magnitude of a property that is meaningfully predicable only of individual mass-points. Since the number of such particles is always finite even if it is large, the mechanical state of a system as a whole is thus specified by a finite number of values of the state coordinates.

The classical definition of mechanical state therefore involves distinctions which immediately suggest a way for classifying alternatives to it. In the first place, a physical state might be defined with the help of an *infinite* rather than a finite number of values of some set of parameters. Such a definition is in fact employed by so-called "field theories," and in particular by electro-magnetic theory, which requires the state of an electro-magnetic field to be specified by the values of two vectors at each point (infinite in number) of the field. In the second place, instead of defining a physical state in terms of *instantaneous* values of state coordinates, the definition might require the values of state parameters at *several* distinct instants or *during* some continuous temporal stretch. This is the alternative mode of defining physical states adopted by theories devised for handling the phenomena of magnetic hysteresis and metal fatigue, and in general is typical of what is sometimes called "hereditary mechanics." And in the third place, a physical state might be defined with the help of certain *statistical* rather than *individual* coordinates. This is the alternative adopted in certain portions of statistical mechanics and, as will eventually appear, in modern quantum mechanics.

There are therefore at least three pairs of alternative requirements which may be used in defining the physical state of a system: the state may have to be specified with the help of either a finite or an infinite number of values of certain coordinates; the values of the coordinates may be instantaneous or involve reference to some non-vanishing duration; and the state coordinates may be individual coordinates or statistical parameters. Accordingly, since there are no relations of logical dependence between alternatives belonging to these different pairs, there are at least eight specifically different ways in which the state of a physical system might be defined. However, only a few of these eight ways appear to have been employed in the history of modern science.

It follows in any event that it is an error to suppose that a theory can be deterministic only if it employs the mechanical definition of physical state. Neither electro-magnetic theory nor the theory of heat flow, for example. defines the notion of physical state in terms of the positions and momenta of particles, and yet each of these theories is deterministic in the same general sense as is classical mechanics: each of these theories establishes a unique correspondence between the theoretical definition of state at one time and the state at any other time.

This conclusion is perhaps obvious and even trivial. For it does not appear to be possible [2] to specify in detail what is the appropriate definition of physical state for a given domain of phenomena until one is in possession of an adequate theory which is deterministic relative to some definition of state. Indeed, the very meaning of "physical state of a system" entails the conclusion that whenever one can specify what is the physical state for a given system, there is available a theory which is deterministic with respect to that physical state. What is not trivial in the above conclusion is that in point of fact theories having a deterministic form, but not employing the mechanical definition of physical state, have been used successfully in several branches of natural science.

III

What light do these various considerations throw on the alleged acausal nature of modern quantum theory? Physicists with years of specialized training and experience are not in agreement on this matter; and a layman who ventures to discuss it risks committing first-class blunders. But even if blunder has not been avoided in the following quite general remarks, they may succeed in bringing into focus central issues in the analysis of quantum theory.

Whether quantum theory is formulated with the help of the Schrödinger wave-equation or the Heisenberg matrix algebra, it successfully accounts for a vast range of phenomena by adopting assumptions concerning processes interior to atoms. As in the case of all theories which postulate sub-microscopic entities, the empirical evidence supporting the various assumptions of quantum theory is indirect and is obtained through experiments conducted in familiar macroscopic domains. In this respect there is nothing novel in quantum theory.

The feature of modern quantum theory which has precipitated acute debate over the status of the principle of causality in recent physics is the deduction from its fundamental assumptions of the Heisenberg Uncertainty Relations. The formula which expresses one of these relations is: $\Delta p.\Delta q \geqq h$. Since "$q$" and "$p$" are usually construed as the coordinates of position and momentum of electrons, protons, and other subatomic elements, "Δq" and "Δp" represent the dispersion of values or the "error" obtained in ascertaining the values of these coordinates by measurement. Accordingly, the above formula is commonly interpreted to assert that the product of the accuracy with which the simultaneous position and the momentum of a subatomic element can be measured is constant. It then fol-

[2] *Cf.* Frank, Philipp, *Modern Science and Its Philosophy*, pp. 53–60.

lows that if one of these coordinates is measured with great precision, the value of the conjugate coordinate becomes quite imprecise; and in particular, if the position of an electron is ascertained with a high degree of accuracy, so that $\triangle q$ is practically zero, then the range $\triangle p$ is practically infinite, so that no determinate value can be assigned to the momentum of the "particle."

It is the occurrence of such Uncertainty Relations within modern quantum mechanics that is held to mark the indeterministic character of that theory. For since the simultaneous positions and momenta of elementary particles cannot be ascertained with unlimited precision, so the argument often runs, the laws of quantum mechanics cannot establish a unique correspondence between positions and momenta at one time and positions and momenta at other times. But since quantum theory does make it possible to calculate the probability with which a particle has a certain momentum when it has a certain position (and vice versa), that theory has an inherent statistical nature though it fails to conform to the requirements of a strictly deterministic theory.

Before examining this fundamental thesis, it will be desirable to consider briefly some of the "explanations" and "interpretations" that have been proposed for the Uncertainty Relations. But we can dismiss as irrelevant the suggestion advanced by some physicists, philosophers and theologians that the Uncertainty Relations express the operation of some sort of "free-will"; and we can likewise dismiss as unilluminating the conception according to which the Uncertainty Relations are evidence for some "radical indeterminism" and "objective chance," where these expressions signify substantival agents of change.

A more sober and prima facie plausible account of the Uncertainty Relations is that they express the relatively large but unaccountable modifications in certain features of subatomic elements, resulting from the interaction between these elements and the instruments of measurement. Heisenberg declares, for example, that though when dealing with large-scale phenomena the effect of instruments of measurement upon the objects measured can be neglected, simply because the magnitudes of the disturbances thus produced are relatively small, in the case of subatomic physics

> the interaction between observer and object causes uncontrollable and large changes in the system being observed, because of the discontinuous character of atomic processes. The immediate consequence of this circumstance is that in general every experiment performed to determine some numerical quantity renders the knowledge of others illusory, since the uncontrollable perturbation of the observed system alters the values of previously determined quantities.[3]

An alternative interpretation of the Uncertainty Relations maintains that they require us to abandon the hope of explaining "all phenomena as relations between objects existing in space and time." The ultimate ground for the failure of the principle of causality in subatomic physics, so propo-

[3] Heisenberg, Werner, *The Physical Principles of the Quantum Theory*, p. 3.

nents of this interpretation urge, is the impossibility of describing subatomic processes in terms of spatio-temporal notions that are adequate only for macroscopic objects. As Heisenberg puts the matter:

> There exists a body of exact mathematical laws, but they cannot be interpreted as expressing simple relationships between objects existing in space and time. The observable predictions of this theory can be approximately described in such terms, but not uniquely. . . .[4]

He therefore proposes the following alternatives: Either we continue to describe subatomic processes in familiar spatio-temporal terms, but at the price of abandoning the possibility of giving causal explanations for those processes; or we retain the possibility of providing such causal explanations, but at the cost of forswearing the interpretation of mathematically formulated causal laws in familiar spatio-temporal terms.

In spite of the high authority supporting these interpretations of the Uncertainty Relations, they are not fully persuasive. Thus, the plausibility of the first-mentioned interpretation is somewhat diminished if it is noted that the Uncertainty Relations are not obtained from a consideration of the experimental facts of measurement, but are simply the consequences of the fundamental assumptions of quantum theory. Thus, the disturbing effect of instruments of measurement on what they measure is well recognized in classical physics, without requiring the adoption of any Uncertainty Relations; for in classical physics the extent of such disturbance can be calculated, at least in principle, with the help of established physical laws. But on the present interpretation of the Uncertainty Relations the central point consists in denying the possibility of calculating such disturbances even in principle, because these latter are the outcome of "uncontrollable changes." There does not, however, appear to be any direct evidence for such uncontrollable changes. Accordingly, if the Uncertainty Relations are accepted, they must be accepted not because of the fact (known in classical physics) that measuring instruments interact with what they measure, but because those Relations follow from the assumptions of quantum theory. Moreover, these Relations set no limits upon the precision with which, say, the coordinate of position of an electron may be measured. In spite of the supposed interaction between electron and measuring apparatus, the coordinate of position is in principle ascertainable with absolute precision. It cannot be the occurrence of such interactions which makes impossible the absolutely precise determination of position and momentum simultaneously.

The second interpretation of the Uncertainty Relations, according to which these Relations set limits upon the explanation of subatomic processes in terms of spatio-temporally localizable objects, does raise an important point, though the manner in which the interpretation is formulated obscures the main issue. The point which requires attention is that when electrons,

[4] *Op. cit.*, p. 64.

protons and other postulated elements of subatomic physics are described as "particles" or "waves," these latter characterizations are used only on the strength of certain analogies. Can it be perchance that these elements cannot be described in spatio-temporal terms, not because spatio-temporal notions are not adequate for subatomic processes, but simply because electrons, protons, etc., are not particles or waves in the familiar and established senses of these terms? This is a suggestion which is at least worth exploring, and in what immediately follows it is proposed to examine the language of quantum theory more closely, in the hope that thereby the allegedly acausal nature of the theory will appear in clearer light.

(1) The subatomic entities postulated by quantum theory are frequently described in a language generally used to describe the mass-points of classical physics. The use of this language thus leads directly to the supposition that the subatomic particles possess both determinate positions and velocities at any time. However, in consequence of the Uncertainty Relations one is also compelled to say that the simultaneous position and velocity of such a particle cannot be determined with unlimited precision. Accordingly, the language employed in discussions of subatomic particles seems to imply that while such particles really do possess absolutely determinate positions and momenta at any instant, it just happens that we cannot possibly discover what their simultaneous values are—although the particles do have certain determinate properties, the simultaneous values of the magnitudes of the properties are inherently inaccessible to human knowledge.

Such a conclusion, were it really necessitated by the facts, would require at least the partial abandonment of the ideal of verifiability which dominates modern science. It is essential to recall, however, that the conclusion depends on characterizing subatomic entities as particles. At the same time, it is only certain formal analogies with the classical conception of particle which lead physicists to employ the particle language in connection with these entities. These analogies, as is well known, are not complete and break down at various points. Physicists are keenly aware of the failures in the analogies, and have felt compelled to amend the particle language used to describe subatomic processes by supplementing it with the language of waves travelling in media. However, the language of waves like the language of particles has been introduced out of considerations of analogy between certain processes familiar from classical physics, and the structure of processes associated with subatomic entities; and as in the case of particles, the wave analogy also breaks down at various crucial points.

Let us therefore keep in mind what the actual situation in quantum physics is like. The fundamental assumptions of quantum theory are expressed with the help of a highly complex mathematical formalism, and once the conditions for applying this formalism to concrete empirical material are specified the content of the theory is contained in that formalism. Nonetheless, it is heuristically advantageous to express the content of the formalism in other ways, for example in terms of more or less visualizable models patterned after more familiar types of physical processes; and in the attempt to do just this, physicists have been led to employ the language developed in connection with the classical notions of particles and waves.[5] At the same time, the formally stated equations of quantum mechanics must be taken to define *implicitly* the various subatomic entities thus postulated, however else these entities are construed; and whatever further characteristics may be associated with these entities, these latter must satisfy the formally expressed conditions or relations of the equations of the theory. Accordingly, the various consequences which are logically derivable from the fundamental equations of the theory—and in particular, the Uncertainty Relations—must be taken as constituting *partial definitions* of what these entities and their properties are.

Thus if certain measurable traits of electrons, to which the names "position" and "velocity" are assigned, must satisfy the conditions stated in the Uncertainty Relations, then these traits in spite of their names must be clearly distinguished from what in classical physics is understood by "position" and "velocity" of "particles." For although in quantum theory the parameters "q" and "p" are *called* the coordinates of "position" and "momentum" of "particles," these words are obviously being employed in unusual senses. According to the usage associated with them in classical physics, a particle has a determinate position and simultaneously a determinate momentum. On that usage it is simply nonsense to say that a particle has a definite position but no determinate momentum, or vice versa; for the meanings of the words are so interrelated that nothing can be said to be a particle which does not possess a determinate position and momentum. It follows that when the formalism of quantum mechanics is interpreted, and electrons are introduced as particles which are precluded by the theory from having determinate values simultaneously for both the properties symbolized by the "q's" and "p's," then either an electron is not a particle in the customary

[5] Consider the following account, contained in a standard textbook on quantum mechanics: "Our store of direct knowledge regarding the nature of the system known as the hydrogen atom consists in the results of a large number of experiments—spectroscopic, chemical, etc. It is found that all the known facts about this system can be correlated and systematized (and, we say, explained) by associating with this system a certain wave equation. Our confidence in the significance of this association increases when predictions regarding previously uninvestigated properties of the hydrogen atom are subsequently verified by experiment. We might then describe the hydrogen atom by giving its wave equation; this description would be complete. It is unsatisfactory, however, because it is unwieldy. On observing that there is a formal relation between this wave equation and the classical energy equation for a system of two particles of different masses and electrical charges, we seize on this as providing a simple, easy, and familiar way of describing the system, and we say that the hydrogen atom consists of two particles, the electron and proton, which attract each other according to Coulomb's inverse-square law. Actually we do not know that the electron and protron attract each other in the same way that two macroscopic electrically charged bodies do, inasmuch as the force between the two particles in a hydrogen atom has never been directly measured. All that we know is that the wave equation for the hydrogen atom bears a certain formal relation to the classical dynamical equations for a system of two particles attracting each other in this way." Linus Pauling and E. Bright Wilson, *Introduction to Quantum Mechanics*, p. 56.

sense of the word, or these symbols cannot refer to positions and momenta in the customary senses of these words.

It is thus simply not the case that certain crucial expressions as used in quantum theory denote the identical traits of things which those expressions signify in classical physics. And outstanding physicists have often called attention to just this point,[6] even if they have not always made the best use of their insight. The use of the language of classical physics in the context of subatomic research is unquestionably valuable, for it calls attention to important analogies and so suggests fresh directions for inquiry. But the use of that language can also be a handicap, in so far as it prevents its users from recognizing important failures in analogy and therefore encourages them to raise misleading questions.

The point under discussion will perhaps be reinforced if we recall another historically important adaptation of old language to new contexts—that which occurred when the word "number" was extended from its use in connection with cardinal and ordinal integers to other kinds of mathematical "entities." As is well known, various operations were first developed for the cardinals (*e.g.*, addition, multiplication, and their inverses), and with their help certain properties of these numbers were defined (*e.g.*, being a perfect square, being odd or even, etc.). Presently, however, the use of the word "number" was extended so as to apply to the ratios of cardinals (usually represented as fractions); for definite operations can be introduced for the ratios of integers which are closely analogous to the operations upon cardinals themselves. Thus, ratios can be "added" and "multiplied," and these new operations exhibit formal patterns which—up to a point—are abstractly the same as the patterns that are exhibited by cardinal addition and multiplication. Nevertheless though the ratios of integers possess many properties that are analogous to those possessed by the cardinals, there are also properties characterizing the latter which are simply not defined for the former. Thus, the property of being a perfect square can be significantly predicated of both cardinals and ratios of cardinals; but the property of being odd (or even) is not defined for the ratios. We are thus unable to answer the question whether ⅔ is odd or even; but our inability stems neither from an insufficiency in our knowledge nor from any inherent in-

[6] For example, von Neumann declares that it would be entirely meaningless to distinguish between a term p.q and a term q.p, if these are construed in the sense specified by classical mechanics. J. von Neumann, *Mathematische Grundlagen der Quantenmechanik*, p. 6. Heisenberg notes that the "uncertainty relation specifies the limits within which the particle picture can be applied. Any use of the words 'position' and 'velocity' with an accuracy exceeding that given by the Uncertainty equation is just as meaningless as the use of words whose sense is not defined." *Op. cit.*, p. 6. And Schrödinger remarks, in commenting on the indeterminacy which quantum mechanics ascribes to material particles, that "On a little reflection it will be clear that the object referred to by quantum mechanics in this connection is not a material point in the old sense of the word. . . . It should neither be disputed nor passed over in tactful silence (as is done in certain quarters) that the concept of the material point undergoes a considerable change which as yet we fail thoroughly to understand." Erwin Schrödinger, *Science and the Human Temperament*, pp. 71–2.

accessibility of properties of ratios—it stems simply from the fact that expressions like "$\frac{2}{3}$ is odd" have no defined sense. And what has just been said in brief about ratios applies with no less force to other entities that have been introduced in the development of mathematics and in the so-called extension of the "number concept"—for example, to matrices and to the failure of the commutative law for matrix multiplication. If anyone views this failure as a paradox, on the ground that the "essential nature" of multiplication requires it to be commutative, he needs to be reminded that the fact is a paradox only because the word "multiplication" is borrowed from one context (in which the operation it names *is* commutative) and then used as a designation for a quite distinct (though in some respect analogous) operation in another context.

In a similar way the quantum-mechanical use of the words "position," "velocity" and "particle" in connection with subatomic elements is to be viewed as an extension of their use in classical physics—an extension that depends on there being certain formal analogies between the mathematical formalism of quantum and classical mechanics. At the same time the actual sense of these expressions in their newer context of usage must be construed in terms of the restrictions imposed upon their possible meanings by the fundamental equations of quantum theory. And since the formal prescriptions which are imposed by quantum and classical physics are different, what these words mean in quantum mechanics is clearly different from their original meanings. To maintain that if we knew enough or had better experimental techniques we might obtain the precise simultaneous values for the "position" and "velocity" of electrons, is to overlook the capital point that in quantum mechanics these expressions are so defined that whatever is designated by them *must* satisfy the conditions stated in the Uncertainty Relations.

(2) It follows from what has now been said that quantum mechanics cannot rightly be characterized as an indeterministic theory merely on the ground that the Uncertainty Relations play an integral role in it. For if the above considerations are at all cogent, it is invalid to conclude that the "position" and "momenta" which these Relations declare to be conjugately uncertain, are identifiable with traits of particles which classical mechanics declares to be subject to a deterministic order.

But another and independent point requires to be made. The view that quantum mechanics is indeterministic rests on the assumption that this theory, like classical mechanics, specifies the physical state of a system in terms of the coordinates of position and momentum. If this assumption could be safely made, there would be at least prima facie reason for the conclusion erected upon it. For since it is impossible to specify at any time the simultaneous instantaneous values of position and momentum for a subatomic "particle," it is obviously impossible to calculate a unique value for these coordinates for some other time.

However, it is just this assumption that requires to be examined: for even if quantum theory is not deterministic with respect to a state description defined in terms of "positions" and "momenta," it does not follow that it may not be quite deterministic with respect to a different state description. And in point of fact, inspection of the formal statements of quantum mechanics does show that this theory does not employ a state description like that of classical mechanics, but that with respect to a mode of state description adopted by the theory it is deterministic in form. The heart of the matter can be stated very succinctly: If quantum theory is considered in its wave-mechanical formulation, the state description adopted by the theory is defined in terms of a certain function, the so-called Psi-function. Moreover, the wave equation has the important property that given the value of this function at one instant and assuming that the boundary conditions for the equation remain fixed, the equation assigns a unique value for that function for any other instant. Quantum mechanics is therefore deterministic with respect to the quantum-mechanical description of state.

Nevertheless, it is not possible to interpret the quantum-mechanical state description in terms of any visualizable model of physical processes. In particular, neither a picture in terms of the motions of classical particles, nor one in terms of the behavior of classical waves, can be used to give a satisfactory "intuitive" or "physical" interpretation for the Psi-function. Just in what way the quantum-mechanical formalism is employed for analyzing and bringing into a system various classes of experimentally ascertained phenomena is a difficult technical problem, far beyond the scope and competence of the present paper. In rough outline the matter appears to be somewhat as follows. The Psi-function is itself complex (in the technical mathematical sense), but the square of its amplitude is of course real (again in the strict mathematical sense). Moreover, the square of this amplitude can be associated with the probability that the electrons for which the Psi-function is the state description occupy a certain region and possess energies of specified magnitudes. The numerical value of this probability can be estimated from experimental data, though these data do not establish a unique value for the Psi-function itself. Accordingly, though quantum mechanics is deterministic with respect to the Psi-function, this function does not possess a direct experimental significance; experiment is capable of ascertaining the initial value of the amplitude of this function, but not the initial value of the function itself. Moreover, both the data that must be supplied to work the wave equation for any concrete case, as well as the physically significant consequences that can be derived from that equation, have a statistical form. For this reason, though quantum mechanics is deterministic with respect to the Psi-function as the state description, it is nevertheless maintained by outstanding quantum theorists that quantum theory is "in the nature of the case indeterministic, and therefore the affair of statistics." [7]

[7] Born, Max, *Atomic Physics*, p. 90.

But it is perhaps worth emphasizing that when the amplitude of the Psi-function is interpreted as a probability—as the relative frequency with which certain types of elementary processes occur—a definite model or picture of physical changes is still being employed. Taken by itself this is not objectionable. However, the model may become an obstacle to understanding if it leads us to suppose that certain properties of electrons and the like, conceived on the pattern of classical particles, are inherently unknowable because of the alleged "indeterministic" nature of the postulated elements. For we must not lose sight of the basic point that though quantum theory is interpreted in terms of some physical model, the equations of the theory do establish unique correspondence between what, from the standpoint of the model, are average values of the magnitudes of properties characterizing the elements of the model. When it is said, for example, that a single electron has some specified configuration or behavior, what needs to be understood by such a statement is that a certain parameter, characterizing the statistical distribution of the properties of a large class of electrons, possesses a certain value and is associated with a certain coefficient of dispersion. And in any event, the equations of quantum theory are so constructed that the value of such a parameter and of its associated dispersion coefficient at one instant uniquely determine the corresponding values of these coordinates at any other instant. It is clear therefore that in terms of the model employed in reading the equations of the theory, the initial data that need to be supplied in applying the theory to a concrete case are interpreted in statistical terms. It should not therefore be surprising or appear paradoxical that all the conclusions obtained with the help of the theory from such data also require to be construed in statistical terms, and do not supply information about any individual member of the statistical aggregate. It would be surprising and paradoxical if the outcome were otherwise.

The remarks of the preceding paragraph are not intended as an argument for some such conclusions as that, since quantum mechanics is deterministic with respect to a statistically specified state-description, there are no important differences between quantum and classical physics. Such a conclusion would be quite incongruous with the known facts, and such a conclusion is not intended. The point of those remarks is to suggest that when quantum theory is characterized as "indeterministic," a tacit interpretation of the formalism of the theory in terms of the behavior of postulated statistical aggregates is being made, while at the same time the use of state descriptions defined in terms of statistical coordinates of state is employed as the sole ground for the characterization. However, if the above analysis of alternative ways for defining the state of a physical system has any merit, that characterization ignores a feature of quantum theory that is at least as central as the one it so emphatically notes.

IV

The belief that subatomic processes are acausal has been often used as the foundation for the further claim that causal laws for macroscopic phenomena cannot be validly affirmed. The argument for this conclusion appears to be as follows. Macroscopic objects are complex structures of subatomic ones; hence the properties possessed by the former can occur only under conditions specifiable in terms of the arrangements and behaviors of the latter. But the behavior of subatomic objects is, by hypothesis, acausal, and the laws formulating this behavior are statistical; hence the interrelations and behaviors of macroscopic objects are also acausal, and the laws formulating them must be indeterministic. Various further consequences have been drawn from this conclusion, among others a number dealing with questions of human freedom and responsible action; but this aspect of the matter will not be pursued here any further.

One premise in this argument—namely, that the laws of quantum physics are indeterministic—has already been examined at considerable length, and has been found not to be fully warranted. However, even if this premise is granted, the argument is less than conclusive; and the remainder of the present paper will attempt to show why it is not.

A tacit assumption in the argument is the view that if a complex is analyzable into a structure of constituent elements, whether these be absolutely or only relatively "simple," the elements are in some special but not altogether clear sense more "ultimate" than or "metaphysically" prior to the complexes. What is perhaps meant is that no property or character has an indisputable place in an account of nature unless such a property can be predicated of the elements into which complexes may be analyzed. But if this is what the assumption means, it is a difficult one to warrant, and there is much to be said against it. Indeed, if the properties which macroscopic objects manifestly possess could be counted among the genuine features of nature only if their more elementary constituents possessed them, there would be no point in developing theoretical explanations for the behavior of macroscopic objects in terms of their elementary parts—for in that case the elementary parts would simply be diminutive duplicates of the macroscopic objects, and would possess all the traits whose very explanation is being sought. In point of fact, when a comprehensive body of theory makes intelligible the behavior of gross objects in terms of microscopic and submicroscopic elements, special laws must be assumed which connect the manifest traits of complexes with certain other traits of the elements; and the presence of such laws would be fatuously absurd, were not the traits of complexes not possessed by their elementary constituents as genuine features of the world as the traits of the elements are assumed to be.

It must also be noted that the phenomenal traits of gross objects do not correspond in a simple one-to-one fashion with the traits and distributions of subatomic elements. Indeed, the central idea in the statistical laws of modern physics is that to a given trait of gross objects—for brevity, let us refer to such trait as a "macro-state"—there corresponds a large number of theoretically possible and distinct combinations (or "micro-states") of the elements. According to classical statistical mechanics, for example, a given state of temperature of a gas corresponds to the mean kinetic energy of the molecules of the gas: the given macro-state thus corresponds to any one of a large number of alternative distributions in the molecular velocities, these alternatives being subject only to the condition that the mean kinetic energy be the same for each. Even if the subatomic elements exhibit only statistical regularities and are not subject to strictly deterministic laws—so that the occurrence of a given micro-state does not uniquely determine some *one* micro-state for another time, but is compatible with the occurrence of *a number of distinct* micro-states at that time—it does not therefore follow that the *macro-states* corresponding to these alternative micro-states are necessarily distinct. In short, though the laws connecting micro-states may be statistical in their structure, the laws connecting the macro-states that correspond to them may nevertheless have a strictly deterministic form.

If these remarks have merit, it follows that the determinate orders in which observable phenomena are found to occur when observable conditions for their occurrence are instituted, are not placed in jeopardy by researches into subatomic process. Such researches certainly enlarge our knowledge through the discovery of hitherto unnoticed factors upon which the occurrence of observable phenomena depends. But the discovery that subatomic processes do not exhibit the same modes of interconnection as do the macroscopic objects of which they are constituents, does not disprove the orders we have established for the latter or reduce them to illusion.

The Two Concepts of Probability *

RUDOLF CARNAP

I. The Problem of Probability

The problem of probability may be regarded as the task of finding an adequate definition of the concept of probability that can provide a basis for a theory of probability. This task is not one of defining a new concept but rather of redefining an old one. Thus we have here an instance of that kind of problem—often important in the development of science and mathematics—where a concept already in use is to be made more exact or, rather, is to be replaced by a more exact new concept. Let us call these problems (in an adaptation of the terminology of Kant and Husserl) problems of *explication;* in each case of an explication, we call the old concept, used in a more or less vague way either in every-day language or in an earlier stage of scientific language, the *explicandum;* the new, more exact concept which is proposed to take the place of the old one the *explicatum.* Thus, for instance, the definition of the cardinal number three by Frege and Russell as the class of all triples was meant as an explication; the explicandum was the ordinary meaning of the word 'three' as it appears in every-day life and in science; the concept of the class of all triples (defined not by means of the word 'triple' but with the help of existential quantifiers and the sign of identity) was proposed as an explicatum for the explicandum mentioned.

Using these terms, we may say that the problem of probability is the problem of finding an adequate explication of the word 'probability' in its ordinary meaning, or in one of its meanings if there are several.

II. The Logical Concepts of Confirmation

In the preparation for our subsequent discussion of the problem of probability, let us examine some concepts which are connected with the scientific procedure of confirming or disconfirming hypotheses on the basis of results found by observation.

The procedure of confirmation is a complex one consisting of components of different kinds. In the present discussion, we shall be concerned

* Reprinted by kind permission of the author and the editor, with slight changes, from *Philosophy and Phenomenological Research,* 5, 1945.

only with what may be called the logical side of confirmation, namely, with certain logical relations between sentences (or propositions expressed by these sentences). Within the procedure of confirmation, these relations are of interest to the scientist, for instance, in the following situation: He intends to examine a certain hypothesis *h*; he makes many observations of particular events which he regards as relevant for judging the hypothesis *h*; he formulates this evidence, the results of all observations made, or as many of them as are relevant, in a report *e*, which is a long sentence. Then he tries to decide whether and to what degree the hypothesis *h* is confirmed by the observational evidence *e*. It is with this decision alone that we shall be concerned. Once the hypothesis is formulated by *h* and the observational results by *e*, then this question as to whether and how much *h* is confirmed by *e* can be answered merely by a logical analysis of *h* and *e* and their relations. Therefore the question is a logical one. It is not a question of fact in the sense that knowledge of empirical fact is required to find the answer. Although the sentences *h* and *e* under consideration do themselves certainly refer to facts, nevertheless once *h* and *e* are given, the question of confirmation requires only that we are able to understand them, i.e., grasp their meanings, and to discover certain relations which are based upon their meanings. If by semantics [1] we understand the theory of the meanings of expressions, and especially of sentences, in a language then the relations to be studied between *h* and *e* may be regarded as semantical.

The question of confirmation in which we are here interested has just been characterized as a logical question. In order to avoid misunderstanding, a qualification should be made. The question at issue does not belong to deductive but to inductive logic. Both branches of logic have this in common: solutions of their problems do not require factual knowledge but only analysis of meaning. Therefore, both parts of logic (if formulated with respect to sentences rather than to propositions) belong to semantics. This similarity makes it possible to explain the logical character of the relations of confirmation by an analogy with a more familiar relation in deductive logic, viz., the relation of logical consequence or its converse, the relation of L-implication (i.e., logical implication or entailment in distinction to material implication). Let *i* be the sentence 'all men are mortal, and Socrates is a man', and *j* the sentence 'Socrates is mortal'. Both *i* and *j* have factual content. But in order to decide whether *i* L-implies *j*, we need no factual knowledge, we need not know whether *i* is true or false, whether *j* is true or false, whether anybody believes in *i*, and if so, on what basis. All that is required is a logical analysis of the meanings of the two sentences. Analogously, to decide to what degree *h* is confirmed by *e*—a question in logic, but here in inductive, not in

[1] Compare Alfred Tarski, "The Semantic Conception of Truth and the Foundations of Semantics," this journal, vol. IV (1944), pp. 341–376; and R. Carnap, *Introduction to Semantics*, 1942.

deductive, logic—we need not know whether *e* is true or false, whether *h* is true or false, whether anybody believes in *e*, and, if so, whether on the basis of observation or of imagination or of anything else. All we need is a logical analysis of the meanings of the two sentences. For this reason we call our problem the logical or semantical problem of confirmation, in distinction to what might be called the methodological problems of confirmation, e.g., how best to construct and arrange an apparatus for certain experiments in order to test a given hypothesis, how to carry out the experiments, how to observe the results, etc.

We may distinguish three logical concepts of confirmation, concepts which have to do with the logical side only of the problem of confirmation. They are all logical and hence semantical concepts. They apply to two sentences, which we call hypothesis and evidence and which in our example were designated by "*h*" and "*e*" respectively. Although the basis is usually an observational report, as in the application sketched above, and the hypothesis a law or a prediction, we shall not restrict our concepts of confirmation to any particular content or form of the two sentences. We distinguish the positive, the comparative, and the quantitative concepts of confirmation in the following way.

(i) *The positive concept of confirmation* is that relation between two sentences *h* and *e* which is usually expressed by sentences of the following forms:

"*h* is confirmed by *e*."

"*h* is supported by *e*."

"*e* gives some (positive) evidence for *h*."

"*e* is evidence substantiating (or corroborating) the assumption of *h*."

Here *e* is ordinarily, as in the previous example, an observational report, but may also refer to particular states of affairs not yet known but merely assumed, and may even include assumed laws; *h* is usually a statement about an unknown state of affairs, e.g., a prediction, or it may be a law or any other hypothesis. It is clear that this concept of confirmation is a relation between two sentences, not a property of one of them. Customary formulations which mention only the hypothesis are obviously elliptical; the basis is tacitly understood. For instance, when a physicist says: "This hypothesis is well confirmed," he means ". . . on the evidence of the observational results known today to physicists."

(ii) *The comparative* (or topological) *concept of confirmation* is usually expressed in sentences of the following forms (a), (b), (c), or similar ones. (a) "*h* is more strongly confirmed (or supported, substantiated, corroborated etc.) by *e* than *h'* by *e'*."

Here we have a tetradic relation between four sentences. In general, the two hypotheses *h* and *h'* are different from one another, and likewise the two evidences *e* and *e'*. Some scientists will perhaps doubt whether a comparison of this most general form is possible, and may, perhaps, restrict the application of the comparative concept only to those situations where two evidences are compared with respect to the same hypothesis (example (b)), or where two hypotheses are examined with respect to one evidence (example (c)). In either case the comparative concept is a triadic relation between three sentences.

(b) "The general theory of relativity is more highly confirmed by the results of laboratory experiments and astronomical observations known today than by those known in 1905."

(c) "The optical phenomena available to physicists in the 19th century were more adequately explained by the wave theory of light than by the corpuscular theory; in other words, they gave stronger support to the former theory than to the latter."

(iii) *The quantitative* (or metrical) *concept of confirmation*, the concept of *degree of confirmation*. Opinion seems divided as to whether or not a concept of this kind ever occurs in the customary talk of scientists, that is to say, whether they ever assign a numerical value to the degree to which a hypothesis is supported by given observational material or whether they use only positive and comparative concepts of confirmation. For the present discussion, we leave this question open; even if the latter were the case, an attempt to find a quantitative explicatum for the comparative explicandum would be worth while. (This would be analogous to many other cases of scientific explication, to the introduction, for example, of the quantitative explicatum 'temperature' for the comparative explicandum 'warmer', or of the quantitative explicatum 'I.Q.' for the comparative explicandum 'higher intelligence'.)

III. The Two Concepts of Probability

The history of the theory of probability is the history of attempts to find an explication for the pre-scientific concept of probability. The number of solutions which have been proposed for this problem in the course of its historical development is rather large. The differences, though sometimes slight, are in many cases considerable. To bring some order into the bewildering multiplicity, several attempts have been made to arrange the many solutions into a few groups. The following is a simple and plausible classification of the various conceptions of probability into three groups [2]: (i) the classical conception, originated by Jacob Bernoulli and Laplace, and represented by their followers in various forms; here, probability is defined as the ratio of the number of favorable cases to the number of all possible cases; (ii) the conception of probability as a certain objective logical relation between propositions (or sentences); the chief representatives of this conception are Keynes [3] and Jeffreys [4]; (iii) the conception of

[2] See Ernest Nagel, *Principles of the Theory of Probability* (International Encyclopedia of Unified Science, Vol. I, 1939, No. 6).

[3] John Maynard Keynes, *A Treatise on Probability*, 1921.

[4] Harold Jeffreys, *Theory of Probability*, 1939.

probability as relative frequency, developed most completely by von Mises [5] and Reichenbach.[6]

In this paper, a discussion of these various conceptions is not intended. While the main point of interest both for the authors and for the readers of the various theories of probability is normally the solutions proposed in those theories, we shall inspect the theories from a different point of view. We shall not ask what solutions the authors offer but rather which problems the solutions are intended to solve; in other words, we shall not ask what explicata are proposed but rather which concepts are taken as explicanda.

This question may appear superfluous, and the fact obvious that the explicandum for every theory of probability is the pre-scientific concept of probability, i.e., the meaning in which the word 'probability' is used in the pre-scientific language. Is the assumption correct, however, that there is only one meaning connected with the word 'probability' in its customary use, or at the least that only one meaning has been chosen by the authors as their explicandum? When we look at the formulations which the authors themselves offer in order to make clear which meanings of 'probability' they intend to take as their explicanda, we find phrases as different as "degree of belief," "degree of reasonable expectation," "degree of possibility," "degree of proximity to certainty," "degree of partial truth," "relative frequency," and many others. This multiplicity of phrases shows that any assumption of a unique explicandum common to all authors is untenable. And we might even be tempted to go to the opposite extreme and to conclude that the authors are dealing not with one but with a dozen or more different concepts. However, I believe that this multiplicity is misleading. It seems to me that the number of explicanda in all the various theories of probability is neither just one nor about a dozen, but in all essential respects—leaving aside slight variations—very few, and chiefly two. In the following discussion we shall use subscripts in order to distinguish these two meanings of the term 'probability' from which most of the various theories of probability start; we are, of course, distinguishing between two explicanda and not between the various explicata offered by these theories, whose number is much greater. The two concepts are: (i) *probability*$_1$ = degree of confirmation; (ii) *probability*$_2$ = relative frequency in the long run. Strictly speaking, there are two groups of concepts, since both for (i) and for (ii) there is a positive, a comparative, and a quantitative concept; however, for our discussion, we may leave aside these distinctions.

Let me emphasize again that the distinction made here refers to two explicanda, not to two explicata. That there is more than one explicatum is obvious; and indeed, their number is much larger than two. But most investigators in the field of probability apparently believe that all the various theories of probability are intended to solve the same problem and

[5] Richard von Mises, *Probability, Statistics, and Truth* (orig. 1928), 1939.

[6] Hans Reichenbach, *Wahrscheinlichkeitslehre*, 1935.

hence that any two theories which differ fundamentally from one another are incompatible. Consequently we find that most representatives of the frequency conception of probability reject all other theories; and, *vice versa*, that the frequency conception is rejected by most of the authors of other theories. These mutual rejections are often formulated in rather strong terms. This whole controversy seems to me futile and unnecessary. The two sides start from different explicanda, and both are right in maintaining the scientific importance of the concepts chosen by them as explicanda—a fact which does not, however, imply that on either side all authors have been equally successful in constructing a satisfactory explicatum. On the other hand, both sides are wrong in most of their polemic assertions against the other side.

A few examples may show how much of the futile controversy between representatives of different conceptions of probability is due to the blindness on both sides with respect to the existence and importance of the probability concept on the other side. We take as examples a prominent contemporary representative of each conception: von Mises, who constructed the first complete theory based on the frequency conception, and Jeffreys, who constructed the most advanced theory based on probability_1. Von Mises [7] seems to believe that probability_2 is the only basis of the Calculus of Probability. To speak of the probability of the death of a certain individual seems to him meaningless. Any use of the term "probability" in everyday life other than in the statistical sense of probability_2 has in his view nothing to do with the Calculus of Probability and cannot take numerical values. That he regards Keynes' conception of probability as thoroughly subjectivistic [8] indicates clearly his misunderstanding.

On the other hand, we find Jeffreys similarly blind in the other direction. Having laid down certain requirements which every theory of probability (and that means for him probability_1) should fulfill, he then rejects all frequency theories, that is, theories of probability_2, because they do not fulfill his requirements. Thus he says: [9] "No 'objective' definition of probability in terms of actual or possible observations . . . is admissible," because the results of observations are initially unknown and, consequently, we could not know the fundamental principles of the theory and would have no starting point. He even goes so far as to say that "in practice, no statistician ever uses a frequency definition, but that all use the notion of degree of reasonable belief, usually without ever noticing that they are using it." [10] While von Mises's concern with explicating the empirical concept of probability_2 by the limit of relative frequency in an infinite sequence has led him to apply the term "probability" only in cases where such a limit exists, Jeffreys misunderstands his procedure completely

[7] *Op. cit.*, First Lecture.
[8] *Op. cit.*, Third Lecture.
[9] *Op. cit.*, p. 11.
[10] *Op. cit.*, p. 300.

and accuses the empiricist von Mises of apriorism: "The existence of the limit is taken as a postulate by von Mises. . . . The postulate is an *a priori* statement about possible experiments and is in itself objectionable." [11] Thus we find this situation: von Mises and Jeffreys both assert that there is only one concept of probability that is of scientific importance and that can be taken as the basis of the Calculus of Probability. The first maintains that this concept is probability_2 and certainly not anything like probability_1; the second puts it just the other way round; and neither has anything but ironical remarks for the concept proposed by the other.

When we criticize the theory of probability proposed by an author, we must clearly distinguish between a rejection of his explicatum and a rejection of his explicandum. The second by no means follows from the first. Donald Williams, in his paper in this symposium,[12] raises serious objections against the frequency theory of probability, especially in von Mises's form. The chief objection is that von Mises's explicatum for probability, viz., the limit of the relative frequency in an infinite sequence of events with a random distribution, is not accessible to empirical confirmation—unless it be supplemented by a theory of inductive probability, a procedure explicitly rejected by von Mises. I think Williams is right in this objection. This, however, means merely that the concept proposed by von Mises is not yet an adequate explicatum. On the other hand, I believe the frequentists are right in the assertion that their explicandum, viz., the statistical concept of probability_2, plays an important role in all branches of empirical science and especially in modern physics, and that therefore the task of explicating this concept is of great importance for science.

It would likewise be unjustified to reject the concept of probability_1 as an explicandum merely because the attempts so far made at an explication are not yet quite satisfactory. It must be admitted that the classical Laplacean definition is untenable. It defines probability as the ratio of the number of favorable cases to the total number of equipossible cases, where equipossibility is determined by the principle of insufficient reason (or indifference). This definition is in certain cases inapplicable, in other cases it yields inadequate values, and in some cases it leads even to contradictions, because for any given proposition there are, in general, several ways of analyzing it as a disjunction of other, logically exclusive, propositions.[13] Modern authors, especially Keynes, Jeffreys, and Hosiasson,[14]

[11] *Op. cit.*, p. 304.

[12] "On the Derivation of Probabilities from Frequencies."

[13] Williams' indications (*op. cit.*, pp. 450 and 469) to the effect that he intends to maintain Laplace's definition even in a simplified form and without the principle of indifference are rather puzzling We have to wait for the full formulation of his solution, which his present paper does not yet give (*op. cit.*, p. 481), in order to see how it overcomes the well-known difficulties of Laplace's definition.

[14] Janina Hosiasson-Lindenbaum, "On Confirmation," *Journal of Symbolic Logic* Vol. V (1940), pp. 133–148.

proceed more cautiously, but at the price of restricting themselves to axiom systems which are rather weak and hence far from constituting an explicit definition. I have made an attempt to formulate an explicit definition of the concept of degree of confirmation (with numerical values) as an explicatum for probability$_1$, and to construct a system of quantitative inductive logic based on that definition.[15] No matter whether this first attempt at an explication with the help of the methods of modern logic and in particular those of semantics will turn out to be satisfactory or not, I think there is no reason for doubting that an adequate explication will be developed in time through further attempts.

The distinction between the two concepts which serve as explicanda is often overlooked on both sides. This is primarily due to the unfortunate fact that both concepts are designated by the same familiar, but ambiguous word 'probability'. Although many languages contain two words (e.g., English 'probable' and 'likely', Latin '*probabilis*' and '*verisimilis*', French '*probable*' and '*vraisemblable*'), these words seem in most cases to be used in about the same way or at any rate not to correspond to the two concepts we have distinguished. Some authors (e.g., C. S. Peirce and R. A. Fisher) have suggested utilizing the plurality of available words for the distinction of certain concepts (different from our distinction); however, the proposals were made in an artificial way, without relation to the customary meanings of the words. The same would hold if we were to use the two words for our two concepts; therefore we prefer to use subscripts as indicated above.

Probability$_1$, in other words, the logical concept of confirmation in its different forms (positive, comparative, and quantitative), has been explained in the preceding section. A brief explanation may here be given of probability$_2$, merely to make clear its distinction from probability$_1$. A typical example of the use of this concept is the following statement: "The probability$_2$ of casting an ace with this die is 1/6." Statements of this form refer to two properties (or classes) of events: (i) the reference property M_1, here the property of being a throw with this die; (ii) the specific property M_2, here the property of being a throw with any die resulting in an ace. The statement says that the probability$_2$ of M_2 with respect to M_1 is 1/6. The statement is tested by statistical investigations. A sufficiently long series of, say, n throws of the die in question is made, and the number m of these throws which yield an ace is counted. If the relative frequency m/n of aces in this series is sufficiently close to 1/6, the statement is regarded as confirmed. Thus, the other way round, the statement is understood as predicting that the relative frequency of aces thrown with this die in a sufficiently long series will be about 1/6. This formulation is admittedly inexact; but it intends no more than to indicate the meaning

[15] These problems are discussed in detail in the book *Logical Foundations of Probability*, Chicago, 1950. The present paper is a modified version of a chapter of the book. The definition of degree of confirmation and some theorems are stated in the Appendix of the book.

of 'probability$_2$' as an explicandum. To make this concept exact is the task of the explication; our discussion concerns only the two explicanda.

IV. The Logical Nature of the Two Probability Concepts

On the basis of the preceding explanations, let us now characterize the two probability concepts, not with respect to what they mean but merely with respect to their logical nature, more specifically, with respect to the kind of entities to which they are applied and the logical nature of the simplest sentences in which they are used. (Since the pre-scientific use of both concepts is often too vague and incomplete, e.g., because of the omission of the second argument (viz., the evidence or the reference class), we take here into consideration the more careful use by authors on probability. However, we shall be more concerned with their general discussions than with the details of their constructed systems.) For the sake of simplicity, let us consider the two concepts in their quantitative forms only. They may be taken also in their comparative and in their positive forms (as explained for probability$_1$, i.e., confirmation, in section II, and these other forms would show analogous differences. Probability$_1$ and probability$_2$, taken as quantitative concepts, have the following characteristics in common: each of them is a function of two arguments; their values are real numbers belonging to the interval 0 to 1 (according to the customary convention, which we follow here). Their characteristic differences are as follows:

1. Probability$_1$ (degree of confirmation)

(a) The *two arguments* are variously described as events (in the literal sense, see below), states of affairs, circumstances, and the like. Therefore each argument is expressible by a declarative sentence and hence is, in our terminology, a proposition. Another alternative consists in taking as arguments the sentences expressing the propositions, describing the events, etc. If we choose this alternative, probability$_1$ is a semantical concept (as in section II). (Fundamentally it makes no great difference whether propositions or sentences are taken as arguments; but the second method has certain technical advantages, and therefore we use it for our discussion.)

(b) A simple *statement* of probability$_1$, i.e., one attributing to two given arguments a particular number as value of probability$_1$, is either L-true (logically true, analytic) or L-false (logically false, logically self-contradictory), hence in any case L-determinate, not factual (synthetic). Therefore, a statement of this kind is to be established by logical analysis alone, as has been explained earlier (section II). It is independent of the contingency of facts because it does not say anything about facts (although the two arguments do in general refer to facts).

2. *Probability*$_2$ (*relative frequency*)

(a) The *two arguments* are properties, kinds, classes, usually of events or things. [As an alternative, the predicate expressions designating the properties might be taken as arguments; then the concept would become a semantical one. In the present case, however, in distinction to (1), there does not seem to be any advantage in this method. On the contrary, it appears to be more convenient to have the probability$_2$ statements in the object language instead of the metalanguage; and it seems that all authors who deal with probability$_2$ choose this form.]

(b) A simple *statement* of probability$_2$ is factual and empirical, it says something about the facts of nature, and hence must be based upon empirical procedure, the observation of relevant facts. From these simple statements the theorems of a mathematical theory of probability$_2$ must be clearly distinguished. The latter do not state a particular value of probability$_2$ but say something about connections between probability$_2$ values in a general way, usually in a conditional form (for example: "if the values of such and such probabilities$_2$ are q_1 and q_2, then the value of a probability$_2$ related to the original ones in a certain way is such and such a function, say, product or sum, of q_1 and q_2"). These theorems are not factual but L-true (analytic). Thus a theory of probability$_2$, e.g., the system constructed by von Mises or that by Reichenbach, is not of an empirical but of a logico-mathematical nature; it is a branch of mathematics, like arithmetic, fundamentally different from any branch of empirical science, e.g., physics.

It is very important to distinguish clearly between *kinds of events* (war, birth, death, throw of a die, throw of this die, throw of this die yielding an ace, etc.) and *events* (Caesar's death, the throw of this die made yesterday at 10 A.M., the series of all throws of this die past and future). This distinction is doubly important for discussions on probability, because one of the characteristic differences between the two concepts is this: the first concept refers sometimes to two events, the second to two kinds of events (see 1(a) and 2(a)). Many authors of probability use the word 'event' (or the corresponding words 'Ereignis' and 'événement') when they mean to speak, not about events, but about kinds of events. This usage is of long standing in the literature on probability, but it is very unfortunate. It has only served to reinforce the customary neglect of the fundamental difference between the two probability concepts which arose originally out of the ambiguous use of the word 'probability', and thereby to increase the general confusion in discussions on probability. The authors who use the term 'event' when they mean kinds of events get into trouble, of course, whenever they want to speak about specific events. The traditional solution is to say 'the happenings (or occurrences) of a certain event' instead of 'the events of a certain kind'; sometimes the events are referred to by the term 'single events'. But this phrase is rather misleading; the important difference between events and kinds of events is not the same as the inessential difference between single events (the first throw I made today with this die) and multiple or compound events (the series of all throws made with this die). Keynes, if I interpret him correctly, has noticed the ambiguity of the term 'event'. He says [16] that the customary use of phrases like 'the happening of events' is "vague and unambiguous," which I suppose to be a misprint for "vague and ambiguous"; but he does not specify the ambiguity. He proposes to dispense altogether with the term 'event' and to use instead the term 'proposition'. Subsequent authors dealing with probability$_1$, like Jeffreys, for example, have followed him in this use.

Many authors have made a distinction between two (or sometimes more) kinds of probability, or between two meanings of the word 'probability'. Some of these distinctions are quite different from the distinction made here between probability$_1$ and probability$_2$. For instance, a distinction is sometimes made between mathematical probability and philosophical probability; their characteristic difference appears to be that the first has numerical values, the second not. However, this difference seems hardly essential; we find a concept with numerical values and one without, in other words, both a quantitative and a comparative concept on either side of our distinction between the two fundamentally different meanings of 'probability'. Another distinction has been made between subjective and objective probability. However, I believe that practically all authors really have an objective concept of probability in mind, and that the appearance of subjectivist conceptions is in most cases caused only by occasional unfortunate formulations; this will soon be discussed.

Other distinctions which have been made are more or less similar to our distinction between probability$_1$ and probability$_2$. For instance, Ramsey [17] says: ". . . the general difference of opinion between statisticians who for the most part adopt the frequency theory of probability and logicians who mostly reject it renders it likely that the two schools are really discussing different things, and that the word 'probability' is used by logicians in one sense and by statisticians in another."

It seems that many authors have taken either probability$_1$ or probability$_2$ as their explicandum. I believe moreover that practically all authors on probability have intended one of these two concepts as their explicandum, despite the fact that their various explanations appear to refer to a number of quite different concepts.

For one group of authors, the question of their explicandum is easily answered. In the case of all those who support a frequency theory of probability, i.e., who define their explicata in terms of relative frequency (as a limit or in some other way), there can be no doubt that their explicandum is probability$_2$. Their formulations are, in general, presented in

[16] *Op. cit.*, p. 5.

[17] F. P. Ramsey, *The Foundations of Mathematics*, 1931; see p. 157.

clear and unambiguous terms. Often they state explicitly that their explicandum is relative frequency. And even in the cases where this is not done, the discussion of their explicata leaves no doubt as to what is meant as explicandum.

This, however, covers only one of the various conceptions, i.e., explicata proposed, and only one of the many different explanations of explicanda which have been given and of which some examples were mentioned earlier. It seems clear that the other explanations do not refer to the statistical, empirical concept of relative frequency; and I believe that practically all of them, in spite of their apparent dissimilarity, are intended to refer to probability$_1$. Unfortunately, many of the phrases used are more misleading than helpful in our efforts to find out what their authors actually meant as explicandum. There is, in particular, one point on which many authors in discussions on probability$_1$, or on logical problems in general, commit a certain typical confusion or adopt incautiously other authors' formulations which are infected by this confusion. I am referring to what is sometimes called psychologism in logic.

Many authors in their general remarks about the nature of (deductive) logic say that it has to do with ways and forms of thinking or, in more cautious formulations, with forms of correct or rational thinking. In spite of these subjectivistic formulations, we find that in practice these authors use an objectivistic method in solving any particular logical problem. For instance, in order to find out whether a certain conclusion follows from given premises, they do not in fact make psychological experiments about the thinking habits of people but rather analyze the given sentences and show their conceptual relations. In inductive logic or, in other words, the theory of probability$_1$, we often find a similar psychologism. Some authors, from Laplace and other representatives of the classical theory of probability down to contemporary authors like Keynes and Jeffreys, use subjectivistic formulations when trying to explain what they take as their explicandum; they say that it is probability in the sense of degree of belief or, if they are somewhat more cautious, degree of reasonable or justified belief. However, an analysis of the work of these authors comes to quite different results if we pay more attention to the methods the authors actually use in solving problems of probability than to the general remarks in which they try to characterize thir own aims and methods. Such an analysis, which cannot be carried out within this paper, shows that most and perhaps all of these authors use objectivistic rather than subjectivistic methods. They do not try to measure degrees of belief by actual, psychological experiments, but rather carry out a logical analysis of the concepts and propositions involved. It appears, therefore, that the psychologism in inductive logic is, just like that in deductive logic, merely a superficial feature of certain marginal formulations, while the core of the theories remains thoroughly objectivistic. And, further, it seems to me that for most of those authors who do not maintain a frequency theory, from the classical period to our time, the objective concept which they take as their explicandum is probability$_1$, i.e., degree of confirmation.

V. Empiricism and the Logical Concept of Probability

Many empiricist authors have rejected the logical concept of probability$_1$ as distinguished from probability$_2$ because they believe that its use violates the principle of empiricism and that, therefore, probability$_2$ is the only concept admissible for empiricism and hence for science. We shall now examine some of the reasons given for this view.

The concept of probability$_1$ is applied also in cases in which the hypothesis h is a prediction concerning a particular "single event", e.g., the prediction that it will rain tomorrow or that the next throw of this die will yield an ace. Some philosophers believe that an application of this kind violates the principle of verifiability (or confirmability). They might say, for example: "How can the statement 'the probability of rain tomorrow on the evidence of the given meteorological observations is one-fifth' be verified? We shall observe either rain or not-rain tomorrow, but we shall not observe anything that can verify the value one-fifth." This objection, however, is based on a misconception concerning the nature of the probability$_1$ statement. This statement does not ascribe the probability$_1$ value 1/5 to tomorrow's rain but rather to a certain logical relation between the prediction of rain and the meteorological report. Since the relation is logical, the statement is, if true, L-true; therefore it is not in need of verification by observation of tomorrow's weather or of any other facts.

It must be admitted that earlier authors on probability have sometimes made inferences which are inadmissible from the point of view of empiricism. They calculated the value of a logical probability and then inferred from it a frequency, hence making an inadvertent transition from probability$_1$ to probability$_2$. Their reasoning might be somewhat like this: "On the basis of the symmetry of this die the probability of an ace is 1/6; therefore, one-sixth of the throws of this die will result in an ace." Later authors have correctly criticized inferences of this kind. It is clear that from a probability$_1$ statement a statement on frequency can never be inferred, because the former is purely logical while the latter is factual. Thus the source of the mistake was the confusion of probability$_1$ with probability$_2$. The use of probability$_1$ statements cannot in itself violate the principle of empiricism so long as we remain aware of the fact that those statements are purely logical and hence do not allow the derivation of factual conclusions.

The situation with respect to both objections just discussed may be clarified by a comparison with deductive logic. Let h be the sentence 'there will be rain tomorrow' and j the sentence 'there will be rain and wind tomorrow'. Suppose somebody makes the statement in deductive logic: "h follows logically from j". Certainly nobody will accuse him of apriorism either for making the statement or for claiming that for its verification no factual knowledge is required. The statement "the probability$_1$ of h on the evidence e is $1/5$" has the same general character as the former statement; therefore it cannot violate empiricism any more than the first. Both statements express a purely logical relation between two sentences. The difference between the two statements is merely this: while the first states a complete logical implication, the second states only, so to speak, a partial logical implication; hence, while the first belongs to deductive logic, the second belongs to inductive logic. Generally speaking, the assertion of purely logical sentences, whether in deductive or in inductive logic, can never violate empiricism; if they are false, they violate the rules of logic. The principle of empiricism can be violated only by the assertion of a factual (synthetic) sentence without a sufficient empirical foundation, or by the thesis of apriorism when it contends that for knowledge with respect to certain factual sentences no empirical foundation is required.

According to Reichenbach's view,[18] the concept of logical probability or weight, in order to be in accord with empiricism, must be identified with the statistical concept of probability. If we formulate his view with the help of our terms with subscripts, it says that probability$_1$ is identical with probability$_2$, or, rather, with a special kind of application of it. He argues for this "identity conception" against any "disparity conception," like the one presented in this paper, which regards the two uses of 'probability' as essentially different. Reichenbach tries to prove the identity conception by showing how the concept which we call probability$_1$, even when applied to a "single event," leads back to a relative frequency. I agree that in certain cases there is a close relationship between probability$_1$ and relative frequency. The decisive question is, however, the nature of this relationship. Let us consider a simple example. Let the evidence e say that among 30 observed things with the property M_1 20 have been found to have the property M_2, and hence that the relative frequency of M_2 with respect to M_1 in the observed sample is $2/3$; let e say, in addition, that a certain individual b not belonging to the sample is M_1. Let h be the prediction that b is M_2. If the degree of confirmation c is defined in a suitable way as an explicatum for probability$_1$, $c(h,e)$ will be equal or close to $2/3$; let us assume for the sake of simplicity that $c = 2/3$.[19] However, the fact that, in this case, the value of c or probability$_1$ is equal to a certain relative frequency by no means implies that probability$_1$ is here the same as probability$_2$; these two concepts remain fundamentally

[18] Hans Reichenbach, *Experience and Prediction*, 1938, see §§ 32–34.

[19] According to Reichenbach's inductive logic, in the case described $c = 2/3$. According to my inductive logic, c is close to but not exactly equal to $2/3$. My reason for regarding a value of the latter kind as more adequate may be found in the book mentioned above, *Logical Foundations of Probability*. A brief statement is in my paper, "On Inductive Logic", *Philosophy of Science*, XII, 1945, § 10. For our present discussion, we may leave aside this question.

different even in this case. This becomes clear by the following considerations (i) to (iv).

(i) The *c*-statement '$c(h,e) = 2/3$' does not itself state a relative frequency although the value of *c* which it states is calculated on the basis of a known relative frequency and, under our assumptions, is in this case exactly equal to it. A temperature is sometimes determined by the volume of a certain body of mercury and is, under certain conditions, equal to it; this, however, does not mean that temperature and volume are the same concept. The *c*-statement, being a purely logical statement, cannot possibly state a relative frequency for two empirical properties like M_1 and M_2. Such a relative frequency can be stated only by a factual sentence; in the example, it is stated by a part of the factual sentence *e*. The *c*-statement does not imply either *e* or the part of *e* just mentioned; it rather speaks about *e*, stating a logical relation between *e* and *h*. It seems to me that Reichenbach does not realize this fact sufficiently clearly. He feels, correctly, that the *c*-value 2/3 stated in the *c*-statement is in some way based upon our empirical knowledge of the observed relative frequency. This leads him to the conception, which I regard as incorrect, that the *c*-statement must be interpreted as stating the relative frequency and hence as being itself a factual, empirical statement. In my conception, the factual content concerning the observed relative frequency must be ascribed, not to the *c*-statement, but to the evidence *e* referred to in the *c*-statement.

(ii) The relative frequency 2/3, which is stated in *e* and on which the value of *c* is based, is not at all a probability_2. The probability_2 of M_2 with respect to M_1 is the relative frequency of M_2 with respect to M_1 in the whole sequence of relevant events. The relative frequency stated by *e*, on the other hand, is the relative frequency observed within the given sample. It is true that our estimate of the value of probability_2 will be based on the observed relative frequency in the sample. However, observations of several samples may yield different values for the observed relative frequency. Therefore we cannot identify observed relative frequency with probability_2, since the latter has only one value, which is unknown. (I am using here the customary realistic language as it is used in everyday life and in science; this use does not imply acceptance of realism as a metaphysical thesis but only of what Feigl calls "empirical realism." [20])

(iii) As mentioned, an estimate of the probability_2, the relative frequency in the whole sequence, is based upon the observed relative frequency in the sample. I think that, in a sense, the statement '$c(h,e) = 2/3$' itself may be interpreted as stating such an estimate; it says the same as: "The estimate on the evidence *e* of the probability_2 of M_2 with respect to M_1 is 2/3." If somebody should like to call this a frequency interpretation of probability_1, I should raise no objection. It need, however, be noticed clearly that this interpretation identifies probability_1 not with

[20] Herbert Feigl, "Logical Empiricism," in *Twentieth Century Philosophy*, ed. D. Runes, 1943, pp. 373-416; see pp. 390 f.

probability$_2$ but with the estimate of probability$_2$ on the evidence e; and this is something quite different. The estimate may have different values for different evidences; probability$_2$ has only one value. A statement of the estimate on a given evidence is purely logical; a statement of probability$_2$ is empirical. The reformulation of the statement on probability$_1$ or c in terms of the best estimate of probability$_2$ may be helpful in showing the close connection between the two probability concepts. This formulation must, however, not be regarded as eliminating probability$_1$. Any estimation of the value of a physical magnitude (length, temperature, probability$_2$, etc.) on the evidence of certain observations or measurements is an inductive procedure and hence necessarily involves probability$_1$, either in its quantitative or in its comparative form.

(iv) The fundamental difference between probability$_1$ and probability$_2$ may be further elucidated by analyzing the sense of the customary references to *unknown probabilities*. As we have seen under (ii), the value of a certain probability$_2$ may be unknown to us at a certain time in the sense that we do not possess sufficient factual information for its calculation. On the other hand, the value of a probability$_1$ for two given sentences cannot be unknown in the same sense. (It may, of course, be unknown in the sense that a certain logico-mathematical procedure has not yet been accomplished, that is, in the same sense in which we say that the solution of a certain arithmetical problem is at present unknown to us.) In this respect also, a confusion of the two concepts of probability has sometimes been made in formulations of the classical theory. This theory deals, on the whole, with probability$_1$; and the principle of indifference, one of the cornerstones of the theory, is indeed valid to a certain limited extent for this concept. However, this principle is absurd for probability$_2$, as has often been pointed out. Yet the classical authors sometimes refer to unknown probabilities or to the probability (or chance) of certain probability values, e.g., in formulations of Bayes' theorem. This would not be admissible for probability$_1$, and I believe that here the authors inadvertently go over to probability$_2$. Since a probability$_2$ value is a physical property like a temperature, we may very well inquire into the probability$_1$, on a given evidence, of a certain probability$_2$ (as in the earlier example, at the end of (iii)). However, a question about the probability$_1$ of a probability$_1$ statement has no more point than a question about the probability$_1$ of the statement that $2 + 2 = 4$ or that $2 + 2 = 5$, because a probability$_1$ statement is, like an arithmetical statement, either L-true or L-false; therefore its probability$_1$, with respect to any evidence, is either 1 or 0.

VI. Probability and Truth

It is important to distinguish clearly between a concept characterizing a thing independently of the state of our knowledge (e.g., the concept 'hard') and the related concept characterizing our state of knowledge with respect to the thing (e.g., the concept 'known to be hard'). It is true that a person will, as a rule, attribute the predicate 'hard' to a thing *b* only if he knows it to be hard, hence only if he is prepared to attribute to it also the predicate 'known to be hard'. Nevertheless, the sentences '*b* is hard' and '*b* is known to be hard' are obviously far from meaning the same. One point of difference becomes evident when we look at the sentences in their complete form; the second sentence, in distinction to the first (if we regard hardness as a permanent property), must be supplemented by references to a person and a time point: '*b* is known to *X* at the time *t* to be hard'. The distinction between the two sentences becomes more conspicuous if they occur within certain larger contexts. For example, the difference between the sentences '*b* is not hard' and '*b* is not known to *X* at the time *t* to be hard' is clear from the fact that we can easily imagine a situation where we would be prepared to assert the second but not the first.

The distinction just explained may appear as obvious beyond any need of emphasis. However, a distinction of the same general form, where 'true' is substituted for 'hard', is nevertheless often neglected by philosophers. A person will, in general, attribute the predicate 'true' to a given sentence (or proposition) only if he knows it to be true, hence only if he is prepared to attribute to it also the predicate 'known to be true' or 'established as true' or 'verified'. Nevertheless 'true' and 'verified by the person *X* at the time *t*)' mean quite different things; and so do 'false' and 'falsified' (in the sense of 'known to be false', 'established as false'). A given sentence is often neither verified nor falsified; nevertheless it is either true or false, whether anybody knows it or not. (Some empiricists shy away from the latter formulation because they believe it to involve an anti-empiricist absolutism. This, however, is not the case. Empiricism admits as meaningful any statement about unknown fact and hence also about unknown truth, provided only the fact or the truth is know*able*, or confirmable.) In this way an inadvertent confusion of 'true' and 'verified' may lead to doubts about the validity of the principle of excluded middle. The question of whether and to what extent a confusion of this kind has actually contributed to the origin of some contemporary philosophical doctrines rejecting that principle is hard to decide and will not be investigated here.

A statement like 'this thing is made of iron' can never be verified in the strictest sense, i.e., definitively established as true so that no possibility remains of refuting it by future experience. The statement can only be more or less confirmed. If it is highly confirmed, that is to say, if strong evidence for it is found, then it is often said to be verified; but this is a weakened, non-absolutistic sense of the term. I think it is fair to say that most philosophers, and at least all empiricists, agree today that the concept 'verified' in its strict sense is not applicable to statements about physical things. Some philosophers, however, go further; they say that, because we can never reach absolutely certain knowledge about things, we ought to abandon the concept of truth. It seems to me that this view is due again to an unconscious confusion of 'true' and 'verified'.[21] Some of these philosophers say that, in order to avoid absolutism, we should not ask whether a given statement is true but only whether it has been confirmed, corroborated, or accepted by a certain person at a certain time.[22] Others think that 'true' should be abandoned in favor of 'highly confirmed' or 'highly probable'. Reichenbach [23] has been led by considerations of this kind to the view that the values of probability (the logical concept of probability$_1$) ought to take the place of the two truth-values, truth and falsity, of ordinary logic, or, in other words, that probability logic is a multivalued logic superseding the customary two-valued logic. I agree with Reichenbach that here a concept referring to an absolute and unobtainable maximum should be replaced by a concept referring to a high degree in a continuous scale. However, what is superseded by 'highly probable' or 'confirmed to a high degree' is the concept 'confirmed to the maximum degree' or 'verified', and not the concept 'true'.

Values of probability$_1$ are fundamentally different from truth-values. Therefore inductive logic, although it introduces the continuous scale of probability$_1$ values, remains like deductive logic two-valued. While it is true that to the multiplicity of probability$_1$ values in inductive logic only a dichotomy corresponds in deductive logic, nevertheless, this dichotomy is not between truth and falsity of a sentence but between L-implication and non-L-implication for two sentences. If, to take our previous example, $c(h,e) = 2/3$, then h is still either true or false and does not have an intermediate truth-value of $2/3$.

It has been the chief purpose of this paper to explain and discuss the two concepts of probability in their role as explicanda for theories of probability. I think that in the present situation clarification of the explicanda is the most urgent task. When every author has not only a clear understanding of his own explicandum but also some insight into the existence, the importance, and the meaning of the explicandum on the other side, then it will be possible for each side to concentrate entirely on the positive task of constructing an explication and a theory of the chosen explicatum without wasting energy in futile polemics against the explicandum of the other side.

[21] I have given earlier warnings against this confusion in "Wahrheit und Bewährung," *Actes du Congrès International de Philosophic Scientifique*, Paris, 1936, Vol. IV, pp. 1–6; and in *Introduction to Semantics*, p. 28.

[22] See, e.g., Otto Neurath, "Universal Jargon and Terminology," *Proceedings Aristotelian Society*, 1940–1941, pp. 127–148, see esp. pp. 138 f.

[23] *Op. cit* (*Experience*), §§ 22, 35.

The Logical Foundations of the Concept of Probability*

HANS REICHENBACH

IN AN EARLIER PAPER [1] I presented my ideas of a solution of the problem of probability. They culminated in the project of a probability logic in which the alternative "true-false" of classical logic is replaced by a continuous scale of probability values; such an extension proved to be necessary in order to overcome the peculiar difficulties of the problem of convergence, which appear in the interpretation of probability as the limit of a frequency. In the meantime I have developed these ideas, published originally only in the form of a program, into a system of probability logic and have arrived at a solution of the problem which appears to me to be final. I should like to give in this paper a summary of my results. I regard it as a particular merit of the new theory that it makes possible a solution of the problem of induction, for which no satisfactory philosophical solution had been known ever since David Hume's outstanding formulation of the problem.

The new theory required a number of mathematical investigations, the results of which, at least in part, I published in other papers.[2] A presentation which includes both the mathematical and the philosophical problems of this complex, will be published in the form of a book in the near future.†
In the present article I should like first to speak briefly about the results of the mathematical studies and then to proceed to an exposition, in the form of a survey, of the ensuing philosophical considerations.

* * *

It was of prime importance for the mathematical investigations of this problem to carry through an axiomatic construction of the calculus of

* Translated by Maria Reichenbach from the German original which appeared in *Erkenntnis* 3, 1932/33 and reprinted with the kind permission of the author and the publisher, Felix Meiner, Leipzig. A few footnotes were added to this translation by the author; they are distinguished from the original footnotes by inclusion in brackets.

[1] "Kausalität und Wahrscheinlichkeit", *Erkenntnis* 1, 1930, p. 158.

[2] "Axiomatik der Wahrscheinlichkeitsrechnung", *Math.Zs.* 34, 1932, p. 568.
"Wahrscheinlichkeitslogik", *Ber. d. Preuss. Akad. d. Wiss.*, phys.-math.Kl., 1932.

† [This remark refers to my book *Wahrscheinlichkeitslehre*, published in 1935 in Leiden, Holland, at A. W. Sijthoff's. An English translation, *Theory of Probability*, was published by the University of California Press in 1949.]

probability, which satisfies both mathematical and logical requirements. Such an inquiry was necessary because, first of all, the assumptions contained in the mathematical calculus of probability had to be formulated. Only when we know these assumptions can we find out which assumptions are made in the application of the calculus of probability to physical reality and which assumptions thus constitute the subject to which the philosophical investigation has to refer. It has turned out that all these assumptions can be reduced to one. In order to explain this result I shall briefly outline the axiomatic construction of the theory of probability.

The construction of the calculus of probability starts with the characterization of the logical structure of the probability statement. The probability is treated as a relation, which is called probability implication. This relation holds between the elements of two classes, with the qualification that these elements must be arranged in the form of a sequence. The probability implication is written in the form [3]

$$(i)\ (x_i \epsilon A \underset{p}{\ni} y_i \epsilon B) \qquad (1)$$

Let us take the following example: if the event x_i is the throw of a die (class A), there exists a probability $p = 1/6$ that the coördinated result y_i belongs to the class B of throws of face "six"; this holds for all elements x_i and y_i. Or another example: if x_i suffers from tuberculosis (class A), there exists a certain probability p that the son y_i of x_i will die of tuberculosis (class B); this holds again for all x_i and y_i. The one-to-one coördination of the x_i and y_i must be known, i.e., there must exist two sequences (x_i) and (y_i) whose elements are coördinated to each other by pairs.

Instead of the notation (1) we shall use the abbreviated form

$$(A \underset{p}{\ni} B) \qquad (2)$$

This expression means the same as (1). It is expedient in many cases to replace (2) by the notation

$$P(A,B) = p \qquad (3)$$

whose meaning is identical with (2).

In addition to the sign for probability the logistic signs enter into the probability formulas. For instance, we can ask for the probability of a disjunction $B \vee C$ (B or C) or for the probability of a conjunction $B.C$ (B

[3] By ϵ we denote according to Russell the membership of the element x_i in the class A. The parenthesis (i) denotes the all-operator and is to be read "for all i". In a more complete notation we would have to write $(x_i)\ (y_i)$, i.e., "for all x_i and y_i". The sign $\underset{p}{\ni}$ denotes the probability implication and is to be read "implies with the probability p". [In adaptation to the English language the German symbol "W" is replaced by "P", standing for "probability". The letters "O", "P", "Q", of the German notation are replaced by "A", "B", "C". The same change was carried through in the exposition in French language, mentioned above, and will also be used in the English translation of my book *Wahrscheinlichkeitslehre*.]

and C). The logistic signs inside probability formulas are treated according to the rules of logistics. For instance, the expression

$$P(A,B\cdot[C\vee D]) \tag{4}$$

can be replaced by

$$P(A,B\cdot C\vee B\cdot D) \tag{5}$$

In this manner the application of the logistic algebra is made possible within the P-symbols.

The whole expression $P(\ )$, for instance the expression (5), possesses the character of a mathematical variable; it stands for a degree of probability. Consequently, the P-symbols can be connected like mathematical quantities, and probability equations can be constructed which determine relations between probabilities. For instance, for mutually exclusive events B and C the relation

$$P(A,B\vee C) = P(A,B) + P(A,C) \tag{6}$$

holds. In this way a calculus is constructed which combines logistics with mathematical methods; within the P-symbols logistics holds, while the P-symbols as wholes are subject to the rules of the mathematical methods of equations. This combined calculus proves to be very expedient, not only for theoretical, but also for practical applications, and makes possible the strict formulation of all theorems of the calculus of probability.

The axioms of the calculus of probability appear as a series of formulas, which contain in addition to logistic signs the sign $\underset{p}{\rightarrow}$, or, in another way of writing, the sign $P(\ )$. These formulas contain rules for the usage of the new sign $\underset{p}{\rightarrow}$, or $P(\ )$, respectively. They are to be conceived as a series of implicit definitions of the concept of probability. Consequently, we can apply the considerations known from the method of implicit definitions, according to which such an axiom system can be conceived in two ways. In the first conception a system can be used formally, i.e., operations with the formulas can be performed although the new sign for probability is not given any interpretation. In the second conception the new sign is given a meaning, or interpretation. Any interpretation is admissible which is compatible with the properties of the sign as formulated in the axioms. The situation is analogous to that of the axiomatic construction of geometry: geometry can be conceived as purely formal; but it is also possible to give to the fundamental geometrical concepts, such as "point", "straight line", etc., an interpretation in terms of small particles, light rays, etc., and thus to proceed to an applied geometry. The coördination of an interpretation to a sign is called coördinative definition.

This double manipulation of the axiomatic system proves to be very valuable for the calculus of probability. We can derive all known theorems of the calculus of probability without referring to an interpretation of the concept of probability. On the other hand, we can transform the formal calculus of probability thus constructed into an interpreted calculus by interpreting the term "probability". For instance, we can interpret probability as a frequency; then our theory comprises all theorems of a calculus of probability based on the frequency interpretation.

The frequency interpretation is introduced by a definition according to which we understand by probability the limit of a frequency, a definition which has first been carried through by R. v. Mises.[4] Our theory, however, differs from v. Mises' theory in that we do not demand any further properties for the concept of probability. In particular, we renounce any rules for the order of probability sequences, as are given by v. Mises in the principle of randomness. Any sequence in which the frequency of events converges towards a limit is a probability sequence in our interpretation. It turns out that, if the frequency interpretation of probability is assumed, all the axioms of the calculus of probability can be proved to be tautologies. This fact proves that the frequency interpretation supplies an admissible model of our axiomatic system.

The calculus of probability so constructed must of course include conceptions concerning the order of probability sequences. It turns out that this task can be accomplished and that a number of different types of order can be defined for probability sequences. Among these types of order the type of extreme randomness is only a special case, which we call *normal sequence;* in addition there are types of a higher degree of order, which step by step lead to the extremely ordered sequence, as is given, for instance, in the alternating sequence $B\ \bar{B}\ B\ \bar{B}\ B\ \bar{B}\ \ldots$ The characterization of the types of order can be carried through by means of rules laying down that certain probabilities referring to subsequences are equal to each other. For instance, the normal sequence has the property that in the subsequence selected by B as predecessor the frequency of B is equal to that in the main sequence; on the other hand, the alternating sequence mentioned above does not possess this property. This illustration indicates the general method by means of which the characterization of special cases of probability sequences can be carried through. Every such characterization consists in the statement that certain probabilities are equal to each other.

I shall not go into the multiple mathematical applications of this theory, but will refer only to one of its results which is essential for the following philosophical considerations. This result is found in the fact that we need only one assumption for the application of the calculus of probability to physical reality. If we possess a method by means of which we can determine the limit of the frequency in a sequence of events, in case there is one, the applicability of the calculus of probability is assured. All that is added by the calculus is tautological transformations, since all the axioms of the

[4] "Grundlagen der Wahrscheinlichkeitsrechnung," *Math.Zs.* 5, 1919, p. 52. Cf. the table of literature on probability in *Erkenntnis*, 2, 1931, p. 189.

calculus of probability are tautologically satisfied for sequences of a limit character. Furthermore we shall determine by the same method, whether a given probability problem possesses the properties of certain special cases. If we can determine the limit of the frequency of a sequence, we can also determine whether two different sequences have the same limit, that is, whether the conditions of the special case are satisfied.

This result has a great bearing upon the philosophical critique of the calculus of probability. Nobody could know a priori whether the calculus of probability does not contain further assumptions. For an illustration we might refer to the difficulties which resulted for logic as long as the introduction of the axiom of reducibility was regarded as necessary. We are free from such difficulties with respect to the calculus of probability and have to answer only the question how to find the limit of the frequency of a sequence. With this investigation, however, we touch upon a number of peculiar problems, which represent the very difficulty of a philosophical solution of the problem of probability.

* * *

The character of these difficulties has repeatedly been treated in the recent literature on probability. These difficulties derive from the fact that the probability sequences occurring in nature are never given by a rule, i.e., are not *intensionally* given, but are presented to us only by enumeration of their elements, i.e., are *extensionally* given. Consequently only an initial section of a finite length is known to us, and we cannot make a definite statement about the infinite rest of the sequence. In particular, it is undetermined towards which limit the frequency of the sequence will converge, because a given initial section can be continued in terms of a different frequency, so that the given beginning can always be made compatible with any value of the limit. The fact that the limit cannot be determined from the initial section makes the meaning of the limit statement questionable. If we assert that a sequence has a certain limit of the frequency, no matter what source we have for our statement, we lack the possibility of verifying this assertion as true or false. It is therefore doubtful whether we can ascribe a meaning to the statement. For a meaningful statement we demand that there exist a method in terms of which the statement, in principle, can be verified as true or false.[5]

We pointed out in the beginning that a way out of this difficulty seems to be possible only if we abandon the alternative *true-false* of classical logic and introduce in its place a continuous scale of probability values. As explained in the paper mentioned above, such a probability logic corresponds to the actual behavior which the man in the street as well as the scientist displays in face of this situation with respect to probability statements. If a long enough section of the sequence with a frequency close to a predicted value p is observed, it will be taken as a confirmation of the pre-

[5] Cf. Rudolf Carnap, "Die Überwindung der Metaphysik durch logische Analyse der Sprache", *Erkenntnis*, 2, 1931, p. 219.

diction, whereas a value of the frequency deviating very much from p will be regarded as a disproof of the prediction. The peculiarity of this judgment consists in the fact that it includes intermediate steps, according as the observed frequency is more or less different from p. Therefore we are no longer concerned with an alternative of judgments but with a judgment in terms of higher or lower probabilities. At first it appears inexplicable on what grounds we base such a judgment about the probability, since there is no reason why we should believe in an unchanged continuation of the observed section of the sequence. I shall postpone the discussion of this problem, which is nothing but the problem of the inductive inference, and develop first the structural form of such a probability logic. The construction of this logic opens up a specific kind of logistic problem, which had to be solved by the use of the mathematico-logical form of the calculus of probability. I shall present briefly the outlines of this solution.

* * *

If the question of a generalization of two-valued logic into a multi-valued logic is to be considered, the grounds of the two-valued character of our logic must first be examined. When we analyze the statements of everyday life or of science from this point of view, we find that the dichotomy can by no means be called necessary. From the example "the weather is summerly" it is easily seen that this statement could very well be called "more or less true". If the weather is warm and the sky cloudless, the statement would be better justified than if clouds appear or a light shower falls, and in the event of extensive cloudiness or heavy downpours the statement will scarcely be regarded as adequate. It would be natural to ascribe to the statement a continuously variable degree w of truth, so that the current meteorological situation would make the statement "true to the degree w". But this treatment of statements is unusual; what is used instead is a division of all meteorological situations into summerly and nonsummerly ones by means of an artificial line of demarcation. In fact, the meteorologists have defined summerly weather by reference to a certain minimum duration of sunlight, a certain minimum value of day-time temperature, and of a certain maximum quantity of rain. In this manner the continuous scale has been transformed into a dichotomy.

This method evidently represents an arbitrary rule, and we have in fact to regard the two-valuedness of our logic as a convention, which could very well be replaced by another rule. All such rules constitute equivalent descriptions in the sense that any such description of nature will be adequate and that it is possible to transform one kind of description into the other. The transition from a continuous scale of truth values to the two-valued one can always be reached by means of an arbitrary dichotomy. We can compare the convention represented by the two-valuedness of our logic with the decimal character of our system of numbers, in which number 10 plays a similar part as the number 2 in two-valued logic; the possibility of translating every multi-valued description into a two-valued one corresponds to the possibility of translating any system of numbers, for instance, the duodecimal system, into the decimal one.

If from this point of view the two-valuedness of our logic appears as a property that can easily be eliminated, these considerations show, on the other hand, that nothing is gained by such an introduction of a multi-valuedness, because we arrive at equivalent descriptions. And indeed, the logic of the probability statement is not identical with a multi-valuedness of the type just described in the example of the summerly weather. This is clear from the fact that the characterization of the weather as "summerly to a certain degree" has no degree of indeterminacy attached to it, of the kind typical for probability statements. The multi-valued characterization of individual statements with respect to the varying degree of their exactness can, therefore, not represent that generalization of logic which we need for probability logic.

The unique problem of probability logic consists rather in the peculiarity that a multi-valued logic has to be constructed which applies although for individual statements we keep to two-valuedness. We call a future event probable, even though we know that a statement about it will be verified as true or false after its occurrence. The problem is to construct a multi-valued logic within the frame of a two-valued logic. This can be done if the concept of probability is given an interpretation, which has always been employed for a solution of the concept of probability: the frequency interpretation. The frequency interpretation derives the degree of probability from an enumeration of the truth values of individual statements and thus reduces the concept of probability to the concept of truth. This is the reason why the degree of probability cannot be conceived as a predicate of individual statements, but has to be referred to more general logical constructions, which are built up from individual statements in a similar way as a sequence is constructed from individual elements.

In carrying through this idea we meet a certain difficulty. Truth is a *property* of statements, i.e., it refers to one statement. Probability, however, is to be conceived as a *relation*, as was formulated in (1) and (2); a sequence of events possesses a probability only with regard to another sequence. It seems therefore difficult to interpret the concept of probability as an analogue of the concept of truth.‡

‡ [My paper of 1933 does not mention the fact that in order to make probability an analogue of truth a certain change in the interpretation of probability is necessary: probability then is not regarded as a property of events, or things, but as a property of linguistic expressions. In other words, the calculus of probability is then incorporated in the metalanguage. This transition is easily achieved for the frequency interpretation, since the numerical value of a probability will be the same whether we count events or the corresponding sentences about the occurrence of the events. Although the paper correctly employs the second interpretation, it would have been advisable to mention the duality of interpretation, which, incidentally, was clearly explained by Boole (G. Boole, *An Investigation of the Laws of Thought*, London, 1854, pp. 247–248).

We can overcome this difficulty by means of the following device. All those x_1 in the sequence of events (x_1), which do not belong to the class A, can be canceled; the remaining elements are renumbered, that is, receive a new subscript i, so that a reduced sequence (x_i) results, for which all x_i belong to A and which we shall call "compact". Likewise we omit all those elements y_i whose corresponding x_i are omitted and renumber the remaining elements y_i. The reduced sequence (x_i) can then be dispensed with; its function for the sequence (y_i) can be assigned to the subscript i, which expresses the enumeration. The frequency of B in the sequence (y_i) is now counted with respect to all elements y_i, no selection from this sequence being referred to. We then can conceive the probability as a property of the sequence (y_i) alone; we count the frequency of B in the sequence (y_i) and call this frequency the probability of B.

The sequence (y_i) so constructed can also be conceived in a different way. We explained above that the enumeration proceeds in terms of $y_i \epsilon B$ being valid or not. Because of the equivalence of classes and propositional functions we can also consider the propositional function ψy_i, which is identical with $y_i \epsilon B$; the counting of the frequency is then equivalent to counting whether the individual values of the propositional function ψ are true or false. The aggregate (ψy_i), which consists of a sequence of individual statements of the form ψy_i, may be called a *propositional sequence.*

The propositional sequence can be conceived as an extension of the concept of statement. The statement is derived from a propositional function by means of a coördination of a special value y_0 of the argument to the propositional function. In a similar way we can conceive the propositional sequence as being constructed by means of a coördination of the argument sequence (y_i) to the propositional function ψ. Just as the aggregate constructed by the coördination of an individual argument to a propositional function possesses a truth value, the aggregate resulting from the coördination of an argument sequence to a propositional function possesses a probability value. Probability is thus a property of propositional sequences in the same sense as truth is a property of statements. Incidentally, propositional sequences need not be infinite; our considerations can also be carried through for finite propositional sequences. This fact makes possible a transition from a propositional sequence to an individual statement: the statement appears as the special case of a propositional sequence in which the argument sequence coördinated to the propositional function consists of only one element.

The preceding considerations supply the fundamentals of probability logic. Probability logic is a logic of propositional sequences and ap-

---

This remark is the only correction I have to add to my paper of 1933. A correct exposition of the duality was given in my paper: "Über die semantische und die Objekt-Auffassung von Wahrscheinlichkeitsausdrücken", *Erkenntnis,* 8, 1939, pp. 50–68.]

pears as a generalization of the logic of statements, which may be likened to the transition from Euclidean geometry to Riemannian geometry. Riemannian geometry is based on the principle that the geometry of the large dimensions can have properties different from those of the geometry of the small dimensions. Similarly the aggregate *propositional sequence* is imbedded in a more general frame than is employed for individual statements, although statements are elements of propositional sequences. The logic of propositional sequences is so to speak a "logic of the large dimensions" and can therefore possess more general properties than the "logic of the small dimensions".

In order to carry through probability logic it is necessary to construct truth tables by analogy with classical logic. This is relatively easy, if the logistic conception of the calculus of probability is taken as a basis. It then is in fact possible to construct truth tables for the logical operations "and", "or", "implication", etc., which on the one hand satisfy the laws of the calculus of probability and on the other hand can be conceived as generalizations of the familiar logistic truth tables. This proof is given by the fact that the truth tables of probability logic, for the special case in which the propositional sequence consists of only one element, become identical with the logistic truth tables. For the formulation of these truth tables and the form of the transition to logistic truth tables we must refer to the paper *Probability Logic* mentioned above.

* * *

It is a peculiarity of the probability logic so constructed that it makes use of the frequency interpretation in the same sense as this interpretation is usually applied in the calculus of probability. Within the calculus of probability the character of being probable is not attached to the individual statement, but to the propositional sequence. The reduction of the probability value to an enumeration of truth values, which is thus accomplished, can be called the *extensional reduction* of probability logic. According to this interpretation we need not regard probability as a property existing independent of the truth value and belonging to the meaning of the statement, but can consider the probability of the propositional sequence as completely determined by the truth values of its individual elements.

With this extensional reduction, however, a fundamental difficulty inherent in the frequency interpretation is transmitted to probability logic. If probability is only a property of propositional sequences, what is the meaning of the degree of probability for the single case? There are numerous instances in everyday life as well as in science where we apparently deal with the probability of a single case; for instance, we may ask for the probability that the weather will be fine tomorrow, or that a certain planned action will be successful, or that a scientific experiment will furnish the result expected. How can probability logic help us in these cases, if probability concerns only a propositional sequence, i.e., a series of propositions similar to each other? This question has often been regarded a fundamental difficulty for any frequency interpretation; but it seems to me that this objection is not tenable. There is a way out which leads to a satisfactory solution of the problem of the single case without a renunciation of the frequency interpretation. We can illustrate this solution by recalling the behavior of a gambler: The gambler has to make a prediction before every game, although he knows that the calculated probability has a meaning only for larger numbers; and he makes his decision by betting, or as we shall say, by *positing* the more probable event. This positing does not mean that he is certain of the result. As a matter of fact, it does not mean any judgment about the single case under consideration; it means only that the decision for the more probable case represents a more favorable action than the opposite decision. The concept "more favorable" can be interpreted by a frequency statement: if the gambler follows the principle of positing always the more probable case, he can count on a greater number of successes in the long run than would obtain for the opposite behavior. The frequency interpretation justifies, indeed, a *posit* on the more probable case. It is true that it cannot give us a guarantee that we shall be successful in the particular instance considered; but instead it supplies us with a principle which in repeated application leads to a greater number of successes than would obtain if we acted against it.

The decisive logical tool in this consideration is the concept of *posit.* To posit a case does not mean to regard it as a necessary event or to regard the statement about it as true; nor, of course, does it mean the contrary. By positing an event we do not assert anything about the event considered, but perform an action about which we know only something more general: that it conforms to a principle which, when honored, leads to the greatest possible number of successes. If from this point of view we look at the numerous actions of daily life where we deal with the "probability of a single case", we notice that the concept of posit supplies a complete solution: we posit that the weather of tomorrow will have the most probable character, or that a planned action will have the most probable result, and although we do not know anything for the single case, we know that in this way we do the most favorable thing that we can do at all—we behave in such a way that we can count on the greatest number of successes. The concept of posit represents the bridge between the probability of the propositional sequence and the compulsion to make a decision in a single case. It is important to realize that the principle of the greatest number of successes is even applicable if we are not concerned with a repetition of cases of the same kind. If we posit in one case fine weather, in another one the satisfactory result of a financial transaction, in a third one the winning of a certain horse in a race, such cases constitute a sequence to which the frequency interpretation is applicable. The calculus of probability includes a theory of sequences which are played from element to element with a variable probability.[6]

We shall call a posit that conforms to the principle of the greatest number of successes the *best posit.* The probability belonging to this posit we call its *weight*; the weight is therefore the probability of the propositional sequence whose element is the posit under consideration. The concept of weight replaces the untenable concept of the probability of a single statement; we cannot coördinate a probability to a single statement, but we can coördinate a weight to it, by which the probability of the corresponding propositional sequence assumes an indirect meaning for the single case.

The best posit has only a restricted use, since it presupposes that we know the corresponding weight, i.e., the probability of the corresponding propositional sequence. There are cases where the probabilities are unknown, and we have to find out what constitutes the most favorable behavior in such cases.

* * *

With this question we enter into the fundamental problem of the concept of probability. We said above that the application of the calculus of probability to physical reality contains only one unsolved problem: in order to apply the calculus of probability we must determine the limit of an extensionally given sequence, of which only a first finite section is known. All other operations of the calculus of probability, we found, are of a tautological nature; only this one method requires critical analysis.

It is evidently the concept of *posit* which we have to employ for an explanation of this method. If in the finite section given we have observed a certain frequency§ f^n, we *posit* that the sequence, on further continuation, will converge towards a limit f^n (more precisely: within the interval $f^n \pm \delta$). We *posit* this; we do not say that it is true, we only posit it in the same sense as the gambler lays a wager on the horse which he believes to be the fastest. We perform an action which appears to us the most favorable one, without knowing anything about the success of this individual action.

In this instance, however, we are concerned with a kind of posit different from the one employed in the case of the best posit. The best posit can be chosen, if its corresponding weight, i.e., the probability of the corresponding propositional sequence, is known. It is true that we can also speak of a corresponding weight for the case of a posit concerning a limit; this weight is given by the probability of the occurrence of a certain probability, i.e., by a probability of the second level. It is very well possible

[6] Problems of this kind are treated by means of a *sequence lattice;* cf. the axiomatic construction of the calculus of probability mentioned above.

§ For notational reasons the number of the element at which the frequency f is considered is indicated by the superscript n.

to extend the theory of probability to such probabilities of a higher level. The frequency interpretation is likewise applicable; the individual sequence is then to be conceived as an element in a series of sequences in which the frequency of a sequence possessing a limit of a certain value is counted. But this determination can only be carried through, if a series of sequences exists; in general we deal only with an individual sequence and are then unable to determine the probability of the second level. Although the determination of a corresponding weight is possible in principle, we are in the peculiar situation that we have to make a posit without knowing the corresponding weight. We do not know, therefore, whether positing the value f^n of the limit is the best posit—yet we make this posit.

These considerations represent the peculiar problem of the inductive inference, since the ascertainment of a limit by the method discussed is identical with the inductive inference. It is true that this inference is usually only considered in the narrower form that an event occurs without exceptions in a great number of cases and we conclude that it will always occur; but this case must be regarded as the special case where the limit has the value 1; the logical problem is the same when the limit possesses any other value f^n. It is an important step to recognize that the inductive inference is not meant to supply a true statement, but a *posit*: we posit that the sequence will go on in the same way as observed. The difficulty lies in the fact that we must make this posit without knowing its weight.

And yet it is possible to give a justification even for this kind of posit. The following consideration will help us. Let us assume for the moment that there is a limit towards which the sequence converges, then there must be an n from which on our posit leads to the correct result; this follows from the definition of the limit, which requires that there be an n from which on the frequency remains within a given interval δ. If we were to adopt, on the contrary, the principle of always positing a limit outside $f^n \pm \delta$ when a frequency f^n has been observed, such a procedure would certainly lead us to a false result from a certain n on. This does not mean that there could not be other principles which like the first would lead to the correct limit. But we can make the following statement about these principles: even if they determine a posit outside $f^n \pm \delta$ for a smaller n, they must, from a certain n on, determine the posit within $f^n \pm \delta$. All other principles of positing must converge asymptotically with the first principle. This is the property which distinguishes the first principle from others: we know that it must eventually lead to the right result, whereas we know nothing about other principles—except that, if they are to be successful, they must eventually converge with the first.

We call such a posit an *approximative posit;* it represents an approximative method because it anticipates the aim and is used as though the aim had already been reached. Positing that the frequency will remain at the value last observed finds a justification, as we saw, by the fact that it will finally lead to the correct result, *if a limit of the frequency exists.* Let us assume temporarily this condition and postpone the question of how to dispense with it to a later discussion.

* * *

The method of the approximative posit requires a supplementation, which we must now explain. These considerations will show us at the same time the part played by probability logic in this connection.

We mentioned before that even the approximative posit is capable of receiving a weight, and that this weight can be found by considering the posit within the frame of a class of similar posits. Such an incorporation of individual posits in a comprehensive class actually occurs when scientific statements are made. Our judgment in the case of a series of individual observations is never based upon this observational series alone, but is also determined by a number of earlier experiences in other fields. If we throw a die, we shall not base the assumption of a probability $1/6$ on the present observational series alone; our judgment will also be influenced by experiences with earlier throws. If we want to be sure, we shall examine the center of gravity of the die by physical experiments and thereby include experiences of a mechanical type in our considerations. In this way a concatenation of all experiences obtains; this concatenation carries the advantage that we can construct probabilities of a higher level, which enable us to assign a weight to the posit pertaining to our series of experiments. This method applies likewise to very different examples. If the physicist measures a number of spectral lines and finds that the observational series can be extrapolated according to a certain rule, his confidence in this rule will be strengthened considerably, if the same rule is confirmed by other series of spectral lines. It is this method by means of which, for instance, a rule like Bohr's rule of the quanta is tested. The probability of the validity of Bohr's rule is thus made a probability of a higher level. This method can lead to the result that the original rules are to be subjected to a correction. If we find after 100 throws, for instance, that for a certain die the frequency is still very far from the required value $1/6$ for a certain face, and if we have made it sure by mechanical tests that the die is not loaded, we shall keep to the posit $1/6$ for the limit of the frequency. The original posit is subject to a correction in terms of the corresponding weight, which says in this case that there exists a high probability of the second level that the frequency of the sequence will converge toward the limit $1/6$.

This method of correction finds an extensive application in science; we may even say that scientific method is nothing but a continuous correction of posits by incorporating them into more general considerations. If the scientist predicts the orbit of a new planet, this prediction is essentially based upon experiences concerning other planets, and the laws which he applies to the movements of the planets are in turn connected with experiences concerning very different objects by means of a concatenation with other mechanical phenomena. The system of scientific knowledge can be conceived as a method of correction, which relates every individual statement to the total system of experience. It is the significance of scientific method that for the prediction of a new phenomenon we are never dependent on the specific observations alone to which the prediction refers, but that we can also make use of the vast domain of experiences in very different fields.

This concatenation of experiences is not so rigid, on the other hand, as to deprive the single event of its independence. If we find that a certain individual sequence *retains* its frequency in repeated continuation, although the total system of experiences makes another limit more probable, we shall finally believe in the deviating value for this single case. The system presents us only with a *probability* for the single case, not with an absolute *certainty*. The peculiar tension between individual fact and system, which is characteristic for all scientific research and which is expressed in the old struggle between experiment and theory, receives its strict formulation within the frame of probability logic. It appears as an interrelation between the individual posit and its weight and obtains in this way its mathematical expression.

Let us analyze more precisely the determination of the probability of the second level. It is based again on a posit, which we may call secondary posit, in contradistinction to the primary posits. That we deal only with a posit follows from the fact that, as always, we are given only a finite number of observed cases and are dependent on the method of the approximative posit. The method of correction can thus be described as follows: at first we make a number of primary posits; by regarding them as valid, we arrive at secondary posits. We can use the secondary posits, on the other hand, to correct the primary posits for an individual case. This is no contradiction, although the determination of the secondary posits presupposes the primary posits as valid. The reason is that certain changes in the primary posits furnish only very small changes for the secondary posits. For example: if an electric current flows through a wire, the wire will generally be heated; the posit that in a certain individual case the wire will be heated by the current is therefore corroborated by the secondary posit that in general the flowing of a current produces heat. If the wire is submerged in liquid helium, the primary posit will be false in this individual case (because of supraconductivity), but this does not mean that in general the secondary posit will be false. Often we even have to retain the secondary posits in order to prove that the primary posit is false in the individual case considered. For instance, the current flowing through the supraconductor may be measured in another sector of the circuit by a heat-ampèremeter so that the statement "in the supraconductor there flows a current which does not cause any heat there" is based upon an observation which assumes the heating as a criterion of the flow of the current. The importance of the method of correction and the adaptability of scientific method to new observational discoveries is founded on the relative independence of secondary posits.

The logical schema explained above can now be incorporated into the frame of probability logic. Scientific knowledge starts with primary posits; but we do not stop with them and go on to secondary posits, which furnish a weight of the primary posits and thereby coördinate to them a degree of probability. The primary posits acquire the character of statements which are not judged as true or false, but as more or less probable. On the basis of the probabilities so determined the primary posits can thus be transformed into best posits on the basis of a known weight. On this step, however, the secondary posits remain without any weight, that is, we do not know whether they are the best ones; they are approximate posits in the sense of our definition. But we can repeat the same method and proceed to tertiary posits, which admit of the determination of weights of secondary posits. The approximative character is thereby shifted to the tertiary posits, and so on. We thus obtain a concatenated system of posits, in which weights are known for the posits of lower levels; only the posits of the last level are made without the knowledge of a corresponding weight.

Scientific knowledge represents, therefore, a system of concatenated posits which has an inner order in terms of the principle of the best posit, but which as a whole is so to speak suspended in midair, since there is no weight known for the posits of the last level. In spite of this apparent indeterminacy we can point out the advantage of such a concatenated system. For the justification of the approximative posits we made use of the idea that if there is a limit of the frequency, the approximative posit will finally lead to success. The difficulty arising for this approximative method originates from the fact that we do not know at which place n of the sequence the convergence is reached, so that under certain conditions we continue to make bad posits for a long time, that is, as long as we are very far away from the place of convergence. It is the significance of the method of correction to make possible a faster convergence. It can be shown that the system as a whole converges better than an individual primary posit. The reason is that the posits of a higher level are relatively independent of the posits of a lower level. Consequently we can count on a faster convergence for a primary posit which has been corrected by the total system.

Let us illustrate this correction by an example. If an observer finds that a low position of the barometer is frequently connected with rain, he will posit rain when he observes a low position of the barometer. This primary posit is not very good, and the observer will be disappointed relatively often. Now the system of scientific experiences shows that we arrive at better predictions, if in addition to the position of the barometer we take into account the humidity of the air; in other words, we find that in those cases in which rain was posited for a low position of the barometer the prediction was confirmed mainly within the narrower class of cases in which the low position of the barometer was associated with a high position of the hygrometer. In this way the primary posit is corrected by a system of more comprehensive experiences. If the scientist belittles the advocate of a primitive empiricism, whose knowledge consists merely in "empirical rules", he is justified in so far as he asks that the total system of experience, at the disposition of the scientist, should be used for a correction of the primary empirical rules. It would be a mistake, however, to believe that the scientist applies a method different in principle from that of the pure empiricist. Even the theorems established by scientific method represent posits; but the superiority of these posits derives from the fact that they are posits of a higher level and therefore lead to a faster convergence.

We must therefore conceive the system of scientific statements, not as a system of true statements in the sense of two-valued logic, but as a system of posits ordered within the frame of probability logic. The inductive inference is the only assumption of a non-analytic nature contained in this system, and we found that this inference is to be interpreted by the concept of the approximative posit. It represents a method of approximation which we are justified to use if the occurring sequences possess a limit character. It is the only approximative system of which, on this condition, we know something positive: we know that this method will lead to our aim if the condition is satisfied. A further result is added by the analysis of the method of concatenation: we know the concatenated system converges better than the individual posit.

This is indeed a far-reaching justification of the inductive inference; but we still have to free ourselves from the last condition which we have used.

* * *

This condition consists in the assumption that we know a limit of the frequency to exist for the sequences considered. Only on this condition does the method of the approximative posit lead to the correct value. If no limit exists, we shall never have success when we posit the persistence of the frequency; and the method of correction is useless, too, because it cannot lead to success either.

It would be all too audacious to contend that for some reason or other all sequences occurring in nature must have a limit of the frequency. The philosophy of the *a priori* would certainly be ready for such a pseudoproof. We must realize, however, that an assumption of this kind, i.e., an assumption above the content of all possible experience, is undemonstrable and that we have no reason to believe it. In spite of this difficulty it can be shown that we may continue the path of our considerations.

What would be the case if the sequences occurring in nature would not possess a limit of the frequency? All systematic predictions would be impossible. A prediction might come true by chance once in a while, but we would have to renounce the possibility of consistently confirming the prediction as well as the possibility of constructing a system of better convergence. The attempt of science to arrive at a system of reliable predictions would be futile.

What conclusion can be drawn? It follows that the approximative posit, i.e., the inductive inference, has *no* justification if we know that the sequences occurring in nature have no limit of the frequency. But this is by no means our situation. It would be false to say: "*we know* that there *exists* a limit of the frequency", but it would likewise be false to say: "*we know* that a limit of the frequency does *not exist*". We are confronted by an indeterminacy: *we do not know* whether there exists a limit of the frequency.

In this situation the approximative posit carries a decisive advantage over all other posits. We know: if the sequences occurring in nature possess a limit of the frequency we shall eventually arrive at reliable predictions by applying the method of the approximative posit; and if there is no limit we shall never attain this goal. If anything can be achieved at all, we shall reach our aim by applying the method of the approximative posit; otherwise we shall not attain anything.

With these considerations the method of the approximative posit, that is, the inductive inference, finds its justification. The inductive inference is the only method of which we know that it leads to the aim if the aim can be reached; this is the reason why we must use it, if we want to reach the aim. The problem of the inductive inference finds its solution by means of the argument that it is not necessary for the application of this inference to know a *positive* condition to hold, but that the application is already justified if a *negative* condition is *not* known to hold.

We are often confronted by similar situations in daily life. We want to reach a certain aim and we know of a necessary step, which we shall have to take in order to attain this aim, but we do not know whether this step is sufficient. He who wants to reach the aim will have to take the step, even if it is uncertain whether he will reach his aim in this way. The businessman who keeps his store well stocked so that he can sell something when a customer comes in, the unemployed who makes an application with reference to an advertisement in the paper, although he does not know whether he will receive an answer, the ship-wrecked man who climbs a cliff, although he does not know whether a rescue-ship will spot him—all these persons find themselves in an analogous situation; they satisfy the *necessary* conditions of reaching an aim without knowing whether the *sufficient* conditions are satisfied. We can apply this analogy because we know that the inductive inference must not be construed as an instrument of finding a true statement, but of finding a posit, and that we derive the conclusion not from the viewpoint of truth, but from the viewpoint of the most favorable step which we can take. The most favorable step toward the aim of prediction is that step of which we know that on repetition it must eventually lead to the aim if this aim is attainable at all—and this is the step made in the inductive inference.

With this result we also overcome an objection which was seen in the fact that the *n* of the place of convergence will forever remain unknown. The argument has been advanced that the limit-character of the sequences is useless for us, because the convergence may start after such a large number of elements that it will remain unattainable during the restricted lifetime of human beings. It is true that in the case of such badly converging sequences predictions would be impossible; this case would in all practical respects have the same consequence as the case in which the sequences do not converge at all. Since we could show, however, that we can even include this more general case into our considerations and still arrive at a justification of the approximative posit, the case of the badly converging sequences is also taken care of. Similar to the situation previously discussed, we must say, not that we *know* of the bad convergence, but that we *do not know* whether a good convergence will take place.

If we now analyze critically the considerations leading to a justification of the inductive inference, we should like to point out the significance of this justification as follows. It has been shown for a long time that a logical justification in the sense of a guarantee of success cannot be given for the inductive inference. It would be incorrect, however, to infer that the inductive inference represents a perfectly arbitrary action, that it is so to speak the private affair of everybody whether or not he wants to act according to the principle of the inductive inference. If this were the case, if we had no reason to prefer the posit determined by the inductive inference to other posits, we would be completely lost in all situations of everyday life. But all our behavior, our persistent adherence to the inductive inference, proves that we believe by no means in an equivalence of all kinds of posits, but that we prefer a certain kind of posit, i.e., the one in accordance with the inductive inference. It is the significance of our theory that it succeeds in establishing the preëminence of this posit. The method of correction which we described can be conceived as the establishment of an order for all posits; although we can in no way claim certainty of success for the method described, we can at least maintain that we have arranged the possible posits in the best order attainable, if success can be reached at all. This is the reason why we may regard our theory of the inductive inference as a solution of the problem; in spite of the uncertainty of future happenings we can prove a logical superiority for all those actions which are performed according to the principle of induction.

Our investigaton has come to an end. We could show that the non-analytic assumptions for the application of the calculus of probability to physical reality, and thus in all empirical sciences, are reducible to one, to the inductive inference. And we are in a position to give an explanation for this inference, which since Hume has been recognized by all empiricists to be the central problem of epistemology. This explanation is achieved by the incorporation of the inductive inference in the frame of probability logic and the proof that it represents a method of approximation which has the character of a necessary condition for the making of predictions. He who wants greater certainty, who does not want to make any predictions before he can believe with certainty in their coming true, cannot be helped. We others are satisfied if we know a method by means of which we can at least *posit* the future—if we know we are doing our best to attain success, since a guarantee for success is not given to us.

The Logic of Quanta *

GUSTAV BERGMANN

"THE PHILOSOPHICAL PROBLEMS of quantum mechanics are centered around two main issues. The first concerns the transition from causal laws to probability laws; the second concerns the interpretation of unobserved objects." All philosophical analysts will agree with this statement of Reichenbach's in the opening paragraph of his recent book [1] as to what they hope to accomplish when they turn their attention to the momentous development of quantum mechanics that took place during the last two decades. But unanimity about the *what* does not imply unanimity as to the *how.* I, for one, am unable to accept the fundamental ideas of Reichenbach's approach; consequently, I find myself in disagreement with several important features of his analysis. Perhaps the present essay would not have been written, were it not for the challenge of his work to all those who, without sharing his philosophical ideas, share his conviction that the philosophy of science, if it is to be significant, must be minute, technical, and—in a loose sense of the terms—operational and positivistic. Reichenbach's book is all this and, to that extent, very admirable. Yet I shall here present my own analysis quite independently and, but for a few incidental remarks, quite unpolemically. I wish to say, however, that Reichenbach's work is one of the two from which I learned most. The other is von Neumann's *Mathematische Grundlagen der Quantenmechanik.*

When I speak of the logic or philosophy of science, or of a certain area of science, I use the terms as I did in some previous papers that appeared in this journal.[2,3] Hence I shall not take time to explain them again in any detail. Briefly, the logical analysis of science is a certain kind of description of science. It is not technical about the things science is technical about, yet it has standards and a technic of its own. To give an illustration, a logician who uses such words as 'causal,' 'operational,' 'measurement,' must try to be as precise as physicists are in speaking about force

* Reprinted by kind permission of the author and the editor from the *American Journal of Physics,* 15, 1947.

[1] H. Reichenbach, *Philosophical foundations of quantum mechanics* (Univ. of California Press, 1944).

[2] G. Bergmann, "Outline of an empiricist philosophy of physics," *Am. J. Physics* 11, 248, 335 (1943). [Reprinted in this volume, pp. 262–287.]

[3] G. Bergmann, "The logic of probability," *Am. J. Physics,* 9, 263 (1941).

and energy. The purpose of the present essay is to outline a description of the modern quantum theory that is technical and, I hope, precise in this sense. The job is still largely undone. Reichenbach's book is the first systematic attempt that goes beyond the obvious generalities.[4] Physicists have given us many valuable hints; but these are mostly isolated flashes of insight. Some other comments they have made are either vague or outright confusing. If, for instance, I read, in a physicist's book on quantum mechanics, that it is "operationally meaningless" to speak of the particle's position and momentum beyond the limits of the indeterminacy relation, I see immediately that the term is not used in any precise and specific sense. So I react as a physicist would react when a speculative philosopher tries to buttress his constructions by an analogical use of 'force' and 'energy.' So-called operational analysis is but one aspect of the description of science and applies only to *empirical constructs.* Appeal to it is quite out of place when one examines those features of a calculus or *computational schema* that determine whether it is a *model,* that is, the kind of schema in which one can—in a certain sense—speak of the "position" and the "momentum" of a "particle." Again, a model's being meaningful does not depend on the possibility of assigning precise numerical values, or any numerical values, to all its magnitudes by means of the *theory* of which it is a part. At any rate, such a criterion of meaning would throw out theories which, though now obsolete, are methodologically quite acceptable.

I wish that I could now define the four italicized terms—empirical construct, computational schema, model, theory—and show the advantages such definitions yield, by way of clarification and through the elimination of pseudo-problems. Unfortunately, a moderately adequate explanation fills 30 columns of this journal.[2] Nor can I, with respect to probability, repeat the exposition and defense of the frequency view that I have undertaken elsewhere. But the reader will, in the first part of the present paper, find as much of this material as could be included without untoward repetition. The first part (Secs. I to III) deals with the fundamental notions of measurement, determinism and mechanism, causality, probability, and statistics. Except for a scattering of anticipatory remarks to hold and direct the attention, these sections contain no direct references to the quantum theory. Taking advantage of the background thus provided, the second part (Secs. IV to VII) begins with an outline of the general structure of the quantum theory. This is followed by a description of the calculus whose construction was begun by Schrödinger and Heisenberg, and an analysis of the position that this calculus—the quantum-mechanical schema—occupies in the total structure of the theory. The last section is a separate discussion of two important problems in the logic of quanta.

[4] This is not meant as a criticism of Philipp Frank's *Interpretations and misinterpretations of modern physics* (Hermann & Cie., 1938), a painstaking and lucid refutation of the various attempts to build a metaphysics of freedom upon the vocabulary of modern physics. But the significance and intention of this book are cultural rather than technical.

I. Measurement

(1) Speaking within physics rather than philosophizing about it, we use the term 'measurement' very broadly. We say that we measure the temperature of a gas, but we also say that we measure the (average) velocity of its molecules. These are two different things. The difference I have in mind is not that in the first case we simply read an instrument, while in the second we derive the numerical value from several such readings through a fair amount of computation. The important difference is, rather, that in the case of temperature we measure an empirical construct, while the second number [5] receives its full meaning or interpretation only as the result of an additional step, the coordination of, say, the classical kinetic model to the empirical constructs and laws of thermodynamics. Ambiguities of this kind are harmless so long as they do not obstruct the precise description of situations where the difference they neglect does make a difference. With respect to 'measure' and 'measurement,' such a situation has arisen in the quantum theory. If, therefore, I shall hereafter speak of 'measurement,' the expression will refer to the *measurement of empirical constructs;* whenever the magnitudes of a model or certain other schemas are involved, I shall speak of the *assignment of numerical values.*

(2) In some discussions of the quantum theory one reads that observation and measurement, by affecting the objects observed or measured, introduce an ineradicably *subjective* factor into all our knowledge. Having delivered himself of this opinion, the writer usually pays a compliment to the positivists or other philosophers whom he believes to have disposed of the fable of an independent or objective reality. All this is very confusing. What the physicist impugns, or has a right to impugn, is not the common-sense realism that we all share but merely the naive belief in the "reality" or "existence" of the classical models. The particles of these models are not, and never were, either observed or unobserved objects, in the only intelligible sense of the term—the sense in which trees, stones, laboratory equipment are objects that may or may not be observed. The confusion stems thus from two sources: first, from an analogical use of 'observed' in such phrases as 'indirectly observed', second, from the unguarded use of 'subjective', 'objective', 'reality' and similarly slippery terms that are better left to the philosophers. (Philosophers of my stripe try very hard to avoid them.)

Measurement is based on the observation of scales, and I have never heard it suggested that we make a needle move by watching it, which is but another way of saying that on the common-sense level of laboratory

[5] Since it is computationally derived from the values of empirical constructs, this number is, in one sense, also an empirical construct. But this sense is trivial; it neglects differences that we feel exist and that should be clarified. An *empirical construct* is—*very* roughly speaking—a concept defined in terms of the immediately observable by a chain of "explicit definitions." See also Sec. II (4), where it is contrasted with the "theoretical constructs" of a model.

objects and their immediately observable properties and relations the language of common-sense realism is the only reasonable one. The ancient puzzle how we can ever know that when we do not watch them stones, trees, and laboratory equipment behave exactly as when we do watch them is better left to the epistemologist. This is a *verbal* puzzle, not a factual assumption that we may be induced to drop by developments, no matter how revolutionary, in theoretical physics. Conversely, the solution of this puzzle—if it is a puzzle—depends on the *grammar* of 'perceive (observe)' and 'exist,' not on the *physiology* of perception, with or without benefit of the indeterminacy relation. To drag physiology or the so-called mind-body problem into the methodological analysis of physics makes no more sense to me than Descartes' "derivation" of the conservation of momentum from the perfection of the Creator. To say the same thing again, in three explicit steps: (i) our observing them makes, on the common-sense level, no difference to the behavior of ordinary physical objects; (ii) this behavior is the subject matter of all measurement and, in a familiar interpretation, of all science; (iii) therefore, it is hard to see how a philosophical or otherwise radical notion of subjectivity could enter into the methodological analysis of science. These are the reasons why I believe that whenever this particular twist has been introduced, it has, far from contributing to it, retarded a precise description of the quantum theory. To quote Reichenbach who, for reasons of his own, makes the same point: "Like all other parts of physics, quantum mechanics deals with nothing but relations between physical things; all its statements can be made without reference to an observer." [6] But then, for Reichenbach a tree and an electron are both "things."

Confused as the talk about subjectivity is, it often appears in remarks about a very fundamental aspect of measurement. Systematically, this aspect is not quite new nor, as a point about measurement, peculiar to the quantum theory. Historically, it seems that this aspect did not receive all the attention it deserved before it was brought up—though often for the wrong reasons and in the wrong context—in recent discussions of the quantum theory. I turn now to the discussion of this aspect.

(3) In measuring an empirical construct exemplified by an object or situation A at a given moment—or, as I shall say briefly, in measuring A—one does not observe A alone but, rather, certain aspects of a situation (A, B), compounded of A and the yardstick or measuring instrument B. There is thus the possibility of an interaction by which the two components of the new situation, A and B, may produce changes in each other. That gives rise to two questions: (i) how can we recognize such changes? (ii) under what conditions is a feature of (A, B) acceptable as a measurement of A, that is, as an index or characterizer of A alone?

The answer to the first question is self-evident. We shall say that A has been changed by being put in the measuring situation if it subsequently

[6] Reference 1, p. 15.

behaves *in some respect* differently from A'—which is *otherwise exactly like* A, but has not been measured—provided that *the difference cannot be attributed to other factors.* If differences occur only while (A, B) is maintained, the change may be called temporary. The three italicized clauses reveal the hypothetical and conventional ingredients that inhere in the notion of change. Their precise discussion, though very laborious, is sufficiently elementary and familiar that we need not bother with it in this paper. The point is simply that whatever we know, on the levels of either science or common sense, we know not by itself but embedded, as it were, in a network of hypotheses (empirical laws) and definitions. If a measurement does not, in this sense, produce a change in A, then its immediate repetition will yield the same value. Clearly, the converse does not hold; there is still the possibility of different or later changes. In accepting the repetition test as a *criterion of noninteraction,* one introduces, therefore, but another convention—though, of course, a plausible one. However, the repetition test has been suggested, not as a criterion of noninteraction, but as part of the *definition of measurement.* The suggestion is unnecessarily restrictive. Perhaps it would not have been made if the distinction between measurement proper and the assignment of numerical values to the magnitudes of the quantum-mechanical schema had been appreciated. But of this I shall speak later. Let me now try to give a nonrestrictive definition of measurement. To do this is to answer the second of the two questions I have proposed.

A property of (A, B) *is a measure of* A *if and only if it enters, together with other such properties of* A *(and of other objects), into empirical laws that predict or postdict the behavior, before or after the occurrence of* (A, B)*, of* A *(or of* A *in interaction with other objects).* To be a measurement in this sense, a property of (A, B) need not satisfy the repetition criterion; yet it seems to me that the definition realizes the scientist's working conception of measurement. To show this, assume that there is, in a world otherwise like ours, a magic rod, such that any expanse laid off against its contracts, virtually instantaneously and permanently, to nine-tenths of its previous length. Since this world is by assumption otherwise like ours, its physicists could discover the curious phenomenon. They would know that an object which, thus measured, is found to be of length l will henceforward behave like such an object; and they would also know that up to the time of the measurement with the magic rod it behaved like an object of length $10/9l$. I wonder what else one could expect measurement to achieve. As a matter of convenience, measurement without interaction is often preferable. But such measurement is not always available. One merely has to think of the measurements of temperature and of electric field strength by means of thermometers and electroscopic devices. Finally, whether or not there is interaction does not depend on the schema, classical or otherwise, that we use in our theories. Measurement, as here defined, is entirely a matter of empirical constructs and empirical laws.

Presently I shall define what we mean by 'accuracy' and 'statistical.' In order not to have to return to the discussion of interaction, I shall first make two remarks that are probably clear already; they will, at any rate, be clear after these further notions have been introduced. (i) Interaction in measurement does not, as such, impose any limits on its accuracy. (ii) Interaction in measurement does not prejudge the form of the empirical laws, whether statistical or nonstatistical, in which the constructs measured occur; nor does it, *a fortiori*, determine whether the theoretical schemas that account for these laws are either statistical or nonstatistical. If the electron and the photon of the classical Compton experiment were ordinary physical objects such as stones and light beams, one could therefore say, as Reichenbach does, that "the disturbance by observation, in itself, does not lead to the indeterminacy of the observation." [7] However, by thus neglecting an important difference this formulation blurs another distinction. The indeterminacy relation, which is a matter of the *quantum-mechanical schema* and not of observation, is *one* thing. The impossibility of assigning, within the *semiclassical model*, precise values to both the position and the momentum of the Compton electron before the collision is *another* thing. Again, this impossibility has nothing to do with interaction in, or the limits of accuracy of, measurement. It is, as we shall see, a consequence of certain empirical laws and of the manner in which the entities of the semiclassical theory are coordinated to the empirical constructs. By 'semiclassical theory' I mean the schema—devised by Bohr, Einstein and others—that was in use before Heisenberg and Schrödinger introduced their radical innovations.

(4) We are, as Bertrand Russell once said, quite certain that Cleopatra had 2 eyes and 1 nose and not, perhaps, 2.000001 eyes and 0.999998 noses. Counting is, indeed, the only empirical use of numbers that is precise and accurate. The measurement of continuous dimensions, such as time and space, is not precise and accurate in the same sense. Familiar as this sounds, it is, I believe, worth while to state carefully what we really mean by such terms as 'precise' and 'accurate.' Before turning to this task, I wish to make two preliminary remarks. They, too, cover familiar ground. *First*, the use of real numbers and continuous functions in the description of the empirical material is but a very successful convention, adopted because of the many conveniences it affords in formulation and computation. Accordingly, 'continuous' as just used in 'continuous function' is a purely arithmetic notion, to be distinguished from the 'continuous' in 'continuous dimension,' a phrase that occurs above. In the latter usage 'continuous' is a qualitative term that does not require further analysis for our purposes. *Second*, there is no direct connection between the 'precision' of the discrete eigenvalues that occur in the quantum-mechanical schema and the 'precision,' or the lack of such, with which we measure position, breadth and intensity of the spectral lines whose behavior we explain by a theory of which that schema is a part. It is, of course, a consequence of this theory as a whole that there are limits

[7] Reference 1, p. 17.

to the accuracy with which we measure empirical constructs. But then, such limitation is also a consequence of the semiclassical or the classical theory or, for that matter, of almost any corpuscular and, in this sense, discontinuous theory of matter. Obvious as all this is, it cuts the ground from under a good deal of loose talk.

One may measure the length of an iron rod with an ordinary yardstick to the nearest full inch, or one may measure the same stick with a more elaborate instrument to the nearest 0.01 in. In either case, as in all measurement, one manipulates physical objects and, eventually, reads a scale. The perceptual exertion required may actually be greater in the first case than in the second. Yet we call the second measurement more precise than the former—or this, at least, is how I shall define 'precision.' *Precision*, then, means *the number of digits of a given unit*. The larger this number, the greater the precision. How precise we can be is a matter of empirical laws and, in particular, of those empirical laws that are sometimes referred to as the theory of the instrument. On the other hand, a measurement whose precision is much less than the best we can do may be completely reliable, a measurement being called *reliable* when *in a large number of repetitions the result is always the same*. (The qualifications due to possible interaction and other factors that may interfere with this sameness need not bother us after what has been said before.) If the necessary care is taken, the first of the two measurements of the iron rod is, in fact, completely reliable. The second measurement, which is more precise, is less likely to be completely reliable. The values obtained will scatter or, as one also says, their standard error will not be equal to zero. Having thus defined precision and reliability, I turn to a definition of *accuracy*. The following is, I believe, an exact statement of that rather fundamental feature of our world to which we refer when we say that there is, in fact, a limit to the accuracy of our measurements. *A measurement as precise as we can make it is never completely reliable. Its standard error, though absolutely decreasing with increasing precision, shows no tendency to decrease in proportion to the last digit*. Conversely, if our most precise measurements were completely reliable, we would not consider them as of limited accuracy. Such a state of affairs, by the way, would not necessarily imply that we must forgo the convenience of real numbers in describing it. Whether at all and under what conditions it would be compatible with a corpuscular theory is not an easy question; it has, I believe, some connection with certain aspects of the Zeno paradoxes.

As is well known, we do not in careful experimental work expect our measurements to be reliable. We repeat them, define their average as the "true value" and operate in the formulation and testing of laws with the value thus obtained. Anybody who wishes to describe this state of affairs by saying that all laws of nature are "statistical" is free to do so. But having made this choice of meaning, he is no longer free to use the same term in a different and more specific sense in which not all but only some empirical laws and theories are statistical. Or, at least, he may not do so without being explicit about it. Furthermore, anybody who is thus explicit will not be tempted to believe that the inaccuracy of measurement, by making all laws "statistical," implies or even suggests the "statistical" nature of the quantum theory. In order to make this point as vigorously as possible, I shall henceforth assume that our measurements can be made ideally accurate. The assumption is, of course, contrary to fact. Its expository value lies in the circumstance that with it the methodological problems of the quantum theory are exactly what they are without it.

II. Mechanism and Determinism

I turn now to questions that are usually considered under the headings "determinism" and "mechanism." It will be best to begin with an illustration. Assume, then, that a physicist observes, over a period of time, a *configuration* consisting of n objects, $P_1, P_2, \cdots, P_n$. From previous observations he knows that each P_i is characterized by a number m_i, the value of an empirical construct called the mass of P_i, so that $dm_i/dt = 0$. The set of numbers $[m_1, m_2, \cdots, m_n]$ is a construct that one may use to characterize the configuration. At a certain moment ($t = 0$) the physicist measures certain empirical constructs characteristic of the *condition* of the configuration at that moment, namely, the $3n$ position coordinates $(q_1, q_2, \cdots, q_{3n})$ and the $3n$ momentum coordinates $(p_1, p_2, \cdots, p_{3n})$. The $7n$ numbers m_i, q_i, p_i, when substituted in a certain formula or computation rule, yield $6n$ functions of a continuous parameter, $q_1(t), \cdots, p_{3n}(t)$. (The computation rule prescribes, of course, the solution of the canonic equations: $\dot{p}_i = -\partial H/\partial q_i$, $\dot{q}_i = \partial H/\partial p_i$.) The $6n$ values $q_1{}^1, \cdots, p_{3n}{}^1$ of these functions for $t = t_1$ are then the values the physicist predicts ($t_1 > 0$) or postdicts ($t_1 < 0$) for the coordinates of $P_1, P_2, \cdots, P_n$ at the time t_1. This is, of course, a philosopher's description—with its characteristic shift in emphasis—of the classical treatment of the problem of n bodies. I shall use it to introduce some distinctions.

Let us first consider the whole thing formally, as a definitional arithmetic *schema* of the sort that is also called a calculus. First, one defines three kinds of entities: systems, states, processes. A *system* is an ordered set of M real numbers $[c_1, c_2, \cdots, c_M]$. A *state* is an ordered set of N real numbers $[x_1{}^0, x_2{}^0, \cdots, x_n{}^0]$; and there is also a rule that determines when a state may be said to be a (possible) *state of a system*. In our illustration, systems are restricted to sets of positive numbers and the rule is, very simply, $N = 6M$. A *process* is an ordered set of N functions—with certain mathematical characteristics—of a continuous parameter t, which is referred to as time, $[x_1(t), \cdots, x_n(t)]$. Next, given a system and one of "its" states $[x_1{}^0, x_2{}^0, \cdots, x_N{}^0]$, there is a rule that allows for the computation of one and only one process so that $x_i{}^0 = x_i(0)$. This rule is the part of the whole schema that is usually spoken of as the calculus; I shall refer to it as the *process formula*. It has, typically, the form of a system of ordinary differential equations. Of the schema as a whole I shall speak as a *process schema*. I could also call it a "causal" schema, but I prefer not to make any technical use of this term.

Several generalizations and variations of the process schema are of interest. In one rather common case, states and systems are not defined as finite ordered sets of numbers, but as functions, or ordered sets of functions, with certain mathematical characteristics, of one or several continuous variables. Such process schemas are called *field* schemas. Their formula has, typically, the form of a system of partial differential equations. Again, if these equations are of a certain special form, the schema is called a *wave* schema. These are the only precise meanings the terms 'field' and 'wave' have in theoretical physics.[8] To mention another possibility, the process formula may allow for the computation of a process not from one of its states, but only from one of its segments ($a \leqslant t \leqslant b$). It is then, typically, a system of integro-differential equations. As Volterra first pointed out, such a schema represents our notion of "historical" lawfulness in one precise sense of the term. In another, weaker sense, all process schemas are historical.

It will be noticed that I have distinguished between configurations and conditions "out there," on the one hand, and systems and states, which are purely arithmetic entities, on the other. Also, I have spoken of schemas (calculi) and, in doing so, avoided the customary term, theory. There is a point to all this circumstantiality. For instance, a certain type of theory[9] —I shall call it *process theory*—can now be described as follows. (i) One designates a class of configurations. For a theory to be considered worth while, this class must be rather comprehensive. Let C be an arbitrary member of it. (ii) One defines a finite class E of kinds of empirical constructs realized in these configurations. (iii) One selects a set of measurements of constructs of E to be performed on C and on any of its momentary conditions. Let the numbers of these measurements be M and N, respectively. (iv) One defines a process schema S. (v) One establishes a special set of rules—the so-called coordinating definitions—such that from each set of $M + N$ measurements, the last N of which characterize the condition of C at time t_0, one and only one set of N numbers can be computed, by means of S, for an arbitrary value t of the parameter. If this latter set, so far as we know, is always identical with the measures that characterize, in proper order, the condition of C at time t, then the theory is said to be successful.

If the theory is successful, then two configurations that yield, literally, identical measurements—this identity is one of numbers—are said to be identical; similarly for conditions of identical configurations. *Identity* in

[8] Some confusion has recently been created in the methodology of the behavior sciences (psychology, sociology) through an ambiguous use of the term 'field.' While some analogies with physical field theories are claimed, the term actually is used in the sense of interaction.

[9] In my earlier paper (reference 2) the term 'theory' was restricted to what is here called a theory with a mechanical model; other "theories" were spoken of as systems of empirical laws. The present change in terminology makes it easier to use 'system' in the way in which it is customarily used in quantum mechanics.

this sense is clearly a matter of definition. It signifies what I expressed, in SEC. I, by speaking of two objects or situations as exactly alike. Also, it is merely an identity with respect to a given theory and cannot even be stated without reference to the success of the latter. The behavior of configurations that allow for such treatment may be said to be "determined" by any of their temporal cross sections (initial conditions). Indeed, we are now ready to select a precise meaning for the term 'determinism.' But, of course, any such choice of meaning is arbitrary in that rather limited and peculiar sense in which one cannot help being arbitrary when one tries to state precisely and abstractly what people speak and think of in terms of concrete cases. For instance, 'mechanism' and 'causality' are sometimes used to connote, among other things, what is here called determinism. What words are used is of no consequence. The important thing is that one does not use any of these elusive terms without first defining them, and that, having defined them, one does not use them in any other sense.

(2) Speculation purporting to prove that there must be or that there cannot be a comprehensive process theory has continued for centuries. Such "metaphysical" preoccupation with "determinism" is, from the viewpoint here taken, irrelevant. Whether and to what extent process theories are successful is entirely a matter of fact. Yet a clear notion of what could be meant by a *comprehensive process theory* is helpful. The way to attain this clarification is to describe the state of affairs that would prevail if we were in possession of such a theory. To do this, consider a finite physical space F, say the office in which I sit while writing this. Now we make two assumptions.

First, we assume that there is a finite class E' of kinds of empirical construct (for example, when the comprehensive theory is "mechanistic," mass, position, momentum) such that the numerical values at any moment t of *all possible* empirical constructs realized in F can be computed from measurements, at t in F, of constructs of the class E'. The formulas allowing for these computations are sometimes referred to as operational definitions. However, the term is better avoided. For, whenever a construct is defined independently of E', then the formula for it is not a definition but an empirical law of the cross-sectional type, such as $pv = RT$. Second, we assume that there is a process theory applying to *all possible* configurations in F, so that E' is identical with the class E of the theory. A theory satisfying these two conditions would be a comprehensive theory for F.

The space F is ordinarily called a closed system or, in case the "action flow" through its boundary does not vanish, a controlled system. Whenever one fails to find a theory, comprehensive or otherwise, for a piece of space F, one can always renew one's efforts for another, larger segment of space. As a bare possibility of thought—since it is hard to see how we would ever know it—there could be a deterministic world without a single closed or controlled part in it. More to the point, the notion of closure, like the notion of identity, cannot even be formulated without reference to the success of a theory. After this inductive feature has once been pointed out, one need not burden one's formulations by always mentioning it. Similarly, the two occurrences of the phrase 'all possible' in the foregoing definition refer, not to a vagueness, but to the possibility of refutation of a successful theory by future experience. Such inductive uncertainty is, according to the view here taken, characteristic of all science and, therefore, always tacitly understood.

If and as long as physics works toward the ideal or under the assumption of an eventual comprehensive theory, we shall say that it is deterministic in the strict sense, or *strictly deterministic*. Instead of speaking of an ideal or an assumption of this kind one could also speak of a frame of reference. These are but different names for the same thing. But then, I believe it is doubtful whether our frame of reference ever was strictly deterministic. Not even Laplace expected that we would eventually be able to predict the outcome of an individual throw of dice under so-called chance conditions. That means that the value of at least one "possible empirical construct" could not be actually computed. There is, however, another, weaker sense, in which physics has been deterministic for a long time. Physics is *deterministic* if, without working toward a comprehensive process theory, it expects to relate all its empirical laws to one and the same process *schema*. Classical physics was deterministic, though not strictly deterministic. Up to the time when the difficulties connected with the ergodic hypothesis suggested certain radical revisions, the schema to which its coordinating definitions related everything was a mechanical model. This is probably the reason why 'mechanistic' and 'deterministic' are sometimes used synonymously. Yet a comprehensive mechanical schema—a comprehensive model—is only one way of realizing determinism in the weaker sense. On the other hand, a comprehensive schema may be "mechanical," at least in the weak sense that it preserves the particle notion, and yet "statistical" in a sense that is not compatible with the process feature of "determinism." All this will be taken up presently. First a few brief comments on the two terms in the phrase 'mechanical model' are in order. In these comments, as throughout this paper, I shall neglect relativistic formulations.

(3) Whether or not it is used as a model, a schema will be called *mechanical* if it is essentially similar to the schema of classical mechanics. Classical mechanics as a theory is, of course, not a model but a so-called phenomenological theory. I shall not bother to repeat what has just been said concerning the fringe of arbitrariness that surrounds such an expression as 'essentially similar.' The essential feature, as I see it, is the notion of *orbit*. The introduction of, say, an inverse-cube instead of Newton's inverse-square formula or, for that matter, any other change in the form of the Hamiltonian function would thus not be considered an essential dissimilarity. A mechanical schema, then, is a schema whose processes can be interpreted as the successive positions and momentums of

points in three-dimensional space. "Momentums," in this formal context, are to be defined as functions of the first derivatives of the "positions" with respect to the parameter "time." A mechanical schema has thus two decisive aspects, the *particle* feature and the *orbit* feature. The particle feature is the occurrence of position-momentum sets; it is not independent of the orbit feature. For wherever there are orbits there are, in this formal sense, also particles. The converse does not hold. Earlier analysts also attributed considerable importance to another feature, the notion of mass and its constancy. More recently, we have come to realize that the only "essential" function of mass was, first, to represent a certain measure of temporal persistence and, second, to serve as identifying tags for the "particles." Further logical analysis has convinced us that such individualization—or spatio-temporal localization, if you please—is already implicit in the notion of orbits.

But there is also the point that in the modern quantum theory the individualization of the particles has been limited in a manner that is natural enough in any theory of particles without orbits. The limitation is represented by the Pauli exclusion principle. For the basic rationale of this principle is that, if we have particles without orbits, the question as to which particle becomes which in two successive temporal cross sections does not even arise. It becomes, as some would rather carelessly say, meaningless. But then, I feel that this particular aspect of the logic of quanta has been sufficiently clarified. So I feel justified in restricting myself to Reichenbach's program as indicated in the opening statement of this paper.

(4) For a proper and tenable analysis of the differences between a *model theory* and a phenomenological theory I must refer to my earlier paper.[2] Here I can only say that a model theory is a theory with a partially coordinated mechanical schema—the model—and that the old kinetic theory before Maxwell and Boltzmann is still the best paradigm for it. Very roughly speaking, one could say that in explaining the empirical reference of the terms of a model theory one will somewhere find a sentence that begins with 'assume' and contains, later on, the word 'really' in connection with the basic entities of a mechanical schema. For instance, in Newton's corpuscular theory: "Assume that, whenever there is a ray of light there is, really, a beam of moving particles so that. . . . " No such "assumption" is ever encountered in the definitional hierarchy of the empirical constructs.[5]

Perhaps the greatest advantage of what I thus take to be the correct logical description of models is that it keeps one from indulging in a certain kind of dilettante speculation about the "real nature" of the physical universe. Upon such a view, it is said, for instance, that "reality" cannot be both particles and waves. In terms of the structural features of a schema or, rather, as I hope to show, a pattern of schemas, it can. Sometimes the gist of this approach is expressed by saying, in the style of Mach, that the particles of a model are merely computational entities. Unfortunately, this formulation is likely to produce very undesirable psychological reactions against the "subjectivization" of science.

Many eminent physicists, Born and Einstein among them, feel very strongly on this point. However that may be, I certainly do not mean to imply that a computational entity in an applicable schema is a fiction or a convention in any foolish or foolishly subjective meaning of these terms.

One of the terminological consequences of the clarification involved is that it restricts the term 'operational' to empirical constructs. If it is to have any specific meaning at all, it makes no sense to use 'operational' or 'operationally meaningless' with reference to a model. All one can require of a model is that it is *somehow* coordinated to the empirical constructs. A model thus coordinated may be redundant in the sense that some of its features are not utilized in the coordinations. To call a redundant feature operationally meaningless makes 'operational' a fashion term, signifying nothing in particular. The worst disadvantage of such loose usage is, perhaps, that it seems to invoke the authority of philosophy to support very specialized physical theories, or conversely. No such support is needed, and none can be given.

Assume, for instance, the classical kinetic theory and the experimental facts in, say, 1890 to have been such that if the former is applied to the latter it becomes a consequence of the former that no experiment that would allow for the assignment of numerical values to the momentums and positions of individual particles [10] could ever be designed. Such a situation would still not have made it "operationally meaningless" or in any other "philosophical" sense objectionable for the physicists of 1890 to speak of the positions and momentums, exactly or approximately, of individual particles in their model. The question, had it been raised, would have been one of economy, not one of meaning. The bearing of this remark on certain formulations that are now being proposed is obvious. I have already hinted at that in the introduction.

III. Causality, Probability, Statistics

The terms 'causal' and 'causality' serve no particular purpose in the philosophy of science or, for that matter, in analytic philosophy as contrasted with philosophical speculation. If used, they have, so far as I can see, one of the following meanings. (i) Sometimes they refer to the fact that there is, so far as we inductively know, a large number of empirical laws and that we have been rather successful in organizing them by means of theory. Some writers wish to apply the terms only to all or some of the laws and theories of the process type. (ii) Sometimes belief in causality amounts to the assertion of either a deterministic or a strictly deterministic frame of reference. (iii) Sometimes, particularly in recent discussions, causal laws are contrasted with statistical or probability laws, just as causal-

[10] Except, of course, within the range of the empirical constructs; for example, the Cartesian position coordinates of the particles in a 1-cm cube of some gas lie, in the proper coordinate system, between 0 and 1 cm.

ity is contrasted with, or related to, probability. In this section I shall examine some of the questions that are usually considered under the last heading.

(1) At the end of SEC. I, on measurement, I introduced a fiction in order to make a point. The fiction was that our measurements are ideally accurate. The point was that there is no connection between the actual inaccuracy of measurement and the issue of causality *versus* probability as raised in philosophical examinations of the quantum theory. With this in mind, I introduce now, *among empirical constructs*, the distinction between *individual* constructs on the one hand and *statistical* constructs on the other. The distinction itself is as simple as it is familiar; my main concern is with a description that is both sufficiently precise and sufficiently abstract for my purpose.

The present height l of Mr. Smith is an individual construct; the present average height $[\bar{l} = (1/N) \sum_{i=1}^{N} l_i]$ of all American males above 20 years of age is a statistical construct; so are the standard error of this measurement $[\Delta l^2 = (1/N) \sum_{i=1}^{N} (l_i - \bar{l})^2]$, its higher momentums, and the so-called distribution of it, either discrete $(f_i, \Sigma f_i = 1)$ or, with the customary assumptions and fictions that allow for the use of real numbers, continuous $\left[\phi(x), \int_{-\infty}^{\infty} \phi(x)dx = 1\right]$. Let me now try to state the thing abstractly.

To determine whether a certain empirical construct is statistical or individual one must trace its definition to what has been called the thing level, or the level of the immediately observable.[2] The construct is statistical if and only if at some place in this definitional chain a class of measurements has been combined into a new term by a "statistical" procedure such as average formation, computation of a distribution or a standard error. 'Statistical,' as used in the phrase 'statistical procedure,' is an arithmetic term with a precise meaning. The characterization is, therefore, not circular.

Everything that has been said so far refers only to empirical constructs such as length, temperature, pressure. Pressure and temperature in particular are, according to the definition, individual constructs, their interpretation in the kinetic theory notwithstanding. Also, it should be noticed that whether a construct is statistical or individual is a matter of its definition, not of the laws and theories in which it occurs.

(2) An empirical law is the inductive statement of a uniformity; it establishes a relation among several empirical constructs in specified configurations; in the limiting case, the temporal behavior of a single empirical construct. In this respect all laws are alike; they are all—in the first meaning of the term given above—causal laws. They are also all alike in that a single counterinstance that cannot be accounted for otherwise refutes the

law, irrespective of whether it is, as some put it, statistical or causal. The difference lies only in what is to be considered as a counterinstance. In the case of so-called statistical laws, though *practically* the law of large numbers works as well as any of our hypotheses, the *logic* of this decision is rather complex. However, the difficulties that beset it are, in principle, not different from those characteristic of all inductions. Their analysis belongs to the logic of probability and cannot be undertaken in this paper.[8, 11] So I turn now to the description of two types of law. They are both, rather inaccurately, referred to as statistical.

An *ensemble* is a configuration consisting of parts—in the literal, spatial sense of 'part'—that are similar in that they all exemplify one and the same measurable feature. To give a trivial illustration, the objects on my desk form an ensemble with respect to weight and volume. Such features can be used to define statistical constructs which are then characteristic of the ensemble. An empirical law that contains such statistical constructs I shall call an *ensemble law*. As is readily seen, there is nothing particularly statistical about the law itself. It may, for instance, be a process law and, in this sense, "causal." (The schema of radioactive decomposition is of this kind.) On the other hand, an ensemble law may also be a statistical law, in the only sense in which I shall speak of statistical laws. This sense is the same as the one sometimes attached to the expression 'probability law.' However, I shall avoid any formal use of 'probability,' just as I have avoided such use of 'causality.' A *statistical law*, then, is a law, not about a process in a configuration, but about the limiting values of frequencies in an infinite series of similar events in the same configuration. The classical illustration of what I have so abstractly expressed is the repeated throw of a die. A statistical law makes no prediction whatsoever about what is in this case the configuration—in ordinary parlance, the individual event. It is a statement about the "ensemble" formed by the series; but this "ensemble" is merely a verbal, not a real ensemble, if I may so express myself. And, most important, there is no longer a notion of process involved, while we have seen that there may be ensemble process laws. There are, nevertheless, many well-known similarities in the mathematical treatment of statistical laws, ensemble process laws and ensemble statistical laws. The factual assumption that guarantees these relations is the so-called independence of the parts of an ensemble. This, indeed, is what is meant by 'independence' when the term is used in this general area.

Just to practice some of our definitions, I shall mention that what some people seem to mean by 'causal law' is what I would have to call a process law about individual constructs. But this is merely by the way; my main motive in making the distinctions of this section is to call attention to the structure of "nonstatistical" ensemble processes and, also, to some related schemas. So I shall now transfer some of these notions to arithmetic schemas. Only two cases will be considered—the distribution process schema and the statistical schema.

[11] See also symposium on probability by Williams, Nagel, Reichenbach, Carnap, Margenau, Bergmann, von Mises and Kaufmann in *Phil. and Phen. Res.* 5–6 (1945).

(3) Formally, the fundamental notion is that of a distribution function or, for short, distribution. A distribution is, in the discrete case, a set of non-negative numbers f_i such that $\Sigma f_i = 1$; in the continuous case, a non-negative function $\phi(x)$ such that $\int_{-\infty}^{+\infty} \phi(x)dx = 1$. With the proper mathematical tools the discrete case becomes a specialization of the continuous one. Remembering what has been said in SEC. II, one sees now the possibility of systems whose states are defined as a distribution (in one or several variables) or as an ordered set of such distributions. Such a schema is a special case of a field schema, or, if the process formula is of a certain kind, of a wave schema. If the states of a process schema are distributions, the systems of which these distributions are the states may themselves be given by a set of functions, perhaps even distribution functions. This will turn out to be the case of the quantum-mechanical schema, but of this I shall speak later; for the moment I merely define a *distribution process schema* as a process schema whose states are either single distribution functions or ordered sets of such. Given the system and one of its states—an ordered set of N distributions for the value t_0 of a parameter—the process formula allows for the computation of one and only one ordered set of N distributions for every value of the parameter. Again, there is nothing particularly "statistical" about this schema; the only feature that could suggest statistics is the occurrence of distributions.

One may be tempted to say that a distribution process schema is always the schema of an ensemble process. However, this is not quite exact. The basic entities that determine the condition of an ensemble are the individual measurements. The resulting distributions are already among the derived or, as one also says, explicitly defined magnitudes of the corresponding schema. In a distribution process schema, on the other hand, the distribution functions are themselves among the basic entities of the calculus. They are, so to speak, not distributions *of* anything. So all one could say is that the schema of an ensemble process contains a part that, taken by itself, is a distribution process schema. Conversely, the question may be raised whether a distribution process schema can be so supplemented that it becomes the schema of an ensemble process *of a certain kind* or *in a certain manner*. Such an attempt may or may not succeed. It will be seen, for instance, that the quantum-mechanical schema cannot be supplemented—in a manner that would be satisfactory in the total context of the theory—to the schema of a "particle ensemble." I shall now explain what I mean by the latter term.

Consider an ensemble whose distributions are those of the positions and momentums of a class of mass points, and make the customary assumption that these distributions are independent within the ensemble. To elucidate the last assumption, assume that $a_i \leqslant q_i \leqslant b_i$ for 30 percent of the particles and that $c_j \leqslant p_j \leqslant d_j$ for 20 percent of the particles. Then 6 percent of them have both coordinates within the limits indicated. Ensembles whose parts are not individual mass points but configurations of such are essentially of the same kind.

Such a schema determines for every position-momentum set the percentage of part configurations that are "in" this mechanical state.[12] In this respect it preserves the notion of a particle. The process formula, on the other hand, does not connect mechanical states, but distributions of such. Is this the pattern of a mechanical schema, as I have defined the term? Yes and no. It has particles and it has a process, but it has no orbits; its process is, as it were, a statistics of orbits. The schema is undoubtedly an intermediate type of its own; so I suggest for it the intermediate name of a *particle ensemble*. It is interesting for two reasons: first, the schema of the kinetic theory, in its radical interpretation (for example, that of von Mises), is a statistics of particle ensembles; second, the quantum-mechanical schema is nonmechanical in the sense that it cannot even be interpreted as a particle ensemble process within the context of the theory.

(4) Turning to the schema of a statistical law, I consider only the case where states are given by a finite ordered set of N numbers $[x_1^0, \cdots, x_n^0]$. The formula is such that it allows for each state the computation of one and only one ordered set of distributions for each value of the parameter t: $\phi_1(x, t), \cdots, \phi_N(x, t)$. What is here problematical is the use of the term 'process.' The only process feature lies in the typical role of the time parameter. Otherwise the rule states, in ordinary parlance, that given any set of values $[x_1^0, \cdots, x_N^0]$ for the zero value of the parameter, the system will in $\phi_1(a_1, t) \cdot \phi_2(a_2, t) \cdots \phi_N(a_N, t)$ percent of the cases [12] be in the state $[a_1, a_2, \cdots, a_n]$ for the value t of the parameter.

In speaking quite naively of percentages I indicate again that I do not wish to deal with the niceties of the logic of probability. But I shall ask again whether this pattern—call it a *statistical schema*—could be called mechanical, even if its states can be read as position-momentum coordinates. As in the case of the particle ensemble, the answer is: Yes and no. What is preserved, in about the same manner, is the particle notion. What has been discarded is, not only the notion of the orbit but, even more radically, the notion of process. One could say that in the ensemble process the individual process has merely been neglected; at least, it has not been excluded. The statistical law goes further in this respect. This is perhaps the main reason why statistical lawfulness and determinism are often contrasted with each other. For any notion of determinism certainly implies that of process. But then, it has also been seen that this is only one ingredient of an intelligible notion of determinism. The mechanical or particle feature, finally, is not essential to either notion.

(5) If the schema of a theory is of the ensemble or the statistical

[12] Technically, I should here speak of an arbitrarily small cell of the phase space and of so-called probability density, not of one position-momentum state and its probability. This obvious consequence of working with continuous distributions has nothing whatever to do with inaccuracy or indeterminacy.

type (or possibly both), it does not follow that all, or even any, of the empirical laws in the theory are either ensemble processes or statistical. That still depends on how the empirical constructs are coordinated to the entities of the schema. But all this is well known from the early states of the kinetic theory.

IV. The General Pattern of the Quantum Theory

In the first part of this paper I spoke sometimes of *quantum mechanics*, sometimes of the *quantum theory*. This was not done haphazardly, as if the two expressions were used synonymously. By 'quantum theory' I mean the whole of the modern theory, using 'theory' as in Sec. II. By 'quantum mechanics' I mean the schema or calculus, the construction of which was begun by Schrödinger and Heisenberg. This section contains a brief statement of what I believe is the gist of the philosophical description of the quantum theory attempted in the next two sections. Here are the main points. (i) Quantum mechanics, a distribution-process schema, is not the whole schema of the quantum theory, but merely a part of it. For reasons that will soon be apparent I shall call it the second schema (*II*). (ii) The other part, referred to as the first schema (*I*), is a statistical modification of the semiclassical particle schema. (iii) Schema *I* preserves fully the particle feature but, being statistical, has no processes and, of course, no orbits. (iv) The relation between *I* and *II* is formally the same as that between the empirical constructs of a theory, as we have so far known it, and its schema. In other words, the relation is established by coordinating terms of *II* to terms of *I*, or—this is but another way of saying the same thing—interpreting *II* in terms of *I*. The only difference between this procedure and that of establishing coordinating definitions is that the latter relate empirical constructs to terms of a schema, while here two schemas are involved.

The last point is in my opinion the crucial one. It is, at any rate, the crucial point of the present analysis. According to this view the pattern of the quantum theory looks like this:

Empirical Constructs→Schema *I*→Schema *II*.

All theories we have so far known follow the simpler pattern:

Empirical Constructs→Schema.

The complexity of the first pattern is something radically new. It is, I believe, at the very root of the philosophical puzzlement the new theory has produced. If this is true, then the puzzles should all disappear after the new pattern has once been recognized; it should be possible to eliminate all apparent paradoxes from our formulations and to identify our initial bewilderment as a psychological and, perhaps, esthetic reaction to the novelty of the pattern. This, I submit, is so. Nor is it particularly difficult to see, in a general manner, how the "philosophical" problems are made to disappear. Each of the two schemas may have features that are very different from, or even incompatible with, some of the other schemas. Since there are two schemas—one piled upon the other, as it were—this causes no difficulty. Assume, for instance, that *I* is a standard mechanical model and *II* a field schema of the classical kind, such as Maxwell's. (Actually things are much more complicated.) Even in this case we would not have to say, as some propose, that we apply sometimes a particle and sometimes a wave interpretation or, even worse, that ultimate physical reality unites in some mysterious fashion these two incompatible features.

One sees by now that it is rather misleading to speak of *I* and *II* as parts of one schema. Since we are faced with a three-level theory, not with the usual two-level pattern, it is preferable to say that the theory has two schemas such that the one (*I*) is the interpretation of the other (*II*) and such that only the first one is directly coordinated to the empirical constructs. With the two schemas thus clearly separated and with the help of the distinctions proposed in the first part of this paper, the "allocation of features" proceeds more conveniently, less ambiguously, and with greater detail.

It has been said, for instance, that the modern theory has statistical as well as deterministic aspects; in our terms, *I* is a statistical schema, *II* the schema of a process. But we can add that the new theory is statistical in that *II* is a schema of distributions, and is mechanistic in the sense that *I* is a schema of particles. (That mechanism and determinism are not always clearly distinguished has been seen in Sec. II.) To touch upon one more point, one sees clearly how *II*, though not itself a particle schema, preserves some of the traits of the particle. The connection between *I* and *II* is such that certain structural and numerical constants of *I*—the number of particles, their masses and charges—enter as structural and numerical constants into schema *II*; so does, in a more complicated manner, the kind of the particles—electron, photon, and so on. By and large this allocation of features is an easy task. I shall return to it briefly in the last section.

In one of the preceding paragraphs I remarked that certain dissatisfactions with the modern theory are psychological and esthetic, rather than indicative of genuine philosophical difficulties. Unless one is very explicit a remark of this kind is almost certain to be misunderstood. I did not deny and do not mean to deny that such dissatisfactions may lead to the construction of new theories that are more satisfactory—in this respect as well as in others that are less elusive. That has happened in the past and may happen again. To achieve such progress is the privilege and burden of the scientist; the philosopher's task, as positivists conceive it, is merely to exhibit the logical structure of the theories *as he actually finds them.* To use Reichenbach's suggestive terms, the philosopher's concern is with the context of justification, not, as the psychologist's and historian's, with the context of discovery.

To give one illustration of this difference, in the latter context de Broglie's models and derivations are of prime importance, in the former they can at present be safely omitted. The same is true of the correspondence principle and some other topics that are very popular in most "philosophical" treatments of the quantum theory. But some seem to believe that logical analysis obstructs the progress of science. More or less politely expressed, this was the opinion of the physicists who opposed Mach's interpretation of the classical particles; it is now the opinion of those who oppose positivistic interpretations of the quantum theory. Such critics are likely to reject the present attempt as the very extreme of positivistic scholasticism; but they also consider Reichenbach's ideas, as well as those Margenau expressed in several articles on our subject, as "too positivistic." Apparently these critics feel that scientists are challenged by the "philosophical" problems they encounter when they take their schemas to be pictures of reality, while there is danger that efforts may slacken in the face of "merely" psychological and esthetic dissatisfactions. As a generalization about the motivation of scientists this is doubtful, to say the least. Besides, there is evidence that unquestionable scientific progress has sometimes accompanied logical analysis of the positivistic type.

In the case of the modern quantum theory the *logical* complexity of the three-level pattern—as distinguished from the *mathematical* complexity of the apparatus, which is merely a matter of technic—is most intriguing. I am sure physicists will not easily be kept from attempts to replace it by the older and simpler pattern. Perhaps this is what will happen after we have turned the next corner. All we know for certain, or as certainly as we know anything in science, is that such a future theory could not be a particle theory of the classical type. On the other hand, the present theory has met with plenty of *non*-philosophical difficulties, particularly when the attempt was made to formulate it so that it becomes consistent with the theory of relativity. As far as I know, these difficulties have come to a head in the quantum theory of electromagnetic fields. So it is perhaps significant that this is also the only part of the theory where the three-level analysis does not quite fit its actual logical structure. For, as Dirac has shown, the electromagnetic field in a vacuum can be quantized directly. The connection between the field vectors, which are empirical constructs, and schema *II* can be established without mediation by the first schema. But then, in the crucial applications one knows of the field only by its interaction with particles whose positions and momentums one computes, from empirical constructs, by means of schema *I*. This will become clear in SEC. VI, the present section being merely a sort of preview and, therefore, the proper place for statements of a more general nature.

I turn now to the actual description of the theory. In the course of this description I shall give reasons, *other than the philosophical ones so far mentioned*, why *I* must be interpolated between *II* and the empirical constructs and why, on the other hand, *I* and *II* should not be considered as parts of one schema.

V. The Quantum Mechanical Schema

The account of the Newtonian schema in Sec. II is so abstract that one need not even know what a differential equation is in order to understand it. Yet I am as skeptical as anyone as to how much a person who knows no mathematics and physics at all could benefit from my account. The point is, rather, that those who do have some background find such abstractions useful and even necessary for the philosophical analysis of science. Now I must try to give a similarly abstract account of the quantum-mechanical schema.

The task is difficult, for the mathematical apparatus is very complex. As far as it was known at all, it was until relatively recently the almost exclusive possession of mathematical specialists. So I shall simplify and omit wherever simplification and omission do not appear to affect the relevant logical structure. I realize, of course, that I do this at my own risk. For instance, I shall not attempt to describe the schema in its full mathematical generality, but shall restrict myself to what is known as the Schrödinger representation. As far as the physical material is concerned, I shall limit myself to the problem of n bodies with $6n$ degrees of freedom. Spin, for instance, will be completely ignored.

Like all schemas this one, too, requires that its functions (or other mathematical entities) fulfill certain mathematical conditions. The members of the class our schema considers—we need not bother to specify the conditions—are called ψ-functions or, for short, ψ's. What are the systems, the states, and the processes of the schema? The most fundamental characteristic of a system is a certain integer, n. Since all ψ's that occur in its definitions and in its states are, in principle, functions of n variables, $\psi(x_1, x_2, \cdots, x_n)$, n may be called the number of variables of the system. I shall describe a system of n variables.

A *system* is, by definition, a subclass S of the class of ψ's (with n variables). The members of S are called the eigenfunctions "of" the system. But not every class of ψ's is a system.

A class is a system if and only if its members stand in certain mathematical relations to a function of $2n$ variables $H\ (\zeta_1, \zeta_2, \cdots, \zeta_n, \eta_1, \cdots, \eta_n)$. So one could say that a system, while it *is* a class of ψ's, is *determined* by an H. The function H itself is not a ψ but, at least for all we need to know, quite arbitrary. Later on we shall see that it plays the decisive role in the coordination of *II* to *I*.

A *state* is, by definition, a ψ. In other words, except for the restriction in the number of variables, which I shall no longer bother to repeat, every ψ is a possible state of every system. Just as a system, while it is a class of ψ's, is determined by an H, so each ψ, which is the state, determines another mathematical entity. This entity—call it D_n—is an ordered set of n distributions $[\phi_1(\zeta_1), \phi_2(\zeta_2), \cdots, \phi_n(\zeta_n)]$. Though it is not quite accurate, it will suffice for our purposes to say that, conversely, each D_n determines a ψ. In other words, there is a set of rules R that coordinates to each ψ one D_n, and conversely. In this sense, a state *is* an ordered set of distributions and the schema, therefore, a distribution schema.

The *process* formula, known as the time-dependent Schrödinger equation, follows the familiar pattern. Take a state ψ and consider it as the state ψ^0 (or $D_n{}^0$) of the "system H" at the time 0; then there is a formula that coordinates to each value t of the time parameter one and only one state ψ^t (or $D_n{}^t$), so that the class of these states, the process, is the process of all of its states. The process formula depends on the function H, for otherwise there would be no point in calling ψ^t a state of the system. This is the bare skeleton of the schema. Some elaboration is necessary.

(1) Every D_n determines in one and only one way a new entity $D_{2(n)}$, an ordered set of $2n$ distributions $[\phi_1(\zeta_1), \cdots, \phi_n(\zeta_n), \phi_{n+1}(\eta_1), \cdots, \phi_{2n}(\eta_n)]$, so that the following is the case. Call ϕ_i and ϕ_{n+i} *canonically conjugate* distributions, ζ_i and η_i canonically conjugate variables. Then $D_{2(n)}$ is determined by any of its subsets of n distributions, either in ζ or in η, provided only that this subset contains a distribution for one of each pair of canonically conjugate variables. Thus one can also consider a state as a $D_{2(n)}$. One merely has to remember that its $2n$ distribution functions are not independent; n properly chosen ones determine the remaining ones.

(2) Each of the $2n$ distributions of a $D_{2(n)}$ has an average or expectation value $\bar{\zeta}_i$, $\bar{\eta}_i$ and a standard error $\Delta\zeta_i$, $\Delta\eta_i$. It is a mathematical consequence of the rules R that for each i

$$\Delta\zeta_i \cdot \Delta\eta_i \geqslant h/4\pi. \qquad (1)$$

Each of the $2n$ distributions may be either continuous[13] or discrete or partly continuous and partly discrete. If entirely discrete, it may, in particular, disappear in all points except one. Such a distribution will be called a *one-value distribution.* Let, for instance, ϕ_1 be such a distribution with the value ζ_1'. One has $\phi_1(\zeta_1') = 1$, $\zeta_1' = \bar{\zeta}_1$, $\Delta\zeta_1 = 0$. All the distributions of a D_n may be one-value distributions, but no more than n of the distributions in a $D_{2(n)}$ can be of this kind. For if two canonically conjugate distributions were both one-value distributions, the product of their standard errors would disappear. This is excluded by the inequality (1).

(3) A set of distributions D_n is something very different from a set of values $[\zeta_1', \zeta_2', \cdots, \zeta_n']$. Call such a set of values V_n. But, on the other hand, a V_n can be considered as a very special D_n, namely, the D_n all of whose distributions are one-value distributions such that $\zeta_1' = \bar{\zeta}_i$. Furthermore, since every D_n determines a ψ, this special D_n also determines a ψ; call it ψ^{Vn} and consider it the ψ determined by V_n. Clearly, the ψ^{Vn} are of a special kind, since the ζ-distributions that belong to a ψ are, in the general case, not all one-value distributions. All this is very important; for, as will be seen presently, on the characteristic asymmetry of this state of affairs

[13] In the continuous case the ϕ is, properly speaking, a distribution density. See reference 12.

hinges the possibility of correlating, system by system, a statistical particle schema (in $2n$ variables) and a nonparticle distribution process (in n variables). So I shall repeat. *A general* ψ *determines a* D_n *(and a* $D_{2(n)}$*), not a* V_n*. But each* V_n *determines a* ψ*. This* ψ*, called* ψ^{V_n}*, is of a special kind;* n *of its distributions are one-value distributions whose values are, in the proper order, the values of* V_n. Take as an example the case $n = 2$ and assume that D_2 consists of a three-value and a two-value distribution:

$$\phi_1(\zeta_1') = a_{11}, \quad \phi_1(\zeta_1'') = a_{12}, \quad \phi_1(\zeta_1''') = a_{13};$$
$$\phi_2(\zeta_2') = a_{21}, \quad \phi_2(\zeta_2'') = a_{22}.$$

This D_2—or its ψ—determines six possible V_2, namely $[\zeta_1', \zeta_2']$, $[\zeta_1'', \zeta_2']$, $\cdots$ $[\zeta_1''', \zeta_2'']$. But not even the set of these six V_2 determines ψ; there are still three degrees of freedom left, namely, the five "probabilities" a_{ik}, subject to the two conditions $\Sigma a_{1i} = 1$, $\Sigma a_{2i} = 1$. Furthermore, since identical ψ determine identical D, each of the six ψ^{V_2} determined by the six V_2 is different from the original ψ.

(4) Can schema *II* be considered as the process schema of a particle ensemble, or an ensemble of particle configurations, in the sense of Sec. III (3)? Assume, for instance, that $n = 3N$. Then one may ask whether the $6N$ distributions of $D_{2(n)}$ could not be considered as characteristic of an ensemble in three-dimensional space so that each part configuration of the ensemble consists of N particles and so that $\phi_1(\zeta_1), \cdots, \phi_n(\zeta_n)$ and $\phi_{n+1}(\eta_1), \cdots, \phi_{2n}(\eta_n)$ are the distributions [13] of the position and momentum coordinates ζ_i, η_i, respectively. The following two remarks show why the answer to this question is negative.

(*a*) Let us remember that the part configurations of an ensemble are, by definition, independent of one another. Hence, if the $6N$ distributions of the position-momentum coordinates are given, the distribution $\bar{\phi}$, in $2n$ variables, of the product $\zeta_1 \cdot \zeta_2 \cdots \eta_{n-1} \cdot \eta_n$ is uniquely determined.[14] So it is natural to ask whether the rules R can be made to yield a distribution $\bar{\phi}$. The following is the case. The rules R can be formulated so as to yield directly distributions for *some* expressions in *several* of the variables ζ_i, η_i. But there are also some *other* such expressions to which, within the framework of the mathematical apparatus, no distributions can be assigned. The products of canonically conjugate variables and the products of these products are of this kind! Noteworthy as that is, in itself it is not prohibitive. For, if we do not get the expected $\bar{\phi}$, we do not, at least, get another one. But the next difficulty is insurmountable.

(*b*) Assume that each configuration consists of one particle ($N = 1$, $n = 3$) and that each of the three distributions in D_3 is a four-value distribution. Then ψ determines 64 V_3. If ψ were characteristic of an ensemble E of, say, M configurations, then E could be considered as the *sum* of 64 ensembles whose ψ's are the respective ψ^{V_3} and whose size (M_i) is de-

[14] As has been pointed out in Sec. III (3), the determinateness of this product is a very essential component of the particle notion.

termined by the probabilities in D_3. By the sum of two ensembles E_1 and E_2 we mean the ensemble whose part configurations are the configurations of E_1 and those of E_2. It follows immediately that if E_1 is an ensemble of M_1 and E_2 one of M_2 parts, and if ϕ_1, ϕ_2 and ϕ are the distributions of *any* magnitude in E_1, E_2 and their sum, respectively, the relation

$$\zeta = \frac{M_1}{M_1 + M_2}\zeta_1 + \frac{M_2}{M_1 + M_2}\zeta_2$$

will obtain. Now we have seen that the ensemble *supposedly* characterized by ψ could always be considered as a sum. Therefore one would have in a self-explanatory symbolism,

$$D = \sum_{i=1}^{64} \rho_i D^{V_3^i}.$$

It is a consequence of the rules R that no such decomposition exists. Hence *schema II cannot*, in the manner indicated, *be considered as the (partial) schema of a particle ensemble process.*

On the other hand, it is well known and we shall presently see that the distributions in $D_{2(n)}$ are, in fact, "interpreted" as the probabilities for the positions and momentums of *a* particle (or particle configuration) in schema *I*. Consequently, in order to be consistent, it is necessary to understand 'interpretation' as I understand it, namely, as the inverse of a coordination relation between two independent schemas. For to consider *I* and *II* as parts of one schema means, as far as I can see, one and only one thing: to consider *II* as a process in a particle ensemble. To say the same thing in language that is often employed in general expositions of the theory, it is very inaccurate and, strictly speaking, false to consider ψ (or $D_{2(n)}$) as a "pilot wave" that determines statistically the mechanical states of the particles in the manner in which, in the semiclassical theory, an electromagnetic magnitude is considered as the pilot wave for the positions of the photons.

(5) To interpret a quantum-mechanical system as an ensemble of particles or particle configurations is one thing; to study ensembles *of* quantum-mechanical systems is another. The first, we have just seen, cannot be done. The second is just another application of familiar statistical technics. Let me note for future reference that there are two kinds of such ensembles. In the first case, called *pure*, all the systems of the ensemble are in the same state ψ. In the second case, called *mixed*, one knows only the relative frequencies β_i of the systems in state ψ_i within the ensemble. Clearly, the set $[\beta_i, \psi_i]$ contains all the information we have about what one may call the state of the ensemble. By means of the mathematical apparatus this information can be conveniently condensed into a single entity, the so-called *statistical operator*. The following is the case. (i) From the statistical operator, one can always tell whether the ensemble is pure or mixed. (ii) If the (independent) systems of an ensemble undergo their

processes, a pure ensemble remains pure. (iii) In any case, if the systems of an ensemble undergo their processes, determined by the H_i, then the statistical operator, in its turn, also undergoes a process. The formula of this process is, of course, determined by the β_i and the H_i.

A ψ is a function (of a kind we have not bothered to specify) in n variables. I shall for the moment indicate the number of variables by a subscript. It is a consequence of the mathematical apparatus that if ψ_n and ψ_m are states of their respective systems, their product $\psi_n \cdot \psi_m$ is a ψ_{n+m}. It is, intuitively speaking, the ψ of a system "compounded" of two independent systems, provided that one defines the H of the "compound system" so that each of the two "subsystems" follow their own processes. In this sense it may be said that two independent subsystems uniquely determine their compound system. If, on the other hand, a system in $n+m$ variables and one of its states is given, it is by no means obvious that it can in one and only one way be "broken up" into independent subsystems of n and m variables, respectively. The following, however, is *under certain conditions* the case. (iv) Given an ensemble of systems in state ψ_{n+m}, each system can be broken up into independent subsystems of states ψ_n and ψ_m so that the ensembles $E^{(n)}$ and $E^{(m)}$ of the respective subsystems are mixed, while the ensemble $E^{(n+m)}$ of the compound systems is pure. Again one may summarize this information by saying that a pure statistical operator can sometimes be broken up into two mixed ones. The expressions 'subsystem,' 'compound system' and 'breaking up,' which I have used in giving this account, should indicate that what happens is not the kind of decomposition that occurs if one puts some of the configurations of an ensemble in one class, some in another. What is being broken up is not the ensemble but each of its component systems.

If one says that when we know its statistical operator we know all that can be known about an ensemble if it is pure, while we do not know it completely if it is mixed—since we do not know which system is in which state—then (iv) may be expressed, somewhat paradoxically, in the following manner: We may know a "system" completely without completely knowing its "parts." Elaboration of (ii), on the other hand, would show that if we know the "parts" completely, we also have complete knowledge of their "sum." This is the way Schrödinger has expressed himself in one of his philosophical papers.[15] Of course, in this formulation 'system,' 'part' and 'sum' are not used as they are ordinarily used in this paper. And what, in general, is the advantage of paradoxical formulations?

VI. The First Schema and the Structure of the Theory

(1) In Sec. III I said that in the later stages of the kinetic theory physics became a statistics of particle ensembles and was thus no longer, strictly speaking, mechanistic. This statement needs some qualification.

[15] *Naturwiss.* 23, 806–12, 823–28, 844–49 (1935).

It is true that the decisive orbit feature of the classical model was abandoned for ensembles of molecules (or atoms); but it was maintained *within* the atom (and molecule). This state of development is marked by Rutherford's conception of the atom as a planetary system. In his model the notion of orbit was preserved; so physical theory still appeared to be mechanistic and deterministic in principle. Nor did the use of statistical methods—or, as one usually says, the fact that the causality of the macrophenomena is but a result of the law of large numbers—cause many intellectual difficulties at that stage. So it was not fully appreciated at first how radical a step it was to abandon the orbit feature anywhere, even if only in the treatment of thermodynamic ensembles. Accordingly, since the old frame of reference still seemed essentially intact, we see Bohr and his collaborators cling to the notion of orbits, though they discarded the process formulas of classical mechanics in stating the first quantum conditions. This, of course, is the state of the Bohr-Rutherford atom and its successive refinements. Einstein's light-quantum hypothesis was more revolutionary. For the conception of the field acting as a statistical pilot wave for the positions of the photons has the structure of a particle ensemble process without orbits. On the other hand, the price Bohr had to pay for the preservation of orbits was high indeed. His famous jumps not only introduced a discontinuity that was incomprehensible in terms of classical mechanics, but they even seemed to eliminate and, as far as we know, actually have eliminated the possibility of any kind of process theory for the individual particles.

Against the background of these remarks it is not difficult to clarify a term I have used before in several incidental comments. In speaking of the *semiclassical schema* I refer to the following tripartite frame of reference: (i) the "old" quantum theory with the Bohr-Rutherford model of the atom, (ii) Einstein's interpretation of electromagnetic fields in terms of light quanta and (iii) the statistical conception of thermodynamics. The third component need not detain us. Its basic ideas have long been quite unproblematic, and the theory itself has not undergone any recent changes sufficiently fundamental to engage the attention of the logical analyst.[16] The first two aspects taken together constitute a particle schema and, in conjunction with their customary interpretation, what has been called a two-level theory. Now I must give reasons for my assertion that a modification of this theory has been preserved; that in the new theory this modification (schema *I*) has been supplemented, rather than replaced, by the quantum-mechanical calculus (schema *II*). The argument is twofold. Its first part proceeds along the lines of operational analysis; the second part deals with the interpretation of schema *II*.

[16] Except, perhaps, the logical connection between the introduction of the new statistics and the abandoning of orbits. See also the remark on the Pauli principle in Sec. II (3).

(*a*) Like all worth while theories the semiclassical theory is quantitative and specific in the sense that measurement in specified experimental situations leads to the assignment of numerical values to some entities of its schema. One builds a piece of apparatus of specified dimensions, puts it into operation, and performs at the time t_0 certain measurements on it or, perhaps, reads some scales that have been built into it. One measures, for instance, intensities of electric currents, positions of spectral lines, locations and breadths of rings on a photographic plate. This is our operational basis—the realm of empirical constructs.

From this basis the old theory "infers" that at the moment t_0 [17] one electron, or an ensemble of such, passed through a certain slit in our apparatus; and it also assigns a numerical value to the speed or, in the case of the ensemble, to the average speed of the particle at that moment. At another time one "infers" that the atoms emitting the light pass from one energy level to another; and again one assigns numerical values to these two levels. Whether the assignment reaches the individual particle or, perhaps, only statistical aggregates depends on the case and is altogether not a matter of very great importance.

In either event, the basis of "inference" and assignment is threefold: empirical laws obtaining among empirical constructs; the model; the way the former are coordinated to the latter. Also, the customary term 'inference' is very misleading. What goes on is not inference of the "indirectly observed" from the directly observable, but coordination according to the rules of a game. Schematically speaking, then, the semiclassical theory is to a very considerable extent a technic of coordinating to experimental situations such statements as 'An electron had at time t_1 the speed v_1.'

These coordinations have not been abandoned; nor has the technic, broadly speaking, been changed. If, for instance, an experiment has been described, in the old theory, as the collision of photons and electrons of numerically specified characteristics, it is still so described in the new theory. The decisive innovation lies in the technic of predicting other such "data of schema *I*" from those already "observed." The computation proceeds no longer within *I* but, instead, by way of *II*; and it is, in principle, of a kind that makes this modification of *I* statistical with respect to the individual particle.

Perhaps this is the best place for a purely psychological remark. Some people, impressed with the fact that so much of *I* is like the old schema, wish to conclude that its entities are really there, that they are, as I put it before, on the level of stones, trees and laboratory equipment. Some others, more impressed with the introduction of *II* and the differences between *I* and the old schema, consider the recent developments as evidence for the intellectual economy of a positivistic analysis.

[17] Or at an earlier moment. That depends, in a familiar manner, on the theory of the measuring process.

(*b*) In coordinating *II* to *I* two steps may be conveniently distinguished: coordination of systems and coordination of states. Take, for instance, the particle configuration in *I* of which we speak as the hydrogen atom. What quantum-mechanical system *S* corresponds to this particle configuration? Which state of *S* corresponds to a given state of the particle configuration? Clearly, these are two different questions. To answer the second some preliminary remarks will be necessary; the first can be answered without further preparation. The particle configuration (hydrogen atom) has in the classical theory a Hamiltonian function *H* whose variables are canonically conjugate position-momentum coordinates of the component particles. We know from Sec. V that an *H* of this kind, considered as a mathematical entity, determines a quantum-mechanical system *S*. This system *S* is coordinated to the hydrogen atom. Here the process formula of the semiclassical theory has entered the picture. Without it, we would not know how to compute the (statistical) predictions of *I*. There is thus a theoretical as well as an operational sense in which it may be said that the new theory modifies and supplements, rather than eliminates, the semiclassical model.

(2) The coordination of states in *II* to states in *I* meets with a peculiar complication, first pointed out by Heisenberg, that is at the basis of some of the characteristic features of the new theory. To fix the ideas, let us assume that the system in *I* is an *n*-particle configuration. Then *H* becomes $H(\zeta_1, \cdots, \zeta_N, \eta_1, \cdots, \eta_N)$ with $N = 3n$. As for the assignment of numerical values to the $2N$ variables, Heisenberg recognized the full significance of the following *fact*. It is a consequence of certain empirical laws that even if absolutely accurate measurement were possible it would still be impossible to assign, within the semiclassical theory, numerical values to all the $2N$ coordinates of the configuration. The best one can do is this. Having computed that ζ_i lies between two values ζ_i' and ζ_i'', so that $d\zeta_i = |\zeta_i'' - \zeta_i'|$, one can also compute two values η_i' and η_i'' with $d\eta_i = |\eta_i'' - \eta_i'|$, such that the value of the canonically conjugate variable η_i lies between η_i' and η_i'', and such that

$$d\zeta_i \cdot d\eta_i \geqslant h/4\pi. \tag{2}$$

Some comments are in order. *First*, the expression 'fact' was chosen deliberately. The limitation expressed by (2) follows, within the *old* theory, from the well-known laws of diffraction. And empirical laws such as these are, in an obvious sense, matters of fact. *Second*, in view of Sec. I and in view of the formal similarity between inequalities (2) and (1) of Sec. V (2), it should be noticed that the intervals $d\zeta_i$ and $d\eta_i$ are "limits of assignment," not limits of the accuracy of measurement. Nor are they standard errors, either of measurement or of anything else. *Third*, let us assume that $d\zeta_i = 0$ for $i = 1, 2, \cdots, N$. It follows from (2) that $d\eta_i = \infty$. We know nothing about the values of the remaining N coordinates. For the purposes of logical analysis it is sufficient to consider this case. It is, in fact, the case best suited for this purpose.

The situation may be summarized in the following manner. We can in the old theory never assign a numerical state description $[\zeta_1', \zeta_2', \cdots, \eta_N']$ to a configuration of *I*; but we can assign to it a *half-state*, say, for instance $[\zeta_1', \zeta_2', \cdots, \zeta_N']$. *To such half-states of I states of II are coordinated.* This is the crucial idea of the coordination in the direction from *I* to *II*. To state the actual rule, we remember from SEC. V (3) that the set $[\zeta_1', \zeta_2', \cdots, \zeta_N']$ is a V_N, and that this V_N determines one and only one ψ, so that "its" ζ-distributions are one-value distributions with the values $\zeta_1', \zeta_2', \cdots, \zeta_N'$, respectively. This ψ—in SEC. V we called it ψ^{VN}—is the state in *II* coordinated to the half-state of *I*. But it is well to remember that the η-distributions of this ψ—the second half of its $D_{2(n)}$—have no correlate in the first schema. Strictly speaking, I should have used different symbols for the ζ, η of *I* and *II*.

(3) So far we have dealt only with the coordination of the systems and states of *II*, by way of *I*, to the empirical material. Now we must attend to the machinery of prediction. Assume an experimental situation that allows, as one usually says, for the observation of an individual particle or particle configuration. Assume, furthermore, the experimental set-up to realize the characteristic case, assignment of a precise half-state,[18] say $[\zeta_1^0, \zeta_2^0, \cdots, \zeta_N^0]$. In other words, we know, as a result of our measurements, the half-state of *I* and the corresponding state ψ^{VN} of *II* at the moment $t = 0$. The task consists obviously in predicting the results of later measurements by assigning to the moment t_1 $(t_1 > 0)$ a state in *II* and either a precise half-state or state-limits compatible with inequality (2) in *I*. Here is the rule. One computes first, by means of the process formula of *II*, the state $\psi(t_1)$ determined by ψ^{VN} considered as $\psi(0)$. Neither the ζ-distributions nor the η-distributions of this state nor any other *N* will, in general, be one-value distributions. Let $\phi_1(\zeta_1), \phi_2(\zeta_2), \cdots, \phi_{2N}(\eta_N)$ be these distributions. Their interpretation in *I* is as follows. The system of *I* will at the time t_1 with the probability $\phi_1(\zeta_1') \cdot \phi_2(\zeta_2') \cdots \phi_{2N}(\eta_N')$ be in the state $[\zeta_1', \zeta_2', \cdots, \eta_N']$.

Several things should be noticed. *First*, there is a characteristic asymmetry between coordination (from *I* to *II*) and interpretation (from *II* to *I*). That is how one manages to correlate, system by system, a process schema with a statistical schema. *Second*, there is no warrant for saying that the configuration of *I* is either in the state $\psi(t_1)$ or, perhaps, simultaneously and with the respective probabilities, in the states ψ^{VN}, as we called them, which correspond uniquely, by coordination from *I* to *II*, to the several half-states in one of which it will probably be "when observed." Any such statement, and all philosophizing or theorizing based upon it,

[18] Or determination of the ζ_i within arbitrarily small limits, which amounts to the same thing; see reference 13.

fails to distinguish between *I* and *II* and leads, therefore, inevitably to confusion. *Third*, the assignment of probabilities to full states in *I* does not conflict with the limitation expressed by inequality (2). This limitation comes into play only when one wishes to test the prediction experimentally. Then one can either arrange the set-up so that the later measurements allow for the assignment of a precise half-state, or so that they yield state-limits. I shall deal with the two cases separately.

(*a*) If one assigns at t_1 a precise half-state, say $[\zeta_1', \zeta_2', \cdots, \zeta_N']$, then one is, according to inequality (2), unable to assign any value to the η_i. The probability of making a measurement that indicates this half-state is, therefore, $\phi_1(\zeta_1') \cdot \phi_2(\zeta_2') \cdots \phi_N(\zeta_N')$; for the probability of an η having some value is 1.

(*b*) Assume, next, $\bar{\zeta}_i$, $\bar{\eta}_i$, $\triangle\bar{\zeta}_i$, $\triangle\eta_i$ to be the averages and the standard errors of the distributions in the $D_{2(n)}$ that belongs to $\psi(t_1)$. It is a consequence of the interpretation of *II*, in conjunction with familiar theorems of statistics, that if one realizes the initial set-up many times, the values of ζ_1 and η_1 at t_1 will almost every time lie in the intervals $\bar{\zeta}_1 \pm a\triangle\zeta_1$ and $\bar{\eta}_1 \pm a\triangle\eta_1$, respectively, where a is a small integer. If, therefore, our later measurements are of a nature that leads to a $d\zeta_1$ and a $d\eta_1$ such that $d\zeta_1 = 2a\triangle\zeta_1$, $d\eta_1 = 2a\triangle\eta_1$, then the two coordinates lie "every time" in the properly located intervals. The last statement no longer looks like a statistical statement. But it is, of course, inaccurate or, rather, it is accurate only in the sense in which it is accurate to say that the entropy of a closed system never increases. Taking account of the similarity between inequalities (1) and (2), one could, with the same inaccuracy, describe this state of affairs by saying that one predicts, not the probabilities of states in a statistical schema, but a state within a process, and that one does this within the limits of inequality (2) or, at least, of a small multiple thereof.

Taken in conjunction with SEC. V (2) and some of the comments in the section on measurement, the last paragraph amounts to a logical analysis of the so-called Principle of Indeterminacy. But this, I trust, is obvious.

VII. TWO SPECIAL PROBLEMS

The two preceding sections contain what I take to be, for all philosophical purposes, a reasonably adequate description of the new theory. In SEC. IV I have indicated, in a general manner, how this description may be used to eliminate pseudoproblems. Several hints to the same effect have been scattered throughout the actual description in SECS. V and VI. I shall conclude with a few more comments. They center around two questions of considerable generality and, therefore, of some philosophical interest. The first concerns the well-known discontinuities of the quantum theory; part of what I shall say on the second is based on von Neumann's analysis of the measuring process in the last chapter of his *Mathematische Grundlagen der Quantenmechanik*.

(1) Physicists who have read this far have probably wondered why I have tied my exposition to the position-momentum coordinates. Perhaps they have also suspected that this almost studied neglect of the energy levels, which are in the physicist's actual practice so much more important, would lead to distortion or outright misinterpretation of some of the most characteristic and, at the same time, most paradoxical features of the new theory. Such apprehensions are unwarranted.

First, the position-momentum coordinates are the natural starting point for an attempt to clarify the fundamental or, if you please, philosophical issues. What is there at stake is, after all, the nature of the particle; and in this context the notion of energy is rather unimportant. For there could be a world—or schema—with particles and orbits, but otherwise so constituted that we would never be led to attribute any significance to the energy construct. *Second*, the approach chosen allows one to "get by" with a minimum of technical information which, as such, is of no interest to the philosopher. *Third*, while the characteristic discontinuities of the quantum theory are undoubtedly best brought out by the energy levels and, generally, by the jumps of the old theory and the eigenfunctions of the new, I shall now show that the present exposition yields at least a reasonably adequate view of this feature.

Assume an experimental set-up in which we always determine precise half-states of a single particle or particle configuration. Inaccurately one might say that we assign, on the basis of measurements, the state $\psi(0)$ to the particle at the time t_0 or, still more misleadingly, that we "observe" the particle in the state $\psi(0)$. This state transforms itself with the lapse of time into the state $\psi(t)$ which, as likely as not, is one that we never "observe." For, it will be remembered, $\psi(0)$ is one of those special states that have N one-value distributions, while $\psi(t)$ may or may not be such a state. If it is not, then what we "observe," at the time t, with a certain probability determined by the interpretation of $\psi(t)$ in *I*, is again the special ψ determined by a half-state. If things are stated in this manner, it looks as if the particle capriciously allowed itself to be "observed" only in some of its states.

The dissolution of the apparent paradox is not difficult. Along purely *logical* lines, one must insist that a ψ is not in any sense a state of a particle or particle configuration. To say that it is amounts to saying that a system of *I* is in a state of *II*. That is clearly nonsense. Furthermore, the apparent paradox is made possible by the characteristic asymmetry between coordination (from *I* to *II*) and interpretation (from *II* to *I*). This asymmetry itself is easily understood; it is, as we have seen, an almost obvious consequence of the fact that of the two schemas correlated the one is statistical and the other a process. As long as one insists on coordinating individual systems to individual systems, I can think of no other way in which such correlation could be achieved. Along the lines of *physical* theory, this correlation implies indeed a restriction of the states in which the systems of *I* may be (not just "be observed"). This, I fear, is not brought out too clearly by the description I have furnished.

Be that as it may, the restriction turns out to be equivalent to the quantum conditions of the old theory, according to which the particle configurations never are in some of the states in which they could be in classical mechanics. And not only is the restriction materially the same; one can, if one wishes, still so express it, though, of course, only in schema *I*. In other words, the quantum conditions impose no restrictions on the states of *II*, nor have they anything to do with limits of measurement. They are essentially a feature of schema *I*, which thus becomes a particle schema of discrete states and which is also, as a statistical schema, without orbits. From a philosopher's vantage point this is rather satisfying. Continuity in the schemas of our theories is merely a convention and, moreover, a convention connected with the idea of orbits. So why should there be continuity without orbits or, as in the old theory (the unmodified schema *I*) orbits without continuity?

(2) If one does not carefully distinguish between *I* and *II*, the characteristic experimental situation which I have just discussed seems to exhibit yet another paradoxical feature. As long as it is not "observed," a particle behaves deterministically according to the process formula of *II*. Observation produces a discontinuity. The particle changes abruptly, according to a certain statistical distribution, into one of a class of distinguished states. Here we are at the very source of the thread from which the skein of spurious philosophical interpretation may be spun: one may be tempted to believe that *the statistical feature of the new theory is due to the limits of measurement or, even more profoundly, to the inevitable subjectivity of all observation.* To disentangle such a skein, one must first attempt a systematic and independent analysis of one's own. This I have tried to do. But after the job has been done, it pays to look back in order to find out what has in the meantime become of the original tangles. This I shall do now, beginning with a more general consideration (*a*) and concluding with a more technical remark (*b*).

(*a*) It will be noticed that the foregoing italicized sentence, which I have singled out as the source of all pseudoproblems, throws the weight—I almost feel like saying the responsibility—of what are felt to be the imperfections of the new theory, not on *II* but on *I* and, by bringing measurement into the picture, on the empirical constructs and, perhaps, the observing subject. As long as we move in *II* we may have our heart's desire: a deterministic process schema.

The use of 'deterministic' here requires some explanation. As the term has been defined in SEC. II (2), a schema as such cannot be called deterministic; a theory with a process schema may be called deterministic if it is, in the sense there explained, comprehensive. But then schema *II* may, after a fashion. be thought of as belonging to a comprehensive theory.[19] All we have to do is to conceive, in our imagination, a ψ and H with a tremendously large number of variables—sufficiently large to take care of all the particles in the world or, at least, in an arbitrarily large closed system. So it seems that the world *is,* in essence, still a deterministic process. The schema is, not the world! As long as one remembers that this and only this is what any more exuberant formulation expresses, nothing is wrong with such formulations. As soon as one forgets it, one is easily lured into a certain kind of philosophizing.

On the other hand, it is perhaps a pertinent observation on our uncritical thought patterns that we incline to think of "the last schema" as most intimately connected with "reality." It has been seen that in the ordinary two-level theory certain thought habits were unshaken as long as certain features could be preserved in the schema. One could still be deterministic, even if physics was not strictly deterministic, as long as one believed in the possibility of a theory with a comprehensive process schema. If we had, or should ever have, a four-level theory, we would perhaps believe that the third schema is a true picture of the universe, and attribute all the discrepancies between its structure and that of the lower levels to limits of measurement, the unavoidable subjectivity of observation, or what not.

(*b*) It is, of course, perfectly true that what occurs in "measurement" does something to the system "measured." *Before* it is interfered with, the system of *II* is in the general state $\psi(t)$; *afterwards,* with a probability determined by $\psi(t)$, in one of the distinguished states. Now one could simply say that what occurs in measurement is, within *II*, represented as the collision of two systems, say, for instance, the system of the "measured" electron and the "measuring" photon in the Compton experiment. So the process formula of either of the two initially independent systems, electron and photon, does no longer apply, since any process formula applies only as long as its system remains undisturbed.

Relatively superficial as this account is, it shows clearly that the measuring process does not offer any difficulties of a fundamental or, if you please, philosophical nature. Physicists, however, could hardly afford to be satisfied with this answer. Rather, they will have to ask themselves the following question. Suppose one considers a more comprehensive system (of *II*) that contains the representations of both the particle measured and the measuring photon. Can one by following the temporal process in this larger system account for what actually happens in measurement? The notion of the more comprehensive system, followed to its extreme, leads to the philosophical ideas I have discussed in the preceding

[19] The assumption of comprehensiveness is sometimes represented by the "axiom" that every physical magnitude has a representative—its Hermitean operator—in the quantum-mechanical calculus. This is, properly speaking, not an axiom of the calculus but, rather, an assumption about its success in application.

paragraphs. But in itself, and as I just formulated it, the question is a perfectly good scientific question. As long as it has not been given a positive answer, at least in principle, one cannot even be sure that the new theory is scientifically adequate. The solution of this problem, given by von Neumann, makes use of the remarkable properties of ensembles of quantum-mechanical systems that I have briefly mentioned in Sec. V (5).

Consider an ensemble each of whose part configurations consists of the representation (in *II*) of a particle measured and of the measuring photon. Before the collision each particle and each photon will be in the same state and the ensemble will, therefore, be a pure ensemble. If this ensemble, *which as a whole is no longer interfered with by a measurement*, develops according to the process formula for its statistical operator, then it remains a pure ensemble. So it will still be a pure ensemble after the collision. We notice further that the ensemble can, before as well as after the collision, be "broken up" into two independent ensembles, the ensemble of the electrons and that of the photons. But while the two ensembles of the subsystems before the collision are by assumption pure, both will be mixed after the collision. The particle ensemble, for instance, will with the proper probabilities contain all the special states into which an individual particle passes if measured—I express myself, for brevity's sake, inaccurately. The original question is thus found to be equivalent to the following mathematical problem: To find a process formula for a pure statistical operator such that at the beginning and the end of a certain time interval the operator can be broken up into two operators that characterize independent ensembles according to the specifications of the physical situation. The time interval is, intuitively speaking, the time during which particle and photon are sufficiently close to interact. This problem is soluble. One of the crucial theorems that make its solution possible is, as one would expect, (iv) of Sec. V (5). Schrödinger's striking formulation of this theorem is, therefore, an account of the peculiarities of what is usually called the measuring process.

The Principle of Anomaly in Quantum Mechanics*

HANS REICHENBACH

THE HEISENBERG RELATION of indeterminacy, which states a limitation of the measurability of simultaneous values of complementary parameters, has left open two questions, which have been repeatedly discussed and which I should like to formulate as follows:

1) Do the unobservable parameters possess precise values, though these values remain unknown to us?

2) If these unobservable values were known, would it be possible to make precise predictions of the results of later measurements of other parameters, i. e., would strict causality be reestablished?

If these two questions were answered affirmatively, the indeterminacy would express a limitation of human knowledge rather than a restriction of the physical world; it would have a subjective meaning, but would not express an objective feature of nature. No wonder that these questions have been much discussed by philosophers who wish to defend so-called apriori principles, including causality, against the attacks of the physicists.

Those who are fortunate enough not to be imbued with any forms of a philosophy of the apriori are inclined to refuse a discussion of these questions. They claim that the questions are not accessible to verification and therefore have no meaning. I would readily subscribe to this answer if I could share the opinion that the questions are not verifiable. The principle that meanings must be reducible to observational facts, which has found its philosophical elaboration in the verifiability theory of meaning, is indispensable for the understanding of the physics of our day. But I should like to show that the above questions can be given an interpretation in which they are verifiable, and that quantum mechanics is capable of answering these questions. I will present here an abbreviated version of this answer, which I have given at greater length at another place.[1]

Let me first explain a kind of answer which I would not regard admis-

* Reprinted by kind permission of the author and the editor from *Dialectica*, 2, 1948.

[1] *Philosophic Foundations of Quantum Mechanics*. Berkeley: University of California Press 1944. This book may be referred to as *PhF*.

sible. Assume somebody says that there exist unobserved parameters which are connected with the observables at a later time by functional relations such that, if, both these unobservables and the functional relations were known, the results of later measurements could be predicted. If the statement does not include further information about the unobserved parameters and the functional relations, it is empty, because, given a set of observed data at a certain time, it is always possible to postulate both a set of unobserved quantities existing at an earlier time and a set of functional relations, such that the observed values are made unique functions of the postulated values. The statement of the existence of such entities would acquire physical meaning only if the postulated quantities were connected by certain rules with observables existing at the same time, and if both these rules and the postulated functional relations were the same for all physical situations. The first condition is merely a paraphrase of the possibility of acquiring knowledge of the postulated values at the time when they exist, and the second condition paraphrases the possibility of knowing the functional relations before the observation of the future values of the quantities. If we always have to observe a quantity before we can know the relation that connects the found value with previous values, i. e., if the functional relations vary with the individual occurrences, they cannot be used for predictions and are therefore not called causal laws.

Some philosophers and physicists, while accepting these conditions, have argued that although a supplementation of quantum-mechanical relations by causal relations of this kind cannot be given today, it might be found at some later time. According to this conception, quantum mechanics is a provisional physics, to be replaced some day by a definitive physics of the classical kind. While such a conception cannot be proved to be false or meaningless, it does not appeal to those who refuse to seriously consider a possibility unless there exists some evidence in its favor. If the conception were true, the laws of quantum mechanics would apply only to a certain kind of physical entities, and there would exist entities of another kind which were controlled by strictly causal laws. On the basis of our present evidence, nobody will be inclined to believe in such a development unless his beliefs are controlled by wishful thinking — if such a solution appears to him desirable at all.

In fact, the quantum mechanical principle that all physical situations are describable in terms of ψ-functions and subject to the rules controlling these functions, must be abandoned if the conception under discussion is to be true. But to save a causal description of nature by assuming that the present physics is false as far as its claims to universality are concerned, means resorting to hope for a *deus ex machina* in the face of empirical evidence to the contrary.

For these reasons, I shall restrict my investigation to physical entities which, apart from some modifications to be explained presently, are controlled by the laws of quantum mechanics. Supposing these laws to be true and universally valid, can we answer the above two questions? I should like to show that we can.

Let us assume, for a moment, the first question to be answered in the affirmative, and let us examine the second question. Since the unobserved values referred to in this question, according to our presupposition, belong to quantum-mechanical entities and are subject to Heisenberg's relation, it is not possible to infer these values from simultaneous observables. When we ask, in spite of this fact, whether we could predict the results of measurements if we knew the unobserved values, such a question means that, for the purpose of our inquiry, we dispense with the Heisenberg restriction of observability, while we assume the statistical predictions of quantum mechanics to hold unchanged. This is the modification referred to above.

Now it is obvious that we cannot tell which values would be observed if the Heisenberg relation did not hold; and for this reason we could never prove the thesis of the second question to be true. It is different, however, if the thesis is false. If we can prove that, whatever be the value of the unobserved entity, causality cannot be restored, the thesis is falsified. This thesis is not completely unverifiable; it represents a case of one-sided verifiability and can be falsified if it is false.

In fact, the proof that the answer to the question is negative can be given. The discussion of the relations holding for a particle may serve as an illustration.

Assume the value of the position q of a particle is measured to a high degree of exactness; the value p of the momentum then remains unknown within a wide interval Δp. Let u be an entity noncommutative with both q and p. If the ψ-function of the system is known, it permits us to foretell the result of a measurement of u with a certain probability; this fact is expressible by saying that the probability distribution $d(u)$ is known, which determines the probability of finding a value u when a measurement is made. The thesis then amounts to saying that, for every value u, there exists an unknown value p within Δp such that it determines u in terms of a causal function $u = f(p)$. The function may be dependent on q; but if q is kept constant, $f(p)$ must be some definitive function which is the same for all situations.

Now it can be shown that this thesis is false. In order to prove its falsehood, we need not know which value p corresponds to u; we can prove that, whatever be the corresponding value p, it is impossible to find a function $f(p)$ which is the same for all situations.

I have given a proof for this negative result in *PhF*, § 26, but I should like to give here a simplified proof. Let p_{un} be an unobserved value of p, while p_{ob} is an observed value. There will exist a distribution $d'(p_{un})$ which is either identical with the distribution $d''(p_{ob})$ [the latter being known from the ψ-function] or which is derivable from $d''(p_{ob})$ in terms of a causal function $p_{ob} = g(p_{un})$. The function g, which expresses the disturbance by the measurement, must be a unique function independent of the situation. The function $f(p)$, which can also be written $f(p_{un})$, must then be so chosen that it transforms the probability distribution $d'(p_{un})$ into the distribution $d(u)$. Combining the transitions from p_{ob} to p_{un} and from p_{un} to u into one step, we can say that there must exist a function $u = k(p_{ob})$ which transforms $d''(p_{ob})$ into $d(u)$. It can be shown that such a function will in general exist.[2] But we also know that the distribution $d''(p_{ob})$, while the measurement of q remains unchanged, is compatible with different ψ-functions (*PhF*, p. 92 and p. 97, footnotes 2 and 3) and therefore with different distributions $d(u)$. The function $k(p_{ob})$ will change with $d(u)$; therefore there exists no function $k(p_{ob})$ which performs the transformation for all possible situations. Consequently, there exists no such function $u = f(p_{un})$ either.

This proof makes use of the fact that any causal relation between u and unobserved values of p, if realized in repeated occurrences, must satisfy the observable statistical relations; and these statistical relations, formulated in quantum mechanics, are so constructed that they exclude a causal interpolation of unobserved values. I should like to explain more fully in what sense the causal supplementation of quantum-mechanical statistics is excluded.

What is shown by this proof is that physical parameters whose statistics is controlled by quantum-mechanical laws do not admit of a causal interpretation in the following sense: it is impossible to make a parameter u a causal function of two complementary parameters p and q, which are also complementary relative to each other. In order to arrive at a determination, there has to be known, in addition, the statistical condition of the system as a whole, expressed through the ψ-function, and causality would thus be dependent, not only on the existing values of the parameters, but also on the possible other values. To illustrate this unusual feature, let me refer to an interference experiment (*PhF*, § 7). If there is radiation going through a diaphragm with two slits, and a particle goes through one slit, its further travel will depend on whether the other slit is open or closed; the possibility that the particle might have gone through the other slit determines its actual behavior. Actuality is made a function of possibility.

The peculiar relationship can also be interpreted as a violation of the principle of action by contact. The causality introduced by artificial interpolation of unobserved values, however these values be chosen, is of such a kind that what happens at one space point depends on conditions at distant space points, while there is no physical transmission of this effect

[2] The problem is to replace the variable p_{ob} in $d''(p_{ob})$ by the variable u, using the function $k(p_{ob})$, so that the resulting function, multiplied by $\frac{dp_{ob}}{du}$, is identical with $d(u)$. It is in general possible to find a function k which achieves this transformation. For the discrete case, i. e., variables of discrete eigen-values, the corresponding transformation is in general impossible, so that for this case a causal interpolation is excluded even without the further considerations.

through space. If there is a causality "behind" the observables of quantum mechanics, it is not of the normal type, but contradicts the principle of action by contact. I have called this result the *principle of anomaly*. This principle is to be added to Heisenberg's principle of indeterminacy, if a complete account of the status of causality within a quantum-mechanical physics is to be given.

After this negative answer to the second question, let us turn now to answering the first question. Do the unobservable parameters possess precise values, though these values remain unknown to us? The answer to this question involves some complications.

Speaking of unobserved objects is meaningful only if such objects are related to observed ones. If we say that a tree exists while we do not look at it, or while nobody looks at it, we interpolate an unobserved object between observables; and we select the interpolated object in such a way that it allows us to carry through the principle of causality. For instance, we observe that a tree casts a shadow; when we see a tree shadow without looking at the tree, we say that the tree is still in its place and thus satisfy the principle of causality. More precisely speaking, we select an interpolation which makes the causal laws of unobserved objects identical with those of observed ones. This qualification is necessary because otherwise we could interpolate different objects and construct for them peculiar causal laws; for instance, we could assume that the unobserved tree splits into two trees, which however cast only one shadow. It is the *postulate of identical causality* for observed and unobserved objects which makes statements about unobserved objects definite. If we abandon this postulate, we arrive at different descriptions of the unobservables. These descriptions are not false, but must be regarded as complicated forms of language which, taken as wholes, are equivalent to the usual description. In fact, we possess a class of equivalent descriptions of unobserved objects. The usual language, according to which the object persists when observation ceases, is constructed by singling out one description among this class; this normal description, or *normal system*, is determined by the postulate of identical causality for observed and unobserved objects. The postulate itself is neither true nor false, but a rule which we use to simplify our language.

For these reasons, the preceding analysis concerning a causal supplementation of quantum-mechanical observables becomes relevant for the problem of the existence of the unobservable values. To say that, if q is measured, p has a definite though unknown value, has a meaning in the sense of classical physics, or of conversational language, only if this interpolation of an unobserved value satisfies the postulate of identical causality for observed and unobserved objects. But it was shown that it is impossible to give to the unobserved quantity a value which satisfies this postulate, since any assumption about the unobserved value leads to causal relations that violate the principle of action by contact, a principle that is known to hold for observables. Hence a statement that the unobserved quantity has a definite value, which only remains unknown to us, does not have the usual meaning associated with the term "unobserved". Like the second question, therefore, the first question is answered negatively.

This does not mean that we have to renounce a description of unobservables. We can introduce such values by definition and, for instance, when q is measured to a certain exactness, select for p a value within the corresponding Heisenberg interval. It is in this sense, that is, in the sense of a definition, that the positive statement about the existence of an unobserved value can be given a meaning. But we should know that there is no way of proving any selected value of the unobservable to be "better" than any other one. For the unobservables of quantum mechanics there exists a class of equivalent descriptions which does not include a normal system. Each of these descriptions violates, at some point, the principle of action by contact. This violation of the rules of causality is the price we pay for any *exhaustive description*, i. e., a description which attributes definite values to the unobservables. And the impossibility of a normal system is the characteristic feature of the quantum-mechanical unobservables.

To make these logical relations clearer, a comparison with the definition of simultaneity in the theory of relativity will appear pertinent. Einstein's principle that there are no causal signals faster than light excludes the ascertainment of time order for certain events; to every event there corresponds, at a distant space point, a time interval the time points of which cannot be said to be earlier or later than the first event.[3] However, we can introduce a time order by selecting one time point of the interval and calling it, by definition, simultaneous with the first event. What distinguishes this logical situation from its quantum-mechanical analogue is the fact that every such definition leads to a normal system, in the sense that it satisfies the conditions of causality, whereas in the quantum-mechanical case none of the possible definitions leads to a normal system.

The duality of wave and corpuscle interpretation finds thus its explanation. Each of these two interpretations is a member of the class of equivalent descriptions. The corpuscle interpretation regards one definite value of the unobserved quantity as existing, while the wave interpretation regards the totality of possible unobserved values as existing simultaneously. Each description is true, but neither is a normal system, because each leads to causal anomalies. The causal anomalies are not the same, though, for each description; occurrences that in one description lead to causal anomalies, are given an interpretation in terms of normal causality through the other description, depending on the problem under investigation. The causal anomalies thus can be transformed away for a specific problem, whereas they cannot be transformed away for the description as a whole. I should like to say a few more words about the anomalies re-

[3] See the author's *Philosophie der Raum-Zeit-Lehre*. Berlin 1928, § 22.

sulting for the wave description, since the existence of these anomalies has been denied by some physicists who believe that the wave interpretation can restore the principle of causality.

According to this conception, causality can be reestablished when the physical state is regarded as given, not by parameters of the q-and-p type, but by the ψ-function. This function is controlled by Schrödinger's differential equation; since a differential equation, so it is argued, expresses action by contact, the ψ-states follow a law of the causal type. This argument overlooks the fact that not all developments to new ψ-states are governed by the Schrödinger equation. As soon as an interaction with other matter occurs, the physicist introduces a new ψ-function by a procedure that is sometimes called a reduction of the wave packet; this transition to a new ψ-function is not governed by Schrödinger's equation and represents a causal anomaly if the ψ-function is regarded as a physical state. Since the latter conception is the same as the wave interpretation, the anomaly can be illustrated by the fact that the whole wave front disappears instantaneously when a narrowly localized flash on a screen occurs (*PhF*, p. 31). Like the particle interpretation, the wave interpretation can secure normal causality only for limited stretches of occurrences, but not for all occurrences.

The following consideration may serve as an illustration showing that the conception of the ψ-function as a physical state does not reintroduce causality. Assume we put into an insulating box a source of radiation together with certain instruments of measurement so that a closed system results; the instruments may be so devised that the results of their operations are laid down in writing on slips of paper. Given the initial data of the system, it is possible (in principle) to determine the function $\psi(t_0)$ pertaining at the time t_0 to the whole system, including the instruments of measurement; this determination is made by the use of a set of rules ρ, such as known from the presentations of quantum mechanics. Schrödinger's equation, then, allows us to compute the form $\psi(t)$ of the function at a later time t. When we now open the box at the time t and look at the writing on the slips, we shall find a new set of data; these data, however, subject to the methods of computation formulated in the rules ρ, do not determine the function $\psi(t)$, but a different function $\psi'(t)$. This difference results from the fact that the indications of the measuring instruments at the time t are predictable, at the time t_0, only with probabilities; the function $\psi(t)$ will represent a mixture of all possible indications of the instruments, each multiplied by its corresponding probability. What the Schrödinger equation determines is, not the actual future state of the system at a given time, but the ordered totality of all its possible future states at that time. The transition from the function $\psi(t)$ to the function $\psi'(t)$, then, represents a causal anomaly, since it is not governed by the Schrödinger equation.[4]

[4] More precisely speaking: assume that no macrocosmic occurrences happen between t_0 and t, and that the first indication of a measuring instrument happens at t; then

The set-up of our imaginary experiment makes clear, too, that it is not permissible to make the act of observation account for the new function $\psi'(t)$. The observation by the human observer is here a purely macroscopic affair; the reading of the slips does not influence the system. As long as we do not open the box we do not know the function $\psi'(t)$ and shall therefore use the function $\psi(t)$ as its best substitute; but in doing so we know that we do not know the actual physical state $\psi'(t)$. By the actual physical state I understand the ψ-function determined by the rules ρ in terms of the macrocosmic occurrences existing at the same time.

At this point I should like to add a remark concerning a frequent misinterpretation. The difference between a pure case and a mixture is well known in quantum mechanics (see for instance, *PhF*, p. 107). But this difference entails a difference as to existential statements. For a pure case not corresponding to a measurement of u, i. e., a ψ-function not representing an eigen-function of u, the statement that there exists a definite value of u, though unknown to us, leads to the usual difficulties, as explained above. However, for a mixture of ψ-functions, each of which is an eigen-function of u, the statement that there exists a definite ψ-function, identical with an eigen-function of u, though unknown to us, is perfectly legitimate and does not lead to logical difficulties; in particular, it does not lead to violations of the complementarity principle. The ψ-function is capable of an observational determination and may be regarded as existing even if it is unknown. This distinction between pure case and mixture answers Schrödinger's [5] paradox of the cat that is enclosed in a box together with a radioactive substance and a poison capsule opening on the disintegration of an atom: the status of the box is a mixture and should be interpreted, not as the living and the dead cat being smeared out over the state, but as a status describable in terms of an "either-or" and certain degrees of probability. There is either a living or a dead cat, each possibility to be expected with a determinate probability — that is a permissible interpretation, which does not violate the rules of complementarity nor leads to causal anomalies.

The given analysis shows that the relation of determination holding between macrocosmic occurrences and the ψ-function is an objective relation and has nothing to do with the existence of a human observer. To conceive the ψ-function as a physical state is meaningful only when the ψ-function is regarded as determined by simultaneous macrocosmic occurrences, in the sense of this objective relation. It follows that ψ-states are not throughout connected by causal chains, and that this breakdown of causality cannot be ascribed to the interference by an observer, or regarded as a consequence of the epistemological distinction between subject and object.

It is sometimes argued that the transition from the function $\psi(t)$ to

---

the function $\psi\ (t - \epsilon)$, where ϵ is a small time interval, represents a physical state for every $\epsilon > 0$. It is the transition from $\psi\ (t - \epsilon)$ to $\psi'\ (t + \epsilon)$ which constitutes the causal anomaly.

[5] *Naturwissenschaften* 23, 1935, p. 812.

the function $\psi'(t)$ must not be judged from the viewpoint of causality, that $\psi'(t)$ is a function based on information different from that leading to $\psi(t)$, and that therefore one cannot speak of a causal anomaly. This objection misses its point because it confuses two interpretations. The argument is correct if the ψ-function is regarded as an instrument of formulating probabilities; the discontinuous transition from $\psi(t)$ to $\psi'(t)$, then, presents no more difficulties than, say, the discontinuous transition from the probability of death computed for a twenty-year-old man to the death probability computed for the same man on the additional information that he has tuberculosis. If, however, the ψ-function is regarded as a physical state, this way out is closed; $\psi(t)$ and $\psi'(t)$, then, are physical states and as such subject to a consideration from the viewpoint of causality. In this interpretation, therefore, the discontinuous transition represents a causal anomaly. The confusion of interpretations is one of the weak spots of the customary discussion of quantum-mechanical issues; it has blinded the eyes of some physicists to the extent that they do not see the causal anomalies unavoidable for every interpretation. The probability interpretation of the ψ-function, of course, has its anomalies, too; they manifest themselves, not in the time development of the ψ-function, but in the behavior of particles, since this interpretation, in its exhaustive form, is identical with the particle interpretation.

I should like to add a remark about the possibility of eliminating the causal anomalies through a change in the conception of the space-time continuum. Although I am well aware of the fact that in very small dimensions the meaning of the usual space-time concepts is questionable and demands revision, I do not think that any such investigation could change the results about causal anomalies. The action at a distance referred to concerns distances of a macroscopic size. The distance between the slits in a diaphragm producing interference patterns can be rather long, and the distance at which a flash on a screen "absorbs" the wave can have astronomical dimensions. [The wave beam can partly pass through a glass and partly be reflected; one beam then will disappear if a flash occurs at a distant point of the other beam.] The space-time order to which the causal anomalies refer can therefore be established by the usual macrocosmic methods.

The considerations presented show that the breakdown of causality, which quantum mechanics has uncovered, is of a twofold nature. On the one hand, quantum mechanics has shown, through Heisenberg's relation of indeterminacy, that observables are predictable only in terms of statistical laws. On the other hand, the principle of anomaly reveals that causality breaks down even for unobservables. It is true, it remains possible to introduce unobservables so as to restore causality *post hoc*, i. e., to connect observed events with past events by causal relations which, though not lending themselves to foretelling the future, represent the present as a causal function of the past. But the causality so established is not of the normal type; it includes action at a distance and does not fulfill the conditions which classical physics has set up for the description of nature.

It is this breakdown of a causality of the unobservables which leads to the ambiguities in the description of unobserved objects. It has sometimes been argued that the physicist need not speak about unobservables because such statements are not verifiable. The argument is invalid: certain statements about unobservables are verifiable. For instance, it is a verifiable statement that any description of unobservables leads to causal anomalies. The physics of the unobservables is a function of the physics of the observables, and quantum mechanics includes, through its system of statistical laws for observables, a peculiar physics of the unobservables. No interpretation of quantum mechanics should overlook this fact.

Yet because of the specific status of the quantum-mechanical unobservables it may appear advisable to separate certain statements from the main body of quantum-mechanical statements and to exclude them from the domain of what is either true or false. Of this kind are statements which do not speak about unobservables in the form of implications but assign definite values to them. I use the name *restrictive interpretation* for any interpretation that puts such statements into a separate class, thus excluding causal anomalies from being assertable. Bohr and Heisenberg have suggested to regard such statements as meaningless; such a procedure appears inadvisable because certain "if-then" combinations of such statements may be verifiable statements. I have therefore suggested to introduce a three-valued logic, in which such statements assume a middle truth value, called *indeterminate*. The rules for the use of this logic have been constructed. As an interesting consequence of this construction I may mention the fact that certain combinations of three-valued statements turn out to be two-valued statements and that thus a formulation of the law of complementarity can be given which makes this law a statement of the ordinary two-valued kind.

I do not wish to say that a restrictive interpretation in which statements of the segregated class are regarded meaningless is impermissible. The problem concerns technical advantages of language systems, not questions of truth or falsehood. But I think that the adherents of such an interpretation are mistaken when they believe they really have got rid of such statements. Though eliminated from the domain of meaning, the statements reappear in other forms, usually in the form of metalinguistic statements. I should like to explain the difference between the two restrictive interpretations in greater detail.

In every language so far considered by logicians the rule is followed that if a statement "P" is meaningful, and if a statement "Q" is meaningful, the statement "P and Q" is also meaningful. This rule, in fact, is so convenient, that it would appear unreasonable to abandon it. Now the difficulties into which this rule leads for quantum mechanics can be explained as follows.

When we define meaning by the possibility of verification, the statement "P" about a future value of the momentum p must be regarded as meaningful since it is possible to make a corresponding measurement. As it is also possible to measure, instead, the value q of position, the statement "Q" about the future position must also be regarded as meaningful. But quantum mechanics has shown that it is not possible to measure both p and q; the statement "P and Q" would therefore turn out to be meaningless.

If, in this situation, the above rule is to be maintained, such can be done only by a change in the definition of meaning. There are two possible changes leading to the desired result.

The first change — and that is the one introduced by the Bohr-Heisenberg definition of meaning — consists in basing the definition of meaning, not on the *possibility* of verification, but on the *actuality* of verification. Only when a measurement is actually made is the statement about the value p, or q, regarded as meaningful. The above rule is thus saved; "P and Q" is not meaningful, but since at a given time t only one of the two sentences "P" and "Q" can be meaningful, the rule is satisfied. It then follows, however, that we cannot regard a statement about a future value p, or q, as meaningful before we know that a measurement has been made; that is, a physics dealing with the future would include reference to statements of which we do not yet know whether they will be meaningful. A physicist asking a question about the future, therefore, would have to retire into the metalanguage; instead of asking, "will the entity q have the value q_1?" he will have to ask: "if the linguistic expression 'the entity q has the value q_1' is meaningful at the time t, will the expression be true or false?"

Such a language is rather inconvenient. Its inadequacy may be illustrated by an application of its principles to macrocosmic physics. For instance, when actuality of verification is required for meaning, the statement that it snows now on the North Pole is meaningless since there is at present no observer at the North Pole. The whole domain of unknown truth would thus be eliminated from physical language and could be discussed only in the metalanguage. If, however, we do not wish to use such a narrow rule of meaning for classical physics, I do not see the reason why we should prescribe it for quantum physics.

The other way out of the difficulty consists, not in narrowing down the definition of meaning, but in widening it. This is the way followed in my interpretation by a three-valued logic. In this interpretation, the statements "P" and "Q" are both meaningful, but the statement "P and Q" is meaningful, too, although it can never be verified as true. The interpretation includes, for this reason, a widening of the definition of meaning:

a statement is meaningful if it is verifiable as true, false, or indeterminate.[6] The principle that meaning is defined in terms of the possibility of verification is thus satisfied. On the other hand, the complementarity of the statements "P" and "Q" is expressed in the fact that the statement "P and Q" can never be true but will be either indeterminate or false.

The complementarity is thus expressed, not by a statement in the metalanguage, but by a statement in the object language. We notice here the decisive advantage of the interpretation by a wider meaning over the interpretation by a narrower meaning: it enables us to formulate the laws of physics in the object language.

I have attempted to give a logical analysis of quantum mechanics which is not influenced by preconceived philosophical conceptions. Those who claim that causality is apriori and extends to unobservables, and those who refuse to speak of the causal behavior of unobservables, are alike in that they commit the mistake of judging quantum mechanics from the viewpoint of certain philosophical doctrines. It is possible to speak about the logical status of quantum mechanics in neutral terms. Instead of asking "how should we interpret quantum mechanics?" I have asked "if we interpret quantum mechanics in this or that way, what are the logical consequences?" This question can be answered irrespective of philosophical preoccupations. Its answer is therefore not a matter of opinion. Those who feel uneasy at the quantum-mechanical answer to the problem of causality, who wish to reestablish classical causality and unambiguous unobservables, should not argue on philosophical ground — they have to prove that quantum mechanics is false and have to replace it by a different physics. There is nothing wrong with the philosophy of quantum mechanics. The conception of physical reality developed with this latest chapter of physics is as consistent as that of classical physics. The philosopher must admit that nature may very well be as the quantum physicist describes it; whether this description is true is a matter of empirical science.

[6] The verification of statements as indeterminate is given through a truth table, according to which a statement about the value of a quantity is indeterminate if no measurement is made (*PhF*, p. 146).

VI

PHILOSOPHICAL PROBLEMS OF BIOLOGY AND PSYCHOLOGY

Philosophy of Organic Life*

MORITZ SCHLICK

THE ULTIMATE and the most basic question of the science of organic life concerns the relation of living to nonliving matter.

Scientific knowledge consists in the explanation of one set of phenomena in terms of another. For biology, this involves the task of explaining all the phenomena of organic life by reducing them to the most general principles that exhibit their common features. Thus, a concept of organic matter, of life in general, is formed which is contrasted only with the concept of inorganic, nonliving matter, the subject-matter of physics. If scientific knowledge can progress at all beyond this stage, then such a further step forward could only amount to a unification of these two concepts. But the question as to whether this is possible awaits us at the end of biological science and contains basically the whole philosophical core of that science.

Man naturally first explained inorganic matter in terms of concepts taken from organic life. That is, it was described in terms of concepts transferred from human life. This was the stage of the mythological explanation of nature which interpreted the objects of nature anthropomorphically, viewing the roaring wind and the babbling brook as living things and perceiving in a thunder storm the wrath of a god. Such explanation of nature does not, of course, fulfill the requirements of scientific thought. But on a higher level a similar attempt is in principle conceivable. Schelling's philosophy of nature makes organic processes into fundamental explanatory principles, thus attempts to reduce nonliving nature to the living. It is well known—and reasons for this will appear much more clearly later—that nowadays only the converse approach is feasible. That is to say, if one is at all of the opinion that the organic and the inorganic are not irreducibly different, then one considers it possible that living phenomena can be explained in terms of the inorganic. Hence, there are only two competing views today: the first believes in the reducibility of living phenomena to nonliving nature, and the other considers a reduction in either direction impossible. The latter position which ascribes to life

* Reprinted with the kind permission of Mrs. Schlick from "Naturphilosophie", originally published in Dessoir, ed., *Die Philosophie in ihren Einzelgebieten,* Ullstein, Berlin, 1925. Translated by H. F. and M. B.

a unique role in the world is, as is well known, called *vitalism.* The first view is the assertion of *mechanism.* (This name is not well chosen; it stems from the time when mechanics was considered the foundation of physics and every physical explanation was viewed as a mechanical one. However, the word has become so customary that it may be retained—but it must be interpreted correctly.). There is a third possibility, according to which both fields might be subsumed under a common supreme principle. But this can be safely ignored, since there is no good methodological reason why any eventually discovered explanatory principle should be assigned to a third domain rather than to physics. This point also will be clarified later.

The older philosophical tradition, from Hellenistic times to the end of the Middle Ages, did not assume a sharp division between living and nonliving nature. Indeed, the transition from one to the other was considered a matter of daily occurrence. It was only in the light of the progress of experimental research that there appeared an unbridgeable gap between the two realms (at least, in the direction from the nonliving to the living). This gave rise to and corroborated the doctrine characterizing and defining organic life by the presence of a special or peculiar force. This "vital force" was said to manifest itself especially in that only with its help was the production of certain substances possible, namely, those chemical substances occurring in organisms, the so-called "organic" substances. With the development of chemistry, these organic compounds were, of course, analyzable into elementary components, but could not be artificially synthesized from these components. Only the "vital force" could achieve such a feat. However, in the year 1828, Wöhler was able to produce in his laboratory a substance which heretofore was found only in living organisms, namely, urea. This refuted once and for all the doctrine that the synthesis of organic compounds requires a special force. Gradually, more and more organic compounds were synthesized and even if today some substances such as the proteins have not as yet been produced in this manner, there is no serious doubt that this is due only to purely technical difficulties engendered mainly by the extremely complex structure of those compounds, not to any impossibility in principle. The present opinion maintains that "organic chemistry" is in a sense a misnomer and that this field of science would more correctly be called the chemistry of carbon compounds. For all substances produced in the biological processes contain carbon and this may well be explained by the fact that carbon atoms are able to link together in the form of chains and rings, thus forming those extremely complex molecules, often composed of thousands of atoms, without which the well-known complex living processes could not occur.

Thus it was established that the compounds formed by elements occurring in organisms are not peculiar to life but can be produced outside of organisms. Scientific interest concentrated upon this question of organic substances simply because of the prominence of the concept of substance in general.

All of this, however, did not contribute much to the solution of the problem of the explanation of organic life. Once it is realized that the concept of substance is merely a very special form of the concept of law, then it becomes clear that the major problem requires for its complete solution an answer to the following question: are the processes of organic life explainable in terms of the same laws that apply to inorganic processes or are they not? This, then, is the manner in which the question of modern biological philosophy must be posed. In this form it includes also the problems concerning the structure, the behavior and the evolution of organisms. The view that organic life possesses its own irreducible laws, that is, the doctrine of the autonomy of organic life, is called "neo-vitalism." Neo-vitalism consists essentially in the formulation and defense of arguments for the uniqueness of biological laws, whereas the mechanistic philosophy consists in the critique of these arguments and in the search for evidence which speaks in favor of the reducibility of biological laws. In what follows, we shall present a survey of the controversy, restricting ourselves to the most significant points on both sides.

* * *

Life and Consciousness

To fuse the concept of organic life with that of consciousness (thereby intending that consciousness be a or even the only necessary and sufficient criterion of organic life) is to proceed down a blind alley. This would amount to asserting that life is accessible only to *psychological* explanation.

Various reasons make this point of view indefensible:

First, there is a *methodological* reason. Whether or not a being is endowed with consciousness is in principle and definitely inaccessible to direct verification. After all, it is a commonplace and a result of even the most modest philosophical reflection that we have immediate knowledge of only one single consciousness, namely, our own. The assumption of another's consciousness can under any circumstances, be supported only by inference from analogy: We perceive in other beings behavior which we know to be accompanied in ourselves by mental processes and we assume that analogous conscious processes occur also in those beings. Thus we infer the presence of mental processes only after we have convinced ourselves of the presence of vital processes. The inference, therefore, proceeds precisely in the converse direction from that which would be made if consciousness could serve as a criterion of life. Furthermore, the conclusion of an analogical inference is never logically necessary, but always only probable. One will gladly attribute the highest probability to this inference when, for instance, we infer the existence of mental life in our fellow human beings or when we declare horses or dogs to be conscious beings (although no less a thinker than Descartes considered all animals as mere nonconscious automatons). But what are we to say of this inference when it concerns the question as to whether the amoeba, or a human spermatozoon (as to whose being alive there can be no doubt) possess consciousness? To ask such unanswerable questions suffices to reveal that it would be methodologically perfectly mistaken to make something that is in principle unobservable—and consciousness, after all, is never an object of observation—into a criterion of organic life.

Secondly, there is a very imposing *empirical* reason for asserting that life and consciousness are not necessarily and intrinsically bound together. It is the fact that apparently consciousness can cease without life doing so. In swooning or total anaesthesia and probably also in deep sleep, consciousness, as far as we know, is completely extinguished, but life calmly goes on—how then is it possible to consider consciousness as a necessary condition of life!

There is a third reason, pertaining to the *theory of knowledge*, hence cutting most deeply. Even if it were permissible to explain organic life by something that is in principle unobservable, this could never be consciousness, for all natural processes demand an interpretation within natural science, and all recourse to concepts of a fundamentally different kind would, from the point of view of philosophy of science, be tantamount to renunciation of any explanation whatsoever. It is of course quite permissible to render understandable the behavior of men or animals through the assumption of mental events. We do proceed in this way in common life, in history and in the other cultural sciences. There the psychological type of explanation and its fusion with the mode of explanation in the natural sciences is admissible because there we are quite generally not concerned with pure knowledge in the strictly theoretical sense, but with a more general type of understanding. But in biology, this sort of understanding can be justified only in a preliminary way as a half-way house toward a genuine explanation. Within the closed cognitive system of the natural sciences psychological concepts can play no role. The epistemological analysis of the relation of physical processes to consciousness shows that these two are not co-ordinated to one another and therefore cannot both appear as links in one and the same causal chain. We do not mean to say that the physical and the mental are two different kinds of reality, but they are—as cannot be justified here in further detail—entirely different conceptual systems, that is different ways in which reality can be symbolized. We call reality mental insofar as it is part of the immediately experienced content of a consciousness: and it is called physical insofar as it is symbolized by the conceptual system peculiar to natural science. A concept is psychological if it directly designates an immediately encountered datum of consciousness. Physical and biological concepts, however, are constructed by a very special procedure of abstraction and combination. (In the case of the physical concepts, the ultimate elements of the construction are the well-known pointer readings.) Scientific explanation simply amounts to representation by means of this very special system of physical concepts. Should this system fail on some occasion, then this would amount to the impossibility of an explanation and no purpose would be served by filling the gaps with altogether heterogeneous psychological concepts. If one believes that it is impossible to carry out an explanation of living phenomena without the "psychical" or "mental", then one must in any case introduce it as a "factor of nature", that is, by a concept to be defined in the manner of natural science and not by recourse to consciousness. The difficulties which, it is true, we encounter in this procedure, we do not have to face at this moment. Even from the vitalistic point of view (H. Driesch), the validity of the foregoing argument against psychological explanation in biology has been fully acknowledged.

Each of the three mentioned reasons is decisive by itself. Thus we may maintain the conclusion that every fusion of the concepts of life and consciousness is to be repudiated and that, no matter what the relation of these two concepts to one another may be, the problem of organic life in biology has to be treated independently of the problem of consciousness.

Organic Teleology and "Finality"

The concepts most frequently adduced in connection with the explanation of organic life are those of purpose and purposiveness.

The processes of metabolism and regeneration, and the adaptation of the various organs and functions to one another, appear extremely "purposive". They all seem to be directed toward a supreme goal, sometimes directly, sometimes in a roundabout fashion. The goal is the preservation and development of the living organisms, both of the individual and of the species. It is this purposiveness of the organisms and their functions which represents itself to many thinkers as the genuine miracle of life that distinguishes it from the lifeless. Hence it is only too understandable that reference to the teleology of organic life constituted throughout the ages the strongest argument in favor of the autonomy of organic life.

A careful analysis of the concepts is indispensable for a clarification of the questions surrounding this issue. First of all, what are we to understand by "purpose"? No doubt this is a concept derived from human action. What we call purpose is nothing but the anticipated outcome of our actions. In each action that is consciously carried out, the goal of the action is envisaged by consciousness. Hence, the existence of a purpose presupposes the presence of a consciousness capable of representation. Wherever consciousness is absent or wherever a conceptual system is utilized which does not refer to consciousness, it is therefore impossible to speak of "purposes" in the original sense of this word. In accordance with what we said before, this term should really be banished from biology right from the start. If it is to be retained at all, then this can be done only by assigning a new meaning to the term "purpose". Such a procedure should be followed only in case of extreme need, for any such change in the meaning of a word only too easily produces much misunderstanding.

However, let us ask what significance one could attribute to this word, if it is to be applied in biology. Since reference to consciousness is to be eliminated, it would seem most plausible to drop the characteristic of conscious representation and to interpret the purpose of organic processes simply as the terminal effect attained and without considering whether or not this effect was anticipated by a consciousness. It thus comes down to the actual effect of these processes. However, the word "effect" in this case formulates fully everything that can be asserted and since this concept is generally applied and available there is thus no reason at all suddenly to introduce a different term into biology. This procedure would merely evoke the impression that the science of living phenomena would require a new and autonomous concept and our thinking would be misguided from the very start. Moreover, it must be said that the new meaning of the word "purpose" deviates in a very essential point from the original one. In the case of a conscious action, the purpose is by no means always identical with the actual effect, for, of course, the intention of the agent can always be thwarted, the attainment of the goal prevented by interfering circumstances. Matters are not improved if one were—in order to assimilate the original meaning—to define purpose in terms of a *normal* effect of the processes, where "normal effect" denotes that effect which invariably occurs when no disturbing influences intervene. Here again, the expression "normal effect" is a term which renders more clearly and simply the intended meaning and which is not misleading.

In short: the concept of purpose is to be eliminated from the scientific investigation of organic life. This, however, does not imply that the concept of purposiveness must suffer the same fate. We have utilized this latter concept already and it can indeed be shown that this can be done legitimately and without misgivings, for this concept can be defined without reference to purposes. One can speak of purposiveness also in those cases where anticipated consciousness is absent. It is sufficient if there are certain relations of natural processes with one another which are never missing in the case of human purposive action and which therefore give the *appearance* of a conscious purpose being pursued. Indeed, the attempt has been made to define the concept of purposiveness by means of this appearance. Thus a biologist (S. Becher) defines: "We designate those organic structures and processes as purposive which appear as if they had been created or controlled by an intelligent being for the sake of the attainment of an anticipated goal." Instead of referring to this appearance and thus giving only an indirect definition, it would certainly be much better to list the characteristics themselves which create this impression. We shall therefore have to say: a group of processes or organs is called purposive with respect to a definite effect, if this effect is the normal effect in the cooperation of the processes or organs. The accent here is on *co-operation*; in a specific case these processes, depending upon the circumstances, may occur in a variety of ways, but they are dependent upon one another and linked together in such a way that on the whole approximately the same sort of effect always ensues. In inorganic processes a certain effect which owes its occurrence to the cooperation of several factors will usually (but not always) fail to occur, if one of these factors is disturbed. But in the case of organic life, the other factors compensate for the disturbance.

Purposiveness, therefore, is tantamount to a certain type of relation, interaction, or concatenation. This can be recognized from the fact that the terminal result of these processes are, within wide limits, independent of external circumstances and disturbances—which precisely makes it appear as if a goal-conscious will were asserting itself. The effect resulting from the cooperation of the functions is first of all the preservation and development of the organism itself and, secondly, the preservation and propagation of the whole species. It may also be, thirdly,—and this has been pointed out by E. Becher—that an organism may be equipped with devices which are useful for other organisms. With this philosopher, we may speak of three different possibilities, which may be characterized as serving the organism itself, serving the species, and serving other organisms.

This concept of purposiveness which is perfectly sufficient for the description of the facts of biology contains nothing that transcends, in principle, the processes and laws characteristic of inorganic matter. While it is true that the far-reaching harmony of the functions with each other is observed only in the world of organisms, it is in no way incompatible with the laws of the nonliving of physics. Purposiveness, therefore, does not signify anything fundamentally new. It amounts to no more than a special form of dependence of the processes upon each other. Thus it is difficult to see why this kind of purposiveness should be regarded as a true sign of the autonomy of organic life. And yet this is being done when it is asserted that purposiveness as described cannot be explained on the basis of physical laws and that the concatenation of organic processes quite generally cannot be accounted for in a causal manner. It is asserted that while perhaps purposiveness may be definable without references to the concept of purpose, it cannot be explained without it. The laws of organic life are here viewed as a special kind, namely, as "finalistic" or "teleological" (*finis* being the Latin, *telos* the Greek word for goal or purpose). The assertion that physical analysis of living processes must necessarily fail will be examined presently. But first let us examine the concept which is to replace physical causality, namely, the concept of teleology or finalism.

Let us see how Johannes Reinke, a representative of the teleological point of view, defines the concept of finalism: "All lawful processes in nature occur with necessity.—Of biological necessity, we know two kinds: causal and final. Every biological process is determined by preceding events: this is causality. But such processes can also be determined by later conditions inasmuch as the preceding ones are indispensable preliminary stages for them: this is finalism.—While causal necessity characterizes all natural sciences alike, finalism prevails exclusively in the field of biology.—In the case of teleological phenomena, the essential conditions lie not in the past but in the future. They do not precede but follow. This is what distinguishes finalism from causality. . . ."

Logical analysis of the concept of causality shows clearly that these ideas are vague, if not completely inadmissible, thus demonstrating the general wrong-headedness of the concept of finalism. The idea of causality is simply identical with the idea of a thorough-going lawfulness of nature. And from the vantage point of this conception it is entirely immaterial whether one says that later conditions are determined by previous ones, or, conversely, that (as in the Principle of Least Action) the course of a process is determined by its beginning as well as by its end. Which one of these views one chooses is entirely arbitrary. Each of these possibilities is always equally available for either organic or inorganic processes. Therefore, these different types of description do not constitute different types of lawfulness in nature. They are merely formally different ways of expressing the thoroughgoing mutual dependence of natural processes, which amounts precisely to the essence of causality. Therefore, whoever acknowledges the inviolable lawfulness of nature is thereby already committed to the doctrine of causality. He who denies it does not thereby facilitate a teleological point of view, for finalism is supposed to involve strict lawfulness too. It is especially instructive to make clear to oneself the uselessness of the idea of finalism for the most prominent type of organic processes, namely, the case of human action. Here everyone applies causal considerations in their usual form. The purposes that guide our actions are obviously by no means something in the future but they precede our actions as causes, in the customary sense of "cause."

In short: if organic life has an autonomous lawfulness at all, then this cannot consist in exemption from causality and domination by finalism. Rather the difference between organic and inorganic processes must be looked for within the frame of causal analysis. This provides the cue for the modern defense of the autonomy of organic life.

Critical Vitalism

The existence of nonphysical processes can be asserted only if one has a strict definition of physical processes. Upon reflection, we find that *spatial* characteristics are the indispensable conditions for a concept of physical science. As soon as an event or an object is assigned a definite place in space (of course, relative to other events or objects), it is thereby marked as a physical object and thus subject to the methods of physical knowledge. The only possibility of demonstrating a factor as nonphysical therefore would consist in showing its nonspatiality. If it were possible to show for some or all organic processes that their causes are not identifiable with any spatially localized events, then it would be proper to assume nonspatial factors as causes, and the autonomy of life would then consist in the fact that organic processes depend upon determining circumstances to which spatial predicates cannot be applied, i.e., which cannot be localized in any place.

Already, E. von Hartmann occasionally maintained that his organic superforces "have no spatial location generally and not even a particular place in space from which they act." But a sharp formulation of this view may be found only in the philosophy of organism as developed by Hans Driesch. His efforts are expressly directed toward demonstrating the impossibility of an explanation of living phenomena on the basis of spatially determinable data. Thus, his views may be classified as critical vitalism.†

It is true that among Driesch's attempted proofs of the autonomy of life there are also some which do not go beyond naive vitalism. Consider, for instance, the argument in which he contrasts the behavior of organisms as an "action" with the processes of inorganic nature. While in inorganic processes definite components of the cause always correspond to quite definite components in the effect, Driesch argues that in the case of organic processes "the single constituents of the effects do not singly depend upon the several constituents of the stimulus but that here a *whole* depends upon another *whole*." This may be best illustrated by the famous "telegram argument". If someone receives a telegram saying "Our son killed in accident," then the action elicited by this message is quite independent of the shape of the letters in the message, whether large or small, printed or written. Even if the message had been in a different language, it might very well have brought about the same action. Thus, considerable differences in the stimuli need not bring about any difference in the response. And yet, a very minute alteration in the cause might bring about an entirely different action. Had the text of the telegram read, "Your son killed in accident," the effect upon the receiver would certainly have been very different, for in this case the significance of the stimuli is different, no matter how small the actual difference in the configuration of the letters. This manner of reacting, so says the argument, is fundamentally different from the processes of nonliving nature and thus makes indispensable the assumption of a special factor called by Driesch, in this case, "psychoid"

† [In an earlier section, here omitted, Professor Schlick distinguishes between "naive" and "critical" vitalism. Naive vitalism bases its arguments for the autonomy of life on an inadequate analysis and understanding of the nature of physics, while critical vitalism supports its case for unique laws of living substances with a careful analysis of the nature of physical events—e.g., in this case, the necessary condition of spatial location. Editors' note.]

(not psyche, for the psyche in the strict sense presupposes consciousness and Driesch rightly rejects the intrusion of consciousness into biological explanations).

A more detailed analysis shows however that the facts of "action" furnish no sufficient reason for a definitive distinction between the organic and the inorganic. Only a difference of degree can be maintained. For it is after all rather easy to conceive of a physical mechanism which responds with similar reactions to extremely different causal conditions but which produces a completely different effect upon certain very minute changes in the "stimulus". Yet this was supposed to be the peculiar feature of the previously described action. Of course one may say that such a mechanism would never be capable of learning and of profiting from experience as is a living being: for in the case of a physical apparatus (such as a phonograph or movie camera) the traces of its previous history are retained in the order once impressed upon it, while in the case of the actions of organisms those traces form a general reservoir of possibilities, the elements of which may be regrouped according to the requirements of the moment. But this produces the impression of a fundamental difference only because one conceives these physical models as composed of the rigid materials of our customary machines. Once one regards the traces of past influence as impressed upon a plastic colloidal substance (protoplasm) in which they can naturally interpenetrate and combine, then one realizes that here again there is only a difference of degree and no fundamental contrast with living matter. Of late Driesch has admitted that one might be able to conceive of an automaton capable of carrying on a conversation but incapable of one thing, namely—lying(!).

Much more important than the reasons based upon "action" are the arguments which concern the *morphogenetic* processes in organisms. There, attention is directed upon the really decisive features, namely, *spatial* relations. The highest degree of organic teleology manifests itself in those processes in which from a germ cell gradually a whole individual is formed (development) or those in which a mutilated individual reforms itself into a complete organism (regeneration). Here the single components and processes organize themselves relative to one another independently of their original spatial orientation to form a whole individual. In the case of normal development a definite part of the embryo becomes a definite organ of the full-grown animal: one part may develop into an eye, another into a foot, etc.; but if through experimental intervention such a part is removed, the mature organism is not necessarily lacking an eye or a foot, since the formation of these organs may be taken over by other parts of the embryo. If a fetus is cut in half at a certain stage of its development, then only the cells for one half of the mature animal in the normal course of development remain. Nevertheless, even from this half a complete individual can develop, though perhaps of subnormal size. As is well known, many lower animals (such as the earthworm) may be cut in many parts and the several parts may each grow into complete individuals. If, e.g., the upper part of a tubularia (a hydroidpolyp) is cut off, then a new part grows from the surface of amputation. However, if the organism is divided in another way, then the very same surface which in the first case produced the head end may now sprout a tail end. In short, one and the same part of certain organisms contains entirely different developmental potentialities; out of it may evolve an eye, a foot, or a head, according to what is most appropriate for the development of a complete organism. It is impossible, continues Driesch, that a purely physical system, a machine, could have such characteristics. After all, it is characteristic of machines that each of its spatial parts is capable of one definite function, for which it is designed. However, these parts cannot arbitrarily take over each other's functions. If one separates a piece from the machine, then this piece is not a machine of the same type as the whole (perhaps in smaller dimensions), but it is an incomplete fragment. The morphogenetic processes of life are therefore declared as not machine-like and as incapable of physical explanation. The characteristics of a definite part of an organism are, of course, entirely determined by its place and its orientation within the organism. But since the experimental facts just related demonstrate that a locally determined part of the organism can play entirely different roles in development (ontogenesis), this development, this fate, of a single small part must be additionally determined by some further factor which cannot be localized at all and may hence be called *nonspatial*. Driesch, appropriating an Aristotelian term, calls it "entelechy." "Let us remember that not every single spatial event that results from the developmental effects of the entelechy has a single external cause. Just because this is not the case we found it necessary to introduce our concept of the entelechy." All organic processes are distinguished by the presence of entelechy upon which is based the autonomy of organic life. The entelechy is "a teleologically directing factor of nature. . . . There is nothing like it in the inorganic world." "Entelechy is not an energy, not a force, not an intensity, not a constant, but—entelechy." "Entelechy relates to space, thus belongs to nature; but entelechy is not *in* space—it acts not in space but into space." It is "indivisible" and "non-localized."

Is this a cogent demonstration of the autonomy of organic life? Do the facts described above necessitate the assumption of nonspatial causes? The assertion that there is a nonphysical agent playing a role in some process is tenable only if it can be proved that there are no spatial changes whatsoever that could be considered as the causes of the process. This would be the case only if out of the very same condition, that is out of exactly similar constellations, different states could ensue, e.g., if out of two perfectly similar eggs (which we assume to be completely known in every detail) two different animals emerged, or if two germ cells, equal down to the smallest detail and under identical external conditions, were to undergo entirely different developments. Since in this case all spatially localizable causes are identical, yet different effects would occur, the principle of causality would urge the assumption of nonspatial and therefore unobservable causes. Of course it might be said that identity of different cases is a theoretical construction which does not occur in reality: and even if through the most precise methods of investigation no differences in initial conditions could be established, it would always remain possible to assume spatial changes as causes of the observed effects, even if these assumptions are hypotheses concerning submicroscopic structures. This is no doubt correct and hence it is always impossible to furnish an absolutely rigorous proof for the existence of nonspatial causes. But one may concede this much to the reasoning of the vitalists, that such a retreat to hypotheses concerning the invisibly minute would not be scientifically satisfactory and that the failure of all attempts to find spatially localized causes would make their nonexistence more and more probable. If the facts of organic life are such that even the most precise and penetrating observation would find all spatial characteristics of the objects actually completely equal, then the vitalistic hypothesis would be rendered quite probable.

But, we must ask, what in fact is proved by the experiments in Driesch's illustrations? It may readily be seen that the assumption of the similarity of all conditions is entirely unjustified. An important factor in all those experiments is obviously the manner of dissection of the organic germ cells, that is, the localization and orientation of the cut. This indeed is entirely different in those different cases and could well be the sufficient cause for the different ensuing courses of development of one and the same tissue part, such that, for example, it may develop once into an ear, another time into an eye. After all, we do not know precisely what sort of influences radiate from these cross-sections. Nothing prevents us from assuming that a complete reordering of the smallest particles will bring about a radical change in the elementary processes such that the course of development of the smallest parts will be very different from that which it would have been without the dissection. Even if it is true that in a "machine" each part fulfills the function for which it is designed, there is no reason why it could not be arranged that in case of dissection of the "machine" the structures and function of single parts may automatically rearrange themselves to fulfill the original function. If it be said that we cannot imagine such a machine, this may be correct but this may simply be an admission of our limited ingenuity. If, however, it is asserted that such a machine is absolutely impossible, then one would have to specify the general major premiss from which such an impossibility follows. But such a major premiss is not known.

Thus we see that the necessity for assuming nonspatial causes of organic processes has not been established and that therefore no demonstration of the autonomy of organic life has been achieved. On the basis of more recent investigations, one may go even further and consider it highly probable that the causes of organic processes are to be identified with spatially localized and spatially propagated, that is, physical processes. Ingenious experiments have shown the following. In the earliest stage in the development of a germ cell the later function or the fate of its several parts is not as yet determined. This is shown by the fact that transplantations of minute parts of the germ cell with one another does not bring about an organism with exchanged organs but a normal individual. In a later stage, however, some parts of the germ cell are determined while other parts are still undetermined; and with progressive development the property of being determined spreads over the whole embryonic organism until finally a definite part develops only into a quite specific organ no matter whether this part remains at its normal place or, due to transplantation, develops at another place in the organism. This gradual and continuous spatial spreading of determination certainly indicates that all causes of this described organic process are spatially localized and capable of transportation, and thus may be subsumed under the concept of the physical. This dependency upon the place and the position would be entirely unintelligible if a nonspatial "entelechy" were responsible for the processes described. If there were such a factor of nature, it should be capable of achieving its aims on any arbitrary material irrespective of its given structure. An absolutely nonspatial determiner should be able to transform any structure into any other arbitrarily chosen one. Out of one and the same egg cell it should be able to produce equally well a chick or a crocodile: and if nature had at its disposal such an entelechy, it would be hard to understand why germ cells have as great structural differences as we actually observe. Why are not the entelechies and their different ways of effecting changes sufficient? Why the far-reaching differences in the spatial structure of organic cells? Driesch appears to assume that the differences in structure are necessary in order, as it were, to inform the entelechy as to what it ought to do so that it may effect the required change upon this stimulus: ". . . we cannot say any more than *that* the entelechy is effected in a certain way by the special given material properties of the system which it is to develop, adapt or reconstitute." This means that the entelechy requires a stimulation through the physical condition of the organism. But if this condition determines completely the activities of the entelechy, then it may just as well be considered as the sufficient cause for all the ensuing processes. In other words, if the spatial processes in the organism are necessary and sufficient to give the required directions to the entelechy for the subsequent processes, then they must also be sufficiently differentiated to contain the sufficient conditions for these further processes in themselves. That is to say, the entelechy thus interpreted plays only the role of a mediator and of an entirely superfluous one at that: it is not clear why the later phases of the organic processes could not directly develop out of the previous ones. If the causes are fully contained in the initial conditions, then there is no reason whatsoever for the assumption of a non-spatial intermediary.

Thus we may well conclude that the arguments so far advanced for the autonomy of life are not convincing. The assertion of vitalism is not proved. Quite to the contrary, the facts of biology encourage us throughout to pursue the reduction of biological to physical laws further and further with fresh hope.

As regards the positive explanation of organic teleology, we have many beginnings but no doubt the decisive scientific advances are yet to be made. To be sure the evolutionary theories of Lamarck, Darwin and others have pointed to important factors which play their part in the formation of the teleological features of organic life. Darwin's idea of "selection" especially makes plausible how through purely random variations, through the struggle for existence and through heredity, given teleological features could be perfected. But there is no question that at present the ideas of these theories are not sufficient to give a full account of the peculiarities of organic processes and structure. It is not likely that we shall be able to do without the assumption that organisms possess a special tendency and capacity for the development of teleological features which brings about adaptation to the environment in a more direct fashion than by the long way over various chance variations and subsequent selection of the fittest. How such a tendency could be explained physically, we can at the present stage of research only very dimly conceive. On the other hand, there is no general principle which would seem to preclude such a reduction of organic processes to inorganic principles. Of late, the psychologist Wolfgang Köhler has pointed to certain similarities between physical and biological processes which seem to indicate that even in physics there are certain structures (the so-called physical gestalten or wholes) similar to the "organism" in biology and the "gestalt" in psychology, so that even in the inorganic world "teleology" in our sense may not be completely absent. Perhaps here are the beginnings for a future explanation. Scientists and philosophers thus have good reason to trust that nature does not consist of two realms separated by an unbridgeable gulf but that it is rather one and the same causality which pervades all its parts.

Teleological Explanation and Teleological Systems*

ERNEST NAGEL

THE ANALYTICAL METHODS of the modern natural sciences are universally admitted to be competent for the study of all non-living phenomena, even those which, like cosmic rays and the weather, are still not completely understood. Moreover, attempts at unifying special branches of physical science, by reducing their several systems of explanation to an inclusive theory, are generally encouraged and welcomed. During the past four centuries these methods have also been fruitfully employed in the study of living organisms; and many features of vital processes have been successfully explained in physico-chemical terms. Outstanding biologists as well as physical scientists have therefore concluded that the methods of the physical sciences are fully adequate to the materials of biology, and many of them have been entirely confident that eventually the whole of biology will be simply a chapter of physics and chemistry.

But despite the undeniable successes of physico-chemical explanations in the study of living things, biologists of unquestioned competence continue to regard them as not entirely adequate for the subject-matter of biology. Most biologists are in general agreement that vital processes, like non-living ones, occur only under determinate physico-chemical conditions and form no exceptions to physico-chemical laws. Some of them nevertheless maintain that the mode of analysis required for understanding living phenomena is fundamentally different from that which obtains in the physical sciences. Opposition to the systematic absorption of biology into physics and chemistry is sometimes based on the practical ground that it does not conform to the correct strategy of current biological research. However, such opposition is often also supported by theoretical arguments, which aim to show that the reduction of biology to physico-chemistry is inherently impossible. Biology has long been an arena in which crucial issues in the logic of explanation have been the subject of vigorous debate. It is therefore instructive to examine some of the reasons biologists commonly advance for the claim that the logic of explanatory

* Reprinted by kind permission of the author and the publisher from S. Ratner, ed., *Vision and Action: Essays in Honor of Horace Kallen on His Seventieth Birthday.* Rutgers University Press, 1953.

concepts in biology is distinctive of the science and that biology is an inherently autonomous discipline.

I

What are the chief supports for this claim? Let us first dispose of two less weighty ones. Although it is difficult to formulate in precise general terms the differences between the living and non-living, no one seriously doubts the obvious fact that there are such differences. Accordingly, the sciences of the living are concerned with special questions that are patently different from those with which physics and chemistry deal. Biology studies the anatomy and physiology of living things, and investigates the modes and conditions of their reproduction, development and decay. It classifies vital organisms into types or species; and it inquires into their geographic distribution, their descent, and into the modes and conditions of evolutionary changes in them. It also analyzes organisms as structures of interrelated parts, and seeks to discover what each part contributes to the maintenance of the organism as a whole. Physics and chemistry, on the other hand, are not specifically concerned with such problems, although the subject-matter of biology also falls within the province of these sciences. Thus, a stone and a cat when dropped from a height exhibit behaviors which receive a common formulation in the laws of mechanics; and cats as well as stones therefore belong to the subject-matter of physics. Nevertheless, cats possess structural features and engage in processes in which physics and chemistry, at any rate in their current form, are not interested. Stated more formally, biology employs expressions referring to identifiable characteristics of living phenomena (such as "sex", "cellular division", "heredity" or "adaptation") and asserts laws containing them (such as "Hemophelia among humans is a sex-linked hereditary trait") that do not occur in the physical sciences, and are not at present definable or derivable within the latter. Accordingly, while the subject-matters of biology and the physical sciences are not disparate, and though the former science makes use of distinctions and laws borrowed from the latter, the science of biology does not at present coincide with the sciences of physics and chemistry.

It is no less evident that the techniques of observation and experimentation in biology are in general different from those current in the physical sciences. To be sure, there are tools and techniques of observation, measurement, and calculation (such as lenses, balances, and algebra) which are used in both groups of disciplines. But biology also requires special skills (such as those involved in the dissection of organic tissues) that serve no purpose in physics; and physics employs techniques (such as those needed for producing high vacua) that are irrelevant in present-day biology. A physical scientist untrained in the special techniques of biological research is no more likely to perform a biological experiment successfully than is a pianist untutored in playing wind-instruments likely to perform well on an oboe.

These differences between the special problems and techniques of the physical and biological sciences are sometimes cited as evidence for the inherent autonomy of biology, and for the claim that the analytical methods of physics are not fully adequate to the objectives of biological inquiry. However, though the differences are genuine, they cartainly do not warrant such conclusions. Mechanics, electro-magnetism, and chemistry, for example, are prima facie distinct branches of physical science, in each of which different special problems are pursued and different techniques are employed. But these are quite obviously not sufficient reasons for maintaining that each of those divisions of physical science is an autonomous discipline. If there is a sound basis for the alleged absolute autonomy of biology, it must be sought elsewhere than in the differences between biology and the physical sciences that have been noted thus far.

What then are the weightier reasons which support that allegation? The main ones appear to be as follows. Vital processes have a prima facie purposive character; for organisms are capable of self-regulation, self-maintenance, and self-reproduction, and their activities seem to be directed toward the attainment of goals that lie in the future. It is usually admitted that one can study and formulate the morphological characteristics of plants and animals in a manner comparable with the way physical sciences investigate the structural traits of non-living things. Thus, the categories of analysis and explanation of physics are generally held to be adequate for studying the gross and minute anatomy of the human kidney, or the serial order of its development. But morphological studies are only one part of the biologist's task, since the latter also includes inquiry into the *functions* of structures in sustaining the activities of the organism as a whole. Thus, biology studies the role played by the kidney and its microscopic structures in preserving the chemical composition of the blood, and thereby in maintaining the whole body and its other parts in their characteristic activities. It is such manifestly "goal-directed" behavior of living things that is often regarded as requiring a distinctive category of explanation in biology.

Moreover, living things are organic wholes, not additive systems of independent parts, and the behavior of these parts cannot be properly understood if they are regarded as so many isolable mechanisms. The parts of an organism must be viewed as internally related members of an integrated whole. They mutually influence one another, and their behavior regulates and is regulated by the activities of the organism as a whole. Some biologists have argued that the coordinated, adaptive behavior of living organisms can be explained only by assuming a special vitalistic agent; others believe that an explanation is possible in terms of the hierarchical organization of internally related parts of the organism. But in either case, so it is frequently claimed, biology cannot dispense with the notion of organic unity; and in consequence it must use modes of analysis and formulation that are unmistakably *sui generis.*

Accordingly, there are two main features that are commonly alleged to differentiate biology from the physical sciences in an essential way. One is the dominant place occupied by *teleological* explanations in biological inquiry. The other is the use of conceptual tools uniquely appropriate in the study of systems whose total behavior is not the resultant of the activities of independent components. We must now examine these claims in some detail.

II

Almost any biological treatise or monograph yields conclusive evidence that biologists are concerned with the functions of vital processes and organs in maintaining characteristic activities of living things. In consequence, if "teleological analysis" is understood to be an inquiry into such functions, and into processes which are directed toward attaining certain end-products, then undoubtedly teleological explanations are pervasive in biology. In this respect, certainly, there appears to be a marked difference between the latter and the physical sciences. It would surely be an oddity on the part of a modern physicist were he to declare, for example, that atoms have outer shells of electrons in order to make chemical unions between themselves and other atoms possible. In ancient Aristotelian science categories of explanation suggested by the study of living things (and in particular by human art) were made canonical for all inquiry. Since non-living as well as living phenomena were thus analyzed in teleological terms—an analysis which made the notion of final cause focal—Greek science did not assume a fundamental cleavage between biology and other natural sciences. Modern science, on the other hand, regards final causes to be vestal virgins which bear no fruit in the study of physical and chemical phenomena; and because of the association of teleological explanations with the doctrine that goals or ends of activity are dynamic agents in their own realization, it tends to view such explanations as a species of obscurantism. But does the procedure of teleological explanations in biology and the apparent absence of such explanations from the physical sciences entail the absolute autonomy of the former? We shall try to show that it does not.

Quite apart from their association with the doctrine of final causes, teleological explanations are sometimes suspect in modern natural science because they are assumed to invoke purposes or ends-in-view as causal factors in natural processes. Purposes and deliberate goals admittedly play important roles in human activities; but there is no basis whatever for assuming them in the study of physico-chemical and most biological phenomena. However, as has already been noted, there are a great many explanations that are counted as teleological which do not postulate any purposes or ends-in-view; for explanations are often said to be "teleological" only in the sense that they specify the *functions* which things or processes possess. Most contemporary biologists certainly do not impute purposes to the organic parts of living things whose functions are investigated; and most of them would probably also deny that the means-ends relationships discovered in the organization of living creatures are the products of some deliberate plan on the part of a purposeful agent. To be sure, there are biologists who postulate psychic states as concomitants and even as directive forces of all organic behavior. But they are in a minority; and they usually support their view by special considerations which can be distinguished from the facts of functional or teleological dependencies that most biologists do not hesitate to accept. Since the word "teleology" is ambiguous, it would doubtless prevent confusions and misunderstandings were it eliminated from the vocabulary of biologists. But as it is, biologists do use it, and say they are giving a teleological explanation when, for example, they explain that the function of the alimentary canal in vertebrates is to prepare ingested materials for absorption into the bloodstream. The crucial point is that when biologists do employ teleological language they are not necessarily committing the pathetic fallacy or lapsing into anthropomorphism.

We must now show, however, that teleological (or functional) explanations are equivalent to non-teleological ones, so that the former can be replaced by the latter without loss in asserted content. Consider some typical teleological statement, for example. "The function of chlorophyll in plants is to enable plants to perform photo-synthesis." But this statement appears to assert nothing which is not asserted by "Plants perform photosynthesis only if they contain chlorophyll", or alternatively by "A necessary condition for the occurrence of photosynthesis in plants is the presence of chlorophyll." These latter statements, however, do not explicitly ascribe a function to chlorophyll, and in that sense are therefore not teleological formulations. If this example is taken as a paradigm, it seems that when a function is ascribed to a constituent of some organism, the content of the teleological statement is fully conveyed by another statement which simply asserts a necessary (or possibly a necessary and sufficient) condition for a certain trait or activity of that organism. On this assumption, therefore, a teleological explanation states the *consequences* for a given biological system of one of the latter's constituent parts or processes; the equivalent non-teleological explanation states some of the *conditions* (though not necessarily in physico-chemical terms) under which the system persists in its characteristic organization and activities. The difference between teleological and non-teleological explanations is thus comparable to the difference between saying that B is an effect of A, and saying that A is a cause or condition of B. In brief, the difference is one of selective attention, rather than of asserted content.

This point can be reinforced by another consideration. If a teleological explanation had an asserted content which is different from the content of every non-teleological statement, it would be possible to cite procedures and evidence for establishing the former which are different from the procedures and evidence required for confirming the latter. But in point of fact, there appear to be no such procedures and evidence. Thus, consider the teleological statement "The function of the leucocytes in human blood is to defend the body against foreign micro-organisms." Now whatever may be the evidence which warrants this statement, it also warrants the statement that "Unless human blood contains a sufficient number of leucocytes, certain normal activities of the body are injured," and conversely. Accordingly, there is a strong presumption that the two statements do not differ in *factual* content. More generally, if as seems to be the case the conceivable empirical evidence for a teleological explanation is identical with the conceivable evidence for a certain non-teleological one, the conclusion appears inescapable that these statements cannot be distinguished with respect to what they *assert*, even though they may differ in other ways.

However, this proposed equation of teleological and non-teleological explanations must face a fundamental objection. Most biologists would perhaps be prepared to admit that a teleological explanation *implies* a non-teleological one; but some of them, at any rate, would maintain that the latter does not in general imply the former, so that the suggested equivalence does not in fact hold. This latter claim can be forcefully stated as follows. If there were such an equivalence, it may be said, not only could a teleological explanation be replaced by a non-teleological one, but a converse replacement would also be possible. In consequence, the customary statements of laws and theories in the physical sciences must be translatable into teleological formulations. In point of fact, however, modern physical science does not appear to sanction such formulations; and physical scientists would doubtless resist their introduction into their disciplines as an unfortunate attempt to reinstate the point of view of Greek and medieval science. Thus the statement "The volume of a gas at constant temperature varies inversely with its pressure" is a typical physical law, which is entirely free of teleological connotations. If it were equivalent to a teleological statement its presumed equivalent would be "The function of a varying pressure in a gas at constant temperature is to produce an inversely varying pressure", or perhaps "Gases at constant temperature under variable pressure alter their volumes in order to keep the product of pressure and volume constant." But most physicists would regard these latter formulations as preposterous, and at best as misleading. There must therefore be some important differences between teleological and non-teleological statements which the discussion has thus far failed to make explicit.

The attitude of physical scientists toward teleological formulations in their own disciplines is doubtless as alleged in this objection. Nevertheless, the objection is not completely decisive on the point at issue. Two general comments are in order which will at least weaken its force.

In the first place, it is not entirely accurate to maintain that the physical sciences never employ formulations that have at least the appearance of teleological statements. As is well known, some physical laws and theories are often expressed in so-called "isoperimetric" or "variational" form, rather than in the more familiar form of numerical or differential equations. When laws and principles are so expressed, they undoubtedly seem to be akin to teleological formulations. For example, the elementary law of optics that the angle of incidence of a light ray with a surface is equal to the angle of reflection, can also be rendered by the statement that a light-ray travels in such a manner that when it is reflected from a surface the length of its actual path is the minimum of all possible paths. More generally, a considerable part of classical as well as contemporary physical theory can be stated in the form of "extremal" principles. What these principles assert is that the actual development of a system is such as to minimize or maximize some magnitude which represents the possible configurations of the system.[1]

The discovery that the principles of mechanics can be given such extremal formulations was once considered as evidence (especially by Maupertuis in the 18th century) for the operation of a divine plan throughout nature. Such theological interpretations of extremal principles is now recognized almost universally to be entirely gratuitous; and no competent physicist to-day supposes that extremal principles entail the assumption of purposes animating physical processes. The use of such principles in physical science nevertheless does show that it can formulate the dynamical structure of physical systems so as to bring into focus the incidence of constituent elements and processes upon certain properties of a system taken as a whole. If physical scientists dislike teleological language in their own disciplines, it is not because they regard teleological notions in this sense as foreign to their task. Their dislike stems in some measure from the fear that, except when such teleological language is made rigorously precise through the use of quantitative formulations, it is apt to be misunderstood as connoting the operation of purposes.

In the second place, the physical sciences unlike biology are in general not concerned with a relatively special class of organized bodies, and they do not investigate the conditions making for the persistence of some selected physical system rather than of others. When a biologist ascribes a function to the kidney, he tacitly assumes that it is the kidney's contribution to the maintenance of the living animal which is under discussion; and he ignores as irrelevant to his primary interest the kidney's contribution to the maintenance of any other system of which it may also be a constituent. On the other hand, a physicist generally attempts to discuss the effects of solar radiation upon a wide variety of things; and he is reluctant to ascribe a "function" to the sun's radiation, because there is no

[1] It can in fact be shown that when certain very general conditions are satisfied, all quantitative laws and principles can be given an "extremal" formulation.

one physical system of which the sun is a part that is of greater interest to him than any other such system. And similarly for the law connecting the pressure and volume of a gas. If a physicist views with suspicion the formulation of this law in functional or teleological language, it is because (in addition to the reasons which have been or will be discussed) he does not regard it his business to assign special importance (even if only by vague suggestion) to one rather than another consequence of varying pressures in a gas.

III

However, the discussion thus far can be accused with some justice of naïveté if not of irrelevance, on the ground that it has ignored completely the fundamental point—namely, the "goal-directed" character of organic systems. It is because living things exhibit in varying degrees adaptive and regulative structures and activities, while the systems studied in the physical sciences do not—so it is frequently claimed—that teleological explanations are peculiarly appropriate for the former but not for the latter. Thus, it is because the solar system, or any other system of which the sun is a part, does not tend to persist in the face of environmental changes in some integrated pattern of activities, and because the constituents of the system do not undergo mutual adjustments so as to maintain this pattern in relative independence from the environment, that it is preposterous to ascribe any function to the sun or to the solar radiation. Nor does the fact that physics can formulate some of its theories in the form of extremal principles—so the objection continues—minimize the differences between biological and purely physical systems. It is true that a physical system develops in such a way as to minimize or maximize a certain magnitude which represents a property of the system as a whole. But physical systems are not organized to *maintain* extremal values of such magnitudes, or to develop under widely varying conditions in the direction of realizing some particular values of such magnitudes.

Biological systems, on the other hand, do possess such organization, as a single example (which could be matched by an indefinite number of others) makes clear. There are complicated but coordinated physiological processes in the human body, which maintain many of its characteristics in a relatively steady state (or homeostasis). Thus, the internal temperature of the body must remain fairly constant if it is not to be fatally injured. In point of fact, the temperature of the normal human being varies during a day only from about 97.3° F to 99.1° F, and cannot fall much below 75° F or rise much above 110° F without permanent injury to the body. However, the temperature of the external environment can fluctuate much more widely than this; and it is clear from elementary physical considerations that the body's characteristic activities would be profoundly curtailed unless it were capable of compensating for such environmental changes. But the body is indeed capable of doing just this; and in consequence, its normal activities can continue, in relative independence of the temperature of the environment—provided, of course, that the environmental temperature does not fall outside a certain interval of magnitudes. The body achieves this homeostasis by means of a number of mechanisms, which serve as a series of defenses against shifts in the internal temperature. Thus, the thyroid gland is one of several that control the body's basal metabolic rate; the heat radiated or conducted through the skin depends on the quantity of blood flowing through peripheral vessels, a quantity which is regulated by dilation or contraction of these vessels; sweating and the respiration rate determine the quantity of moisture that is evaporated, and so affect the internal temperature; adrenalin in the blood also stimulates internal combustion, and its secretion is affected by changes in the external temperature; and automatic muscular contractions involved in shivering are an additional source of internal heat. There are thus physiological mechanisms in the body such that its internal temperature is automatically preserved, despite disturbing conditions in the body's internal and external environment.[2]

Three separate questions that are frequently confounded are raised by such facts of biological organization. Is it possible to formulate in general but fairly precise terms the distinguishing structure of "goal-directed" systems, but in such a way that the analysis is neutral with respect to assumptions concerning the existence of purposes or the dynamic operation of goals as instruments in their own realization? Is the fact, if it is a fact, that teleological explanations are customarily employed only in connection with "goal-directed" systems, decisive on the issue whether a teleological explanation is equivalent to some non-teleological one? Is it possible to explain in purely physico-chemical terms—that is, exclusively in terms of the laws and theories of current physics and chemistry—the operations of biological systems? This third question will not concern us in this paper; but the other two require our attention.

IV

There have been many attempts since antiquity at constructing machines and physical systems which simulate the behavior of living organisms in one respect or another. None of these attempts has been entirely successful, for it has not been possible thus far to manufacture in the workshop and out of inorganic materials any device which acts fully like a living being. Nevertheless, it has been possible to construct physical systems which are self-maintaining and self-regulating up to a point, and which therefore resemble living organisms in one important respect. In an age in which servo-mechanisms no longer excite wonder, and in which the language of cybernetics and "negative feed-backs" has become widely

[2] Cf. Walter B. Cannon, *The Wisdom of the Body*, New York, 1932, Chap. 12.

fashionable, the imputation of "goal-directed" behavior to purely physical systems certainly cannot be rejected as an absurdity. Whether "purposes" can also be imputed to such physical systems, as some expounders of cybernetics claim,[3] is perhaps doubtful, though the question is in large measure a semantic one; in any event, the issue is not relevant in the present context of discussion. Moreover, the possibility of constructing self-regulating physical systems does not constitute proof that the activities of living organisms can be explained in exclusively physico-chemical terms. However, the occurrence of such systems does suggest that there is no sharp division between the teleological organization which is often assumed to be distinctive of living things, and the goal-directed organization of many physical systems; and it does offer strong support for the presumption that the structure of such organizations can be formulated without the postulation of purposes or of goals as dynamic agents.

With the homeostasis of the temperature of the human body before us as an exemplar, let us now state in general terms the structure of systems which have a goal-directed organization.[4] The characteristic feature of such systems is that they continue to manifest a certain state or property *G*, or to develop "in the direction" of attaining *G*, in the face of a relatively extensive class of changes in their external environments or in some of their internal parts—changes which, if not compensated by internal modifications in the system, would result in the vanishing of *G* or in an altered direction of development. This feature can be formulated more precisely though schematically as follows.

Let *S* be some system, *E* its external environment, and *G* some state or property which *S* possesses or is capable of possessing under suitable conditions. Assume for the moment—this assumption will be presently relaxed—that *E* remains constant in all relevant respects, so that its influence upon *S* can be ignored. Suppose also that *S* is analyzable into a structure of parts, such that the activities of a certain number of them are causally relevant for the occurrence of *G*. For the sake of simplicity, assume that there are just three such parts, the state of each of which at any time can be specified by a determinate form of the complex predicates "*A*", "*B*", and "*C*", respectively; numerical subscripts will serve as indicators of such determinate forms. Accordingly, the state of *S* at any time causally relevant to *G* will be expressed by specializations of the matrix "$(A_x B_y C_z)$". One further general assumption must now be made explicit.

[3] Cf. Arturo Rosenblueth, Norbert Wiener, Julian Bigelow, "Behavior, Purpose and Teleology", *Philosophy of Science*, Vol. 10 (1943); Norbert Wiener, *Cybernetics*, New York 1948; A. M. Turing, "Computing Machines and Intelligence", *Mind*, Vol. 59 (1950); Richard Taylor, "Comments on a Mechanistic Conception of Purposefulness", *Philosophy of Science*, Vol. 17 (1950), and the reply by Rosenblueth and Wiener with a rejoinder by Taylor in the same volume.

[4] The following discussion is heavily indebted to R. B. Braithwaite, "Teleological Explanation", *Proc. of the Aristotelian Society*, Vol. 47 (1947), and G. Sommerhoff, *Analytical Biology*, London, 1950. Cf. also Alfred J. Lotka, *Elements of Physical Biology*, New York, 1926, Chap. 25.

Each of these state-variables (they are not necessarily numerical variables) can be assigned any determinate values that are compatible with the known character of the part of *S* whose state it specifies. In effect, therefore, the states which can be values for "A_x" must fall into a certain class K_A; and there are corresponding classes K_B and K_C for the other two state variables. The reason for this restriction will be clear from an example. If *S* is the human body, and "A_x" states the degree of dilation of peripheral blood-vessels, it is obvious that this degree cannot exceed some maximum value; for it would be absurd to suppose that a blood-vessel could acquire a mean diameter of, say, five feet. On the other hand, the possible values of one state-variable at a given time will be assumed to be independent of the possible values of the other state variables at that same time. Accordingly, any combination of values of the state variables will be a permissible specialization of the matrix "$(A_x B_y C_z)$", provided that the values of each variable belong to the classes K_A, K_B, and K_C respectively. This is tantamount to saying that the state variables which are stipulated to be causally relevant to *G* are also postulated to be capable of having values at a given time which are mutually independent of one another.

Suppose now that if *S* is in the state $(A_0 B_0 C_0)$ at some given time, then *S* either has the property *G*, or else a sequence of changes will take place in *S* in consequence of which *S* will possess *G* at some subsequent time. Call such an initial state of *S* a "causally effective state with respect to *G*", or a "*G*-state" for short. Not every possible state of *S* need be a *G*-state; for one of the causally relevant parts of *S* may be in such a state at a given time, that no combination of possible states of the other parts will yield a *G*-state for *S*. Thus, suppose that *S* is the human body, *G* the property of having an internal temperature lying in the range 97° to 99° F, A_x again the state of peripheral blood-vessels, and B_y the state of the thyroid glands; it may happen that B_y assumes a value (e.g., corresponding to acute hyperactivity) such that for no possible value of A_x will *G* be realized. It is also conceivable that no possible state of *S* is a *G*-state, so that in fact *G* is never realized in *S*. For example, if *S* is the human body and *G* the property of having an internal temperature lying in the range 150° to 160° F, then there is no *G*-state for *S*. On the other hand, more than one possible state of *S* may be a *G*-state, though only one of them will be actual at a given time; but if there is more than one possible *G*-state, we shall assume that the one which is realized at a given time is uniquely determined by the actual state of *S* at some previous time. In short, we are assuming that *S* is a deterministic system with respect to the occurrence of *G*-states. The case in which there is more than one possible *G*-state for *S* is of particular relevance to the present discussion, and we must now consider it more closely.

Assume again that at some initial time t_0, *S* is in the *G*-state $(A_0 B_0 C_0)$. But suppose now that a change occurs in *S* so that in consequence A_0 is caused to vary, and that at time t_1 subsequent to t_0 the state variable "A_x"

has some other value. Which value it will have at t_1 will depend on the particular changes that have occurred in S. We shall assume, however, that there is a range of possible changes, and that the values which "A_x" may have at time t_1 fall into some class K'_A (a sub-class of K_A) which contains more than one member. To fix our ideas, suppose that A_1 and A_2 are the members of K'_A; and assume further that neither $(A_1B_0C_0)$ nor $(A_2B_0C_0)$ is a G-state—that is, a variation in A_0 alone would take S out of a G-state. Accordingly, if the changes mentioned thus far were the only changes in the state of S, S would no longer be in a G-state at time t_1. Let us, however, make the contrary assumption. Assume S to be so constituted that if A_0 is caused to vary so that the value of "A_x" at time t_1 falls into K'_A, there will also be further compensatory changes in the values of some or all of the other state variables. More specifically, these further changes are stipulated to be of the following kind: if K'_{BC} is the class of sets of values which "B_y" and "C_z" have at time t_1, then for each value of "A_x" in K'_A there is a unique set in K'_{BC} such that S continues to be in a G-state at time t_1; but these further changes unaccompanied by the first-mentioned ones would take S out of a G-state—that is, if at time t_1 the state variables of S have a set of values such that two of them belong to a set in K'_{BC} while the remaining one is not the corresponding member in K'_A, then S is not a G-state. For example, suppose that if A_0 is changed into A_1, the initial G-state $(A_0B_0C_0)$ is changed into the G-state $(A_1B_1C_1)$ with $(A_0B_1C_1)$ not a G-state; and if A_0 is changed into A_2, the initial G-state is changed into the G-state $(A_2B_1C_0)$, with $(A_0B_1C_0)$ not a G-state. In this example, K'_A is the class $\{A_1, A_2\}$, and K'_{BC} the class of sets $\{[B_1, C_1], [B_1, C_0]\}$, with A_1 corresponding to $[B_1, C_1]$ and A_2 *to* $[B_1, C_0]$.

We now introduce some definitions, based upon the above discussion. Assume S to be a system satisfying the following conditions: (1) S can be analyzed into a structure of parts, a certain number of which (say three) are causally relevant to the occurrence in S of some property or feature G; and the causally relevant state of S at any time can be specified by means of a set of state-variables. These state-variables at any given time can be assigned values independently of each other, though the possible values of each variable are restricted to some class of values. (2) If S is in a G-state at some time t_0 during period T, and a variation occurs in one of the state parameters (say "A") such that this variation alone would take S out of its G-state, then the possible values of this parameter at time t_1 subsequent to t_0 but still in T fall into a certain class K'_A. Call this variation a "primary variation" in S. (3) If the state parameter "A" varies in the indicated manner, then the remaining parameters also vary so that their variation alone would take S out of its G-state, and so that their possible values at time t_1 constitute sets belonging to a class K'_{BC}. (4) The elements of K'_A and K'_{BC} correspond to each other in a uniquely reciprocal fashion, such that when the state of S is specified by these corresponding values S is in a G-state at time t_1. Call the variations in S which are represented by the members of K'_{BC} the "adaptive" variations in relation to the variations represented by members of K'_A. When these assumptions hold for *S*, the parts of *S* that are causally relevant to *G* will be said to be "directively organized during the period *T* with respect to *G*"—or more shortly "directively organized", if the reference to *T* and *G* can be taken for granted. This definition can be easily generalized for a larger number of state-variables, and for the primary variation of more than one state-variable; but the present incompletely general definition will suffice for our purposes.

It will be clear from this account that if *S* is directively organized, the persistence of *G* is in a certain sense independent of the variations (up to a point) in any one of the causally relevant parts of *S*. For although it is the state of these parts which by hypothesis determine the occurrence of *G*, an altered state in one of them may be compensated by altered states in the other parts of *S* so as to preserve *S* in its *G*-state. The structure or character of so-called "teleological" systems is therefore expressed by the indicated conditions for a directively organized system; and these conditions can be stated, as we have seen, in a manner not requiring the adoption of teleology as a fundamental or unanalyzable category. What may be called the "degree of directive organization" of a system, or perhaps the "degree of persistence" of some trait of a system, can also be made explicit in terms of the above analysis. For the property *G* is maintained in *S* (or *S* persists in its development which eventuates in *G*) to the extent that the range of K'_A of the possible primary variations is associated with the range of induced compensatory changes K'_{BC} such that *S* is preserved in its *G*-state. The more inclusive the range K'_A that is associated with such compensatory changes, the more is the persistence of *G* independent of variations in the state of *S*. Accordingly, on the assumption that it is possible to specify a measure for the range K'_{BC} the "degree of directive organization" of *S* with respect to variations in the state-parameter *A* can be defined as the measure of this range.

We may now relax the assumption that the external environment *E* has no influence upon *S*. But in dropping this assumption, we merely complicate the analysis, without introducing anything novel into it. For suppose that there is some factor in *E* which is causally relevant to the occurrence of *G* in *S*, and whose state at any time can be specified by some determinate form of the state-variable "F_w". Then the state of the system *S'* (which includes both *S* and *E*) that is causally relevant to the occurrence of *G* in *S* is specified by some determinate form of the matrix "$(A_xB_yC_zF_w)$"; and the discussion proceeds as before. However, it is generally not the case that a variation in any of the internal parts of *S* produces any significant variation in the environmental factors. What usually is the case is that the latter vary quite independently of the former; that they do not undergo changes which compensate for changes in the state of *S*; and that while a limited range of changes in them may be compensated by changes in *S* so as to preserve *S* in some *G*-state, most of the states which environmental factors are capable of assuming cannot be so compensated by changes in *S*. It is customary, therefore, to talk of the "degree of plasticity" or the "degree of adaptability" of organic systems in relation to their environment, and not conversely. However, it is possible to define these notions without reference to organic systems in particular, in a manner analogous to the definition of "degree of directive organization" already suggested. Thus suppose that the variations in the environmental state *F*, compensated by changes in *S* so as to preserve *S* in some *G*-state, all fall into the class K'_F; then if a measure for this class is available, the "degree of plasticity" of *S* with respect to *G* in relation to *F* can be defined as the measure of K'_F.

V

This must suffice as an account of the structure of "teleological" or "goal-directed" systems. The account is intended to formulate only the gross pervasive features of such systems, and undoubtedly suffers from neglect of many important complications. Moreover, it does not pretend to indicate what the detailed mechanisms may be which are involved in the occurrence of such systems. It is therefore deliberately neutral with respect to such issues as whether these mechanisms are explicable entirely in physico-chemical terms, or whether the notion of "feed-back" is required in analyzing them. But if the account is at least approximately adequate, it implies a positive answer to the question whether the distinguishing features of "goal-directed" systems can be formulated without invoking purposes and goals as dynamic agents.

However, there is one matter that must be briefly discussed. The definition of directively organized systems has been so stated that it may apply both to biological as well as to non-vital systems. It is in fact easy to find illustrations for it from either domain. The human body with respect to the homeostasis of its temperature is an example from biology; a building equipped with a furnace and thermostat is an example from physico-chemistry. But though the definition is not intended to distinguish between vital and non-vital systems—the difference between such systems must be stated in terms of the *specific* properties and activities they manifest—it *is* intended to set off systems which have a prima facie "goal-directed" character, from systems which are usually not so characterized. The question therefore remains whether the definition does achieve this aim, or whether on the contrary it is so inclusive that almost *any* system (whether it is ordinarily judged to be goal-directed or not) satisfies it.

Now there certainly are many physico-chemical systems which are ordinarily *not* regarded as being "goal-directed", but which appear to conform to the definition of directively organized systems proposed above. Thus, a pendulum at rest, an elastic solid, a steady electric current flowing through a conductor, a chemical system in thermodynamic equilibrium, are obvious examples of such systems. It seems therefore that the definition of directive organization—and in consequence the proposed analysis of "goal-directed" or "teleological" systems—fails to attain its intended objective. However, two comments are in order on the point at issue. In the first place, though we admittedly do distinguish between systems that are goal-directed and those which are not, the distinction is highly vague, and there are many systems which cannot be classified definitely as being of one kind rather than another. Thus, is the child's toy sometimes known as "the walking beetle"—which turns aside when it reaches the edge of a table and fails to fall off, because an idle wheel is then brought into play through the action of an "antenna"—a goal-directed system or not? Is a virus such a system? Is the system consisting of members of some species which has undergone certain lines of evolutionary development, a goal-directed one? Moreover, some systems have been classified as "teleological" at one time and in relation to one body of knowledge, only to be reclassified as "non-teleological" at a later time when knowledge concerning the physics of mechanisms had improved. "Nature does nothing in vain" was a maxim commonly accepted in pre-Newtonian physics, and on the basis of the doctrine of "natural places" even the descent of bodies and the ascent of smoke were regarded as goal-directed. Accordingly, it is at least an open question whether the current distinction between systems that are goal-directed and those which are not has an identifiable objective basis (i.e., in terms of differences between the actual organization of such systems), and whether the *same* system may not be identified in alternative ways depending on the perspective from which it is viewed and on the antecedent assumptions that are adopted for analyzing its structure.

In the second place, it is by no means clear that physical systems such as the pendulum at rest, which is not usually regarded as goal-directed, really do conform to the definition of "directively organized" systems proposed above. Consider a simple pendulum which is initially at rest, and is then given a small impulse (say by a sudden gust of wind) and assume that apart from the constraints of the system and the force of gravitation the only force that acts on the bob is the friction of the air. Then on the usual physical assumptions, the pendulum will perform harmonic oscillations with decreasing amplitudes, and will finally assume its initial position of rest. The system here consists of the pendulum and the various forces acting on it, while the property G is the state of the pendulum when it is at rest at the lowest point of its path of oscillation. By hypothesis, its length and the mass of the bob are fixed, and so is the force of gravitation acting on it, as well as the coefficient of damping. What is variable, is the impulsive force of the gust of wind, and the restoring force which operates on the bob as a consequence of the constraints of the system and of the presence of the gravitational field. However, and this is the crucial point, these two forces are *not* independent of one another. Thus, if the effective component of the former has a certain magnitude, the restoring force will have an equal magnitude with an opposite direction. Accordingly, if the state of the system at a given time were specified in terms of state-variables which take these forces as values, these state variables would not satisfy one of the stipulated conditions for state-variables of directively organized systems: for the value of one of them at a given time is uniquely determined by the value of the other at that same time. In short, the values at any specified time of these proposed state-variables are not independent. It therefore follows that the simple pendulum is *not* a directively organized system in the sense of the definition given. And it is possible to show in a similar manner that a number of other physical systems, currently classified as non-teleological, fail to satisfy this definition. Whether one could show this for all such systems is admittedly an open question. But there is at least some ground for holding that the definition does achieve what it is intended to achieve, and that it states the distinctive features of systems commonly characterized as "teleological".

VI

We can now settle quite briefly the second question we undertook to discuss—namely, whether the supposed fact that teleological explanations are usually reserved for "goal-directed" systems casts doubt on the claim that teleological and non-teleological explanations are equivalent in asserted content. But if such systems are always analyzable as directively organized ones, in the sense of the above definition, the answer to this question is clearly in the negative. For the defining characteristics of such systems can be formulated entirely in non-teleological language; and in consequence, every teleological explanation (that is, every explanation which contains a teleological expression) must be translatable into an equivalent statement (or set of statements) which is non-teleological.

Why, then, does it seem odd to render physical statements such as Boyle's law in teleological form? The obvious answer is that we do not usually employ teleological statements except in the context of discussing systems which are assumed to be directively organized. A teleological version of Boyle's law appears strange and unacceptable, because such a formulation is usually taken to imply that any gas enclosed in a volume is a directively organized system, in contradiction to the tacit assumption that it is not such a system. In a sense, therefore, a teleological explanation does assert more than its prima facie equivalent non-teleological translation does. For the former tacitly assumes, while the latter often does not, that the system under consideration is directively organized. But if the above discussion is sound in principle, this "excess" meaning of teleological statements can always be expressed in non-teleological language.

On the assumption that a teleological explanation can always be equated to a non-teleological one with respect to what each asserts, let us now make more explicit in what respects they do differ. The difference appears to be as follows: Teleological explanations focus attention on the culminations and products of specific processes, and upon the contributions of parts of a system to its maintenance. They view the operations of things from the perspective of certain selected wholes to which the things belong; and they are therefore concerned with properties of parts of such wholes only in so far as these properties are relevant to some complex features or activities assumed as characteristic for those wholes. Non-teleological explanations, on the other hand, place chief emphasis on certain conditions under which specified processes are initiated and persist, and on the factors upon which the continued operation of given systems are contingent. They represent the inclusive behavior of a thing as the the operation of certain selected constituents into which the thing is analyzable; and they are therefore concerned with features of complex wholes only to the extent that these features are related to the assumed characteristics of those constituents. The difference between teleological and non-teleological explanations, as has already been suggested, is one of emphasis and of perspective in formulation.

It is sometimes objected, however, that teleological explanations are fallaciously parochial; for they tacitly assume a privileged status for a special set of complex systems, and so make focal the role of things and processes in maintaining just those systems and no others. Processes have no inherent termini, so it is argued, and cannot rightly be assumed to contribute exclusively to the maintenance of some unique set of wholes. It is therefore misleading to say that *the* function of the white cells in the human blood is to defend the human body against foreign micro-organisms. This is admittedly *a* function of the leucocytes; and it may even be said to be *the* function of these cells from the perspective of the human body. But leucocytes are elements in other systems as well—for example, in the system of the blood stream considered in isolation from the rest of the body, in the system composed of some virus colony as well as these white cells, or in the more inclusive and complex solar system. These other systems are also capable of persisting in their "normal" organization and activities only under definite conditions and from the perspective of *their* maintenance the leucocytes possess other functions.

One obvious reply to this objection is a *tu quoque*. It is as legitimate to focus attention on consequences, culminations and uses, as it is on antecedents and conditions. Processes do not have inherent termini, but neither do they have absolute beginnings; things and processes are not in general exclusively involved in maintaining some unique whole, but neither are wholes analyzable into a unique set of constituents. It is nevertheless intellectually profitable in causal inquiries to focus attention on certain earlier stages in the development of a process rather than on later ones, and on one set of constituents of a system rather than another set. And similarly, it is illuminating to select as the point of departure for the investigation of some problems certain complex wholes rather than others. Moreover, as we have seen, some things are parts of directively organized systems, but do not appear to be parts of more than one such system. The study of the unique function of such parts in such unique teleological systems is therefore not a preoccupation that assigns without warrant a special importance to certain systems. On the contrary, it is an inquiry which is sensitive to fundamental and objectively identifiable differences in nature.

There is nevertheless a point to the objection. For the operation of human interest in the construction of teleological explanations is perhaps more often overlooked than in the case of non-teleological analyses. In consequence, certain end-products of processes and certain directions of changes are frequently assumed to be inherently "natural", "essential" or "proper", while all others are then labelled as "unnatural", accidental" or even "monstrous". Thus, the development of corn seeds into corn plants is sometimes said to be natural, while their transformation into the flesh of birds or men is asserted to be accidental. In a given context of inquiry, and in the light of the problems which initiate it, there may be ample justification for ignoring all but one direction of possible changes, and all but one system of activities to whose maintenance things and processes contribute. But such disregard of other wholes and of other functions which their constituents may have, does not warrant the conclusion that what is ignored is less genuine or natural than what receives selective attention.

VII

One final point in connection with teleological explanations in biology must be briefly noted. As has already been mentioned, some biologists maintain that the distinctive character of biological explanations appears in physiological inquiries, in which the functions of organs and vital processes are under investigation, even though most biologists are quite prepared to admit that no special categories of explanation are required in morphology or the study of structural traits. Accordingly, great stress has been placed by some writers on the contrast between structure and function, and on the difficulties in assessing the relative importance of each as a determinant of living phenomena. It is generally conceded that "the development of functions goes hand in hand with the development of structures", and that neither does vital action exist apart from a material structure, nor does vital structure exist save as a product of protoplasmic activity. In this sense, structure and function are commonly regarded as "inseparable aspects" of biological organization. Nevertheless, eminent biologists believe it is still an unresolved and perhaps insoluble problem "to what extent structures may modify functions or functions structures", and regard the contrast between structure and function to present a "dilemma".[5]

But what is this contrast, why do its terms raise an apparently irresolvable issue, and what does one of its terms cover that allegedly requires a mode of analysis and explanation that is specific to biology? Let us first remind ourselves in what way a morphological study of a biological organ, say the human eye, differs from the corresponding physiological investigation. A structural account of the eye usually consists in a description of its gross and minute anatomy; and such an account therefore specifies the various parts of the organ, their shapes and relative spatial arrangements with respect to each other and other parts of the body, and their cellular and physico-chemical compositions. The phrase "structure of the eye" therefore ordinarily signifies the spatial organization of its parts, together with the physico-chemical properties of each part. On the other hand, a physiological account of the organ specifies the activities in which its various parts can or do participate, and the role these parts play in vision. For example, the ciliary muscles are shown to be capable of contracting and slackening, so that because of their connection with the suspensory ligament the curvature of the lens can be accommodated to near and far vision; or the lachrymal glands are identified as the sources of fluids which lubricate and cleanse the conjunctival membranes. In general, therefore, physiology is concerned with the character, the order, and the consequences of the activities in which the parts of the eye may be engaged.

If this example is typical of the way biologists employ the terms, the contrast between structure and function is evidently a contrast between, on the one hand, the *spatial* organization of anatomically distinguishable parts of an organ and, on the other hand, the *temporal* (or spatio-temporal) organization of changes in those parts. What is investigated under each term of the contrasting pair is a mode of organization or a type of order. In the first case, the organization is primarily if not exclusively a spatial one, and the object of the investigation is to ascertain the spatial distribution of organic parts and the modes of their linkage; in the latter case, the organization has a temporal dimension, and the aim of the inquiry is to discover sequential and simultaneous orders of change in the spatially ordered and linked parts of organic bodies. It is evident, therefore, that structure and function (in the sense in which biologists appear to use these words) are indeed "inseparable." For it is difficult to make sense of any

[5] Cf. Edwin G. Conklin, *Heredity and Environment*, Princeton, 1922, p. 32, and Edmund B. Wilson, *The Cell*, New York, 1925, p. 670. In a more recent volume Conklin declares that "the relation of mechanism to finalism is not unlike that of structure to function—they are two aspects of organization. The mechanistic conception of life is in the main a structural aspect, the teleological view looks chiefly to ultimate function. These two aspects of life are not antagonistic, but complementary", *Man: Real and Ideal*, New York, 1943, p. 117.

supposition to the effect that a system of activities which has a temporal organization is not a system of spatially structured parts manifesting these activities. In any event, there is obviously no antithesis between an inquiry directed to the discovery of the spatial organization of organic parts, and an inquiry addressed to ascertaining the spatio-temporal orders that characterize the activities of those parts. A comparable distinction between inquiries can also be introduced in the physical sciences. Descriptive physical geography, for example, is concerned primarily with the spatial distribution and spatial relations of mountains, plains, rivers, and oceans; historical geology and geophysics, on the other hand, investigate the temporal and dynamic orders of change in which such geographic features are involved. Accordingly, if inquiries into structure and function were antithetical in biology, a comparable antithesis would also occur within the non-biological sciences. Any inquiry involves discriminating selection from the great variety of patterns of relations that are exhibited by the subject-matter; and it is undoubtedly convenient to direct some inquiries to certain kinds of such patterns and other inquiries to different kinds. There seems to be no reason for generating a fundamental puzzle from the fact that living organisms exhibit both a spatial and a spatio-temporal order of their parts.

What then is the unsolved or irresolvable issue raised by the biological distinction between structure and function? Two questions can be distinguished in this connection. It may be asked, in the first place, what spatial structures are required for the exercise of specified functions, and whether a change in the pattern of activities of an organism or of its parts is associated with any change in the distribution and spatial organization of the constituents of that system. This is patently a matter to be settled by detailed empirical inquiry, and though there are innumerable unsettled problems in this connection, they do not raise issues of fundamental principle. There is a school of philosophers and biological theorists, for example, which maintains that the development of certain comparable organs in markedly different species can be explained only on the assumption of a "vital impulse" which directs evolution toward the attainment of some future function. Thus, the fact that the eyes of the octopus and of man are anatomically similar though the evolution of each species from eyeless ancestors has followed different lines of development, has been used as evidence for the claim that no explanation of this convergence is possible in terms of the mechanisms of chance variation and adaptation; and that fact has been used to support the view that there is an "undivided original vital impulse" which so acts on inert matter as to create appropriate organs for the function of vision.[6] But even this hypothesis, however vague and otherwise unsatisfactory it may be, involves in part factual issues; and if

[6] Cf. H. Bergson, *Creative Evolution,* New York, 1911, Chap. 1; and the brief but incisive critique of views similar to those of Bergson in George G. Simpson, *The Meaning of Evolution,* New Haven, 1949, Chap. 12.

most biologists reject it, it is largely because the available factual evidence supports more adequately a different theory of evolutionary development.

In the second place, one may ask just why it is that a given structure is associated with a certain set of functions, or conversely. Now this question may be understood as a demand for an explanation, perhaps in physico-chemical terms, for the fact that when a living body has a given spatial organization of its parts it exhibits a certain pattern of activities. When the question is so understood, it is far from being a preposterous one; for although we may not possess answers to it in most cases, we do have reasonably adequate answers in at least a few others, so that we have some ground for the presumption that our ignorance is not necessarily permanent.

However, such explanations must contain as premises not only statements about the physico-chemical constitution of the parts of a living thing and about the spatial organization of these parts, but also statements of physico-chemical laws or theories; and at least some of these latter must assert connections between the spatial organization of physico-chemical systems and their pattern of activities. But if the question continues to be pressed, and an explanation is demanded for these latter connections as well, an impasse is finally reached. For the demand then in effect assumes that the temporal or causal structure of physical processes is deducible simply from the spatial organization of physical systems, or conversely; and neither assumption is in fact tenable. It is possible, for example, to give quite an accurate account of the spatial relations in which the various parts of a clock stand to one another. We can specify the sizes of its cogwheels and the linkages between them, the shapes and positions of its pointers, the location of the main-spring and the escapement-wheel, and so on. But although such knowledge of the clock's spatial structure is indispensable, it is not sufficient for understanding how the clock will operate. We must also know the laws of mechanics, which formulate the temporal structure of the clock's behavior by indicating how the spatial distribution of its parts at one time is related to the distribution at a later time. However, this temporal structure cannot be deduced simply from the clock's spatial structure (or its "anatomy"), any more than its spatial structure at any given time can be derived from the general laws of mechanics. Accordingly, the question why a given biological structure is associated with specified functions may be irresolvable, not because it is beyond our capacities to answer it, but simply because the question in the sense intended asks for what is *logically* impossible. In short, structure does not *logically* determine function, though as a matter of *contingent* fact the specific structure possessed by an organism does set bounds to the kinds of activities in which the organism can engage. And conversely, the pattern of behavior exhibited by an organism does not *logically* imply a unique anatomical structure, though in point of *contingent* fact an organism manifests specific modes of activity only when its parts possess a determinate structure of a definite kind.

It follows from these various considerations that the distinction between structure and function covers nothing which distinguishes biology from the physical sciences, or which necessitates the use in the former of a distinctive logic of explanation. It has not been the aim of this paper to deny the patent differences between biology and other natural sciences with respect to the role played in them of functional analyses. Nor has it been its aim to cast doubt on the legitimacy of such explanations in any domain in which they are found to be appropriate because of the special character of the systems investigated. The objective of this essay has simply been to show that the prevalence of teleological explanations in biology does not constitute a sufficient basis for the claim that the pattern of explanation in biology is fundamentally different from what it is in the physical sciences, nor for the further claim that for this reason biology must be regarded as an inherently autonomous discipline.

The Philosophy of Science in Gestalt Theory*

EDWARD H. MADDEN[1]

1. The Problem. Although the point of departure for Gestalt theory has been for the most part psychological investigation, nevertheless Gestalt theory is more inclusive than Gestalt psychology. Within psychology Gestalt theory claims to be the basis of the only scientific theory that can explain the empirical facts of psychology, but on a more general level Gestalt theory comprehends a philosophy of science, and positions in epistemology, metaphysics, and value theory. According to Wertheimer, Gestalt theory is "a palpable convergence of problems ranging throughout the sciences and the various philosophic standpoints of modern times" (1: 3). He also asserts that Gestalt theory was the result of concrete work done in psychology, logic, and epistemology (1: 1). In this paper we will be concerned only with the Gestaltist interpretations of and claims for the method and structure of science in general.

Wertheimer and Koehler both regard the Gestaltist view as a new interpretation of the structure and method of science insofar as it offers an alternative to the "analytical" interpretations of science. Wertheimer and Koehler both reject the universality of "analytical" method, their thesis being that this traditional approach cannot account for some aspects of science which can be done justice only in Gestaltist terms. Wertheimer's most formal condemnation of the analytical view of science and his thesis that there are areas to which it does not apply is to be found in his address of 1924 to the *Kantgesellschaft.*

It has long seemed obvious—and is, in fact, the characteristic tone of European science—that "science" means breaking up complexes into their component elements. Isolate the elements, discover their laws, then reassemble them, and the problem is solved. All wholes are reduced to pieces and piecewise relations between pieces. (1: 2)

The word science has often suggested a certain outlook, certain fundamental assumptions, certain procedures and attitudes—but do these imply that this is the only possibility of scientific method? Perhaps science already embodies

* Reprinted by kind permission of the author and the editor from *Philosophy of Science*, 19, 1952.

[1] The theses of this paper stem from Professor Gustav Bergmann's lectures on systematic psychology and philosophy of science. I thank Professor Bergmann for permitting me to use them here and in my doctoral dissertation, "An Examination of Gestalt Theory," State University of Iowa, 1950.

methods leading in an entirely different direction, methods which have been continually stifled by the seemingly necessary, dominant ones. . . . Even though the traditional methods of science are undoubtedly adequate in many cases, there may be others where they lead us astray. (1: 2)

Koehler takes the same position in saying that if problems of self-distribution in macroscopic physics were more familiar "the belief would not be so general that physics is under all circumstances an 'analytical' science in which the properties of more complex extended facts are deduced from the properties of independent local elements" (5: 205).

In this examination of Gestalt theory as an interpretation of the structure and method of science we will first give an exposition of the Gestaltist views and then go on to construct an "analytical" terminology by means of which we try to show a) that all legitimate distinctions of the Gestalters can be rendered in this language and b) that Gestalters use such terms as "additive," "bundle," "interaction," and "field" both ambiguously and misleadingly.

2. *Exposition of Gestalt Theory*. Following the example of K. Grelling and P. Oppenheim (2) we begin by distinguishing between W-Gestalts and K-Gestalts, the former term referring to a pattern or configuration which determines the nature of its parts and the latter term to systems of functional interdependence.

Concerning what we have called "W-Gestalts" Wertheimer writes,

There are wholes, the behaviour of which is not determined by that of their individual elements, but where the part-processes are themselves determined by the intrinsic nature of the whole. It is the hope of Gestalt thory to determine the nature of such wholes. (1: 2)

A whole the behavior of which determines the nature of its individual elements is formally the negation of complexes the behavior of which is determined in the piecewise fashion. Wertheimer's schema for the latter kind of complexes follows:

If I have a_1 b_1 c_1 and b_2 c_2 are substituted for b_1 c_1, I then have a_1 b_2 c_2. We are dealing essentially with a summative multiplicity of variously constituted components (a "bundle") and all else is erected somehow upon this and-summation. (1: 12)

Any complex which transcends the nature of a summation or a "bundle" is a W-Gestalt. Examples are simple and numerous. The effect of transposing a melody is a familiar classic illustration. A melody made up of one series of notes is heard as the same as a melody composed of another series of different notes. In other words, a melody persists and is recognized even when played in different keys. According to the Gestalters it is this identification of melodies when the individual elements (notes) are different that supports the interpretation that the melody is not merely a sum of its parts but that as the whole it determines how the parts shall be heard. In addition Wertheimer discusses many factors, largely relational, which are intended to demonstrate the inadequacy of part-summation and the priority of wholes in determining perception. Such factors are likeness, nearness, common fate, objective set, closure, position and so forth (1: 71 ff.).

Turning to the K-Gestalt, a system of functional interdependence, we find that Koehler makes a basic distinction between microscopically and macroscopically organized physical states (5: 194 ff.). As a help in establishing the difference, Koehler refers to a network of pipes—three sections connected to the same inlet and outlet—through which water flows. He points out that the behavior of the water in each branch is not a local affair independent of any condition outside the particular pipe. If a valve in one pipe is closed the current will flow faster in those pipes remaining open, and if other pipes are added to the original three the current in the original ones will be slower. Knowledge of these interdependencies is contingent, of course, on one's observing the activity in a larger part of the network than one branch. If one considers activity within a branch pipe as well as what goes on in the rest of the network then the activity in the branch is seen to be relatively microscopic because it is not independent of outside occurrences and interferences. The entire network or, for that matter, any part larger than a branch is, relative to that branch, a macroscopic entity. According to Koehler, a certain kind of analysis of macroscopic entities is possible, a kind of analysis which tells us how events act within a macroscopic context. However, he points out, "More often . . . analysis is expected to give us *independent* elementary facts, the mere synthesis of which would yield the complex entities found in primary observation" (5: 201). Analysis in this sense, Koehler concludes, is incompatible with the nature of macroscopic states.

The example of the pipes is a special case of "dynamic interaction" because the rigid channels permit interaction only at specific points. Koehler also considers the case of a single vessel with one opening for the incoming water and another for the outgoing water. How will the current be distributed in this continuous volume and how will alteration in the position of the openings affect the distribution? The important point in this case is that the current at each point depends more directly on the current at all points because the system is no longer restricted in its points of interaction. In these situations an equation for the steady distribution as a whole must be found if the equation for the steady flow at a point is to be found. Koehler contends that if such problems as these were more familiar "the belief would not be so general that physics is under all circumstances an 'analytical' science in which the properties of more complex extended facts are deduced from the properties of independent local elements."

3. Analytical Science and the W-Gestalt. What one must do to refute the Gestalter's claim that certain aspects of science cannot be described adequately in analytical terms but must be described in Gestaltist terms is to show that what the Gestalters say about relations, wholes, interaction, and fields—or better, everything they say legitimately about them—can also be stated in analytical terms. This reformulation in analytical terms of those features of science which the Gestalters emphasize and think that only they adequately describe might be called "methodological refutation." Semantically such a procedure amounts to a clarification of such terms as "additive," "interaction," and "field." More particularly, our methodological refutation must show that the features which Koehler thinks are unique to "macroscopic" situations are present already in what he calls the "analytical parts of physics"—i.e., where "the properties of more complex extended facts are deduced from the properties of independent local elements." We begin our methodological refutation by describing in analytical terms the classical Newtonian problem of *n* bodies.

We will assume that the classical Newtonian problem of *n* bodies is known and we will simply stress those features which are important for our purposes. We must distinguish two things at the outset, namely, description and explanation. First, there is the *configuration* of *n* bodies and its initial and subsequent *conditions* at any given moment of time; second, there is the *law* which yields the values of the variables characteristic of one condition from those of an earlier or later condition (prediction or postdiction). All that pertains to the former—the masses and the position and momentum coordinates—constitutes a scientific *description*; all that pertains to the latter constitutes a scientific *explanation*. A W-Gestalt, which we have defined as a pattern or configuration, is a concept primarily relevant to scientific description; a K-Gestalt, which we have defined as a system of functional interdependence, is a concept primarily relevant to scientific explanation. We turn our attention first to scientific *description*.

Given a configuration of *n* objects (mass points), $o_1, o_2, \cdots, o_n$, the physicist knows from previous observations that each o is characterized by a number which is the value of an empirical construct called mass, which remains constant in time $\left(\frac{dm_i}{dt}\right) = 0$. The mass of a physical object is thus an "index," a constant characterizer which is the non-configurational element entering into gravitational behavior. At least it is non-configurational (non-relational) as long as we do not push our analysis into an operational definition of mass itself. However it is not necessary to do this for our purposes because all we would gain would be a repetition of the situation we wish to discuss, repetition on a level more elementary in the sense of ultimate epistemological reduction but less suitable for our expository purposes.

At a particular time ($t = 0$) the physicist can obtain measurements which, as a class, determine the *condition* of the configuration at that moment. (The configuration itself is determined by the values of the masses.) The constructs measured are the positions and momenta of the *n* bodies. These, we notice, are *relational* concepts; for the rest we assume that the distances and the time intervals out of which they are defined can be measured in some meaningful fashion without further analyzing these ideas.

The statement of these data at $t = 0$ as a *logical conjunction* ("and" connection) of, say, k sentences constitutes a "description" of the initial configuration. *E.g.*, "(The mass of o_1 is m_1) & (The mass of o_2 is m_2) & · · · (The distance between o_1 and o_2 is $r_{1,2}$)& · · · & S_k." In stating this conjunction of k sentences S_1, S_2, · · · , S_k, one is asserting the truth of all the sentences so conjoined; if at least one of the member sentences is false, then the whole conjunction is false. Such a logical product will constitute a description of the system and its condition at any time t.

In the light of this illustration let us now examine Wertheimer's thesis that "the whole is more than the sum of its parts," interpreting it at the moment as an emphasis on configuration or pattern, and let us see what are the possible meanings of it in analytical terms. In the analytical terminology of initial condition (description of the configuration at time t_0) and prediction of the condition at time t (description of the configuration at time t_1), Wertheimer's thesis simply means that a description consists of several statements about physical objects, non-relational properties of such objects, and also statements of relations obtaining among them. Insofar as Wertheimer is emphasizing that statements of relations such as "a is to the left of b" are fundamental and not defined in terms of statements about objects or their properties, he is making an important point. In this case, however, his meaning is formulable in ordinary analytical terms. In fact we just did so formulate it. Only the classical materialists have tended to neglect the fundamental role undefined relation terms play in the description of nature.

In analytical terms another just and perfectly correct meaning can be given in the area of description to the classical adage that the whole is more than the sum of its parts. Consider a Newtonian system consisting of, say, six mass points. We can *conceptually* decompose this system into two sub-systems of three bodies each. One sub-system (P_1) of the whole system can be described as consisting of the masses of three bodies (m_1, m_2, m_3), their momenta, and their three distances. The remaining sub-system (P_2) likewise can be described in the same manner. With descriptions P_1 and P_2 conceived as constituting the meaning of the term "parts," the term "whole" may be applied to a system P composed of P_1 and P_2. Then it will be found that the description of P is not simply the conjunction of the descriptions of P_1 and of P_2 but contains *as further conjunctive terms at least some of the mutual distances between the bodies of the two parts of sub-systems*. In this sense it may be said that even in the realm of description the whole is more than the sum of its parts. This meaning of part and whole may of course be generalized. A "part," then, is a description of a sub-system of any group of entities. The description of the "whole" consists of the descriptions of all sub-systems *plus* the descriptive characters which indicate the relations between the sub-systems of the "whole" (in our example, mutual distances).

However, because Wertheimer's rejection of the "and" or "bundle" hypothesis indiscriminately includes both the "and" of description and the "and" of explanation and because he maintains that the latter—which would hold that the behavior of two systems S_1 and S_2 in spatial juxtaposition or partial overlap is the sum of the behavior of the two systems in isolation—is untenable, he consequently is insisting that the former—which is a logical "and" and simply means that the statements about objects, properties of objects, and relations between them are asserted together—is also untenable. The "and" of explanation does not in fact even have a clear meaning and should be rejected, but this does not impair the legitimacy of the logical "and" in description. To think that it does rests on a confusion between description and explanation.

That Wertheimer does consider the "and" of description untenable is implicit in his further consideration of the melody illustration:

> . . . other explanations were also proposed. One maintained that in addition to the six tones there were intervals—relations—and that *these* were what remained constant. In other words we were asked to assume not only elements but "relations-between-elements" as additional components of the total complex. But this view failed to account for the phenomenon because in some cases the relations *too* may be altered without destroying the original melody. (1: 4)

Here Wertheimer attempts to discredit the elementaristic or summative view by showing the empirical inadequacy of adding new elements, relational ones, to the individual notes in an effort to account for the recognition of a melody despite a transposition. But even if it is true that a melody may be recognized even when the relations are not all maintained in transposition, it is not evidence detrimental to the legitimacy of the logical "and." In analytical terms we would say that the description of initial conditions, which are conjoined by the logical "and," is not complete. Let us amplify the notion of complete description in connection with the classical Newtonian n-body problem.

In the classical Newtonian n-body problem one says that a *complete description* embraces only mass points, distances, and speeds. But how does one know that the initial description is complete when only these constituents are listed? How does one know, for example, that the color of the bodies is not also a determining factor? Completeness simply means finding the empirical law; no *a priori* criterion for the completeness of a description exists. One must continue to add constituents to the initial description until he can state a law enabling him to predict subsequent conditions. The experimental check on this procedure is obvious. One observes several systems equated in all respects mentioned in the description. If the same results do not occur, then there is an "uncontrolled variable" that needs to be added. When it is discovered and added (by the logical "and") the description is complete.

Let us apply this analytical insight to Wertheimer's discussion of the melody. If indeed the relations between notes can be changed without altering the perceived melody, then we would say that adding relations to the notes still does not complete the description. If the constancy of response to groups of different elements (notes) cannot be attributed to something already contained in the description of the initial conditions we should (1) recognize the description as incomplete and (2) try to supplement it in one of the two possible ways: either add new basic data or derive new relations (*e.g.*, ratios of ratios) from data already present. However there is nothing in this situation that justifies the belief that our account of description is in principle inadequate because it is too elementaristic.

The Gestalters would probably object at this point because we are consistently dealing with physical stimuli rather than with how the subject "sees" the stimuli. In our descriptions the statements refer to frequencies, to the ratio of frequencies, and to other matters of the "geographical environment." All we shall say now is that how a subject "sees" the stimuli is a matter of a lawful relationship between the subject's behavior and a complex stimulus situation rather than of the behavior *of* the elementary components *in* the complex. We shall return to this point later.

4. Analytical Sciences and the K-Gestalt. We turn now to an analysis of the K-Gestalt and a formulation of its characteristic features in analytical terms. Given the values of mass, position, and momentum at time T_0 the physicist can substitute these values in a formula—let us call it the computation rule—which will yield the values of these same variables at any time t (that is, the computation rule yields the values of the variables as functions of the initial conditions and a continuous time parameter). The computation rule, of course, will be different when different numbers of objects exist simultaneously. The curve (law) for two bodies is different from the curve for three bodies and so forth. In the case of two bodies we have the law of a conic orbit; in the case of three or more bodies more complicated curves occur. In analytical terms any such empirical curve (law) will constitute an "explanation." An explanation, then, is any function connecting subsequent descriptions of a system. When properties occur in any curve which do not occur in the curves of any lesser number of bodies, we will speak of this situation as *novelty* in respect to laws.

Let us assume that we have a computation rule for two bodies, so that a physicist could predict the future conditions for any given configuration of two bodies. Now this computation rule tells us nothing about the behavior of three or four . . . or n bodies together. However, we can take the combination of three bodies, for example, and conceptually decompose it into sub-complexes (elements). The "elements" involved in the three-body configuration would be three configurations of two bodies each. Now we can apply our two-body computation rule to each of the elements separately. Next we discover inductively a rule which will produce the law for the three-body complex by combining in some definite manner the computation rules for the elements (in this example the rule is the so-called vector addition of forces). We will call this rule, which we discovered for predicting the behavior of a complex configuration out of the re-application of the computation rule to the "elements" of the complex, a *composition rule*. The general idea of the composition rule is to discover a single rule which will enable one to derive the computation rule for any given number of bodies. It must be emphasized that such a composition rule is just as much an empirical law, albeit independent of the empirical laws that obtain for the elementary configurations, as these laws themselves.

The success of this technique in wide areas of science is a fact. If one wishes to describe it by saying that science is "elementaristic," "mechanistic," or "additive," one is free to do so. Regardless of how one chooses his terms, though, it is important to note that "additive" in this sense has a different meaning from the "additive" whose meaningful and nonsensical connotations we tried to distinguish in the area of description. In particular, a composition rule is not a logical summation or "and" connection. (The terms "vector addition" and "vector sum" are rather unfortunate in this context and probably are among the causes of the confusion.) Nor does a composition rule, if it holds, imply that the parts of a whole independently go through the processes they would go through if they existed in isolation. Thus this "additive," "analytical," or "mechanistic" feature of science does not deny dynamic interaction of the parts of a whole. This point is sufficiently important to bear further elaboration and repetition.

As we have seen, Koehler stresses interaction in the sense that a change in one element causes alteration in all areas of a system. This is essentially what is meant by saying that a K-Gestalt is a system of functional interdependence. In analytical language, given a prediction which holds for one set of initial conditions, this prediction will in general not hold in *any* of its particulars if even *one* of the variables in the initial conditions is changed. The interrelations that actually obtain find their complete and exhaustive expression in the mathematical structure of the process law. Likewise, interaction is accounted for in the correct statement of the composition rule. In the case of planetary laws, if we know the Newtonian law for two bodies and for three bodies we still do not know *a priori* what the law for five bodies will be. This must be determined as a matter of fact. The deduction of the law of a complex from the laws of the elements is not a matter of linking together two laws by a logical "and." It is patently false to say that the composition rule is additive in the descriptive sense because in the case of planetary systems we would have planets with more than one orbit; planets in two places at once! A composition rule is *another* law, not a pre-existing rule for getting a logical product; this shows that Koehler is confused when he complains that in "analytical" science "the properties of more complex extended facts are deduced from the properties of independent local elements."

In summary, we see that both scientific description and explanation have several features which are rightly stressed by the Gestalters but which may be rendered in analytical terms. Moreover, by thus rendering them in analytical terms we have shown that some of these features are not quite what the Gestalters think they are and do not carry the implications which they think they do. The usual answer to this kind of claim is that the entire Gestalt thesis is not captured in these reformulation tactics, that the essence of the whole escapes the analytical net. We now turn to these "something more" aspects of the Gestalter's position.

5. Intrinsic Wholes and Explanatory Emergence. Wertheimer says that "there are wholes, the behaviour of which is not determined by that of their individual elements, but where the part-processes are themselves determined by the intrinsic nature of the whole" (1: 2). In criticism we shall say, first, that no psychologist, whether or not he is a Gestalter, would hold that a response to a stimulus S_1 is the same as the response to a stimulus P of which S_1 is a constituent even if the subject has been given the "analytical" set of responding to S_1, which is thus once the whole and once a part of the presented stimulus configuration. In the analytical schema

$$\begin{array}{ll} (1)\ S_1 \rightarrow R_1 & \text{(organism "constant"} \\ (2)\ \underbrace{S_1 \text{ and } \cdots}_{P} \rightarrow R_2 & \text{in both situations)} \end{array}$$

The "and" in (2) is of course the logical "and" of description, so the total stimulus is different and there is therefore no reason why the response should not be different. Whether or not it actually is different is a matter of the law that happens to govern this particular situation. We may summarize by saying that sometimes the behavior of a subject toward a stimulus is (in part) determined by the whole or complex of which it is a part. But when Wertheimer claims that the intrinsic nature of the parts is determined by their being in a whole, we must confess that we do not know what he means. Is not S_1, as an event, S_1 whether or not it appears alone or in conjunction with something else? The thing which may or may not change, according to conditions, is the *response* to S_1. This response is determined both by the elementary stimulus event and its context. But this event is the same in isolation or in context.

This discussion has concerned the "something more" aspect of the Gestalist doctrine in the area of description. In the area of explanation this "something more" aspect of the Gestaltist doctrine can be considered as a belief in *explanatory emergence.* Like other historical formulations of emergence the Gestaltist formulation is not particularly clear. It usually takes the form of denying the possibility of predicting one set of characteristics from another. Koffka writes,

Moreover, hydrogen occurs in nature in a form in which it is not composed of hydrogen atoms but of hydrogen molecules, each composed of two hydrogen atoms. Thus we have H, H_2, H_2O. This sounds like a straight molecular theory, but it is not anything of the kind. For H, H_2, H_2O have all different properties which cannot be derived by *adding* properties of H's and O's. (6: 57)

This assertion is misleading because scientifically no matter of fact by itself forms the basis for predicting the occurrence of another fact. *Predictability is always a matter of a set of conditions and a law or a theory in terms of which a future set of conditions can be predicted.* We will characterize the matter in greater detail. First, Koffka is not contending in his chemical example that it is a case of novelty of laws but rather an analytical characterization of what he might mean is *explanatory emergence* in the sense that *composition rules* or theories using them break down not only in the organic realm, as the vitalist contends, but already in the physical realm. The assertion of the breakdown of a theory however is not a metaphysical assertion; rather it is the empirical meaning of the doctrine of emergence. Nor is the adequacy or breakdown of a composition rule an *a priori* matter. Whether or not a composition rule is adequate and to what extent it is adequate is a matter of scientific ascertainment. The allegedly "novel" and superadditive characters of the classical chemical illustrations, already favored by J. S. Mill, are by now in fact "mechanistically" explained in terms of quantum chemistry. That the Gestalters do not seem to realize the logic of this situation is borne out in Koehler's *Mentality of Apes* and other Gestaltist literature in which the main contention is, in our terms, that empirical laws of insight are not only novel but also must be theoretical or explanatory emergents with respect to trial and error learning.

Any breakdown of a theory with composition rules at a certan level of complexity would be a case of explanatory emergence. The Gestalters, misled by their conceptions of "additive" and "analysis," claim that this level is already to be found in physics itself, not only in the realm of organic behavior, where it seems at least *prima facie* more plausible that organisms are, as the classical vitalists claimed, the kinds of wholes that resist explanation by means of a set of composition rules unless there is an explanatory emergence. It is plausible to conjecture that this claim of explanatory emergence occurring already in physics has something to do with the halo with which the Gestalters have surrounded the notion of "field," for fields, of course, occur already in physics. It is in order, then, that we say a few words about fields and the role this notion plays in Gestaltist thinking.

6. Field Theory. Koehler always speaks of the necessity of *field theory* in psychology. Concerning field theory in perception and in its physiological correlates, he writes,

By this [field theory] we mean that the neural functions and processes with which the perceptual facts are associated in each case are located in a continuous medium; and that the events in one part of this medium influence the events in other regions in a way that depends directly on the properties of both in their relation to each other. This is the conception with which all physicists work. (4: 55)

Whether in physics or elsewhere, as methodologists we can and must distinguish two meanings of the terms "field" and "field theory." In its more general meaning the term "field" simply designates a system of interaction; in its special meaning it refers to theories that work with a continuously spread medium and, accordingly, use the mathematical technique of partial differential equations. The planetary system, e.g., treated in the Newtonian manner, *like all scientific theories*, is a field theory in the first sense; but all scientific theories are not field theories in the second sense.

In order to understand better the second notion of "field theory" we will return to the *n*-body paradigm. Even though the concrete terms "configuration," "conditions," and "objects" were used, we must not lose sight of the formal arithmetical schema—which we can call a calculus and which is coordinated with the empirical data. The system is in this case the finite and discrete ordered set of positive real numbers "corresponding" to the masses; a state is the finite and discrete ordered set of real numbers "corresponding" to the positions and momenta that determine a temporal cross section of the process; a process is always a continuous series of the states of the system as a function of time. So in the Newtonian case of *n*-bodies a process is an ordered set of *6n* functions of time. This discreteness and finiteness are characteristic of systems of interaction which are not fields in the second sense. A process schema is called a field schema in this second, narrower sense when either states or systems or both are not defined as finite ordered sets of numbers but as functions or ordered sets of functions spread out continuously through space like, e.g., temperature or electric field strength. That psychology has no field theory in this second sense is obvious when one examines the present state of this science. That it must be a field theory in the general sense is an analytical truth which results from its being a science; for every science is a field theory in the sense of interaction because, as we have seen, a change in one variable at time t_0 may alter all conditions at time t_1, and if L_1 and L_2 are laws of the parts of the whole in isolation it does not follow that "L_1 and L_2" is the law of the whole. The Gestalters have consistently blurred the distinction between the general and specific meanings of "field."

The reasons for this blurring may be found on at least two levels. Everybody familiar with the history of Western thought during the last century knows that certain specious semantic dichotomies have been erected upon the slender foundation of science half understood. Newtonian *mechanics* is not a field theory in the second sense; Maxwell's contribution to electro*dynamics* is a field theory in the second sense. And so, of course, is Einstein's general theory of relativity. Field theories, therefore, have prestige and supersede mechanics. "Mechanics," furthermore, is in our cultural tradition associated with "mechanistic," "elementaristic," and "analytical." And Wundt is "elementaristic" and "analytical" and, of course, the Gestalters are always in revolt against him.

On a different level, we can say that the Gestalters seize upon fields in the second sense because they feel, rightly or wrongly, that such systems share an intuitively clear "structural" characteristic with perceptual phenomena. In other words, this reason for their preference for fields in the narrower sense, like the distribution of charges on a conductor or in an electrolyte, is grounded in their principle of isomorphism. The kind of interaction that can be observed in such physical systems is peculiarly attractive to them simply because they believe its nature to be immediately translatable into terms of perception. As an example of this intuitivity one may cite the concept of a "good Gestalt." The left and right halves of a face, for example, are perceived as symmetrical although physically the face is more often than not only approximately symmetrical. As Koehler says,

> So long as a face is at least approximately symmetrical and, thus, sufficiently near a standard condition of clearness and simple regularity, organization of this face as a percept will tend to overcome such minor irregularities as exist objectively. With regard to symmetry it will have "too good" an appearance. (5: 254)

Then Koehler goes on, characteristically, to point out that macroscopic physical states like electric currents in electrolytes show exactly the same tendency. Such systems tend to develop in the direction of maximum "regularity" and "simplicity."

We hope that by now we have carried out what we proposed as the task of this paper. What the Gestalters wish to say in their characteristic way about science can be said more clearly in the ordinary, analytical way which they reject as in principle inadequate. Some of what they actually do say in their own characteristic way turns out to be misleading. Thus, we believe, their claim that Gestalt theory is, among other things, a new philosophy of science is ill-founded.

REFERENCES

(1) Ellis, Willis D., *A Source Book of Gestalt Psychology*. New York: The Humanities Press, 1950.

(2) Grelling, K. and P. Oppenheim, "Der Gestaltbegriff im Licht der neuen Logik," *Erkenntnis*, 1938, 7, pp. 211–224.

(3) Koehler, Wolfgang, *Gestalt Psychology: An Introduction to New Concepts in Modern Psychology*. New York: Liveright Publishing Co., 1947.

(4) ———, *Dynamics in Psychology*. New York: Liveright, 1940.

(5) ———, *The Place of Value in a World of Facts*. New York: Liveright, 1938.

(6) Koffka, Kurt, *Principles of Gestalt Psychology*. New York: Harcourt, Brace and Co., 1935.

(7) Wertheimer, Max, "Gestalt Theory," *Social Research*, 1944, *11*, 78–99. (This account of Wertheimer's 1924 address to the *Kantgesellschaft* is more complete than the one in the Ellis volume.)

The Postulates and Methods of 'Behaviorism'*

KENNETH W. SPENCE

THERE WAS A TIME when the term 'behaviorism' in the title of a speech required no further specification. Every psychologist at least knew the referent to be that new brand of psychology, introduced by Watson, which proposed to break with tradition and deny that psychology had anything to do either with a mentalistic entity called consciousness or a method known as introspection. Today the situation is not so simple. The term 'behaviorism' may, on the one hand, merely imply a very general point of view which has come to be accepted by almost all psychologists and thus does not point to any particular group or theoretical position. Or, on the other hand, it may refer to any one of several varieties of behaviorism which have been offered as supplementations or modifications of the original formulation of Watson (*e.g.*, molecular behaviorism, molar behaviorism, operational behaviorism, purposive behaviorism, logical behaviorism—to mention only some of the varieties). While these current formulations usually acknowledge some debt to Watson, for various reasons which we cannot stop to discuss they almost invariably take great pains to differentiate themselves from what has come to be known as 'Watsonian Behaviorism' or 'Watsonianism.' In fact, so far as I know, there are no proponents today of the original Watsonian version. Proper care should be taken to note, however, that this statement holds true only for the particular pattern of assumptions that Watson advanced. Many of the basic postulates of his formulation are to be found in the present-day varieties of behaviorism and, what is more important, probably, in the underlying working assumptions of the great majority of present-day American psychologists.

Now that I have taken the precaution to differentiate the behaviorisms of today from the original version of behaviorism, I should like to call attention to the further interesting fact that with the exception possibly of Tolman very few, if any, current psychologists ever seem to think of themselves, or at least explicitly refer to themselves, as behaviorists. Such labeling, when it occurs, is usually the contribution of psychologists who

* Reprinted from the *Psychological Review,* 55, 1948, by kind permission of the author, the *Psychological Review,* and the American Psychological Association.

consider themselves opposed to behaviorism. Undoubtedly, one of the reasons underlying this absence or lack of 'old-school-tie' spirit is that a large majority of present-day American psychologists just take for granted many of the behavioristic assumptions and, occupied as they have been with the details of developing and applying their specific research tools, they have had little time or inclination to give much thought to the more general methodological and systematic problems of their science.

Even the more theoretical-minded of the behavioristically-oriented psychologists seem to have been too preoccupied with matters of detail to get around to the consideration of a more general theoretical framework. Instead of attempting to formulate a complete system of psychology, these theorists have been more concerned with the elaboration of relatively specific hypotheses concerning rather limited realms of data—*e.g.*, theories of simple learning phenomena, motivational theories, theories of personality development, etc. As a consequence we find that instead of being built up around the symbol 'behaviorism,' allegiances tend to become attached to such labels as associationism, conditioning, reinforcement theory, frustration hypothesis, etc. It seems, in other words, that these psychologists have outgrown the stage of schools.

Under these circumstances, I cannot and I shall not undertake to present a fixed set of articles of faith, articulately and self-consciously held by a group of men calling themselves behaviorists. Instead, I shall attempt to formulate a few methodological principles that are, I believe, exemplified in the work of certain contemporary psychologists who would undoubtedly acknowledge a heavy historical debt to that earlier formulation known as the school of behaviorism.

The first problem that I shall discuss has to do with the behavior scientist's conception of the nature of psychological events. In the older, classical psychologies, whether of the structural or act varieties, the point of view taken was that psychology, if it was a natural science, was, to say the least, a somewhat unique one. Instead of being conceived like physics, for example, as concerning itself with events mediated by or occurring in the consciousness or immediate experience of the observing scientist, psychology was said to observe and analyze by a kind of inner sense immediate experience *per se*. Sensations, emotions, thoughts were regarded as observable aspects of direct experience rather than systematic constructs which, like the physicist's atoms and electrons, were inferred from immediate experience.

Fortunately, the relationship of immediate experience (consciousness) to the data and constructs of science has been considerably clarified in recent years by the writings of several different groups of thinkers. The philosophers of science, particularly the logical positivists (1, 5, 6, 7), philosophically-minded scientists such as Bridgman (3) and, within psychology, such writers as Boring (2), Pratt (15), and Stevens (18) have succeeded, I believe, in making the point that the data of all sciences have the same origin—namely, the immediate experience of an observing person, the scientist himself. That is to say, immediate experience, the initial matrix out of which all sciences develop, is no longer considered a matter of concern for the scientist qua scientist. He simply takes it for granted and then proceeds to his task of describing the events occurring in it and discovering and formulating the nature of the relationships holding among them.

Boring stated this matter very clearly for psychologists in his book of some years ago, *The Physical Dimensions of Consciousness*. He wrote: "Thus the events of physics, as Wundt said, are mediate to experience, which stands in the background as the dator of scientific data, unrealizable as reality except inductively. In the same way psychology must deal with existential reals which are similarly mediate to experience. There is no way of getting at 'direct experience' because experience gives itself up to science indirectly, inferentially, by the experimental method" (2, p. 6).

More recently Pratt, in his *Logic of Modern Psychology* (15), has hammered home this same point with considerable effectiveness. As he points out, the subject matter of psychology is exactly the same in kind as all other sciences; any differentiation among the sciences is merely a matter of convenience, a division of scientific labor resorted to as the amount of detailed knowledge increases beyond the capacity of a single person's grasp.

I think that it is of some historical interest to note in connection with this point that in the first of his articles introducing the behavioristic position, Watson took essentially the same stand. He wrote: "It [psychology] can dispense with consciousness in a psychological sense. The separate observation of 'states of consciousness' is, on this assumption, no more a part of the task of the psychologist than of the physicist. We might call this the return to a non-reflective and naive use of consciousness. In this sense consciousness may be said to be the instrument or tool with which all scientists work" (21, p. 176).

Acknowledging, then, that the psychologist conceives his task as that of bringing order and meaning into the realm of certain events provided by immediate experience, we now turn to the question of what these particular observed events are. In attempting to answer this question, attention should first be directed to the fact that the sense events in the experience of the observing scientist may depend upon or result from two different classes of conditions, intra-organic and extra-organic, the former exciting the interoceptors and the latter, the exteroceptors. The physical sciences, it should be noted, moreover, deal only with events of an extra-organic origin—*i.e.*, those received through the exteroceptors. The data of classical psychology, on the other hand, were regarded as involving primarily sense events initiated through the interoceptors. These latter were regarded as being stimulated by such internal mental activities as thinking, desiring, emotional reactions, perceiving, etc., and hence were thought of as providing primary data concerning them.

It is apparent, however, that these internally initiated experiences differ rather markedly from the externally aroused ones in the extent to which they are publicly controllable and communicable. At least, if we can judge from the interminable disagreements of the introspective psychologists themselves, this class of experiences does not meet too well the requirements of social verification and acceptance demanded by the scientist. It was in the face of this difficulty that Watson made his suggestion that the psychologist, like all other scientists, should confine himself to those segments of his experience which have their origin in extra-organic conditions. In other words, the events studied by the psychologist, Watson held, should consist in observations of the overt behavior of *other* organisms, other persons than the observing scientist himself, and not in the observation of the scientist's own internal activities.

As everyone knows, however, most behavior scientists have continued more or less to make use of this latter type of material in the form of the objectively recordable verbal reports of their subjects. Indeed, the scientist himself, in certain circumstances, may assume a dual role and serve as both subject and experimenter. In this event his own introspective report is recorded as a linguistic response and becomes a part of the objective data. To some critics of the behavioristic viewpoint, this acceptance of the verbal reports of their subjects as a part of the data has seemed to represent an abandonment of the strict behavioristic position and a return to the conception that psychology studies *experiential* events as well as overt behavior.

Such a contention, it seems to me, fails to note a very important difference in the two positions. The introspectionist, it should be recalled, assumed a strict one-to-one relationship between the verbal responses of his subjects and the inner mental processes. Accordingly, he accepted these introspective reports as *facts* or *data* about the inner mental events which they represented. The behavior scientist takes a very different position. He accepts verbal response as just one more form of behavior and he proposes to use this type of data in exactly the same manner as he does other types of behavior variables. Thus he attempts to discover laws relating verbal responses to environmental events of the past or present, and he seeks to find what relations they have to other types of response variables. He also makes use of them as a basis for making inferences as to certain hypothetical or theoretical constructs which he employs. In contrast, then, to the introspectionist's conception of these verbal reports as mirroring directly inner mental events, *i.e.*, facts, the behaviorist uses them either as data in their own right to be related to other data, or as a base from which to infer theoretical constructs which presumably represent internal or covert activities of their subjects. We shall return later to the use made of such language responses in the theorizing of the behaviorist.

From this all too cursory discussion of the initial data of the behavioristic psychologist, I should like now to turn to a consideration of the nature of the concepts which he employs to record and describe these events. I do not believe it is necessary for me to discuss at any length the position of the behaviorist with respect to the movement known as operationism. The insistence of the early behaviorists on a thoroughgoing operational analysis of the traditional mentalistic concepts was really nothing more than an anticipation of this somewhat overemphasized program. That a body of empirical knowledge cannot be built up without providing for verifiability of the terms in use is simply taken for granted by the behaviorist. Instead, then, of talking about operational definition of psychological concepts, I should like to discuss certain matters related to a second criterion of acceptability of a scientific concept—namely, its *significance.*

One often hears criticism to the effect that behavioristic concepts are too elementaristic, too atomistic, or that they fail to portray the real essence or true meaning of man's behavior. These latter critics often complain bitterly about the impoverishment of the mind, and of the lack of warmth and glowing particulars in the behaviorist's picture of psychological events. Some of these criticisms merely reflect, of course, a lack of appreciation on the part of some 'psychologists' as to the difference between scientific knowledge of an event on the one hand and everyday knowledge, or the kind of knowledge the novelist or poet portrays, on the other. Either by reason of training or because of their basically non-scientific interests, these critics have never really understood the abstract character of the scientific account of any phenomenon. The only reply that can be made to such a critic is to point out that the scientist's interests are quite different from his. There are, of course, other legitimate interpretations of nature and man than the scientific one and each has its right to be pursued. The behavior scientist merely asks that he be given the same opportunity to develop a scientific account of his phenomena that his colleagues in the physical and biological fields have had. If there are aspects of human or animal behavior for which such an account cannot ever be developed, there are not, so far as I know, any means of finding this out without a try. Unfortunately, the attitudes of too many psychologists with regard to this matter are not such as are likely to lead them to the discovery of such knowledge. The difficulty, I fear, is that too many persons whose interests are non-scientific have become psychologists under the mistaken impression that psychology is one of the arts.

As to the criticisms that the behaviorist's concepts are too elementaristic, I must confess to the belief that the term 'elementarism' is merely one of those stereotypes, or 'rally-round-the-flag' words which the Gestalt psychologist has used in the defense and exposition of his holistic doctrines. However fervently the Gestalt psychologist may claim that he deals only with wholes, with total situations, the fact remains that if he is interested in discovering uniformities or scientific laws he must, of necessity, fractionate or abstract out certain features of the total events he observes. Such uniformities or laws describe ways in which events repeat themselves. Total concrete events, however, are seldom if ever repeated. Only certain features of events are repeated and since this is the case science must always abstract.

The problem here is really one of the size of the 'units of description' that the scientist is to employ and this brings us back to the criterion of acceptability of a scientific term which we referred to as *significance*. By the *significance* of a scientific concept is here meant the extent to which a concept or variable aids or enters into the formulation of laws. Significant concepts in science are those which are discovered to have functional relations with other concepts. Unfortunately, there are few if any rules for deciding *a priori* which concepts will and which ones will not be significant. Whether elementaristic concepts or units of description which, like the Gestaltists, are nearer the 'meaningful' common sense level, are to be chosen is entirely a pragmatic matter of which ones are most successful —*i.e.*, which ones lead to the discovery of laws. This can be ascertained only by trying them out.

Attention might also be called here to the further fact that it is entirely conceivable that different sizes or levels of descriptive units may be employed for the same set of events. The physical sciences provide us with numerous instances of this sort of thing and we see examples of it in psychology both in the description of behavior and stimulus events. Thus, employing the terms of Brunswik (4) and Heider (8), we may make use of either a proximal or distal account of the stimulus situation, and behavior may be described either in terms of movements (muscular patterns) or in terms of gross achievements. The particular alternative chosen, molecular or molar, depends upon the interest and purpose of the scientist, the kind of law he expects to find or use. As Hull (11) has pointed out in discussing this matter, some of the seeming disagreements among current psychologists are merely that one prefers to use more molar concepts than another.

Such different descriptions, however, do not necessarily represent fundamental disagreements. If the two systems of concepts should each be successful in leading to the discovery and formulation of laws, it should also be possible to discover coordinating definitions which will reveal the interrelations of the two systems. Or, as Hull (11) suggests, the postulates or primary assumptions of those working at a more molar level may ultimately appear as theorems in a more molecular description.

To sum up, then, the position which the behavior scientist takes with respect to the selection of the descriptive concepts to be employed in his science, recognizes (1) that the *significance* of a concept is to be measured in terms of the extent to which it leads to the formulation of laws about the phenomena; (2) that a scientific law is always, in some greater or less degree, abstract in the sense that it refers only to certain properties of the events or sequence of events it describes and ignores other properties which are irrelevant to the particular momentary purpose; (3) that the method of elementary abstraction or analysis has been highly successful in all fields of science. While the disentanglement of the great complexes of properties and relations (sequences) among psychological events is undoubtedly much more difficult than in the case of physical phenomena, the difference between them need not be regarded as more than one of degree. On the basis of this assumption there would seem to be little reason for abandoning the method of abstraction or analysis.

We have said that the primary aim of the behavior scientist is to bring order and meaning into the particular realm of events he studies. Ordering a set of observable events for the scientist consists in discovering relationships between the events or, as we say, in the finding of empirical laws. The scientist seeks to establish laws relating his concepts or variables because they make possible explanation and prediction.

In the case of such areas of science as physics, the finding of empirical laws has involved chiefly the process of inductive generalization from observation and experimentation. In other words, in physics it has been possible to isolate sufficiently simple systems of observation to arrive at such laws in this manner. The situation in psychology and the other behavior sciences is quite different. Primarily because of the greater complexity of psychological as compared with physical phenomena, the psychologist has either been unable to isolate, experimentally, simple systems, or he has not found satisfactory means of measuring all of the relevant variables in the system under observation. In this circumstance he has resorted to guesses or postulations as to the uncontrolled or as yet unmeasurable factors. As a result of this difference the term 'theory' has, as I have pointed out elsewhere (17), come to have a very different connotation in psychology from that which it has in physics. Theories in physics are constructions which serve primarily to integrate or organize into a single deductive system sets of empirical laws which previously were unrelated. The classical example is, of course, the Newtonian integration of the previously unconnected areas of mechanics and astronomy by the gravitational theory. Other well-known examples are the electromagnetic theory of light and the kinetic theory of gases.

In psychology, on the other hand, theories serve primarily as a device to aid in the formulation of the empirical laws. They consist in guesses as to how the uncontrolled or unknown factors in the system under study are related to the experimentally-known variables. To these hypothetical constructs Tolman (20) has applied the very appropriate term 'intervening variable' because they are assumed to intervene between the measurable environmental and organic variables, on the one hand, and the measurable behavior properties on the other.

The manner in which the behavior scientist has used these hypothetical, intervening constructs may be shown by considering the various kinds of laws which the psychologist seeks to discover. Confining ourselves for the moment to laws which do not involve any hypothetical components, we find that the variables studied by the behavioristic psychologist fall into two, or possibly three, main groups:

(1) Response variables: measurements of behavior properties.

(2) Stimulus variables: measurements of properties of the physical and social environment.

(3) Organic variables: measurements of neuroanatomical or neurophysiological properties of the organism.

The different types of empirical relationships or laws in which psychologists have been interested are as follows:

1. $R = f\ (R)$
2. $R = f\ (S)$
3. $R = f\ (O)$
4. $O = f\ (S)$

Type 1 laws are laws of association of behavior properties. A great deal of use is made of the statistical constant, the coefficient of correlation, in the formulation of these laws and, as is well known, this type of law is investigated extensively in the field of psychological testing.

Type 2 laws may be concerned with the present environment or with past environmental events. Thus in the case of the typical perception experiments, we are interested in the effects of variation of aspects or features of the environmental stimulus on the perceptual or discrimination responses of the subject. Best examples of laws relating behavior to past events in the environment are laws of learning, laws of secondary motivation, etc.

For the most part the present-day behavioristic psychologists tend to concentrate their energies on these two classes of laws and to a very considerable extent they have favored the use of the molar rather than molecular concepts. A few psychologists whose interests have been in mediational problems have concerned themselves with type 3 and type 4 laws. These latter are obviously in the field of neurophysiological psychology and have in the main been concerned only with the simplest kinds of behavior phenomena—*e.g.*, sensory responses. Indeed, our inability to develop measures of this class of events (*i.e.*, organic variables) in the case of the more complex behavior phenomena has been one of the factors underlying the substitution of the hypothetical intervening constructs in their place.

Figure 1 continues this analysis of the laws of psychology. In this diagram I have attempted to portray, in addition to the four types of empirical laws which we have been discussing, the new hypothetical or guessed-at types of relationships which are involved in the introduction of the hypothetical intervening constructs. These latter are indicated as I_a and I_b and are represented as *hypothetical state variables* (enclosed within the rectangle). The environment or world situation at three different time intervals is represented by $S_t - n$ (past) $S_t = o$ (present) $S_t + n$ (future). These S's and also the R's represent empirical variables. I have also represented the class of experimental neurophysiological variables of the first figure by the symbol O, to the left of the rectangle. The four classes of empirical laws, listed at the right side of the figure, are represented by the solid curved lines. The guessed-at or postulated laws relating the hypothetical state variables (I_a, I_b, etc.) to the various experimental variables are represented by the dotted lines. Thus No. 5 type of 'law' defines or

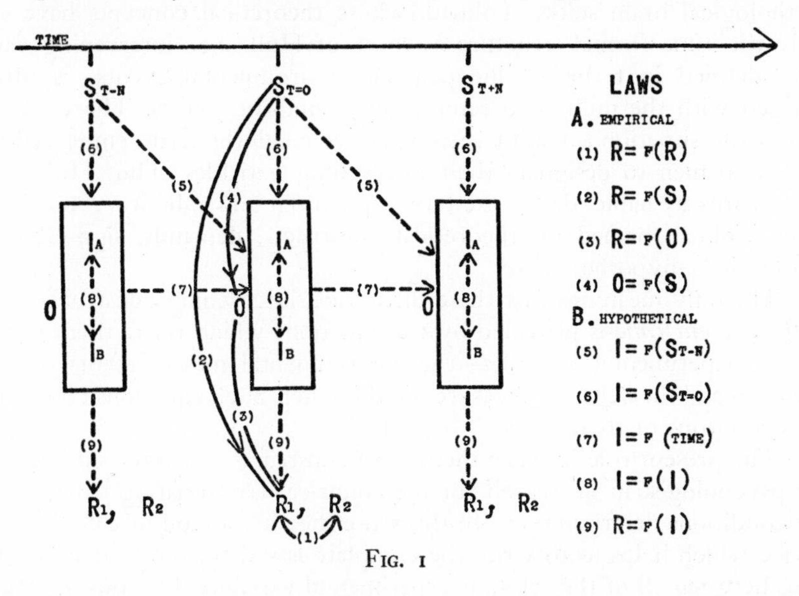

FIG. 1

introduces the intervening variables in terms of past events; No. 6 type relates them to the present environmental variables and No. 7 to time; No. 8 'laws' present interrelations assumed between these intervening variables, and, finally, the relations represented by No. 9 relate the intervening variables to the response variables. That is to say, these dotted lines should be thought of as representative of different classes of postulated relationships, not the usual notion of an S–R connection.

Those who are acquainted with the theoretical constructs of Hull (11) will recognize specific examples of these hypothetical laws. Thus his postulate or definition of the construct habit strength, or $_SH_R$, as a function of the number of past reinforcements is a good example of class No. 5 'law.' His assumption of the nature of the manner in which H and D interact to determine E falls in Class No. 8 and his postulate as to how the construct of reactive inhibition (I_R) is assumed to change (disintegrate) with time is an instance of No. 7 type of 'law.' Incidentally, it will be noted that this last relationship is the only one which is similar to the so-called dynamic or process laws of physics. This type of law states or describes the laws governing the changes that occur within a system in time.

A question concerning these theoretical constructs that invariably seems to arise is whether they represent some kind of internal, presumably neurophysiological, process or state. The persistence with which misunderstanding arises on this point is truly surprising. It is probably to be explained in terms of the difficulty and resistance we have in shedding old, familiar meanings of words. In this connection it is not a little amusing to note that whereas Hull is usually accused of stuffing the organism with mythological brain states, Tolman, whose theoretical concepts have exactly the same formal structure as those of Hull—*i.e.*, intervening variables defined in terms of independent environmental events—is often charged with the guilt of dreaming up mentalistic ghosts. The explanation of this situation is readily seen when we recall the terms employed by these two men to designate their intervening variables. Thus Hull used such words as habit, drive, excitatory potential and inhibitory potential while Tolman named his theoretical constructs, demands, sign-Gestalt-expectations, hypotheses, etc.

The only meanings that these theoretical intervening constructs have *at the present time* is provided by the equations which relate them to the known experimental variables—the environmental measurements on the one hand and the behavior measures on the other. Such equations constitute the definitions of these terms.

The present role of these theoretical constructs we have said is to aid the psychologist in his search for the empirical laws relating behavior to the conditions determining it. In this sense they are a kind of calculational device which helps us to write the complete law describing the interrelations between all of the relevant experimental variables. In a recent article (17) on this problem of theory construction in contemporary psychology I called attention to the point that it is possible in the case of the theoretical formulation of simple learning behavior developed by Hull to substitute in the successive equations introducing the intervening theoretical constructs and obtain a single equation which states the response measure as a function of the several antecedent environmental variables. In this equation the intervening theoretical variables are represented among the parameters of the equation.

While both Tolman and I have emphasized the heuristic value of this type of theoretical construction in the formulation of the complete form of the laws, Hull (12) has called attention to another use which these constructs serve. Such constructs as habit and excitatory potential also provide, he claims, convenient, quantitative representations or indices of the particular complex of experimental variables for which they stand. Thus instead of having to state that the subject has had so many reinforcements in the situation under conditions in which the goal was of such-and-such a magnitude and was delayed for such-and-such a period, it is possible to substitute the calculated value of habit strength.

Finally, there remains the possibility, at least, that these intervening constructs may turn out to have their counterparts somewhere under the skin of the organism. Hull in particular has been quite prone to accept this possibility and has not hesitated to add further statements about these constructs which suggest their possible locus and functioning in the nervous system. His justification, however, has always been that such conjectures provide experimental hints to persons interested in making such coordinations of our knowledge. His main theoretical efforts have been primarily at the molar-behavioral level.

In concluding this discussion of the theoretical framework of the behavioristic psychologist, I should like to emphasize that it is as yet only in a very primitive state of development, a fact which has unfortunately been lost sight of by many of the current critics of this position. The theorist in this field apparently has to choose between attempting to lay down the general theoretical framework of the whole range of behavior phenomena or working out the detailed nature of one small realm of data. Tolman has, for the most part, chosen the former alternative with the consequence that his treatment is characterized by an obvious lack of detailed specification of his theoretical constructs. Hull, on the other hand, has elected to follow the second method. His recent book, *Principles of Behavior*, dealt only with the most *simple* instances of laboratory learning phenomena, classical and instrumental conditioning, and he and his students are now engaged in extending the fundamental laws there discovered to the major phenomena of individual behavior.

So far as theoretical constructs are concerned, it is obvious that the simple behavior phenomena dealt with by Hull and other behavioristic-oriented psychologists have not required (to any great extent) a whole class of hypothetical intervening variables that must ultimately be postulated. Thus the theoretical constructs in Hull's recent book—habit, excitatory and inhibitory potential, drive, etc.—are what might be referred to as *state variables*. Each of these constructs represents a hypothetical condition or state of the organism which is assumed to have resulted from and is defined in terms of the past interactions of the organism and its environment. In contrast the new theoretical constructs referred to above will represent, not states, but hypothetical, non-observable responses, implicit processes, occurring in the individual. Thus, in dealing with the more complex types of animal and human behavior, implicit emotional responses, covert verbal responses and not easily observable receptor-exposure and postural adjustments will have to be postulated in addition to these state variables. As yet only a bare beginning has been made in the use of such theoretical constructs—*e.g.*, anxiety reactions and their secondary reinforcing effects (14), fractional anticipatory goal reactions as the basis of purposive behavior (9, 10).

It is in this realm of theorizing that the verbal reports of human subjects are likely to be of most use to the behavior theorist, for presumably these reports can be made the basis on which to postulate the occurrence of these inferred activities. There are, of course, many pitfalls in the use of such verbal reports and considerable caution needs to be exercised in their use. However, careful control and checking in terms of other, non-verbal responses should provide a means of detecting distortions, both deliberate and otherwise, in this source of data (16).

A discussion of behaviorism, especially when it occurs in conjunction with a symposium which includes Gestalt psychology, requires at least some comment on the distinction often made between field and non-field theories in psychology. The Gestalt psychologists, in particular, have been very fond of this contrast and they have not hesitated to imply that their theoretical structures are similar in some respect to the type of field theory in physics represented by the Maxwell electromagnetic theory and Einstein's gravitational theory. In some instances the further implication has been made that behavioristic theories are a mechanical type of theory and as such are just as outmoded as the mechanistic theories of physics. Now I have often wondered what our theoretical brethren from the field of physics would think of these claims if perchance they were ever to take a serious look at these two groups of theories. Certainly the behavioristic theoretical structure I have been talking about uses neither the mechanical models—*i.e.*, particles with their attracting forces—nor the type of mathematical equations that characterize a mechanical theory. Nor do I believe that there is anything even remotely resembling the field equations of Maxwell and Einstein in the theoretical formulations of the Gestalt psychologists. In the sense, then, in which the theoretical physicist understands the dichotomy, mechanical versus field theory, no such distinction, in my opinion, exists in psychology today.

If, on the other hand, the concept of field refers in psychology essentially to the notion of a system of interdependent variables, with its implication that the behavior of an organism at any moment is a resultant of the totality of relevant variables, then there is not to my knowledge any behavioristic theory today which would not also be a field theory. Furthermore, if we accept the additional notion that it is the pattern of interrelationships between the determining variables that is the crucial factor differentiating psychological field theories from non-field theories, I do not believe that the behavior theories which I have been describing would fail to qualify as field theories. The hypothetical equations which Hull (11) postulates in the introduction of his theoretical constructs provide in precise mathematical form these very patterns of interrelationship. Finally, as to the characteristic of field theory emphasized by Lewin (13) under the principle of contemporaneity—namely, that the behavior at any moment is a function of the situation *at that moment only* and not a function of past or future situations,—I find it difficult to believe that any present-day psychologist believes that other conditions than those of the present moment determine the behavior of this moment. Even the psychoanalyst never held, as Lewin sometimes seems to imply, that past events somehow jump through time to determine the present behavior, but, instead, conceived of these past events leaving their effects in the organism and through them determining the behavior of the moment. The behaviorist takes exactly the same view of the matter.

The development of our science has not been helped, in my opinion, by such distinctions as field and non-field theory. A much more useful procedure would be to examine in detail these differing theoretical positions with a view to ascertaining to what extent they differ in the particular variables they believe to be relevant in a particular instance and what differences, if any, exist in their postulation as to the pattern of the interrelationships involved—*i.e.*, in the form of the hypothetical laws they assume. It is my personal belief that if this procedure were followed there would be much less in the way of specific disagreements to settle than is usually thought. I base this prediction not only on the well-known fact that the Gestaltists, psychoanalysts and behaviorists have to a considerable extent been interested in very different realms of psychological phenomena and that hence their theories are not in competition with one another, but also on the fact that very little real theorizing, particularly in the matter of specifying the precise form of the interrelations between the variables, has actually been done. It is most imperative that psychologists attempt to formulate their theories in as precise and articulate a manner as possible, for it is only by means of such theorizing that psychology can hope, finally, to attain full-fledged scientific statehood.

REFERENCES

1. Bergmann, G. The subject matter of psychology. *Phil. Sci.*, 1940, 7, 415–433.
2. Boring, E. G. *The physical dimensions of consciousness.* New York: The Century Company, 1933.
3. Bridgman, P. W. *The logic of modern physics.* New York: Macmillan Company, 1928.
4. Brunswik, E. The conceptual focus of some psychological systems. *J. Unified Sci. (Erkenntnis)*, 1939, 8, 36–49.
5. Carnap, R. Testability and meaning. *Phil. Sci.*, 1936, 3, 419–471; 1937, 4, 1–40.
6. ——. *Philosophy and logical syntax.* London: Kegan Paul, Trench, Trubner & Co., Ltd., 1935.
7. Feigl, H. Operationism and scientific method. *Psychol. Rev.*, 1945, 52, 243–246.
8. Heider, F. Environmental determinants in psychological theories. *Psychol. Rev.*, 1939, 46, 383–410.
9. Hull, C. L. Knowledge and purpose as habit mechanisms. *Psychol. Rev.*, 1930, 37, 511–525.
10. ——. Goal attraction and directing ideas conceived as habit phenomena. *Psychol. Rev.*, 1931, 38, 487–506.

11. Hull, C. L. *Principles of behavior.* New York: D. Appleton-Century Co., 1943.
12. ——. The problem of intervening variables in molar behavior theory. *Psychol. Rev.*, 1943, 50, 273–291.
13. Lewin, K. Defining the "field" at a given time. *Psychol. Rev.*, 1943, 50, 292–310.
14. Mowrer, O. H. A stimulus-response analysis of anxiety and its role as a new forcing agent. *Psychol. Rev.*, 1939, 46, 553–565.
15. Pratt, C. C. *The logic of modern psychology.* New York: The Macmillan Company, 1939.
16. Skinner, B. F. The operational analysis of psychological terms. *Psychol. Rev.*, 1945, 52, 270–278.
17. Spence, K. W. The nature of theory construction in contemporary psychology. *Psychol. Rev.*, 1944, 51, 47–68.
18. Stevens, S. S. The operational definition of psychological concepts. *Psychol. Rev.*, 1935, 42, 517–527.
19. Tolman, E. C. *Purposive behavior in animals and men.* New York: The Century Company, 1932.
20. ——. The determiners of behavior at a choice point. *Psychol. Rev.*, 1938, 45, 1–41.
21. Watson, J. B. Psychology as the behaviorist views it. *Psychol. Rev.*, 1913, 20, 158–177.

The Operational Analysis of Psychological Terms*

B. F. SKINNER

An answer to Question 6[1] will define the position to be taken in what follows. Operationism is not regarded as a new theory or mode of definition. The literature has emphasized certain critical or hitherto neglected instances, but no new kind of operation has been discovered and none should be singled out. There is no reason to restrict operational analysis to high-order constructs; the principle applies to all definitions (Question 9). This means, in answer to Question 1 (a), that we must explicate an operational definition for every term unless we are willing to adopt the vague usage of the vernacular.

Operationism may be defined as the practice of talking about (1) one's observations, (2) the manipulative and calculational procedures involved in making them, (3) the logical and mathematical steps which intervene between earlier and later statements, and (4) *nothing else*. So far, the major contribution has come from the fourth provision and, like it, is negative. We have learned how to avoid troublesome references by showing that they are artifacts, which may be variously traced to history, philosophy, linguistics, and so on. No very important positive advances have been made in connection with the first three provisions because operationism has no good answer to Question 10. It has not developed a satisfactory formulation of the effective verbal behavior of the scientist.

The operationist, like most contemporary writers in the field of linguistic and semantic analysis, is on the fence between logical 'correspondence' theories of reference and empirical formulations of language in use. He has not improved upon the mixture of logical and popular terms usually encountered in casual or even supposedly technical discussions of scientific method or the theory of knowledge (*e.g.*, Bertrand Russell's recent *An inquiry into meaning and truth*). 'Definition' is a key term but is not rigorously defined. Bridgman's original contention that the 'concept

* Reprinted from the *Psychological Review*, 52, 1945, by kind permission of the author, the *Psychological Review* and the American Psychological Association.

[1] [The questions referred to formed the basis of a "Symposium on Operationism" of which this article was a part. These questions will be found listed at the end of this paper. Editors' note.]

is synonymous with the corresponding set of operations' cannot be taken literally, and no similarly explicit but satisfactory statement of the relation is available. Instead, a few roundabout expressions recur with rather tiresome regularity whenever this relation is mentioned. We are told that a concept is to be defined '*in terms of*' certain operations, that propositions are to be '*based upon*' operations, that a term denotes something only when there are '*concrete criteria for its applicability*,' that operationism consists in '*referring any concept for its definition* to . . . concrete operations . . . ,' and so on. We may accept expressions of this sort as outlining a program, but they do not provide a general scheme of definition, much less an explicit statement of the relation between concept and operation.

The weakness of current theories of language may be traced to the fact that an objective conception of human behavior is still incomplete. The doctrine that words are used to express or convey meanings merely substitutes 'meaning' for 'idea' (in the hope that meanings can then somehow be got outside the skin) and is incompatible with modern psychological conceptions of the organism. Attempts to derive a symbolic function from the principle of conditioning (or association) have been characterized by a very superficial analysis. It is simply not true that an organism reacts to a sign 'as it would to the object which the sign supplants' (Stevens, 2, p. 250). Only in a very limited area (mainly in the case of autonomic responses) is it possible to regard the sign as a simple substitute stimulus in the Pavlovian sense. Modern logic, as a formalization of 'real' languages, retains and extends this dualistic theory of meaning and can scarcely be appealed to by the psychologist who recognizes his own responsibility in giving an account of verbal behavior.

It is not my intention to attempt a more adequate formulation here. The fundamental revision is too sweeping to be made hastily. I should like, however, to try to make a small but positive contribution to this symposium by considering a few points which arise in connection with the operational definition of psychological terms. Much of the material which follows is adapted from a much longer work now in preparation, in which the necessary groundwork is more carefully prepared.

The operational attitude, in spite of its shortcomings, is a good thing in any science but especially in psychology because of the presence there of a vast vocabulary of ancient and non-scientific origin. It is not surprising that the broad empirical movement in the philosophy of science, which Stevens has shown (2) to be the background of operationism, should have had a vigorous and early representation in the field of psychology—namely, behaviorism. In spite of the differences which Stevens pretends to find, behaviorism has been (at least to most behaviorists) nothing more than a thoroughgoing operational analysis of traditional mentalistic concepts. We may disagree with some of the answers (such as Watson's disposition of images), but the *questions* asked by behaviorism were strictly operational in spirit. I also cannot agree with Stevens that American behaviorism was 'primitive.' The early papers on the problem of consciousness by Watson, Weiss, Tolman, Hunter, Lashley, and many others, were not only highly sophisticated examples of operational inquiry, they showed a willingness to deal with a wider range of phenomena than do current streamlined treatments, particularly those offered by logicians (*e.g.*, Carnap) interested in a unified scientific vocabulary. But behaviorism, too, stopped short of a decisive positive contribution—and for the same reason: it never finished an acceptable formulation of the 'verbal report.' The conception of behavior which it developed could not convincingly embrace the 'use of subjective terms.'

A considerable advantage is gained from dealing with terms, concepts, constructs, and so on, quite frankly in the form in which they are observed—namely, as verbal responses. There is then no danger of including in the concept that aspect or part of nature which it singles out. (Several of the present questions seem to mix concept and referent; at least they seem to become trivial when, in order to make the mixture less likely, 'term' is substituted for 'concept' or 'construct.') Meanings, contents, and references are to be found among the determiners, not among the properties, of response. The question 'What is length?' would appear to be satisfactorily answered by listing the circumstances under which the response 'length' is emitted (or, better, by giving some general description of such circumstances). If two quite separate sets of circumstances are revealed, then there are two responses having the form 'length' (Question 2), since a verbal response-class is not defined by phonetic form alone but by its functional relations. This is true even though the two sets are found to be intimately connected. The two responses are not controlled by the same stimuli, no matter how clearly it is shown that the different stimuli arise from the same 'thing.'

What we want to know in the case of many traditional psychological terms is, first, the specific stimulating conditions under which they are emitted (this corresponds to 'finding the referents') and, second (and this is a much more important systematic question), why each response is controlled by its corresponding condition. The latter is not necessarily a genetic question. The individual acquires language from society, but the reinforcing action of the verbal community continues to play an important rôle in maintaining the specific relations between responses and stimuli which are essential to the proper functioning of verbal behavior. How language is acquired is, therefore, only part of a much broader problem.

We may generalize the conditions responsible for the standard 'semantic' relation between a verbal response and a particular stimulus without going into reinforcement theory in detail. There are three important terms: a stimulus, a response, and a reinforcement supplied by the verbal community. (All of these need more careful definitions than are implied by current usage, but the following argument may be made without digressing for that purpose.) The significant interrelations between these terms may be expressed by saying that the community reinforces the response only when it is emitted in the presence of the stimulus. The reinforcement of the response 'red,' for example, is contingent upon the presence of a red object. (The contingency need not be invariable.) A red object then becomes a discriminative stimulus, an 'occasion,' for the successful emission of the response 'red' (1).

This scheme presupposes that the stimulus act upon both the speaker and the reinforcing community; otherwise the proper contingency cannot be maintained by the community. But this provision is lacking in the case of many 'subjective' terms, which appear to be responses to *private* stimuli. The problem of subjective terms does not coincide exactly with that of private stimuli, but there is a close connection. We must know the characteristics of verbal responses to private stimuli in order to approach the operational analysis of the subjective term.

The response 'My tooth aches' is partly under the control of a state of affairs to which the speaker alone is able to react, since no one else can establish the required connection with the tooth in question. There is nothing mysterious or metaphysical about this; the simple fact is that each speaker possesses a small but important private world of stimuli. So far as we know, his reactions to these are quite like his reactions to external events. Nevertheless the privacy gives rise to two problems. The first difficulty is that we cannot, as in the case of public stimuli, account for the verbal response by pointing to a controlling stimulus. Our practice is to *infer* the private event, but this is opposed to the direction of inquiry in a science of behavior in which we are to predict response through, among other things, an independent knowledge of the stimulus. It is often supposed that a solution is to be found in improved physiological techniques. Whenever it becomes possible to say what conditions within the organism control the response 'I am depressed,' for example, and to produce these conditions at will, a degree of control and prediction characteristic of responses to external stimuli will be made possible. Meanwhile, we must be content with reasonable evidence for the belief that responses to public and private stimuli are equally lawful and alike in kind.

But the problem of privacy cannot be wholly solved by instrumental invasion. No matter how clearly these internal events may be exposed in the laboratory, the fact remains that in the normal verbal episode they are quite private. We have not solved the second problem of how the community achieves the necessary contingency of reinforcement. How is the response 'toothache' appropriately reinforced if the reinforcing agent has no contact with the tooth? There is, of course, no question of whether responses to private stimuli are possible. They occur commonly enough and must be accounted for. But why do they occur, what is their relation to controlling stimuli, and what, if any, are their distinguishing characteristics?

There are at least four ways in which a verbal community which has no access to a private stimulus may generate verbal behavior in response to it:

(1) It is not strictly true that the stimuli which control the response must be available to the community. Any reasonably regular accompaniment will suffice. Consider, for example, a blind man who learns the names of a trayful of objects from a teacher who identifies the objects by sight. The reinforcements are supplied or withheld according to the contingency between the blind man's responses and the teacher's visual stimuli, but the responses are controlled wholly by tactual stimuli. A satisfactory verbal system results from the fact that the visual and tactual stimuli remain closely connected.

Similarly, in the case of private stimuli, one may teach a child to say 'That hurts' in agreement with the usage of the community by making the reinforcement contingent upon public accompaniments of painful stimuli (a smart blow, tissue damage, and so on). The connection between public and private stimuli need not be invariable; a response may be conditioned with merely periodic reinforcement and even in spite of an occasional conflicting contingency (1). The possibility of such behavior is limited by the degree of association of public and private stimuli which will supply a net reinforcement sufficient to establish and maintain a response.

(2) A commoner basis for the verbal reinforcement of a response to a private stimulus is provided by collateral responses to the same stimulus. Although a dentist may occasionally be able to identify the stimulus for a toothache from certain public accompaniments as in (1), the response 'toothache' is generally transmitted on the basis of responses which are elicited by the same stimulus but which do not need to be set up by an environmental contingency. The community infers the private stimulus, not from accompanying public stimuli, but from collateral, generally unconditioned and at least non-verbal, responses (hand to jaw, facial expressions, groans, and so on). The inference is not always correct, and the accuracy of the reference is again limited by the degree of association.

(3) Some very important responses to private stimuli are descriptive of the speaker's own behavior. When this is overt, the community bases its instructional reinforcement upon the conspicuous manifestations, but the speaker presumably acquires the response in connection with a wealth of additional proprioceptive stimuli. The latter may assume practically complete control, as in describing one's own behavior in the dark. This is very close to the example of the blind man; the speaker and the community react to different, though closely associated, stimuli.

Suppose, now, that a given response recedes to the level of covert or merely incipient behavior. How shall we explain the vocabulary which deals with this private world? (The instrumental detection of covert behavior is again not an answer, for we are interested in how responses to private stimuli are normally, and non-instrumentally, set up.) There are two important possibilities. The surviving covert response may be regarded as an accompaniment of the overt (perhaps part of it), in which case the response to the private stimulus is imparted on the basis of the public stimulus supplied by the overt response, as in (1). On the other hand, the covert response may be *similar to*, though probably less intense than, the overt and hence supply the *same* stimulus, albeit in a weakened form. We have, then, a third possibility: a response may be emitted in the presence of a private stimulus, which has no public accompaniments, provided it is occasionally reinforced in the presence of the same stimulus occurring with public manifestations.

Terms falling within this class are apparently descriptive only of behavior, rather than of other internal states or events, since the possibility that the same stimulus may be both public and private (or, better, may have or lack public accompaniments) seems to arise from the unique fact that behavior may be both covert and overt.

(4) The principle of transfer or stimulus induction supplies a fourth explanation of how a response to private stimuli may be maintained by public reinforcement. A response which is acquired and maintained in connection with public stimuli may be emitted, through induction, in response to private events. The transfer is not due to identical stimuli, as in (3), but to coinciding properties. Thus, we describe internal states as 'agitated,' 'depressed,' 'ebullient,' and so on, in a long list. Responses in this class are all metaphors (including special figures like metonymy). The term 'metaphor' is not used pejoratively but merely to indicate that the differential reinforcement cannot be accorded actual responses to the private case. As the etymology suggests, the response is 'carried over' from the public instance.

In summary, a verbal response to a private stimulus may be maintained in strength through appropriate reinforcement based upon public accompaniments or consequences, as in (1) and (2), or through appropriate reinforcement accorded the response when it is made to public stimuli, the private case occurring by induction when the stimuli are only partly similar. If these are the only possibilities (and the list is here offered as exhaustive), then we may understand why terms referring to private events have never formed a stable and acceptable vocabulary of reasonably uniform usage. This historical fact is puzzling to adherents of the 'correspondence school' of meaning. Why is it not possible to assign names to the diverse elements of private experience and then to proceed with consistent and effective discourse? The answer lies in the process by which 'terms are assigned to private events,' a process which we have just analyzed in a rough way in terms of the reinforcement of verbal responses.

None of the conditions that we have examined permits the sharpening of reference which is achieved, in the case of public stimuli, by a precise contingency of reinforcement. In (1) and (2) the association of public and private events may be faulty; the stimuli embraced by (3) are of limited scope; and the metaphorical nature of those in (4) implies a lack of precision. It is, therefore, impossible to establish a rigorous scientific vocabulary for public use, nor can the speaker clearly 'know himself' in the sense in which knowing is identified with behaving discriminatively. In the absence of the 'crisis' provided by differential reinforcement (much of which is necessarily verbal), private stimuli cannot be analyzed. (This has little or nothing to do with the availability or capacity of receptors.)

The contingencies we have reviewed also fail to provide an adequate check against fictional distortion of the relation of reference (*e.g.*, as in rationalizing). Statements about private events may be under control of the drives associated with their consequences rather than antecedent stimuli. The community is skeptical of statements of this sort, and any attempt by the speaker to talk to himself about his private world (as in psychological system making) is fraught with self-deception.

Much of the ambiguity of psychological terms arises from the possibility of alternative or multiple modes of reinforcement. Consider, for example, the response 'I am hungry.' The community may reinforce this on the basis of the history of ingestion, as in (1), or collateral behavior associated with hunger, as in (2), or as a description of behavior with respect to food, or stimuli previously correlated with food, as in (3). In addition the speaker has (in some instances) the powerful stimulation of hunger pangs, which is private, since the community has no suitable connection with the speaker's stomach. 'I am hungry' may therefore be variously translated as 'I have not eaten for a long time' (1), or 'That food makes my mouth water' (2), or 'I am ravenous' (3) (compare the expression 'I was hungrier than I thought' which describes the ingestion of an unexpectedly large amount of food), or 'I have hunger pangs.' While all of these may be regarded as synonymous with 'I am hungry,' they are not synonymous with each other. It is easy for conflicting psychological systematists to cite supporting instances or to train speakers to emit the response 'I am hungry' in conformity with a system. With the balloon technique one might condition the verbal response exclusively to stimulation from stomach contractions. This would be an example of either (1) or (2) above. Or a speaker might be trained to make nice observations of the strength of his ingestive behavior, which might recede to the covert level as in (3). The response 'I am hungry' would then describe a tendency to eat, with little or no reference to stomach contractions. Everyday usage reflects a mixed reinforcement. A similar analysis could be made of all terms descriptive of motivation, emotion, and action in general, including (of special interest here) the acts of seeing, hearing, and so on.

When public manifestations survive, the extent to which the private stimulus takes over is never certain. In the case of a toothache, the private event is no doubt dominant, but this is due to its relative intensity, not to any condition of differential reinforcement. In a description of one's own behavior, the private component may be much less important. A very strict external contingency may emphasize the public component, especially if the association with private events is faulty. In a rigorous scientific vocabulary private effects are practically eliminated. The converse does not hold. There is apparently no way of basing a response entirely upon the private part of a complex of stimuli. *A differential reinforcement cannot be made contingent upon the property of privacy*. This fact is of extraordinary importance in evaluating traditional psychological terms.

The response 'red' is imparted and maintained (either casually or professionally) by reinforcements which are contingent upon a certain property of stimuli. Both speaker and community (or psychologist) have access to the stimulus, and the contingency may be made quite precise. There is nothing about the resulting response that should puzzle anyone. The greater part of psychophysics rests upon this solid footing. The older psychological view, however, was that the speaker was reporting, not a property of the stimulus, but a certain kind of private event, the sensation of red. This was regarded as a later stage in a series beginning with the red stimulus. The experimenter was supposed to manipulate the private event by manipulating the stimulus. This seems like a gratuitous distinction, but in the case of some subjects a similar later stage could apparently be generated in other ways (by arousing an 'image'), and hence the autonomy of a private event capable of evoking the response 'red' in the absence of a controllable red stimulus seemed to be proved. An adequate proof, of course, requires the elimination of other possibilities (*e.g.*, that the response is generated by the procedures which are intended to generate the image).

Verbal behavior which is 'descriptive of images' must be accounted for in any adequate science of behavior. The difficulties are the same for both behaviorist and subjectivist. If the private events are free, a scientific description is impossible in either case. If laws can be discovered, then a lawful description of the verbal behavior can be achieved, with or without references to images. So much for 'finding the referents'; the remaining problem of how such responses are maintained in relation to their referents is also soluble. The description of an image appears to be an example of a response to a private stimulus of class (1) above. That is to say, relevant terms are established when the private event accompanies a controllable external stimulus, but responses occur at other times, perhaps in relation to the same private event. The deficiencies of such a vocabulary have been pointed out.

We can account for the response 'red' (at least as well as for the 'experience' of red) by appeal to past conditions of reinforcement. But what about expanded expressions like '*I see* red' or '*I am conscious of* red'? Here 'red' may be a response to either a public or a private stimulus without prejudice to the rest of the expression, but 'see' and 'conscious' seem to refer to events which are by nature or by definition private. This violates the principle that a reinforcement cannot be made contingent upon the privacy of a stimulus. A reference cannot be narrowed down to a specifically private event by any known method of differential reinforcement.

The original behavioristic hypothesis was, of course, that terms of this sort were descriptions of one's own (generally covert) behavior. The hypothesis explains the establishment and maintenance of the terms by supplying natural public counterparts in similar overt behavior. The terms are in general of class (3). One consequence of the hypothesis is that each term may be given a behavioral definition. We must, however, modify the argument slightly. To say 'I see red' is to react, not to red (this is a trivial meaning of 'see'), but to one's reaction to red. 'See' is a term acquired with respect to one's own behavior in the case of overt responses available to the community. But according to the present analysis it may be evoked at other times by *any private accompaniment* of overt seeing. Here is a point at which a non-behavioral private seeing may be slipped in. Although the commonest private accompaniment would appear to be the stimulation which survives in a similar covert act, as in (3), it might be some sort of state or condition which gains control of the response as in (1) or (2).

The superiority of the behavioral hypothesis is not merely methodological. That aspect of seeing which can be defined behaviorally is basic to the term as established by the verbal community and hence most effective in public discourse. A comparison of cases (1) and (3) will also show that terms which recede to the private level as overt behavior becomes covert have an optimal accuracy of reference, as responses to private stimuli go.

The additional hypothesis follows quite naturally that being conscious, as a form of reacting to one's own behavior, is a social product. Verbal behavior may be distinguished, and conveniently defined, by the fact that the contingencies of reinforcement are provided by other organisms rather than by a mechanical action upon the environment. The hypothesis is equivalent to saying that it is only because the behavior of the individual is important to society that society in turn makes it important to the individual. The individual becomes aware of what he is doing only after society has reinforced verbal responses with respect to his behavior as the source of discriminative stimuli. The behavior to be described (the behavior of which one is to be aware) may later recede to the covert level, and (to add a crowning difficulty) so may the verbal response. It is an ironic twist, considering the history of the behavioristic revolution, that as we develop a more effective vocabulary for the analysis of behavior we also enlarge the possibilities of awareness, so defined. The psychology of the other one is, after all, a direct approach to 'knowing thyself.'

The main purpose of this discussion has been to answer Question 10 by example. To be consistent the psychologist must deal with his own verbal practices by developing an empirical science of verbal behavior. He cannot, unfortunately, join the logician in defining a definition, for example, as a 'rule for the use of a term' (Feigl); he must turn instead to the contingencies of reinforcement which account for the functional relation between a term, as a verbal response, and a given stimulus. This is the 'operational basis' for his use of terms; and it is not logic but science.

The philosopher will call this circular. He will argue that we must adopt the rules of logic in order to make and interpret the experiments required in an empirical science of verbal behavior. But talking about talking is no more circular than thinking about thinking or knowing about knowing. Whether or not we are lifting ourselves by our own bootstraps, the simple fact is that we *can* make progress in a scientific analysis of verbal behavior. Eventually we shall be able to include, and perhaps to understand, our own verbal behavior as scientists. If it turns out that our final view of verbal behavior invalidates our scientific structure from the point of view of logic and truth-value, then so much the worse for logic, which will also have been embraced by our analysis.

REFERENCES

1. SKINNER, B. F. *The behavior of organisms: an experimental analysis.* New York: D. Appleton-Century Co., 1938.
2. STEVENS, S. S. Psychology and the science of science. *Psychol. Bull.*, 1939, 36, 221–263.

These are the questions. They are referred to in the text by their numbers.

1. (a) What is the purpose of operational definitions? When are they called for?

Since it is obviously impossible to explicate an operational definition for every construct-term used in scientific discussion, there must be some principle which determines when operational definitions are useful.

(b) Logically, operational definitions could form an infinite regress, since the construct-terms used in describing an operation are themselves in need of definition.

How is this regress limited in scientific practice?

2. When the same construct is defined by two independent operations, should it be said that there are really two constructs? For instance, it has been said that tape-measured distance and triangulated distance are really two kinds of distance and should perhaps have different names.

Against this view it can be argued that these are operations for showing the equivalence of operations, *e.g.*, for demonstrating the identity of taped and surveyed short distances.

3. (a) Are hypothetical operations which are physically impossible with present available techniques, of scientific use? Is the other side of the moon what you would see if you went there?

It is arguable that an unperformable operation has value in stating the conditions by which a construct could be validated. Such a statement shows that the construct is not at the moment valid.

(b) Is there a use for hypothetical operations that would define constructs which are actually at the moment nonexistent?

Red and green are supposed to be derived from yellow in the course of evolution. The discriminatory operations which would establish the existence of two new colors, derived similarly from blue, could be stated, although they could not be performed at the present stage of evolutionary development. The operations which would define a new invisible planet are similar.

(c) Is there a use for hypothetical operations which could never be performed?

The definition of infinity depends on operations which can never be completed.

4. Is *experience* a proper construct for operational definition?

It has been held that experience is ultimate, subject to immediate intuition but not to operational definition.

5. Are there scientifically good and bad operations, and how are operations evaluated if they differ in value?

Objectivists hold that the data of experience can always be operationally defined if the data become public, because the operations of publication define the datum. It is, however, argued further that the operations of verbal report are 'poorer' than the operations of discriminatory choice (C.R.; jumping stand) because the verbal response itself involves terms that are less rigorously defined.

6. Is operationism more than a renewed and refined emphasis upon the experimental method (as understood already by Galileo, if not even by Archimedes)—*i.e.*, a formulation of modern scientific empiricism and pragmatism (especially of the Peirce-Dewey variety), mainly of criteria of factual meaningfulness and empirical validity?

7. Must operationists in psychology relegate theorizing of all sorts to the limbo of metaphysics? Bridgman in physics is perfectly aware of the value of theories as long as they are in keeping with his operational requirements. The Gestaltists, particularly Köhler and Koffka, have repeatedly attacked positivism (an identical twin of operationism), reproaching it for its (alleged) opposition to theoretical construction. C. C. Pratt (*Logic of Modern Psychology*, pp. 147–154) on the basis of his operationism maintains that all theoretical explanation is circular or tautological. Köhler (*Dynamics in Psychology*, pp. 107–125) holds a strictly opposite view. Which position is the most adequate for psychological research?

8. Some radical operationists assert that the meaning of a quantitative concept lies exclusively in the set of measuring operations which determine the application of the concept. (*E.g.*: "Intelligence is what the intelligence test tests.") But how can we then know what it is that we are after in constructing tests; and what possible meaning is there in talking about improving or revising tests and measurements if there are no criteria outside the chosen test methods?

9. Are *all* scientifically legitimate definitions operational in character? This is (at least in part) a terminological question, but certainly one that it would pay to settle (not only) among psychologists.

10. What is a definition, operational or otherwise? It is important to know whether one is presupposing a logical apparatus for dealing with the language of science or intending through a psychological analysis to justify such an apparatus.

11. For the purpose of operational definition, what class or classes of events may be used properly as defining-operations? Specifically, can a phenomenon be identified or its properties be defined in terms of the events (operations) which are effective to produce, or occur as results of, the phenomenon?

Hypothetical Constructs and Intervening Variables *

KENNETH MacCORQUODALE
AND PAUL E. MEEHL

As THE THINKING of behavior theorists has become more sophisticated and self-conscious, there has been considerable discussion of the value and logical status of so-called 'intervening variables.' Hull speaks of "symbolic constructs, intervening variables, or hypothetical entities" (5, p. 22) and deals with them in his theoretical discussion as being roughly equivalent notions. At least, his exposition does not distinguish among them explicitly. In his presidential address on behavior at a choice point, Tolman inserts one of Hull's serial conditioning diagrams (11, p. 13) between the independent variables (maintenance schedule, goal object, etc.) and the dependent variable ('behavior ratio') to illustrate his concept of the intervening variable. This would seem to imply that Tolman views his 'intervening variables' as of the same character as Hull's. In view of this, it is somewhat surprising to discover that Skinner apparently feels that his formulations have a close affinity to those of Tolman, but are basically dissimilar to those of Hull (10, p. 436, 437). In advocating a theoretical structure which is 'descriptive' and 'positivistic,' he suggests that the model chosen by Hull (Newtonian mechanics) is not the most suitable model for purposes of behavior theory; and in general is critical of the whole postulate-deductive approach.

Simultaneously with these trends, one can still observe among 'tough-minded' psychologists the use of words such as 'unobservable' and 'hypothetical' in an essentially derogatory manner, and an almost compulsive fear of passing beyond the direct colligation of observable data. 'Fictions' and 'hypothetical entities' are sometimes introduced into a discussion of theory with a degree of trepidation and apology quite unlike the freedom with which physicists talk about atoms, mesons, fields, and the like. There also seems to be a tendency to treat all hypothetical constructs as on the same footing merely because they are hypothetical; so that we find people arguing that if neutrons are admissible in physics, it must be admissible

* Reprinted from *Psychological Review*, 55, 1948, by kind permission of the authors, the *Psychological Review* and the American Psychological Association.

for us to talk about, *e.g.*, the damming up of libido and its reversion to earlier channels.

The view which theoretical psychologists take toward intervening variables and hypothetical constructs will of course profoundly influence the direction of theoretical thought. Furthermore, what *kinds* of hypothetical constructs we become accustomed to thinking about will have a considerable impact upon theory creation. The present paper aims to present what seems to us a major problem in the conceptualization of intervening variables, without claiming to offer a wholly satisfactory solution. Chiefly, it is our aim here to make a distinction between two subclasses of intervening variables, or we prefer to say, between 'intervening variables' and 'hypothetical constructs' which we feel is fundamental but is currently being neglected.

We shall begin with a common-sense distinction, and proceed later to formulations of this distinction which we hope will be more rigorous. Naively, it would seem that there is a difference in logical status between constructs which involve the hypothesization of an *entity*, *process*, or *event* which is not itself observed, and constructs which do not involve such hypothesization. For example, Skinner's 'reflex reserve' is definable in terms of the total available responses without further conditioning, whereas Hull's 'afferent neural interaction' involves the notion of processes within the nervous system which presumably occur within the objective physical system and which, under suitable conditions, we might observe directly. To take examples from another science in which we psychologists may have less stake in the distinction, one might contrast the notion of 'resistance' in electricity to the notion of 'electron.' The resistance of a piece of wire is what Carnap has called a *dispositional concept*, and is defined by a special type of implication relation. When we say that the resistance of a wire is such-and-such, we mean that "so-and-so volts will give a current of so-and-so amperes." (For a more precise formulation of this see Carnap, 3, p. 440.) Resistance, in other words, is 'operational' in a very direct and primitive sense. The electron, on the other hand, is supposedly an *entity* of some sort. Statements about the electron are, to be sure, supported by means of observational sentences. Nevertheless, it is no longer maintained even by positivists that this set of supporting sentences exhaust the entire *meaning* of the sentences about the electron. Reichenbach, for example, distinguishes *abstracta* from *illata* (from Lat. *infero*). The latter are 'inferred things,' such as molecules, other people's minds, and so on. They are believed in on the basis of our impressions, but the sentences involving them, even those asserting their existence, are not reducible to sentences about impressions. This is the epistemological form, at rock bottom level, of the distinction we wish to make here.

The introduction of the word 'entity' in our discussion has served merely to indicate the distinction, but in any crucial case there could be dispute as to whether a stated hypothesis involved the positing of an entity. For instance, is Hull's 'habit strength' an entity or not? Is 'drive' an entity? Is 'super-ego'?

Previous analyses of this difference may enable us to give a somewhat more precise formulation. These two kinds of concepts are variously distinguished by writers on philosophy of science. Feigl (personal communication) refers to *analytic* versus *existential* hypotheses. Benjamin (1) distinguishes between *abstractive* and *hypothetical* methods. In the abstractive or analytic method we merely neglect certain features of experience and group phenomena by a restricted set of properties into classes; relations between such classes can then be discovered empirically, and nothing has been added to the observed in the process. The hypothetical method, on the other hand, relates experiences "by inventing a fictitious substance or process or idea, in terms of which the experiences can be expressed. A hypothesis, in brief, correlates observations by adding something to them, while abstraction achieves the same end by subtracting something" (1, p. 184).

This quotation suggests to us at least three ways of stating the distinction we have in mind. First, it may be pointed out that in the statement of a hypothetical construction, as distinguished from an abstractive one, there occur words (other than the construct name itself) which are not explicitly defined by (or reduced to) the empirical relations. Once having set up sentences (postulates) containing these hypothetical words, we can arrive by deduction at empirical sentences which can themselves be tested. But the words themselves are not defined directly by or reducible to these empirical facts. This is not true of abstractive concepts, such as resistance or solubility or, say, 'drive' as used by Skinner. (We may neglect wholly non-committal words such as *state*, which specify nothing except that the conditions are internal.)

A second apparent difference between abstractive and hypothetical concepts is in their logical relation to the facts, *i.e.*, the observation-sentences and empirical laws which are the basis for believing them. In the case of sentences containing only abstractive concepts, the truth of the empirical laws constitutes *both the necessary and sufficient conditions* for the truth of the abstractive sentences. For sentences involving hypothetical concepts, this is well known to be false. The empirical laws are necessary for the truth of the hypothetical sentences, since the latter imply them; but they are not sufficient. All scientific hypothesizing is in the invalid 'third figure' of the implicative syllogism. We neglect here the impossibility, emphasized by Reichenbach and others, of equating even an abstractive sentence or empirical 'law' to a *finite* number of particular observation sentences; this is of importance to philosophers of science but for help in the understanding of theories is of no particular consequence. We shall be assuming the trustworthiness of induction throughout and hence will treat 'direct' observational laws as universal sentences or as sentential functions. One can deduce empirical laws from sentences involving hypothetical constructs, but not conversely. Thus, beginning with the hypothesis that gases are made up of small particles which obey the laws of mechanics, plus certain approximating assumptions about the relation of their sizes to their distances, their perfect elasticity, and their lack of mutual attraction, one can apply mathematical rules and eventually, by direct substitution and equation, lead without arbitrariness to the empirical equation $PV = K$. However, one cannot rigorously reverse the process. That is, one cannot commence with the empirical gas law $PV = K$ and arrive at the full kinetic theory. The mathematics is reversible, granted that certain arbitrary breakups of constants etc., are permitted; but beginning with the empirical law itself there is no basis for these arbitrary breakups. Furthermore, aside from the equations themselves, there are coordinated with these equations certain existence propositions, and assertions about the properties of the entities hypothesized. We state that there exist certain small particles, that they collide with the walls of the container, that the root mean square of their velocities is proportional to the temperature, etc. These assertions can of course not be deduced from the empirical law relating pressure and volume.

This suggests a third distinction between concepts of the two kinds. In the case of abstractive concepts, the quantitative form of the concept, *e.g.*, a measure of its 'amount,' can be derived directly from the empirical laws simply by grouping of terms. In the case of hypothetical concepts, mere grouping of terms is not sufficient. We are less assured of this distinction than of the other two, but we have not been able to think of any exceptions. It seems to us also that, in the case of Hull, this is the point which makes our distinction between hypothetical constructs and intervening variables most obvious. Let us therefore consider Hull's equations as an example.

In *Principles of Behavior*, the influence of certain independent variables such as number of reinforcements, delay in reward, stimulus-response asynchronism, etc., upon response strength is experimentally investigated. In the study of the influence of each of these, the other independent variables are held constant. The experimental findings lead to the formulation of the separate laws of dependence as a set of growth and decay functions. We shall neglect for the moment the complication of drive and of all other variables which intervene between the construct ${}_sH_r$ and the empirical measure of response. That is to say, we shall deal only with the variables introduced in Hull's Postulate 4. The mathematical statement of Postulate 4 is

$${}_sH_r = M(1-e^{-kw})e^{-jt}e^{-ut'}(1-e^{-iN}). \quad (5, \text{p. } 178)$$

This equation asserts that habit strength is a certain joint function of four variables which refer to direct empirical quantities—number of reinforcements, delay in reinforcement, amount of reinforcement, and asynchronism between the discriminative stimuli and the response. It is important to see that in this case Hull does not distinguish the four experimentally separated laws combined in the equation by separate concept-names; the only intervening variable introduced is habit strength, which is written as an explicit function of four empirical variables w, t, t', and N. It would be quite possible to introduce an intervening variable referring to, say, the last bracket only; it might be called 'cumulative reinforcement' and it would be a function of only one empirical variable, N. This would be the most reasonable breakdown of habit strength inasmuch as the other three growth functions (two negative) serve merely to modify the asymptote M (5, p. 181). That is to say, given a certain (maintained) rule for the amount of reinforcement given and two time-specifications concerning the constant relation of the response to two other operations, we have determined a parameter m for a dynamic curve describing the course of acquisition of habit strength. The quantity $(1-e^{-iN})$ (which we are here calling 'cumulative reinforcement') is then an intervening variable which is multiplied by the parameter m in order to determine the value of habit strength after N reinforcements have occurred.

Suppose now that a critic asks us whether our 'cumulative reinforcement' really *exists*. This amounts to asking whether we have formulated a 'correct statement' concerning the relation of this intervening variable to the anchoring (empirical) variables. For since the statement of 'existence' for the intervening variable is so far confined to the equations above, the 'existence' of cumulative reinforcement reduces strictly to the second question. And this second question, as to whether the statement about the intervening variable's relation to the facts is correct, is in turn equivalent to the question, "Are the empirical variables related in such-and-such a way?" In other words, to confirm the equation for habit strength, it is merely necessary to state that (as Hull assumes in his earlier chapters) with drive, etc., constant, some empirical measure of response strength R is a linear function of habit strength. Then we can write directly,

$$R = C({}_sH_r) = C \cdot F(w)G(t)H(t')J(N) = Q(w, t, t', N).$$

To confirm or disconfirm this equation is a direct empirical matter. It is possible to multiply out the bracketed quantities in various combinations, so as to make the arbitrary groupings disappear; what will mathematically persist through all such regroupings will be the rather complicated joint function Q of the four empirical variables w, t, t', and N. By various arbitrary groupings and combinations we could define 15 alternative and equivalent sets of intervening variables. Thus, we might multiply out three of the four brackets in the basic equation but for some reason choose to put $e^{-ut'}$ separately into the denominator. This would give us

$$R = \frac{F(w, t, N)}{e^{ut'}}$$

as the particular form for our empirical relation. $F(w, t, N)$ could then be given an appropriate 'intervening variable' name, and the stimulus-response asynchronism t' would then define an intervening variable $e^{ut'}$.

It may be objected that 'habit strength' presumably refers to some state of the organism which *is* set up by reinforcing N times under specified conditions; whereas $e^{ut'}$ cannot refer to any such state. This seems plausible; but the point is that to establish it as a state, it would be necessary to coordinate to the groupings within equations certain existence propositions, *i.e.*, propositions that do *more* than define a term by saying "Let the quantity $G(x, y, z)$, where x, y, z are empirical variables, be designated by the phrase so-and-so." This setting up of existence propositions could presumably be done even for a quantity such as $e^{ut'}$, by referring to such hypothetical processes as, say, diminishing traces in the neural reverberation circuits activated by a certain discriminative stimulus.

In the above example we have considered the fractionation of the intervening variable ${}_sH_r$ into others. This reasoning can also be extended in the upward direction, *i.e.*, in the direction of fusion rather than fractionation. Let us treat 'habit strength' as Hull would treat our 'cumulative reinforcement,' by not giving it a name at all. It is still possible to set up equations to fit the Perin-Williams data (5, p. 229, 255) without referring to habit strength, writing merely

$$n = F(N, h),$$

where N and h are again both purely empirical variables.

We do not mean to imply that the divisions made by Hull (or Tolman) are of no value. It is convenient to have some term to refer to the result of a certain maintenance schedule, instead of having to say "that part of the general multivariable equation of response strength which contains '*hours since eating to satiety*' as an independent variable." We merely wish to emphasize that in the case of Hull's intervening variables, it is both necessary and sufficient for the truth of his 'theory' about the intervening variables that the empirical facts should be as his equations specify. The latter are merely names attached to certain convenient groupings of terms in his empirically fitted equations. It is always possible to coordinate to these quantities, which as written mathematically contain parameters and experimental variables only, certain existence propositions which would automatically make the construct 'hypothetical' rather than 'abstractive.' This giving of what Reichenbach calls 'surplus meaning' automatically destroys the equivalence between the empirical laws and the theoretical construct. When habit strength *means* the product of the four functions of w, t, t' and N, then if the response strength is related to these empirical variables in the way described, habit strength 'exists' in the trivial sense that the law holds. Our confidence in the 'correctness' of the intervening variable formulation is precisely as great as our confidence in the laws.

When, however, habit strength means not merely this product of empirical functions but something more of a neural or other physiological nature, then the theory could be false even if the empirical relations hold.

It seems to us that Tolman himself, in using one of Hull's serial conditioning diagrams as a set of intervening variables (11, p. 13), departs from his original definition. He has first described the situation in which the 'behavior ratio' is a complex function f_1 of the independent experimental variables. He goes on to say,

"A theory, as I shall conceive it, is a set of intervening variables. These to-be-inserted intervening variables are 'constructs' which we, the theorists, evolve as a useful way of breaking down into more manageable form the original complete f_1 function" (11, p. 9).

His reason for introducing intervening variables does not seem to us very cogent as he states it. He says that empirically establishing the form of f_1 to cover the effects on behavior of all the permutations and combinations of the independent variables would be a 'humanly endless task.' If this means that all of the verifying instances of a continuous mathematical function cannot be empirically achieved it is true; but that is equally true for a function of one variable only. In order to utilize the proposed relationship between Tolman's function f_3 (11, p. 10) which describes the relation of the behavior to the intervening variables, it is still necessary to establish empirically that the relationship holds—which amounts essentially to trying several of the infinitely many permutations and combinations (as in the Perin-Williams study) until we are inductively satisfied by ordinary scientific standards.

However cogent the arguments for intervening variables may be, it seems clear from Tolman's description that they are what we are calling *abstractive* rather than *hypothetical.* His notion of them involves nothing which is not in the empirical laws that support them. (We may speak of 'laws' here in the plural in spite of there being just the single function f_1, just as Boyle's and Charles' laws are distinguished in addition to the more general gas law $PV/T = R$.) For Tolman, the merit of an intervening variable is of a purely 'summarizing' character. One can determine the function f_1 by parts, so to speak (11, p. 17), so that the effect of a given maintenance schedule upon one part of f_1 may be referred to conveniently as *drive.* For a given drive, we can expect such-and-such behavior ratios in a diversity of situations defined by various combinations of the other independent variables.

It has been observed earlier that in introducing one of Hull's well-known serial conditioning diagrams as an example of intervening variables outside Tolman's own system, we see a departure from the definition Tolman gives. The Hull diagrams contain symbols such as r_g (fractional anticipatory goal response) and s_g (the proprioceptive impulses produced by the movements constituting r_g). These symbols refer to hypothetical processes within the organism, having an allegedly real although undetermined neuromuscular locus. These events are in principle directly observable. In fact, here the case for speaking of an objective reality is even stronger than Reichenbach's examples of electrons, molecules, etc.; since even the criterion of *technical* verifiability, admitted by all positivists to be too strong a restriction, would not exclude these hypotheses as empirically meaningless. Even without penetrating the organism's skin we have some direct observational evidence of r_g in the work of Miller (7). Whether r_g occurs and actually plays the role described is not relevant here; the point is that the diagrams and verbal explanations of Hull involve the supposition that it does. He assumes the existence of certain processes which are not logically implied by the empirical laws in the sense of strict equivalence. Even if, by using the notion of fractional anticipatory goal response, Hull deduced all of the empirical laws relating independent and dependent variables, alternative hypotheses could be offered. Because of the 'surplus meaning' contained in concepts like r_g and s_g, these concepts are not really 'anchored' to the facts in the sense implied by Tolman's definition of intervening variables or by Hull's diagram on page 22 of the *Principles*. Hull states in reference to this diagram,

> When an intervening variable is thus securely anchored to observables on both sides it can be safely employed in scientific theory (5, p. 22).

We presume that Hull means in this statement that the anchoring in question is not only a sufficient but a necessary condition for scientific admissibility. We feel that the criterion is too strong, assuming that the structure of modern physical science is to be allowed. This sort of anchoring makes the intervening variable strictly reducible to the empirical laws, which is, to be sure, what Tolman's original definition implied. But it excludes such extremely fruitful hypotheses as Hull's own fractional anticipatory goal responses, for which the strict reducibility does not exist.

It occurs to us also in this connection that Hull seems to have moved in the direction of Skinner and Tolman in his treatment of intervening variables. The use of the postulate-theorem approach is maintained more as a form in the *Principles* than as an actual instrument of discovery. In this respect, the *Principles* is much less like Hull's Newtonian model than was the *Mathematico-deductive theory of rote learning*. The justification of 'postulates' in the usual sense is their ability to mediate deductions of empirical laws which are then verified. In the *Principles*, the 'postulates' are verified directly, by the experimental device of holding all variables constant except the one for which we want to find a law. This is quite unlike the derivation of the gas law in physics. The only sense in which any postulates are 'assumed' is in the assumption, referred to by Hull on page 181 of the *Principles*, that the separately verified parts of Postulate 4 will in fact operate according to his equation 16 when combined. This is certainly a 'postulate' only in a very attenuated sense, since it amounts essentially to an empirical extrapolation which can be verified directly, as Hull suggests.

At this point any distinction between the type of theory advocated by Hull and that advocated by Skinner or Tolman would seem to disappear, except for the relatively non-contributory 'neural' references contained in the verbal statement of Hull's postulates. Insofar as this neural reference is taken seriously, however, we are still dealing with concepts of a hypothetical rather than abstractive character. There are various places in Hull's *Principles* where the verbal accompaniment of a concept, which in its mathematical form is an intervening variable in the strict (Tolman) sense, makes it a hypothetical construct. Thus, the operational definition of a *pav* of inhibition (5, p. 281) would seem merely to mean that when we know from the independent variables that the combined habit strength and drive, together with a discriminative stimulus located so many j.n.d.'s from the original, would yield a reaction potential of so many *wats*, it requires an equal number of *pavs* of inhibition to yield an effective reaction potential of zero. However, in the accompanying verbal discussion (5, p. 281) Hull refers to the removal of the inhibitory substance by the blood stream passing through effector organs as determining the quantitative law of spontaneous loss of inhibition as a function of time. 'Afferent neural interaction' is another example of a concept which is mathematically represented as a relation of intervening variables in Tolman's sense, but to which are coordinated verbal statements that convey the surplus meaning and make it an hypothesis.

The question might be raised, whether this is not always the difference—that the mathematical assertions are definitive of intervening variables but the verbal additions lend the hypothetical character to such concepts. We do not believe this is the essential difference. There are mathematical expressions whose meaning is not defined in the absence of verbal existential accompaniment, because the quantities involved refer to non-observational (*i.e.*, hypothetical) processes or entities. There are other mathematical expressions for which this is not true, since their component symbols have direct observational reference. In the case of our 'cumulative reinforcement' term $(1 - e^{-iN})$, no coordinated existential proposition is required. We simply say, "Response probability is such-and-such a multivariate function of such-and-such experimental variables. Within this function can be isolated a simple growth function of one variable, whose value as a function of N is referred to as *cumulative reinforcement*." This may be taken as an adequate reference for $(1 - e^{-iN})$. On the other hand, in the derivation of the law $PV = K$ there occur statements such as "When the gas is maintained at the same temperature, $mv^2/2$ does not change." Neither m nor v is an empirical variable. This statement does not tell us anything *until* we are informed that v refers to the velocity which each molecule of the gas could be assumed to have in order that their mean kinetic energy should be what it is. In other words, in the derivation of the gas laws from kinetic theory there occur mathematical assertions whose meaning is unclear without the accompanying existence assertions, and *which cannot be utilized to take the subsequent mathematical steps in the chain of inferences unless these assertions are included.* Thus, to get from a purely mathematical statement that a molecule on impact conserves all of its momentum, to a mathematical statement whose terms refer to the empirical concept of 'pressure on the walls,' it is necessary to know (from the accompanying verbal description) that in the equations of derivation, m refers to the mass of a hypothetical particle that strikes the wall, v to its velocity, and so on. This example shows that some mathematical formulations are themselves incomplete in the sense that they cannot mediate the desired deductions unless certain existential propositions are stated alongside, so as to render certain necessary substitutions and equations legitimate. Therefore it is not merely the matter of mathematical form that distinguishes a 'pure' intervening variable from a hypothesis.

In the second place, it seems to us that the use of verbal statements without mathematical formulations does not guarantee that we are dealing with a hypothetical construct rather than an intervening variable. Consider Skinner's definition of emotion as a 'state of the organism' which alters the proportionality between reserve and strength. This is not defined as a direct proportionality, and in fact Skinner nowhere deals with its quantitative form. No mathematical statement is given by him; yet we would contend that the use of the word 'state' does not in any way make the notion of emotion existential, any more than drive is existential in Skinner's usage. The 'state' of emotion is not to be described in any way except by specifying (a) The class of stimuli which are able to produce it and (b) The effects upon response strength. Hence emotion for Skinner is a true intervening variable, in Tolman's original sense. We conclude from these examples that whether a given concept is abstractive or hypothetical is not merely a matter of whether it is an equation with or without accompanying verbal exposition.

On the basis of these considerations, we are inclined to propose a linguistic convention for psychological theorists which we feel will help to clarify discussion of these matters. We suggest that the phrase 'intervening variable' be restricted to the original use implied by Tolman's definition. Such a variable will then be simply a quantity obtained by a specified manipulation of the values of empirical variables; it will involve no hypothesis as to the existence of nonobserved entities or the occurrence of unobserved processes; it will contain, in its complete statement for all purposes of theory and prediction, no words which are not definable either explicitly or by reduction sentences in terms of the empirical variables; and the validity of empirical laws involving only observables will constitute both the necessary and sufficient conditions for the validity of the laws involving these intervening variables. Legitimate instances of such 'pure' intervening variables are Skinner's *reserve*, Tolman's *demand*, Hull's *habit strength*, and Lewin's *valence*. These constructs are the behavioral analogue of Carnap's 'dispositional concepts' such as solubility, resistance, inflammability, etc. It must be emphasized that the setting up of a definition or reduction for an intervening variable is not a wholly arbitrary and conventional matter. As Carnap has pointed out, it often happens that we give alternative sets of reduction sentences for the same dispositional concept; in these cases there is empirical content in our statement even though it has a form that suggests arbitrariness. The reason for this is that these separate reductions for a given dispositional concept imply that the empirical events are themselves related in a certain way. The notion of amount of electric current can be introduced by several different observations, such as deposition of silver, deflection of a needle, hydrogen separated out of water, and so on. Such a set of reductions has empirical content because the empirical statements together with the reductions must not lead to contradictions. It is a contingent fact, not derivable from definitions alone, that the deposition of silver will give the same answer for 'amount of current' as will the deflection of a needle. A similar problem exists in Hull, when he sets up 'momentary effective reaction potential' as the last intervening variable in his chain. In the case of striated muscle reactions, it is stated that latency, resistance to extinction, and probability of occurrence of a response are all functions of reaction potential. Neglecting behavior oscillation, which does not occur in the formulation for the second two because they involve many repetitions of the situation, this means that the empirical variables must be perfectly correlated (non-linearly, of course). The only possible source of variation which could attenuate a perfect correlation between probability of occurrence and resistance to extinction would be actual errors of experimental measurement, since there are no sources of uncontrolled variation left within the organism. If we consider average latency instead of momentary latency (which is a function of *momentary* effective reaction potential and hence varies with behavioral oscillation), latency and resistance to extinction should also be perfectly correlated. It remains to be seen whether the fact will support Hull in giving simultaneously several reductions for the notion of reaction potential.

As a second linguistic convention, we propose that the term 'hypothetical construct' be used to designate theoretical concepts which do *not* meet the requirements for intervening variables in the strict sense. That is to say, these constructs involve terms which are not wholly reducible to empirical terms; they refer to processes or entities that are not directly observed (although they need not be in principle unobservable); the mathematical expression of them cannot be formed simply by a suitable grouping of terms in a direct empirical equation; and the truth of the empirical laws involved is a necessary but not a sufficient condition for the truth of these conceptions. Examples of such constructs are Guthrie's M.P.S.'s, Hull's r_g's, S_d's, and *afferent neural interaction*, Allport's *biophysical traits*, Murray's *regnancies*, the notion of 'anxiety' as used by Mowrer, Miller, and Dollard and others of the Yale-derived group, and most theoretical constructs in psychoanalytic theory. Skinner and Tolman seem to be almost wholly free of hypothetical constructs, although when Skinner invokes such notions as the 'strain on the reserve' (10, p. 289) it is difficult to be sure.

We do not wish to seem to legislate usage, so that if the broader use of 'intervening variable' has become stuck in psychological discourse, we would propose alternatively a distinction between intervening variables of the 'abstractive' and of the 'hypothetical' kind. Since our personal preference is for restricting the phrase *intervening variables* to the pure type described by Tolman, we shall follow this convention in the remainder of the present paper.

The validity of intervening variables as we define them cannot be called into question except by an actual denial of the empirical facts. If, for example, Hull's proposed 'grand investigation' of the Perin-Williams type should be carried out and the complex hyperspatial surface fitted adequately over a wide range of values (5, p. 181), it would be meaningless to reject the concept of 'habit strength' and still admit the empirical findings. For this reason, the only consideration which can be raised with respect to a given proposed intervening variable, when an initial defining or reduction equation is being written for it, is the question of convenience.

In the case of hypothetical constructs, this is not so clear. Science is pursued for many reasons, not the least of which is *n Cognizance.*† Since hypothetical constructs assert the existence of entities and the occurrence of events not reducible to the observable, it would seem to some of us that it is the business of a hypothetical construct to be 'true.' It is possible to advance scientific knowledge by taking a completely 'as if' attitude toward such matters, but there are always those whose theoretical-cognitive need dictates that existential propositions should correspond to what is in fact the case. Contemporary philosophy of science, even as represented by those who have traditionally been most cautious about discussing 'truth' and most highly motivated to reduce it to the experiential, gives psychologists no right to be dogmatic about the 'as if' interpretation of theoretical knowledge (*cf.* especially Carnap, 4, p. 598, Kaufmann, 6, p. 35, Russell, 9, Introduction and Chapter XXI, and Reichenbach, 8, *passim*). We would find it rather difficult to defend the ingenious conditioning hypotheses developed in Hull's series of brilliant papers (1929–) in the *Psychological Review* on the ground that they merely provide a "convenient shorthand summarization of the facts" or are of value in the 'practical manipulation' of the rat's behavior. We suspect that Professor Hull himself was motivated

† [The term is H. A. Murray's, defined as "(Inquiring attitude). To explore (moving and touching). To ask questions. To satisfy curiosity. To look, listen, inspect. To read and seek knowledge." *Explorations in Personality*, Oxford University Press, New York, 1949, p. 744. Editors' note.]

to write these articles because he considered that the hypothetical events represented in his diagrams may have actually *occurred* and that the occurrence of these events represents the underlying truth about the learning phenomena he dealt with. In terms of practical application, much (if not most) of theoretical psychology is of little value. If we exclude the interesting anecdotes of Guthrie, contemporary learning theory is not of much use to school teachers. As a *theoretical* enterprise, it may fairly be demanded of a theory of learning that those elements which are 'hypothetical' in the present sense have some probability of being in correspondence with the actual events underlying the behavior phenomena, *i.e.*, that the assertions about hypothetical constructs be true.[1]

Another consideration may be introduced here from the standpoint of future developments in scientific integration. Even those of us who advocate the pursuit of behavioral knowledge on its own level and for its own sake must recognize that some day the 'pyramid of the sciences' will presumably catch up with us. For Skinner, this is of no consequence, since his consistent use of intervening variables in the strict sense genuinely frees him from neurophysiology and in fact makes it possible for him to impose certain conditions upon neurophysiological explanations (10, pp. 429–431). Since he hypothesizes nothing about the character of the inner events, no finding about the inner events could prove disturbing to him. At most, he would be able to say that a given discovery of internal processes must not be complete because it cannot come to terms with his (empirical) laws. But for those theorists who do not confine themselves to intervening variables in the strict sense, neurology will some day become relevant. For this reason it is perhaps legitimate, even now, to require of a hypothetical construct that it should not be manifestly unreal in the sense that it assumes inner events that cannot conceivably occur. The 'as if' kinds of argument sometimes heard from more sophisticated exponents of psychoanalytic views often seem to ignore this consideration. A concept like *libido* or *censor* or *super-ego* may be introduced initially as though it is to be an intervening variable; or even less, it is treated as a merely conventional designation for a class of observable properties or occurrences. But somewhere in the course of theoretical discussion, we find that these words are being used as hypothetical constructs instead. We find that the libido has acquired certain hydraulic properties, or as in Freud's former view, that

[1] It is perhaps unnecessary to add that in adopting this position we do not mean to defend any form of metaphysical realist thesis. The ultimate 'reality' of the world in general is not the issue here; the point is merely that the reality of hypothetical constructs like the atom, from the standpoint of their logical relation to grounds, is not essentially different from that attributed to stones, chairs, other people, and the like. When we say that hypothetical constructs involve the notion of 'objective existence' of actual processes and entities within the organism, we mean the same sort of objective existence, defined by the same ordinary criteria, that is meant when we talk about the objective existence of Singapore. The present discussion operates within the common framework of empirical science and common sense and is intended to be metaphysically neutral.

the 'energy' of libido has been converted into 'anxiety.' What began as a name for an intervening variable is finally a name for a 'something' which has a host of causal properties. These properties are not made explicit initially, but it is clear that the concept is to be used in an explanatory way which requires that the properties exist. Thus, libido may be introduced by an innocuous definition in terms of the 'set of sexual needs' or a 'general term for basic strivings.' But subsequently we find that certain puzzling phenomena are *deduced* ('explained') by means of the various properties of libido, *e.g.*, that it flows, is dammed up, is converted into something else, tends to regress to earlier channels, adheres to things, makes its 'energy' available to the ego, and so on. It is naive to object to such formulations simply on the ground that they refer to unobservables, or are 'hypothetical,' or are not 'statistical.' None of these objections is a crucial one for any scientific construct, and if such criteria were applied a large and useful amount of modern science would have to be abandoned. The fundamental difficulty with such theories is two-fold. First, as has been implied by our remarks, there is the failure explicitly to announce the postulates concerning existential properties, so that these are introduced more or less surreptitiously and *ad hoc* as occasion demands. Secondly, by this device there is subtly achieved a transition from admissible intervening variables to inadmissible hypothetical constructs. These hypothetical constructs, unlike intervening variables, are inadmissible because they acquire the existence of entities and the occurrence of processes which cannot be seriously believed because of other knowledge.

In the case of libido, for instance, we may use such a term legitimately as a generic name for a class of empirical events or properties, or as an intervening variable. But the allied sciences of anatomy and physiology impose restrictions upon our use of it as a hypothetical construct. Even admitting the immature state of neurophysiology in terms of its relation to complex behavior, it must be clear that the central nervous-system does not in fact contain pipes or tubes with fluid in them, and there are no known properties of nervous tissue to which the hydraulic properties of libido could correspond. Hence, this part of a theory about 'inner events' is likely to remain metaphorical. For a genuine intervening variable, there is no metaphor because all is merely shorthand summarization. For hypothetical constructs, there is a surplus meaning that is existential. We would argue that dynamic explanations utilizing hypothetical constructs ought not to be of such a character that they *have* to remain only metaphors.

Of course, this judgment in itself involves a 'best guess' about the future. A hypothetical construct which seems inherently metaphorical may involve a set of properties to which hitherto undiscovered characteristics of the nervous system correspond. So long as the propositions about the construct are not stated in the *terms* of the next lower discipline, it is always a possibility that the purely formal or relational content of the construct will find an isomorphism in such characteristics. For scientific theories this is enough, since here, as in physics, the associated mechanical imagery of the theorist is irrelevant. The tentative rejection of libido would then be based upon the belief that no neural process is likely to have the *combination* of formal properties required. Strictly speaking, this is always problematic when the basic science is incomplete.[2]

Summary

1. At present the phrases 'intervening variable' and 'hypothetical construct' are often used interchangeably, and theoretical discourse often fails to distinguish what we believe are two rather different notions. We suggest that a failure to separate these leads to fundamental confusions. The distinction is between constructs which merely abstract the empirical relationships (Tolman's original intervening variables) and those constructs which are 'hypothetical' (*i.e.*, involve the supposition of entities or processes not among the observed).

2. Concepts of the first sort seem to be identifiable by three characteristics. First, the statement of such a concept does not contain any words which are not reducible to the empirical laws. Second, the validity of the empirical laws is both necessary and sufficient for the 'correctness' of the statements about the concept. Third, the quantitative expression of the concept can be obtained without mediate inference by suitable groupings of terms in the quantitative empirical laws.

3. Concepts of the second sort do not fulfil any of these three conditions. Their formulation involves words not wholly reducible to the words in the empirical laws; the validity of the empirical laws is not a sufficient condition for the truth of the concept, inasmuch as it contains surplus meaning; and the quantitative form of the concept is not obtainable simply by grouping empirical terms and functions.

4. We propose a linguistic convention in the interest of clarity: that the phrase *intervening variable* be restricted to concepts of the first kind, in harmony with Tolman's original definition; and that the phrase *hypothetical construct* be used for those of the second kind.

5. It is suggested that the only rule for proper intervening variables is that of convenience, since they have no factual content surplus to the empirical functions they serve to summarize.

6. In the case of hypothetical constructs, they have a cognitive, factual reference in addition to the empirical data which constitute their support. Hence, they ought to be held to a more stringent requirement in so far as our interests are theoretical. Their actual existence should be compatible with general knowledge and particularly with whatever relevant knowledge exists at the next lower level in the explanatory hierarchy.

[2] We are indebted to Dr. Herbert Feigl for a clarification of this point.

REFERENCES

1. Benjamin, A. C. *An introduction to the philosophy of science.* New York: Macmillan, 1937.
2. Carnap, R. Testability and meaning, Parts I–III. *Phil. Sci.*, 1936, 3, 419–471.
3. Carnap, R. Testability and meaning, Part IV. *Phil. Sci.*, 1937, 4, 1–40.
4. ——. Remarks on induction and truth. *Phil. & phenomenol. res.*, 1946, 6, 590–602.
5. Hull, C. L. *Principles of behavior.* New York: Appleton-Century, 1943.
6. Kaufmann, F. *Methodology in the social sciences.* London: Oxford University Press, 1944.
7. Miller, N. E. A reply to 'Sign-Gestalt or conditioned reflex.' *Psychol. Rev.*, 1935, 42, 280–292.
8. Reichenbach, H. *Experience and prediction.* Chicago: University of Chicago Press, 1938.
9. Russell, B. *Inquiry into meaning and truth.* New York: Norton, 1940.
10. Skinner, B. F. *Behavior of organisms.* New York: Appleton-Century, 1938.
11. Tolman, E. C. The determiners of behavior at a choice point. *Psychol. Rev.*, 1938, 45, 1–41.

The Mind-Body Problem in the Development of Logical Empiricism*

HERBERT FEIGL

THE CLUSTER OF puzzles and perplexities that constitute the Mind-Body-Problem of modern philosophy owes its origin to a great variety of motives and considerations. The central issue, however, may justly be located in the disputes between Dualism and Monism. The dualistic doctrines have a twofold root: Firstly, there are the mythological, animistic, theological, and religious-moral contentions as to the sharp distinction, if not actual separability, of the mental and the physical. The deep-seated and culturally fairly widespread wishful belief in some form of survival after bodily death, as well as the exaltation of the spirit and the deprecation of the flesh in so many eastern and western religions and moral codes may be regarded as the emotional root of dualism. The other, scientific, root of dualism may be found in the rise of science, most prominently beginning with the seventeenth century, although at least adumbrated in ancient thought. The striking success of the method of the physical sciences was, at least historically, contingent upon a clear-cut division of the physical and the mental, and the relegation of the latter to the limbo of a sort of secondary or epiphenomenal existence. But the development of modern psycho-physics and psycho-physiology from the nineteenth century on, culminating in present-day neuro-physiology, Gestalt-psychology, psycho-somatic medicine, and cybernetics, has revived the interest in monistic interpretations. One discrepant tendency may of course be seen in the dualistic claims of the researchers in the still highly questionable fields of Parapsychology (extra-sensory perception, psychokinesis, etc.). Another and very different kind of opposition comes from philosophers of various schools who either on the basis of their metaphysical commitments or simply in the name of clear thinking insist that the physical and the mental are *toto genere* and irreconcilably distinct and different, so that any monistic attempts at their identification must be rejected on purely logical grounds.

This is not the place to review even in outline the history of dualistic and monistic arguments and systems from Descartes and Spinoza down to

* Reprinted with their kind permission from *Revue Internationale de Philosophie*, 4, 1950.

our time. Two notable conclusions seem to emerge from a study of this history:

1. The clarification of the badly tangled issues requires as an indispensable first step the discrimination between the factual and the logical questions involved in the mind-body-problem. The factual questions depend for their solution on the progress of scientific research, such as in psychophysiology. The philosopher *qua* logical analyst has no business either imaginatively to anticipate or dogmatically to endorse hypotheses that can be established only by painstaking empirical investigations. Since the philosopher is concerned with the analysis of meanings, he can at best examine the consistency of various hypotheses and clarify their precise content by an examination of their logical implications.

2. It is evident that different thinkers have been impressed with different aspects of the very complex problem of the relations of the mental and the physical. Descartes was puzzled with the question how something of the nature of a non-spatial substance (thinking) could be causally related with a spatial substance (matter). Some philosophers of the nineteenth and twentieth centuries tried to tackle another "spatial" problem: the location of sense data. Still others have tried to account for the difference of the mental and the physical in terms of the distinctions of the qualitative and the quantitative or of content and structure. Some were intrigued with the "private" character of consciousness and the "public" character of behavior and of neurophysiological processes. Others again, found in the "meaningful," "intentional," "referential" nature of mental states an insuperable obstacle to the attempted identification with "blind" brain-states. Similar objections arose out of the considerations of "purpose," "free choice," "reason" on the mental side as juxtaposed with "mechanism," "determinism," "cause" on the physical side. Normative and critical predications (like "correct," and "incorrect," "success" and "failure," "responsible" and "irresponsible," "justified" and "unjustified," (morally) "right" and "wrong," etc.,) seem to apply meaningfully only to minds, mental states, attitudes or functions but not to physical things, processes or events.

This list of juxtapositions, which could easily be expanded, may serve as a reminder that any present-day advocate of monism (in the sense of an identity-theory) is confronted with a considerable task. Recent naturalistic philosophical and psychological movements, such as positivism, pragmatism, neo-realism, critical realism, behaviorism and some phases of analytic philosophy, have in one way or another attempted various resolutions of the puzzles posed by the apparent incompatibilities of the essential features of the mental and the physical. A good many of the traditional questions in the total complex of the problem have fairly generally been recognized as pseudo-problems, arising out of conceptual confusions. This may be asserted with assurance in the case of the free choice *vs.* determinism perplexity. Almost equally definite seem to me the clarifications of the problems of spatial localization, of emergent novelty and of teleology. The proper view of the referential, normative and critical functions of "mind" or "reason" depends on an adequate formulation of rule-guided behavior. Although a good deal of work along these lines is still required, it is evident even now that some of these questions pertain not so much to the distinction of the mental and the physical, but rather to that of logical structure to psychological (or behavioral) fact. Common to all these issues, however, is the irrepressible and most controversial question: In which sense is the identification of the mental and the physical to be understood? It is interesting to note that Logical Empiricism in the twenty-five years of its career since its beginnings in the Vienna Circle has in succession embraced three different monistic views and has temporarily countenanced also a more agnostic (parallelistic) form of dualism. In recent years Logical Empiricists have prepared a return to their first monistic position, however, reformulated in a more cautious and therefore more auspicious manner. In connection with the very brief review of the four previous positions that I am now going to present, it must be kept in mind that the affinities these positions display with the more traditional metaphysical doctrines are, on the whole, more of the nature of historical analogies than genuine identities of theoretical import. Logical empiricists have from the beginning disclaimed any intention of pronouncing ontological truths. Their sole concern has been the analysis of language and meaning. It was precisely on the basis of such reflections that ontologies of *all* sorts were declared as devoid of factual meaning. The metaphysicians, understandably hurt in their pride and unconvinced by the negativism of the positivists, kept reading into the logical analysis of the latter all the traditional tenets and categories. As already admitted, the flavor of the traditional monisms (or of parallelism) was there, but only historically-culturally speaking. The first position, for example, can easily be regarded as a double-aspect, or double knowledge, view of the type held by critical realism. This was Schlick's [1] outlook before the formation of the Vienna Circle, i.e., before the impact of the ideas of Carnap and Wittgenstein.[2] However, even anticipating the later emphases of logical positivism Schlick regarded the difference of the mental and the physical as a difference between two conceptual systems, of which the physical, as a matter of fundamental empirical fact, is universally applicable, whereas the psychological pertains only to a small part of the total realm of reality. This early point of view is therefore more appropriately characterized as a "double-language" theory.

With the first phase of logical positivism, most markedly represented

[1] M. Schlick, *Allgemeine Erkenntnislehre*, 2nd ed., Springer, Berlin, 1925.

[2] This widely held position may be traced back to Spinoza, and is represented in various metaphysical versions also by Leibniz (in a certain sense also by Kant), Schopenhauer, Fechner, Clifford, Riehl, Paulsen, the American monistic critical realists, especially R. W. Sellars, D. Drake, C. A. Strong; by one phase of B. Russell's thought; by R. Ruyer in France; by the psychologists Ebbinghaus, M. Prince, Warren; the Gestalt psychologists, especially Köhler and Koffka; by L. T. Troland, E. G. Boring, C. K. Ogden, and others.

by Carnap's "*Der Logische Aufbau der Welt*," the rational reconstruction of empirical knowledge was pursued on a phenomenalistic basis. It is therefore not surprising that metaphysicians misinterpreted this approach as a revival of a Berkeleyan subjective idealism. While Carnap explicitly disavowed any claims regarding the ultimate reality-problems of the mental and the physical, he shared of course with Berkeley, Hume, Condillac, Mill, Mach, and Avenarius the conviction that there is no ontological mind-body problem that could be legitimately formulated. The only genuine problem, Carnap claimed, was one of logical analysis, i.e., the question of the formal relations between the concepts that describe the data of first-person-experience, the concepts of physics, and those of (behavioristic) psychology. The "basic situation" of the mind-body-relation was identified with the parallelism of data that a person would experience if he were to observe by means of some "cerebroscope," his own cerebral processes alongside with the stream of images or feelings which "correspond" to those brain processes. But the internal difficulties of a strictly phenomenalistic reconstruction were soon recognized. The translatability of statements about physical objects into statements about phenomenal data could no longer be held to obtain in the sense of mutual deducibility. And the absurdities of a metaphysical solipsism were parallelled by the absurdities of a phenomenal language that was doomed to be "private," "soliloquistic," "incommunicable."

The second phase of logical positivism arose largely out of a reaction against the phenomenalism (experientialism) of the first phase. Under the influence of O. Neurath's and K. Popper's critical suggestions, Carnap [3] formulated his *physicalism*. It was easy again for metaphysically minded opponents to misconstrue this position as a variant of ontological materialism. But Carnap's aim was, just as in the previous phase, merely that of an analysis of language. He outlined a logical reconstruction of factual knowledge on the basis of an intersubjective (physicalistic) thing-language. This position, though independently arrived at, was generally akin to the methodological behaviorism that had been formulated even somewhat earlier but with much less formal precision by E. A. Singer and K. S. Lashley.[4] It is important to distinguish two phases in the development of physicalism. The first phase was rather rash in its claim of the translatability of the statements of physics and those of psychology into those of the thing-language. Availing ourselves of the material idioms (realistic language), this radical and crude form of physicalism may be said to amount to an identification of mental states with overt behavior. Early behaviorism (especially that of J. B. Watson) has been rightly accused of just this falla-

[3] R. Carnap, *The Unity of Science*, Kegan Paul, London, 1938; "Ueber Protokollsaetze", *Erk.* 3, 1932; "Les concepts psychologiques et les concepts physiques, sont-ils foncièrement differents?" *Revue de Synthese*, 1935: "Logical Foundations of the Unity of Science," *Int. Ency. of Unified Science*, I, 1, 1938.

[4] E. A. Singer, *Mind as Behavior*, Columbus, Ohio, 1924; K. S. Lashley, "Behaviorism and consciousness," *Psych. Rev.*, 30, 1923.

cious reduction. This view was essentially revised and corrected in the later formulations.[5] Strict translatability depends of course on explicit definitions. But no explicit definitions that would serve the purpose could plausibly be constructed. The concepts of physics and psychology could perhaps be *introduced* by means of test-condition-test-result-conditionals but not in any way be regarded as synonymous with concepts of the thing-language (or purely logical compounds thereof). Carnap [6] advanced his reduction sentences as a possible formulation of those conditionals. While it has become increasingly doubtful that this formulation is logically adequate, the underlying and related ideas of confirmability and degree of confirmation are now quite generally accepted. No statement of physics nor of (intersubjective) psychology can be considered as completely and directly verifiable (or refutable) by the observations as formulated in the protocol-statements of the thing-language. These protocol-statements confer only a degree of confirmation upon the statements in the scientific languages of physics and psychology.

Reichenbach's version of scientific empiricism [7] had for many years opposed the narrow verifiability criterion of the Viennese positivists. His emphasis on probability and induction led him to advocate a more inclusive confirmability criterion, amounting approximately to the same delimitation of factual meaning as Carnap's criterion (in the second phase of physicalism). Reichenbach's account of the mind-body problem, based on his empirical realism, represents in many ways a position similar to that of Schlick in his early realistic approach. Before we turn to a fuller discussion of this view we must briefly mention a more agnostic position which arose out of a reaction against the earlier, rather immature arguments in favor of mind-body identity.

Felix Kaufmann, and similarly also Norman Jacobs,[8] generally in sympathy with the principles of Logical Empiricism, insisted that strict identity would have to be tantamount to *logical* equivalence of phenomenal (introspective) descriptions of mental states with the descriptions of the "correlated" neurophysiological processes. But it seems obvious, so Kaufmann argued essentially, that the investigations of psycho-physiology are of a factual-empirical character. Which mental state is correlated with which neural processes can be determined only by experimental investigations. The statement of the correlation is therefore synthetic and the "equivalence" of the two descriptions thus can at best be only of (universal) *empirical* character. Reading this conclusion again in terms of traditional metaphysics it may be taken as a formulation of dualistic parallelism. Wolf-

[5] "Testability and Meaning," reprinted this volume; "Logical Foundations of the Unity of Science," *loc. cit.*

[6] "Testability and Meaning."

[7] H. Reichenbach, *Experience and Prediction*, Chicago, 1938; "Logistic Empiricisms in Germany," *Jl. of Phil.*, 33, 1936.

[8] F. Kaufmann, *Methodology of the Social Sciences,* Oxford Univ. Press, 1944.

gang Köhler in one of his later works,[9] and other thinkers trying to be cautious in such delicate matters, have essentially retreated to this obviously safer (because less daring) position. If anyone (like, e.g., E. G. Boring [10]) wanted to account for the parallelism by means of a supposed more fundamental identity, he usually availed himself of the help of the principle of parsimony.

The principle of parsimony itself needs careful analysis. Occam's razor has really, as it were, *three* blades. The simplicity it advocates may be the descriptive or purely formal (or logico-mathematical) expediency that distinguishes, e.g., the heliocentric from the geocentric description of the planetary system. It may be the factual (or inductive) simplicity that arises from a reduction of the number of independent empirical hypotheses. This is probably the purport of Newton's first *regula philosophandi*. But finally, Occam's razor may be used to cut away metaphysical entities. In what follows I shall contend that this third blade, the confirmability criterion of Carnap and Reichenbach, if properly applied, removes the metaphysical surplus, without cutting into the flesh of knowledge. I shall contend also that this new point of view involves (1) a fundamental revision of phenomenalistic positivism and radical operationism (and behaviorism); (2) a re-instatement of a clarified critical realism on the basis of pure semantics and pure pragmatics; (3) a return to a reinterpreted identity (or double-language) view of mind and body.

1. The slogan of Vienna Logical Positivism: "The meaning of a statement is the method of its verification"; [11] and the slogan of Bridgman's operationism: [12] "A concept is synonymous with the set of operations" [which determine its applications] were excellent preventives of the transcendent type of metaphysical speculations. They have had a most salutary purifying effect. Logical empiricism in its later development, however, had to replace these radical principles by more conservative ones. As already indicated, the meaning of scientific statements cannot in general be identified with their confirming evidence. This is obvious in all those cases in which the evidence must in principle be indirect. Historical statements concerning past events, predictions of future events; existential hypotheses concerning radiations, subatomic processes in physics; genes, filterpassing viruses in biology; unconscious motivations in psychology; etc., are only some of the more striking types of assertions whose meanings (i.e., the states of affairs to which they refer) cannot be identified with the states of affairs that can conceivably serve as evidence for them. For a more specific but very simple example we may refer to the concept of the temperature of a body. As ordinary and scientific commonsense (untouched by ultra-

[9] *The Place of Values in a World of Facts*, Liveright, New York, 1938.
[10] *The Physical Dimensions of Consciousness*, Appleton, New York, 1933.
[11] M. Schlick, "Meaning and verification," *Philos. Rev.* 45, 1936; reprinted in Feigl and Sellars, *Readings in Analytical Philosophy*.
[12] P. W. Bridgman, *The Logic of Modern Physics*, Macmillan, New York, 1927.

positivistic reductionism) would put it, thermometer (or pyrometer) readings, spectroscopic findings, and other types of measurement merely indicate something about the body in question, namely the intensity of heat which is a state of that body. No matter whether this heat intensity is construed in terms of classical (macro-) thermodynamics or in terms of statistical (micro- or molecular) thermodynamics, it is in any case only *evidenced by but not identical with* those indications. Similarly for psychology: The overt symptoms and behavior that indicate an emotion, like e.g., anxiety, are confirmable and measurable in terms of skin-temperature, endocrine secretions, psychogalvanic reflexes, verbal responses, etc. but must not be confused with the emotion itself. Generally, the "theoretical constructs," i.e., the hypothetically assumed entities of the sciences cannot be identified with (i.e., explicitly defined in terms of) concepts which apply to the directly perceptible facts as they are manifest in the contexts of ordinary observation or of experimental operations.

2. The required correction and emendation of the phenomenalistic phase of positivism and operationism can best be achieved by means of a reconstruction in terms of pure semantics and pure pragmatics. Semantics as developed primarily by Tarski and Carnap enables us in a precise way to speak, in a metalanguage, about the relation of designation that holds between the symbols of a given language (the object language) and the objects, properties, relations and states of affairs they symbolize. The required metalanguage must of course have a sufficiently rich vocabulary to allow for this. It is in the field of pure pragmatics (thus far only sketched in outline by Wilfrid Sellars) that the rules and the scope of the metalanguage are determined. The pragmatic prerequisites of a workable scientific language extend far beyond the conditions that must be fulfilled for the sake of logical consistency and for the purposes of deductive inference. They also include the condition of confirmability, with all that this implies: a set of proper names (or co-ordinates) and of predicates only some of which correspond to directly confrontable items of immediate experience; a set of relationships that connect the directly verifiable with the only (indirectly) confirmable predicates and statements. With such a reconstruction a distinction necessarily neglected by phenomenalism can be reinstated. It is the important distinction between the evidential basis and the factual reference of terms and statements. In acknowledging this distinction we retain the empiricist conditions for meaningfulness and for factual adequacy: Only if our terms are nomologically related to terms that designate items or aspects of what is directly observable can they be factually meaningful; and only if statements are supported at least by incomplete and/or indirect evidence can they be justifiably asserted. But in the recognition of the incompleteness and indirectness of the verification of practically all scientific statements we implicitly allow for a genuinely critical realism. This new version of realism is free from the objectionable metaphysical elements in the older forms of realism. Much of the perplexities in the time-honored

reality-problems arose out of a confusion of the intuitive, experiential idea of reality with the cognitive, objective concept of reality. The agonies that attend all attempts to solve the "problem of transcendence" can be avoided once it is realized that this is a pseudo-problem. The solution that had been sought involved plainly an inconsistency: The non-given was to be proved just as real as the given. But if by "real" one means *given*, then obviously the wish for a demonstration is doomed because of the self-contradiction. If however one wishes to connect with the word "real" not an ineffable but a cognitively expressible significance then the usage of this term in common life and in science may profitably be taken as a standard. "Real" and "unreal" are of course ambiguous and often emotively tinged words. But in the context of the traditional realism-phenomenalism controversy it is clear that the distinction connoted by these terms cannot be intended to achieve a division among things, events or processes. Once anything is at all classified under one of these three headings it is *eo ipso* considered real. Dreams and delusions are (even according to common-sense) real enough as occurrent events. What is not real are the referents (designata) of certain terms or assertions that we sometimes formulate on the basis of certain *interpretations* of dream or delusion-experiences.

The realistic correction of positivism consists in the identification of meaning with factual reference. This conforms well with customary usage according to which a statement *means* a state of affairs; and is *true* if that state of affairs is fulfilled ("is real," "exists"). This is the obvious grammar of "meaning," "truth," and "reality." Metaphysical problems cannot arise as long as we combine those definitions with the empiricist requirement that in order to be meaning*ful*, a statement must in principle be confirmable. The confirmation rules which formulate the connections between the evidential basis and the factual referents of statements are the metalinguistic correlate of those laws without which inference of specific unobserved or unobservable states of affairs would be impossible. Just which network of laws and existential assumptions will most adequately and parsimoniously serve for a comprehensive and predictively fruitful organization of the data can of course not be settled in any a priori fashion. Nevertheless, only within the frame of a language that makes such a network possible can we legitimately assign probabilities to hypotheses on the basis of relevant evidence. The ("realistic") frame itself however cannot be justified by considerations of inductive probability. The adoption of this frame can be vindicated only by its fruitfulness for the purposes which it helps to fulfill. Like other principles which rationalists mistake for synthetic a priori presuppositions this is, from the viewpoint of logical reconstruction, a basic convention, capable only of pragmatic but not of cognitive justification.[13]

[13] The realism of pure semantics and pragmatics is outlined in H. Feigl, "Existential Hypotheses: realistic versus phenomenalistic interpretations," *Phil. of Sci.*, 17, 1950; W. S. Sellars, "Realism and the new way of words," *Philos. and Phenom. Rev.*, 8, 1948 (reprinted in Feigl and Sellars, *loc. cit.*) and "Acquaintance and description

3. We are now ready to develop the implications of the just outlined clarified empirical realism for the mind-body problem. There are three demonstrably mistaken reductions by means of which monistic solutions have been attempted. There is firstly the crude and simple-minded identification of the stimulus-aspects with the mental qualities. Obviously we cannot say that a color sensation is identical with the radiation (of a certain intensity and frequency-pattern) which, under certain conditions merely elicits that sensation. Secondly, in our critique of phenomenalism we have also refuted the identification of physical bodies with complexes or configurations of elements of direct perception. Thirdly, the behavioristic identification of mental states with the responses (including linguistic utterances) of organisms is equally fallacious. It is of course granted that the confirmation of objective statements concerning "physical" bodies is possible only on the basis of the evidence of direct experience. Similarly, intersubjectively meaningful statements concerning mental states are confirmable only on the basis of behavioral evidence. If we are to avoid the errors of phenomenalist reduction and quite generally of the negativism of orthodox positivism then all the relationships mentioned are not identities, but —at best—lawful (causal) connections between distinguishable states or events. The equivalence of statements about each pair of states or events can therefore be only of the empirical type. The precipitous assertion of a logical equivalence was of course based on the phenomenalistic claims of the explicit definability of the entities in one realm in terms of the entities of the corresponding other realm. This, as we have tried to point out, was completely unwarranted.

Curiously enough, the same sort of critique has been applied also to the identification of mental states with processes inside the organism, i.e., neurophysiological processes. It seemed quite incredible how a color sensation, a remembrance of things past, an act of thought concerning mathematical relations or a feeling of indignation, could in any sense whatsoever be "the same" as some brain-process or other. Here again it was urged that the relation can be no other than, at best, that of a lawful correspondence or parallelism of simultaneous events. The many arguments in favor of this view are well known. One of the more important among these arguments contends that the attributes of mental states and events and the attributes of the corresponding neurophysiological processes are so different that the respective predicates characterizing each of the two types of processes can stand only in the relation of general (empirical) equivalence but never in that of a logical equivalence. Hume argued that statements of specific causal relations are synthetic a posteriori because alternatives are always conceivable without self-contradiction. Similarly, it is contended that a brain process which a future neurophysiology might characterize as of a definite

---

again", *Jl. of Phil.*, 46, 1949. An analysis of the problem of justification may be found in H. Feigl, "De principiis non disputandum? On the meaning and the limits of justification," in *Philosophical Analysis*, M. Black, ed., Cornell Univ. Press, 1950.

type could conceivably be associated with a phenomenologically described immediate experience of a type radically different from that with which, as a matter of empirical regularity it is actually associated (say a sentiment of nostalgia). Eddington once argued that even the most detailed physiological and physical knowledge of the behavior and the nervous processes in the human organisms occurring on some November 11th at 11 A.M. in London could not possibly indicate to a Martian super-scientist unfamiliar with human history and unendowed with human sentiments that these events "mean" a commemoration of the armistice. This fascinating argument however, rests on two fallacies. Correcting these errors, it may be said, firstly, such a utopian knowledge of the neurophysiological processes would enable the Martian to derive the actual and potential verbal behavior of the Londoners; it would also enable him to reconstruct the physical account of the origin of the ritual (two minutes' silence, etc.) and thus to know, in principle, everything that can be known about those events in an intersubjective manner. Secondly, this can be achieved even if the Martian, because of the differences or limitations in his repertoire of emotions, cannot empathize, let alone share, the sentiments in question. A congenitally blind man, equipped with modern physical devices, could investigate not only the physics of colored surfaces, of light radiations reflected by them, etc., but also the (behavioristic) psychology of color sensation, discrimination, and perception (on the part of subjects equipped with eyesight). Similarly, a Martian could *know* all *about* human feelings and emotions without having *knowledge of* them, i.e., without directly experiencing them or being *acquainted* with them by intuition or imagination.

Quite generally, one of the difficulties that are so frequently adduced in the critique of the identity-theory of mind and body rests on a confusion of *acquaintance* with *knowledge*. No one denies that the *image* of a brain, as perceived by a surgeon or as pictured in terms of an atomic model has totally different properties from a melody-as-heard or a sentiment-of-elation-as-actually-lived-through. But images or other directly experienced acts or data are not in and by themselves concepts. Knowledge proper is always conceptual. This insight is an important point of agreement between such otherwise divergent recent philosophers as Poincaré, Bergson, James, Dewey, Russell, Eddington, R. W. Sellars, C. I. Lewis, Schlick, Wittgenstein, and Carnap. What then is meant by "conceptual knowledge"? What is meant by "concept"? The best answer we can give today rests on a repudiation of psychologism and upon the results of pure semiotic. Concepts are meanings (intensions) of symbols constituted by the syntactical, semantical, and pragmatic rules which determine the relations of those symbols to one another, to their designata and to their evidential basis. The crucial question then concerns the conditions of the identity of concepts. What is the criterion for identity? We can safely follow Leibniz' *principium identatis indiscernibilium*, here as elsewhere. If two terms are defined by the same set of rules, they are merely different symbols for the same meaning, they represent the same concept. Such synonymy however may arise in various ways. The most obvious and trivial case is that of explicit definition in which we arbitrarily stipulate the unrestricted mutual substitutibility of symbols. More interesting and more relevant for our problem is the case of epistemic (or "systemic") synonymy. We may determine certain meanings uniquely by different definitions of the type known as "definite descriptions" (Russell). Thus two explorers may unwittingly have observed the same mountain from different directions, and only after comparing notes come to realize that it was really identically the same mountain. This is a systemic identity in that it can be established only if the system of empirical geometry and optics is presupposed. Quite analogously, the identity of the morning star with the evening star (ever since Frege a much used example in logical analyses) is based on the recognition that one and the same trunk of world-lines (the four-dimensional representation of the planet Venus) is the object of reference of the two designations, referring to alternative segments of that trunk. Only within the system of Kepler's kinematics and of ordinary geometrical optics can this identity be explicated and warranted. This and the preceding example concerned the identity of things (continuants), or more precisely speaking, the identity of the designation of a name with the designatum (descriptum) of a description or else the identity of the descripta of two descriptions of thing-like entities.[14] But quite similar considerations hold for concepts (predicates of various levels). The identity of the concept of "electric current" defined by various definite descriptions such as those based on the magnetic, chemical or thermal indications can be defended against empiricist or operationist doubts only after a full fledged system of electrodynamics enables us to *deduce* those various effects from a unitary theory of electricity, magnetism, electrolysis, and heat. Those doubts could of course never be removed with finality. We not only admit but would even emphasize the empirical or inductive basis which underlies all such identifications in the realm of factual knowledge. The only kind of identification that can be proved with finality is found in the purely formal sciences. Despite the fundamental difference between the situation in empirical knowledge and that in pure mathematics, there is an instructive structural analogy here. Two different infinite series, for example, may be used for the definition (unique description) of one and the same number, as, e.g., in the case of π. But such mathematical proofs of identity also presuppose a frame of concepts and postulates. Only within such a frame can we assert meaningfully and demonstrate validly the identity of the object of two descriptions. (A perfectly obvious illustration is the arithmetical identity of 2^3 with $\sqrt{64}$). The frame of arithmetic, i.e., the postulate system of Peano in the Frege-Russell interpretation, is logically or analytically valid. The situation is radically different in empirical geometry. For example, the identity of

[14] Even these first two examples could be analyzed in terms of individual-concepts (unit-classes) instead of things, whose identity is under examination.

two points or line-segments characterized in different ways depends upon the factual adequacy of the geometrical postulates. The same holds, *a fortiori*, for the identifications in the natural sciences. Returning to an illustration previously introduced, the identification of the temperature of a gas with the mean kinetic energy of its molecules depends of course upon the truth of the molecular-statistical theory of heat. But if the truth of the theory is assumed, the strict identity of reference becomes a matter of logical deduction. Temperature as a macro-concept refers to the state of a body which is only more fully characterized by the theoretical description of its micro-structure. Once the theory is adopted it would make no sense to speak of the temperature as something distinct and different from that set of micro-conditions. Only the pictorial connotations of the word "temperature" that remind us of thermometers or of the directly felt heat of a body seem to make the corresponding concept merely "parallel" to that of molecular thermodynamics.

The logical principle that underlies our argument is, as indicated before, simply a variant of Leibniz' principle of identity. The meaning of a concept is determined, not by its pictorial connotations, but by the system of rules which implicitly defines that meaning. If two terms, no matter what words or symbols they are and no matter what pictorial appeals they may convey, are mutually substitutible for each other because they fulfill precisely the same functions in a system of rules, then they have the same meaning, they are the same concept.

The application of these considerations to the mind-body problem must by now be fairly obvious. Relative to the "molar" (or macro-) account given by behavioristic psychology, the neurophysiological account is a micro-description of the very same events and processes. The pictorial connotation of the two accounts are of course different, since the images attaching to the behavioristic terms represent stimulus-response situations, while the images connected with the neurophysiological language are apt to represent observations of nervous tissues. The notoriously greatest difficulty however arise here from the pictorial connotations of the mentalistic terms that owe their introduction to a third avenue of approach to the same processes—*introspection.* The qualities of direct awareness, the facts of stimuli and responses, the directly observable data of the neurophysiologist are of course not to be identified with one another. We have already warned against the fallacies involved here. But we contend that the designata of the mentalistic language are identical with the descripta of the behavioristic language, and that both are identical with the designata of the neurophysiological language. Utilizing the distinction suggested before, we may say that the factual reference of some of the terms in each of these different languages (or vocabularies) may be the same while only their evidential bases differ. A state of mind, conceived as an event in the spatio-temporal-causal structure of the world may thus be characterized by concepts that are evidentially anchored in quite heterogeneous areas. It is this anchoring that gives the concepts their particular place in one or the other vocabulary. But if we are sure not to confuse their factual reference with their evidential base we may rightly say that they have the same meaning. This holds unless we countenance in principle unconfirmable assertions or unless the facts of psychology themselves force upon us an interactionistic dualism. The last proviso indicates the systemic nature of the proposed identifications. On the whole, I should think, the available evidence points with remarkable consistency in the direction of a system of psychology, psycho-physics and psychophysiology which provides for the monistic solution here outlined. But this is the empirical, the factual issue which philosophical analysis cannot decide and should not prejudge. We can do no more than clarify the logical structure of the problem and remove unfounded objections to the identity theory which perhaps owing to a "failure of nerve" seems to have been temporarily eclipsed by a return to parallelism —if not even interactionism. The view we are proposing here should not be construed as a metaphysical doctrine. It again has merely some historical affinities with certain forms of epiphenomenalistic materialism, panpsychism, or the double-aspect or double-knowledge theories. If a label is wanted, then perhaps "double-language-theory" is still the least misleading I can suggest. Within the conceptual system which fulfills the intersubjective confirmability condition and is at the same time the simplest account compatible with the accumulated facts of psychology, the terms of the behavioral-psychological and of the introspective language are (systemically) synonymous. If further factual discoveries should force upon us a radical revision of the conceptual system, then, conceivably, this claim of synonymy may have to be modified or even abandoned. In the meantime it is well to remember that the tentative identifications which generally underlie synonymies of this type are among the most fruitful devices in the search for unifying explanations in the progress of science. The identification of light with a special kind of electromagnetic oscillating field; ferro-magnetism with the spin of electrons; of heat with molecular motion; of chemical valences with certain dynamical features of the atoms; of the medium of inheritable traits with the gene-structure of the chromosomes, etc., are only some of the more noteworthy cases in point.

One last critical question requires discussion. The entire preceding argument, it may be argued, depends upon the presupposition that the vocabulary of introspection is part of an intersubjective language and thus really interpreted behavioristically. Introspective terms are then introduced on the evidential basis of linguistic responses and are therefore in any case logically on a par with those terms that have their basis in non-linguistic responses of the organisms. Thus, it may be urged, that the real difficulty of the mind-body problem has been avoided rather than resolved. This objection obviously implies that the language of introspection is to be taken as phenomenal, purely experiential and thus strictly subjective. My reply, very briefly, is this: The problem thus proposed is the epistemological question of the relation between the "private" (if not solipsistic) language of data (phenomena) to the language of "public," intersubjective "constructs" (thing-concepts). It is highly questionable as to whether the idea of a phenomenal language in this sense can even be consistently maintained, let alone fully elaborated. But to those who cling to this "Aufbau"-phase of positivism I would offer the suggestion that there can be only a correspondence, but never a translation between the phenomenal language and the thing-language. If introspective descriptions are not to be taken as referring to events which are at least in principle confirmable by the much more indirect route of behavioral (or physiological) evidence then they are indeed severed from the language of intersubjective communication and doomed to solipsistic privacy. There is no bridge between such a private language and the language of science except one of isomorphic correspondence. Structurally the situation bears a certain resemblance to the one in the reconstruction of the rational numbers on the basis of the natural numbers. Certain ordered pairs of natural numbers are introduced, they define rational numbers. But the rational numbers (like $\frac{3}{1}$, for example) which represent integers (3 in this example) merely correspond to them, but are not identical with them. This isomorphism here consists not only in the one-to-one correspondence of certain elements of one realm to all elements in another, but in the one-to-one correspondence of the results of all arithmetical operations with corresponding elements. The analogy with the (however much more complex) field of epistemology lies in the isomorphism between certain statements in the phenomenal language and those in the intersubjective scientific language. As Carnap pointed out long ago [15] epistemological reconstruction may be attempted in either of two ways. The protocol-propositions may be part of the system of the scientific language or they are outside of it. In the latter case we must have some statements in the scientific language that correspond to the protocol propositions. This correspondence, however, must not be confused with what is traditionally called psycho-physical or psycho-physiological parallelism. Parallelism has always been a doctrine according to which two different types of processes or two aspects of one and the same process are related by laws of coexistence or contemporaneity. The correspondence of the protocol propositions with propositions of the intersubjective system is a purely formal relation which arises exclusively out of the constructive definitions, involving differences in Russellian type-levels, by means of which the terms of the physical language are supposedly constituted out of terms belonging to the language of data. This is the position a consistent phenomenalist must take. But the many difficulties of that position have impelled Carnap and other physicalists to replace it by the reconstruction on an intersubjective basis. The analogy of this procedure in mathematics

[15] R. Carnap, "Ueber Protokollsaetze," *loc. cit.*

is of course the axiomatic method by means of which the total system of numbers (real numbers) is introduced and no problems of the "Aufbau"-type are then encountered. If the protocol propositions, i.e., the names and predicates occurring in them, are part of the total symbolic system of the language of science, then we have here before us the sort of "realistic" reconstruction which underlies the systemic identity view of mind and body.

Résumé: Logical Empiricism in its present phase possesses the logical tools for a reformulation of the identity or double-language view of the mental and the physical. As in so many other issues of philosophy, this solution represents an equilibrium that has been reached only after several oscillations toward untenable extreme positions. The identity proposed is neither the reductive definitional one of phenomenalism or of behaviorism, nor is it an identity that presupposes a metaphysical realism. It is rather the hypothetical identity of the referents of terms whose evidential bases are respectively: introspective, behavioral or physiological. It is granted that the relations between the evidential indicators (linguistic responses, overt behavior and the data of neuro-physiology) must be interpreted as empirical laws. But this does not in the least preclude the identity of the factual reference of the concepts which characterize the causal processes and events in terms of which the facts in each sphere of evidence may become explainable and predictable to an ever increasing extent. It is this hypothetical, systemic, referential identity that has been overlooked by those who retreated to a timid parallelism. The alleged difficulties of the identity view are mainly due to a confusion of pictorial appeals with cognitive meanings. A more adequate discussion of the points touched upon as well as of the many related questions and difficulties would of course require much more space than is available here.

On Some Methodological Problems of Psychology*

GUSTAV BERGMANN[1]

At the end of the last century, there began a movement away from traditional philosophy and towards a closer contact of philosophical thought with empirical science. Philosophers following this course were met halfway by groups of scientists, mostly physicists and mathematicians, who in their own field had found themselves face to face with problems which traditionally belonged to philosophy. But since neither of these two groups was inclined to respect conventional boundaries, they joined forces and the result of their endeavors proved challenging to both philosophy and science. Various aspects and representative theses of this movement are known to-day as logical positivism, operationism, physicalism or scientific empiricism. For the movement as a whole, however, the term *logical positivism* is now becoming generally used. The present paper should be considered as a selective and partly historical survey of the methodological discussion in psychology from the standpoint of logical positivism.

I. Logical Behaviorism

At the time the logico-positivistic movement first gained momentum and influence outside the disciplines from which it started, psychology was still struggling against its metaphysical heritage, the earmark of its origin from traditional philosophy. At this state, Watsonian behaviorism was most consciously aware of the necessity of getting rid of this encumbrance, and this explains the sympathy logical positivists have always felt for behaviorism. There was no harm in the profession of this sympathy as long as the most liberal (and hence the most orthodox) application of Occam's razor

* Reprinted by kind permission of the author and the editor from *Philosophy of Science*, 7, 1940.

[1] I now (1952) consider some of the formulations in this paper as not sufficiently precise. Some of the epistemological asides I now believe to be outright mistaken. The following three references contain together a complete statement of my present views on the logic of psychology in general and on psychoanalysis in particular: "The Logic of Psychological Concepts," *Philosophy of Science*, 18, 1951; the chapter on "Theoretical Psychology" in *Annual Review of Psychology* (vol. 4, 1953); "Psychoanalysis and Experimental Psychology," *Mind*, 52, 1943.

was the operation most urgently needed by the nonphysical disciplines (biology, psychology, social sciences, in the following referred to as "biological sciences"). For these historical reasons the term *logical behaviorism*, coined by Hempel for the application of the logico-positivistic method to psychology, is amply justified.

In the meantime, however, the scene has changed. To-day, every scientific psychology is practically behavioristic, and in its methodological discussions psychology seems to have reached a complete understanding with logical positivism. But on the other hand, there is still some mistrust and uneasiness among psychologists and sociologists as to logical positivism. Therefore it might not be superfluous to state most expressedly just at this moment: Logical behaviorism does not identify itself either with physiological nor with any molar behaviorism, or with any special psychological theory at all. It does not offer anything but logical criteria and formal methodological schemes and it is not able to take sides between various theoretical approaches within a science, provided that all these approaches comply with its purely formal requirements. The anachronistic prerogative of philosophy to decide ex cathedra among the various scientific theories has been completely and sincerely renounced.

Sociological excursus. The resistance against logical positivism, widespread among scientists, especially in Europe, and based upon the suspicion that it is nothing but a kind of disguised, refined materialism, is a very interesting sociological fact in itself. But there are sufficient reasons to be found in history of ideologies for this ever-ready suspicion. It might be perfectly true that the value system behind logical positivism is psychologically and genetically akin to the materialistic attitude; but one must keep in mind that in this context "materialistic" is a sociologico-psychological term and has nothing to do with philosophical materialism. On the other hand, more conceptually-minded sociologists, specialising in the investigation of theoretical systems as such and their historical filiation, might be equally right in describing logical positivism as a "dialectic" outgrowth of the perennial antagonism between materialism and empiricism at the one and idealism and rationalism at the other end of the scale of philosophic tempers. Both standpoints can be clearly distinguished in the system of logical positivism (formal logic and language analysis on the one side, empiricism on the other). After all, logical positivists never claimed to be a parthenogenetic offspring of that Absolute which they fight and deny so ardently. It is true, however, that they did not give much attention to the clarification of their own historical position. This in turn, though certainly no merit in itself, is perfectly understandable by the very nature of the momentum which led to their achievements. The great enlightenment of the 18th century was not very historically-minded either.

As a matter of fact, logical behaviorism, in spite of the connotations of the term, does not mean anything but the consistent application of

1. The principles of operationism to the terms used in psychology and the laws connecting them,
2. Logical (language) analysis of the theoretical systems in which these terms and laws occur.

In this formulation logical behaviorism seems to be almost unrestrictedly accepted by psychology to-day. Let us outline a few consequences of these two main aspects for psychology. If, by virtue of the clarification reached by psychology itself, these remarks seem rather obvious and self-explanatory, it is a symptom of the progressive integration of scientific thought and to the credit of both psychology and logical positivism.

1. One should be most careful in substituting the term *physicalism* for logical behaviorism. In accordance with Feigl † the term physicalism has two meanings. Only one of these is equivalent to the thesis of empiricism and operationism, while the second is merely a hypothesis and no essential part of the system of logical positivism. Physicalism in the first sense is sometimes formulated in this way: A scientific theory is meaningful if and only if operational relations between its constructs and those of physics can be established, i.e., if its language can be "translated" into that of physics. For what that means in psychology, Tolman's book on purposive behavior with its famous glossary is the already classical example. The physicalistic hypothesis (strict physicalism), however, claims that the laws of any science can be "reduced" to and "derived" from the terms and laws of physics. Applied to psychology, this hypothesis is practically equivalent to the claim of physiological behaviorism, that psychology is a part of physiology. But this is, at the present state of affairs, nothing but a prognosis and an opinion as to what line future research should preferably follow. Logical behaviorism will not be affected by the success or failure of such a program.

2. The anti-mentalistic and anti-introspectionistic thesis of early behaviorism was philosophically biased. Purified from ontological admixture, it yields two methodological problems, viz.:

a. Whether at all, and if so, in which systematical position, verbalizations should be used for the definition of psychological constructs, and
b. Whether mentalistic terms like consciousness, intention, thought, and so forth, should be introduced into the system language (theory) of psychology.

As soon as that became clear, the whole issue lost its interest entirely. Apparently it was just its concomitant metaphysical meaning which stirred up all those violent reactions at that time.

3. Even if the thesis of strict physicalism is anticipated, it does not mean the discarding of all non-physical language levels. The choice of the

† [See the paper "Unity of Science and Unitary Science" reprinted in this collection. Editors' note.]

system language is an entirely pragmatic decision. Even the hypothetical ideal physicist will not most suitably describe psychological and biological phenomena in terms of electrons and protons. Physics itself does not always push reduction as far as possible, and it is not probable that microphysical theories as such will ever be used to design or describe a locomotive. Only the experts can decide which language level suits best the purposes of their special science. To-day physicalism certainly carries the danger of a too high level of aspiration for psychologists. This might be one more reason why strict physicalism, if explicitly stated, is frowned upon even by psychologists who implicitly adopt its thesis throughout the whole line of their thought.

4. Every-day language is a kind of primitive scientific system, constructed over the (individual) *protocol.* The protocol (of an individual) consists of sentences like "Now hungry", "Now here red circle". It does not use the personal pronoun "I". Certain structural properties of the various (individual) protocols, e.g., their relation to the (intersubjective) system language of physics, the similarity they show in many respects, their spatio-temporal coherence, express themselves by the use of the personal pronouns, verbs such as "to think", "to feel" and nouns such as "mind", "wish", "reality". The traditional epistemological problems and statements induced by this linguistic use, among them all ontological questions, cannot even be formulated in any scientific language. If partial translation into a meaningful language is possible, they turn out most frequently to belong to the subject-matter of psychology. The gradual elaboration of the concept of behavior-object (Ding) by modern psychology is probably the most impressive example. The historical development from elementaristic stimulus-psychology through Gestalt theory to the investigations into the genesis and the structure of "behavior-objects" and stimulus equivalence covers all meaningful aspects of philosophical realism. In line with these cautious discriminations, the workers in the field systematically closest to physiological reduction (reflexology) now distinguish most carefully between a model and an actual reduction.

5. In an elaborate scientific theory the coordinating definitions are established only for a basic subclass of its constructs. The term *basic* in this statement should not be confounded with *elementary*. Syntactically "elementary" means the lowest level of the linguistic structure. Science, however, when discussing e.g., whether some isolated "atomistic" sensory data and their traces or perceptual wholes are elementary, uses the term in a strictly empirical, sometimes even phenomenological, and not in any methodological sense. Therefore reasons for establishing the correspondence between the very levels of these different kinds of "elementary" are of a merely pragmatic character and no methodological arguments against an "atomistic under-structure" can be derived from them. Physics, at any rate, starts its theoretical construction deeply "below" the protocol, which in turn is at the basis of all semantic coordinations.

II. Historical vs. Systematic Laws

The analysis of general terms like scientific law, theory, causality, as performed and systematized by logical positivism, has been abstracted from and elaborated in closest contact with the actual development of physics. This historical fact is often used as a starting point for criticism. Even those who admit that a suitable framework for the methodological problems of physics has been built up, argue sometimes against the straightforward and unqualified application of the same tools in the biological sciences. The historical source of this resistance is easy to trace. It leads back to vitalistic ideas (Bergson) and that line of psychological thought, particularly deep-rooted in Germany (Dilthey, Spranger), which stresses the fundamental rôle of "understanding." The trend in psychology, however, is unmistakable. Pseudo-problems have almost completely disappeared in the methodological discussion, and certainly the logico-positivistic analysis has had its part in this development. On the other hand logical positivists were not very much concerned with the special problems of the biological disciplines and often dealt with them in a rather summary way. There are, therefore, some rather general questions particular to these disciplines, which have not been given quite the attention they deserve. The issue connected with the antithesis of historical vs. systematic laws (theories, concepts and so forth) seems to belong to this group. In Lewin's recent work on theoretical psychology the dichotomy is very strongly emphasized. But his arguments are often so closely interwoven with other considerations, that a few more general remarks might be justified, taking his terms merely as a point of departure.

If one looks from outside at modern psychology, the most striking traits are the strong tendency towards quantification, simultaneous efforts to eliminate "merely" statistical laws as much as possible, and the great emphasis laid upon hypothetico-deductive derivation. It is quite obvious that physics is the model science for those psychologists and there is ample evidence for that in their writings (Hull, Lewin). The term "systematic" is sometimes also used to characterize this trend, but as opposite to "historical" it has a more specific meaning. In this sense, too, physics is regarded as representative of the systematic approach. Let us then consider the classical example of a physical law, Newton's formula:

$$\text{(S)} \qquad \frac{d^2x_i}{dt^2} = f_i[x_1(t), x_2(t), \ldots, x_n(t)], \qquad i = 1, 2, \ldots. n,$$

a system of differential equations connecting the (second) derivatives of the spatial coordinates of the masses (as functions of the time t) with the momentary positions of these masses. As far as the future is concerned, it is well known and exhaustively clarified how this typical form of the descriptive equation system has determined our ideas on causality (Laplace's world formula). In line with this clarification the teleological argument as against "mechanistic" causality is no longer used in scientific discussions in order to prove the particular character of the biological sciences as opposed to physics. As to the past, a very obvious generalisation of (S), given below, might prove useful to illustrate the structure of a "historical law."

Given a certain physical set-up, let (S) be the system needed for its description. For actual evaluation, certain measurements have to be carried out, to determine the constants and the initial values of the variables in these equations. Sometimes it is also necessary to consider the effects of the measuring procedures themselves. Always, however, it is assumed that

a) All the measurements necessary can be carried out "at present" and that one does not need the values of any of the variables at any time point before t, and that
b) The describing function themselves do not change their "form" with time.

In physics everybody knows what b) means, but one should be clear that in a more general context this statement is rather vague and somewhat arbitrarily separated from a).

Both assumptions are indispensable for the possibility and the usefulness of those set-ups called *experiments* in physics. Wherever laboratory set-ups are supposed to have the same systematic position within a science that experiments have in physics, it is silently presupposed that the investigated properties of the material conform at least approximately to a) and b). As a matter of fact, we see psychology immediately resorting to the method of case study when those assumptions seem questionable. The very stress which theoretical psychology lays upon the systematic difference between case study and experimentation shows that it is well aware of its fundamental importance. It should also be mentioned in this context that the statement: "No experimentation is possible in history" has two meanings, viz., 1) no experimentally controllable sociological set-up in the large can be arranged (problem of extrapolation), and 2) assumptions a) and b) are not sufficiently warranted. All this applies similarly to experimentation proper, as opposed to other methods of fact finding, in social psychology.

The claim that psychology is a systematic science means, as far as I can see, that psychological constructs and psychological laws connecting them, for which a) and b) are valid, can be found, and that it will be possible to cover the whole field of psychology in such terms. In this statement the occurrence of the term "psychological" is essential. For the thesis is not that after reduction of psychology to physiology, and, if necessary, a further reduction of the latter to physics, it will be possible to derive all the "historical" relations in psychology (and the social sciences) from the systematic laws of physics. The meaning is rather that this can be done on the level of a "genuinely psychological" theory. Although "genuinely psychological" is certainly no sharp concept, there will be hardly any misunderstanding as to what this expression intends to convey, and we shall not try to define it. It is just one of the results of logico-positivistic analysis (theory of the unity of science) that there is little point in such attempts. Moreover, the occurrence of (overt or covert) mentalistic terms and the description of processes where the individual is somehow involved as a whole is still a practically sufficient criterion for a psychological theory.

To make predictions about such molar behavior, Lewin starts out with the equation

$$\text{(L)} \qquad B = f(P, E)$$

B being the behavioral unit, P the psychological person and E the psychological environment. Again the adjective psychological is essential and marks the first step necessary to obtain systematic laws, for the reaction of the "same" individual to the same physical environment depends quite obviously upon the individual's history. A rat in a maze behaves differently after starvation periods of different lengths and according to its previously acquired "knowledge" about what he is going to find in the goal-box. Moreover, the person is a very complex variable and there is, even with rats, the problem of individual differences. Consequently the systematic approach has to start from a set of "intervening variables" of a *purely inferential character*. Each of these variables might be operationally related to the person as well as to the environment. This is expressed by integrating the variables at the right side of (L) into the concept of *life space*. The probable interdependence of these variables is expressed by the term *field*, which thus is entirely identical with the term "Gestalt" in its meaning as "system of interaction". The claim of the systematic approach then is:

a_1) Methods to determine at present the "structure and dynamics of the life space" (to measure all the constants and the present values of those to-be-defined variables) can be devised.

b_1) There are functions f of a given, unchanging form, by means of which the behavior B can be derived from those measurements.

In view of the peculiarities of the psychological material it might not be superfluous to isolate one more self-explanatory assumption:

c_1) All the measurements mentioned in a_1) can be carried out independently from the actual occurrence of B, the behavior to be predicted, and the state of the field is not essentially affected by these manipulations.

Two more remarks should rule out any possible misunderstanding:

1) The determination of the values of variables at earlier time points, e.g., by asking a human subject, is an historical procedure, and if these values actually occur in the describing equations, the law is a historical law. Otherwise the whole issue would be an entirely trivial question of terminology.

2) There is no objection from the systematic standpoint against using historical methods to determine present states, if they are technically preferable, provided only that there are also systematic

methods to do it. To starve a rat for a certain time might be an easier method to determine its present state of hunger than the carrying out of certain physiological measurements to the same effect.

The concept of a historical law, on the other hand, involves the dependence of the descriptive functions not only upon the values of the variables at the given time point t, but also on their values at a (finite or infinite) number of previous time points (or intervals) t_1, t_2, ... Perhaps, it should be mentioned that the term "systematic" is sometimes used to eliminate an obvious misinterpretation of the term "historical," viz.: No reasonable attempt would try to tie the present values to certain absolute time points. To say the same thing in a more vague but more suggestive language, it is not empty time per se, but rather its content, the temporal development of the process which is thought of as influencing the present. The simplest interpretation of this idea as to the variables and the form of the laws by a mathematical model then would be:

a_2) The values to be substituted into the empty places of the functions f to make the evaluation at the time point t possible are not the momentary values of the variables $x_1, x_2, \cdots x_n$, but values derived by certain operations from the values of (all) the variables during time intervals preceding t. A very general expression for these to-be-filled-in values would be:

$$\text{(T)} \qquad \int_{-\infty}^{t} \phi(x_1(t), x_2(t), \ldots, x_n(t))\,dt$$

Substituting this, e.g., in a system like (S), one obtains

$$\text{(H)} \qquad \frac{d^2x_i}{dt^2} = f_i\left[\int_{-\infty}^{t} \phi_1(x_1(t), \ldots, x_n(t))\,dt, \ldots, \int_{-\infty}^{t} \phi_n(x_1(t), x_2(t) \ldots, x_n(t))\,dt\right] \qquad i = 1, 2, \ldots n.$$

This is an integro-differential equation of the type investigated by Volterra. It is a mathematical model of a historical law, in which the idea of the constancy of the functional relation (assumption b) is given a concrete interpretation by the form of the functions f. Let us add a few remarks concerning (H):

1. By the occurrence of earlier values of the variables any science using historical laws is faced with the methodological problem of defining the criteria of historical truth.

2. The functions ϕ in (T) cover a wide range of possible structures. The fact, for instance, that the events previous to a certain time point t_1 have no effect within the present constellation, would be expressed by $\phi = 0$ in the time interval from the lower limit to t_1.

3. There are no historical laws of the form (H) in physics of to-day.

Therefore the question comes up as to whether the occurrence of historical laws is compatible with the hypothesis of strict physicalism. Of course, one could always say that on the way to actual and complete physicalisation one would discover "physical" laws of a still unknown type. Applied to biology, this is about the empirical meaning of vitalism. But physicalists would not like this answer, and it does not seem that they would have to resort to it. At least there is no simple mathematical reason, why those molar combinations of solutions of systems (S), which *correspond* to the terms of the biological sciences should not in reasonable approximation fulfill equations of type (H). On a more or less speculative level so-called "trace" theories seem to anticipate this expectation.

III. Experimental and Historical Psychoanalysis

Although in the recent methodological discussions psychoanalysis has not been given quite the amount of attention one would expect after the breakdown of the antimentalistic prejudice, the various tendencies towards a rapprochement are beginning to make themselves felt. Nevertheless, "behaviorization" and "experimental proof" of psychoanalysis seem to be accepted as a realistic and even desirable program by so-called academic psychology. Certainly direct operational links for a sufficiently large subclass of psychoanalytic concepts should be most carefully established. The very fact that many mentalistic terms, such as consciousness, wish, memory, ego, had to be stratified and modified in the psychoanalytic theory, suggests that such an attempt would be of more than methodological interest. Moreover it will help to bridge what is still left of the original gap between psychoanalysis and the rest of psychology. But such a translation, if it is not to destroy the finer structure of the theory, might prove to be a very hard job; at any rate it is far beyond the scope and the ambition of the present paper. A few remarks, however, will be ventured.

1. There are some parts of the theory which can be subjected to an experimental test. The hypnotic experiments, arranged to demonstrate the general "knowledge" of the symbols, cannot fail to be mentioned once more in this context. It is also possible to furnish statistical evidence for the amount of correlation actually obtaining between personality traits, for which the psychoanalytic theory predicts such an interdependence. The same might hold true for correlations between personality traits and biographical facts, and there seem to be still many other ingenious ways to use psychoanalytical ideas for experimental explorations in personality. But psychoanalysis is essentially a historical theory. Because of this fact it is not easy to see how experimental verification can be extended beyond certain limits.

2. By giving very neat and strictly empirical definitions of such terms as libido, ambivalence, sublimation, aggression, and by eliminating all "unscientific" pictures and analogies from the relations describing the various

possibilities of their functional and genetic interdependence, one might build a marvelous airplane, but there would still be no airports providing firm landing ground. For psychoanalysis claims (and there is every possible evidence that this claim is consistent with the whole structure of the theory): To make any concrete prediction about an individual's behavior (to bring about any therapeutic effect) one must

a) Determine the special kind of linkages (drive history, history of ego and superego formation) which have taken place with the individual in question, and that

b) The only procedure by which this can be achieved, is the analytical treatment itself.

Thus the "protocol" from which any meaningful operational approach to psychoanalysis will have to start, is not the writings of the analysts, but a sufficient number of phonographic records of real analyses.

3. It is the privilege of historical theories in the biological sciences to give us the stimulating experience and the pragmatically invaluable help of "understanding" by a lucid interpretation of the past. But for a historical theory, too, the crucial test is the possibility of predictions. This implies for instance for history in the usual sociological meaning of this term: A scientific theory of history must be able to answer questions of the following type: "Given a concrete historical situation, which changes can be effected and by which means?." This is a point to be made before any question of reliability. If an approach to history does not provide such concrete answers, its claim to be a scientific theory should be dismissed without a hearing. What now is the result, if one applies this criterion to the historical theory of psychoanalysis? Here, as in any other clinical field, the main question seems to be whether successful cures are possible and how to perform them. If there is sufficient evidence that healings at a rate exceeding chance are being obtained, and if the reports of the analysts about what they are doing with their patients *in camera caritatis* are true, the objection of *subjectivity* will need a careful rewording. The therapeutic effect of a treatment can be tested by objective methods. The possible use of phonographic records has already been mentioned.

4. With respect to the "subjectivity" due to the rôle the analyst himself plays in the treatment, let us finally mention another formal criterion any historical theory must fulfill. Both, the statesman unleashing a propaganda drive and the analyst who starts a cure are going to change the "natural course of events." Consequently their theories must be constructed in a way which accounts for the effect of this interference, otherwise the theory is not *closed.* As to psychoanalysis, a detailed explanation of the mechanism of the treatment is a rather carefully integrated part of the theory. Thus this formal requirement is fulfilled. There is a certain analogy between this phenomenon of closure of a historical theory and the necessity of considering the effect of the measuring procedures in an experimental discipline.

Law and Convention in Psychology*

PAUL E. MEEHL

IN HIS RECENT REVIEW on "The History and Present Status of the Law of Effect," Postman (19) lays considerable emphasis on the problem of "circularity" which he sees as crucial in the formulation of the law. He says:

> Whereas some critics were most concerned with the mechanisms mediating effect, others focussed their attention on the nature of the satisfiers and annoyers to which reference is made in Thorndike's law. Although Spencer and Bain, in whose tradition Thorndike continued, frankly invoked pleasure and pain as agents responsible for the fixation and elimination of responses, Thorndike's law has been a law of *effect*, not *affect*. He carefully defines satisfiers and annoyers in terms independent of subjective experience and report. "By a satisfying state of affairs is meant one which the animal does nothing to avoid, often doing such things as to attain and preserve it. By a discomforting state of affairs is meant one which the animal avoids and abandons." Although admittedly free of hedonism, such a definition of satisfiers and annoyers has faced another serious difficulty: the danger of circularity. The critic may easily reword the definition to read: "The animal does what it does because it does it, and it does not do what it does not do because it does not do it." This *reductio ad adsurdum* is probably not entirely fair, but it points up the danger of the definition in the absence of an *independent* determination of the nature of satisfiers and annoyers. The satisfying or annoying nature of a state of affairs can usually be determined fully only in the course of a learning experiment and cannot then be invoked as a causal condition of learning without circularity. In their experimental work Thorndike and his associates have made no significant attempts to establish the satisfying or annoying nature of their rewards and punishments independently of the learning experiment (19, p. 496).

And a little later Postman says:

> Stripped of virtually all defining properties and qualifications, the law does indeed have a very wide range of applicability but only at the expense of vagueness. The sum and substance of the argument now is that something happens in the organism (nervous system) after an act is performed. The fact that something happens influences further action. This something is, however, so little defined that it has almost no predictive efficiency. The O.K. reaction has no measurable properties, the conditions for its occurrence are so general as to embrace almost every conceivable situation. Hence the operation of O.K. reaction can be inferred only *ex post facto*, after learning has taken place. But here we are again impaled on the horns of the dilemma of circularity (19, p. 497).

* "On the Circularity of the Law of Effect," *Psychological Bulletin*, 47, 1950. Reprinted by kind permission of the author and the editor.

And still further:

In attempting to evaluate the controversy which has raged around the definition of satisfiers one is struck by the key importance of the hedonistic issue. Certainly hedonism is an immediate ancestor of the law, and now that the principle of effect has reached an uneasy maturity it is clear that it cannot deny its origin without sacrificing much of its vigor. When the law is stripped of hedonistic implications, when effect is not identified with tension-reduction or pleasure (as by Thorndike), the law of effect can do no more than claim that the state of affairs resulting from a response in some way influences future responses. Such a statement is a truism and hardly lends itself to the rigorous deduction of hypotheses and experimental tests. If a neohedonistic position is frankly assumed (as, e.g., by Mowrer) the law becomes an important tool for research, provided "satisfaction" is independently defined and not merely inferred from the fact that learning has occurred (19, p. 501).

Throughout Postman's paper this problem is constantly lurking behind the scenes even when the author does not single it out for specific mention. I am in complete agreement with Postman's final remark that "at the present state of our knowledge the law of effect as a monistic principle explaining all learning has not been substantiated," and Postman performs a service by emphasizing this problem of circularity in his discussion of the "law." I am inclined, however, to think that he has settled the question of circularity somewhat too easily, and that his settlement of it has an effect upon much of his argumentation. I gather from the above quotations that Postman looks upon any definition of effect or reinforcement in terms of the resulting change in response strength as "circular," where that word has a pejorative sense. If he is right in this it is very serious. While the law of effect has many difficulties, I do not believe that "circularity" is among them. To show this is the aim of the present paper.

I shall consider the problem of circularity in the law of effect as identical with the problem of circularity in the definition of *reinforcement* in instrumental conditioning. I take it that Postman does the same, since in the first quotation above he cites a passage from Hilgard and Marquis' *Conditioning and Learning*, where the two problems are considered together and with free interchange of the two terminologies. These authors say:

It is apparent that no definition of effect provides an independent measure of the strength of reinforcement. The degree of satisfaction, of complacency, or of tension reduction has not been objectively determined. The strength of reinforcement can be given comprehensive definition only in terms of the amount of learning resulting from it. This is, of course, a circular definition, if strength of reinforcement is to be used as a factor determining degree of learning. A partial escape from circularity is achieved by the fact that a stimulus such as food which is found to be reinforcing in one situation will also be reinforcing in other situations, and with other animals (9, p. 83).

Writing in 1948, however, Hilgard states concerning Thorndike's "operational" definition of satisfiers and annoyers:

These definitions are not circular, so far as the law of effect is concerned. That is, the states of affairs characterized as satisfying and annoying are specified independently of their influence upon modifiable connections. The law of effect then states what may be expected to happen to preceding modifiable connections which are followed by such specified states. The objection that Thorndike was lacking in objectivity in the statement of the law of effect is not a valid one (8, p. 24).

Hilgard is willing to let the concept of reinforcement (effect, satisfaction, reward) be introduced on the basis of behavior, but only because there are behavioral criteria of seeking and avoiding other than the effect of reinforcement upon *modifiable* connections. Whether this restriction is necessary needs to be considered carefully.

Skinner dismisses the whole problem in two sentences:

> A reinforcing stimulus is defined as such by its power to produce the resulting change. There is no circularity about this; some stimuli are found to produce the change, others not, and they are classified as reinforcing and nonreinforcing accordingly (22, p. 62).

Spence (23) takes essentially the same tack in his recent discussions of secondary reinforcement. The stimuli which impinge upon an organism may be divided, he says, into two classes: those which produce an increment in response strength, and those which do not. It seems from the several preceding quotations that there is a lack of agreement as to whether or not the law of effect or the principle of reinforcement involves an unavoidable circularity, or, if it does not, how circularity is to be avoided. In what follows, I make no claim to originality, since the essence of my development is contained in the previous quotations, together with the work of Tolman. But I feel it worthwhile to bring the arguments together in one context, and to show that the problem merits somewhat more extended treatment than is usually given it. Without claiming to present a definitive solution, I shall indicate the general direction which I believe the solution might take, and in the process introduce certain distinctions and terminological proposals which I feel might clarify our discussion and experimentation.

The Meaning of Circularity

It must be pointed out that there are two meanings of the word "circular" in common use. We have on the one hand circularity in *definition,* in which an unfamiliar term is defined by using other terms which are (directly or ultimately) defined by the term in question. There is no question of circularity in this sense in a definition of the Skinner-Spence type. Let us accept as a crude preliminary formulation the following: "A reinforcing stimulus is one which increases the subsequent strength of responses which immediately precede it." The words *stimulus,*[1] *strength, increase* and *re-*

[1] "Stimulus" will be used broadly to include "stimulus change," and stimulus configurations of all degrees of patterning and complexity.

sponse are all definable without any reference to the fact or theory of reinforcement. The definitions of these terms, particularly the term "response," present terrible difficulties; but I do not know of anyone who maintains that they involve the notion of reinforcement. Words such as these are current in the vocabulary of many kinds of psychological theorists who do not accept the Law of Effect as a principle of learning and in the absence of any indications to the contrary, I shall assume that we can tell what we mean by them. We can determine empirically when the strength of a response has increased without knowing anything about reinforcing stimuli, drives, satisfactions, and the like. It seems clear that the definition of a reinforcing stimulus in terms of its effect on response strength does not involve circularity in *this* sense.

The other meaning of the word circularity refers not to meanings (definition of terms) but to the establishment of propositions. We speak of *proofs* as being circular if it can be shown that in the process of establishing (proving) a proposition we have made use of the probandum. I am not aware that any responsible theorist has attempted to "prove" the Law of Effect in this way. It is true that those who look upon the law as fundamental are skeptical when they hear of a case of increase of response strength which does not *seem* to involve any obvious reinforcing consequences so that they begin to invent hypotheses to explain the results. There is no harm in this so long as the proposed explanations are in principle confirmable on the basis of some other experimental consequences, however remote. If an animal learns a response sequence without being given food, water, or any of the usual rewards, I suspect most Hullians would begin to talk about secondary reinforcement present in the situation. One can, of course, be careless with this kind of explanation, but there is nothing intrinsic to the concept that entails non-confirmability. The establishment of secondary reinforcing effects as explanations of a given experimental result consists in combining the facts known about primary reinforcers with facts about the animal's life history, in terms of which we understand how certain stimuli have acquired their secondary reinforcing powers. People on both sides of the present controversy over reinforcement theory are performing many different sorts of experiments in order to confirm or disconfirm the Law of Effect. It would seem that if the law of effect *were* being treated by anyone as a consequence of definition, or established by some hidden assumption of its truth, the experiments would not be going on.

Can "Reinforcement" be Independently Defined?

Nonetheless, when we think about this definition we feel uncomfortable. I do not think we have in mind either a circularity in definition or a begging-the-question fallacy, but some sort of peculiar pseudo-circularity in which it seems to us vaguely that the law *could* be "derived" from the proposed definition, even though no one in fact seems to be trying to do it this way. The problem can be stated very simply: How can we introduce the concept of reinforcement in terms of effect upon strength, and still have a "law of effect" or "principle of reinforcement" which has the empirical content that everybody seems to be taking for granted in experimentation?

1. Suppose we reject the Thorndike-Skinner-Spence procedure of defining reinforcement in terms of response strength, and decide to define the term quite independently of the learning process. The first possibility, which we shall dismiss rather dogmatically, is to do it subjectivistically in terms of pleasure, experiences of satisfaction, and the like. Aside from the general behavioristic objections, and the specific problems of measurement created, this approach is not feasible because it leaves us without any basis for speaking of reinforcing value in the case of that very important class of motivations that are unconscious or at least inadequately verbalized in the human case; and it makes impossible the establishment of reinforcing value in the case of lower organisms. At the present time there are probably very few psychologists who would consider this alternative seriously.

2. Secondly, we might try to define reinforcers in terms of certain physical properties on the stimulus side. I shall attempt to show below that this is a procedure which *follows* the introduction of the generic notion of a reinforcer, and which at a later stage becomes very important. But no one wants to group together an arbitrary class of physical objects or stimuli and call them "reinforcers," since the aim of our concept formation is to make possible the statement of laws. The possibility of identifying common physical properties of that large class of stimuli already grouped together as "rewarding" seems very remote. Besides, we would set up these properties or sets of properties by examining the members of the reinforcing class, which we already have set apart on some basis or other; and the question is: How have we arrived at the members of that class?

3. A third possibility, seen in the work of Hull, is to define reinforcement ultimately in terms of drive reduction, that is, in terms of the inner physiological events involved. Here again, I do not suppose that anyone would be able to give even the vaguest specification of the defining property of all neural events which are reinforcing. Even for the so-called primary physiological needs such as hunger, the evidence as to their exact physiological basis is most incomplete. No psychologist today is willing to equate "hunger" with "stomach contractions," in the light of the experimentation on visceral denervations, specific sub-hungers, and the like. In other cases, we have practically no information on the neurophysiology, e.g., the neurophysiologic basis of the reinforcing effect of the presence of another organism, the turning off of a light in the Skinner box, or the going through of "exploratory" behavior on the other side of a grill. There is some reason to suppose that certain stimuli retain their secondary reinforcing value in the absence of the primary drive (2, 16), which complicates the problem further.

These considerations force a return to the *effect* of stimuli as a basis for specifying that they are reinforcers, and this leads to the paradox. If we define a reinforcing agent by its effect upon learning, then it seems that whenever learning is effected, we know ("by definition") that we have given a reinforcement. For surely, when the organism behaves, some stimulus change occurs, if nothing else than the proprioceptive effects of responding. If the behavior increases in strength, then these stimulus changes, which were in fact preceded by the response, are reinforcers. Hence, it seems that a definition of reinforcement in terms of an increase of habit strength makes the law tautological and devoid of factual content. This train of thought, which I am sure is familiar to most readers, seems obvious and straightforward. But I believe it can be shown to be mistaken, once the law is stated *explicitly* in the way we all really think of it *implicitly* when we perform experiments or try to explain a given case of learning.

An Empirical Derivation of Reinforcement

Let us begin afresh by going to the behavior itself in a situation in which there is little or no disagreement as to what occurs. Consider a bright, inductively inclined Martian, who had never experienced any needs or satisfactions (except perhaps *n Cognizance*!) † and who was observing the behavior of a rat in successive runnings in a T-maze. For the moment we shall simply consider a "standard rat," neglecting the individual differences in parameters and the accidents of personal histories that generate special secondary reinforcing properties. These refinements need to be added later, but as is usually the case will have to be added by being integrated into the whole structure of reinforcement theory, since we cannot treat everything at once. At the beginning, the Martian observes that the organism turns to the right or left with, let us say, about equal frequency. With further trials, a change occurs until finally the rat is responding close to 100% of the time by turning to the right. A Martian could obviously discover this with no notion of rewards, pleasure and the like. If he is ingenious enough to think of the possibility that the strength of a response might be influenced by the events that follow it in time, he would then proceed to investigate the changes that are contingent on this right turning.[2] He notes that when the rat turns to the right he brings about the following states of affairs on the stimulus side which he does not bring about when he turns to the left: He ends up nearer to the right-hand wall, which is painted green; he twists his own body to the right in responding; he ends up in a wooden box having knots in the wood; he ends up nearer the North pole; and to a dynamo on the other side of the campus; and he comes into the presence of a cup of sunflower seeds. These are the stimuli (stimulus changes) which are contingent on right turns. Is it possible that the gradual strengthening of the right turning is dependent upon one, some, or all of these changes follow-

† [See footnote † on p. 607 for definition of *n Cognizance*. Editors' note.]

[2] Actually, no great ingenuity is involved here. Study of the events immediately *preceding* a run, e.g., the manner in which the experimenter handles the rat, what orientation he gives its head in placing it in the entry box, etc., would fail to reveal any systematic factor related to the direction of a preference. Considering this, together with the fact that before any runs have been made no preference exists, the Martian would be led to ask whether it is something that happens *after* the run (or during it) that affects the probability of a similar choice in subsequent runs.

ing it? Our scientist from Mars would proceed to study a series of standard rats in the situation, altering the above variables systematically by usual inductive procedures. As a matter of empirical fact, he would discover that, within certain very wide limits, alterations in the first five have no effect. The sixth, the sunflower seeds, have a tremendous effect. He finds that he can alter the geographical direction, the direction of the body twist required, the wall color approached, etc.—that he can introduce all manner of modifications in the other factors; and so long as the sunflower seeds are presented, the rat will tend to go to where they are. On the other hand, if the sunflower seeds are omitted, and nothing else put in their place, a preference fails to develop as a function of these remaining differences.

But we have already greatly over-simplified. Actually, the Martian would discover that the effect of finding sunflower seeds in some cases is almost too slight to be detected; furthermore, even after a preference has been acquired, it may on some occasions fail to show itself. Now, it has already been apparent that when he comes upon these sunflower seeds, the rat behaves toward them in a characteristic way, that is, he ingests them. In seeking to understand the variability in the development and manifestation of a preference, one would notice a correlation between the strengthening of a preference and the rate, strength, and consistency of ingestive responses in the presence of the food. Identifying the same rat on successive days, it is found that on those days on which a preference already established broke down, very frequently the ingestive response in the presence of the sunflower seeds was at a very low or even zero strength. Failing to find anything varying in the maze situation itself to account for these differences, one can study the experiences of the animals between runs. Here appears a very striking correlate of both preference strength *and* the ingestive response in the maze: that which a human experimenter would call the "feeding schedule." The Martian would observe that when sunflower seeds were made available to the rats in their cages, they behave with respect to them in the same way as they do when they come upon the sunflower seeds in the goal box: namely, with ingestive responses. He would discover, again by systematic variation in these conditions, that such matters as the chemical nature of the substance made available, the periodicity of its availability, the lapse of time between when it was last available and the maze run; the rate of ingestion manifested at the moment of beginning deprivation (i.e., how close the rat was to satiety when interrupted), and so on, all exert an effect upon the maze response. By far the most intimate correlate would be the lapse of time since feeding. To quote Skinner again,

The problem of drive arises because much of the behavior of an organism shows an apparent variability. A rat does not always respond to food placed before it, and a factor called its "hunger" is invoked by way of explanation. The rat is said to eat only when it is hungry. It is because eating is not inevitable that we are led to hypothesize the internal state to which we may assign the variability. Where there is no variability, no state is needed. . . . In dealing with the kind of behavior that gives rise to the concept of hunger, we are concerned with the strength of a certain class of reflexes and with the two principal operations that affect it—feeding and fasting (22, pp. 341, 343).

For a considerable class of stimuli found to affect choice behavior in the maze, there is a fairly well demarcated class of events in the extra maze activities which exert an effect. Food, water, a female rat, all depend for their efficacy upon a deprivation schedule of some sort. For other stimuli, the rest of the day's activities seem of less relevance. For example, the effects of turning off a light in the Skinner box upon the lever pressing response would not depend upon a schedule of extra box illumination in any such obvious way as the effects of a food pellet depend upon the extra maze operations of feeding and fasting. Even here, at the extremes, it is likely that the schedule has some effect. Although I know of no experimental material on the point, it would be surprising if rats raised and maintained in a dark or extremely bright living cage would show the same response to light-off as a reinforcing agent. In order to keep the discussion quite general, I shall refer to *schedule-reinforcer* combinations, which will be understood to include those combinations in which almost any life-maintaining schedule is adequate. Whether there are any such does not need to be settled here. The stimulus presented is a *reinforcer,* and the presentation of it (an "event") is a *reinforcement.*

We are now in possession of a rather simple set of empirical facts. A certain stimulus, for a rat which has been under a specified schedule, for instance the sunflower seeds for a rat who has not ingested anything for 23 hours, will exert a strengthening effect. We can formulate a "law" stated crudely as follows: "In a rat which has not recently ingested sunflower seeds, bran mash, Purina chow, etc., a response of turning in a given direction in the T-maze will be increased if the fairly immediate presentation of sunflower seeds, etc., is made contingent upon that response." Similarly, we would find such a specific law to hold for thirst and water, sex and a mate, and so on. The general form of such special laws would be: "On schedule M, the termination of response sequence R, in setting S, by stimulus S^1 is followed by an increment in the strength of S.R." Such a law may be called a *situational-reinforcement* law, where the "reinforcement" is understood to stand for "presentation-of-a-reinforcer-following-a-specified-maintenance-schedule," and the term "situational" covers "response R in situation S."

Actually, in any given case, M, R, S, S^1 are classes. This is indicated by the suspicious-looking "etc." in the first "law" above. There is nothing shady about this "etc.," inasmuch as what is actually involved here is a class of operations and effects which are ultimately to be specified by locating each instance with respect to a whole complex set of dimensions. For example, Guttman (6) shows a relation between concentration of sugar solution used as a reinforcing agent and the strength of the lever pressing response. Heron and Peake (7) have studied protein as a specific component of reinforcement. There is to be discovered a vast number of such rather special laws which are comparable to the myriads of laws in chemistry concerning the solubility of substance Y in substance X and the like.

The next thing to notice is that while the schedule, reinforcement, response, and situation are all classes showing certain relations to one another, in general the schedule and reinforcer are related to one another more intimately than either is to the situation or response. The strength of a response which is maintained by food reinforcement is heavily dependent upon the feeding-fasting schedule, whereas the effect of a food reinforcement upon a response is relatively independent of, say recency of copulatory activity, so that a given schedule-reinforcement pair are "tied" to one another. But the Martian observes that the strengthening effect of a given schedule-reinforcement combination is relatively (not wholly!) neutral with respect to the response we are trying to strengthen and the situation in which we are trying to strengthen it. For a hungry rat, right turning depends heavily upon finding food; for a satiated rat, it depends very little. So the feeding schedule is intimately related to the reinforcing agent's efficacy. However, this "hungry-food" schedule-reinforcement combination seems to be capable of strengthening chain-pulling, lever-pressing, wheel-turning, marble-rolling, gnawing-through-paper, and so on through a very wide range of behaviors differing greatly in their topography and in their stimulus conditions. This leads to the question, will a certain schedule-reinforcer combination increase the strength of *any* response, in *any* setting? This question turns out empirically to be answered in the negative, since we find at least three limitations upon the generality of a schedule-reinforcer combination as response strengthener. Leaving out the trivial case in which the response is anatomically impossible, e.g., to teach an elephant to thread a needle, we find:

1. No situation-response sequences may involve stimulus dimensions which are not discriminable by the organism. (Tolman's "discriminating capacities.")

2. Some response sequences seem on the basis of their sequence, timing, or "complexity" not to be learnable by members of a given species, or subgroups within a species. It appears impossible to teach a rat a quintuple alternation problem, or to teach a human moron integral calculus.

3. There are cases in which the response we wish to strengthen is incompatible with responses at a very high (and relatively unmodifiable) strength under the schedule-stimulus combinations we are employing. For example, it would probably be next to impossible to teach a very hungry cat to carry a piece of fresh liver across the room, deposit it in a box, and return to receive food as a reinforcement. "Defensive" and "anxiety-related" responses are among the most important examples of this case.

How do we discover what responses have these characteristics? Experimentally, as we discover anything else. Let us call a situation-response combination having none of these properties *learnable*. A positive definition will be given below. What we find is that whereas learnable responses seem to differ somewhat in their "readiness" under different schedule-reinforcement combinations, this is a matter of parameters and does not invalidate the following tentative "law," which is stated qualitatively: "Any learnable response will be strengthened by sunflower seeds as a reinforcer." The general form of such a law is "the stimulus S^1 on schedule M will increase the strength of any learnable response." I shall call such a law a *trans-situational reinforcement* law. It must be noted carefully that such a law is still about a *particular* reinforcing agent, having, to be sure, a class character; but the particular reinforcing agent (and its associated necessary schedule, if any) is no longer tied to the response sequence first studied. The reinforcing property of sunflower seeds was noted first in the T-maze. The Martian will discover that white rats *can* learn to pull chains, press levers, and roll marbles. He finds that these learnable responses can also be strengthened by making the feeding of sunflower seeds contingent upon them. He makes the inductive generalization that sunflower seeds would exert this effect upon all learnable responses in the rat.

He now asks the obvious question: Are all schedule-reinforcer combinations like this? That is to say, when we study a new schedule-reinforcer combination and find it strengthens a response, can we assume that it will increase the strength of all learnable responses? Naturally, our confidence in the general reinforcing power of any particular one will increase as we try it out on more and more learnable responses. But we do not know whether a higher-order inductive statement is justified, so long as we study sunflower seeds only or study several kinds of agents but in only one situation each.

Having found a particular reinforcer in a particular situation, we have discovered that it is trans-situational. Next we discover that all of the reinforcers that we have investigated have turned out to be trans-situational. The next induction is, "If a learnable response is followed by a stimulus which is known to be a reinforcer of learnable responses the strength will increase." A shorter way of saying this, having first defined a reinforcer as "a stimulus which will increase the strength of at least one learnable response," is simply: *all reinforcers are trans-situational.* Nothing is said as to the *amount* of strengthening. It is sufficient, in order to demonstrate the trans-situational character of a reinforcing agent, to show that it produces an increment in strength. If equal increments were required, it is probable that very few (if any) reinforcers would be trans-situational because of the varying behavior readinesses and different parameters of habit acquisitions from one drive to another and from one situation to another.

This assertion, that all reinforcers are trans-situational, I propose to call the *Weak Law of Effect*. It is not our problem in this paper to discuss whether the Weak Law of Effect holds or not. A "proof" of the Weak Law of Effect consists, as usual, of establishing inductively many instances of it in a variety of situations with our confidence increasing on the basis of the usual inductive canons. A "disproof" of the Weak Law of Effect would involve showing that a certain stimulus change acts as a reinforcing agent for one response, i.e., that the presentation of this stimulus following the response will increase the latter's strength; but that another response, previously established as learnable, cannot be strengthened by a presentation of this agent. A failure of the Weak Law of Effect to hold strictly would not be particularly serious, since one could (at the very least!) specify the exceptions and would hope to be able to generalize about them, that is, to discover empirically what are the kinds of reinforcers, or kinds of differences among situations, which reveal its invalidity. Actually, here again we have a case in which the law is stated in a qualitative all-or-none form; but the development of a science of behavior would eventually result in substituting a multiplicity of laws indicating the extent to which the reinforcing (strengthening) property generalized over various dimensions of the stimulus side, the reinforcing agent, and the "required" response properties. Assuming the Weak Law of Effect to have been established inductively, where are we now in our development? We have specific situation-reinforcer laws which state that a given stimulus is a reinforcing agent for a specified kind of response in a specified situation. As an example, we discover that for a standard rat, sunflower seeds will strengthen right turning in the T-maze. Having established several such specific situation-reinforcer laws, we find it convenient to introduce a definition, saying that a situational reinforcer is a stimulus which occurs as a term in such a specific situation-reinforcer law. Sunflower seeds are hence situational reinforcers. This definition is "arbitrary" or "conventional" in the usual sense, but clearly leads to no circularity. We cannot tell from the definition whether or not there is such a thing as a situational reinforcer, just as we cannot tell from the definition of a unicorn or of the phrase "King of France" whether such a thing exists. All we stipulate in the definition is that if a thing having certain properties turns out to exist, we will call it by this name. That there are situational reinforcers, that is to say, that we can find stimuli that do increase the strength of responses in a certain situation, is an empirical result. It is obvious that the specific situation-reinforcer laws have a perfectly good factual content (e.g., each such law could be false) in spite of the conventional character of the definition.

If our science contained nothing but a collection of such situational-reinforcer laws, we would still be in possession of valuable information. But we discover inductively that we can actually say more than this. For any given reinforcer, we discover that it can in fact be used to increase the strength of responses differing very greatly in topography from the one which originally led us to infer that it was a reinforcer, and in very different stimulating fields. It is true that there are a few special cases, as our cat with the liver, in which we cannot increase the strength of a *kind* of a response (carrying an object from one place to another) which we know from independent study this species is able to learn. But in all such cases we are able to specify an interfering response at such high strength that the behavior in question does not get a chance to be emitted, and hence cannot be reinforced. With this exception, we are able to say that a given reinforcer will increase the strength of all learnable responses of the species; although there will be quantitative differences which remain to be discovered and generalized about after much painstaking experimentation. We define a reinforcer which is of this sort as trans-situational, and from a study of numerous reinforcers we conclude that they are all of this type. The second order induction that all reinforcers are trans-situational (the Weak Law of Effect) is then made.

This last is certainly a very rich and powerful induction. It is true that to make predictions we must study at least one learnable response in order to find out whether a given stimulus change is reinforcing, and we must know for any contemplated response whether it is learnable. Experience with a given species need not be too extensive in order to get a general idea of the kinds of behavior which are possible and learnable; and once having this, we proceed to strengthen responses by means of reinforcing agents which have never been utilized before in connection with these responses. This is so commonplace that we are likely to underestimate its theoretical significance. So far as I know, no animal psychologist has the least hesitation in utilizing any of a very large class of reinforcing objects called "food" in experimentation upon practically any kind of behavior which he is interested in studying. Should he find a failure of response strength to increase, the chances of his asking what is wrong with the food are negligible. His inductive confidence in the Weak Law of Effect is such that he will immediately begin to investigate what is wrong with the stimulus field, or what requirements concerning the response properties he has imposed which transcend the powers of the organism. I am stressing this point because there is a tendency to say that since we have to study the effects upon strength in order to know whether an agent is reinforcing, we do not really "know anything" when we have enunciated the Law of Effect. I think it should be obvious from the diversity of both the class called learnable and the class of agents called reinforcing that to the extent that this law holds almost without exception, when we have enunciated it we have said a great deal.

The man from Mars might be tempted here to take a final step which would be suggested by the ubiquity of the manifestations of the Weak Law of Effect. It might occur to him that the great majority of the instances in which changes in response strength occur seem to involve the operation of the Weak Law, i.e., the presentation of a member of the reinforcing class. Perhaps it is not only true that any learnable response can be strengthened by the presentation of a trans-situational reinforcer but may it not be that this is the *only* way to increase the strength of responses (by learning)? Response strength may be increased by surgical and drug procedures, and also by maturation; but the demarcation of learning as a very general mode of response change, while it presents difficult problems, need not concern us here. Assuming that we have some satisfactory basis for distinguishing an increase in the strength which is based upon "experience" rather than upon interference with the reaction mechanism or biological growth determined by genetic factors given minimal (viable) environments, we may ask whether learning takes place on any *other* basis than the Weak Law of Effect. Certain apparent exceptions to this statement of reinforcement as a necessary condition would appear, but the Martian might ask whether these exceptions are more apparent than real. The formulation of such a law would run something like this: "Every learned increment in response strength requires the operation of a trans-situational reinforcer." I shall designate this rash inductive leap as the *Strong Law of Effect.*

It appears obvious that this also is a statement far from being experimentally empty or in any sense a consequence of definition. I have heard psychologists translate the statement "he learns because he was reinforced" as being tantamount to "he learns because he learns." Postman suggests the same kind of thing in the first quotation above. This is too easy. The expanded form which I suspect everyone has implicitly in mind when he talks about the Strong Law of Effect is: "He learns following the presentation of a stimulus change which for this species has the property of increasing response strength; and, other things being equal in the present setting, if this change had *not* occurred he would not have learned." Such a statement can clearly be false to fact, either because no such trans-situational reinforcer can be shown to have been present, or because the same learning can be shown to be producible without it in the present setting. The claim of the reinforcement theorist to explanation is (at this stage of our knowledge) of exactly the same character as "he developed these symptoms because he was invaded by the Koch bacillus, and we know that the Koch bacillus has these effects." This is not a very *detailed* explanation, because the intermediate or micro-details of the causal sequence are not given; but it is certainly neither factually empty nor trivial.

In our initial quotation from Postman, we find him saying, "The satisfying or annoying nature of a state of affairs can usually be determined fully only in the course of a learning experiment and cannot then be invoked as a causal condition of learning without circularity." The trouble with this remark lies in the ambiguity of the phrase "*a* learning experiment." That we cannot know what is reinforcing without having done *some* experimentation is obvious, and is just as it should be in an empirical science. But once having found that a certain state of affairs *is* reinforcing for a given species, there is no reason why a given case of learning cannot be explained by invoking the occurrence of this state of affairs as a causal condition. The definition of force does not entail the truth of Hooke's law. It is only by an experiment that we find out that strain is proportional to stress. Once having found it out, we are all quite comfortable in utilizing Hooke's law to account for the particular cases we come across. I am confident that Postman would not be disturbed if in answer to the question, "Why does that door close all the time?" someone were to reply, "Because it has a spring attached to it on the other side." There is no more "circularity" in this kind of causal accounting than in any other kind. It is perfectly true that this kind of "lowest-order" explanation is not very intellectually satisfying in some cases, although even here there is a considerable variability depending upon our familiarity with the situation. For a detailed consideration of these problems by more qualified persons I refer the reader to papers by Hospers (10), Feigl (4, 5), and Pratt (20).

I think it is obvious that this is the way we think of the Law of Effect, whatever we may think as to its truth. When an apparent case of learning in the absence of reinforcement occurs, those who are interested in preserving the status of the Law of Effect (in my terminology, in preserving the status of the *Strong* Law of Effect) begin to search for changes following the response which can be shown to be of the reinforcing sort. They do not simply look for *any* stimulus change and insist ("by definition") that it is a reinforcement. The statement that a given case of apparently non-reinforcement learning is actually based upon secondary reinforcement is essentially a claim that some stimulus change can be shown to have followed the strengthened response, and that this stimulus change has (still earlier) been put in temporal contiguity with a stimulus change of which we know, from a *diversity* of situations, that it exerts a reinforcing effect.

Abandoning the charge of circularity, a critic might offer a "practical" criticism, saying, "What good does it do to know that a reinforcer strengthens, when the only way to tell when something is a reinforcer is to see if it strengthens?" The trouble here lies in the vagueness, since the *generality* is not indicated, and this failure to indicate generality neglects the usual advantages of induction. That a describable state of affairs *is* reinforcing can only be found out, to be sure, by experimenting on some organisms utilizing *some* learnable response. But it is not required (if the Weak Law of Effect is true) that we, so to speak, start afresh with each new organism of the species and each new response. As a matter of fact, after we have considerable experience with a given species, we can generalize about the physical properties of a stimulus class. So that finally "food" means many substances which may never yet have been tried in a learning situation, and may never have been presented in natural circumstances to the members of a particular species. Wild rats do not eat Purina Chow. Here we begin to approach inductively one of the previously rejected bases of defining reinforcement, namely, the physical character of the stimulus change itself. To ask for a definition of reinforcers which will tell us beforehand for a given species which objects or stimuli will exert the reinforcing effect is to ask that a definition should tell us what the world is like before we investigate it, which is not possible in any science. It happens that the psychologist is worse off than others, because species differences, individual hereditary differences, and differences of the reactional biography make a larger mass of facts necessary in order to know whether a given agent will reinforce a particular organism. But at worst the Weak Law of Effect in conjunction with its member laws is far from useless. When I know inductively that all non-toxic substances containing sugar will act as reinforcers for organisms from rat to man and therefore that I can almost certainly strengthen all responses learnable by any of these species on the basis of the presentation of any of these substances, I know a great deal and my science has a very considerable predictive power.

An Analogous Problem in Physics

It is instructive to consider a somewhat analogous problem in physics, in the definition of "force." Once mass has been defined by some such artifice as Mach's acceleration-ratio technique, and acceleration defined in terms of time and distance, Newton's second law is a *definition* of force. I neglect here other attempts to introduce the notion such as the "school of the thread" (18), utilizing Hooke's law in the form of a definition rather than a law, or its modern variants, e.g., Keenan's (13) recent effort. Force is "that which accelerates mass." Mach's introduction of the concept of mass was somewhat disturbing to certain of his contemporaries because of a suggested circularity. Mach saw that it was the *inertial* character of mass, rather than "weight" or "quantity of matter" which was crucial in setting up the definition of force. Accordingly, he proceeds as follows:

a. *Experimental Proposition.* Bodies set opposite each other induce in each other, under certain circumstances to be specified by experimental physics, contrary *accelerations* in the direction of their line of junction. (The principle of inertia is included in this.)

b. *Definition.* The mass-ratio of any two bodies is the negative inverse ratio of the mutually induced accelerations of those bodies.

c. *Experimental Proposition.* The mass-ratios of bodies are independent of the character of the physical states (of the bodies) that condition the mutual accelerations produced, be those states electrical, magnetic, or what not; and they remain, moreover, the same, whether they are mediately or immediately arrived at.

d. *Experimental Proposition.* The accelerations which any number of bodies A, B, C, . . . induce in a body K, are independent of each other. (The principle of the parallelogram of forces follows immediately from this.)

e. *Definition.* Moving force is the product of the mass-value of a body into the acceleration induced in that body. Then the remaining arbitrary definitions of the algebraical expressions "momentum," "vis viva," and the like, might follow. But these are by no means indispensable. The propositions above set forth satisfy the requirements of simplicity and parsimony which on economico-scientific grounds, must be exacted of them. They are, moreover, obvious and clear; for no doubt can exist with respect to any one of them either concerning its meaning or its source; and we always know whether it asserts an experience or an arbitrary convention (17, pp. 243–244).

In the appendix to the second English edition, Mach replies to critics of this procedure as follows:

A special difficulty seems to be still found in accepting my definition of mass. Streintz has remarked in criticism of it that it is based solely upon gravity, although this was expressly excluded in my first formulation of the definition (1868). Nevertheless, this criticism is again and again put forward, and quite recently even by Volkmann. My definition simply takes note of the fact that bodies in mutual relationship, whether it be that of action at a distance, so called, or whether rigid or elastic connexions be considered, determine in one another changes of velocity (accelerations). More than this, one does not need to know in order to be able to form a definition with perfect assurance and without the fear of building on sand. It is not correct as Höfler asserts, that this definition tacitly assumes *one and the same force* acting on both masses. It does not assume even the notion of force, since the latter is built up subsequently upon the notion of mass, and gives then the principle of action and reaction quite independently and without falling into Newton's logical error. In this arrangement one concept is not misplaced and made to rest on another which threatens to give way under it (17, pp. 558–559).

It is obvious that Mach defines mass in the way he does *so that* the definition of force by $F = ma$ will lead to the kinds of laws we want. That is, a previous "knowledge" of the law of gravity based upon a cruder notion of mass is involved historically in the formulation of such a definition. But the crucial point is that it is involved only in the context of discovery, not in the context of justification (21, pp. 6–7). There is nothing wrong with making use of any notions, including vague anthropomorphic experiences of pleasure, in deciding how we shall formulate definitions, since our aim is to erect concepts and constructs which will fit into the most convenient and powerful system of laws. The point is that we wish to come out with explicit notions that are free of this vagueness and which do not require any notions which cannot be finally introduced objectively. There is probably a remnant of hedonism in the thinking of the most sophisticated contemporary reinforcement theorists, and there is no reason why anybody should pretend that when he talks about rewards he does not have some faint component in his thinking which involves the projection of such pleasure-pain experiences. But this does not mean that these notions are made part of the scientific structure he erects, in the sense that either the definitions of terms or the establishment of the laws requires such associated imagery in his readers. I suggest that Thorndike's critics are in the same position as Mach's.

One might ask, why would a physicist be upset should he attend a spiritualist seance and find tumblers leaping off tables and floating through the air? If the concept of force is given simply by the relation $F = ma$, then, if a glass tumbler undergoes an acceleration, a force must act and his definition assures him that the physical world will not surprise him. I do not think the answer to this question is far to seek. While it is admittedly a question of decision, I doubt that most physicists would decide to say that an acceleration occurred in the absence of a force. If the genuineness of the phenomenon were satisfactorily established, I do not think there would be a re-definition of the *concept* of force, but rather that the existence of "forces" on other bases than those previously known would be assumed. That is, the physicist would not say "here is a case of acceleration without a force," but he would rather say "here is a case of force not arising from the usual mechanical, gravitational, or electro-magnetic situations which I have thought, up to now, were the sole bases on which forces came into being." It is certainly no criticism of a Newtonian definition of force (I leave out the fact that Newton, while he defined force in this way, apparently also treated his second law as one of empirical content) to say that having thus defined force you cannot know beforehand what are the conditions in the world under which forces will appear. The mechanical forces involved in direct contact, the force of gravity, and certain electrostatic and magnetic forces were known to Newton. There is nothing about his definition of force which tells us that a peculiarly directed force will exist between a wire carrying an electric current and a compass needle, nor that attracting or repelling forces will exist between parallel wires each of which carries a current. The discovery of these conditions under which forces exist was an empirical contribution of Oersted and Ampère.

Similarly, the psychologist defines what is meant by a reinforcer, and proceeds to search for the agents that fall under this definition. There are undoubtedly kinds of stimulus changes of which we are as yet unaware which will turn out to have the reinforcing property. Dr. Wilse Webb (personal communication) has found in preliminary experiments that at least in one kind of Skinner box the click produced by the operation of an empty magazine will exert a reinforcing effect in an animal whose experience has never given this stimulus an opportunity to acquire secondary reinforcing properties. This is surprising to us. What are the conditions under which this will occur? Suppose it should be found that almost *any* stimulus change within a fairly wide range (avoiding extreme intensities which are anxiety-producing) would exert a slight reinforcing effect in the Skinner box or in any similar apparatus in which there is a considerable stimulus restriction and a marked constancy in the homogeneity of the visual and auditory fields. It might be discovered that when a member of this species has remained in such a homogeneous field for a period of time, stimulus *changes* (not otherwise specified) exert a reinforcing effect. Maybe the rat is "bored" and just likes to make something happen! A difficult notion to nail down experimentally, to be sure. But its complexity and the number of things to be ruled out, does not take it out of the realm of the confirmable.

Let us consider a very extreme case. Suppose in the T-maze situation a systematic increase in the strength of the right turn should be discovered for a standard rat. Suppose that the most thoroughgoing, exhaustive manipulation of the external effect of right-turning should fail to reveal any condition necessary for the effect. "No member of the reinforcing class is to be found." I think that at this point we would begin reluctantly to consider a reinforcing property of the response itself. Perhaps turning to the right is inherently reinforcing to this species. It seems, for instance, that "fetching" behavior in certain species of dogs is self-reinforcing (or at least that it has a biologically replenished reserve). The only reason for calling right-turning "self-reinforcing" rather than simply saying that it is a response of innately high strength in the species is that a *change* in strength occurs with successive runs, otherwise "turning to the right" is simply a kind of tropism. Is the "self-reinforcing" idea factually empty? Although many people would disagree with me at this point, I do not think it is. But it has factual meaning only intradermally. There is no reason why we could not study the proprioceptive effects of a right turn and find out whether, if they are cut out, the increase in response strength continues to occur. In principle we could create the proprioceptive effects of a right turn by artificial means and on that basis strengthen a topographically different response such as lifting the fore paw, wiggling the whiskers, or the like. Here there are difficulties, but I would be prepared to argue that in principle the self-reinforcing effect of right-turning is an empirically meaningful notion.

An interesting side-light is that even the Strong Law of Effect is, as stated, compatible with the latent learning experiments. I am not interested in avoiding the consequences of those experiments by shrewd dialectics, but in the interests of clarity it should be pointed out that in, e.g., the Blodgett design, the big drop in errors *does* follow a reinforcement. So long as the Strong Law of Effect is stated qualitatively and does not explicitly mention amounts and times, it would be admittedly difficult to design an experiment in which it could be refuted. A neo-Hullian interested for some reason in preserving the Strong Law of Effect might simply add a quantitative postulate. He might assume that when a response undergoes an increment in strength on the basis of a minimally reinforcing agent (that is, one in which the asymptote of the acquisition of habit strength is relatively low), then, if subsequently a strong reinforcement is introduced, the parameter in the new growth function which determines the rate of approach to the new asymptote is greater than it would have been without the original learning. Since in the Blodgett design there is evidence of acquisition of differential habit strengths during the latent phase, such a postulate would lead to a preservation of the Strong Law of Effect. The main reason that we are concerned to deal with latent learning material of the Blodgett type is that in the reinforcement theory as now formulated, the effect of a reinforcer is implicitly assumed to operate immediately.

Relationship of Reinforcement to Drive

Perhaps a comment is needed on the way in which reinforcement has been treated here as the primary notion whereas drive, need, or demand is defined in terms of it. I do not mean to imply that need or drive is not the more "basic" factor, if by this is meant that what is a reinforcer or what acquires reinforcing properties depends upon a certain relevance to need. But this manner of speaking refers to the causal reconstruction of behavior, and reverses the epistemological order. The needs of an organism are inferred from changes in behavior strength as a function of certain states of affairs. That is to say, we "get a fix" on a need by being able to induce the chief defining properties of those states of affairs to which behavior is shown to tend. I do not see how there is any possibility in proceeding otherwise at the level of molar behavior. Whether it will be feasible or desirable to hypothesize a kind of state called need in the case of all reinforcers is a moot point at present. I gather that Hull would argue it will, whereas Skinner would argue it will not. One can consider a sort of continuum of reinforcing states of affairs at one end of which it is most easy and natural and obviously very useful to speak in terms of a need, e.g., the case of food or water; whereas at the other end, e.g., the reinforcing effects of hearing a click or turning off a light, the notion of needs seems relatively less appropriate. But the *causal* primacy of needs in our final reconstruction of behavior laws must not be confused with the epistemological status of needs, i.e., the operations by which we arrive at a conception of the needs. Whether the reduction of need is a necessary condition for learning is a question that is not involved in my formulation of either the Weak or the Strong Law of Effect since need-reduction is not equated to reinforcement. This independence of the notions of reinforcement and need-reduction is seen not only in the question of whether need-reduction is (for a sophisticated organism) a necessary condition for reinforcing effect, but it is the intention of these definitions to leave it an open question as to whether a kind of event called need-reduction is involved in reinforcing effects at any stage. The alternative to this is to exhaust completely the concept of need by defining an intervening variable via a class of reinforcing agents, i.e., the organism's "need" is not specified in any way except to say that it is "whatever state" within the organism is involved in the reinforcing effect of a stimulus change known experimentally to exert such an effect. In this case, of course, a rat may be said to have a "need" to keep the light off, to be with another rat, to hear a sound, etc. Whether this is a desirable way of speaking we need not consider here.

In the preceding developments, I have avoided consideration of refinements which would be necessary to complete the theoretical picture. The most important of these is the apparent exception to the Weak Law of Effect in which a change in strength does not occur in spite of the presentation of a known reinforcing agent because certain other dominant factors are at work. As an example, we may consider the "fixation" of a response which is followed by anxiety reduction to the point that an opposing response consistently reinforced with food fails to develop an increase in strength. In any particular situation it is the task of experimental analysis to show what the relations are; as a nice example of this I may refer to the recent work of Farber (3). Of course, if the response does not have sufficient opportunity to *occur*, be reinforced, and hence develop strength, the Weak Law of Effect is not violated. Those cases in which this is not an adequate explanation must be dealt with by considering the opposing forces, leaving open the question as to whether these opposing forces can themselves be satisfactorily subsumed under the Strong Law of Effect. The case here is not essentially different from the case in mechanics where we introduce the concept of force as a dynamic concept (that is, by accelerations produced) and subsequently apply the same notions to systems which are in equilibrium. In physics, one makes use of the laws about force which are based upon the dynamical notion of it in order to explain those cases in statics in which no motion results. Whereas the detailed reconstruction of the causal system remains as a task for the future, I do not believe there are any fundamental logical difficulties involved in the notion that a reinforcing state of affairs is initially defined by an increase in strength, and subsequently the failure of such a state of affairs to exert the effect is explained in terms of the occurrence of other operations or states which oppose it.

Summary

Let me conclude by summarizing the development, using Mach as a model. For convenience I neglect here the specification of a schedule:

a. *Experimental Proposition:* In the rat, if turning to the right in the T-maze is followed by the presentation of sunflower seeds, the strength of the right-turning response will increase. (A situational-reinforcer law.)

b. *Definition:* A stimulus or stimulus change which occurs as the strengthening condition in a situational-reinforcer law is a *reinforcer*.

This empirical law together with the above definition enables us now to assert (as an empirical statement) "sunflower seeds are a reinforcer." The empirical content of this is that there is at least one response which the presentation of sunflower seeds will strengthen.

The presentation of a reinforcer is called *reinforcement*.

c. *Definition:* If the strength of a response may be increased as a function of behavior in an exposure to a situation (rather than by surgical, drug, or maturational changes), such a response is *learnable* by the organism. No reference to reinforcement is made here; we simply require that response strength be shown to increase following "experience," of whatever sort.

d. *Experimental Propositions:* Following suitable manipulation of their experiences, rats will show increases in the strength of pressing levers, pulling chains, rolling marbles, turning to the right at certain choice points, gnawing through paper, digging through sawdust, turning wheels, etc. (Expanded, this would consist simply in a long list of specific "laws" asserting the learnability of certain response classes.)

e. *Experimental Propositions:* Sunflower seeds may be used to strengthen lever pressing, chain pulling, etc. In general, sunflower seeds may be used to strengthen all learnable responses in the rat. (This asserts the generality of the reinforcing effect of sunflower seeds and is what I am calling a trans-situational reinforcer law.)

f. *Definition:* A trans-situational reinforcer is a stimulus which will strengthen all learnable responses. (We have already defined reinforcer so that it does not commit us to its generality, that is, a reinforcer is *at least* a situational reinforcer. If there are any reinforcers which exert the reinforcing effect upon all learnable responses, they are trans-situational.) This definition with the immediately preceding experimental propositions enables us to say, "Sunflower seeds are a trans-situational reinforcer."

Such a collection of specific empirical laws in combination with the above general definition leads to a large set of laws such as these last stated ones so that in the end we find the following:

g. *Experimental Proposition:* All reinforcers are trans-situational. (The Weak Law of Effect.)

h. *Experimental Proposition:* Every increment in strength involves a trans-situational reinforcer. (The Strong Law of Effect.)

It seems clear that in the above sequence both the definitional and the factual (empirical) elements are present, and in a simple, commonplace form. The definitional and conventional elements appear in the specification of the circumstances under which a stimulus is to be called "reinforcing." Such a stipulation, however, cannot tell us whether any such stimuli exist. That they do exist, which no one doubts, is an empirical finding; and the numerous statements about them constitute situational-reinforcer laws which are in a sense the special "sub-laws" of effect. These are related to the Weak Law of Effect somewhat in the same way that the particular empirical laws about the properties of bromine, fluorine, chlorine, and so on, are related to the Periodic Law. That the stimuli which occur in the situational-reinforcer laws have a generality of their reinforcing power is also an empirical finding, at present less well established (the Weak Law of Effect). That all cases of learning require certain time relationships to the presentation of such general reinforcers is yet a further factual claim, at present very much in dispute (the Strong Law of Effect).

I can see no reason why any theorist, whatever his position, should find the preceding treatment objectionable as an explication of the Law of Effect. I do not see any way in which the Strong Law of Effect, which is after all the big contemporary issue, has been surreptitiously put into the definitions in such a way that what is intended as an empirical proposition is effectively made a consequence of our use of words. The status of the Strong Law of Effect and even to some extent the Weak Law is presently in doubt. Further, some of the words used in these definitions, e.g., the word "response," are difficult to define in a way that makes them behave in the total system as we wish them to. I have not tried to deal with all these problems at once, but I hope that there are no difficulties springing from the problem of circularity which have not been met. That it is difficult to untangle the learning sequence which has given the reinforcing property to some states of affairs, particularly in the human organism, is admitted by everyone. That a large amount of detailed work of the "botanizing" type, not particularly ego-rewarding, needs to be done before the special sub-laws of effect are stated in terms of quantitative relations is quite clear. Finally, it would be very nice if in some magical way we could *know* before studying a given species exactly what stimulus changes would have the reinforcing property; but I have tried to indicate that this is an essentially irrational demand. In the light of the previous analysis I think the burden of proof is upon those who look upon a sophisticated formulation of the Law of Effect as circular, in either of the ordinary uses of that word.

BIBLIOGRAPHY

1. Carr, H. A., *et al.* The Law of Effect: a roundtable discussion. *Psychol. Rev.*, 1938, 45, 191–218.
2. Estes, W. K. A study of motivating conditions necessary for secondary reinforcement. *Amer. Psychologist*, 1948, 3, 240–241. (Abstract.)
3. Farber, I. E. Response fixation under anxiety and non-anxiety conditions. *J. exp. Psychol.*, 1948, 38, 111–131.
4. Feigl, H. Operationism and scientific method. *Psychol. Rev.*, 1945, 52, 250–259.
5. Feigl, H. Some remarks on the meaning of scientific explanation. In H. Feigl & W. Sellars, *Readings in philosophical analysis.* New York: Appleton-Century-Crofts, 1949. Pp. 510–514.
6. Guttman, N. On the relationship between resistance to extinction of a bar-pressing response and concentration of reinforcing agent. Paper presented at the meeting of the Midwestern Psychological Association, Chicago, Ill., April 29, 1949.
7. Heron, W. T., & Peake, E. Qualitative food deficiency as a drive in a discrimination problem. *J. comp. physiol. Psychol.*, 1949, 42, 143–147.
8. Hilgard, E. R. *Theories of learning.* New York: Appleton-Century-Crofts, 1948.
9. Hilgard, E. R., & Marquis, D. G. *Conditioning and learning.* New York: Appleton-Century, 1940.
10. Hospers, J. On explanation. *J. Philos.*, 1946, 43, 337–356.
11. Hull, C. L. Thorndike's *Fundamentals of learning. Psychol. Bull.*, 1935, 32, 807–823.
12. Hull, C. L. *Principles of behavior.* New York: Appleton-Century, 1943.
13. Keenan, J. Definitions and principles of dynamics. *Sci. Mon.*, 1948, 67, 406–414.
14. Lenzen, V. F. *The nature of physical theory.* New York: John Wiley, 1931.
15. Lindsay, R. B., & Margenau, H. *Foundations of physics.* New York: John Wiley, 1936.
16. MacCorquodale, K., & Meehl, P. E. "Cognitive" learning in the absence of competition of incentives. *J. comp. physiol. Psychol.*, 1949, 42, 383–390.
17. Mach, E. *The science of mechanics* (Transl. by T. J. McCormack). Second English Ed. Chicago: Open Court Publishing Co., 1902.
18. Poincaré, H. *The foundations of science.* New York: Science Press, 1913.
19. Postman, L. The history and present status of the Law of Effect. *Psychol. Bull.*, 1947, 44, 489–563.
20. Pratt, C. C. Operationism in psychology. *Psychol. Rev.*, 1945, 52, 262–269.

21. REICHENBACH, H. *Experience and prediction.* Chicago: Univ. of Chicago Press, 1938.
22. SKINNER, B. F. *The behavior of organisms.* New York: Appleton-Century, 1938.
23. SPENCE, K. W. Studies on secondary reinforcement. Address given to the Minnesota Chapter of Psi Chi, Minneapolis, April 22, 1948.
24. TAYLOR, L. W. *Physics, the pioneer science.* New York: Houghton, Mifflin, 1941.
25. THORNDIKE, E. L. *The fundamentals of learning.* New York: Teachers College, Columbia Univ., 1932.
26. THORNDIKE, E. L. *Animal intelligence.* New York: Macmillan, 1911.
27. THORNDIKE, E. L. *The original nature of man.* New York: Teachers College. 1913.
28. THORNDIKE, E. L. *The psychology of learning.* New York: Teachers College, 1913.
29. TOLMAN, E. C. *Purposive behavior in animals and men.* New York: Century, 1932.

VII

PHILOSOPHY OF THE SOCIAL SCIENCES

Reason in Social Science*

MORRIS R. COHEN

The great Poincaré once remarked that while physicists had a subject-matter, sociologists were engaged almost entirely in considering their methods. Allowing for the inevitable divergence between the sober facts and heightened Gallic wit, there is still in this remark a just rebuke (from one who had a right to deliver it) to those romantic souls who cherish the persistent illusion that by some new trick of method the social sciences can readily be put on a par with the physical sciences with regard to definiteness and universal demonstrability. The maximum logical accuracy can be attained only by recognizing the exact degree of probability that our subject-matter will allow.

From the fact that social questions are inherently more complicated than those of physics or biology—since the social involves the latter but not vice versa—certain observations as to methodologic possibilities follow at once.

(A) The Complexity and Variability of Social Phenomena

In the first place, agreement based on demonstration is less easy and actually less prevalent in the social than in the natural sciences, because the greater complexity of social facts makes it less easy to sharpen an issue to an isolable point and to settle it by direct observation of an indefinitely repeatable fact. The issue between the Copernican and the Ptolemaic astronomy in the days of Galileo was reduced to the question whether Venus does or does not show phases like the moon's, and this was settled by looking through a telescope. If Venus did not forever repeat her cycle, and if the difference between a full circle of light and one partly covered by a crescent shadow were not so readily perceived, the matter could not be so readily settled.

With the greater complexity of social facts are connected (1) their less repeatable character, (2) their less direct observability, (3) their greater variability and lesser uniformity, and (4) the greater difficulty of isolating

* Reprinted by kind permission of Felix S. Cohen from M. R. Cohen, *Reason and Nature*, Harcourt, Brace & Company, Inc., New York, 1931, pp. 250–263.

one factor at a time. These phases are so dependent on one another that we shall not treat them separately.

The practical difficulties of repeating social facts for purposes of direct observation are too obvious to need detailed mention. What needs to be more often recognized is that social facts are essentially unrepeatable just to the extent that they are merely historical. The past fact cannot be directly observed. Its existence is established by reasoning upon assumed probabilities. In the case of physical history or geology our proof rests on definitely established and verified laws of natural science. In the case of human history the principles assumed are neither so definite nor so readily verifiable.[1]

The greater variability of social facts may, if we wish, be viewed as another phase of their complexity. Any cubic centimetre of hydrogen will for most purposes of physics or biology be as good as another. But observation on one community will not generally be so applicable to another. Even purely biologic facts, e.g. the effects of diet, seem to be more variable in the human than in other species. Reasoning from examples in the social realm is intellectually a most hazardous venture. We seldom escape the fallacy of selection, of attributing to the whole class what is true only of our selected instances. To urge as some philosophers do that this is true only because physical knowledge is thinner and depends more upon the principle of indifference, is to urge an interpretation, not a denial, of the fact.

It is, of course, true that for certain social questions we can treat all individuals as alike. Thus, for vital statistics every birth or death counts the same, no matter who is involved. Likewise, in certain economic or juristic questions we ignore all individual differences. Yet there can be no doubt that the applicability of such rules in the social sciences is more limited and surrounded with greater difficulty than the application of the laws of the natural sciences to their wider material.

J. S. Mill in his *Logic* has raised the interesting question as to why it is that in certain inquiries one observation or experiment may be decisive while in other cases large numbers of observations bring no such certain results. In the main this difference holds between physical and social observation.

I venture to suggest a rather simple explanation of this fact—a fact that puzzled Mill because he did not fully grasp the logic of hypothesis. In any fairly uniform realm like that of physics, where we can vary one factor at a time, it is possible to have a crucial experiment, that is, it is possible to reduce an issue to a question of yes or no, so that the result refutes and eliminates one hypothesis and leaves the other in possession of the field. But

[1] Thus it is difficult to refute the assertion that race differences are constant and not changed in the course of time by direct or selective influence of the environment. For if history fails to record any extensive intermarriage of a race like the Hebrew with other peoples and yet shows marked changes in physiognomy as members of the race settle in different lands, it is still open to proponents of the theory to assert that they *must have* intermarried.

where the number of possible causes is indefinitely large, and where we cannot always isolate a given factor, it is obviously difficult to eliminate an hypothesis; and the elimination of one hypothesis from a very large number does not produce the impression of progress in the establishment of a definite cause.

The last observation suggests that the greater complexity and variability of social fact also make its purely theoretical development more difficult. In general, social situations are networks in which one cannot change one factor without affecting a great many others. It is, therefore, difficult to determine the specific effects of any one factor. Moreover, social elements seldom admit of simple addition. The behaviour of the same individuals in a large group will not in general be the same as their behaviour in a smaller group. This makes it difficult to apply the mathematical methods which have proved so fruitful in the natural sciences. For these mathematical methods depend upon our ability to pass from a small number of instances to an indefinitely large number by the process of summation or integration.

Where the number of units is indefinitely large we can assume continuity in variation. But the application of continuous curves to very limited groups of figures to which our social observation is usually restricted produces pseudo-science, for example, the assertion that if our distribution is skewed we have a proof of teleology.

The relatively small number of observations that we generally have to deal with in the social sciences makes the application of the probability curve a source of grave errors. For all the mathematical theorems of probability refer only to infinite series (for which we substitute as a practical equivalent "the long run"). Where the number is small there is no assurance that we have eliminated the fallacy of selection. The mathematical error of applying a continuous curve to a discrete number of observations produces ludicrous results. It is vain to expect that the crudeness of our observation and the vagueness of our fundamental categories will be cured by manipulation of the paraphernalia of statistical methods. The mathematical theory of probability enables us to manipulate complex probabilities when we have some determinate ratio to begin with, such as that American pennies fall heads as often as tails. But social scientists seldom take the trouble to formulate the material assumptions of probability (or "indifference") which underlie their conclusions as to the probability of a given event, e.g. a rise in the price of gold. They thus endow their reasoning with the magical appearance of bringing forth material propositions out of the forms of pure mathematics. Actually the material assumptions of statistical workers are often purely aesthetic in origin, being dictated by an unintelligent regard for smoothness and symmetry in graphs.

Physical categories have themselves been clarified by analysis. The dimensions of the different categories that we talk about—energy, action, force, momentum, etc.—are numerically determined in terms of m (mass), *l* (length), and *t* (time). In the social sciences the very categories that we use are hazy, subject to variable usage and to confusing suggestion. Does law determine the state, or the state make the law? How many thousands of learned men have discussed this and similar questions without fixing the precise meaning of the terms "state" and "law." [2]

It is a familiar observation that the difficulty of framing exact concepts in the social realm causes much confusion through ambiguity. To this it should be added that vague concepts make possible the constant appeal to vague propositions as self-evidently true. Open any book on social science at random and you will find the author trying to settle issues by appealing to what seems self-evident. Yet most of such self-evident propositions are vague, and when we ask for their precise meaning and for the evidence in their favour, our progress stops. In the natural sciences the questioning of what seems self-evident is relatively simple because when we have a simple proposition we can more readily formulate a true or an exclusive alternative. In social matters where difference of opinion is greater and demonstration more difficult, we cling all the more tenaciously to our primary assumption, so that our assumptions largely mould what we shall accept as facts.

Any one who naïvely believes that social facts come to us all finished and that our theories or assumptions must simply fit them, is bound to be shocked in a court of law or elsewhere to find how many facts persons honestly see because they expected them rather than because they objectively happen. That psychoanalysts, economists, sociologists, and moralists labour more or less in the same situation, the tremendous diversity of opinion among them amply indicates. Will a classical anthropologist admit that some Indians had a patriarchal form of kinship before adopting the matriarchal type? Is it a *fact* that the suppression of certain desires, deliberately or as a result of imitation, necessarily produces pathologic states of mind? One has but to scrutinize the statement to see how much must be assumed before it can be shown that a fact is involved here.

Is corporal punishment in schools, or free divorce, an evil or not? Under the influence of general opinions one can readily maintain it as a fact that all the consequences of such practices are evil. But one who refuses to admit that these practices are evils can be equally consistent.

Is this true in the natural sciences? Certainly not to the same extent. Because theories do not to the same extent influence what we shall regard as physical or biologic fact, false theorems have never been such serious obstacles to the progress of natural science. The statements in popular histories that the Ptolemaic, the phlogiston, or the caloric hypothesis stopped the progress of science have no foundation. On the contrary these and other false theories in physics were useful in suggesting new lines of research. It is

[2] Before Fourier definitely established the exact "dimensions" of the various physical categories, physicists could dispute (as the Cartesians and the Leibnizians did) as to the proper measure of "living" forces. Social science likewise needs a system of categories the exact dimensions of which are so clear as to make impossible the many confusions of which the example in the text is only one illustration.

this fact that led Darwin to remark that false observations (on which others rely) are much more dangerous to the progress of science than false theories. Now in the social sciences we certainly do not have the elaborate safeguards against false observation that the natural sciences with their simpler material and many instruments of precision find it necessary to cultivate. The very circumstance that social facts are apt to be more familiar makes it easier to be misled as to the amount of accurate knowledge that we have about them.

From another point of view we may express this by saying that in the social sciences we are more at the mercy of our authorities with regard to what are the facts. The social worker or field anthropologist has less opportunity to preserve his specimens than the naturalist or the laboratory worker. If a later social worker or field anthropologist finds the fact to be different from what was reported by his predecessor, there is the possibility not only that they have observed different things but also that the social facts have changed.

In this connection it is well to note that the invention of a technical term often creates facts for social science. Certain individuals become *introverts* when the term is invented, just as many people begin to suffer from a disease the moment they read about it. Psychiatry is full of such technical terms; and if a criminal is rich enough he generally finds experts to qualify his state of mind with a sufficient number of technical terms to overawe those not used to scrutinizing authorities. The technical terms of natural science are useful precisely because they carry no aroma of approval or disapproval with them.

(B) Are There Any Social Laws?

In view of the paucity of generally recognized laws in social science it is well to ask categorically if the search for them is fully justified. The existence of similarities in different societies at different times and places has been used as a proof of the existence of "a uniform law in the psychic and social development of mankind at all times and under all circumstances." [3] But *similarities* of customs and beliefs, even if they are not superficial or due to the prepossession of the observer, are not laws. As human beings resemble one another in their physical, biologic, and psychologic traits, we naturally expect that their social expressions will have points of resemblance, especially when the outer material is similar. If the number of human traits were known and within manageable compass, the principle of limited possibilities (enunciated by Dr. Goldenweiser) might be a clue to the laws of social life. But even a finite or limited number of facts may be too large for our manipulation.

Physical laws are in fact all expressed in relatively simple analytic functions containing a small number of variables. If the number of these variables should become very large, or the functions too complicated, physical

[3] Lester Ward, *Pure Sociology*, pp. 53, 54.

laws would cease to be readily manipulated or applicable. The science of physics would then be practically impossible. If, then, social phenomena depend upon more factors than we can readily manipulate, even the doctrine of universal determinism will not guarantee an attainable expression of laws governing the specific phenomena of social life. Social phenomena, though determined, might not to a finite mind in limited time display any laws at all.

Let us take a concrete example. A man says to a woman, "My dear!" The physical stimulus is here a very definite set of sound waves, and we have reason to believe that the physical effect of these waves is always determinate. But what the lady will in all cases say or do in response depends upon so many factors that only an astonishing complacency about our limited knowledge of human affairs would prompt a confident answer.

The a priori argument that there must be laws is based on the assumption that there are a finite number of elements or forms which must thus repeat themselves in an endless temporal series. But why may not the repeatable forms and elements be only those which enter our physical laws? What guarantee is there that in the limited time open to us there must be a complete repetition of social patterns as well?

In any case, those who think that social science has been as successful as physical science in discovering and establishing laws may be invited to compile a list of such laws and to compare the list in respect to number, definiteness, and universal demonstrability, with a collection such as Northrup's *Laws of Physical Science.*

We may approach this issue more positively by considering three types of laws:

(1) Every general fact that can be authenticated can be regarded as a law. Thus, that gold is yellow is the assertion of a law, i.e. whenever you find a substance having a certain atomic weight, etc., it will also be yellow in colour. We do not generally call statements of this sort laws, because a long list of such statements would hardly constitute what is distinctive of advanced *science*. In the latter such statements are connected with others by logical principles. Nevertheless such laws or facts are basic to science, and in the social realm they do not seem so numerous or so readily authenticated. Is it a fact, for instance, that the negro race is not ambitious?

(2) The second type of law is that of empirical or statistical sequences, e.g. "Much sugar in a diet will be followed by decayed teeth." In natural science we regard these also as but the starting points of the scientific search for the third type of law. Why do such sequences hold? We answer this question if we find some more general connecting link, e.g. some chemical process connecting sugar with the tissue of the teeth.

The situation in the social sciences is logically similar. Empirical sequences are not scientifically satisfactory laws. We are more apt, in the social realm, to find correlations that confirm our opinions and to neglect items that do not. If the graduates of a college get into *Who's Who* the college compiles such lists and claims credit. If they get into jail the college does not hold itself responsible.

(3) The third type of law is the statement of a universal abstract relation which can be connected systematically with other laws in the same field. Such laws we may indeed find in the social sciences, e.g. the laws governing the exchange of goods under free competition as worked out mathematically by Walras, Pareto, H. Schultz,[4] et al., but always these laws are on a plane of abstraction from which translation to actual experience is difficult and dangerous. The ideal entities represented by "free competition" and "economic man" are, to be sure, no more abstract than the ideal entities of physics, but nevertheless economics is a poorer basis for predicting actual events than is physics. For in physics the transition from laws governing rigid bodies to those applying to (say) lead bullets is made on the basis of new laws of compressibility or elasticity, while in economics the transition from our laws of supply and demand in an ideal market to those determining (say) New York Stock Exchange transactions is still largely a matter of guess-work.

On a similar plane is the law of social inertia, parallel in motive to Newton's first law of motion. If, following the suggestion of the law of inertia, we assume that all social phenomena persist unless something is brought into play to change them, we have a useful principle of methodic procedure. Similarly we may assume the law of social heredity—all social institutions will be transmitted by parents to children, or people will believe and act as did their fathers before them except in so far as certain factors produce changes in our social arrangements and in our ideas and sentiments. Similar remarks may be made about the law of imitation or the law of differentiation in the division of labour, which certainly help to explain certain elementary aspects of most social phenomena.

The law of imitation has of course to take account of the impulse to do things differently in order to attract attention, and the law of social differentiation has to note the factors which make for uniformity, just as the biologic law of differentiation must be checked by noting the phenomena of convergent evolution. But until opposite tendencies or forces can be more precisely measured, these laws will not go very far to explain actual happenings.

All laws are abstract. They state what would be true of a given factor if all other things remained indifferent. In physics other things do remain in a measure indifferent. But in the social field the variation of one factor produces all sorts of disturbances in others.

Physical phenomena, in other words, do show certain abstract uniformities of repetition which enable us to predict what will happen with greater certainty than in the social realms.

These observations are reinforced by considering the precise meaning of social causation and social forces—terms borrowed by the social from

[4] See *The Meaning of Statistical Demand Curves.*

the natural sciences, generally without regard for their precise meaning or their applicability to the questions of social science.

(C) Social and Natural Causation

The notion of cause originates in the field of legal procedure. A cause (αἰτία) is a case or ground for an action. The Stoics, basing themselves on certain notions of Heraclitus, brought the notion of law into the conception of natural happenings. Law to them meant not mere uniformity that just happens to exist, but something decreed by the World-Reason or λόγος. Violations of it are possible but reprehensible. This is still the popular view, which speaks of certain acts as unnatural and of nature punishing all violations of her laws. The notion of a law of nature as a non-purposeful but absolute uniformity, so that a single exception would deny its validity, arises from the modern application of mathematics to physics. The proposition that all *x*'s are *y*'s is simply false if one *x* is not a *y*.

Modern physics seeks to attain such laws by the process of abstraction. Thus, the proposition that all bodies fall to the earth suggests itself as such a law. But if we remember the behaviour of smoke, of birds or balloons, some modification of this statement is necessary if universality is to be attained. This is achieved in the statement that all bodies attract one another. For in the case of bodies which do not fall we can show the presence of some force which counteracts the attraction of the earth so that the latter force is thus recognized. If the counteracting forces did not themselves operate according to a known law, the law of gravitation would be useless. We can predict phenomena only because the gravitational and the counteracting forces are independently measurable. Unless similarly social forces are measurable and there is some common unit or correlation of social forces, the whole notion of law as employed in the physical sciences may be unapplicable. When religious and economic interests pull individuals in different directions, which force will prevail? Such a question can certainly not be answered on any scientific basis. We do not know how many units of one social force will counteract another. All we can say is that in some cases religious motives prevail over economic ones, in some cases the reverse is true, and in most cases we cannot separate the motives at all.

The difference between social and natural causation is confused by the doctrine that social "forces" are psychic, and that at least one of them, desire, acts like a physical force—indeed, that it obeys the Newtonian laws of motion.[5] Obviously if social phenomena are not merely physical, the term "social force" can at best be only a metaphor and we should be careful to note its real difference from physical force.

This difference is ignored when a popular sociologist speaks of social motion as following the line of least resistance even more closely than does

[5] Lester F. Ward, *Psychic Factors in Civilization*, pp. 94, 123.

nature herself.[6] In natural science we know what a straight line is before considering any given physical process. But what is denoted by the metaphor, the "straight line" or the "line of least resistance" in any given social process, is something that we arbitrarily tell only after the event. Psychic forces are not physical forces.

If purely psychic forces operate at all, it is in the way of desire as an actually felt state of mind. But as we have seen before in our discussion of psychic causality, desire can be said to bring about results only if there happens to be also some adequate physical or physiologic mechanism at hand, so that the relation between the desire and what follows does not replace the physical causation but is an entirely different type of relation.

Similarly, social forces are not merely psychological. What is called social causation may be regarded as a teleologic relation. But the fact that in social relations we deal with large groups enables us to depart from individual psychology. We can thus say with greater certainty that an economic opportunity will be utilized, or that the religion of their fathers will be followed by a large group of persons, than that it will be utilized or followed by a single individual whose specific disposition we do not know. We cannot tell what a given individual will think of the next war, but we can be fairly certain that every nation will, like Rome, manage to be convinced that its side is the just one.

Social causation, then, need not be like that of individual purposes. The overcrowding in cities does not intentionally bring about certain social diseases, any more than the invention of the cotton-gin was intended to bring about the economic changes which led to the fall of the older southern aristocracy and the political changes which led to the Civil War. It is of greater importance to recognize that social science is for the most part concerned not like physics with laws expressing the invariant repetition of elements, nor with laws of individual psychic events, but with laws about the relation of very complex patterns to one another.

Consider a number of examples of social causations. It is surely significant to inquire as to the effects of density of population. Is feminism a cause or an effect of the greater economic opportunity open to women? Is poverty the cause or the effect of a higher birth rate? In all such cases a causal relation means some connection not between individual events, or mere sums of such events, but between diverse patterns of distribution, sometimes of the same group of events. If social institutions as specific groups of events are themselves called events, we must distinguish the different levels of the term *events*. It will, however, prevent confusion if we remember that a social institution is a mode of viewing or grouping a number of events and is, therefore, strictly speaking, not a datable event, although the constituent events may occur between two dates.

Thus it is that in social causation the cause does not disappear when

[6] E. A. Ross, *Foundations of Sociology*, p. 43.

it produces an effect, but can be said to continue and to be modified by its effects. A system of education may affect the commerce of a people and that in turn may modify the system of education. That is possible because "system of education" is not a single temporal event but a pattern of events actually coeval with the pattern of events called "the commerce of a people." The causal relation or the interaction between them is predominantly a matter of logical analysis of groups of phenomena.

The purely scientific interest is thus best served by isolating some one aspect of social phenomena—e.g. the economic, the political, the religious—and tracing the effect of changes in that aspect. Even the historian must select and restrict himself to certain phases of social events. But the practical interest in social outcome is not immediately satisfied by uniform sequences nor by the merely necessary conditions of social happenings which are too numerous to be very interesting. It needs, rather, a knowledge of the quantitative adjustments of *all* the factors necessary to produce a desired effect. This is seldom attainable. We can under certain conditions tell, for example, that a reduction of price or certain forms of advertising will increase sales. But the variation of any one factor due to local conditions is very large, and our concrete practical knowledge always involves guesswork. Hence, it can never guarantee us against fatal errors.

(D) Tendencies as Laws

One of the most usual ways of generalizing from insufficient instances and ignoring or lightly disposing of contrary facts is to call our generalization a tendency. There is an apparent analogy to this situation in the popular formulation of the laws of physics, e.g. when the law of gravitation is stated as a tendency of two bodies to move toward each other. The word *tendency*, however, can always be eliminated from physics if we remember the law of composition of forces. As the force of gravity and the resistance of a table to a falling body can both be independently measured, there is no logical difficulty in saying that the law or force of gravity is operative even when the body is brought to rest on the table.

But in the social sciences, where single factors cannot be easily isolated and independently measured, an essential indeterminateness in discussion is inevitably produced by reliance on the notion of "tendency." For conflicting schools or parties can begin with the assertion of opposite tendencies and never really join in a definite issue. Thus one party may base its political theory on the assertion that all men love or tend to love liberty, and dismiss contrary facts as sacrifices which men make in the interest of peace, etc. The opposing party can base itself on the opposite assertion that men inherently tend to love order and to fear or hate the burden of responsibility so much that they prefer to obey even insane tyrants; and the facts which cannot be so described can be attributed to exceptionally unbearable conditions, etc. Obviously if the strength of these opposing tendencies were measurable and determined, the seemingly opposite assertions might be seen to be theoretically equivalent, that is to say, they would lead to the same predictions as to whether people will or will not obey under given conditions. Of course the emotional bias in favour of one set of words over the other will, so long as words have emotional associations, make people of different experience or temperament cling to different formulae. But the outstanding fact of methodologic importance is the indetermination involved in the use of the notion of tendency, and the vain and interminable disputes that it makes possible.

It is of course scientifically useful to resist the suggestion of proposed plausible generalization by discovering contrary "tendencies." Also the existence of opposite "tendencies" must be considered before we can proceed to measure them. But the temptation to set up tendencies as laws makes social science essentially indeterminate in the sense that diverse schools set up diverse principles all with the same show of truth. Thus when the Durkheim school of anthropology says all religion is totemic in origin, or that all magic is simply an illegitimate use of the supernatural, many phenomena are aptly described, but others are ignored. Rival schools start with these other facts and deny Durkheim's theory in toto. Both sides are right if they admit that they are describing some facts, and both are wrong if they pretend to describe all the facts of religion or magic. The way out of such typical sloughs of social science is to recognize that while full description of some of the facts may be needed in the beginning of social science, the ideal end is to attain universal statements about partial aspects of all the phenomena in a given class.[7]

[7] To call a correlation a tendency is to admit that we have not yet purified the concepts correlated of the foreign ingredients which block the regular manifestation of some causal relationship.

If what the grocer sells as sugar is in fact not uniformly sweet, we may say that grains of the stuff *have a tendency to be* sweet. It will require the careful work of a chemist to distinguish the $C_{12}H_{22}O_{11}$ that *is* sweet from the other substances that *are not* sweet. It is just this work of analysis and refining, a hundred times more difficult with social institutions than with sugar, that a complacent reliance upon "tendencies" as the substance of social science discourages. Like fictions, metaphors, and false theories, "tendencies" are valuable stimulants for scientific thought, but they will not take the place of food.

Can the Social Sciences Be Value-Free?*

J. A. PASSMORE

MOST OF THE CRITICISMS which have been levelled against positivism leave it quite untouched, at the vital points. First, it is asserted that the positivist cannot help having social preferences. This is obviously true; an interest in social policy is what first leads him to the social field and it is bound to determine, very largely, the kind of problem on which he concentrates. This will seem a fatal objection only if we think that physical science is an exercise in pure reason, in which the scientist lays aside all human passions. This would simply be bad psychology. It is his special interests which lead a man to physics and to particular problems in that field. Certainly, anti-theoretical passions are more likely to be stirred up in the social than in the purely physical field. This makes social science difficult, but not impossible.

Secondly, the anti-positivist asserts that positivism is often used as a mask for the propagation of particular social policies. This must be admitted (cf. the "scientific ethics" of the Darwinians). Scientific-sounding words like "efficiency" disguise value-judgments; and factual-seeming statements like "the State is . . ." are often highly misleading ways of formulating social policies. It is certainly better to state social policies openly than to cover them over with pseudo-science. It is part of the task of the social sciences to expose subterfuges of this sort; the mere fact that they are known to exist shows that the contrast can be made between fact and policy — in other words, that a positive social science is not impossible.

Thirdly, anti-positivists argue that a positivistic social science must distort the facts, because values, aspirations, principles are part of the substance of social life. This the positivist need not at all deny, but only that in order to study morality it is necessary to moralise about it.

The vital point for the positivist is to show that there are non-trivial theoretical problems in the social sciences. We may distinguish, as a first approximation, theoretical problems, technical problems and problems of policy. Theoretical (including historical) problems can be settled by finding out what happens. We propose hypotheses, make observations, and thus, if we are lucky, solve our problem. Not everybody may agree with us,

* Reprinted by kind permission of the author and the publishers from summary of a paper originally printed in the *Proceedings of the Tenth International Congress of Philosophy*, North-Holland Publishing Co., Amsterdam, 1949.

but if our facts and our hypotheses are accepted, there are objective ways of showing that the problem has been solved.

A problem of policy (e.g., "Ought we to abolish class distinctions?") is not solved in this way. Two disputants might agree that the abolition of class distinctions would decrease servility but diminish cultural variety. One concludes: "It follows that we ought to abolish them", the other, that we ought not to do so. How can we decide which is right? In a way, neither; for nothing follows from observations of this sort about what ought to be done. We have still our decision to make after the theoretical work is finished. Our policy is determined in the light of the facts, but it is not deduced from them. If all questions in the social field were problems of policy, then a positive social science cannot answer them; but also, unless there are theoretical issues problems of policy would be quite undiscussable. To discuss a policy is to make testable assertions about its character and consequences. But that there are such testable assertions is all that the positivist account of social science is concerned to assert. Anti-positivists have really to deny the possibility of social discussion; but it clearly takes place, even if often in a rather muddled sort of way, with no clear distinction between what is discussable and what is not.

Technical problems are of the form: "How can something be constructed to such-and-such specifications?" A technical question is only a particularised theoretical question, but serious confusion may be caused because problems of policy are often framed as if they were merely technical. Take the question: "How can child-delinquency be prevented in wartime?" If this were simply a technical question it would be answerable by naming a method. But suppose we answer: "By devoting one third of the total manpower to child-care". We would be told: "That's no solution". What is really being asked is: "How ought we to deal with child-delinquency?" To give a "satisfactory" answer, we should not only have to solve the theoretical question "What social changes would prevent child-delinquency?" but also to find changes which would not conflict with an unstated social policy. Scientists sometimes profess to be giving "merely technical advice" when in fact they are tacitly assuming a particular social policy. This gives encouragement to the view that "positive social sciences" are a sham. But, of course, genuine technical problems can also be found; they are contained within the sham sort; what the sham sort does is to include in the technical specifications factors which it does not mention. It has still to settle certain technical problems even if they are not quite the ones it pretends to be deciding.

The last refuge of the anti-positivist is that although there are theoretical problems in the social sciences these are all of a trivial kind and that the actual effect of positivism in the social sciences is to lead to the production of a vast quantity of work which boasts of being scientific but is empty and commonplace. Now, "trivial" has two senses: a question like "Where will that bomb land?" is methodologically trivial because the answer to it will (usually) have no effect on the theoretical structure of physics, but it can none the less be a question we are tremendously anxious to answer.

When the social sciences are called trivial, sometimes all that is meant is that they fail to tell us many of the things we should particularly like to know. This, of course, is not a serious objection. But a good deal of positivistically-inspired social science is also trivial in a methodological sense. This is sometimes because the scientist wrongly believes that science is the collection of information, sometimes because he thinks that to be a scientist he must leave moral issues alone, in the sense of avoiding any question which involves them, or which might stir up the passions of the investigator. Since these are usually the facts of central importance to the understanding of social life, the natural result of this panic-stricken approach is triviality. Unfortunately, positivists have sometimes held very simple-minded views about morality; they have thought it is just a matter of taste and have grossly under-estimated its social importance. The positivist needs a better understanding of his own position. Then he will see that it is not positivism but cowardice which leads him into trivialities. What he has to do is to produce theories about the structure of morality which are genuinely theories and do not involve the advocacy of any particular social policy. Unless he is prepared to face the central issues, he can abandon the hope of a positive social science which is anything but a collection of commonplaces. A positive social science must be value-free in the sense that it is not social advocacy in disguise, but not in the sense that it has nothing to say about values. Such a theory will have the limitations characteristic of the physical sciences. It will not tell us what we ought to do, any more than physics tells us whether to build a bridge or to be content with a ferry. It will not (usually), any more than physics, tell us when a particular event is going to occur, but it will not be trivial, any more than physics is trivial.

The Operation Called *Verstehen**

THEODORE ABEL

THE ADVOCATES OF *Verstehen*[1] define it as a singular form of operation which we perform whenever we attempt to explain human behavior. The idea behind this claim is by no means of German origin. Long before Dilthey and Weber, Vico acclaimed mathematics and human history as subjects about which we have a special kind of knowledge. This he attributed to the fact that the abstractions and fictions of mathematics are created by us, while history, too, is "made by men." He claimed that human beings can possess a type of knowledge concerning things they themselves produce which is not obtainable about the phenomena of nature.

Comte, too, implied that a special procedure is involved in the interpretation of human behavior. He held that the methods used in sociology embrace not only observation and experiment but a further process of verification which makes use of what he vaguely referred to as "our knowledge of human nature." According to him, empirical generalizations about human behavior are not valid unless they are in accord with our knowledge of human nature. Comte was the first to establish what may be termed "the postulate of *Verstehen*" for sociological research, for he asserted that no sociological demonstration is complete until the conclusions of historical and statistical analyses are in harmony with the "laws of human nature."

In the American sociological field Cooley is the outstanding protagonist of the idea that we understand the human and the social in ways different from those in which we understand the material. His theory is that we can understand the behavior of human beings by being able to share their "state of mind." This ability to share other people's minds is a special knowledge,

* Reprinted by kind permission of the author and the University of Chicago Press from *American Journal of Sociology*, 54, 1948.

[1] To avoid confusion, we prefer to use the German term instead of its English equivalent, which is "understanding." Understanding is a general term approximating the German *Begreifen* and does not convey the specific meaning intended by the term *Verstehen*, which implies a particular kind of understanding, applicable primarily to human behavior. Understanding is synonymous with comprehension, and Lundberg is perfectly right when he asserts (in *Foundations of Sociology* [New York: Macmillan Co., 1939], p. 51) that "understanding is the end at which all methods aim, rather than a method in itself." In this sense "understanding" is the goal of all sciences. *Verstehen*, on the other hand, is viewed by its proponents as a method by means of which we can explain human behavior. The purpose of this paper is to clarify this point and evaluate its significance.

distinct from the kind of perception gleaned from tests and statistics. Statistical knowledge without "empathic" knowledge is superficial and unintelligent. Between the two, Cooley claims, "there is a difference in kind which it would be fatuous to overlook." [2]

The notion of *Verstehen* is included in Znaniecki's concept of the "humanistic coefficient" and particularly in the role he ascribes to "vicarious experience" as a source of sociological data. According to Znaniecki, vicarious experience enables the student of human behavior "to gain a specific kind of information which the natural experimenter . . . ignores altogether." [3]

Similarly, Sorokin stresses the need for *Verstehen* when he insists that the causal-functional method is not applicable to the interpretation of cultural phenomena. He points out that the social sciences must employ the logico-meaningful method which enables us to perceive connections which "are much more intimately comprehensible, more readily perceived, than are causal-functional unities." [4]

MacIver, too, speaks of a special method which must be used whenever we study social causation. He calls this process "imaginative reconstruction." He claims the causal formula of classical mechanics cannot be applied to human behavior. However, the student of human behavior will find this compensated for by "the advantage that some of the factors operative in social causation are understandable as causes; are validated as causal by our own experience." [5]

As these brief references indicate, there is no dearth of tradition and authority behind the idea of *Verstehen*.[6] It is, therefore, surprising to find that, while many social scientists have eloquently discoursed on the existence of a special method in the study of human behavior, none has taken the trouble to describe the nature of this method. They have given it various names; they have insisted on its use; they have pointed to it as a special kind of operation which has no counterpart in the physical sciences; and they have extolled its superiority as a process of giving insight unobtainable by any other methods. Yet the advocates of *Verstehen* have continually neg-

[2] H. E. Cooley, *Sociological Theory and Social Research* (New York: Scribner's, 1930), p. 290.

[3] Florian Znaniecki, *The Method of Sociology* (New York: Farrar & Rinehart, 1934), p. 167.

[4] Pitirim Sorokin, *Social and Cultural Dynamics* (New York: American Book Co., 1937), p. 26.

[5] R. M. MacIver, *Social Causation* (Boston: Ginn & Co., 1942), p. 263.

[6] The more important works dealing with *Verstehen* are K. Bühler, *Die Krise der Psychologie* (Jena: Fischer, 1927); W. Dilthey, *Ideen ueber eine beschreibende und zergliedernde Psychologie* (Leipzig: Teubner, 1894); T. Erisman, *Die Eigenart des Geistigen* (Leipzig: Quelle, 1924); P. Häberlin, *Der Geist und die Triebe* (Berlin: Springer, 1924); K. Jaspers, *Allgemeine Psychopathologie* (Berlin: Springer, 1920); H. Rickert, *Die Grenzen der naturwissenschaftlichen Begriffsbildung* (Tübingen: Mohr, 1913); E. Rothacker, *Logik und Systematik der Geisteswissenschaften* (Bonn: Bouvier, 1947); G. Simmel, *Geschichtsphilosophie* (Berlin: Duncan, 1920); E. Spranger, *Lebensformen* (Halle: Niemeyer, 1924); and Max Weber, *Gesammelte Aufsaetze zur Wissenschaftslehre* (Tübingen: Mohr, 1920).

lected to specify how this operation of "understanding" is performed—and what is singular about it. What, exactly, do we do when we say we practice *Verstehen?* What significance can we give to results achieved by *Verstehen?* Unless the operation is clearly defined, *Verstehen* is but a vague notion, and, without being dogmatic, we are unable to ascertain how much validity can be attributed to the results achieved by it.

I. The Operation Illustrated

Our first task is to ascertain the formula according to which the operation of *Verstehen* is performed. To do so, we had best examine a few illustrations of behavior analysis. For this purpose we shall use three examples: the first will deal with a single case; the second, with a generalization; and the third, with a statistical regularity.

Case 1.—Last April 15 a freezing spell suddenly set in, causing a temperature drop from 60 to 34 degrees. I saw my neighbor rise from his desk by the window, walk to the woodshed, pick up an ax, and chop some wood. I then observed him carrying the wood into the house and placing it in the fireplace. After he had lighted the wood, he sat down at his desk and resumed his daily task of writing.

From these observations I concluded that, while working, my neighbor began to feel chilly and, in order to get warm, lighted a fire. This conclusion has all the earmarks of an "obvious fact." Yet it is obvious only because I have fitted the action of my neighbor into a sequential pattern by assuming that the stimulus "drop in temperature" induced the response "making a fire." Since I recognize a relevant connection between the response and the stimulus, I state that I understand the behavior of my neighbor. I may even say that I am certain of it ("The case is obvious"), provided I note carefully to what this certainty refers. I *cannot* be certain that this is the *correct* or true explanation of his conduct. To be sure my explanation is correct, I need additional information. I can go over to him and ask him why he lighted the fire. He may confirm my interpretation. However, I cannot stop there. Suppose he has another, hidden, intention? He may be expecting a guest and wish to show off his fireplace. Or suppose he himself is not aware of the "true" motive? Perhaps he was impelled by a subconscious motive of wanting to burn down his house so as to punish the fellow who harasses him about paying off the mortgage. If so, his lighting the fire would have a symbolic function. Of what, then, am I certain? I am certain only that my interpretation *could* be correct.

Hence, *Verstehen* gives me the certainty that a given interpretation of behavior is a possible one. I *know* that it can happen this way, even though I cannot be certain that such was the case in this instance. My interpretation in itself is not a hypothesis; only its application to the stated case is hypothetical.

Whence comes this certainty that I achieve through *Verstehen?* Since the case is simple, the answer is simple: I have enacted it myself. Feeling chilled, I have gathered wood and lighted a fire; therefore, I *know*. The sense of relevance is the result of personal experience; the connection has been established by me before, so I am *certain* of its possibility.

However, the answer as stated does not give us a clear picture of the operation the act of *Verstehen* involves. It will, therefore, be necessary to schematize the evidence and show the steps taken to perform the operation.

Two sets of observations are given in our example. First, there is a sequence of bodily movement (chopping wood, lighting a fire, etc.); second, there is a thermometer reading of a near-freezing temperature. The act of *Verstehen* links these two facts into the conclusion that the freezing weather was the stimulus which set off the response "making a fire." An elementary examination shows that three items of information are utilized to reach this conclusion:

1. Low temperature (A) reduces the temperature of the body (B).
2. Heat is produced (C) by making a fire (D).
3. A person "feeling cold" (B') will "seek warmth" (C').

Through this interpretation the three items are linked together as follows:

$$A - B \qquad\qquad C - D$$
$$B' - C'$$

We immediately recognize the third item as the significant element of the interpretation. The two conditions (A–B), together with their known consequences (C–D), are disparate facts. We link them into a sequence and state that C–D is the consequence of A–B by "translating" B and C into feeling-states of a human organism, namely, B' and C'. Introducing these intervening factors enables us to apply a generalization concerning the function of the organism (behavior maxim), from which we deduce the drop in temperature as a possible "cause" of my neighbor's behavior.

By specifying the steps which are implicit in the interpretation of our case, we have brought out two particulars which are characteristic of the act of *Verstehen*. One is the "internalizing" of observed factors in a given situation; the other is the application of a behavior maxim which makes the connection between these factors relevant. Thus we "understand" a given human action if we can apply to it a generalization based upon personal experience. We can apply such a rule of behavior if we are able to "internalize" the facts of the situation.

These propositions require further elucidation, but, before we attempt this, let us consider two other examples of behavior analysis.

Case 2.—In one of Lundberg's articles we find the following generalization:

> Faced by the insecurity of a changing and hostile world, we seek security by creating "eternal verities" in our thoughts. The more inadequate we feel, the more we indulge in this type of wishful thinking. Conversely, as the clergy has always complained, in times of prosperity and security, man tends to neglect

his gods. It has been suggested that the Platonic preference for the changeless may be due to the fact that the Greeks did not have a mathematical technique such as the calculus for dealing with modes and rates of change.[7]

The opening sentence of this quotation asserts a relevant connection between "belief in eternal verities" (verbal response) and "a changing and hostile world" (stimulus). The subsequent sentences hint at a possible statistical basis for the generalization and cite two historical examples as illustrations. Clearly there is insufficient evidence to substantiate the validity of the interpretation as a tendency in some of us toward idealistic philosophy. We can recognize, though, that the connection asserted by the generalization is relevant; that is, we "understand" it, and so consider it possible.

The act of *Verstehen* which is implied here involves the same operation we have observed in the first example. We internalize "change and hostility" (*B*), which we observe to be an attribute of "the world" (*A*), into "feeling of inadequacy" (*B'*). The connotation "changeless" (*C*), which the concept "eternal verities" (*D*) implies, we internalize into "feeling of security" (*C'*). Having thus internalized the situation, we can now apply the behavior maxim that a person who feels inadequate (when facing change) will seek security (in something changeless). This procedure provides the mediating links *B'–C'*, which enable us to "understand," or recognize, the relevancy of the causal connection brought out in the generalization.

Case 3.—Competent statistical research has established a high correlation ($r = .93$) between the annual rate of crop production and the rate of marriage in a given year. There are, of course, statistical methods for proving whether or not this correlation is spurious. In this case, however, we feel that we can forego such tests because the correlation as such does not present a problem to us. We regard the connection as relevant; in short, we say we "understand" why the rate of marriage in farming districts closely follows the rate of crop production.

The act of *Verstehen* which this reasoning implies can be shown to involve the same procedure we have observed in the other examples. We use as items of information the fact that failure of crops (*A*) materially lowers the farmer's income (*B*) and the fact that one is making new commitments (*C*) when one marries (*D*). We then internalize *B* into "feeling of anxiety" (*B'*) and *C*—since the behavior in question is "postponement of marriage"—into "fear of new commitments" (*C'*). We are now able to apply the behavior maxim: "People who experience anxiety will fear new commitments" (*B'–C'*). Since we can fit the fact of fewer marriages when crops fail into this rule, we say we "understand" the correlation.

7 "Thoughtways of Contemporary Sociology," *American Sociological Review*, I (1936), 703.

II. The Operation Analyzed

The examples show that the characteristic feature of the operation of *Verstehen* is the postulation of an intervening process "located" inside the human organism, by means of which we recognize an observed—or assumed—connection as relevant or "meaningful." *Verstehen*, then, consists of the act of bringing to the foreground the inner-organic sequence intervening between a stimulus and a response.

The examples also suggest that there are special conditions which determine the need for making the intervening process explicit. Some connections appear to be obvious; that is, we recognize their relevancy instantaneously and without any awareness of the implicit assumptions upon which the recognition is based. These are usually connections of which we have direct knowledge, because we ourselves established such connections in the past; or they are connections we have previously examined, so that their occurrence is accepted as an expected or familiar happening.

The need for making the intervening process explicit arises whenever behavior is not routine or commonplace. This is clearly the case when we are puzzled. For example, when we were confronted with the evidence that in army units in which promotion was easy there was much more griping about "injustice" than in those units in which very few were promoted, we were puzzled. We would expect the contrary. It is only by internalizing the situation—namely, by introducing the intervening factor of "expectation"—that we are able to understand the connection. If we then assume that in units in which promotion is easy there will be greater expectation of promotion, we can apply the behavior maxim: "The higher one's expectations, the greater one's disappointment if those expectations are not fulfilled." This enables us to "understand" the seemingly paradoxical behavior.

Another condition for making the intervening inner-organic sequence explicit arises whenever we are called upon to explain the reason for asserting a connection between occurrences. This is particularly so when no experimental or statistical data are available and recourse is taken to arguments in support of an interpretation. This happens frequently when interpretations of individual historical events are attempted, as, for example, establishing the cause of a war. Here the behavior in question can be related to earlier events solely on the basis that in terms of assumed feeling-states such a relation is a plausible one.

As has been indicated, the operation of *Verstehen* involves three steps: (1) internalizing the stimulus, (2) internalizing the response, and (3) applying behavior maxims. The questions now arise as to how to go about the process of internalizing and where we get our knowledge of behavior maxims.

1. *Internalizing the stimulus.*—To the best of my knowledge, no one has yet specified a technique by which we can objectively attribute certain

feeling-states to persons faced by a particular situation or event. The arbitrary procedure we employ to internalize a stimulus consists of *imagining* what emotions may have been aroused by the impact of a given situation or event. Sometimes we are able to employ definite clues which we have gathered while observing the impact. These may have been gestures, facial expressions, or exclamations or comments. Where there are no such clues, we note the effect produced by an event or situation. Then we imagine how we would have been affected by such an impact. For example, not being a farmer, I never experienced the consequence of crop failure. However, observing that its effect is a curtailment of income, I attribute to the farmer a feeling of anxiety which I recall having felt—or imagine I might feel—under similar circumstances. Thus the internalizing of a stimulus depends largely upon our ability to describe a situation or event by categorizing it and evoking a personal experience which fits into that category.

2. *Internalizing the response.*—Here, too, no specific techniques are known which permit a definite association between feeling-states and observed behavior. All that can again be said is that we use our imagination when we ascribe a motive to a person's behavior—for example, "fear of new commitments" as the reason for postponing marriage; or, in another instance, when we view the behavior as expressive of some emotion—namely, when we infer that the "griping" of soldiers over promotions evokes a feeling of disappointment. We generally infer the motive of an act from the known or observed modification it produces. If we express this consequence of an act in general terms, we can utilize our personal experience with motives or feelings we had when we ourselves acted in order to produce a similar result.

In cases where both stimulus and response are stated, imagination is facilitated by the fact that both can be viewed as part of a complete situation. This enables us to relate to each other whatever inferences we make about the stimulus and the response. We then select the inferences which "fit" one another in such a way that the given behavior can be recognized as the "solution" (release of tension) of the "problem" (tension experience) created by the impact of the stated event.

3. *Behavior maxims.*—The generalizations which we call "behavior maxims" link two feeling-states together in a uniform sequence and imply a functional dependence between them. In the cases cited it can be seen that the functional dependence consists of the fact that the feeling-state we ascribe to a given human action is *directed* by the feeling-state we presume is evoked by an impinging situation or event. Anxiety directs caution; a feeling of cold, the seeking of warmth; a feeling of insecurity, a desire for something that will provide reassurance.

Behavior maxims are not recorded in any textbooks on human behavior. In fact, they can be constructed *ad hoc* and be acceptable to us as propositions even though they have not been established experimentally. The relation asserted appears to us as self-evident.

This peculiarity of behavior maxims can be accounted for only by the assumption that they are generalizations of direct personal experience derived from introspection and self-observation. Such personal experiences appear originally in the form of what Alexander has called "emotional syllogisms." He has this to say about them:

> Our understanding of psychological connections is based on the tacit recognition of certain causal relationships which we know from everyday experience and the validity of which we accept as self-evident. We understand anger and aggressive behavior as a reaction to an attack; fear and guilt as results of aggressiveness; envy as an outgrowth of the feeling of weakness and inadequacy. Such self-evident connections as "I hate him because he attacks me" I shall call emotional syllogisms. The feeling of the self-evident validity of these emotional connections is derived from daily introspective experience as we witness the emotional sequences in ourselves. . . . Just as the logic of intellectual thinking is based on repeated and accumulated experiences of relations in the external world, the logic of emotions is based on the accumulated experiences of our own emotional reactions.[8]

Emotional syllogisms when stated in the form of general propositions are behavior maxims. This explains their familiar ring and accounts for the facility with which they can be formulated. In generalizing emotional syllogisms we proceed on the assumption that the emotions of others function similarly to our own.

We find, then, that in all its essential features the operation of *Verstehen* is based upon the application of personal experience to observed behavior. We "understand" an observed or assumed connection if we are able to parallel either one with something we know through self-observation does happen. Furthermore, since the operation consists of the application of knowledge we already possess, it cannot serve as a means of discovery. At best it can only confirm what we already know.

III. The Operation Evaluated

From the foregoing description of the operation of *Verstehen* we can draw several inferences as to its limitations and possibilities. The most obvious limitation of the operation is its dependence upon knowledge derived from personal experience. The ability to define behavior will vary with the amount and quality of the personal experience and the introspective capacity of the interpreter. It will also depend upon his ability to generalize his experiences. In some cases it may be possible to secure objective data on the basis of which the verification of an interpretation can be approximated. However, owing to the relative inaccessibility of emotional experiences, most interpretations will remain mere expressions of opinion, subject only to the "test" of plausibility.

[8] Franz Alexander, "The Logic of Emotions and Its Dynamic Background," *International Journal of Psychoanalysis*, XVI (October, 1935), 399.

Regardless of the relative ability of people to use it, a second limitation to the use of the operation itself lies in the fact that it is *not a method of verification.* This means that what in the realm of scientific research we consider a quality of crucial importance is not an attribute of the operation of *Verstehen.*

When we say we "understand" a connection, we imply nothing more than recognizing it as a possible one. We simply affirm that we have at least once in direct experience observed and established the connection or its equivalent. But from the affirmation of a possible connection we cannot conclude that it is also probable. From the point of view of *Verstehen* alone, any connection that is possible is *equally* certain. In any given case the test of the actual probability calls for the application of objective methods of observation; e.g., experiments, comparative studies, statistical operations of mass data, etc. We do not accept the fact that farmers postpone intended marriages when faced with crop failure because we can "understand" the connection. It is acceptable to us because we have found through reliable statistical operations that the correlation between the rate of marriage and the rate of crop production is extremely high. We would continue to accept the fact even if we could not "understand" it. In this instance the operation of *Verstehen* does no more than relieve us of a sense of apprehension which would undoubtedly haunt us if we were unable to understand the connection.

The postulate of *Verstehen* can now be viewed from a proper perspective. It cannot be made to imply that if we do not "understand" a connection it surely, or most probably, is false. It does, however, imply that our curiosity concerning human behavior does not rest until we have in some way been able to relate it to our personal experience. The satisfaction of curiosity produces subjective increment but adds nothing to the objective validity of a proposition. Thus, all assertions based solely on the evidence of "understandability" can be viewed as cases of "misplaced familiarity."

These limitations virtually preclude the use of the operation of *Verstehen* as a scientific tool of analysis. Still there is one positive function which the operation can perform in scientific investigations: It can serve as an aid in preliminary explorations of a subject. Furthermore, the operation can be particularly helpful in setting up hypotheses, even though it cannot be used to test them.

In dealing with human behavior, we create hypotheses whenever we ask for the "stimulus" which produced a given response, or when we attempt to predict what "response" will follow from a given occurrence. It is an accepted fact that, in formulating hypotheses, we start with some "hunch" or "intuition." Now it appears highly probable that the hunches which lead us to certain hypotheses concerning human behavior originate from the application of the operation of *Verstehen.* This follows from the fact that the operation—in addition to using the stated stimulus or response

—allows the use of another item of knowledge (a behavior maxim), which permits us to "reach out" from a given observation to its unknown counterpart. The diagram representing the reasoning about the neighbor seen chopping wood clearly indicates how behavior maxims can serve as a source of "hunches." Suppose *C–D* were given as an item of observation. By internalizing *C*, we obtain *C′*, to which we can then apply a behavior maxim, which gives us *B′*. *B′*, in turn, provides a clue to the nature of the situation or event which may be the possible stimulus (*A–B*) to the behavior in question. Lundberg's generalization (Case 2) is an example of a hypothesis derived in this fashion. By postulating that people who assert "eternal verities" are seeking security, he inferred a strong feeling of anxiety as the counterpart to this motive. He then surmised that the "changing and hostile world" might be the anxiety-producing condition. A "hunch" similarly reached was used by Durkheim in his study of suicide. When he found the rate of suicide varying in different groups, he was confronted by the problem of selecting the most likely determinant from a multitude of attributes of group life. From Merton's statement of the "paradigm of Durkheim's theoretic analysis," we can infer that Durkheim first internalized rates of suicide as "functions of unrelieved anxieties and stresses to which persons are subjected." [9] He then viewed such emotional states as the result of a lack of "psychic support," such as is provided by intimate associations with others. This suggested the possibility of social cohesion being the crucial factor which determines the characteristic rate of suicide in a group. Subsequent investigations established a high degree of probability for this inference because Durkheim was able to show that the rate of suicide varies consistently in inverse ratio with the degree of group coherence.

By reversing the procedure, we arrive at hunches about possible responses to given or expected occurrences. That is, we internalize the situation by projecting it as a problem experience and then, by means of a behavior maxim, infer the problem-solving response (intention). However, to guess the particular form the response will take requires information which the operation of *Verstehen* does not provide. It would not, for example, be of use in trying to conjecture specific ways and means of aggression which may be employed by a group in response to a provocation by another group. The operation gives us "hunches," and it points out the general character of possible factors, but it does not enable us to evaluate probabilities.

The findings with regard to the operation of *Verstehen* may be summarized in the following propositions:

The operation of *Verstehen* is performed by analyzing a behavior situation in such a way—usually in terms of general "feeling-states"—that it parallels some personal experience of the interpreter.

Primarily the operation of *Verstehen* does two things: It relieves us

[9] R. K. Merton, "Sociological Theory," *American Journal of Sociology*, L (May, 1945), 470.

of a sense of apprehension in connection with behavior that is unfamiliar or unexpected and it is a source of "hunches," which help us in the formulation of hypotheses.

The operation of *Verstehen* does not, however, add to our store of knowledge, because it consists of the application of knowledge already validated by personal experience; nor does it serve as a means of verification. The probability of a connection can be ascertained only by means of objective, experimental, and statistical tests.

The Logic of Historical Analysis *

ERNEST NAGEL

According to Aristotle, poetry, like theoretical science, is "more philosophic and of graver import" than history, for the former is concerned with the pervasive and universal, and the latter is addressed to the special and the singular. Aristotle's remark is a possible historical source of a widely held current distinction between two allegedly different types of sciences: the nomothetic, which seek to establish abstract general laws for indefinitely repeatable processes; and the idiographic, which aim to understand the unique and nonrecurrent. It is often maintained that the natural sciences are nomothetic, whereas history (in the sense of an account of events) is idiographic; and it is claimed in consequence that the logic and conceptual structure of historical explanations are fundamentally different from those of the natural sciences. It is my aim here to examine this and related issues in the logic of historical analysis.

I

Even a cursory examination of treatises in theoretical natural science and of books on history reveals the prima facie difference between them, that by and large the statements of the former are general in form, and contain few if any references to specific objects, places, and times, whereas the statements of the latter are almost without exception singular and replete with proper names, dates, and geographic specifications. To this extent, at least, the alleged contrast between the natural sciences as nomothetic and history as idiographic appears to be well founded.

It would, however, be a gross error to conclude that singular statements play no role in the theoretical sciences or that historical inquiry makes no use of universal ones. No conclusions concerning the actual character of specific things and processes can be derived from general statements alone; and theories and laws must be supplemented by initial or boundary conditions when the natural sciences attempt to explain any particular occurrence. Nor does the familiar and often useful distinction between "pure" and "applied" natural science impair the relevance of this point. For, clearly,

* Reprinted by kind permission of the author and the editor from *The Scientific Monthly*, 74, 1952.

even the pure natural sciences can assert their general statements as empirically warranted only on the basis of concrete factual evidence, and therefore only by establishing and using a variety of singular statements. And there are branches of natural science, such as geophysics and animal ecology, that are concerned with the spatiotemporal distribution and development of individual systems. It follows, in short, that neither the natural sciences taken as a whole nor their purely theoretical subdivisions can be regarded as being exclusively nomothetic.

Neither can historical study dispense with at least a tacit acceptance of universal statements of the kind occurring in the natural sciences. Thus, although the historian may be concerned with the nonrecurrent and the unique, he selects and abstracts from the concrete occurrences he studies, and his discourse about what is individual and singular requires the use of common names and general descriptive terms. Such characterizations are associated with the recognition of various kinds or types of things and occurrences, and therefore with the implicit acknowledgment of numerous empirical regularities. Again, one phase of a historian's task is to establish the authenticity of documents and other remains from the past, the precise meaning of recorded assertions, and the reliability of testimony concerning past events. For the effective execution of this task of external and internal criticism, the historian must be armed with a wide assortment of general laws, borrowed from one or the other of the natural and social sciences. And, since historians usually aim to be more than mere chroniclers of the past, and attempt to understand and explain recorded actions in terms of their causes and consequences, they must obviously assume supposedly well-established laws of causal dependence. In brief, history is not a purely idiographic discipline.

Nonetheless, there is an important asymmetry between theoretical and historical sciences. A theoretical science like physics seeks to establish both general and singular statements, and in the process of doing so physicists will employ previously established statements of both types. Historians, on the other hand, aim to assert warranted singular statements about the occurrence and interrelations of specific actions; and though this task can be achieved only by assuming and using general laws, historians do not regard it as part of their task to *establish* such laws. The distinction between history and theoretical science is thus somewhat analogous to the difference between medical diagnosis and physiology, or between geology and physics. A geologist seeks to ascertain, for example, the sequential order of geologic formations, and he is able to do so by applying various physical laws to the materials he encounters; it is not the geologist's task, qua geologist, to establish the laws of mechanics or of radioactive disintegration that he may employ.

The fact that historical research is concerned with the singular, and seeks to ascertain the causal dependencies between specific occurrences, does not warrant the widespread contention that there is a radical difference between the logical structure of explanations in the historical and the generalizing sciences. I shall consider only one specific argument to support the claim that there is such a difference. It has been said that there is a demonstrable *formal* difference between the "general concepts" of the theoretical sciences and the "individual concepts" assumed to be the goals of historical inquiry. Concepts of the first kind are alleged to conform to the familiar logical principle of the inverse variation of the extension and intension of terms: when a set of general terms is arranged in order of their increasing extensions, their intensions decrease. But quite the reverse is said to be the case for the individual concepts of historical explanations, since the more inclusive the "scope" of such a concept, the richer and fuller is its "meaning." Thus, the term "French Enlightenment" is claimed to have not only a more inclusive scope than the term "the life of Voltaire," but also to possess a fuller intension.[1]

But this is simply a confusion, derived in part from a failure to distinguish the relation of *inclusion* between the extensions of terms, from some form of *whole-part* relation between an instance of a term and a component of that instance. Thus, the French Enlightenment may be said to "contain" as one of its "components" the life of Voltaire; and it is doubtless correct to maintain that the term "French Enlightenment" is "richer in meaning or content" than the term "the life of Voltaire." But the *extension* of the term "French Enlightenment" does *not* include the *extension* of the term "the life of Voltaire," so that the logical principle under discussion cannot be significantly applied to these terms.

More generally, there appears to be no good reason for claiming that the general pattern of explanations in historical inquiry, or the logical structure of the conceptual tools employed in it, differs from those encountered in the generalizing and the natural sciences. The explanatory premises in history, as in the natural sciences, include a number of implicitly assumed laws, as well as many explicitly (though usually incompletely) formulated singular statements of initial conditions. The tacitly assumed laws may be of various kinds. They may be statements of regularities well attested in some special science, or they may be uncodified assumptions taken from common experience; they may be universal statements of invariable concomitance, or they may be statistical in form; they may assert a uniformity in temporal sequence, or they may assert some relation of co-existent dependence. The singular statements of initial conditions are of comparable variety, and although the truth of many of them is often incontrovertible it is frequently highly conjectural. Indeed, the relevance of such singular statements to the specific problems under investigation, as well as their truth, are questions upon which historians are often undecided or unable to achieve unanimity. There are, in fact, several problems in this connection that are of much concern to historical research, although they are not

[1] Rickert, H. *Die Grenzen der naturwissenschaftlichen Begriffsbildung*. Tübingen: J. C. B. Mohr, 281 (1921).

without relevance to other branches of social science as well. I therefore turn to consider briefly some of the real and alleged difficulties that plague the pursuit of historical knowledge.

II

It is a platitude that research in history as in other areas of science selects and abstracts from the concrete occurrences studied, and that however detailed a historical discourse may be it is never an exhaustive account of what actually happened. Curiously enough, it is the very selectivity of history that generates many of the broader questions relating to the nature of historical inquiry and is sometimes made the occasion for wholesale skepticism concerning the possibility of "objective" explanations in historical matters. Since a historian exercises selection in choosing problems for study, and also in his proposed solutions to them, it will be convenient to examine some of the relevant issues under these two heads.

1) Historians do not all concern themselves with the same things, and there are undoubtedly many past events that have received attention from no historian. Why does one historian occupy himself with ancient Greece, another with modern Germany, still another with the development of legal institutions in the American colonies, a fourth with the evolution of mathematical notation, and so on? Is there some general feature which differentiates those occurrences that are of concern to historians from those that are not? And, above all, is a historian prevented from giving a warranted or objective account of things because of his initial choice of a limited problem?

It is clear that there is no uniform answer to the first of these queries, for in historical inquiry as in other branches of science a variety of circumstances may determine what problems are to be investigated. It may be individual preference and endowment, controlled by education and the influence of teachers; it may be professional obligation or the desire for financial gain; it may be national pride, social pressure, or a sense of political mission. Historians of ideas have given some attention to this matter, and have uncovered interesting data concerning stimuli to specific investigations. But there is no prima facie reason to believe that, because a historical inquiry begins with a specific problem, or because there are causal determinants for his choice, a historian is in principle precluded—any more than is a natural scientist—from rendering an adequate account of the subjects he is investigating.

Many writers maintain, however, that the selectivity of history is peculiar in that the historian is inescapably concerned with "value-impregnated" subject matter. Thus, according to one influential view, an individual or process can be properly labeled as "historical" only if it is "irreplaceable," either because it uniquely embodies some universally accepted cultural value or because it is instrumental to the actualization of such a value. In consequence, the supposition that historical inquiry can ignore theoretical value relations is said by some writers to involve a self-deception,[2] whereas other commentators have concluded that unlike the physical sciences "history is violently personal," since "stars and molecules have no loves and hates, while men do." [3] There is, however, no basis for the claim that historical study is addressed exclusively to value-impregnated occurrences, unless indeed the word "history" is arbitrarily redefined so as to conform with the claim. For, although undoubtedly much historical inquiry is concerned with events that may be so characterized, there are also many investigations commonly called "historical" that are not of this nature—for example, inquiries into the development of the stars, biological species, and much else. More generally, there appears to be no warrant for any of the various claims that the occurrences studied by historians are distinguished by some inherent differentiating feature from those that are not. Moreover, even when a historian is concerned with admittedly value-impregnated subject matter or with occurrences manifesting various passions, it by no means follows that he must himself share or judge those values or passions. It is an obvious blunder to suppose that only a fat cowherd can drive fat kine. It is an equally crude error to maintain that one cannot inquire into the conditions and consequences of values and evaluations without necessarily engaging in moral or aesthetic value judgments.

There is also the broad question whether historical inquiry is inevitably guilty of distorting the facts because it is addressed to limited problems and is concerned only with certain selected materials of the past. The supposition that it is entails the view that one cannot have competent knowledge of anything unless one knows everything, and is a corollary to the philosophic doctrine of the "internality" of all relations. It will suffice here to note that, were the doctrine sound, not only would every historical account ever written be condemned as a necessarily mutilated and distorted version of what has happened, but a similar valuation would have to be placed on all science, and indeed on all analytical discourse. In short, the fact that inquiry is selective because it originates in a specific and limited problem places the historian in no worse position than it does other scientists with respect to the possibility of achieving what is commonly characterized as objectively warranted knowledge.

2) Historical inquiry is selective not only in its starting point; it is also selective in proposing solutions to its problems. A variety of skeptical doubts about the possibility of an objective history has been expressed in consequence.

One such expression takes the form that, in view of the inexhaustibly numerous relations in which a given event stands to other events, no account can ever render the "full reality" of what has occurred. Accordingly, since every historical account covers only a few aspects of an occurrence and

[2] *Ibid.*, 254.

[3] Nevins, A. *The Gateway to History*. New York: Appleton-Century, 29 (1938).

stops at some point in the past in tracing back its antecedents, every proposed explanation of that occurrence is said to bear the mark of arbitrariness and subjectivity. Part of this objection can be summarily dismissed with the reminder that it is never the task of any inquiry initiated by a specific problem to *reproduce* its subject matter, and that it would be a gratuitous performance were a historian in the pursuit of such a problem to formulate "all that has been said, done, and thought by human beings on the planet since humanity began its long career." Not only is the bare fact that inquiry is selective no valid ground for doubting the objectively warranted character of its conclusions; on the contrary, unless an inquiry were selective it would never come near to resolving the specific question by which it is generated.

However, the objection under discussion also rests on another misconception: it in effect assumes that since every causal condition for an event has its own causal conditions, the event is never properly explained unless the entire regressive series of the latter conditions are also explained. It has been maintained, for example, that

> A Baptist sermon in Atlanta, if we seek to explain it, takes us back through the Protestant Reformation to Galilee—and far beyond in the dim origins of civilization. We can, if we choose, stop at any point along the line of relations, but that is an arbitrary act of will and does violence to the quest for truth in the matter.[4]

But is there any violence to the truth? Is *B* not a cause of *A* simply because *C* is a cause of *B*? When some future position of a planet is predicted with the help of gravitational theory and information about the initial condition of the solar system at some given time, is there ground for skepticism simply because the assumed initial conditions are in turn the outcome of previous ones? These are rhetorical questions, for the answers to all of them are obviously in the negative. Moreover, precisely what is the problem in connection with the Baptist sermon in Atlanta? Is it why a given individual delivered it at a stated time and occasion, or why he chose a particular text and theme, or why that occasion happened to arise, or why Baptists flourished in Atlanta, or why they developed as a Protestant sect, or why the Protestant Reformation occurred, or why Christianity arose in antiquity? These are all quite different questions, and an adequate answer for one of them is not even relevant as a proposed solution for the others. The supposition that, when a problem is made definite a regressive chain of answers must be sought if any one answer is to be objectively warranted, is patently self-contradictory. On the other hand, the fact that one problem may suggest another, and so lead to a possibly endless series of new inquiries, simply illustrates the progressive character of the scientific enterprise; that fact is no support for the claim that unless the series is terminated, every proposed solution to a given problem is necessarily a mutilation of the truth.

[4] Beard, C. A. *The Discussion of Human Affairs.* New York: Macmillan, 68–9 (1936).

Skepticism concerning the possibility of objectively warranted explanations in human history takes a more empirical turn when it bases its negations on the influence of personal and social bias upon such inquiry. The doubt embodied in the *aperçu* that history is written by the survivors is by no means a novelty; but in recent years it has been deepened and given a radical form by many sociologists of knowledge. According to some of them, all thought is conditioned and controlled by the "existential situation" in which it occurs; and, especially when thinking is directed to human affairs, the interpretation of observed facts, the selection of problems for inquiry and the methods employed for resolving them, and the standards of validity accepted are all functions of the thinker's unconscious value commitments and world outlook, his social position, and his political and class loyalties. Every cognitive claim concerning matters of vital human interest is therefore said to be valid only within the particular social setting in which it emerges; and the belief that it is possible to obtain explanations that are "true" for everyone, irrespective of his position in a given society, is declared to be part of the self-deception (or "ideology") of a culture.

There appear to be four distinct issues raised by this form of skepticism. In the first place, the choice of particular problems for study, especially inquiries into human affairs, is undoubtedly controlled by the character of a given culture, and sometimes by the status of the student in that culture. An investigation of traffic problems is not likely to be made in an agricultural society, and a man's interest in labor history may very well be causally related to his social position. But, as has already been seen, this form of selective activity on the part of an inquirer does not necessarily jeopardize the objectivity of his findings.

In the second place, no inquiry takes place in an intellectual vacuum, and every investigator approaches his task with information and guiding ideas derived in large measure from his culture. But it does not follow from this circumstance alone that the conscious and unconscious value commitments associated with the social status of an investigator inevitably influence his acceptance of one conclusion rather than another. The preconceptions he brings to the analysis of a given problem may be neutral to all differences in social values, even when that problem is concerned with human affairs. And, in point of fact, there are many questions in the social as well as in the natural sciences upon which there is complete agreement among students, despite their different social positions and loyalties.

It is undoubtedly the case, in the third place, that the standards of validity operative in an inquiry are *causally* related to other cultural traits, and that social status, class and national bias, and general world perspectives frequently influence what conclusions a man accepts. For example, the degree of precision currently demanded in experimental work is certainly not independent of the current state of technology; and a comparison of Southern and Northern histories of the period of reconstruction following the American Civil War makes amply clear the force of sectional and race bias. This is an area of study that has not yet been systematically exploited, although sociologists of knowledge have already illuminated the genesis of many ideas and the manner in which social pressures enforce their acceptance. In any event, biased thinking is a perennial challenge to the critical historian of human affairs; and research into the causal determinants of bias is of undoubted value for recognizing its occurrence and for mitigating if not always eliminating its influence. The very fact that biased thinking may be detected and its sources investigated shows that the case for objective explanations in history is not necessarily hopeless. Indeed, the assertion that a historian exhibits bias assumes that there is a distinction between biased and unbiased thinking, and that the bias can be identified—for otherwise the assertion would at best be simply futile name-calling. In consequence, it is possible, even if frequently difficult, to correct the bias and to obtain conclusions in better agreement with the evidence. Accordingly, if doubt concerning the objectivity of a historical explanation is based on considerations relating to the causal influence of various social factors upon the evaluation of evidence, it is often salutary and well taken; but it does not entail a wholesale skepticism concerning the possibility of such explanations.

This brings me to the final issue. It is sometimes argued that the social perspective of a student of human affairs is not only causally influential upon his inquiry, but is *logically* involved both in his standards of validity as well as in the meaning of his statements. And it is also maintained that one must therefore reject the thesis that "the genesis of a proposition is under all circumstances irrelevant to its truth." [5] On the other hand, the radical skepticism concerning objective explanations of human affairs that results is qualified by the further claim that a "relational" type of objectivity can nevertheless be achieved. Thus, students who share the same social perspective and employ the same conceptual and categorical apparatus will allegedly arrive at similar conclusions on any problem when the standards characteristic of their common perspective are correctly applied. And students operating within different social perspectives can attain objectivity in a "roundabout fashion" by construing their inevitable differences in the light of the differences in the structures of their perspectives.

There are, however, grave factual and dialectical difficulties in these several claims. There is no factual evidence to show that the "content and form" of statements, or the standards of validity employed, are *logically* determined by the social perspective of an inquirer. The facts commonly cited establish no more than some kind of causal dependence between these items. For example, the once much-publicized view that the "mentality" or logical operations of "primitive" social groups are different from those typical of European civilization—a difference that was once attributed to institutional differences in the societies compared—is now generally rec-

[5] Mannheim, K. *Ideology and Utopia.* New York: Harcourt, Brace, 243, 259 (1936).

ognized to be without foundation. Moreover, even the most extreme proponents of the sociology of knowledge admit that there are many assertions (those usually mentioned come from mathematics and the natural sciences) which are neutral to differences in social perspective and whose genesis is irrelevant to their validity. Why cannot assertions about human affairs exhibit the same neutrality? If, as no one seems to doubt, the truth of the statement that two horses can in general pull a greater load than either horse alone is logically independent of the social status of the one who asserts it, what inherent social circumstance precludes such independence for the statement that two laborers can in general dig a ditch of given dimensions more quickly than either laborer working alone?

Second, what is the logical status of the claim that social perspectives enter essentially into the content and warrant of all assertions about human affairs? Is the claim itself meaningful and valid only for those occupying a certain social status? In that case, its validity is narrowly self-limited, no student with a different social perspective can properly understand or evaluate it, and it must be dismissed as irrelevant by most inquirers into social questions. Or is the claim peculiarly exempt from what it asserts, so that its meaning and truth are not logically dependent upon the social status of those who assert it? In that case, then, there is at least one conclusion about human affairs which may be "objectively valid" in the usual sense of this phrase; and if there is one such conclusion, there is no clear reason why there may not be others.

Finally, the relational type of objectivity which the claim admits as attainable is nothing other than objectivity in the customary sense, which the claim appears to deny as possible. A translation formula which renders the "common denominator" of seemingly diverse conclusions stemming from differing social perspectives, cannot in turn be "situationally determined" in the sense under dispute. Indeed, the search for such formulas is but a well-known phase of theoretical research in all areas of inquiry. It is a search for objective invariants in numerically and qualitatively distinct processes; and when the quest is successful, as it often is, it terminates in laws of greater or less generality, with whose help what is relevant to the occurrence of an event or to the continuance of a process can be distinguished from what is not.

In brief, therefore, although the historian is undoubtedly selective in the conduct of his inquiries, and although personal and social bias frequently color his judgment and control what conclusions he accepts, none of these facts precludes the possibility of warranted explanations for the events he studies.

III

The elimination of theoretical objections to the possibility of warranted explanations in history obviously does not ensure the realization of that possibility. As a matter of fact, there are serious obstacles, other than those already mentioned, which frequently do obstruct the quest for such explanations.

The search for explanations is directed to the ideal of ascertaining the necessary and sufficient conditions for the occurrence of phenomena. This ideal is rarely achieved, however, and even in the best-developed natural sciences it is often an open question whether the conditions mentioned in an explanation are indeed sufficient. Most historical inquiry is even further removed from this ideal, since the full circumstances are often quite complex and numerous and are usually not known. Historians therefore frequently cite only what they regard as the "main," "primary," "principal," "chief," or "most important" causal factors and cover their ignorance of the others by the convenient phrase "other things being equal." To mention but one example, the "main" cause of America's entrance into the first world war is declared by one careful student to be Germany's adoption of an unrestricted submarine warfare, though the factor cited is not assumed to be sufficient for producing the effect.

The "weighting" of causal factors in respect to their "degree of importance" is sometimes dismissed as essentially "arbitrary" and "meaningless" —partly on the ground that there is no warrant for selecting one occurrence as the cause of a given event rather than some prior cause of that occurrence (for example, since unrestricted submarine warfare was Germany's response to the British blockade, this latter occurrence is allegedly as much the cause of America's entrance into the war as is the former), and partly on the ground that no verifiable sense can be attached to such characterizations as "chief" or "most important" in connection with causal factors. It must be admitted that the natural sciences do not appear to require the imputation of relative importance to the causal variables that occur in their explanations; and it is easy to dismiss the question of whether there is any objective basis for such gradations of variables, with a peremptory denial on the ground that, if a phenomenon occurs only when certain conditions are realized, all these conditions are equally essential, and no one of them can intelligibly be regarded as more basic than the others. And it must also be acknowledged that most historians do not appear to associate any definite meaning with their statements of relative importance, so that the statements often have only a rhetorical intent, from which no clear empirical content can be extracted. Nevertheless, we often do make such claims as that broken homes constitute a more important cause of juvenile delinquency than does poverty, or that the lack of a trained labor force is a more fundamental cause of the backward state of an economy than the lack of natural resources. Many people might be willing to admit that the *truth* of such statements is debatable, but few would be willing to grant that they are totally without *meaning* so that anyone who asserts them is invariably uttering nonsense.

It is desirable, therefore, to make explicit what such statements may be intended to convey. In point of fact, ascriptions of relative importance to determinants of social phenomena appear to be associated with a variety of meanings, some of which I shall try to distinguish. If *A* and *B* are two adequately specified factors upon which the occurrence of a phenomenon *C* is supposed to depend in some fashion, the statements I wish to consider will be assumed to have the schematic form "*A* is a more important (or basic, or fundamental) determinant of *C* than is *B*."

1) *A* and *B* may both be necessary for the occurrence of *C*, though perhaps their joint presence is not sufficient for that occurrence. Then one sense in which *A* might be said to be a more important determinant of *C* than is *B* is simply this: variations in *B* occur infrequently and may be neglected for all practical purposes, whereas variations in *A*, with consequent variations in *C*, are quite frequent and perhaps uncontrollable. Thus, suppose that dislike of foreigners and need for economic markets are both necessary conditions for the adoption of an imperialist policy by some country; but suppose that xenophobia in that country varies little if at all during a given period, whereas the need for foreign markets increases. In this first sense of more important, need for foreign markets is a more important cause of imperialism than is dislike of foreigners.

2) But there is another though more difficult sense of more important. Assume again that *A* and *B* are both necessary for the occurrence of *C*. But suppose that there is some way of specifying the magnitude of variations in *A*, *B*, and *C*, respectively, and that, although changes in one may not be comparable with changes in another, the changes within each item are comparable. Suppose, further, that a greater change in *C* is associated with a given proportional change in *A* than with an equal proportional change in *B*. In that event, *A* might be given a more important rank as a determinant of *C* than is assigned to *B*. For example, assume that a supply of coal and a trained labor force are both necessary for industrial productivity; but suppose that, say, a 10 per cent variation in the labor force produces a greater alteration in the quantity of goods produced (as measured by some convenient index) than does a 10 per cent variation in the coal supply. Accordingly, the availability of a trained labor force could be said to be a more important determinant of productivity than the availability of coal.

3) Suppose now that the joint presence of *A* and *B* is not necessary for the occurrence of *C*, so that *C* can occur under conditions *A* and *Y*, or under conditions *B* and *Z*, where *Y* and *Z* are otherwise unspecified determinants. In this case, also, there is a sense of more important analogous to the first sense mentioned above. More explicitly, the frequency with which the first condition *B* and *Z* are realized may be small when compared with the frequency of the realization of *A* and *Y*; and this possibility may then be expressed by saying that *A* is a more important determinant of *C* than is *B*. Thus, assume that automobile accidents occur either because of negligence or because of mechanical failure; and suppose that the fre-

quency with which there is such failure that leads to accidents is very much less than the frequency with which carelessness terminates in accidents. In that case, negligence may be said to be a more important cause of accidents than is mechanical failure.

4) Assume, again, that the joint presence of *A* and *B* is not necessary for the occurrence of *C*; and suppose that the relative frequency with which *C* occurs when the condition *A* is realized but *B* is not is greater than the relative frequency of *C*'s occurrence if *B* is realized but *A* is not. It is such a state of affairs which is sometimes intended by the assertion that *A* is a more important determinant of *C* than is *B*. For example, a statement such as that broken homes are a more fundamental cause of juvenile delinquency than is poverty is frequently best interpreted to mean that the relative frequency of delinquency among juveniles coming from broken homes is much greater than among children coming from homes marked by poverty.

5) One final sense of more important must be mentioned. Suppose that a theory *T* is formulated with the help of *A* as a fundamental theoretical term; and suppose that *T* can account for the phenomenon *C* when *T* is supplemented by appropriate data which involve reference to *B*. In consequence, though reference to *B* is essential for explaining *C* with the help of *T*, reference to *B* is not always necessary when *T* serves to explain phenomena other than *C*. Accordingly, since the range of phenomena which fall within the province of *T* (and therefore within the range of application of *A*) is more inclusive than the phenomena for which *B* is relevant, *A* may be said to be a more basic determinant of *C* than is *B*. Something like this sense of more basic appears to be intended by those who claim that the social relations that govern the production and distribution of wealth constitute a more basic determinant of the legal institutions of a society than do the religious and moral ideals professed in that society.

Other senses of more important or more basic can undoubtedly be distinguished, but the five here mentioned appear to be those most frequently used in discussions of human affairs. It is essential to note that, although a definite meaning may thus be associated with ascriptions of greater importance to assumed determinants of social processes, it does not follow that the available evidence does in fact warrant any given assertion of such a claim. Accordingly, even when a historian does intend to convey a verifiable content by such assertions, it is doubtful whether in most cases they are actually supported by competent evidence. There is next to no statistical material bearing on the relative frequency of occurrence of the phenomena of special concern to students of human affairs. Historians are therefore compelled, willy-nilly, to fall back upon guesses and vague impressions in assigning weights to causal factors. There are often wide divergences in judgment as to what are the main causes of a given event, and one man's opinions may be no better grounded than another's. Whether this defect in current causal imputations in historical research can eventually be remedied is an open question, since the probable cost of remedial measures in terms of labor and money seems staggering. Meanwhile, however, a judicious skepticism concerning the warrant for most if not all judgments of relative importance of causal factors (among those assumed to be relevant to an event) appears to be in order.

Doubtless the basic trouble in this area of inquiry is that we do not possess at present a generally accepted, explicitly formulated, and fully comprehensive schema for weighing the evidence for any arbitrarily given hypothesis so that the logical worth of alternate conclusions relative to the evidence available for each can be compared. Judgments must be formed even on matters of supreme practical importance on the basis of only vaguely understood considerations; and, in the absence of a standard logical canon for estimating the degree in which the evidence supports a conclusion, when judgments are in conflict each often appears to be the outcome of an essentially arbitrary procedure. This circumstance affects the standing of the historian's conclusions in the same manner as the findings of other students. Fortunately, though the range of possible disagreement concerning the force of evidence for a given statement is theoretically limitless, there is substantial agreement among men experienced in relevant matters on the relative probabilities to be assigned to many hypotheses. Such agreement indicates that, despite the absence of an explicitly formulated logic, many unformulated habits of thought embody factually warrantable principles of inference. Accordingly, although there are often legitimate grounds for doubt concerning the validity of specific causal imputations in history, there appears to be no compelling reason for converting such doubt into wholesale skepticism.

Dialectic in Society and History*

SIDNEY HOOK

The term "dialectic" is almost as old as the practice of philosophy. Like many other labels of great antiquity, it has been used as a tag for concepts, activities, and situations of the most heterogeneous variety. Few philosophers have ever employed the term in the same sense as any of their predecessors. Indeed, rarely is it the case that any philosopher has consistently adhered to any one meaning in his writings. What *the* dialectic is, therefore, can no more be adequately treated short of a history of its definitions in use from Plato to the present than we could straightway say what *the* empirical, *the* reasonable, *the* sensible, *the* romantic, and similar terms mean in the history of philosophy. What is true of Plato, Aristotle, and Plotinus —all of whom employ the term "dialectic" and all in different senses—is the general rule for every other period of philosophy.

None the less, it is possible to indicate the chief classes of meaning within which the various uses of the term fall, and to investigate the kinds of problems and intellectual motivations which have impelled philosophers to distinguish between what is dialectical and what is not. It is also possible to point out certain characteristic errors and dangers which have accompanied the use of the term "dialectic." The only alternative to this procedure is to present one's own theory of dialectic. This I shall not do. Instead I shall argue that it would be best in the interests of clarity to let the term sink into the desuetude of archaisms. Further, I shall try to show that this is the only legitimate moral that can be drawn from any critical investigation of the assumptions and types of procedure most frequently designated as dialectical in the history of thought.

There are two generic conceptions of dialectic under which the various meanings of dialectic may be subsumed. The first is the conception of dialectic as a pattern of existential change either in nature or society or man where the "or" is not exclusive. The second is the view that dialectic is a special method of analyzing such change. Usually, but not always, it is held that the method of dialectical analysis in some sense "reflects" or "corresponds to" the dialectical pattern of change. In any case, there is always a distinction drawn, though with no great regard for consistency,

* Reprinted by kind permission of the author from Sidney Hook, *Reason, Social Myths and Democracy*, Humanities Press, New York, 1951, Ch. 11.

between the dialectical type of change and other kinds. When the dialectic is identified with change as such, it is explicitly contrasted with some other natural or supernatural element which is regarded as undialectical, e.g., unchanging form or pattern. Similarly with the conception of dialectic as method. Whether taken as a method of analysis or discovery or both, it is always distinguished from other methods called undialectical, i.e., metaphysical, scientific, commonsensical, etc. This last distinction is of the first importance. For the alleged justification of the dialectic method consists in its power to lead us to the discovery of new truths or to a deeper and more adequate understanding of old truths not accessible to us by any other method.

1. Dialectic as the Pattern of Existential Change

What is the dialectic when it is conceived as a constitutive principle in history and culture? Here we must distinguish between three subclasses of conceptions.

1. Dialectic as Pendular Rhythm

The first of these is the view that the pattern of dialectical change in history is found in a pendular rhythm or eternal repetitive seesaw between tendencies, forces, institutions, styles of thought, and morals. On this view, every activity, in virtue of its very pervasiveness and triumph, tends by force of immanent necessity to bring about its own opposite. Convention leads to revolt and revolt to convention, peace to war and war to peace, despotism to democracy and democracy to despotism, empiricism to rationalism and vice versa. So far as I am aware, no one has understood the concept of pendularity as involving a literal return to some previous phase, for this would mean that the initial polarity was the final polarity. The history of culture or of any aspect of culture would then be sufficiently described in one formula and no allowance made for the rich variety of forms that fall outside the arc of the pendular swing. And, in fact, even when it is admitted that oscillations between tendencies never carry the pendulum back to the very same place, the whole notion of periodicity seems inadequate to the *historical* character of cultural phenomena. It is nothing but a mechanical analogy imposed upon a material which in large measure reveals continuities, transitions, cumulative developments. Its inadequacy is expressed by the arbitrary character of the time span it takes for this swing rhythm to fulfill itself. Its use in suggesting points of similarity between anything present and past is blind and irrelevant except in relation to some specific hypothesis that involves references to other factors which do not necessarily have periodic character. And without such an hypothesis, the analogy is likely to distract our attention from what is historically new in any given epoch. The uncritical comparisons between modern totalitarianisms and those of ancient or medieval times is a case in point.

The most serious defect, however, of this view of dialectic is in its conception of immanent necessity. It states some periodic law on the basis of a simple and risky induction from a few cases. It then uses the law to explain and predict other historical events. It thus combines a kind of mystical rationalism with a crude empiricism. It overlooks the fact that in scientific inquiry the observation of a genuine periodicity or fluctuation is rarely taken as a brute fact or ultimate datum. It marks the beginning of a problem, not the close of an inquiry. And the problem usually is to discover how the periodic changes are functionally related to, or determined by, other factors in the environmental medium or background. Here there are no immanent necessities.

II. Dialectic as Struggle

The second conception of existential dialectic in society and history identifies it with the fact and pattern of struggle. On this view, wherever human beings live in association with each other, struggles, conflicts, and oppositions of varying intensity are bound to ensue. The conditions under which, the objects over which, and the occasions on which struggle breaks out—vary from one dialectical theory to another. When it is consistently held, it flatly contradicts the naïve belief that the social harmony and peace, envisaged by all chiliastic doctrines, can ever prevail in the relations between men. But the view is rarely held in a consistent way. In the interests of political mythology, the dialectic of struggle is usually restricted to a certain set of antagonisms assumed to be basic to all others. With the elimination of the conditions which breed these antagonisms, it is predicted that all other antagonisms will disappear. The result is either an *a priori* belief that social war is an inexpugnable feature of all social life or chiliasm in pseudo-scientific dress—a belief in a predestined day when all men will be brothers and no one will re-enact the role of Cain.

The trouble with both of these alternatives is that they deal with "struggle" in the large. Like all vague monisms, despite their suggestive character, they are incapable of scientific verification. Verbally, they are compatible with any known state of affairs. Empirically, we do not know struggle but struggles. And these are neither absolute nor unconditional. That is to say, the same individuals who are members of groups engaged in some specific struggle may also be members of groups engaged in some specific form of co-operation or solidarity. And every specific struggle is contingent upon factors which if not modifiable are at least variable. In the absence of a precisely defined schedule of the kinds of struggle, their degree of pervasiveness, and their interrelationships, significant causal analysis is very difficult. Thought moves on a pre-scientific level contenting itself with some traditional conception of human nature. The traditionalism of social neo-Darwinism, which from propositions about man's biological organism makes inferences about history and society to the end of all time, is matched by the fantasies of millenary Utopianism which, from evidence that *some* socially undesirable traits of historical behavior may be removable, makes inferences about the future which would require that man cease being a biological organism.

III. Dialectic as Historical Interaction

The third and most common objective reference of dialectic is to the pattern of interaction between "objective conditioning features of the environment," and man considered as an active agent in the historical process. The dialectical problem par excellence on this view is how man changes himself, or how men, as a class, change their social status, by reacting upon a changing social environment. Sometimes concern seems to be with the way in which "the will," operating within a causally or finalistically determined system, expresses its own form of determination as a principle of freedom, making a difference to the system and at the same time making itself different. Sometimes the concern seems to be with the way in which qualities of feeling and emotion, whether derived from inner impulses or outer impacts, become transformed by virtue of the ideas and activities in which they are expressed. Most often, the problem is to account for the fact that ideals or resolutions, which are an outgrowth of that which is apparently neither, are capable none the less of modifying their own conditions. The idealistic version of dialectic meets the difficulty by assimilating things to mind; the materialistic version of dialectic interprets mind as a specific form of adaptive behavior. In both types of solution human activity, informed by ideals, introduces changes in the original situation whose difficulties provoke action. The dialectical nub of the process is considered to be the element of creative redetermination produced in the self or the world by human ideals and practice, and the subsequent modification of human nature by the control of things and institutions.

Now strictly considered, all these forms of activity and the problem of interaction associated with them, fall within the realm of individual and social psychology, and testify to the fact that the latter is a comparatively undeveloped discipline whose very key concepts are subject to ambiguity and dispute. Particularly is this true for what may be called the field of personal psychology. Those who regard the problems of individual life in the dramatic form in which they are experienced when momentous decisions, conversions, and actions occur, as the only genuine concern of the philosophical psychologist, seem to me, for all their elaborate verbal constructions, to be expressing in a disguised way only their own concern or preference for certain problems which have autobiographical significance. Their new and arresting vocabulary baptizes the events in question so that we know that they are crisis phenomena not in the life of man, as is alleged, but in the lives of some men. But they do not explain them. At best, they convey a sense of their high importance. So far as I can see, the chief insights of Kierkegaard, Heidegger, Jaspers, *et al.*, are already involved in the dictum of Lichtenberg that the verbs which express personal existence are irregular in all languages, which even on the most *outré* metaphysical theory of language justifies the not very exciting conclusion that the mode of man's existence is in some ways different from that of other things in this world.

The crucial problem suggested by the use of dialectic in this sense is not the existence of the facts of social, personal, and moral experience, nor whether they have a call upon our attention, but whether the *descriptions* of these facts in the *language* of dialectic are valid, and by what objective techniques of inquiry the validity of these descriptions is to be established. The most momentous conclusion which is hung upon the allegedly dialectical character of consciousness, individual or historical, is that its investigation entails an abandonment of the principles of scientific empirical procedure, not to speak of ordinary canons of logic, which are granted a limited validity in other fields, and the adoption of a new dialectic method of thought or apprehension. What this dialectic method is we shall discuss later. But there is nothing in the descriptive account of the phenomena of conscious human action that makes necessary an appeal to non-scientific types of investigation and inference. Suppose it is true that every act of inquiry affects the quality of the state of personality which is being investigated; suppose it is true that in knowing, processes are set up that transform the situation which is being known; suppose, to use another of the stock illustrations of the dialectic situation, it is true that human beings, whose behavior has been predicted, are influenced to some extent in their behavior by that prediction. In all of these cases, the situation becomes more complicated, the observed data and effects are indirectly connected with the quaesitum, and reliable knowledge may be harder to get. But the complexity of a problem is an invitation to extend and refine existing methods of analyses and inquiry, particularly if they have proved adequate to the solution of simpler problems in their respective fields. It does not warrant a jump to a distinction between two kinds of knowledge or to two radically different methods of acquiring knowledge.

2. Dialectic as a Method of Understanding Change

We now turn to a consideration of those conceptions of dialectic which identify it with a method of thought—conceived not merely as a mode of analysis which uncovers assumptions and elicits the consequences of asserted meanings, i.e., the familiar method of clarifying ideas—but dialectic as a fruitful method of discovering truths. Those who hold that there is something dialectical in the world of nature or history usually assert that truths about it can be disclosed by the dialectical method alone: there are some, however, who deny that there is an existential dialectic, but affirm that whatever *is* in the world can be understood with the help of the dialectical method. The exercise of the dialectic method is usually attributed to a certain intellectual power or faculty, reason as distinct from the understanding, synoptic insight as distinct from discursive thought.

What is this dialectic method? Here again we can only understand it by examining the intellectual procedures of those who claim they are using it.[1] When we do this we find not one but several basic notions or principles of procedure in the writings of those who identify themselves as dialecticians.

I. Dialectic as Interrelatedness

One of the most important categories of dialectic method is the principle of *interrelatedness*. Used in social inquiry, this has led, since the time of Hegel, to the perception that certain cultural patterns and ideals are so pervasive that a sharp separation of the fields of law, religion, politics, and economics from each other makes unintelligible the structure, problems, and indeed the very history of those fields. Used in the analysis of individual acts of behavior, it often uncovers not merely the physical and biological systems in which they appear as elements, but a pattern of social values to which these acts owe their distinctive significance. From this point of view, a culture may not be a seamless web, but it is more than an aggregate of unrelated individual activities in a frame of chance-assorted institutions. No matter what we understand by "understanding" in social inquiry, it always presupposes that a thing is placed in context, connection, or relationship with other things. Now so much, every theory of scientific method would assert, and not merely for social inquiry but *all* inquiry. What is distinctive, however, about the category of interrelatedness in the dialectic method is that it recognizes no limitation upon the principle. For it, *all* things are interrelated in a definite kind of pattern whose nature we shall later indicate; and this is asserted not as a heuristic principle, subject to the *piecemeal* verification of scientific method but as a dogma. It is not enough on this view to say that some cultural wholes are related in some determinate ways to other wholes. What is asserted is that all wholes are related to each other in the same or similar way as the parts of any whole are related to each other. Where this cannot be established for any event or for a whole domain of events, the dogma is not modified, but the event or domain in question is characterized as in so far incomplete, unintelligible, accidental, and an "inferior" order of "reality" is attributed to it.

The excesses to which the dialectic method, conceived as the principle of cultural interrelatedness, can go is best illustrated in Spengler, for whom one style of the soul informs and unites such apparently different things

[1] I have omitted specific discussion of Marx in this connection because, whether or not we regard his findings as valid, I believe it can be shown that he made no distinction between the dialectic method, as he understood it, and scientific method as applied to the historical and cultural sciences.

as oil painting perspective, printing, the credit system, long range weapons, contrapuntal music, and differential calculus; while another style of the soul is found organically unifying the nude statue, coin-currency, the city state, Euclidean geometry, and the burning of the dead. Here we have organicism gone mad, buttressed by dubious scholarship, substituting impressionist principles of integration for clearly defined forms of interrelation, and in the end compelled to rule out as atypical, "unreal," or as cultural aberrations whatever does not yield to arbitrary intuition. Spengler is the best but by far not the only representative of this tendency. Many orthodox dialectical materialists proceed in the same fashion, except that instead of the style of the soul they substitute the style (forces) of production which "in the last instance" determines everything significant in art, biology, physics, military warfare, the clothing industry, and the movies.

II. Dialectic and Holism

It is clear, then, that the concept of interrelatedness as used by the dialectic method goes hand in hand with the concept of *totality*. In many writers it is this term which receives the chief emphasis. Here, too, in so far as it is a way of asserting that there are no ready-made atomic facts, observation of which is a final validation of an isolated judgment, it states what is recognized by every adequate account of scientific method. Even the most rigorous analysis takes its point of departure from some vaguely apprehended qualitative whole or situation; and every significant observation involves a whole body or system of knowledge. But what distinguishes the scientific from the dialectic use of totality is its attempt to predict, with the greatest exactness possible to the material, the behavior of some particular whole by formulating certain abstract general laws that hold for the elements of all totalities in the same relevant class. According to the customary use of dialectic method, on the other hand, it is *theoretically* impossible to formulate laws that are instrumentally valid for individual totalities without these laws being *necessarily* modified by their organic interrelation with other aspects of totality. That is to say, not merely is it asserted that no set of laws can completely determine all the specific aspects of the behavior of an individual totality—which every student of scientific method would grant—the dialectic method affirms that the very meaning and validity of these laws must of necessity be affected by the structure of the concrete totality to which it is applied. This, of course, is involved in the Hegelian theory of the concrete universal and its doctrine that all relations are internal. From them it follows not merely that scientific knowledge is incomplete, but that it necessarily distorts, not merely that abstractions are for certain purposes inadequate, but that they are vicious, and that the laws which state how they are related are unintelligible.

In actual practice those who have used the dialectic method most plausibly in the cultural disciplines have done little more than to show that the totalities of culture and history are more inclusive than those of natural science, and that consequently although the laws of natural science retain their validity in the more inclusive situations, it is possible to formulate social laws to do justice to the distinctive character of cultural and historical totalities. But this does not justify the belief that the rationale or logic of scientific method becomes altered when its subject matter is historical and social rather than physical. Theoretically, there is no reason to deny the possibility that social and historical laws may be reduced to special expressions of more general physical laws (i.e., given certain general physical laws, certain special data of observation, and certain rules governing inferences for the class of phenomena in question, it may be possible to deduce biological or social laws). But on the other hand, there is no reason to assert that they necessarily must be reducible, except in a special technical sense that applies not to laws, but to how concepts are to be introduced, a sense which has nothing to do with traditional "reductionism." The empirical fact is that social life is the most inclusive form of totality that we know, that *some* but not *all* forms of biological and psychological interaction, observed to hold outside of a social context, are modified when they are found within this totality. The investigation of the extent to which, and the specific ways in which, this is accomplished, however, needs no special dialectic logic to reach scientifically valid conclusions.

III. Dialectic and Inquiry

Historically, the actual technique of the dialectic method from Proclus to Hegel, where it is not synonymous with logical analysis or the art of clarifying a position by question and answer, consists in showing that every concept or category or judgment implicitly involves its contradictory, and that these contradictories together, instead of negating each other, logically involve another concept or category or judgment in which, for the moment, they enjoy a differentiated compatibility. This is the famous *dialektischer Dreitakt* by which logical thinking marches to the One or the Absolute Idea. Logically, of course, the whole process does not survive a second glance. The confusion between the concepts of contraries, contradictories, opposition, and otherness is palpable. Just as Nicholas von Cusa calmly uses the phrase *coincidentia oppositorum*—the identity of opposites—interchangeably with *connexio oppositorum*—the unity of opposites—so Hegel speaks of the *Einheit* and *Identität* of *Widersprüche* and *Gegensätze* as if they meant the same.

Looking away from the fatal difficulties which attend any attempt to take the dialectic method literally, we may ask: What do we discover to be the case when those who claim to be using dialectical procedures reach conclusions or make analyses which on *other* grounds we are prepared to admit as valid? In all such cases, I think that what we find is this. We begin with some vague conceptions and definitions which are set to work to solve some felt difficulty in a situation. We develop therefrom an ordered set of implications which are established as a system in terms of which the structure or behavior of the given and similar situations are so described that the felt difficulty or problem is resolved. We then discover (1) either that certain incompatible judgments follow from the premises, or (2) that some particular subject matter which is outside of our system and yet seems to be continuous in certain respects to the subject matter within the system, cannot be intelligibly characterized. In the first case, we go back to our premises and clarify ambiguities; in the second, we redefine the terms in our premises or add new premises with a direct eye to the new material. Both are special cases of the logic of redefinition as it functions in inquiry. Illustrations abound on all sides, e.g., changes in the definition of number to include the so-called irrational and imaginary numbers; in the definition of atom from Democritus to the present; in the definition of organism to include unicellular entities; in the definition of property to include copyrights and good will, etc.

Procedures of this kind are familiar in all fields. They are phases of scientific inquiry. Far from affirming, they contradict the claims made for the dialectic method. For what is called the movement of dialectic method is here obviously neither universal, nor necessary, nor immanent, as all versions of the theory contend it must be. The synthetic construction in any situation can never be deduced from the logical character of what the dialectic miscalls contradictories. There is always a number of syntheses or supra-ordinate systems that can be constructed to resolve "oppositions." The particular syntheses made are always oriented to a problem, an interest, a need, i.e., to the exigencies of something outside the conceptual system. *In abstracto* all oppositions may be solved, but *in concreto* what prevents us from admitting that some oppositions may be irreconcilable? What, indeed, save the unverifiable dogma that there must be some underlying harmony in the scheme of things, that all difficulties and problems must have single, determinate solutions? Here again specific answers can be given only to specific problems.

IV. Dialectic and Destiny

The presupposition of the dialectic method is not merely that whenever it is applied some totality is present. So much, we have seen, any method of inquiry, with certain modifications, grants. What is usually asserted is that the whole which the dialectic method explores is also a value whole. Again not merely in the sense that the quest for an answer involves the recognition of the value of truth, nor, in the sense that values provide, in Rickert's phrase, "an historical center" around which the materials of culture study and history can be organized. What is meant is that each System has a value co-ordinate. Without reference to this value co-ordinate, the direction of the development of the system is unintelligible and all description therefore becomes a correlation of unessentials. This value is at least as objective as any other feature of the system, and is more important because by some hidden telic causality it controls what is ultimately realized and what not. The dialectic method presumably shows that the ground-consequent, cause-effect, and stimulus-response relationships within any system can exist only as part of the means-end relation. Not the means-end relation of ordinary purposive action but Means-End relation in some cosmic sense.

Thus, for Hegel, particular passions and interests may have particular causes and be directed towards particular human ends, but the final result, guaranteed by an inner necessity, is not the accomplishment of these empirical ends but of some Divine End—Self-consciousness or Freedom. Other Hegelians differ from Hegel merely in the character of the End which they spell out of immanent social processes. Whenever, in the field of natural science, a distinction is made between scientific and dialectic method, the latter is supposed to demonstrate that some organisms are higher and better (in an absolute sense) than others, that the processes of nature are such that the appearance of man on this earth or elsewhere is not contingent but necessary, and similar conclusions. In history and politics, whenever the dialectic method is distinguished from the scientific method, it is harnessed to the belief that history has some goal which will inevitably be realized, that temporary setbacks and defeats are necessary to the ultimate triumph of man's highest ideals, meaning one's own. In other words, it is not the patterns of causality which the dialectic method uncovers but the patterns of destiny.

3. Sense and Nonsense in Dialectic

In the first class of conceptions of dialectic we have considered, i.e., where dialectic is taken existentially, it is clear that we are confronted by a set of material hypotheses concerning the organization of society and the historical course it will take. The difficulty with all of these hypotheses is that, as formulated, they are so vague that no matter how events turn out, it is possible to claim some validation for them. They then function somewhat like the conceptions that Henri Poincaré calls "neutral hypotheses," i.e., assumptions such that even if we had started with opposite ones, it would not be necessary to change any of the empirical results. These neutral hypotheses are always dangerous if their character is misunderstood, for they may lead us to bring our inquiry to a halt just at the point where it really should begin.

Suppose that we accept for the moment the conception that history develops in periodic or swing rhythm. What, even if taken in conjunction with specific data, can we predict from it? Merely, that no matter how history turns out a time will come when we will be able to construct *some* periodic classificatory scheme which will illustrate the principle. But our primary scientific interest is in predicting as closely as we can the specific form of the institutions of tomorrow. To do this, we must proceed from a whole cluster of assumptions about (1) the relevant factors that may be now observed at work, and these are always many; (2) the relative weight of these factors; and (3) the historical effects of knowledge and ignorance of (1) and (2). The hypothesis of oscillating rhythms in history enables us to make no predictions except that the civilization of the future, in certain, not too carefully defined respects, will be different from the civilization of today—if there is a civilization.

Or let us look for a moment at the dialectic conceived as the principle of class struggle. Here we have an hypothesis according to which class struggles, where a class is defined by reference to the role which a group plays in production, are the key to juridical, political, national, religious, and even philosophical conflicts. Predictions have been made on the basis of it which to some extent have been verified. But I am acquainted with no theory of the class struggle at present which does not use the term "class," not to speak of "struggle," in several different senses, so that it is easy for the uncritical-minded to interpret almost any kind of struggle as a "manifestation" of class struggle. Even on the rare occasions when the writers of this school adhere to a single meaning of the term "class struggle" and recognize the existence of other kinds of struggle, the conclusions are hardly testable. The predictions that (1) the class struggles of tomorrow will take a certain form because of the character, intensity, and conditions of the class struggles of today, and (2) that the national and ideological conflicts of tomorrow will take a certain form because of the character, intensity, and conditions of the class struggles of tomorrow—can receive scientific confirmation only when we develop some commonly-agreed-on measure of the intensity of class struggles, and can evaluate the independent strength of other types of struggle—and their effect upon class struggles.

We may put the point we are making in this way. Every theory in this existential sub-type of dialectics begins with an initial monism which it is compelled to qualify by reference to the reciprocal and interactive effects of many different factors. The monism is then abandoned and it is asserted that Spirit or mode of production, technology, or the great man is the dominant (or most fundamental or most important) cause of historical or social development. But there is no way to "measure" the dominant factor in general unless this means that many more cultural phenomena can be shown to depend upon X than upon any other factor. This is a proposition about comparative frequencies and could only be established as a result of a vast statistical study of cultural dependencies which no one has ever adequately undertaken.

The confusion comes from speaking of the dominant factor in relation to society or history as a whole, when it only makes sense to speak of something as dominant or most important in relation to some problem to be solved or difficulty to be overcome. There is no such thing as the most important factor in the health or functioning of the human organism. But once trouble arises, analysis may indicate that for its elimination, certain functions of the organism may be more important than others, i.e., restoration at some points is more urgent than others. So in social inquiry What those who speak of dialectic must mean if they are to avoid tautologies or contradictions is that in reference to some problem or felt difficulty, which may vary with the different values of different groups, the use of certain instrumentalities is more valid than others.

This leaves the third type of hypothesis with which the dialectic in society is identified, viz., the interaction between objective conditions and human ideals, volition, need, and knowledge. Strictly speaking, what we have here is not an hypothesis to be developed but a delimitation of a subject matter in terms of a convenient organizing category. That is to say, dialectic in this sense means that we are to regard the differentiating categorical feature of social and historical subject matter to be value-centered human activity; that no matter how values are to be interpreted, once we know how words designating them are introduced into discourse, explanation in value terms is legitimate but not mandatory in historical and social inquiry; that although they do not function independently of those objective features of the environment which lack value, the distinctive characters of *human* life lie precisely in the way physical and biological energies are organized in a value-making way.

4. Dialectic and the Doctrine of Two "Truths"

When we consider the set of conceptions identified with dialectic as a method of analysis and discovery, we notice that they represent a characteristic exaggeration of some features found exhibited in non-dialectical scientific inquiry. The characteristic exaggeration can always be traced to the more or less explicit assumption that there is some all-pervading plan or purpose in history. The intent of the dialectic method is not to investigate the relationships between the specific empirical *valuings* of men in concrete interaction with the world and each other, but to discover how one great objective Value or Good is being realized in the social and historical process. It is a means of getting by faith what cannot be reached by evidence, obscured by the logically vicious illusion that what has been begged by faith can be demonstrated as a scientific conclusion.

Where faith has political power, i.e., where this objective Value or Good is interpreted by a political party or a church, the sciences are expected to reach conclusions that may be used in some way to justify or rationalize a political program. Where scientific conclusions seem to run counter to the necessities of faith, they, together with the scientists, are "corrected" by the allegedly higher methods suggested by the slogan of "the Bolshevization of Science" [2] in one country, and "the Aryanization of

[2] The indispensability of the dialectic method and its superiority to all other forms of thought is a cardinal tenet of all varieties of Leninism. The three most important

Science" in another. I do not mean to suggest that all proponents of the dialectic method are necessarily committed to such harsh faiths. But I do mean that they are committed to some cosmic faith, and that in distinguishing between dialectical methods and the mundane methods of empirical science, they are driven to the theory of two truths. In practice, if a clash between them is recognized, one is subordinated to the other, i.e., the truths of science are abridged in the light of the more inclusive "truths" of faith.

One does not have to believe in the existence of a special principle of dialectic in the world to recognize that the life of man in society is one which reveals modes of behavior that are characteristic of man and not of an ant-hill, or carbon chain, or spinning electron; that in addition to breathing and fighting, he works, loves, and prays. We do not have to desert the empirical plane to discover this. Nor does one have to believe that there is a special dialectic method, distinct from scientific method, to describe and understand this. The investigation is difficult because of the complexity of the phenomena and because our emotional interests are so strongly engaged. But whatever difficulties there are must be resolved *not* by abandoning the rationale of scientific method as we know it in the field of our most reliable knowledge—the quest for verifiable hypotheses, the deduction of consequences, experiment under controlled conditions, or where this is not possible, careful use of the comparative method of agreement and difference—but by elaborating specific methods of inquiry within the basic unity of scientific method. True, the work will never be finished. True, there will always be some need for redefinition. And these are the only truths that can be distilled from the pretentious pronouncement of the dialectic method—truths that may be recommended more appropriately to absolutist metaphysicians than to scientists.

Looking back upon the long history of the use of the term "dialectic," it seems to me that a justified moral emerges from our discussion, viz., that the term "dialectic" is so infected with ambiguity, that it is not likely to function as a serviceable designation for any concept or intellectual procedure in any inquiry which aims at the achievement of reliable knowledge about ourselves and the world we live in.

---

schools of Leninism, those headed by Stalin, Trotsky, and the late Bukharin, are in agreement on this point. Criticism of the dialectic method is proof positive in their eyes of "petty-bourgeois opportunism," and consistently followed must lead to counter-revolution. Since in the eyes of each one the other two are counter-revolutionists, it is questionable whether even from their own standpoint rejection of dialectic is either a necessary or sufficient condition of counter-revolution. In actual fact, the epithet "undialectical" is used by them as a weapon in political struggle when the political position itself cannot be defended on grounds that seem reasonable to their own erstwhile followers. It functions as a kind of ritualistic abracadabra to bolster authority, and to reinforce belief in scientifically untenable doctrines which the leader finds politically exigent to uphold.

Physics and the Problem of Historico-sociological Laws*

EDGAR ZILSEL

THE QUESTION as to the existence of laws in history has frequently been discussed. A new discussion may yet be useful, since some misconceptions based on incorrect comparisons with the natural sciences have been brought forward by both advocates and opponents of historical laws. We shall try to clarify the problem by applying a few ideas familiar to physicists and astronomers to the conditions peculiar to history. Physics is the most mature of all empirical sciences as to method. In physics the law-concept has been used for three hundred years. It may be assumed, therefore, that most of the difficulties in its application to other fields have their physical counterpart and can be clarified most easily with the help of physical concepts. A few preliminary examples of historical laws will be given towards the end of the article.

I

The relationship between historical laws and historical prophecies has sometimes been misrepresented. Astronomers can not predict from Newton's law what the position of the planet Mars will be on next New Year's Eve. In addition to the law they need the knowledge of the positions, velocities, and masses of a few celestial bodies at some given time: they need knowledge of "initial conditions" as the physicist puts it. Knowledge of a law, therefore, is not a sufficient but only a necessary condition of prediction. Evidently the same holds for history. Even if laws according to which wars between industrialized countries proceed were known, it might still be impossible to predict the outcome of the present war. Among other more intricate things we do not know is e.g. the number of airplanes on both sides. This knowledge will not be achieved before the war is ended, when it will be too late for prediction. As far as the past is concerned many analogous deficiencies, probably, never will be removed. Probably, we shall never know how large the population was in ancient Babylonia and how

* Reprinted by kind permission of Paul R. Zilsel and the editor from *Philosophy of Science*, 8, 1941.

great the percentage of priests, noblemen, merchants, farmers, and slaves. This ignorance not only impairs our knowledge of the initial conditions but, unfortunately, also of the laws. Every scientific law asserts subsistence of recurrent association or regular connection of certain conditions and events. When and where we are completely ignorant of essential initial conditions, we shall never find recurrent associations. Or to put it more exactly: the more incomplete our knowledge of the initial conditions is, the more difficult is discovery of laws. We shall be very modest, therefore, in our expectations regarding historical laws.

In a few natural sciences laws appear in formulations which, beyond mere statements of recurrent associations, seem to include logical necessity. This necessity, however, springs from the deductive form only attained by those sciences. In physics e.g. the three laws of Kepler can be deduced from Newton's law; likewise virtually all laws of electromagnetism are deducible from Maxwell's equations. Yet this is a mere matter of logical form that does not affect the empirical content. When Galileo discovered the law of falling bodies by experimentation and measurement, he did not deduce it from more general mechanical laws, since such were not yet known. Deductive connection with other laws was not achieved before Newton, for deductive theories are almost always constructed a considerable time after discovery of single empirical laws. This is relevant to our problem. Investigation of historical laws still is in an embryonic stage. For a long time to come these laws must not be compared to the laws of nineteenth century mechanics or electromagnetics but to the laws of young and still undeveloped sciences such as stellar physics. Based on numerous observations e.g. the law of Leavitt-Shapley asserts the existence of a functional relation between period and luminosity of variable stars of a certain type. This and many similar isolated empirical regularities in fixed star astronomy are well verified laws [1] without any regard to the hypothetical attempts of deducing them theoretically from more general physical principles. In history where investigation of laws has hardly begun, construction of deductive theories would only impair empirical research. At any rate, however, there is no basic difference between isolated empirical laws and laws connected by deduction.

There is one more reason why historical laws on the one hand and mechanical and electromagnetic laws on the other do not compare. The latter are found in laboratories. Laboratories contain artificial apparatus built for specific ends. All physical apparatus are carefully safeguarded against mechanical shock; conforming to their objectives they are isolated electrically or thermally, they are constructed airtight or protected by lead against X-rays, etc. Therefore creation of 'isolated systems', i.e. of systems not affected by undesirable interference from without, is among

[1] E.g. Kohlschuetter-Adams: intensity of certain spectral lines and luminosity of the star; Adams-Joy: precision of spectral lines and luminosity; Lindblad: intensity of the continuous spectrum and luminosity.

the chief aims of laboratory physics. In nature on the other hand there are, except for astronomy, practically no isolated systems. Particularly in history all systems are very incompletely isolated: cultures, countries, states always interfere with each other spiritually, politically, economically. Ancient Greece was influenced by the Orient; the Roman Empire was invaded by Germanic tribes, the civilization of these tribes was changed by classical culture and christianity; modern China is influenced by Western capitalism, modern Western philosophy by Chinese and Indian ideas, etc. There are no airtight compartments, no isolated systems in history. History, therefore, must never be compared to laboratory physics. It compares only to geophysics, i.e. to physics of earthquakes and sea-currents, to volcanology and meteorology. This is a triviality but, strangely enough, has been forgotten in most of the analyses. Moreover, the aid of laboratory physics which forms the background of meteorology and geophysics and supplies laws from which deductions can be attempted is lacking in history. All this taken into account, historical phenomena are scarcely more difficult to predict than the weather and certainly not more difficult than volcanic eruptions and earthquakes. What would scientists think of a geophysicist who gives up the search for geophysical laws because of their inexactness?

II

Psychological laws deal with the behavior of human individuals, historical laws with large groups of individuals, namely with cultures, states, nations, occupations, classes, etc. They do not correspond, therefore, to the laws of impact by which in classical gas-theory the behavior of the single molecules is regulated ('micro-laws'), but to the gas-laws ('macro-laws'). Historical and sociological groups, however, compare to gases considerably differing from those studied in our laboratories. They are contained in vessels with permeable walls; they consist of comparatively few molecules that do not move at random but in a partially orderly way. Moreover, the impulse of some of them is considerably greater than that of others. Little wonder that under such conditions the 'gas-laws' do not hold very exactly. These difficulties must be analyzed one by one.[2]

1. The 'permeable walls', i.e. the incomplete isolation of the historical systems has already been discussed.

2. An ordinary gas vessel in a laboratory contains about 10^{23} molecules. Since at present the whole population of the earth amounts to about 10^9 individuals, all historical groups are by many orders of magnitude smaller than statistical systems in physics. Although the accuracy of macro-laws is dependent not only on the numbers of individuals involved, in gen-

[2] On the other hand the problems of modern quantum-mechanics have no bearing on our problem. Historical laws are macro-laws. Heisenberg's principle of indeterminacy questions the existence of physical micro-laws; the validity of macro-laws is not affected by quantum-mechanics. The same holds for the so often discussed problem of determinism. Even individuals with "free" will could follow statistical macro-laws.

eral statistical laws of smaller groups are less exact. Certain historical groups are particularly small. E.g. a law of some intellectual development might be concerned with not more than a hundred or even as few as ten philosophers or authors. Provided all authors concerned are taken into account, investigation of macro-laws is still justified, since the authors have been singled out from considerably larger groups. Several years ago the statistician Bortkiewicz obtained his 'law of small numbers' by studying soldiers of the German army who had died from having been kicked by a horse. We do not insist on the correctness of this special law of Bortkiewicz,[3] but the method in general is justified. E.g. a law of intellectual history would be fairly well founded, though it is based on the observation of only fifty French philosophers, these having been singled out from forty million Frenchmen. Astronomers also investigate laws of the behavior of supernovae and 'white dwarfs' though only exceedingly few of such stars are known at present. Astronomers, however, do not pick out or leave out objects according to value concepts and personal predilections.

3. Boltzmann based his theory of gases on the assumption that the molecules move 'at random' ('hypothesis of disorder'), a hypothesis formulated more exactly in modern statistical physics (von Mises). For historico-sociological groups analogous hypotheses are valid to a limited degree only. E.g. states are 'organized', i.e. they consist of orderly hierarchies of subgroups. Yet, even in states a residuum of 'disorderly' behavior remains. There is, however, a statistical theory of crystals too in modern physics. In crystals the atoms are arranged in three dimensional 'lattices'. Since over this order random oscillations are superimposed, a statistical theory of e.g. electric and thermal conductivity in crystals is possible. The same holds for historico-sociological groups: modern statistical investigation of public opinion is not prevented by the fact that states are 'organized'.

4. The historical influence of human individuals shows a much greater variety than the physical effectiveness of atoms. Here two kinds of human inequalities must be distinguished. The effectiveness of persons can differ because they hold different positions in an organization. If in an army a general commits treason the effects are incomparably greater than in the case of a private doing the same. Therefore, counting generals and privates, heads of states or public officials and plain civilians with the same weight can become absurd in certain statistical investigations. In states, armies, and similar organizations inequality of position is of decisive importance. For this reason the validity of historical laws certainly is smallest in political history. In this field 'chance', i.e. psychological, biological, and other individual circumstances, might greatly impair macro-regularities. Macro-laws might play a greater part in the history of civilization and ideas, of art, science, philosophy, and religion where differentiated organizations are less important.

[3] It asserts that dispersion is nearly "normal" in such exceedingly small groups. Cf. L. v. Bortkiewicz: *Das Gesetz der kleinen Zahlen,* Leipzig 1898.

On the other hand human individuals influence history to different degrees because they differ in their personal gifts and abilities: there are good and bad artists, good and bad scientists and philosophers. Whether these differences are great enough to make statistical investigation and macro-laws impossible can not be decided by a priori arguments, but only by the results of empirical search after such laws. At any rate a 'statistical' history, aiming at laws of intellectual, artistic, and religious developments, would greatly differ from traditional historiography. It can neither dwell on masterpieces nor disregard the mass of mediocrities. The question as to whether an artistic or theoretical work is the product of a genius or a bungler would not even enter its investigation. Certain components of these value concepts, however, would reappear in other and more objective shapes. The distinction between long- and short-lived ideas must appear also in 'statistical' history, if it should represent the facts. And the same holds for both the difference between new creations and mere repetitions and the stratification of literary and artistic taste according to social ranks and various levels of education and sophistication.

III

Time is contained as a variable in some physical laws but not in others. E.g. the second law of thermodynamics asserts a temporal process, stating that the entropy of an isolated system increases with time. The law of Wiedemann-Franz, on the other hand, asserts that, without regard to time, electric and thermal conductivity of metals are proportional to each other, good electric conductors being good thermal ones and vice versa. These two kinds of regularity may be called temporal laws and simultaneity-laws.[4]

Both types of laws may be expected in history. We shall give a few examples of the first type (in preliminary and vague formulations) and indicate the empirical evidence in brackets.

1. In isolated historical systems tribal organization precedes the beginnings of the state (empirical evidence: ancient China, ancient Jews, ancient Greece, Germanic states of the early Middle Ages et al. Under external influence, i.e. in non-isolated systems, the development can proceed in a different way: British dominions, U. S. A.).

2. Individualized art and poetry are preceded by anonymous folk-art and poetry, signed paintings and sculptures by non-signed works. Or to put it more generally: the collective mindedness of the period of self-sufficient domestic economy and barter economy precedes the individualistic spirit of the period of money economy and economic competition (rise of individualism in Greece in the sixth and fifth, in Rome in the third and

[4] In physics the terms 'dynamic' and 'static' laws are often used. This terminology has been avoided here, since it is too narrow and since, in philosophy and the social sciences, use of the word 'dynamic' often covers deficiencies in scientific analysis. The magic and animistic connotations of this term, discarded in physics three hundred years ago, have not quite disappeared from the social sciences.

second centuries B.C.; the Middle Ages and the Renaissance). This law goes back to Hegel and Jacob Burckhardt and has been generalized by Carl Lamprecht.

3. Free artists e.g. sculptors, painters, and architects, gradually develop from craftsmen, such as stonedressers, whitewashers, and masons (China, ancient Greece, the Renaissance).

4. Worship of eminent individuals first takes sides and is partial, i.e. persons with opposite or divergent aims are not admired or worshipped by the same people; impartial admiration and worship of divergent great personalities develop later: biased hero-worship precedes impartial genius-worship (classical antiquity, the pre-romantic and the post-romantic period in Europe; cf. the study of the genesis of the concept of genius mentioned in footnote 5).

All these 'laws' are yet incomplete in so far as only necessary but not sufficient conditions are given. They describe temporal processes in yet rather vague formulations and may be called 'historical' laws in a narrower sense. On the other hand there are in history also simultaneity-laws. Though they are usually called 'sociological' laws, there is no basic difference between sociological and historical regular connections. The separation is entirely artificial, since sociology by no means disregards investigation of temporal processes. We give a few examples of simultaneity-laws.

5. Wherever learned priests are entrusted with the task of teaching priest-candidates, they systematize the vague and contradictory mythological traditions of the past and develop rational distinction, classification, and enumeration as scientific methods. Even if they turn to worldly subject-matters they develop causal investigation in a very small degree and never investigation of physical laws (Medieval Arabic and Catholic Scholasticism; Jewish Talmudism; the five orthodox Indian "philosophical" systems, especially Sankhya; Buddhistic Scholasticism in Japan).

6. If under favorable circumstances a past culture is revived after centuries, the initiators and bearers of this intellectual movement are characterized by the following traits: they do not belong to the clergy; they are scribes and secretaries in political services and develop under favorable circumstances to free literati; exceedingly proud of their ability of writing and reading they disdain the illiterate; in their idea the educated man is chiefly distinguished by perfection of his literary style; as patterns of style serve literary documents of the past, the authors of these documents are looked upon as authorities superior to all representatives of subsequent periods (the European Renaissance; the two Renaissances of Confucianism under the Han and Tang dynasties in China; probably also the Renaissance movement in the New Empire of ancient Egypt and the Neo-Parthian Renaissance).

All these historical 'laws' have to be considered as preliminary and more or less probable assertions only. They are meant as examples to illustrate what form, approximately, historical laws would take and also on what kind of empirical evidence they have to be based.[5] Since experiments are not feasible in history, comparison of various countries and cultures is the only way of finding historical laws.[6] The cultures compared ought to be as independent from each other and as numerous as possible. E.g. Europe and America, the modern era and antiquity, the civilizations of India, China, Egypt, and Persia must be compared and investigated from identical points of view if historical laws are to be established. In this program the only real difficulty in the application of the law-concept to history is revealed. It originates in the comparatively small number of independent historical systems. If in the natural sciences hypothetical laws are to be tested, it is in most cases easy to find suitable instances that do not influence each other. In history it is only among the primitive cultures that the number of independent instances is considerable. Higher civilizations are in most cases connected by spatial interaction or the temporal links of tradition. This is a serious obstacle to verification of laws. E.g. analogous intellectual developments in eighteenth century France and England may be due to mutual influence and consequently must not be extrapolated and generalized. Practically the same holds for classical antiquity and modern Europe. Yet analogies e.g. in medieval Catholic and in Japanese Buddhistic Scholasticism may offer a sufficiently reliable basis for extrapolation. Far remote cultures, therefore, are particularly illuminating and convincing in investigation of historical laws. But also in the other cases painstaking scientific criticism may often succeed in separating direct influence from actual recurrence of the same phenomenon under analogous conditions. However, prediction will always stand as the ultimate test for the correctness of a law. Evidently prediction must not be taken in a temporal meaning only. If a historical regularity, obtained by comparing certain historical systems, is confirmed in other and independent systems, it may be considered, at least for the present, as verified.

On the other hand lack of perfect analogies neither speaks against the possibility of historical laws nor does it form a basic difference between history and the natural sciences. This had been assumed erroneously by the Windelband-Rickert-school and has often been repeated since. True, no

[5] After collection of the historical material about twenty other hypothetical laws have been given by the author of this article at the end of his *Die Entstehung des Geniebegriffes. Ein Beitrag zur Ideengeschichte der Antike und des Fruehkapitalismus*, Tuebingen 1926, pp. 324–326. With the necessary scientific accuracy a historical law has been given for the first time in Frederick J. Teggart: *Rome and China. A Study of Correlations in Historical Events*, Berkeley 1939. Professor Teggart verifies statistically that there is a correlation between political disturbances in Western China and the Asiatic frontier regions of the Roman empire on the one hand and barbaric invasions in the Danube and Rhine region on the other. Teggart's law, however, belongs to a more special type than the "laws" indicated above. It holds, although for many events, for late antiquity only. Evidently this does not impair its scientific value. Mechanics of rigid bodies also is valid in a limited period only. There were no rigid bodies 10^{10} years ago. In empirical science all laws hold as long only as the objects and systems they are concerned with exist.

[6] Cf. F. J. Teggart, *loc. cit.*, p. 245.

two historical individuals are completely alike and history never repeats itself. However, the repetitions in natural science are overestimated by those only who are rather remote from this field of research. He who has ever worked in a laboratory knows that even every apparatus, if it is somewhat more complex, has its individual characteristics and has to be handled with its own special tricks. No two reflectors of the same brand are perfectly alike and even less two planets. In natural science the variety of objects is mastered by the method of gradual approximation: objects may be handled as analogous in the first approximation; their differences are taken into account later in second and third approximations, when they are put together and compared in new groups. Variety of historico-sociological phenomena surpasses variety of other objects in degree only. There is no reason, therefore, why the method of gradual approximation should not be applied in comparative history too. The conformities in the cultural ideals of Renaissance humanists and Chinese literati-officials can be established first; the differences may be taken into account later.

On the other hand the method of "understanding" ("insight") which has often been recommended for social science is not sufficient when investigating historical laws. "Understanding" means psychological empathy: psychologically a historical process is "understood" if it is evident or plausible. The main objection to this criterion of the correctness of a historical assertion is that virtually always opposite historical processes are equally plausible.[7] When a city is bombed it is plausible that intimidation and defeatism of the population result. But it is plausible as well that the determination to resist increases. It would not be plausible, on the other hand, if the bombing changed the pronunciation of consonants in the bombed city. Which process actually takes place can not be decided by psychological empathy but by statistical observation only. In the final analysis the method of understanding is equivalent to the attempt to deduce historico-sociological laws from laws of introspective psychology. However, before regularities are established it is premature to attempt to deduce them. In the construction of new empirical sciences the predeductive stage can not be skipped.

There is even the possibility that certain historical laws may never become psychologically evident. Certainly history is based on the behavior of human individuals reacting psychologically. Yet there are in the natural sciences macro-laws that are similar to micro-laws and others that are not. Maxwell's equations hold for the macro-phenomena caused by electric currents as well as for the behavior of (free) electrons: in this case macro- and micro-laws not only assert the same functional relations but contain also the same variables (electric and magnetic field, etc.). On the other hand the gas laws entirely differ from the laws of elastic impact regulating the behavior of molecules in classical gas-theory. In this case the macro-laws con-

[7] This originates in the fact that the patterns of *consent-refusal* and *affirmation-negation* predominate in the province of emotional and intellectual processes.

nect variables, such as pressure, volume, and temperature of the gas, which have no application at all to single molecules.[8] Likewise there may be historical macro-laws connecting parameters only that are meaningless when applied to human individuals; no term that fits emotional or intellectual processes might enter them. In this case the historical law would be deprived of the possibility of psychological understanding and empathy. Yet it might be well verified empirically, since observable facts can be put into a correspondence also with very complex and abstract logical constructs. The law of the shifting of consonants in the Indo-European languages approaches to this type of "non-understandable" historical regularities. The number of such laws may be considerable, e.g. in economic history.

History has grown out of other roots than the natural sciences. A man who, desiring to lift a load, is interested in the principle of the lever is the prototype of a natural scientist. A father who takes pictures of his son every year and collects and keeps them may serve as an analogy to the origin of historiography. He is not interested in regular connections and predictions but in the gradual development of his object because he likes it. Nobody will argue against this kind of historiography. It will always persist as long as men love their countries, their communities, and their culture. On the other hand, however, investigation of historical laws should not be obstructed by methodological objections. The greatest danger in this field is the danger of dilettantism and superficiality. The investigator of historical laws must collect, interpret, and compare an immense and highly complex material. Which scholar is an expert on modern and classical, Egyptian and Chinese history simultaneously? Astronomers have mastered analogous difficulties by division of labor and cooperation. The observatories have divided and distributed the problems, have collected, each in its field, the immense material according to identical principles and have thus produced the star catalogues and maps which form the basis of their laws. There is yet no analogous cooperation and division of labor in comparative history. Yet its problems are extremely interesting and may become important in a practical way in the future. Many scientists must establish a common program of research and cooperate according to it. By collecting and comparing the material with philological accuracy historical laws will be discovered at last not by general methodological discussions like ours.

[8] The correspondence of one macro-parameter to a set of quite different micro-parameters is an instance of the relationship that, with a rather vague term, has been called *emergence*.

Ideal Types and Historical Explanation*

J. W. N. WATKINS

1. Introduction

In this paper I shall consider: first, what sort of creatures ideal types should be if they are to be used in the construction of social theories; and secondly, what we do when we try to explain historical events by applying such theories to them.[1]

2. Holistic and Individualistic Ideal Types

It is only decent to begin a discussion of ideal types by considering Weber's views; but he held two successive conceptions of what an ideal type should be and do, without, I think, realising what important differences lay between them.

* Revised and expanded version of a paper that originally appeared in *The British Journal for the Philosophy of Science*, 3, 1952. Reprinted by kind permission of the author and the editor.

[1] It has been established by Professor K. R. Popper that the formal structure of a prediction is the same as that of a full-fledged explanation. In both cases we have: (*a*) initial conditions; (*b*) universal statements; and (*c*) deductive consequences of (*a*) plus (*b*). We explain a given event (*c*) by detecting (*a*) and by postulating and applying (*b*); and we predict a future event (*c*) by inferring it from some given (*a*) and postulated (*b*). Nevertheless, I think that in social science explanation and prediction should be considered separately, for two reasons. First, as Professor G. C. Hempel has pointed out in a most illuminating discussion of this problem (see his 'The Function of General Laws in History' in *Readings in Philosophical Analysis*, ed. H. Feigl and W. Sellars, New York, 1949, pp. 462–5) in history we often have to be content (and in fact *are* content) with what he calls an explanation *sketch*, i.e. a somewhat vague and incomplete indication of (*a*) and (*b*) from which (*c*) is not *strictly* deducible. And if we go back to a time when (*a*) but not (*c*) has occurred, this partial sketch of (*a*) and (*b*) will not allow us to predict (*c*). For example, we may be satisfied by the explanation that Smith insulted Jones because Jones had angered him, although we should *not* be prepared to admit that if Jones angers Smith in the future, Smith will necessarily react by insulting Jones.

Secondly, even the social scientist who can provide a *full-fledged* explanation of a past event will run into difficulties if he tries to predict similar events, because they will occur in a system which is not isolated from the influence of factors which he cannot ascertain beforehand. The Astronomer Royal can prepare a Nautical Almanac for 1953 because he is predicting the movements of bodies in a system isolated from

His earlier version is set out in an article translated under the title '"Objectivity" in Social Science and Social Policy.'[2] At this time (1904) Weber believed that the social scientist should not try to imitate the natural scientist's procedure of systematically subsuming observation-statements and low order theories under more comprehensive laws. The social scientist should first decide from what point of view to approach history. Having decided, say, to treat its economic aspect, he should then select from this some unique configuration of activities and institutions, such as 'the rise of capitalism.' Then he should pin down and describe its components. His final task is to draw in the causal lines between these components, imputing 'concrete effects to concrete causes.'[3]

This programme could never be carried out; 'in any actual economic system so many factors are at work simultaneously that the effect of a single factor by itself can never be known, for its traces are soon lost sight of.'[4] And separate facts cannot be linked together as causes and effects with no reference to general laws. However, I will not press these criticisms of a methodological position which Weber tacitly abandoned later.

To assist the social scientist in this task of explaining particular events by relating them to their particular antecedents, Weber proposed his first version of the ideal type. This was to be constructed by abstracting the outstanding features from some (more or less clearly demarcated) historical complex, and by organising these into a coherent word-picture. The ideality of such a type lies in its simplification and aloofness from detail: it will be free from the detailed complexity of the actuality to be analysed with its aid. As this kind of ideal type emphasises the 'essential' traits of a situation considered *as a whole,* I call it 'holistic,' in contrast with the 'individualistic' ideal type described by Weber in Part I of his posthumous *Wirtschaft und Gesellschaft.*[5]

In this work he held that the social scientist's first task was to build up a generally applicable theoretical system; and for arriving at this he proposed the use of ideal types similar to the models used in deductive economics. These are constructed, not by withdrawing from the detail of social life, but by formalising the results of a close analysis of some of its significant details considered in isolation. The holistic ideal type was supposed

extraneous influences, but the Chancellor of the Exchequer cannot prepare an Economic Almanac for 1953 because, even if he possessed sufficient knowledge to explain completely the 1951 levels of prices, production, investment, exports, etc., his predictions of future levels would undoubtedly be upset by unforeseeable, world-wide disturbing factors, the effects of any of which might be cumulative.

Hence, the problem of social prediction raises questions not raised by the problem of historical explanation; and this paper is not concerned with the former.

[2] Max Weber, *The Methodology of the Social Sciences*, trans. and ed. E. A. Shils and H. A. Finch, Illinois, 1949, ch. 2.

[3] *Op. cit.*, p. 79.

[4] Walter Eucken, *The Foundations of Economics*, trans. T. W. Hutchison, London, 1950, p. 39.

[5] Translated by A. R. Henderson and Talcott Parsons as *The Theory of Social and Economic Organisation,* introd. by Talcott Parsons, London, 1947.

to give a bird's eye view of the broad characteristics of a whole social situation, whereas the individualistic ideal type is constructed by inspecting the situations of actual individuals, and by abstracting from these: (*a*) general schemes of personal preferences; (*b*) the different kinds of knowledge of his own situation which the individual may possess; and (*c*) various typical relationships between individuals and between the individual and his resources. An individualistic ideal type places hypothetical actors in some simplified situation. Its premisses are: the form (but not the specific content) of the actors' dispositions, the state of their information, and their relationships. And the deductive consequences of these premisses demonstrate some principle of social behaviour, e.g. oligopolistic behaviour. The ideality of *this* kind of ideal type lies: (i) in the simplification of the initial situation and in its isolation from disturbing factors; (ii) in the abstract and formal, and yet explicit and precise character of the actors' schemes of preferences and states of information; and (iii) in the actors' rational behaviour in the light of (ii). It is not claimed that a principle of social behaviour demonstrated by an individualistic ideal type will often have an exact empirical counterpart (though the principle of perfect competition has been precisely manifested, for instance in commodity-markets). But economists do claim that there is a limited number of basic economic principles, and that any economic phenomenon is a particular configuration of some of these, occurring at a particular place and time, which can be explained by a synthesis of the relevant ideal types, and by specifying the content of their formal premisses.[6]

Weber was no Platonist; he proposed both kinds of ideal type as heuristic aids which, by themselves, tell you nothing about the real world, but which throw into relief its deviations from themselves. The individualistic ideal type was to assist in the detection of disturbing factors, such as habit and tradition, which deflect actual individuals from a rational course of action—a proposal I shall examine later. Now I shall examine the assumptions underlying Weber's earlier proposal to use holistic ideal types.

One might improve one's appreciation of the shape of a roughly circular object by placing over it an accurate tracing of a circle. This analogy

[6] 'This morphological study of economic history reveals a *limited* number of pure forms out of which *all* economic systems past and present are made up.' Eucken, *op. cit.*, p. 10 (my italics). The 'de-idealisation' of the pure principles of economic theory which occurs when they are combined into a particular configuration which is applied to an empirical counterpart, is exactly paralleled in the natural sciences. For example, Galileo combined the Law of Inertia (which describes the motion of a body not acted upon by any force—a condition which can never be realised), and the Law of Gravity (which describes the motion of a body in a vacuum which the experimenter cannot obtain), and the principles of air resistance, into a theoretical configuration which allows complete prediction of the trajectories of e.g. cannonballs, if the initial conditions are known. 'All universal physical concepts and laws . . . are arrived at by idealisation. They thereby assume that simple . . . form which makes it possible to reconstruct any facts, however complicated, by synthetic combination of these concepts and laws, thus making it possible to understand them.' (Ernst Mach, quoted by F. Kaufmann, *Methodology of the Social Sciences*, New York, 1944, p. 87.)

brings out Weber's conception of the purpose, and manner of employing, holistic ideal types in three respects. (i) By comparing an impure object with an ideal construction the deviations of the former from the latter are thrown into relief; and Weber did regard this kind of ideal type as a 'purely ideal *limiting* concept with which the real situation . . . is *compared* and surveyed for the explication of certain of its significant components.' [7] (ii) Both the object and the construct are considered *as a whole*. (iii) The analogy involves what is presupposed by the idea of comparison, namely, a simultaneous awareness of the characteristics of both things being compared. And in 1904 Weber did assume that the social scientist can place his knowledge of a real situation alongside his knowledge of an ideal type he has himself constructed, and compare the two.[8] It is the simultaneous knowability of the features of both which enables holistic ideal types to be 'used as conceptual instruments for *comparison* with and *measurement* of reality.' [9]

At this point an awkward question arises: If the characteristics of a historical situation have already been charted *before* the ideal type is brought into play, why bother with ideal types? They are not hypotheses [10] which guide the social scientist in his search for facts, for they are not supposed to be realistic, or empirical. A holistic ideal type is not a guess about reality, but an *a priori* word-picture—in other words, a definition. What Weber's earlier proposal amounts to is that holistic ideal types should be used as explicit definitions of those 'hundreds of words in the historian's vocabulary [which] are ambiguous constructs created to meet the unconsciously felt need for adequate expression and the meaning of which is only concretely felt but not clearly thought out.' [11]

Thus the holistic ideal type transpires to be something of a mouse, a mere demand for definitions; [12] and I shudder when I imagine each of those 'hundreds of words' being replaced by lengthy verbal definitions, though such defining *may* be helpful in particular circumstances. For instance, to order and classify a collection of variegated instances it may be necessary to construct a scale with limiting ideal types at either end. The survey of the constitutions of 158 Greek states was probably tidier and more systematic than it would have been if Aristotle's 'Monarchy-Aristocracy-Polity' and 'Tyranny-Oligarchy-Democracy' scales, or some equivalent, had not been used.

[7] *Methodology*, p. 93.

[8] Thus he speaks of 'the relationship between the logical structure of the conceptual system . . . and what is immediately given in empirical reality' (*op. cit.*, p. 96). The term 'immediately given' should not, I think, be taken too seriously. What this phrase does imply is that the social scientist's knowledge of ideal type and corresponding reality are on an equal footing.

[9] *Op. cit.*, p. 97.

[10] *Op. cit.*, p. 90.

[11] *Op. cit.*, pp. 92–3.

[12] For a criticism of such demands, see K. R. Popper, *The Open Society and Its Enemies*, London, 1945, vol. 2, ch. 11, sect. ii.

But such scales are for classifying facts already analysed, not for analysing raw material; and the real weakness of Weber's earlier proposal lies in the method of historical analysis which was to accompany the use of holistic ideal types. With *individualistic* ideal types, it will be remembered, we *start* with individuals' dispositions, information and relationships, and work outwards to the unintended consequences of their interaction (deducing a price-level, for example, from demand and supply schedules). But with *holistic* ideal types the analysis is supposed to proceed in the opposite direction. Here, the historian is supposed to start with the broad (or 'essential') characteristics of an entire historical situation, and then to *descend* to an ever closer definition of its deviations from the ideal type with which it is being compared. In principle, this descent from overall traits to detailed ingredients might continue until, *at the end of the analysis*, the relevant dispositions, information, and relationships of the people concerned had been established.

The idea that we can apprehend the overall characteristics of a social situation *before* learning something of the individual situations of the actors in it *appears* to be borne out by a statement such as, 'The British economy in 1850 was competitive.' This statement apparently attributes an overall characteristic to a demarcated whole, while saying nothing about individuals (just as 'The lake's surface was calm' says nothing about water-particles). Now the unintended merit of the holistic ideal type is that its use forces us to recognise the falsity of this idea. If, in order to assess the competitiveness of the British economy in 1850, we try to establish an ideal type of 'perfect competition' we shall at once find that we can only define it in terms of the preferences, information and relationships of individuals—an assertion which can be confirmed by turning to any economics text-book. In other words, we shall have established an *individualistic* ideal type.[13] But if knowledge of the general characteristics of a social situation is always derivative knowledge, pieced together from what is known of individuals' situations, then it is not possible for historical analysis to proceed *from* overall characteristics *towards* individuals' situations. The former is logically derivative from the latter. Weber's earlier conception of an ideal type presupposed that one can detect the essential traits of some historic 'whole' while remaining aloof from the detail of personal behaviour; but this belief is shown to be false when we actually construct such a type. It was probably this experience which later led Weber tacitly to abandon holistic ideal types and the impossible method associated with them, in favour of individualistic ideal types and the method of reconstructing historical phenomena with their aid.[14]

[13] Similarly, if we try to construct an ideal type for 'feudalism,' say, we shall at once find ourselves speaking of people's obligations and privileges towards their superiors, inferiors, the land, and so on.

[14] What I call a 'holistic ideal type' roughly corresponds to what Eucken called a 'real type,' a name he used to denote the 'stages,' such as 'city economy,' 'early capitalism,' 'mature capitalism,' through which, according to the Historical School of

The assertion that knowledge of social phenomena can only be derived from knowledge about individuals requires one qualification. For there are certain overt features [15] which can be established without knowledge of psychological facts, such as the level of prices, or the death-rate (but *not* the suicide-rate). And if we detect more or less regular changes in such overt features we have something eminently suitable for analysis. But some people, over-impressed by the quasi-regularity of, for example, a long-term 'wave' in economic life, have supposed that such a thing possesses a sort of internal dynamic, and obeys its own laws; and that while *it* must therefore be taken as a datum, many other phenomena (such as bursts of inventiveness, emigration movements, outbreaks of war) can be explained as consequences of it.[16]

This is a sort of blasphemy. The Israelites also imputed their fortunes and misfortunes to a superior entity immune from their own activities; but they rightly called this 'God.' But economic cycles do not possess a quasi-divine autonomy. They are mere human creations—not deliberate creations, of course, but the unintended product of the behaviour of interacting people.

For the last few paragraphs a basic methodological principle has been struggling to emerge and the time has come to bring it into the open in order to clarify its meaning and status.

---

economists, any economic system develops. He also rejected such types in favour of individualistic ideal types (which he simply called 'ideal types') and he criticised Weber for confusing the two, but from a somewhat different viewpoint to my own. His fascinating book, *The Foundations of Economics*, contains a sustained plea for the fertile marriage of abstract theory and concrete fact, and a powerful criticism of the Historical School for blurring the distinction between the two; whereas I am arguing against methodological holism, and for methodological individualism. Our arguments tend to coincide because 'historicism' is closely related to 'holism': the belief in laws of development presupposes a 'whole' which undergoes the development. (See K. R. Popper, "The Poverty of Historicism," *Economica*, XI, 1944, pp. 91–2.) For Eucken's discussion of real and ideal types, see especially pp. 347–9.

[15] By 'overt feature' I do not mean something which can necessarily be directly perceived—it may be a highly theoretical construct. But whether it be the price of a marked article in a shop-window, or the average level of prices in 1815, an overt feature is something which can be ascertained without referring to people's dispositions, etc. See R. Stone, *The Role of Measurement in Economics*, Cambridge, 1951, p. 9.

[16] I have written the above with the Russian economist Kondratieff in mind. He asserts that the view that long waves 'are conditioned by casual, extra-economic circumstances and events, such as (1) changes in technique, (2) wars and revolutions, (3) the assimilation of new countries into the world economy, and (4) fluctuations in gold production . . . reverse[s] the causal connections and take[s] the consequence to be the cause.' (N. D. Kondratieff, 'The Long Waves in Economic Life,' *Readings in Business Cycle Theory*, Blakiston Series, London, 1950, ch. 2, p. 35.) In other words, the long wave is *the* fundamental datum, in terms of which even such a strictly individual and psychological matter as human inventiveness is to be explained.

3. The Principle of Methodological Individualism

This principle states that social processes and events should be explained by being deduced from (*a*) principles governing the behaviour of participating individuals and (*b*) descriptions of their situations.[17] The contrary principle of methodological holism states that the behaviour of individuals should be explained by being deduced from (*a*) macroscopic laws which are *sui generis* and which apply to the social system as a whole, and (*b*) descriptions of the positions (or functions) of the individuals within the whole.

There is clearly an important difference between these two principles. What are my grounds for accepting the individualistic, and rejecting the holistic, method?

(1) Whereas physical things can exist unperceived, social 'things' like laws, prices, prime ministers and ration-books, are created by personal attitudes. (Remove the attitudes of food officials, shop-keepers, housewives, etc., towards ration-books and they shrivel into bits of cardboard.) But if social objects are formed by individual attitudes, an explanation of their formation must be an individualistic explanation.

(2) The social scientist and the historian have no 'direct access' to the overall structure and behaviour of a system of interacting individuals (in the sense that a chemist does have 'direct access' to such overall properties of a gas as its volume and pressure and temperature, which he can measure and relate without any knowledge of gas-molecules). But the social scientist and the historian can often arrive at fairly reliable opinions about the dispositions and situations of individuals. These two facts suggest that a theoretical understanding of an abstract social structure should be derived from more empirical beliefs about concrete individuals.[18]

But neither (1) the truism that social objects are created by personal

[17] This principle does not apply to the study of purely physical, biological or behaviouristic properties of human groups. Professor Hayek has drawn a very useful distinction between the 'natural sciences of society', such as vital statistics and the study of contagious diseases, and the 'social sciences' proper. (*Individualism and Economic Order*, London, 1949, p. 57.) Typical problems of the social sciences are war, unemployment, political instability, the clash of cultures. Professor M. Ginsberg has asserted that principles of historical interpretation 'are not necessarily exclusively psychological or even teleological: there may well be social laws *sui generis* . . .' (*Aristotelian Society, Supplementary Volume* XXI, 1947, 'Symposium: The Character of a Historical Explanation,' p. 77). The only example he gives of something determined by such laws is phonetic change. But phonetic change is either an unconscious, behaviouristic process to be studied by a natural science of society, or a deliberate process, in which case it can be explained individualistically, e.g., in terms of a man's desire to raise his social status by acquiring a superior accent.

[18] 'The social sciences . . . do not deal with "given" wholes but their task is to *constitute* these wholes by constructing models from the familiar elements. . . .' 'The whole is never directly perceived but always reconstructed by an effort of our imagination.' F. A. Hayek, *The Counter-Revolution of Science: studies on the abuse of reason*, The Free Press, Glencoe, Illinois, 1952, p. 56 and p. 214.

attitudes, nor (2) the 'invisibility' of social structures, *entail* methodological individualism; they only support it.

(1) The fact that prices, for instance, are charged and paid by people, the fact that they are human creations, does not, by itself, entail that the whole price-system may not be governed by some overall law which is underivable from propositions about individuals. (2) A holist who denied that 'the English State, for example, is a logical construction out of individual people',[19] and who asserted that it is an organism which develops, and responds to challenges, according to underivable holistic laws, might also admit that only its individual components were visible and that any operational definition of the laws it obeyed would be in terms of individual behaviour.

Moreover, an extremely unlikely circumstance is conceivable in which methodological individualism would have to be demoted from a rule to an aspiration; for it apparently suffers this humiliation in the study of certain non-human societies.

One can see what upsets methodological individualism by considering three different systems of interacting components: (*a*) the solar system as conceived by classical mechanics; (*b*) the economic system as conceived by classical economics; and (*c*) a bee-hive.

(*a*) Here, methodological individualism is altogether adequate. The behaviour of the whole system can be explained by applying the inverse square law and the law of inertia to the system's components, if their relative positions, masses and momenta are known. Indeed, methodological individualism in the social sciences is analogous to the method of resolution and re-composition which characterizes Galilean and Newtonian physics: the method, namely, of analysing a complex whole into its atomic constituents, and into the simplest principles which they obey, and of deductively reconstructing the behaviour of the whole from these.

(*b*) Adam Smith stated that the individual

> generally, indeed, neither intends to promote the public interest, nor knows how much he is promoting it . . . ; by directing [his] industry in such a manner as its produce may be of the greatest value, he intends only his own gain, and he is in this, as in many other cases, led by an invisible hand to promote an end which was no part of his intention. (*The Wealth of Nations*, Bk. 4, Ch. 2.)

But the invisible hand is, strictly, gratuitous and misleading. What Smith actually showed was that individuals in competitive economic situations are led by nothing but their *personal dispositions* to promote unintentionally the public interest. Here again, methodological individualism is altogether adequate.

(*c*) Mr E. S. Russell, basing himself on experiments by Rösch, has reported the following strange fact[20] (strange, that is, to the methodological individualist). If young worker-bees (whose normal function is to feed

[19] A. J. Ayer, *Language, Truth and Logic*, 2nd. ed., London, 1948, p. 63.
[20] See *The British Journal for the Philosophy of Science*, 1950, I, pp. 113–14.

the larvae from their salivary glands) are segregated into one half of a hive sealed off from the other half, in which have been segregated the older worker-bees (whose salivary glands have atrophied and whose normal function is to produce wax from their newly developed wax-glands, and later, to forage), then the following will occur: after two days' dislocation and near-starvation some of the young workers will start foraging and their salivary glands will atrophy prematurely; while the atrophied salivary glands of some of the older workers will revive and continue functioning long after the normal period, enabling them to feed the larvae in their half of the hive. The bees' functions will be increasingly differentiated until the division of labour in both halves approximates that of a whole hive. Here it really is as if individual bees were led by an invisible hand, not merely to promote the interest of the whole half-hive, but to adapt drastically their biological structure in order to do so. It seems extremely difficult to believe that the emergence of these two new systems of specialised functions could be explained individualistically, in terms of the situations and principles of behaviour of each bee, because all the bees in each half-hive were of a similar type and in approximately the same situation, yet only the requisite number adapted themselves to new functions. Thus each half of the bifurcated bee-hive appears to be an organism in the sense that its components' behaviour is determined by teleological principles which apply to the whole half-hive and which cannot be derived from a knowledge of individual bees—though one hopes that this appearance is misleading and that the re-emergence of specialization will eventually be explained individualistically.

The principle whose status I have been trying to elucidate is a methodological rule which presupposes the factual assertion that human social systems are not organisms in the above sense. There is no evidence to suggest that this presupposition is false; but one cannot assert *a priori* that it is true. What one *can* assert is that *if* any social system were such an organic entity then it would be something utterly different from anything so far imagined. For the only sorts of organism so far imagined are (*a*) physical or biological; (*b*) mental; and (*c*) social; and it will be shown that social systems are none of these.

(*a*) It is at any rate plausible to say that the personalities of a mating couple are sometimes submerged beneath the biological laws of their physical union. But it would be stretching terms to call this a 'social system'; and in the case of such social organizations as the Comintern or the International Red Cross, it is clear that what holds these bodies together is not physical ties but the ideals, loyalties, discipline and beliefs of their dispersed members.

(*b*) Is the behaviour of a number of individuals ever regulated by some super-individual *mental* entity? It is just possible that this is so in the case of a panicking crowd or of an ecstatic revivalist meeting. But in general, 'group-minds' are very rightly out of fashion; for to impute a big social phenomenon (such as war) to a big mental counterpart (such as a 'nation's' aggressive spirit) is not to explain but to duplicate.[21] Moreover, social phenomena which nobody wants are precisely those whose occurrence most needs explaining; and it would obviously be absurd to impute mass unemployment, for instance, to some mental counterpart such as a 'nation's' laziness.

(*c*) When a sociologist proffers a holistic law the entity whose behaviour it is supposed to determine is usually thought of as a special sort of organism, neither physical nor biological nor mental, but *social*. Alleged social entities such as 'The State', 'Capitalism', etc., however, are only hypostatizations of sociological terms. As we have seen, whenever we try to make these terms precise we find ourselves speaking individualistically.

Hence society is not an organism in any existing sense of the term. The ontological basis of methodological individualism is the assumption that society is not some unimagined sort of organism, but really consists only of people who behave fairly intelligibly and who influence each other, directly and mediately, in fairly comprehensible ways.

This section was intended to clarify and justify methodological individualism. We can now revert to the construction and use of ideal types.

4. Concluding Remarks on Ideal Types

The argument of section 2 can be summarised thus: An understanding of a complex social situation is always derived from a knowledge of the dispositions, beliefs, and relationships of individuals. Its overt characteristics may be *established* empirically, but they are only *explained* by being shown to be the resultants of individual activities.[22]

All this was recognised by the later Weber. In *The Theory of Social and Economic Organisation* ideal type construction means (not detecting and abstracting the overall characteristics of a whole situation, and organising these into a coherent scheme, but) placing hypothetical, rational actors in some simplified situation, and in deducing the consequences of their interaction.

Such intellectual experimenting *may* be fruitful even if some of the premisses are very unrealistic. For instance, the concept of a static economy in equilibrium aids the analysis of the changes and disequilibria of actual economies. And gross exaggeration of one factor may show up an influence which would otherwise have been overlooked. This is particularly impor-

[21] This criticism is parallel to Aristotle's chief criticism of Plato's theory of Forms, to the effect that instead of accounting for their perceptible likenesses the Forms merely divert attention to transcendent duplicates. *Met.*992a27.

[22] An explanation may be in terms of the *typical* dispositions of more or less anonymous individuals, or in terms of the peculiar dispositions of specific individuals. (This is the basis of my distinction between 'explanation in principle' and 'explanation in detail.' See p. 733.) Thus, you might try to explain an election result in terms of how 'the Lancashire shop-keeper' and 'the non-party professional man' etc., felt; or, if you had an unlikely amount of knowledge, in terms of the dispositions of each elector.

tant in social science where the influence of different factors can seldom be accurately calculated. If E is the *sort* of effect produced by F_1, and if F_1 and E are both present, the social scientist tends to assume that F_1 is *the* cause of E, whereas F_1 may have caused only a *part* of E, and an undetected factor F_2 may have caused the rest of E. For example, the domestic economic policy of country A will be a major influence on its own economy; but this may also be influenced by the domestic economic policy of country B. In order to show up this secondary influence, we might assume provisionally that A exports *all* its production to, and imports *all* its consumption from, B, and then deduce the effect on A of a change of policy in B.[23]

But that would be a preliminary intellectual experiment. The premisses of a finished ideal type should be sufficiently realistic for it to be applicable to historical situations. I now turn to the problem of application.

5. Historical Explanation

I shall consider three levels of historical explanation: (I) colligation (where ideal types play no significant role); (II) explanation in principle (which is the field *par excellence* for ideal types); and (III) explanation in detail (where ideal types are mostly constructed *ad hoc*, and rendered increasingly realistic until they become empirical reconstructions).[24]

(I) *Colligation.* The term 'colligation' has been revived by Mr Walsh[25] to denote a procedure which is important, not because it is methodologically powerful, but because most 'literary' historians do in fact use it when they write, for example, constitutional history. It means 'explaining an event by tracing its intrinsic relations to other events and locating it in its historical context.'[26] Thus we begin to understand why a bill was enacted in May 1640 condemning Strafford to death when we learn of such matters as: his autocratic power in Ireland; Parliament's fear of the Irish army and Pym's ruthlessness as a parliamentary leader; the King's dependence on Parliament to pay indemnities to the Scottish army in the north; and the angry anti-royalist mob which beset Westminster during the bill's passage. It may also be better understood by being colligated with *subsequent* events. Thus the Long Parliament's later treatment of Laud and Charles suggests that its treatment of Strafford was not eccentric, but part of a campaign against extra-parliamentary power.

However, as Mr Walsh admits, colligation yields only what he calls

[23] I owe this example to Professor J. E. Meade.

[24] Professor F. A. Hayek also draws a distinction between explaining in principle and explaining in detail, but he wishes to distinguish an explanation of why, say, a price will rise under certain conditions, from a quantitative prediction of the amount by which it will rise (*The Counter-Revolution of Science*, pp. 42–3); whereas I wish to distinguish between explanations in terms of *typical* dispositions, etc., and explanations in terms of the characteristics and personal idiosyncrasies of the principal actors concerned.

[25] See W. H. Walsh, *An Introduction to Philosophy of History*, London, 1951, ch. 3, §3.

[26] *Op. cit.*, p. 59.

a 'significant narrative', which is more than a chronicle, but less than a full explanation, of the events colligated.

(II) *Explanation in Principle.* The principle of the automatic governor can be demonstrated in a simple model which shows that a fall in some temperature, voltage, speed, pressure, etc., below a certain level will move a lever which will increase the supply of heat, etc.; and *vice versa.* Understanding this, you can explain the constant temperature of your car's circulating water *in principle* if you know that an automatic governor controls it, although you do not understand its detailed operation.[27]

Analogous explanations are used in applied economics. Consider the bargaining process. The principle of this is demonstrated in the following ideal type. Two rational agents are postulated. Each possesses one homogeneous, divisible good, and each knows the schedule of those combinations of various portions of his own and the other's good which he would exchange indifferently for the whole of his present good. These premisses are highly precise, and also highly formal. Call them α and β. From these it is deduced that only the limits within which a bargain will be struck are determined, and that within those limits the outcome will be arbitrary. Call this consequence ω. Now consider post-war Anglo-Argentinian trade negotiations. Here, we can, I think, detect factors A, B, c, d, . . . Z where: A and B are the resources and policies of the trade delegations, and are concrete examples of α and β; c, d, . . . are minor factors whose small influences on Z may partly cancel out; and Z is the outcome of the negotiations, the actual instability of Anglo-Argentinian trade relations, which is a rough empirical counterpart of ω. The 'α, β, ω' ideal type explains in principle the 'A, B, c, d, . . . Z' situation.[28]

In this example I have assumed that only one main economic principle, demonstrable in a single ideal type, was at work in the historical situation. But the situation will usually be more complex. Consider a wage-bargain. Perhaps there is a closed shop and limited entry into the trade union. The firm, a centrally planned organisation, buys its raw materials, which are rationed, through a government agency, and its machinery at the best price it can get from oligopolistic suppliers. By law it must export a proportion of its produce, and the export market is highly competitive. Its home prices are fixed by a cartel agreement.[29] The general situation is inflationary.

Here, the outcome of the bargaining process will be shaped by a num-

[27] It is the principle of an invention rather than its physical detail which is usually described in patents. See M. Polanyi, *The Logic of Liberty*, London, 1951, p. 21.

[28] I owe this example to Professor Lionel Robbins.

[29] The definitions of perfect competition, oligopoly and monopoly provide, incidentally, good illustrations of the principle of methodological individualism. An entrepreneur faces: (*a*) perfect competition if the price at which he sells is determined for him; (*b*) oligopoly, if he can alter his price, but if this alteration may lead to price changes by his competitors which may force him to make further, undesired alterations to his own price; and (*c*) monopoly, if he can alter his price without causing undesired repercussions. Competition, oligopoly and monopoly are nothing but the outcome of the behaviour of interacting individuals in certain relationships.

ber of economic principles besides that illustrated in the previous example. And in order to understand the whole situation in principle it would be necessary to build up a complex model from the relevant simple ideal types. Here, an '(α, β), (λ, μ), (σ, τ), . . . ω' model would be used to explain in principle an 'A, B, c, . . . L, M, n, . . . S, T, u, . . . Z' situation (where c . . ., n . . ., u . . . represent comparatively uninfluential factors).

The social scientist's explanations in principle lack the quantitative precision of explanations in mathematical physics. But he may claim that his explanations are at any rate 'intelligible' and 'satisfying,' whereas those of the natural scientist are not. The most universal laws which the latter applies in his explanations and predictions contain terms (e.g. 'elementary quantum of action') whose connotation the layman cannot 'picture' or 'grasp.' Moreover, the status of these most universal laws is probably only temporary: they will probably come to be subsumed under higher order laws.

But the ultimate premisses of social science are human dispositions, i.e. something familiar and understandable (though not introspectable since they are not mental events). They 'are so much the stuff of our everyday experience that they have only to be stated to be recognised as obvious.'[30] And while psychology may try to explain these dispositions, they do provide social science with a natural stopping-place in the search for explanations of overt social phenomena. The social scientist might claim more. The natural scientist cannot, strictly speaking, *verify* valid hypotheses; he can only *refute* false ones.[31] He can say, 'If H, then E. But not-E. Therefore not-H.' But if he says, 'If H, then E. Moreover E. Therefore H' he commits the fallacy of affirming the consequent.[32] But a social scientist might claim that a valid social theory *can* be verified because both its conclusions *and* its premisses can be confirmed—'you assent to the former because they correspond with recognised social facts; and you assent to the latter because they correspond with your ideas of how people behave.' An example of the belief that a social theory can be wholly verified by being confirmed at both ends is to be found in Keynes' *General Theory*. There he asserts 'the fundamental psychological law, upon which we are entitled to depend with great confidence . . . from our knowledge of human nature . . . , that men are disposed, as a rule and on the average, to increase their consumption as their income increases, but not by as much as the increase in their income'; and *vice versa*.[33] He then shows that the empirical fact that no depression has worsened until 'no one at all was employed' is a deductive

[30] Lionel Robbins, *The Nature and Significance of Economic Science*, London, 1935, p. 79.

[31] See K. R. Popper, *Logik der Forschung*, Vienna, 1935, *passim*.

[32] See F. S. C. Northrop, *The Logic of the Sciences and the Humanities*, New York, 1948, pp. 108–9; and e.g. H. W. B. Joseph, *An Introduction to Logic*, Oxford, 1916, pp. 522–3.

[33] *The General Theory of Employment, Interest and Money*, London, 1936, p. 96.

consequence of this law.[34] The theory is thus doubly confirmed, and therefore verified: 'it is *certain* that experience would be extremely different from what it is if the law did not hold.' [35] No natural scientist could claim so much for *his* laws. His explanations are 'surprising' in the sense that he explains the familiar in terms of the unconfirmable unfamiliar. But the social scientist explains the familiar in terms of the familiar. The element of surprise in *his* explanations lies in the logical demonstration of connections which had not been seen before between facts which are *prima facie* discrete.

But a double caution must be entered against the idea of double confirmation in social science: (i) The same conclusion can, of course, be deduced from different sets of premisses, and we cannot be certain that our set of psychological assumptions is the correct set. (ii) Even if our psychological assumptions *are* correct, and even if we *do* find that their deductive consequences correspond to recognised facts, we may nevertheless be mistaken if we explain these facts as a consequence of those psychological factors. This is because we can seldom calculate the relative influence of different psychological factors.[36] Thus Keynes' belief that people are disposed to save a smaller proportion of their income if their income diminishes may well be correct; his demonstration that this general disposition would not allow depressions to worsen indefinitely is immaculate; and the fact that depressions do not worsen indefinitely is undoubted. It is nevertheless conceivable that *no* depression has been halted because of this disposition. One may have been halted by an outbreak of war, another by an upsurge of confidence, another by a public works policy, and so on. In explaining social phenomena we must not be content with the detection of one factor which, singly, would have produced, after an unstated period, an unstated amount of an effect which may, in any particular situation, have been caused mainly by quite different factors.

If I am right in supposing that social theories derive sociological conclusions from dispositional premisses, we should expect to find that major theoretical advances in social science consist in the perception of some typical feature of our mental make-up which had previously been disregarded, and in its formulation in a way which is more deductively fertile and which goes to explain a wider range of facts, than the psychological generalisations relied on hitherto. And this is precisely what we do find. I think that it would be generally conceded that economics is the most mature social science, and that the two most striking advances made in economics during the last century are: (i) the 'revolution' which occurred

[34] *Op. cit.*, p. 252.

[35] *Op. cit.*, p. 251 (my italics).

[36] I was myself inclined to accept the idea of double confirmation until Professor Popper pointed out to me the relevance of this consideration.

in the early 1870's when Jevons, Menger and Walras introduced the concept of marginal utility; and (ii) the Keynesian 'revolution.'

(i) The classical economists saw that the price of a good must be partly determined by the demand for it, and that that demand must reflect the buyers' estimates of the good's utility—and yet diamonds, whose utility is low, fetch a far higher price than water, whose utility is high. So they tried to escape from their dilemma by saying that the price of a good is determined by the cost of its production, though this would obviously be untrue of an unwanted good which had been expensively produced. This difficulty dissolved with the introduction of the idea of the utility, not of a whole good, but of its least important, or 'marginal,' unit. For—and this is the recognition of a psychological contour-line which had not been clearly mapped before—it is in terms of that unit that we tend to value a whole good; and the more we have of the same good, the more its marginal utility diminishes. Hence, if diamonds became abundant and water very scarce, their subjectively determined values would be reversed. F. H. Knight has given a vivid description of the elegance and power of the concept of marginal utility:

> To its admirers it comes near to being the fulfilment of the eighteenth-century craving for a principle which would do for human conduct and society what Newton's mechanics had done for the solar system. It introduces simplicity and order, even to the extent of making it possible to state the problems in the form of mathematical functions dealt with by the methods of infinitesimal calculus.[37]

(ii) The reader who is unfamiliar with Keynes' contribution to the theory of employment must take its value on trust, for it is impossible to describe it briefly. But here again we find that what it rests on is the perception and precise formulation of certain human dispositions which Keynes regarded as 'ultimate independent variables,'[38] and from which he could deduce such dependent variables (or overt phenomena, as I have called them previously) as the amount of employment and the general level of prices. At the heart of his *General Theory* Keynes placed 'three fundamental psychological factors, namely, the psychological propensity to consume, the psychological attitude to liquidity and the psychological expectation of future yield from capital-assets.'[39]

(III) *Explanation in Detail.* The mark of an explanation in principle is its reliance on typical dispositions and its disregard of personal differences. But it is often impossible to disregard these, for instance, in diplomatic history. Here, the premisses of a historical explanation must be the specific dispositions, beliefs and relationships of actual people. This is what I call 'explanation in detail.'

[37] F. H. Knight, *The Ethics of Competition,* London, 1935, p. 158.

[38] *Op. cit.,* p. 246. Of course, the variables are only 'independent' from the social scientist's point of view. The psychologist would probably consider them 'dependent'.

[39] *Op. cit.,* pp. 246–7.

So far, I have allowed two questions to lie dormant: (i) What is the status of these dispositions, and wherein lies their explanatory power? (ii) What assumptions concerning people's rationality are we obliged to make when we explain something in terms of their dispositions and beliefs? These questions were not acute so long as explanations in principle were being considered. An explanation requires a general statement as its major premiss; and when we postulate a typical disposition we assert that all men (with trivial exceptions and minor deviations, and, perhaps, within a limited historico-geographical area) are prone to behave in a certain kind of way; and this gives us the generality we require. And we explain in principle by combining types which are, after all, ideal, and which may therefore be expected to contain idealised simplifications of real life, such as the assumption of fully rational behaviour in the light of preferences and beliefs.

But when we turn to explanations in detail these two questions do become acute. For we are here concerned with the variegated dispositions of actual people, and these appear to lack the generality which the major premiss of an explanation needs. And actual people do not behave altogether rationally, which suggests that we cannot go on assuming that they do. I shall discuss the first question under the head of 'Personality', and the second under the head of 'Rationality and Purposefulness'.

(i) *Personality*. A series of occurrences constitutes a person's life, and a complex and evolving system of dispositions constitutes his personality.[40] Dispositions 'are not laws, for they mention particular things or persons. On the other hand they resemble laws in being partly "variable" or "open." '[41] The dispositions which comprise a unique personality are, so to speak, 'laws' which apply to only one man over a limited period of time. It is as if the laws of chemistry concerning, say, mercury, applied only to a period in the life of one solitary bottle of mercury which has come into existence, matured, and will dissolve, and whose twin, we may confidently assume, never has existed, and never will.

All this presupposes that men do have personalities, i.e. that their behaviour is fairly consistent over a period of time if their personalities are

[40] I have adopted the terminology of Professor G. Ryle's *Concept of Mind* (London, 1949; see especially ch. 5), but not that book's famous denial that a man has 'privileged access' to his own mind. Sitting beside the driver of a car who turns white and wrenches the steering-wheel over, I may perceive instantaneously *that* he fears an accident, but I do not *feel* his fear. Moreover, the historian is usually in the position of the policeman who tries to reconstruct what happened from skid-marks and reports of witnesses; and for him the dualism between uninterpreted overt behaviour (e.g. Jan Masaryk's fall from a Prague window) and its interpretation in psychological terms is very real.

But the following characteristic remarks suggest that Professor Ryle has now modified his original anti-dualism: 'We have . . . a sort of (graduatedly) privileged access to such things as palpitations of the heart, cramps, and creaks in the joints.' 'I have elsewhere argued for the idea that a tickle just *is* a thwarted impulse to scratch. . . . But I do not think now that this will do.' ('Feelings,' *The Philosophical Quarterly*, April 1951, I, 198–9).

[41] Ryle, *Concept of Mind*, p. 123.

not subjected to dissolvent shocks. This assumption of the quasi-permanence of personalities corresponds roughly—very roughly—to the natural scientist's belief in the permanence of the natural order.

The generalisations of psychology fit into this scheme in the following ways: (*a*) Some attribute a certain disposition to all men. The theory of the association of ideas is an example. (*b*) Others attribute certain dispositions to a certain type of man, e.g. the 'introvert.' (*c*) Yet others attempt to describe the dynamics of personality-development, deriving later dispositions from prior determining conditions in the light of psychological theory. (It is this search for the primitive determining conditions which leads back to the 'formative years' of early childhood.) An example is the theory of the 'incest-complex,' which asserts that a man who idealised his sister as a child will be prone to hypoæsthesia on marriage.

A disposition attributed to one man is no weaker than the same disposition attributed to all men in explaining and predicting that one man's behaviour. 'X will accept office' can be deduced from the minor premiss, 'X believes that if he refuses the office he has been offered he will find himself in the wilderness' in conjunction with *either* (*a*) the major premiss, 'All men seek power,' *or* (*b*) the major premiss, 'X is a power-seeker'; but whereas (*b*) may be true, (*a*) is the sort of statement which is likely to be false because men are not uniform.[42]

Similarly, a detailed description of one man's chess-playing dispositions (his knowledge of the rules, evaluations of the different pieces, and ability to see a certain number of moves ahead) together with his present beliefs about his opponent's intentions and the positions of the pieces, imply his next move, which could not be deduced from propositions about chess-players in general in conjunction with a description of the present state of the game.

Thus the idea that the historian's interpretative principles are simply generalisations about human nature, into which he must have special insight, is inadequate.[43] His knowledge of human nature in general has to be supplemented by a knowledge of the peculiar personalities of the principal actors concerned in the situation he is trying to understand, whether his problem be X's behaviour, or the chess-player's next move, or the rise of Christianity, or the Congress of Vienna.

The dispositions which the historian attributes to a personality he is trying to reconstruct resemble scientific laws in two further ways.

(*a*) They are postulated hypotheses which correspond to nothing

[42] On law-like dispositions of very limited generality, see R. Peters, 'Cure, Cause and Motive,' *Analysis*, April 1950, 10, no. 5, p. 106.

[43] This idea underlies Mr Walsh's contribution to the symposium on 'The Character of a Historical Explanation' (*Aristotelian Society, Supplementary Volume* XXI, 1947). From it he infers that, since 'men's notions of human nature change from age to age' we must recognise 'the subjective element which history undoubtedly contains' (p. 66). The point is, do historians' notions of, say, Napoleon's personality change from age to age (not because of the discovery of fresh evidence, etc., but) arbitrarily?

observable, although observable behaviour can be inferred from them in conjunction with factual minor premisses. Consequently, in judging their validity we want to know, not the mental process by which the historian arrived at them, but their degree of success in accounting for what is known of the man's behaviour. The hypothetical dispositions postulated by the historian who has 'sympathetically identified himself with his hero' may be richer than those of the historian who has not done so, but it is not this which gives them a certificate of reliability. Professor Hempel has put the matter very clearly:

> The method of empathy is, no doubt, frequently applied by laymen and by experts in history. But it does not in itself constitute an explanation; it is rather essentially a heuristic device; its function is to suggest certain psychological hypotheses which might serve as explanatory principles in the case under consideration.[44]

And the historian is no more precluded from reconstructing a strange and unsympathetic personality than is the scientist from reconstructing the behaviour of an atom which does things he would not dream of doing himself.[45]

(*b*) The dispositions which constitute a personality also resemble scientific laws in that they form a hierarchical system; and this is of considerable methodological importance. It is, of course, essential that the dispositions which a historian attributes to a historical figure should not be mere *ad hoc* translations of known occurrences into dispositional terms. It is no explanation of Brutus' behaviour to say that he was disposed to assassinate Caesar, though it would be a ground for an explanation to say that Brutus was disposed to place his loyalty to the State above his loyalties to his friends, if independent evidence were found to support this hypothesis. Moreover—and it is here that the idea of a hierarchy of dispositions is important—the historian who can explain some aspect of a person's behaviour *up to a certain time* in terms of certain disposition, although his *subsequent* behaviour conflicts with this disposition, must not merely say that at that

[44] *Op. cit.*, p. 467. Failure to realise this is, I think, the weakness of R. G. Collingwood's *The Idea of History* (ed. T. M. Knox, Oxford, 1946).

[45] Failure to recognise this vitiates, I think, some of the argument in Professor F. A. Hayek's 'Scientism and the Study of Society' (*The Counter-Revolution of Science*, Part One). There, despite all the work done in abnormal psychology, he asserts: 'When we speak of mind what we mean is that certain phenomena can be successfully interpreted on the analogy of our own mind. . . . To recognise mind cannot mean anything but to recognise something as operating in the same way as our own thinking.' From this false premiss he correctly infers the false conclusion that 'history can never carry us beyond the stage where we can understand the working of the minds of the acting people because they are similar to our own' (pp. 77–9). Only a war-like historian can tackle a Genghiz Khan or a Hitler! Moreover, if it were true that people, young and old, do not recognise as mind what they cannot interpret on the analogy of their own mind, they would never learn to speak. For children must unconsciously realise that adult noises differ importantly from their own gibberish in being meaningful before they can begin to understand adult talk.

I hasten to add that I owe much to other parts of Professor Hayek's argument.

time the earlier disposition gave way to another. He should find a *higher order* disposition which helps to explain both earlier and later lower order dispositions, and hence the whole range of the person's behaviour. For example: suppose that Russian foreign policy is controlled by a consistent, integrated personality. Before 1939 Russia was disposed to pursue an anti-fascist foreign policy. But in 1939 came the Russo-German Pact. In order to explain this aberration it is not enough for the historian to say that the anti-fascist disposition was replaced. He must find a higher order disposition (e.g. 'Russian foreign policy is determined by considerations of national expediency, not by ideological factors') from which, in conjunction with factual premisses, the change in policy is derivable. In doing this it is clear that the historian will *not* be translating an occurrence (the signing of the pact) into dispositional terms, but deriving both the occurrence and the change in lower order dispositions from a more permanent and fundamental disposition.

In conclusion it should be said that the personality of a man in society comprises dispositions both of a more private and temperamental kind, and of a more public and institutional kind. Only certain individuals are disposed to weep during the death-scene in *Othello*, but all policemen are disposed to blow their whistles under certain circumstances and any Speaker in the House of Commons is disposed to disallow parliamentary criticism of exercises of the Prerogative. And these more public and institutional dispositions, which may vary very little when one man undertakes another's role, can be abstracted from the total, variegated flux of dispositions, and so provide the social scientist with a fairly stable subject-matter.[46]

(ii) *Rationality and Purposefulness.* Before asking what assumptions the historian is obliged to make about the rationality of those whose behaviour he is trying to interpret, we must establish a satisfactory 'definition in use' of the term 'rational behaviour.' Weber defined it, very austerely, as the deliberate and logical choice of means to attain explicit goals, in the light of existing factual knowledge. This is unsatisfactory for two reasons. (*a*) Whitehead said somewhere that 'civilisation advances by extending the number of important operations we can perform without thinking about them.' This morning's tooth-brushing was not irrational because done from habit and not from deliberations on dental hygiene. Our pursuit of goals need not be conscious in order to be rational. (*b*) Behaviour often does not conform to the end-means pattern. I may tell the truth, or go fishing, simply from a desire to do so, with no further end in mind.[47]

We escape these difficulties by saying that a person has behaved rationally if he *would* have behaved in the same way if, with the same *factual* information, he had seen the full *logical* implications of his behaviour,

[46] See Hayek, *Counter-Revolution*, p. 34.

[47] 'We invest our capital reluctantly in the hope of getting dividends. . . . But the angler would not accept or understand an offer of the pleasures without the activities of angling. It is angling that he enjoys, not something that angling engenders.' Ryle, *op. cit.*, p. 132. See also H. A. Pritchard, *Moral Obligation*, Oxford, 1949, pp. 10–11.

whether he actually saw them or not. And if we define purposeful behaviour as trying (consciously or otherwise) to do or achieve something wanted, it follows that fully rational behaviour is a limiting case of purposeful behaviour.

The historian who tries to interpret overt behaviour must assume that it is purposeful but not necessarily fully rational.[48] Consider a *crime passionel* committed by an enraged husband. A judge who assumed that the husband had behaved purposelessly could reconstruct the event in a number of quite arbitrary ways—perhaps cramp caused his finger to contract round the trigger of a gun which happened to be pointing at his wife's lover. But while the judge must not assume purposelessness he need not assume full rationality. The husband would probably have confined himself to threats and remonstrances if he had paused to consider the less immediate consequences of a violent course of action.

The assumption of purposefulness is constantly made by those who attempt the most intensive analysis of human behaviour, i.e. practising psycho-analysts. It has often been pointed out that the psycho-analyst is on the side of rationality in that he tries to cure his patients. More interesting from our point of view is his assumption that the behaviour of an *uncured* patient is thoroughly purposeful. Suppose a patient forgets to wind his watch, and so arrives late at his father's funeral. Unlike the layman, the psycho-analyst will not attribute the stopped watch to accidental forgetfulness, to a purposeless psychic aberration. He will ask his patient *why* he *wanted* his watch to stop—maybe he felt guilty on having a death-wish fulfilled and so created an excuse for avoiding the funeral. This would certainly be purposeful behaviour, and might even be regarded as rational behaviour based on misinformation.[49]

(iii) *Conclusion.* Having considered the status of dispositions and the problem of rationality, we can now return to explanations in detail.

Weber advocated using individualistic ideal types, which depict rational behaviour, to show up the partial irrationality of actual behaviour. But this is unacceptable. Suppose that a historian wishes to interpret a general's behaviour during a battle. He has reconstructed, as best he can, both the dispositions which constitute that aspect of the general's personality with which he is concerned, and the general's information about the military situation. Suppose that, in conjunction, these dictate retreat as the rational course of action, but that the general is known to have given the signal to advance. Now the historian, like the psycho-analyst, will not want to leave puzzling overt behaviour uninterpreted; but according to Weber he should simply call this a deviation from the ideally rational course of action implied by the premisses of his theoretical reconstruction of the situation. But since an irrational aberration can be attributed to

[48] See Robbins, *op. cit.*, ch. 4, sect. 5.

[49] The mixture of rationality and misinformation due to childhood associations which psycho-analysis brings to the surface was pointed out to me by Professor Popper.

anything from boredom to panic, this procedure would result in thoroughly arbitrary reconstructions. Rather, the historian must discover the most satisfactory amendment to the premisses of his ideal type (constructed more or less *ad hoc* to depict the main features of the general's personality and situation) which will remove the discrepancy between what it implies and what happened. Perhaps there is independent evidence to suggest that the general was more lion-hearted than the historian had supposed; or perhaps he had underestimated the enemy's strength, or, in estimating the immediate consequences of an advance, he had overlooked a more distant undesirable repercussion. When *ad hoc* ideal types are used in detailed historical explanations, they have to be amended and amended until they cease being ideal constructs and become empirical reconstructions. The historian who claims to have interpreted a historical situation should be able to show: (*a*) that the behaviour of the actors in it flows from their personalities and situational beliefs; and (*b*) that significant events which no one intended are resultants of the behaviour of interacting individuals.

6. Summary

An individual's personality is a system of unobservable dispositions which, together with his factual beliefs, determine his observable behaviour. Society is a system of unobservable relationships between individuals whose interaction produces certain measurable sociological phenomena. We can apprehend an unobservable social system only by reconstructing it theoretically from what is known of individual dispositions, beliefs and relationships. Hence holistic ideal types, which would abstract essential traits from a social whole while ignoring individuals, are impossible: they always turn into individualistic ideal types. Individualistic ideal types of explanatory power are constructed by first discerning the form of typical, socially significant, dispositions, and then by demonstrating how, in various typical situations, these lead to certain principles of social behaviour.

If such a principle, or a number of such principles, is at work in a historical situation, the outcome of that situation can be explained anonymously, or in principle, by an application to it of the relevant ideal type, or combination of ideal types. If the idiosyncrasies of the actors concerned significantly influenced the outcome, it must be explained in terms of their peculiar dispositions and beliefs. In either case, the hypothetico-deductive method is used. The hypotheses consist of postulated dispositions, beliefs and relationships of (anonymous or specific) individuals; and their test lies in the correspondence or otherwise between their deductive consequences and what is known of the overt characteristics of the situation being reconstructed. How the historian establishes the overt characteristics of a vanished situation is another story.

The Scope and Method of Economics *

OSCAR LANGE

1. The Subject Matter of Economics

Economics is the science of administration of scarce resources in human society. Human beings, living within the framework of a given historical civilisation, experience various wants, such as of food, shelter, clothing, education, social prestige, entertainment, expression of religious, national, or political attitudes, and others. Some of the wants result from biological needs which must be satisfied for the very preservation of life. Most of them, however, are products of life in civilized society, frequently of the very existence of the means to satisfy them, and even the wants which result from biological needs assume forms determined by the standards of the particular civilization under which the human beings live. The wants can be satisfied by means of appropriate objects called *goods*, e.g. land, coal, cattle, buildings, ships, railroads, machinery, stocks of raw materials and the uses of such objects or of persons called *services*, like of transportation, of housing, of workingmen, of teachers, of managers, and of artists, etc. The goods and services are the *resources* which serve to satisfy human wants. Some of the resources, air, for instance, are so plentiful that all wants dependent upon them can be fully satisfied. Others, however, e.g. oil or the services of human beings, exist only in quantities which are not sufficient to satisfy all wants dependent upon these resources. In this case, we say that the resources are *scarce*. When resources are scarce, certain wants must go unsatisfied. Men make decisions which, given the organisation and institutions of society, determine the distribution of the scarce resources among the different persons as well as the uses to which the scarce resources are put. In other words: the resources are administered. The study of the ways in which scarce resources are administered is the task of the science of economics.

The administration of scarce resources is influenced by the standards of civilisation and by the organisation and institutions of the society in which men live. The influence is a two-fold one. The wants which the resources serve to satisfy are products of standards of civilisation historically developed in society. The ways in which scarce resources are procured,

* Reprinted by kind permission of the editor from *Review of Economic Studies*, 13, 1945–6.

adapted to various purposes, distributed among different persons are all results of social organisation and social institutions. Forms of ownership, institutions like corporations and banks, technical knowledge acquired in institutes of research and transmitted by schools, regulation by government agencies, habits and moral standards all influence the ways of administering scarce resources. Economics is thus a *social science,* i.e. it deals with a subject which depends on the standards and forms of life in human society. It differs from sociology, the science of social actions and relations (patterns of repeated social actions) between men, by being interested in the actions of men toward the scarce resources which serve to satisfy their wants. These actions are dependent upon social actions but are distinct from them. We shall call them *economic actions.* While dependent on social actions, economic actions, in turn, influence and even create social actions and relations. The last mentioned influence provides subject-matter for a special field of study. We might name it *economic sociology,* the science of the effect of economic actions upon social actions and relations. Subjects such as the sociology of industrial relations, bureaucracy in corporations, trade-unionism, belong to this field. The present essay is limited to economics, i.e. the study of economic actions. This includes a study of the influence of social organisation and institutions upon the ways and methods of administration of scarce resources.

Like any other science, economics is not content with merely descriptive knowledge. It tries to discern general patterns of uniformity in the administration of scarce resources. The possibility of establishing such patterns of uniformity is based on two observed facts. Human actions with regard to scarce resources are subject to uniform patterns of repetition. For instance, most people react to an increase in their income by spending more money on goods and services. Within the framework of given social organisation and institutions, the uniformities in economic action of individuals or groups of individuals produce certain uniformities in the distribution and use of scarce resources. Thus, an increase in the quantity of bank loans to businessmen or corporations makes them increase their demand for resources with a consequent rise in employment and/or prices. The branch of economics which deals with such patterns of uniformity and combines them in a coherent system is called *theoretical economics* or *economic theory* (also economic analysis). Statements enunciating the patterns of uniformity are referred to as *economic laws.* Economic laws are, like all other scientific laws, conditional statements. They assert that such and such happens regularly whenever such and such conditions are satisfied (i.e. whenever such and such other observations take place). No scientific law applies when its prerequisite conditions do not occur. Since the administration of scarce resources is influenced by social organisation and institutions, such organisation and institutions are among the conditions implied in economic laws. Consequently, economic laws which hold under one type of social organisation may fail to do so under another type. Most economic laws are thus "limited historically" to certain given types of social organisation and institutions. This, however, does not imply any basic difference between the laws of economics (or of other social sciences) and the laws of the natural sciences. The latter, too, are contingent upon conditions which are subject to change. Different laws of the natural sciences have different degrees of historic permanence, usually a much higher one than the laws of economics, though even this is not always the case (some laws of meteorology are less permanent than some laws of economics). The difference is but one of degree. Like all scientific laws, economic laws are established in order to make successful prediction of the outcome of human actions. In economics the laws serve to predict the result of policies, i.e. of actions of public or private agencies with regard to the administration of scarce resources. Such predictions, however, are difficult. This is due to the fact that the number of conditions circumscribing the validity of economic laws is very great, and it is difficult to ascertain whether they are all satisfied in any particular situation. Notwithstanding, some successful predictions are being made with the aid of economic science.

Theoretical economics does not exhaust the field of economic inquiry. Economics also studies and describes the particular ways and methods of administering scarce resources as they occur in the history of human society, past and present. Observations are made and classified and interpreted with the aid of the uniformities established by economic theory. This pursuit provides the subject-matter of *applied economics*. Applied economics is subdivided into several parts. The most important are economic history—the study of administration of scarce resources in the human societies of the past—and institutional economics, the study of the influence of particular social institutions upon the administration of scarce resources. The effect of trade-associations upon prices, quality and output of goods, or the effect of collective farming in agriculture on the efficiency of production are examples of problems which fall in the last-mentioned field.

Theoretical economics puts the patterns of uniformity in a coherent system. This is done by presenting the laws of economics as a deductive set of propositions derived by the rules of logic (and of mathematics) from a few basic propositions. The basic propositions are called assumptions or postulates, the derived propositions are called theorems. Theoretical economics thus appears (like all other theoretical sciences) as a deductive science. This, however, does not make it a branch of pure mathematics or logic. Like the rest of economics, economic theory is an empirical science. Its assumptions or postulates are approximative generalisations of empirical observations; e.g. the assumption that business enterprises act so as to maximise their money profit. Some inaccuracy of approximation (e.g. some considerations, like safety, may keep enterprises from maximising money profit) is accepted for the sake of greater simplicity. The theorems, in turn, are subjected to test by empirical observation. A deductive set of theorems to be subjected to empirical test is also called a *theory*, *hypothesis*, or a *model*. We can thus say that theoretical economics provides hypotheses or models based on generalisation of observations and subject to empirical test.

Since the assumptions (postulates) underlying a model are only approximative, the theorems do not correspond directly to results of empirical observations. In order to establish such a correspondence, special procedures must be provided. First, the concept used in theoretical models are not adequate representations of empirical observation. For instance, a theoretical model speaks at "the price" of a specified good, but experience fails to produce anything like the specified "good" and its "price." There are hundreds of quality-grades and thousands of sellers each charging a different price. Experience is much richer than the language of science can make allowance for. In order to bridge the gap between theoretical concepts and empirical observations, it is necessary to have a procedure of *identification*, which contains rules establishing a correspondence between the two. Such procedures have to be provided by the different branches of applied economics. Furthermore, the theorems of theoretical economics are never borne out exactly by empirical observation. At best, they do so only "approximately." This raises the question as to what is to be considered as an acceptable degree of approximation inducing us to accept a hypothesis as "true" and what degree of approximation is to be judged as insufficient, making us reject the hypothesis as "incompatible with the facts." The question can be answered only in terms of a procedure of *verification* (testing) which establishes rules according to which hypotheses are accepted as "empirically verified" or rejected as "empirically unverified" or "empirically refuted." A recently developed special branch of economics deals with such procedures of verification. It is called *econometrics* and is based on the principles of mathematical statistics.

The administration of scarce resources empirically observed can be evaluated in terms of certain social objectives. Such objectives may consist in the best satisfaction of the wants of private persons according to their own preferences or in marshalling scarce resources for certain collective enterprises—e.g. industrialisation of a country according to time-table, as in the Soviet Union, or successful prosecution of war, or enactment of certain ideas of social justice—or, finally, of a combination of all. The social objectives being given, rules of use of scarce resources can be found which are most conducive to the attainment of these objectives. The use of resources which follows these rules is referred to as the "ideal" use. The rules of "ideal" use of resources provide a standard by which the actual use can be evaluated as to its social desirability. The use of resources empirically observed may be compared with the "ideal" use and measures may be recommended to bring the actual use into closer correspondence with the "ideal" one. This provides subject-matter for another branch of economic science, usually called *welfare economics* (also normative economics or social economics). The rules of "ideal" use of resources are general statements; they express uniform patterns of economic action which, if adopted, are most conducive to the social objectives aimed at. They are conditional statements because they are valid only under given social objectives and given empirical conditions; they require empirical verification. (A rule of "ideal" use of resources may prove in practice not to be conducive to the social aims desired.) The rules of "ideal" use of resources can thus be considered as a special kind of economic laws. This makes it convenient to include welfare economics in theoretical economics as a supplementary branch of the latter.

2. The Objectivity of Economic Science

The statements of economic science have objective validity. This means that two or more persons who agree to abide by the rules of scientific procedure are bound to reach the same conclusions. If they start with the same assumptions, they are bound, by the rules of logic, to derive the same theorems. If they apply the same rules of identification and verification, they are bound to reach agreement as to whether the theorems should be accepted as "true" or rejected as "unverified" or "false." The test of verification decides whether the assumptions are adequate or not. In the latter case, they have to be replaced by new ones which lead to theorems able to stand the test of verification. The final verdict with regard to any statement of economic science is thus based upon an appeal to facts, i.e. to empirical observations. "The proof of the pudding is in the eating." This verdict has interpersonal validity because facts are interpersonal, i.e. can be observed by everyone.

The interpersonal validity of statements holds also for welfare economics. There is no necessary interpersonal agreement about the social objectives which provide the standard of evaluation for welfare economics. Different persons, social groups and classes may, and frequently do desire different social objectives. Once, however, the objectives are stated and certain assumptions are made about empirical conditions, the rules of "ideal" use of resources are derived by the rules of logic and verified by the rules of verification. This procedure is interpersonally objective, i.e. everyone who applies it is bound to reach the same conclusions. The situation may be compared with that of two physicians treating a patient. There is no necessity of interpersonal agreement about the objective of the treatment. One physician may want to heal the patient, the other may want to kill him (e.g. the patient may be a Jew in a Nazi concentration camp; one physician may be a fellow prisoner who wants to help him, the other physician may be a Nazi acting under orders to exterminate Jews). But once the objective is set for the purpose under discussion (either of the two physicians may, of course, refuse to act upon it), their statements as to whether a given treatment is conducive to the end under consideration have interpersonal validity. Any disagreement between them can be settled by appeal to fact and to the rules of scientific procedure.

Our conclusion about the objectivity of economic science may seem startling. Economists are rather notorious for being unable to reach agreement and for being divided into opposing "schools of thought," "orthodox" and "unorthodox," "bourgeois" and "socialist," and many others. The existence of profound disagreement among economists, however, does not refute our thesis about the objectivity of economics as a science. The disagreements can all be traced to one or more of the following sources:

(1) Disagreement about social objectives. This is the most frequent source of disagreement, but acts as such only as long as it is implicit and unrecognised. If the social objectives are stated explicitly, the disagreement disappears. For any given set of social objectives and with given assumptions as to empirical conditions, conclusions are drawn with interpersonal validity by the rules of logic and of verification.

(2) Disagreement about facts. Such disagreement can always be resolved by further observation and study of the empirical material. Frequently, however, the empirical data necessary to resolve the disagreement are unavailable. In such cases the issue remains unsettled. The conclusion that the issue cannot be settled with the data available has interpersonal validity. Agreement is reached to withhold judgment.

(3) Failure to abide by the rules of logic, of identification and of verification. The disagreement can be removed by correct application of these rules.

The disagreements are thus all due to failure to abide by the rules of scientific procedure and can be resolved by strict application of these rules. Economists, as well as other scientists, however, are not automatons acting on the basis of the rules of scientific procedure. As human beings they are subject to a great multiplicity of influences, some conscious, most of them subconscious, which determine their conclusions as laid down in the literature of economics. There are influences, sociological and psychological, which sometimes are unfavourable and sometimes favourable to the application of scientific procedure. The persistence of disagreements indicates that the harmful influences are very strong. It is desirable to have a picture of these influences, harmful as well as helpful.

Economists, like other human beings, live under the institutions of a historic society and under the standards of its civilisation. They share in its beliefs and values, prejudices and interests, horizons and limitations. They depend for their living, advancement, and recognition on the institutions of the society in which they live, e.g. on universities, research institutes, publishers, press, government, and business establishments. Most of these institutions have other, more important, objectives than the "untrammelled pursuit of truth," and even those which have this objective are dependent on the rest of society and must make their adjustments and compromises. Furthermore, economists are brought up as members of a particular nation, social class, religious or philosophical group, and political tradition, etc. All this exposes economists, and also other scientists, to a multiplicity of influences other than the rules of scientific procedure. Those influences which are conscious are easily recognised and overcome if they interfere with honest application of scientific procedure. Though even in this case, many may choose to limit their scientific inquiry to "safe" fields where there is little danger of conflict with powerful and dominant interests and prejudices. The really important influences, however, are those which are subconscious. The economist subject to them is unaware of their existence; the influences operate through processes of rationalisation of subconscious motivations. The result is the production of *ideologies*, i.e. systems of beliefs which are held not on grounds of their conformity to scientific procedure but as rationalisations of subconscious, non-logical, motives. Ideologies have no interpersonal validity. They convince only those who share the same subconscious motivations and undergo the same processes of rationalisation.

The study of ideologies, of the conditions of their origins and influences, has become the subject-matter of a special discipline, the *sociology of knowledge*. This discipline has established valuable insights into the sociological and psychological conditions of scientific inquiry. Its most important contribution is the recognition of the fact that all scientific production contains an ideological element. This holds for the natural sciences as well as for the social sciences. The history of the Copernican theory in astronomy and of the theory of evolution in biology provides an example. For a long time the attitude of astronomers and of biologists to these theories was influenced by their general attitude, friendly or hostile, to dominant ecclesiastic doctrines and by their personal dependence or lack of dependence on ecclesiastic institutions. The history of economics is full of instances of the ideological element in economic science. The most important stepping-stones in the development of economics were not merely scientific but also ideological with far-reaching social consequences.

The existence of an ideological element in each science has caused some representatives of the sociology of knowledge to deny the objective validity of scientific statements, particularly in the domain of the social sciences. Such a conclusion is unwarranted. The validity of scientific statements can be ascertained with impersonal objectivity through an appeal to facts. Predictions derived from scientific statements are or are not borne out under the test of verification. The outcome is entirely independent of human motivations, conscious or subconscious; it depends entirely on the correctness of the scientific procedure applied in establishing the statements. Eclipses predicted do or do not occur, bridges stand the stress of traffic or break down, patients get healed or die, whatever the personal motivations of the astronomer, the engineering scientist or the medical man. Certain economic situations lead to unemployment or to inflation, whatever the economist's personal liking or disliking of the capitalist system. The validity of scientific statements does not depend on human motivations; it depends entirely on the observations of the rule of scientific procedure and is, therefore, interpersonal.

The ideological element in scientific inquiry need not always be a handicap in reaching interpersonally valid results. If this was not the case, little scientific progress would have been made. Ideological motivation may also stimulate the development of science. Discoveries have been made in physics and chemistry as a consequence of the desire to make profits or to promote national defence (indeed, the very development of these sciences is closely related to modern industry and warfare). Biological science has been stimulated by motivations of human sympathy for the sick and the suffering. Most important contributions of the social sciences are due to passion for social justice and betterment. The discoveries of classical economics were thus ideologically motivated by passion for freedom and justice as well as by the interests of the industrial middle class. The progress of institutional economics was substantially motivated ideologically by the desire for justice and for the improvement of the lot of the industrial working class. Some relation seems to exist between the nature of the motivations and their favourable or unfavourable influence upon the development of economics and other social sciences. "Conservative" motivations, i.e. motivations resulting from the desire to maintain established social institutions and standards of civilisation tend to disfavour, while "progressive" motivations which result from the desire to change and improve social institutions and standards of civilisation tend to favour the attainment of scientifically valid results in the domain of the social sciences. For it is the desire for change and betterment, whether conscious or subconscious which creates the inquisitiveness of mind resulting in scientific investigation of human society.

3. The Postulate of Rationality

. . . The pursuit by firms of a single magnitude for an objective implies the desire to maximise it. A unit in pursuit of money profit but not desirous of maximising it obviously must be striving for additional objectives. It is ready to sacrifice some money profit for the attainment of some other objective or objectives. Thus, there appears to be an essential difference between firms and households. Firms pursue a single objective, a magnitude which they want to maximise; households, instead, are concerned with the satisfaction of many different wants, theirs being a multiplicity of objectives. However, since resources are scarce, wants must be weighed against each other and decisions must be made as to which wants to satisfy and to what extent; resources must be allocated accordingly. This implies the existence of given preferences which guide the household in choosing one allocation rather than another. We may now ask whether these preferences can be ordered along a scale. When this is possible, the household can be interpreted as pursuing a single objective, namely, the most preferred allocation of the resources among its different wants. The household appears then as maximising a magnitude. We call this magnitude *utility*. The decisions of the household are interpreted, in this case, in a way similar to those of firms, i.e. as resulting from the pursuit of a single objective.

The possibility of interpreting decisions of households in a way similar to decisions of firms suggests the adoption of a general postulate covering both cases. We call it the *postulate of rationality*. A unit of economic decision is said to act rationally when its objective is the maximisation of a magnitude. Firms thus act rationally, by definition, while households do so only when their preferred allocations of resources among different wants can be ordered along a scale. The postulate of rationality is the assumption that all units of economic decision act rationally. This assumption provides us with a most powerful tool for simplification of theoretical analysis. For, if a unit of decision acts rationally, its decisions in any given situation can be predicted by mere application of the rules of logic (and of mathematics). In absence of rational action such prediction could be made only after painstaking empirical study of the uniformities in the decision patterns of the unit. For a unit which acts rationally, these uniformities or laws can be deduced immediately by logic and the decisions predicted, accordingly. Thus, the postulate of rationality is a short-cut to the discovery of laws governing the decisions of units and to the prediction of their actions under given circumstances.

Though a short-cut designed to save elaborate empirical investigation, the postulate of rationality is, nevertheless, but an empirical assumption. It is a hypothesis which, in each case, must be verified by confronting the logical deductions obtained from the postulate with the observations of experience. The use of the postulate is justified only when the logical deductions agree with the results of empirical observation with an acceptable degree of approximation. Otherwise, the postulate would lead us to make predictions which fail to be borne out by observed facts. This needs to be stressed because some economists believe that the postulate of rationality can be used as an *a priori* principle, not subject to empirical verification. In such case, however, the conclusions derived from the postulate of rationality could not have any empirical relevance, either. Theoretical economics would become a branch of pure logic or mathematics without empirical implications, whatsoever. If the laws deduced from the postulate of rationality are to serve as a basis of making predictions about the decisions of units encountered in experience, this postulate must be treated as an empirical hypothesis.

The hypothesis that producing units act rationally, i.e. with the objective of maximising money profit, is verified with satisfactory approximation in the capitalist economy. It serves, therefore, as a useful tool of simplification in the study of that economy. The situation is more doubtful with regard to households. Here the verification of the hypothesis is much more precarious, and we must expect much larger discrepancies between results of empirical observation and conclusions derived from the postulate of rationality. There seems, however, to be some difference between households operating in the capitalist economy and households of the domestic economy of pre-capitalist societies. The dominance of business enterprises with a tangible and quantified magnitude (money profit) as their objective has created a mental habit of considering all kinds of decisions as a pursuit of a single objective, expressed as a magnitude. Some authors call this mental habit the "capitalist spirit." It spreads beyond the specific decisions of business enterprises and affects the mode of operation of other units, including households. Under the influence of the mental habit mentioned, households are encouraged to order their preferences along a scale, i.e. to maximise utility. In capitalist society, therefore, the decisions of households are more likely to conform to the deductions derived from the postulate of rationality than in societies which preceded the rise of modern capitalism.

Public services act rationally when the social objective they aim at can be expressed as a single magnitude to be maximised. The magnitude is then called *public welfare*. Public welfare exists as a magnitude when the community, or more exactly the agencies of the community responsible for the judgment, have preferences as to the distribution of resources among members of the community as well as to the allocation of resources among the various wants of each member, and when, furthermore, these preferences can be ordered along a scale. In this case, the decisions of public services in any given situation can be derived by the rules of logic from the postulate of rationality. But the community seldom has such definite and ordered preferences. Because of this, the study of the operation of public services has to be based on the observations of institutional economics and economic history rather than on logical deductions from the postulate of rationality. However, there is a different way in which the postulate of rationality is useful in the study of public services. Instead of accepting it as an empirical hypothesis, we can consider conformity of public services with the postulate of rationality as a social objective. In other words: we can set up a chosen set of ordered preferences, i.e. some concept of public welfare, as our own (i.e. the student's) social objective and require that all public services be guided by this objective as a norm. This leads to rules of "ideal" use of resources and provides a basis for critical evaluation of the actual administration of resources by public services as well as by firms and households. The postulate of rationality becomes then the basis of a theory of welfare economics.

There is a difference between the rationality of households and firms and the rationality, whether (approximately) actual or normative (as in welfare economics) of public services. The first involves the pursuit of a private objective—utility or profit, respectively; the latter involves pursuit of a social objective, namely, public welfare. We can speak of *private* and *social rationality*, accordingly. Private rationality need not necessarily exclude social rationality. If the community's preferences as to allocation of resources among the various wants of each member coincide with the individual preferences of the members, then each member, by maximising his private utility, contributes to the attainment of maximum public welfare. Under certain conditions the maximisation of money profit by firms implies maximisation of public welfare too. In such cases, their own private rationality makes the members of the community act as if they were public services; private rationality then implies social rationality. The existence of such situations underlies the idea of the service economy. If all firms were always subject to these conditions, the capitalist economy could be considered as a special case of a service economy in which it is found expedient to delegate all production to private firms. This, indeed, is the famous doctrine of *laissez faire* which maintains that the capitalist economy, provided it is not hampered by government planning, spontaneously operates in such a way that it secures the maximum of public welfare. Accordingly, non-interference in the spontaneous operation of the capitalist economy is considered to be the best way of assuring the "ideal" use of resources. Most contemporary students of welfare economics consider this claim to be false and point out many conflicts between the private rationality of business enterprises and social rationality as postulated by welfare economics. The private rationality of business enterprises is also in conflict with the social objectives accepted by most citizens of modern democratic society. This accounts for the increasing tendency toward planning under contemporary capitalism and also for the socialist movements present in most capitalist countries.

A final observation has to be made about the procedure of verification of the postulate of rationality. There is some difference in procedure between firms, on the one hand, and households and public services on the other. Money profit is a quantity which can be observed empirically (like, for instance, velocity in physics). The theoretical concept of money profit, therefore, can be easily identified with corresponding empirical observations (the procedure of identification involves an interpretation of bookkeeping categories). Direct observation tells, then, whether firms do or do not maximise money profit. Utility and public welfare, instead, are purely theoretical constructs; there are no empirical observations which would serve as their counterparts (just like in the case of the concept of potential in physics). But this does not preclude verification by indirect devices. The uniformities of decision patterns are different when utility or public welfare, respectively, are maximised than when they are not. This difference in the uniformities mentioned makes it possible to verify empirically the hypothesis of rationality of acts of households and of public services.

VIII

EPILOGUE

The Limits of Science*

EUGENE P. WIGNER

THE PRESENT DISCUSSION is not put forward with the usual pride of the scientist who feels that he can make an addition, however small, to a problem which has aroused his and his colleague's interest. Rather, it is a speculation of a kind which all of us feel a great reluctance to undertake: much like the speculation on the ultimate fate of somebody who is very dear to us. It is a speculation on the future of science itself, whether it will share, at some very distant future, the fate of "Alles was entsteht ist wert dass es zu Grunde geht." Naturally, in such a speculation one wishes to assume the best of conditions for one's subject and disregard the danger of an accident that may befall it, however real that danger may be.

THE GROWTH OF SCIENCE

The most remarkable thing about Science is its youth. The earliest beginning of chemistry, as we now know it, certainly does not antedate Boyle's *Sceptical Chemist* which appeared in 1661. More probably, one would place the birthyear of chemistry around the years of activity of Lavoisier, between 1770 and 1790, or count its years from Dalton's law in 1808. Physics is somewhat older, Newton's *Principia*, a rather finished work, became available in 1687. Archimedes discovered laws of physics around 250 B.C. but his discoveries hardly can be called the real beginning of physics. On the whole one is probably safe in saying that Science is less than 300 years old. This number has to be compared with the age of Man, which is certainly greater than 100,000 years.

The number of people who devote years of their life to the acquisition of knowledge had an equally spectacular rise. Thus about ten per cent of the American youth are graduated from college, a percentage that has lately doubled in every twenty years. Harvard College was founded in 1636 and it was certainly not a scientific college at that time. The American Association for the Advancement of Science is one-hundred years old and had originally 461 members. Today, it has more than half a million and its membership increased by almost 10,000 in a single half year. The growth of col-

* Reprinted by kind permission of the author and the American Philosophical Society from *Proceedings of the American Philosophical Society*, 94, 1950.

lege attendance was less spectacular in some other countries, probably more spectacular in Russia.

Man's increased mastery of the Earth can be directly traced to his increased knowledge of the laws of nature. The surface of the Earth, as a whole, has not been affected by Man for 99,700 years but vast areas were deforested or the surface's store of some minerals depleted since the birth of Science. For 99,700 years, a man equipped with a good telescope on the moon might not have discovered Man's existence on the Earth. He could not have overlooked it during the last three-hundred years. There is no natural phenomenon that is comparable with the sudden and apparently accidentally timed development of science, except perhaps the condensation of a supersaturated gas or the explosion of some unpredictable explosives. Will the fate of science show some similarity to one of these phenomena?

Actually, if one views detachedly the rapid growth of science, and of the power of man, one cannot help fearing the second alternative. Surely man has not been able to adjust his spiritual outlook to the responsibility which his increased power imposed on him and one has to fear a catastrophe as a consequence of this maladjustment. This has come to be so well recognized recently, particularly as a result of the development of atomic weapons and the subsequent failure of man to cope, or even to come to grips, with the problems created by these weapons, that it is almost a commonplace. Nevertheless, this possibility will be disregarded here, and the limits of the growth of science will be considered under the assumption that no cataclysmic effect will interrupt this growth. The following speculations therefore apply only if we should be able to avoid the cataclysm which threatens us, and science can develop in a relatively peaceful atmosphere. They will look for the inherent limitations of science, rather than the limitations imposed by external effects, whether or not these external effects are influenced by science.

What Can We Call "Our Science"

What might be considered as the natural limit of our science will become perhaps best apparent if we try to define what "our science" is. It is our store of knowledge of natural phenomena. The question then is, what is "our" store? This question will be approached by giving both too broad and too narrow definitions and then attempting an acceptable compromise. A set of volumes, containing information and theories, certainly does not become our store of knowledge by our mere possession of it: the renaissance, or rather the preceding dark ages, teach us that physical possession is not enough. Is it then necessary that anybody know all the contents of those volumes before they can be called "our science"? This may be a defensible point of view but if it were accepted science would have reached its limits already, might have reached them quite some time ago. Is it then enough that there be, in our society, for every volume a person who is fully familiar with it? No, because there may be contradictions between the statements of the various volumes which would remain hidden if everyone knew only part of them. Science is an edifice, not a pile of bricks, valuable as such a pile may be.

I would say that a store of knowledge can reasonably be called "our science" if there are people who are competent to learn and use any part of it, who would like to know each part of it even if they realize that they cannot, and if one has good assurance that the parts are not contradictory but form a whole. The section on elasticity must use the same picture of the structure of iron on which the section on magnetism is based.

Limits of "Our Science"

If the above is accepted as a fair description of what may be called "our science" then its limitations are in the human intellect, in its capacity for interest and learning, in its memory and facilities for communication. All these are surely related to the finite span of the human life. In fact, if we accept the above, science is already changing not only by acquiring new territories, but partly also by shifting from older to new fields. We forget things and focus our attention on more recent developments. Right now, the older parts of science cease to be parts of our science not so much because we have no assurance that they fit into the new picture—I believe they do—but rather because nobody has a strong desire to know them, at least nobody who is interested in the new parts.

Surely, the possibilities of this type of growth are very far from being exhausted. Today, we are neglecting the theory of solids in which a student has to study perhaps six-hundred papers before he reaches the frontiers and can do research on his own; we concentrate instead on quantum electrodynamics in which he has to study six papers. Tomorrow, we may give up a whole science, such as chemistry, and concentrate on something that is less explored. These changes in interest are, furthermore, surely not arbitrary but in most cases well justified inasmuch as the new subject is deeper than the abandoned one, starts from more fundamental realizations, and embraces the old one. The properties of solids follow from the principles of quantum electrodynamics and this discipline is, in addition, able to deal with many phenomena besides those important for solids.

One should realize, nevertheless, that the embracing of the old subject by the new discipline is somewhat illusory. Thus the theory of solids is relinquished by the student of quantum electrodynamics in a very real sense because the human intellect is not powerful enough to derive the important properties of solids from quantum theory, unless it has made a particular, both experimental and theoretical, study to develop the idealizations and approximations which are useful for the description of solids. Only an unusual intellect could guess on the basis of the principles of ordinary quantum theory that there are solids and that they consist of regular lattice-like arrangements of the atoms. No human intellect could overlook, as a matter of course, the significance and role of the defects of these lattices. The equations of quantum theory may form the words of a magic oracle which describes the phenomena of crystal physics in a wonderfully condensed fashion. However, no human intellect can understand this oracle without using a commentary to its words, the length of this commentary being in the same proportion to the condensate of the oracle as is the whole Bible to Leviticus 19, 18. There is clearly a limit beyond which condensation, elevating though it may be as a purpose *per se*, is not useful any more for storing information. Present-day condensation in physics has certainly reached this limit.

Shift of the Second Type

The question now comes up whether science will at least be able to continue the type of shifting growth indefinitely in which the new discipline is deeper than the older one and embraces it at least virtually. The answer is, in my opinion, no, because the shifts in the above sense always involve digging one layer deeper into the "secrets of nature," and involve a longer series of concepts based on the previous ones which are thereby recognized as "mere approximations." Thus, in the example above, first ordinary mechanics had to be replaced by quantum mechanics, thus recognizing the approximate nature and limitation of ordinary mechanics to macroscopic phenomena. Then, ordinary mechanics had to be recognized to be inadequate from another point of view and replaced by field theories. Finally, the approximate nature and limitation to small velocities of all of the above concepts had to be uncovered. Thus, relativistic quantum theory is at least four layers deep; it operates with three successive types of concepts all of which are recognized to be inadequate and are replaced by a more profound one in the fourth step. This is, of course, the charm and beauty of the relativistic quantum theory and of all fundamental research in physics. However, it also shows the limits of this type of development. The recognizing of an inadequacy in the concepts of the tenth layer and the replacing of it with the more refined concepts of the eleventh layer will be much less of an event than the discovery of the theory of relativity was. It will, furthermore, require a much more elaborate and a much longer study to arrive at an understanding of the roots of the evil than was the study needed to appreciate the discrepancies which were eliminated by the theory of relativity. It is not difficult to imagine a stage in which the new student will not be interested any more, perhaps will not be able any more, to dig through the already accumulated layers in order to do research at the frontier. The number of physics graduate students will then drop and the shift of science to new territories will be more drastic than the shifts we are accustomed to: the new discipline in fashion will not embrace physics any more in the same way, as, for instance, quantum theory embraces classical physics. I will call this type of shift the shift of the second type.

The above picture assumes that, in order to understand a growing body of phenomena, it will be necessary to introduce deeper and deeper concepts into physics and that this development will not end by the discovery of the final and perfect concepts. I believe that this is true: we have no right to expect that our intellect can formulate perfect concepts for the full understanding of inanimate nature's phenomena. However, the second type of shift will occur also if we do, because science does not seem to be viable if no research is being done on its outskirts and the interest will soon flag in a completed subject. It is possible also that neither of the two alternatives will come to pass, that it will never be decided whether the concepts of the tenth layer are adequate "in principle" for the understanding of the inanimate world. Absence of interest and the weakness of the human intellect may easily combine to postpone indefinitely the determination of the full adequacy of the *n*th layer of concepts. In that case physics will be left by the wayside, in a somewhat similar fashion to the way in which the phenomena connected with superconductivity are apparently being left by the wayside, most physicists not feeling an acute sense of unhappiness about it.

The second type of shift will not be all resignation. In fact, many feel nowadays that the life sciences and the science of the minds of both animals and men have been already neglected too long. Our picture of the world would surely be more rounded if we knew more about the minds of men and animals, their customs and habits. The second type of shift may mean, however, the acknowledgment that we are unable to arrive at the full understanding of even the inanimate world, just as, a few centuries ago, man came to the conclusion that he has no very good chance to foresee what will happen to his soul after the death of his body. We all continue to feel a frustration because of our inability to foresee our soul's ultimate fate. Although we do not speak about it, we all know that the objectives of our science are, from a general human point of view, much more modest than the objectives of, say the Greek science, were; that our science is more successful in giving us power than in giving us knowledge of truly human interest. The development of the natural sciences was, however, not less vigorous because of the ensuing sense of frustration. Similarly, the vigor of work in the fields to which the second type shifts will lead, will not be smaller because we shall have abandoned the full realization of our dreams concerning an earlier field.

However, the second type of shift will mean some new resignation and also mark a turning point in the existence of science, taking science in the sense of our definition. When shifts of the second type will have occurred in relevant numbers, science will lose some of the attraction on the young mind which it now holds. It will be something altogether different, a bit less fascinating. The wonderful elation which we scientists now are experiencing, and which comes from the new feeling of the power of our intellect, will be somewhat dampened by the recognition of the limits of that power. We will have to acquiesce in the fact that our intellect's toil cannot give us a satisfactory picture of the world such as the Greeks dreamed to attain in an effortless way, by easy speculation.

Stabilizing Forces

Many of us will be inclined to make light of the preceding argument and say that science has a natural vitality by which it will overcome the limits which we, small minds of today, imagine to perceive in its path. There surely is much truth in this statement and we shall shortly turn to elements of elasticity in the whole picture which support it. However, I believe that the darker picture is the fundamentally correct one and that our instinctive desire not to believe it is the desire and ability of the human mind not to think of repugnant events in the future if their threat has no accurately foreseeable date. However, great changes, and often very unwanted changes, do take place and the elasticity of nature only delays them: buffaloes did die out as sources of food; the role of the individual warrior has vanished; the detailed explanation of the holy writings, once the only subject worthy of human studies, has ceased to be an element of our culture; Malthus' dire predictions are sure to come true at least in some respects. All the forecasts predicting these events were once resented by large groups just as we resent and resist the statement of the insufficiency of science.

Can we see even today signals of the crisis in science? Perhaps. The difficulty in penetrating to the frontiers of physics has been mentioned before. It is already so serious for the average human mind that only a negligible fraction of our contemporaries really feels the force of the arguments of quantum and relativity theories. Chemistry has grown so big that very very few people can keep an even loose acquaintance with all its ramifications. Shifts of the first type are going on in these sciences constantly, some of them being the butts of constant jokes.

The clearest sign of the growing realization that the capacity of our intellect limits the volume of science is the number of queries which we hear every day, whether this or that piece of research "is worth doing." In almost all such cases, the problem posed is interesting, the proposed method of attack shows elements of ingenuity, and the answer, whatever it may turn out to be, can be expected to be worth remembering. However, the questioner realizes how great is the number of problems of similar importance, how limited the time and memory of those to whom the results will be of interest. He wonders whether his proposed work would not remain submerged in the mass of literature, with nobody taking time and energy fully to understand and appreciate it. Hence the query. Similar doubts on the "worth" of some proposed research must have arisen at all times. It seems to me doubtful, however, that they ever were as deep as they are now, and concerned as intrinsically interesting problems. I believe I have observed an increase in the frequency of these queries and doubts even during my own short scientific life.

Recently, Mr. Fierz, in a very thoughtful article, has pointed to what may well become in time a shift of the second type. He pointed out that both physics and psychology claim to be all embracing disciplines: the first because it endeavors to describe all nature; the second because it deals with all mental phenomena, and nature exists for us only because we have cognizance of it. Fierz points out that the pictures of the world which these two disciplines project into us are not necessarily contradictory. However, it surely is difficult if not impossible to recognize the two pictures as only different aspects of the same thing. Furthermore, it is hardly an exaggeration to say that no psychologist understands the philosophy of modern physics. Conversely, only the exceptional physicist understands the language of the psychologist. Of course, psychology's philosophy is as yet too vague to draw definite conclusions. However, it is not impossible that we, or our students, are going to witness a real split of science right here.

It would be foolish to draw far-reaching conclusions from the emergence of two sciences, both of which may claim to be all embracing and between the concepts and statements of which one cannot, at present, see any real similarity. Both may yet be united into a deeper common discipline without overtaxing our mind's capacity for abstraction. Altogether, there are many favorable stabilizing effects which can delay the balkanization of science for very long periods. Some of these are methodological: as we understand discoveries more fully, we will be able to explain them better. It is certainly no accident that we have scores of excellent books on thermodynamics but had surely until recently nothing comparable in quantum theory. Relativity theory was understood, so it was claimed, twenty-five years ago only by two—today we teach its principles to undergraduates. Examples of improving teaching techniques by both minor simplifications and by spectacular "condensations" and generalizations are in fact too obvious to bear enumeration.

Another important stabilizing effect will be the reduction of the size of disciplines by elimination of parts of it. An example which must have struck everyone of my age is that the theory of ellyptic functions—a theory as spectacular in its methods and successes as any part of modern mathematics—is right now falling into oblivion. This is a shift of the first kind to which even the queen of sciences is not immune. As such it keeps mathematics more learnable.

Finally, it is not impossible that we'll breed during the coming centuries a human whose power of recollection, whose facility of abstraction, is greater than ours. Or at least that we make a greater and more aptly guided effort to select among the young those best suited for furthering science.

There is, on the other hand, a circumstance which will undoubtedly have an opposite effect. Thirst for knowledge, curiosity concerning the extent of one's mental faculties, and a healthy sense of rivalry, are strong stimulants of the young scientist and will continue to spur him along also in the future. They are, however, not his only motives: the desire to improve the lot of mankind, to extend its power, is also a traditional trait of scientists. These latter incentives are, however, waning, at least as far as the natural sciences are concerned, with the advent of man's full mastery of the element, with the increasing realization that the economic welfare of man is a question of organization rather than a problem of production. The effect of the loss of this incentive will certainly be present; its magnitude is unpredictable.

Co-operative Research

If science is expected to grow so great, both in the comprehensiveness of its subject and also in depth, that the human mind will not be able to embrace it, that the life span of man will not be long enough to penetrate to its fringes in time to enlarge it, could several people not form a team and accomplish jointly what no single person can accomplish. Instead of returning with Shaw to Methuselah, can we find a new way to enlarge the capacity of human intellect by the juxtaposition of several individual intellects rather than by extending a single one? This is a possibility which is so little explored that all that one may say about it must remain highly speculative—much more speculative, I believe, than the rest of this article. The possibilities of co-operative research have to be explored, however, to a much greater extent than they have been so far because they form the only visible hope for a new lease on life for science when it will have grown too large for a single individual.

Most of us scientists are too individualistic to take co-operative research too seriously. As the founder of relativity theory once remarked, he cannot imagine how relativity theory could have been conceived by a group. Indeed, if we think of the present-day research groups, working under a group leader who received his assignment through a section chief, the idea becomes amusingly absurd. Clearly, no fundamental change in our way of thinking can come about that way and no such fundamental change is intended by the groups referred to.

The case against group research can be stated more rationally on the basis of Poincaré's keen analysis of the nature of mathematical discovery. It is, I believe, our intuitive awareness of the facts which he and Hadamard have expressed so aptly which makes us smile at the idea of group research. Poincaré and Hadamard have recognized that, unlike most thinking which goes on in the upper consciousness, the really relevant mathematical thinking is not done in words. In fact, it happens somewhere so deep in the subconscious that the thinker is usually not even aware of what is going on inside of him.

It is my opinion that the role of subconscious thinking is equally important in other sciences, that it is decisive even in the solution of apparently trivial technical details. An experimentalist friend once told me (this was some twenty years ago) that if he could not find the leak in his vacuum system he usually felt like going for a walk, and very often, when he returned from the walk, he knew exactly where the leak was. The problem of group research is therefore, to give free rein to the inventiveness of the subconscious of the individual but, at the same time, have available for him the whole store of knowledge of the group.

It is certainly impossible to tell now whether and how this can be accomplished. It will surely need a much more intimate symbiosis between collaborators than has been established to date. Part, but only part, of this more intimate symbiosis will be a higher faculty for the communication of ideas and information than we have developed so far. If group research is to be fully effective, it will also need a much deeper understanding of the functioning of the human mind than we now have. However, neither of these is impossible; in fact we may be closer to both than we suspect.

Meanwhile, we should keep two facts in mind. The first is that the difficulty in the future development of science, which we have envisaged before, is based in the first place on the limited capacity of the human mind, not on its limited depth. Even if the depth, which is more intimately based on subconscious thinking, could not be increased, the first obstacle, the limitation of the capacity, might well be cut back by teamwork. Second, we should not forget that while it is true that relativity theory could not have been conceived by teamwork, the structure of the George Washington Bridge, and probably even that of the Hanford nuclear reactors, could not have been thought out by a single individual. The problem of group research is to avoid suppressing the subconscious thinking of the individual but to make available for him the information and to some degree even the unfinished ideas of his collaborators. Success of this may mean that the limitations of "our science" which were described above, are limitations only for individualist science.

It is depressing for every scientist and for every person to have to conclude that his principal motive, or that of his epoch, is not here to stay. However, humanity's goals and ideals have shifted already several times during our known history. In addition, it must fill us with pride to believe that we are living in the heroic age of science, in the epoch in which the individual's abstract knowledge of nature, and, we may hope, also of himself, is increasing more rapidly and perhaps to a higher level than it ever has before or will afterwards. It is unconformable to believe that our ideals may pass as the Round Table's illusions disappeared. Still, we live in the heroic age of these ideals.

Causality and the Science of Human Behavior*

ADOLF GRÜNBAUM

IT IS NOT uncommon to find that even those who have complete confidence in the continued success of the scientific method when applied to inanimate nature are highly skeptical of its applicability to the study of human behavior. Some go so far as to assert quite categorically that the methods of the natural sciences are in principle incompetent to yield predictions of man's individual or social behavior. Thus, for example, Dilthey and his followers in the *Geisteswissenschaften* movement [1] insist on the methodological autonomy of psychology and the social sciences, claiming that intelligent goal-seeking, which is so characteristic of man, calls for a method differing *toto genere* from that of the physical sciences.

Several important arguments have been offered against the hypothesis that cause-effect relationships exist in human behavior. These arguments are intended to deny the possibility of making the predictions which only the existence of such relationships would render feasible. In this article I shall attempt to show that the arguments in question are invalid and that there are good reasons for accepting the causal hypothesis against which they are directed. Many of the ideas to be discussed here have been previously outlined or developed by other authors in diverse contexts; wherever possible, references are given to these writings.

Before analyzing critically some of the reasons which have been given for supposing that human behavior is inherently unpredictable, I wish to point out several important consequences of this widely held belief, and also of its denial. It is essential to state explicitly what these consequences are, since few of the proponents of this doctrine realize all of its implications.

If human behavior, both individual and social, does not exhibit cause-

* Reprinted by kind permission of the author and the editor from *American Scientist*, 40, 1952.

[1] In the latter part of the nineteenth century, W. Dilthey spearheaded an influential movement whose representatives claimed that the theoretical task of the natural sciences is fundamentally different from that of the social sciences and humanities. The aim of the natural sciences was said to be generalization, whereas the social sciences were held to seek the articulation of individuality.

effect sequences, then the scientific method is essentially irrelevant to the elucidation of the nature of man, and both scientific psychology and the social sciences are permanently barred from achieving the status of sciences. This conclusion follows, since it is the essence of a scientific explanation in any field outside of pure mathematics to "explain" a past phenomenon or predict a future event by showing that these are instances of a certain law (or laws) and that their occurrence is attributable to the fact that the conditions for the applicability of the relevant law(s) were satisfied. Therefore, scientific or rational learning from past experience consists in ascertaining causal regularities from which to anticipate the future. Accordingly, to deny the existence of uniformities in human behavior, both individual and social, is to assert that significant lessons cannot be drawn from the past and that man's future is capricious and elusive. Nevertheless, some historians and social scientists tell us that the absence of causal law is the distinguishing feature of their subject as contrasted with the natural sciences. In the same breath, they maintain that the only way in which individuals and nations will become manageable is by a drastic intensification in the cultivation of the social studies. It is plain that this position is untenable. For nothing can be learned from history regarding the wise conduct of international relations, if no such wisdom is to be found in history. The distinction between wisdom and foolishness in practical affairs first becomes meaningful through the existence of cause-effect relationships in human behavior and by reference to the predictions which the existence of these relationships makes possible. Rules for managing individuals and nations can be based only on causal laws which tell us that *if* such and such is done, it is likely that the outcome will be thus and so, either in all cases or in an explicitly stated percentage of cases. It is useless to bemoan the great gap between our mastery of physical nature and our scientific understanding of man, if one denies the existence of the conditions which alone would make a scientific analysis of man possible. Only if human behavior does display some kind of causal law is it significant to emphasize the need for closing the dangerous gap between man's control over physical nature and his scientific knowledge of himself lest he destroy himself.

By contrast, the assumption that causal laws are discoverable in human behavior presents enormous possibilities. For in this case we can ask the social scientist to ascertain what means will bring about given ends. Thus it is possible to get a factually true rather than an emotional answer to some of the burning questions of our time. For example, we could hope for an authentic answer to the question, What system of organizing economic relationships will in fact lead to the maximum satisfaction of certain types of human needs? Whatever the answers to such questions, they would merit the assent of all rational men who share the same goals. To be sure, the history of physical science does record the defiance and acrimony evinced by men whose theories failed to be confirmed by the evidence.

Nevertheless, we have learned to reject physical theories which fail to pass the test of observable fact, no matter how ingenious the theory or how dear it may be to our hearts when first propounded. For this reason the history of physical science is in a sense the history of discarded theories. What an advance toward sanity it would be, if it were equally generally accepted that theories of human nature, like physical theories, need careful, disciplined checking through observation. In our time, the ordinary person is very much aware of the need for scrupulous care in ascertaining the facts of nature but will hold forth dogmatically and evangelically about the alleged facts of "human nature." Despite the serious divisions among mankind today, most scientific knowledge concerning inanimate nature commands assent among thinking men everywhere. It would seem, therefore, that scientific knowledge of man, specifying the requirements for attaining given ends, would also merit such universal assent. In so far as this assent would actually be forthcoming, it would constitute a partial step toward human brotherhood.

So much for the implications of rival answers to the issue under discussion. Let us now deal directly with the merits of the answers themselves.

Arguments against Causality in Human Behavior, and Their Refutation

There are four arguments which I wish to consider against the hypothesis that causality is present in human behavior. These are:

1. Human behavior is not amenable to causal description and therefore not predictable, since each individual is unique and not exactly like anyone else.
2. Even if there is a causal order in the phenomena of human behavior, it is so complex as to elude discovery permanently.
3. In the physical sciences, a present fact is always determined by past facts, but in human behavior present behavior is oriented toward future goals and thus "determined" by these future goals.
4. If human behavior were part of the causal order of events and thereby in principle predictable, it would be futile to attempt to make a choice between good and evil, meaningless to hold men responsible for their deeds, unjust to inflict punishment, and naive to take seriously such remorse or guilt as is professed for past misdeeds. In short, the argument is that to assume the principle of causality in human behavior is incompatible with the known fact that people respond meaningfully to moral imperatives.

In the following pages I shall try to show that all four of these arguments are the result of superficial or specious analysis. The fourth has been by far the most influential and was invoked in the pages of this journal a few years ago [5].

Argument from the Uniqueness of Human Individuals. This objection to the possibility of constructing a scientific psychology rests on several misunderstandings of the meaning of causality in science. To remove these misunderstandings it must be pointed out that *all* particulars in the world are unique, whether they are physical objects like trees, physical events like light flashes, or human beings. The mere assertion that a thing is a particular, means that it is in one way or another unique, different from all other objects of its own kind or of other kinds. Every insignificant tick of my watch is a unique event, for no two ticks can be simultaneous with a given third event. With respect to uniqueness, each tick is on a par with Lincoln's delivery of the Gettysburg address! It is clear, however, that the uniqueness of physical events does not prevent them from being connected by causal laws, for present causal laws relate only *some* of the features of a given set of events with *some* of the features of another set of events. For example, frictional processes are accompanied by the development of heat in so far as they are frictional, whatever else they may be. A projectile fired under suitable conditions will describe a parabolic orbit regardless of the color of the projectile, its place of manufacture, and so on. Since the cause-effect relation is a relation between *kinds* of events, it is never necessary that all the features of a given cause be duplicated in order to produce the same kind of effect. It follows that when scientific psychologists assume the existence of causal laws for human behavior, this standpoint is not incompatible with the existence of great individual differences among men, nor does it infringe on the uniqueness and dignity of each particular person.

Every individual is unique by virtue of being a distinctive assemblage of characteristics not precisely duplicated in any other individual. Nevertheless, it is quite conceivable that the following psychological law *might* hold: If a male child having specifiable characteristics is subjected to maternal hostility and has a strong paternal attachment at a certain stage of his development, he will develop paranoia during adult life. If this law holds, then children who are subjected to the stipulated conditions would in fact become paranoiacs, however much they may have differed in other respects in childhood and whatever their other differences may be once they are already insane.

A variant of the argument against scientific psychology is that no psychologist can ever feel exactly like each of the diverse people whose feelings and behavior he is trying to understand. This form of the argument contains an additional misconception of the kind of understanding or explanation that is sought by science—the impression that in order to explain aspects of human experience or behavior scientifically, the psychologist must himself directly have the experience in question in all its complexity. One who objects to scientific psychology on these grounds virtually equates scientific understanding with genuinely empathic understanding. To understand a phenomenon scientifically, however, is, in the first place, to know the conditions necessary for its occurrence. A physician interested in understanding cancer (including the psychic consequences of that disease) is not interested in becoming a cancer victim himself but only in knowing the conditions associated with the occurrence and non-occurrence of cancer. Strictly empathic understanding may have great heuristic value and sometimes aesthetic value as well. However, from the standpoint of achieving scientific understanding and making the predictions which such mastery makes possible, the empathic method in psychology and in history (Dilthey) is quite insufficient.

The Argument from the Complexity of Human Behavior. This argument, it will be recalled, is to the effect that human behavior involves so complex a proliferation of factors that it is futile to attempt to unravel them. A glance at the history of science will deprive this point of view of such plausibility as it may possess. Consider what a person advancing such an argument about psychology today would have said about the physics of motion before the time of Galileo. Probably he would have said that it is hopeless to attempt to reduce the vast diversity of terrestrial and celestial motions to a few simple laws of motion. Before the rise of scientific chemistry, this kind of person would have dismissed the possibility of reducing the seemingly unsurveyable variety of substances in nature to some 96 elements. This argument rests its case on what is not known, and therefore, like all such arguments, it has no case.

The Argument from the "Determination" of the Present by the Future in Goal-seeking Human Behavior. If a person is now taking action toward the realization of a future goal, it is argued that the immediate action is the effect of a future cause—a kind of causation not encountered among physical phenomena. The answer to this contention is that, not the future goal-event, but rather the present expectation of its realization causally controls forward-looking behavior. Indeed, the goal sought may never be attained. Moreover, both the motives for achieving the given goal and the contemplation of action in its behalf function as antecedent conditions in the same way as the causal factors in physical phenomena. Thus in motivational situations causal determination is quite unaffected by the ideational reference of motives to the future [3, 4].

The Argument from Moral Choice. The name "determinism" is applied to the thesis that all phenomena, including those of human behavior, fall into causal patterns. This formulation of determinism is logically objectionable in some respects, but it will suffice for this discussion. It is clear that determinism is one of the key (regulative) principles of all scientific research. The denial of determinism is called "indeterminism," and the indeterminist argument from moral choice to be considered here has been summarized by a critic somewhat as follows [8]: If determinism is true, then my will also is always determined by my character and my motives. Hence I do not make free choices and should not be held responsible for my acts, since I can do nothing about my decisions and cannot help doing what I do. If the determinist is right, I have not chosen either my motives or my character; my motives come to me from both external and internal causes and my character is the necessary product of the influences which have been effective during my lifetime. Thus determinism and moral responsibility are incompatible. Moral responsibility presupposes freedom, that is, exemption from causality.

The question before us is whether the argument of the indeterminist is valid. Before arguing that the answer to this question is emphatically in the negative, I wish to distinguish between two types of determinism and attempt to show that they must each be objectionable to the indeterminist, once he has set forth his argument from moral choice.

The first type of determinism is the 100 per cent type, which maintains that under specifiable conditions a specifiable outcome will occur in all cases. For example, whenever a metal is heated (under ordinary conditions) it will expand. The second type of determinism is the statistical type, which maintains (roughly) that under specifiable conditions a certain result will occur but only in an explicitly stated percentage of cases. An instance of this is the statement that of all the people born in slums, 80 per cent will commit a crime at some time during their lifetime. The claim which I wish to make first is that if the moral argument of the indeterminist were valid against the 100 per cent type of determinism, it would also have relevance against the statistical type of determinism. This point is particularly important, since many indeterminists attempt to acknowledge the incontestable existence of an impressive measure of regularity in human behavior by emphasizing that they object on moral grounds only to the 100 per cent type of determinism and not to the statistical type.

To establish my case, let us suppose that, contrary to fact, we knew that all hunters are subject to the following 100 per cent deterministic law: All hunters commit homicide at some time after returning from jungle life. The indeterminist would say that if these hunters were really subject to such a causal law, they could not help becoming murderers and therefore we should have no right to punish them for their crimes. What would the position taken by the indeterminist have to be if we had a statistical type of law stating with near certainty that, of all the people born in slums, in the long run 80 per cent will commit a crime at some time during their lifetime? To be sure, this statistical law would not entitle us to say that any particular individual(s) born in the slums will become criminal; hence, it does not preclude the possibility that some particular person (or persons) be among the 20 per cent whose conduct is legal and that, to this extent, the person in question be regarded as having acted "freely" in the indeterminist sense. In so far as responsibility is an individual matter, it might even seem that our statistical law would permit the indeterminist to employ his own criteria for assigning individual responsibility to as many as 20 per cent of those persons originating in the slums. But if the 80 per cent who actually did commit a crime at some time during a long interval of time were simultaneously brought to trial before a judge holding the indeterminist point of view, the statistical law in question would deny him the logical right of making individual assignments of responsibility; this law would not enable the judge to designate among the culprits any one or any group of whom it could meaningfully be said that they "could" have avoided the crime by being among the 20 per cent who did, in fact, avoid it. For if a procedure for carrying out such a designation were possible—which it is not—the statistical law would remind us that not only all the remaining defendants arraigned before the judge but also some of those actually belonging to the 20 per cent *could then not have helped* violating the statutes. This means that if over a long period of time we select all those having originated in a slum and not guilty of any crime, the remainder having a similar origin will *always* as a matter of fact commit a crime and will constitute 80 per cent of those born in slums. Thus by the indeterminist's own criteria for assigning responsibility, the judge would not be able to carry out such an assignment individually as he must, because sufficient causality is assured by the statistical law to preclude his doing so consistently with indeterminist premises. If the indeterminist denies the justice of punishment, as he does in the case of 100 per cent determinism, he cannot assent to the punishment of individuals belonging to groups concerning which statistical laws make only a statistical prediction of conduct. Accordingly, the indeterminist must have moral objections to 100 per cent determinism and statistical determinism alike. This means that he must be a foe of the belief that any kind of scientific study of man is possible!

To establish the invalidity of the moral argument offered by the indeterminist, I shall now try to show that there is no incompatibility between the deterministic assumptions of scientific psychology on the one hand and the meaningful assignment of responsibility, the infliction of punishment, and the existence of feelings of remorse or guilt on the other.

Causality and Moral Responsibility

The first point to be made clear is that determinism should never be identified with the prescientific and primitive doctrine of fatalism. The fatalist says that regardless of what we do, the outcome will be the same. By contrast, the determinist says that *if* we do such and such, *then* the effect will be thus and so. The fatalist thinks that if you go into combat, and if "some bullet has your name on it," you will be killed no matter what you do. Thus he would say that when a natural disaster occurs, it does not matter whether you are at the scene of the disaster or not; if you are not there but are "destined to die" that day, you will be destroyed some other way. The determinist maintains that a person will die on a certain day only if the conditions which lead to death materialize for that person on that day, as indeed they do at some time for each of us. Unlike fatalism, determinism allows causal efficacy to human actions.

The second point to keep in mind is that physical laws do not in any sense force bodies to behave in a certain way, but merely describe how, as a matter of fact, they do behave. Similarly, psychological laws do not force us to do or desire anything against our will. These laws merely state what, as a matter of fact, we do or desire under certain conditions. Thus if there were a psychological law enabling us to predict that under certain conditions a man will desire to commit a certain act, this law would not be making him act in a manner contrary to his own desires, for the desire would be his. It follows that neither the causes of our desires nor psychological laws, which state under what conditions our desires arise, compel us in any way to act in a manner contrary to our own will.

An illustration will show that district attorneys are determinists, since they assume in their work a definite causal connection between motives and acts. In a recent French film we find a district attorney married to a rather unsophisticated lady whom he had been suspecting of violating her marital vows. While speaking to her, he found a seemingly innocent way of mentioning the name of his rival. She promptly gulped, and then tried to maintain with studied innocence that she had had no motive at all for gulping. He insisted that she had had a very definite motive, and as it turned out he was right.

It should not be thought that the indeterminist is now prepared to surrender, for he has yet to use his strongest weapon. Says he: "We are all familiar with the fact that when we look back upon past conduct, we frequently feel very strongly that we could have done otherwise. If the determinist is right in saying that our behavior was unavoidably determined by earlier causes, this retrospective feeling of freedom either should not exist or else it is fraudulent. In either case, the burden of proof rests upon him." The determinist gladly accepts this challenge, and his reply is as follows: Let us carefully examine the content of the feeling that on a certain occasion we could have acted other than the way we did, in fact, act. What do we find? Does the feeling we have inform us that we could have acted otherwise *under exactly the same external and internal motivational conditions?* No, says the determinist, this feeling simply discloses that we were able to act in accord with our strongest desire at that time, and that we could indeed have acted otherwise if a different motive had prevailed at the time. Thus the determinist answer is that the content of this "consciousness of freedom" consists in our awareness that we were able to act in response to our strongest motive at the time,[2] and that we were not "under compulsion" in that sense. But the determinist reminds us that our feeling of "freedom" does not disclose that, given the motives which acted on us at the time and given their relative strength and distribution, we could have acted differently from the way in which we did, in fact, act. Neither do we feel that we could have responded to the weaker

[2] The claim that we act in response to our strongest conscious or unconscious motive is not a covert tautology. Cf. [8], Ch. II.

of two contending motives, or acted without a cause or motive, or chosen the motives which acted upon us. Since the retrospective feeling of freedom that we have does not report any of these results, its deliverances contain no facts incompatible with the claim of the determinist [8, 11, 7, 4].

The analysis we have offered is applicable at once to the case of remorse, regret, or guilt. We sometimes experience remorse over past conduct when we reconsider that conduct in the light of *different* motives. Once we bring a different set of motives to bear on a given situation, we may feel that a different decision is called for. If our motives do not change, we do not regret a past deed no matter how reprehensible it would otherwise appear. Regret is an expression of our emotion toward the disvalue and injustice which issued from our past conduct, as seen in the light of the new motives. The regret we experience can then act as a deterrent against the repetition of past behavior which issued in disvalue. If the determinist expresses regret concerning past misconduct, he is applying motives of self-improvement to himself but not indulging in retroactive self-castigation or blame. Retroactive blame is futile, since the past will never return again. Thus, by responsibility the determinist does not mean retroactive blameworthiness, but rather liability to reformative or educative punishment. Punishment is educative in the sense that when properly administered it institutes counter-causes to the repetition of injurious conduct. The determinist rejects as barbarous the primitive vengeful idea of retaliatory punishment. He fails to see how the damage done by the wrongdoer is remedied by the mere infliction of pain or sorrow on the culprit, unless such infliction of pain promises to act as a *causal* deterrent against the repetition of evil conduct. We recall that the indeterminist accused the determinist of cruelly punishing people who, if determinism is true, cannot help acting as they do. The determinist now turns the tables on his antagonist and accuses him of being gratuitously vengeful, on the grounds that the indeterminist is committed by his own theory to a retaliatory theory of punishment. The indeterminist cannot consistently expect to achieve anything better than retaliation by inflicting punishment; for were he to admit that punishment will causally influence all or some of the criminals, then he would be abandoning the basis of his entire argument against the determinist. We see that determinism does not entail the doctrine *tout comprendre, c'est tout pardonner.*

What does the determinist believe about the application of punishment? From his point of view, punishment should be administered to the person upon whom the decisive motive acted, for that person is the essential junction of causes, and it is he who is likely to cause harm again if unpunished. Thus the doctrine of the determinist does not commit him to punishing the parents or social environment of the culprit for the culprit's deeds, even though they are the basic cause of his misconduct. Such a procedure would be of no avail if the aim is to rehabilitate the wrongdoer. There are two types of cases, however, in which the determinist does not apply punishment. When a person is acting under compulsion, he is being prevented from implementing his own desires. In that event, his internal state is irrelevant to what he does. Since his internal state needs no reforming, punishment would be completely misplaced in such a case. Again, in the case of insane behavior the determinist does not apply punishment, since insane people provide no unified point for the application of a counter-motive. More specifically, their internal state is not responsive to the external influences of punishment, and therefore the infliction of punishment upon them cannot be counted on to change their future behavior in the desired direction. Once Ophelia had lost her mind, even Hamlet's words could have no effect on her, and similarly for Marguerite and Faust.

It is apparent that the entire problem of responsibility can be solved within the domain of deterministic assumptions. Thus the issue is not *whether* conduct is determined but rather *by what factors* it is determined, when responsibility is to be assigned [2]. Far from facing insuperable difficulties with the problem of responsibility, the determinist and the scientific psychologist now challenge the indeterminist to provide a logical foundation for the penal system.

Other Arguments of the Indeterminist

It is sometimes said that, when applied to man, the deterministic doctrine becomes untenable by virtue of becoming self-contradictory. This contention is often stated as follows: "The determinist, by his own doctrine, must admit that his very acceptance of determinism was causally conditioned or determined. Since he could not help accepting it, he cannot argue that he has chosen a true doctrine." To justify this claim, it is first pointed out rightly that determinism implies a causal determination of its own acceptance by its defenders. Then it is further maintained, however, that since the determinist could not, by his own theory, help accepting determinism, he can have no confidence in its truth. Thus it is asserted that the determinist's acceptance of his own doctrine was forced upon him. I submit that this inference involves a radical fallacy. The proponent of this argument is gratuitously invoking the view that if our beliefs have causes, these causes *force* the beliefs in question upon us, against our better judgment, as it were. Nothing could be further from the truth. My belief that I am now looking at symbols on paper derives from the fact that their presence is causally inducing certain images on the retinas of my eyes, and that these images, in turn, cause me to infer that corresponding symbols are actually present before me. The reason why I do not suppose that I am now addressing a group of students in a classroom is that the images which the students would produce are not now in my visual field. The causal generation of a belief in no way detracts from its reliability. In fact, if a given belief were not produced in us by definite causes, we should have no reason to accept that belief as a correct description of the world, rather than some other belief arbitrarily selected. Far from making knowledge either adventitious or impossible, the deterministic theory about the origin of our beliefs alone provides the basis for thinking that our judgments of the world are or may be true. Knowing and judging are indeed causal processes in which the facts we judge are determining elements along with the cerebral mechanism employed in their interpretation. It follows that although the determinist's assent to his own doctrine is caused or determined, the truth of determinism is not jeopardized by this fact; if anything, it is made credible.

We have yet to consider the bearing of developments in atomic physics on this problem, since a number of writers have argued that these developments provide evidence for the indeterminist position.

It is known that for measurements in the domain of subatomic dimensions, the Heisenberg Uncertainty Relation comes into play. This relation states that for a given uncertainty or vagueness in the value of an observable quantity like position, there is a definite limit, imposed by the laws of nature, on the accuracy with which the simultaneous value of another empirical quantity like velocity can be known, and that this limit is independent of the particular apparatus or method used in the determination. Since the apparatus used in measurement disturbs the system under observation, it would seem that the possibilities for refining measurements are not unlimited and that the dream of classical physics can therefore never come true. No refinement of experimental technique could ascertain the present values of the observables of a physical system accurately enough to enable us to make a *precise* prediction of the future values. Consequently, the new quantum mechanics is content to specify the frequencies or probabilities with which different values will be found in a given set of measurements. These probability predictions are thus based on a statistico-determinism for the micro-processes of subatomic physics rather than upon the 100 per cent type of determinism which prevails in the physics of the macrocosm.

What are the implications of this situation for the controversy between the philosophical indeterminist and the scientific psychologist? In his *Atomic Theory and the Description of Nature*, Bohr gives several reasons for supposing that the most precise experimentally ascertainable knowledge of the momentary state of the constituent particles of the nervous system and of the external stimuli affecting it permits only a statistical prediction and not a completely detailed prediction of the fate of these stimuli in the nervous system. Nevertheless, there are important reasons why the philosophical indeterminist can derive no comfort from this situation. It has already been shown that if the moral argument for indeterminism is to be valid, statistico-determinism is objectionable along with 100 per cent determinism. For genuine free will would prevail only if the quantum theory were to conclude that all human acts (macrophenomena) can occur with the same frequency. But the theory does not make this assertion at all. The microscopic probabilities yielded by the theory are such that the acts which a macroscopic psychology would predict are overwhelmingly likely to occur. From the standpoint of the macrophenomena of human conduct, a 100 per cent type of determinism holds, to all intents and purposes. As Cassirer has stated, the extent of the determination of human behavior is so great that the free will of the philosophical indeterminist can find no refuge in it [1]. Schrödinger has aptly summarized these conclusions in the following words: "According to the evidence . . . the space-time events in the body of a living being which correspond to the activity of its mind, to its self-conscious or any other actions, are (considering also their complex structure and the accepted statistical explanation of physico-chemistry) if not strictly deterministic at any rate statistico-deterministic. To the physicist I wish to emphasize that in my opinion, and contrary to the opinion upheld in some quarters, *quantum indeterminacy* plays no biologically relevant role in them, except perhaps . . . in such events as meiosis, natural and X-ray-induced mutation and so on . . . let me regard this as a fact, as I believe every unbiased biologist would, if there were not the well-known, unpleasant feeling about 'declaring oneself to be a pure mechanism' " [9].

Conclusion

In this paper an attempt has been made to show that the arguments advanced against the possibility of a scientific study of man are without foundation. Of course, the truth of either strict determinism or statistico-determinism has not been established conclusively; for this cannot be done by logical analysis alone, but requires actual success in the scientific search for uniformities. Since the important arguments against determinism which we have considered are without foundation, the psychologist need not be deterred in his quest and can confidently use the causal hypothesis as a regulative principle, undaunted by the *caveat* of the philosophical indeterminist.

REFERENCES

1. Cassirer, E. Determinismus und Indeterminismus in der modernen Physik. Elanders Boktryckeri Aktiebolag, Göteborg, 1937.
2. Frank, P. Das Kausalgesetz und seine Grenzen. Springer, Vienna, 1932.
3. Hempel, C. G., and Oppenheim, P. Studies in the logic of explanation. *Philosophy of Science*, *15*, 135, 1948. [Reprinted in this volume.]
4. Jeans, J. Physics and philosophy. Cambridge University Press, 1945.
5. Petrunkevitch, A. *Am. Scientist*, *33*, 189, 1945.
6. Planck, M. Vorträge und Erinnerungen. Hirzel, Stuttgart, 1949.
7. Russell, B. Our knowledge of the external world. Allen and Unwin, London, 1914. Chap. 8. [Reprinted, in part, in this volume.]
8. Schlick, M. Problems of ethics. Prentice-Hall, New York, 1939.

9. SCHRÖDINGER, E. What is life? Macmillan, New York, 1945.
10. SCHRÖDINGER, E. Science and humanism. Cambridge University Press, 1951. Pp. 58–64.
11. UNIVERSITY OF CALIFORNIA ASSOCIATES. The freedom of the will. *In:* Readings in philosophical analysis, ed. by FEIGL, H., and SELLARS, W. Appleton–Century–Crofts, New York, 1949. Pp. 594–615.
12. WEYL, H. Philosophy of mathematics and natural science. Princeton University Press, 1949. Appendix C: Quantum physics and causality.

The Laws of Science and the Laws of Ethics*

ALBERT EINSTEIN

SCIENCE SEARCHES FOR relations which are thought to exist independently of the searching individual. This includes the case where man himself is the subject; or the subject of scientific statements may be concepts created by ourselves, as in mathematics. Such concepts are not necessarily supposed to correspond to any objects in the outside world. However, all scientific statements and laws have one characteristic in common: they are "true" or "false" (adequate or inadequate). Roughly speaking, our reaction to them is "yes" or "no."

The scientific way of thinking has a further characteristic. The concepts which it uses to build up its coherent systems do not express emotions. For the scientist, there is only "being," but no wishing, no valuing, no good, no evil — in short, no goal. As long as we remain within the realm of science proper, we can never encounter a sentence of the type: "Thou shalt not lie." There is something like a Puritan's restraint in the scientist who seeks truth: he keeps away from everything voluntaristic or emotional. Incidentally, this trait is the result of a slow development, peculiar to modern Western thought.

From this it might seem as if logical thinking were irrelevant for ethics. Scientific statements of facts and relations, indeed, cannot produce ethical directives. However, ethical directives can be made rational and coherent by logical thinking and empirical knowledge. If we can agree on some fundamental ethical propositions, then other ethical propositions can be derived from them, provided that the original premises are stated with sufficient precision. Such ethical premises play a similar role in ethics to that played by axioms in mathematics.

This is why we do not feel at all that it is meaningless to ask such questions as: "Why should we not lie?" We feel that such questions are meaningful because in all discussions of this kind some ethical premises are tacitly taken for granted. We then feel satisfied when we succeed in tracing back the ethical directive in question to these basic premises. In the case of lying,

* Reprinted by kind permission of the author and the publisher from *Relativity—A Richer Truth*, foreword, The Beacon Press, 1950.

this might perhaps be done in some way such as this: Lying destroys confidence in the statements of other people. Without such confidence, social co-operation is made impossible or at least difficult. Such co-operation, however is essential in order to make human life possible and tolerable. This means that the rule "Thou shalt not lie" has been traced back to the demands: "Human life shall be preserved" and "Pain and sorrow shall be lessened as much as possible."

But what is the origin of such ethical axioms? Are they arbitrary? Are they based on mere authority? Do they stem from experiences of men and are they conditioned indirectly by such experiences?

For pure logic all axioms are arbitrary, including the axioms of ethics. But they are by no means arbitrary from a psychological and genetic point of view. They are derived from our inborn tendencies to avoid pain and annihilation, and from the accumulated emotional reaction of individuals to the behavior of their neighbors.

It is the privilege of man's moral genius, expressed by inspired individuals, to advance ethical axioms which are so comprehensive and so well founded that men will accept them as grounded in the vast mass of their individual emotional experiences. Ethical axioms are found and tested not very differently from the axioms of science. *Die Wahrheit liegt in der Bewährung.* Truth is what stands the test of experience.

SELECTED BIBLIOGRAPHY

SELECTED BIBLIOGRAPHY

The following abbreviations for names of periodicals are used in the list below:

Amer. Math. Mo. for *American Mathematical Monthly*
Arist. Proc. for *Proceedings of the Aristotelian Society*
Arist. Suppl. for *Aristotelian Society, Supplementary Volume*
British Jl. for Phil. of Sci. for *British Journal for Philosophy of Science*
Erk. for *Erkenntnis*
Jl. of Phil. for *The Journal of Philosophy*
Jl. of Symb. Log. for *Journal of Symbolic Logic*
Phil. and Phen. Res. for *Philosophy and Phenomenological Research*
Phil. Rev. for *The Philosophical Review*
Phil. of Sci. for *Philosophy of Science*
Philos. Studies for *Philosophical Studies*
Psych. Rev. for *The Psychological Review*
Sci. Mon. for *The Scientific Monthly*

General Works in the Philosophy of Science

Books

Bavink, B., *The Natural Sciences*, Century, New York, 1932.
Benjamin, A. C., *The Logical Structure of Science*, Kegan Paul, London, 1936.
———, *An Introduction to the Philosophy of Science*, Macmillan, New York, 1937.
Cassirer, E., *Substance and Function and Einstein's Theory of Relativity*, Open Court, Chicago, 1923.
———, *The Problem of Knowledge*, transl. by W. H. Woglom and C. W. Hendel, Yale Univ. Press, 1950.
Churchman, C. W., *Theory of Experimental Inference*, Macmillan, New York, 1948.
———, and Ackoff, R., *Methods of Inquiry*, Educational Publishers, Inc., St. Louis, 1950.
Cohen, M. R., *Reason and Nature*, Harcourt, New York, 1931.
Dingle, H., *Science and Human Experience*, Macmillan, New York, 1932.
———, *Through Science to Philosophy*, Clarendon Press, Oxford, 1937.
———, *The Scientific Adventure*, Philosophical Library, New York, 1953.
Enriques, F., *Problems of Science*, Open Court, Chicago, 1914.
Feigl, H., and Sellars, W., *Readings in Philosophical Analysis*, Appleton-Century-Crofts, New York, 1949.
Frank, P., *Modern Science and Its Philosophy*, Harvard Univ. Press, 1949.
Jörgenson, J., *The Development of Logical Empiricism*, Vol. II, No. 9 of the *International Encyclopedia of Unified Science*, Univ. of Chicago Press, 1951.
Mach, E., *Erkenntnis und Irrtum: Skizzen zur Psychologie der Forschung*, Barth, Leipzig, 1905.

MACH, E., *Popular Scientific Lectures*, Open Court, Chicago, 1898.

MISES, R. VON, *Positivism: A Study in Human Understanding*, Harvard Univ. Press, 1951.

MORRIS, C. E., *Foundations of the Theory of Signs*, Vol. I, No. 2 of the *International Encyclopedia of Unified Science*, Univ. of Chicago Press, 1938.

NORTHROP, F. S. C., *The Logic of the Science and the Humanities*, Macmillan, New York, 1947.

PAP, A., *Elements of Analytic Philosophy*, Macmillan, New York, 1949.

PEARSON, K., *Grammar of Science*, Dent, London, 1937.

PEIRCE, C. S., *Collected Papers*, ed. by Charles Hartshorne and Paul Weiss, Harvard Univ. Press, 1931 ff.

PLANCK, M., *Where Is Science Going?* Norton, New York, 1932.

POINCARÉ, H., *The Foundations of Science*, Science Press, New York, 1929.

POLANYI, M., *Science, Faith and Society*, Oxford Univ. Press, 1946.

POPPER, K. R., *Logik der Forschung*, Springer, Vienna, 1935.

RAMSPERGER, A. G., *Philosophies of Science*, Crofts, New York, 1942.

REICHENBACH, H., *The Rise of Scientific Philosophy*, Univ. of California Press, 1951.

RUSSELL, B., *Mysticism and Logic*, Norton, New York, 1929.

———, *Our Knowledge of the External World*, 2nd ed., Norton, New York, 1929.

———, *The Scientific Outlook*, Norton, New York, 1931.

SCHLICK, M., *Philosophy of Nature*, Philosophical Library, New York, 1949.

SCHRÖDINGER, E., *Science and the Human Temperament*, Norton, New York, 1935.

———, *Science and Humanism*, Cambridge Univ. Press, 1952.

TOULMIN, S. E., *Philosophy of Science*, Hutchinson, London, 1953.

WERKMEISTER, W. H., *A Philosophy of Science*, Harper, New York, 1940.

———, *The Basis and Structure of Knowledge*, Harper, New York, 1948.

WEYL, H., *Philosophy of Mathematics and Natural Science*, Princeton Univ. Press, 1949.

WHITEHEAD, A. N., *An Enquiry Concerning the Principles of Natural Knowledge*, Cambridge Univ. Press, 1919.

———, *The Concept of Nature*, Cambridge Univ. Press, 1920.

WHITTAKER, E., *From Euclid to Eddington*, Cambridge Univ. Press, 1949.

ZILSEL, E., *Problems of Empiricism*, Vol. II, No. 8 of the *International Encyclopedia of Unified Science*, Univ. of Chicago Press, 1941.

Articles

BENJAMIN, A. C., "On Defining 'Science'," *Sci. Mon.*, Vol. LXVIII, No. 3, March, 1949, pp. 192–198.

CARNAP, R., "Die Aufgabe der Wissenschaftslogik" (*Einheitswiss.*) Vienna, 1934. French transl.: "Le Problème de la Logique de Science", Paris, 1935.

———, "Von der Erkenntnistheorie zur Wissenschaftslogik", Actes du Congrès Internationale de Philosophie Scientifique, Paris, 1936.

COHEN, M. R., "Method, Scientific", *Encyclopedia of the Social Sciences*, Macmillan, New York, 1932.

FEIGL, H., "De principiis non disputandum? On the Meaning and the Limits of Justification", in M. Black, ed., *Philosophical Analysis*, Cornell Univ. Press, 1950.

———, "Logical Empiricism", in D. D. Runes, ed., *Twentieth Century Philosophy*, Philosophical Library, New York, 1943. Also reprinted in Feigl and Sellars, *Readings*.

FRANK, P., "Introduction to the Philosophy of Physical Science on the Basis of

Logical Empiricism", *Synthese*, Vol. VIII, Nos. 1 and 2, 1950–51, pp. 28–45.
LENZEN, V. F., "Helmholtz's Theory of Knowledge", *Studies and Essays in the History of Science and Learning in Honor of George Sarton*, 1946, pp. 301–319.
———, "Regulative Principles in Physical Science", *Univ. of Calif. Pub. in Phil.*, Vol. VII.
NAGEL, E., "Malicious Philosophies of Science", *Partisan Review*, Jan.–Feb., 1943.
———, "Russell's Philosophy of Science", in P. A. Schilpp, ed., *The Philosophy of Bertrand Russell*, Northwestern Univ. Press, 1944, pp. 317–349.
REICHENBACH, H., "Dewey's Theory of Science", in P. A. Schilpp, ed., *The Philosophy of John Dewey*, Northwestern Univ. Press, 1939, pp. 159–192.
———, "Logistic Empiricism in Germany and the Present State of Its Problems", *Jl. of Phil.*, 33, 1936, pp. 141–160.
———, "Rationalism and Empiricism", in *Phil. Rev.*, 57, 1948.

I. THE NATURE OF SCIENTIFIC METHOD

Books

BOLL, M., *Elements de logique scientifique*, Dunod, Paris, 1942.
BRIDGMAN, P. W., *Dimensional Analysis*, rev. ed., Yale Univ. Press, 1931.
———, *The Nature of Some of Our Physical Concepts*, Philosophical Library, New York, 1952.
———, *The Logic of Modern Physics*, Macmillan, New York, 1927.
———, *Reflections of a Physicist*, Philosophical Library, New York, 1950.
CAMPBELL, N. R., *An Account of the Principles of Measurement and Calculation*, Longmans, New York, 1928.
———, *What Is Science?* Methuen, London, 1921.
CARNAP, R., *Physikalische Begriffsbildung*, Braun, Karlsruhe, 1926.
———, *The Unity of Science*, Kegan Paul, London, 1938.
COHEN, M. R., *Studies in Philosophy and Science*, Holt, New York, 1949.
———, and NAGEL, E., *An Introduction to Logic and Scientific Method*, Harcourt, New York, 1934.
Contributions to the Analysis and Synthesis of Knowledge, Vol. 80, July, 1951, issue of the *Proc. Am. Acad. of Arts and Sciences.*
DEWEY, J., *Logic, the Theory of Inquiry*, Holt, New York, 1939.
DINGLER, H., *Das Experiment*, Reinhardt, München, 1928.
EATON, R. M., *General Logic*, Scribner, New York, 1931.
FRANK, P., *Foundations of Physics*, Vol. I, No. 7 of the *International Encyclopedia of Unified Science*, Univ. of Chicago Press, 1946.
HELMHOLTZ, H. VON, *On Counting and Measuring*, Van Nostrand, New York, 1930.
HEMPEL, C. G., *Fundamentals of Concept Formation in the Empirical Sciences*, Vol. II, No. 7 of the *International Encyclopedia of Unified Science*, Univ. of Chicago Press, 1952.
———, and OPPENHEIM, P., *Der Typusbegriff im Lichte der Neuen Logik*, Sijthoff, Leiden, 1936.
JEFFREYS, H., *Scientific Inference*, Cambridge Univ. Press, 1931.
JEVONS, W. S., *The Principles of Science*, Macmillan, New York, 1900.
LENZEN, V. F., *Procedures of Empirical Science*, Vol. I, No. 5 of the *International Encyclopedia of Unified Science*, Univ. of Chicago Press, 1938.
———, *The Nature of Physical Theory*, Wiley, New York, 1931.
LINDSAY, R. B., and MARGENAU, H., *Foundations of Physics*, Wiley, New York, 1936.

MACE, C. E., *The Principles of Logic,* Longmans, London, 1933.

MILL, J. S., *A System of Logic,* Longmans, New York, 1947.

NAGEL, E., ed., *John Stuart Mill's Philosophy of Scientific Method,* Hafner, New York, 1950.

———, *On the Logic of Measurement,* Ph.D. thesis, Columbia Univ., New York, 1930.

RITCHIE, A. D., *Scientific Method,* Harcourt, New York, 1923.

ROBINSON, R., *Definition,* Clarendon Press, Oxford, 1950.

RUSSELL, B., *The Analysis of Matter,* Harcourt, New York, 1927.

SMITH, B. O., *Logical Aspects of Educational Measurement,* Columbia Univ. Press, 1938.

STEBBING, L. S., *A Modern Introduction to Logic,* 6th ed., Humsinger Press, New York, 1948.

WESTAWAY, F. W., *Scientific Method,* 4th ed., rev. and enl., Hillman-Curl, New York, 1937; London, 1931.

WILSON, E. B., *An Introduction to Scientific Research,* McGraw, New York, 1952.

WOLF, A., *Essentials of Scientific Method,* G. Allen, London, 1928.

Articles

BERGMANN, G., "An Empiricist's System of the Sciences", *Scientific Monthly,* 59, 1944.

BURES, C. E., "Operationism, Construction, and Inference", *Jl. of Phil.,* 37, 1940.

CARNAP, R., "Uber Protokollsatze", *Erk.* 3, pp. 215–228.

FEIGL, H., "Confirmability and Confirmation", *Revue Internationale de Philosophie,* 5, 1951.

———, "Operationism and Scientific Method", *Psych. Rev.,* 52, 1948, p. 250. Reprinted with some alterations in Feigl and Sellars, *Readings.*

HEMPEL, C. G., "Problems and Changes in the Empiricist Criterion of Meaning", *Revue Internationale de Philosophie,* Vol. IV, No. 11, 1950. Also reprinted in Linsky, ed., *Semantics,* Univ. of Illinois Press, 1952.

———, "Studies in the Logic of Confirmation", *Mind,* 54, 1945.

———, "Vagueness and Logic", *Phil. of Science,* 6, 1939.

———, "The Concept of Cognitive Significance", *Proc. Am. Acad. Arts and Sciences,* 80, 1951, pp. 61–71.

———, and OPPENHEIM, PAUL, "L'importance Logique de la notion de type", *Actes du Congres International* at Sorbonne, Paris, 1935; Paris, 1936, Vol. II, pp. 41–49.

HUXLEY, J., "Towards the New Systematics", in Julian Huxley, ed., *The New Systematics,* Clarendon Press, Oxford, 1940, pp. 1–46.

KAPLAN, A., "Definition and Specification of Meaning", *Jl. of Phil.,* 43, 1946.

———, and SCHOTT, H. F., "A Calculus for Empirical Classes", *Methodos,* 1951.

MEHLBERG, H., "Positivisme et Science", *Studia Philosophica,* 3, 1948.

NAGEL, E., "Measurement", *Erk.,* 2, 1931, pp. 313–333.

———, "Verifiability, Truth and Verification", *Jl. of Phil.,* 31, 1934.

SCHLICK, M., "Meaning and Verification", *Phil. Rev.,* 45, 1936. Reprinted in Feigl and Sellars, *Readings.*

STEVENS, S. S., "On the Theory of Scales of Measurement", *Science,* 103, 1946, pp. 677–680.

WAISMANN, F., "Verifiability", *Arist. Suppl.,* 19, 1945.

II. Philosophy of the Formal Sciences

Books

Black, M., *The Nature of Mathematics*, Harcourt, New York, 1933.
Carnap, R., *Philosophy and Logical Syntax*, Kegan Paul, London, 1935.
———, *Abriss der Logistik*, Springer, Vienna, 1929 (new edition forthcoming).
———, *Meaning and Necessity*, Univ. of Chicago Press, 1947.
———, *The Logical Syntax of Language*, Harcourt, New York, 1937.
———, *Foundations of Logic and Mathematics*, Vol. I, No. 3 of the *International Encyclopedia of Unified Science*, Univ. of Chicago Press, 1939.
Chwistek, L., *The Limits of Science*, Harcourt, New York, 1948.
Dubislav, W., *Die Philosophie der Mathematik in der Gegenwart* (*Philosophische Forschungsberichte*, Vol. 13, Berlin, 1932).
———, *Die Definition*, Meiner, Leipzig, 1931.
Enriques, F., *The Historic Development of Logic*, transl. by J. Rosenthal, Holt, New York, 1929.
Fraenkel, A., *Einleitung in die Mengenlehre*, 3rd ed., Dover, New York, 1946.
Frege, G., *The Foundations of Arithmetic*, transl. by J. L. Austin, Philosophical Library, New York, 1950.
Hahn, H., *Logik, Mathematik und Naturerkennen*, Springer, Vienna, 1925.
Hilbert, D., and Bernays, P., *Grundlagen der Mathematik*, Vols. I–II, Springer, Berlin, 1934–1938.
Hölder, O., *Die Mathematische Methode*, Springer, Berlin, 1924.
Jordan, Z., *On the Development of Mathematical Logic and of Logical Positivism in Poland*, Oxford Univ. Press, 1946.
Kaufmann, F., *Das Unendliche in der Mathematik und seine Ausschaltung*, Deuticke, Vienna, 1930.
Kershner, R. B., and Wilcox, L. R., *The Anatomy of Mathematics*, Ronald Press, New York, 1950.
Keyser, C. J., *Mathematical Philosophy*, Dutton, New York, 1922.
Kleene, S. C., *Introduction to Metamathematics*, Van Nostrand, New York, 1952.
Quine, W. V., *Mathematical Logic*, Norton, New York, 1940.
Ramsey, F. P., *The Foundations of Mathematics and Other Logical Essays*, Harcourt, New York, 1931.
Reichenbach, H., *Elements of Symbolic Logic*, Macmillan, New York, 1947.
Rosenbloom, P. C., *The Elements of Mathematical Logic*, Dover, New York, 1950.
Rosser, J. B., Logic for Mathematicians,, McGraw-Hill, New York, 1953.
Russell, B., *Introduction to Mathematical Philosophy*, G. Allen, London, 1948 (originally 1919).
———, *The Principles of Mathematics*, 2nd ed., Norton, New York, 1938.
Tarski, A., *Introduction to Logic and to the Methodology of the Deductive Sciences*, Oxford Univ. Press, 1941.
Waismann, F., *Introduction to Mathematical Thinking*, Ungar, New York, 1951.
Whitehead, A. N., and Russell, B., *Principia Mathematica*, Vols. I–III, Cambridge Univ. Press. 1st ed., 1910; 2nd ed., 1925. Reprinted 1935, 1950.
Wilder, R. L., *Introduction to the Foundations of Mathematics*, Wiley, New York, 1952.
Young, J. W., *Lectures on the Fundamental Concepts of Algebra and Geometry*, Macmillan, New York, 1911.

Articles

CARNAP, R., "Die logizistische Grundlegung der Mathematik", *Erk.*, 2, 1931.
———, "Die Mathematik als Zweig der Logik", *Blätter fur deutsche Philosophie*, IV, 1930.
———, "Die alte und die neue Logik", *Erk.*, 1, 1930.
CHURCH, A., "Logic, formal", an article in D. D. Runes, ed., *Dictionary of Philosophy*, Philosophical Library, New York, 1942.
GASKING, D., "Mathematics and the World", in A. G. N. Flew. ed., *Logic and Language* (2nd series), Philosophical Library, New York, 1953.
HARDY, G. H., "Mathematical Proof", *Mind*, 30, 1929.
KNEALE, W. C., "The Truths of Logic", *Arist. Proc.*, 46, 1945–46.
———, "Are Necessary Truths True by Convention?", *Arist. Suppl.*, 21, 1947.
MENGER, K., "The New Logic", *Phil. of Sci.*, 4, 1937.
NAGEL, E., "Some Theses in the Philosophy of Logic", *Phil. of Sci.*, 5, 1938.
———, "Logic Without Ontology", in Y. H. Krickorian, ed., *Naturalism and the Human Spirit*, Columbia Univ. Press, 1944. Also, in part, reprinted in Feigl and Sellars, *Readings*.
POPPER, K. R., "Why Are the Calculuses of Logic and Mathematics Applicable to Reality?" *Arist. Suppl.*, 20, 1946.
QUINE, W. V., "Truth by Convention", in O. H. Lee, ed., *Philosophical Essays for A. N. Whitehead*, Longmans, New York, 1936, pp. 90–124. Reprinted in Feigl and Sellars, *Readings*.
REICHENBACH, H., "Bertrand Russell's Logic", in P. Schilpp, ed., *Philosophy of Bertrand Russell*, Northwestern Univ. Press, 1944, pp. 23–54.
RYLE, G., "Why Are the Calculuses of Logic and Mathematics Applicable to Reality?" *Arist. Suppl.*, 20, 1946.
WAISMANN, F., "Ist die Logik eine deduktive Theorie?" *Erk.*, 7, 1938.
WEYL, H., "The Mathematical Way of Thinking", *Science*, 92, 1940.
———, "Mathematics and Logic", *Amer. Math. Mo.*, 53, 1946.

III. SPACE, TIME AND RELATIVITY

Books

BORN, M., *Einstein's Theory of Relativity*, Methuen, London, 1924.
BROAD, C. D., *Scientific Thought*, Harcourt, New York, 1923.
BURTT, E. A., *The Metaphysical Foundations of Modern Physical Science*, Harcourt, New York, 1925; reissued by Humanities Press, New York.
CARNAP, R., *Der Raum: Ein Beitrag zur Wissenschaftslehre*, Ergänzungshefte d. Kant-Studien, Nr. 56, Berlin, 1922.
CLEUGH, M. F., *Time and Its Importance in Modern Thought*, Methuen, London, 1937.
D'ABRO, A., *The Evolution of Scientific Thought from Newton to Einstein*, 2nd ed., Dover, New York, 1950.
DENNES, W. R., *Time as Datum and as Construction—With Some Consideration of Philosophical Method*, *Univ. of Calif. Pub. in Phil.*, Vol. 18, 1935.
EINSTEIN, A., *Sidelights of Relativity*, Dutton, New York, 1923.
———, and INFELD, L., *The Evolution of Physics*, Simon & Schuster, New York, 1938.
FRANK, P., *Einstein, His Life and Times*, Knopf, New York, 1947.
JOHNSON, M. C., *Time, Knowledge and the Nebulae*, Dover, New York, 1947.
———, *Science and the Meanings of Truth*, Faber and Faber, London, 1946.
MACH, E., *Space and Geometry*, Open Court, Chicago, 1943.

NICOD, J., *Foundations of Geometry and Induction*, Harcourt, New York, 1930.
REICHENBACH, H., *Philosophie der Raum-Zeitlehre*, de Gruyter, Berlin and Leipzig, 1928.
———, *Axiomatik der Relativistischen Raum-Zeit-Lehre*, Vieweg, Braunschweig, 1924.
SCHILPP, P., ed., *Albert Einstein: Philosopher-Scientist*, Evanston, Ill., Library of Living Philosophers, Inc., 1949. Reprinted by Tudor, New York, 1951.
SCHLICK, M., *Space and Time in Contemporary Physics*, transl. by H. L. Brose, Oxford Univ. Press, 1920.
WHITEHEAD, A. N., *The Principle of Relativity*, Cambridge Univ. Press, 1922.

Articles

BLACK, M., "Conventionalism in Geometry", *Phil. of Sci.*, 9, 1942.
BROAD, C. D., "Is Space Euclidean?", *Mind*, 24, 1915.
GRÜNBAUM, A., "Some Highlights of Modern Cosmology and Cosmogony", *The Review of Metaphysics*, 5, 1952.
HEMPEL, C. G., "Geometry and Empirical Science", *Amer. Math. Mo.*, 52, 1945. Reprinted in Feigl and Sellars, *Readings.*
LENZEN, V. F., "The Schema of Time", *Univ. of Calif. Pub. in Phil.*, 1936.
MEHLBERG, H., "Essais sur la theorie causale du temps", *Studia Philosophica* I, 1935; *ibid.*, II, 1937.
NAGEL, E., "The Formation of Modern Conceptions of Formal Logic in the Development of Geometry", *Osiris*, 7, 1939.
ROBERTSON, H. P., "Geometry as a Branch of Physics", essay in P. Schilpp, ed., *Albert Einstein: Philosopher-Scientist*, Tudor, New York, 1951.

IV THE LOGIC OF SCIENTIFIC EXPLANATION AND THEORY CONSTRUCTION

Books

BRIDGMAN, P W., *The Nature of Thermodynamics*, Harvard Univ. Press, 1941.
———, *The Nature of Physical Theory*, Princeton Univ. Press, 1936.
BROAD, C. D., *Perception, Physics and Reality*, Cambridge Univ. Press, 1914.
CAMPBELL, N R., *Physics: the Elements*, Cambridge Univ. Press, 1920.
CARNAP, R., *Logical Foundations of the Unity of Science*, Vol. I, No. 1 of the *International Encyclopedia of Unified Science*, Univ. of Chicago Press, 1938.
DUHEM, P., *L'evolution de la Mecanique*, Paris, 1903.
———, *La Theorie physique: son objet et sa structure*, Paris, 1906; English transl. by P. Wiener, Princeton Univ. Press, 1953.
EDDINGTON, A., *The Nature of the Physical World*, Macmillan, New York, 1928.
———, *New Pathways in Science*, Macmillan, New York, 1935.
———, *Philosophy of Physical Science*, Macmillan, New York, 1939.
HOLTON, G., *Concepts and Theories in Physical Science*, Addison-Wesley, Cambridge, Mass., 1952.
KRAFT, V., *Mathematik, Logik und Erfahrung*, Springer, Vienna, 1947.
MACH, E., *Principles of Physical Optics*, Methuen, London, 1926.
———, *The Science of Mechanics*, Open Court, Chicago, 1942.
———, *Prinzipien der Wärmelehre*, 2nd ed., Barth, Leipzig, 1900.
MARGENAU, H., *The Nature of Physical Reality*, McGraw, New York, 1950.
PAP, A., *The A Priori in Physical Theory*, King's Crown Press, New York, 1946.
STEBBING, S. L., *Philosophy and the Physicists*, Methuen, London, 1937.
SWANN, W. F. G., *The Architecture of the Universe*, Macmillan, New York, 1934.
WATSON, W. H., *On Understanding Physics*, Cambridge Univ. Press, 1938.

WEIZSÄCKER, C. F. VON, *The World View of Physics*, Univ. of Chicago Press, 1952.
WHITTAKER, E., *A History of the Theories of Aether and Electricity*, Philosophical Library, New York, 1951.

Articles

ALTSCHUL, E., and ERWIN, B., "The Validity of Unique Mathematical Models in Science", *Phil. of Sci.*, 15, 1948.
BLUMBERG, A. E., "E. Meyerson's Critique of Positivism", *Monist*, 42, 1932.
BOLTZMANN, L., "Models", *The Ency. Britannica*, 11th ed., Vol. 18, 1910.
BRAITHWAITE, R. B., "Review of Eddington's *Philosophy of Science*", *Mind*, 49, 1940.
———, "Eddington's Gifford Lectures: *Review of Nature of Physical World*", *Mind*, 38, 1929.
BROAD, C. D., "Review of Eddington's *Philosophy of Physical Science*", *Phil.*, 15, 1940.
CAMPBELL, N. R., "The Errors of Sir Arthur Eddington", *Phil.*, 6, 1931.
EINSTEIN, A., "Physics and Reality", *Jl. of the Franklin Inst.*, 221, 1936.
FEIGL, H., "Logical Reconstruction, Realism and Pure Semiotic", *Phil. of Sci.*, 17, 1950.
———, "Existential Hypotheses: Realistic Versus Phenomenalistic Interpretations", *Phil. of Sci.*, 17, 1950.
FRANK, P., "Comments on Realistic Versus Phenomenalistic Interpretations", *Phil. of Sci.*, 17, 1950.
HARDIE, C. D., "Logical Positivism and Scientific Theory", *Mind*, 47, 1938.
HEMPEL, C. G., "A Note on Semantic Realism", *Phil. of Sci.*, 17, 1950.
HOSPERS, J., "On Explanation", *Jl. of Phil.*, 43, 1946.
KEENAN, J., "Definitions and Principles of Dynamics", *Sci. Mon.*, 67, 1948.
———, and SHAPIRO, A. H., "History and Exposition of the Laws of Thermodynamics", *Mechanical Eng.*, 1947.
LENZEN, V. F., "Experience and Convention", *Erk.*, 7, 1938.
MUNITZ, M. K., "Scientific Method in Cosmology", *Phil. of Sci.*, 19, 1952.
NAGEL, E., "The Meaning of Reduction in the Natural Sciences" in Robert C. Stauffer, ed., *Science and Civilization*, Univ. of Wisconsin Press, 1949.
———, "Some Reflections on the Use of Language in the Natural Sciences", *Jl. of Phil.*, 42, 1945.
———, "Science and Semantic Realism", *Phil. of Sci.*, 17, 1950.
———, "The Logic of Reduction", *Erk.*, 5, 1936.
NEURATH, O., "Physicalism. The Philosophy of the Viennese Circle", *Monist*, 41, 1931.
REICHENBACH, H., "Die Philosophische Bedeutung der modernen Physik", *Erk.*, 1, 1930.
SCHLICK, M., "Positivismus und Realismus", *Erk.*, 3, 1933; transl. by Rynin in *Synthese*, 1950.
SCHRÖDINGER, E., "What Is an Elementary Particle?" *Endeavour*, 9, 1950.
SELLARS, W. S., "Realism and the New Way of Words", *Phil. and Phen. Res.*, 8, 1948. Also reprinted in H. Feigl and W. Sellars, *Readings.*
SIMON, H. A., "The Axioms of Mechanics", *Philosophical Magazine*, 38, 1952.
SMART, J. J. C., "Theory Construction", *Phil. and Phen. Res.*, 11, 1951.
STEBBING, L. S., "Realism and Modern Physics", *Arist. Suppl.*, 9, 1929.
STRAUSS, M., and TORNEY, L. VON, "Der Analogiebegriff in der modernen Physik", *Erk.*, 6, 1936.
WEINBERG, J. R., "The Idea of Causal Efficacy," *Jl. of Phil.*, 47, 1950.
WERKMEISTER, W. H., "Science, Its Concepts and Laws", *Jl. of Phil.*, 46, 1949.

V. Causality, Determinism, Indeterminism, and Probability

Books

Bergmann, H., *Der Kampf um das Kausalgesetz in der jungsten Physik*, Vieweg, Braunschweig, 1929.
Bohr, N., *Atomic Theory and the Description of Nature*, Macmillan, New York, 1934.
Born, M., *Natural Philosophy of Cause and Chance*, Oxford Univ. Press, 1949.
———, *The Restless Universe*, Harper, New York, 1936.
Carnap, R., *Probability and Induction*, I: *Logical Foundations of Probability*, Univ. of Chicago Press, 1950.
———, *The Nature and Application of Inductive Logic*, Univ. of Chicago Press, 1951.
Cassirer, E., *Determinismus und Indeterminismus in der modernen Physik*, Goteborg, Elanders Boktryckeri Aktiebolag, 1937.
Frank, P., *Das Kausalgesetz und Seine Grenzen*, Springer, Vienna, 1932.
———, *Interpretations and Misinterpretations of Modern Physics*, Hermann, Paris, 1938.
Heisenberg, W., *The Physical Principles of the Quantum Theory*, Univ. of Chicago Press, 1930.
Jeffreys, H., *Theory of Probability*, Clarendon Press, Oxford, 1939.
Keynes, J. M., *Treatise on Probability*, Macmillan, London, 1921.
Kneale, W. C., *Probability and Induction*, Clarendon Press, Oxford, 1949.
Mises, R. von, *Probability, Statistics, and Truth*, Macmillan, New York, 1939 (originally 1928).
Nagel, E., *Principles of the Theory of Probability*, Vol. I, No. 6 of the *International Encyclopedia of Unified Science*, Univ. of Chicago Press, 1939.
Reichenbach, H., *Theory of Probability*, Univ. of Calif. Press, 1949.
———, *Philosophic Foundations of Quantum Mechanics*, Univ. of California Press, 1944.
———, *Experience and Prediction*, Univ. of Chicago Press, 1938.
Russell, B., *Human Knowledge*, Simon & Schuster, New York, 1948.
Silberstein, L., *Causality*, Macmillan, London, 1933.
Williams, C. D., *The Ground of Induction*, Harvard Univ. Press, 1947.
Wisdom, J. O., *Foundations of Inference in Natural Science*, Methuen, London, 1952.
Wright, G. H. von, *A Treatise on Induction and Probability*, Routledge, London, 1951.

Articles

Bergmann, G., "The Logic of Probability", *Amer. Jl. of Physics*, 9, 1941.
———, "Frequencies, Probabilities, and Positivism", *Phil. and Phen. Res.*, 6, 1945.
Birkhoff, G. D., and Lewis, D. C., "Stability in Causal Systems", *Phil. of Sci.*, 2, 1935.
———, and Neumann, J. von, "The Logic of Quantum Mechanics", *Annals of Math.*, 37, 1936.
Black, M., "The Justification of Induction", in his *Language and Philosophy*, Cornell Univ. Press, 1949.
Bohr, N., "Causality and Complementarity", *Phil. of Sci.*, 4, 1937.
Broad, C. D., "Indeterminacy and Indeterminism", *Arist. Suppl.*, 10, 1931.
———, "On the Relation Between Induction and Probability", *Mind*, Part 1, 27, 1918; Part 2, 29, 1920.

BRODBECK, MAY, "An Analytic Principle of Induction?" *Jl. of Phil.*, 49, 1952.
———, "Coherence Theory Reconsidered", *Phil. of Sci.*, 16, 1949.
———, "The New Rationalism: Dewey's Theory of Induction", *Jl. of Phil.*, 46, 1949.
BURES, C. E., "The Concept of Probability", *Phil. of Sci.*, 5, 1938.
CARNAP, R., "Probability as a Guide in Life," *Jl. of Phil.*, 44, 1947.
———, "Remarks on Induction and Truth", *Phil. and Phen. Res.*, 6, 1946.
———, "On the Application of Inductive Logic", *Phil. and Phen. Res.*, 8, 1947.
———, "On Inductive Logic", *Phil. of Sci.*, 12, 1945.
CHISHOLM, R., "The Contrary-to-Fact Conditional", *Mind*, 55, 1946. Reprinted in Feigl and Sellars, *Readings.*
COPELAND, A. H., "Predictions and Probabilities", *Erk.*, 6, 1936.
DOOB, J. L., "Probability and Statistics", *Transactions of the American Mathematical Society*, Vol. 36, No. 4, 1934.
EDDINGTON, SIR A., "Indeterminacy and Indeterminism", *Arist. Suppl.*, 10, 1931.
DE FINNETTI, B., "La Prévision: ses lois logiques, ses sources subjectives", *Annales de l'Institut Henri Poincaré*, VII, 1937.
FREUND, JOHN E., "On the Confirmation of Scientific Theories", *Phil. of Sci.*, 17, 1950.
GOODMAN, N., "The Problem of Counterfactual Conditionals", *Jl. of Phil.*, 44, 1947. Reprinted in Linsky, *Semantics*, Univ. of Illinois Press, 1952.
HAY, W. H., "Professor Carnap and Probability", *Phil. of Sci.*, 19, 1952.
———, "Carnap's *Continuum of Inductive Methods*", *Phil. Rev.*, 62, 1953.
HELMER, O., and OPPENHEIM, P., "A Syntactical Definition of Probability and Degree of Confirmation", *Jl. of Symbolic Logic*, 10, 1945.
HEMPEL, C. G., and OPPENHEIM, P., "A Definition of 'Degree of Confirmation' ", *Phil. of Sci.*, 12, 1945.
HOPF, E., "On Causality, Statistics and Probability", *Jl. of Math. and Physics*, 13, 1934.
HOSIASSON, J., "Why Do We Prefer Probabilities Relative to Many Data?" *Mind*, 40, 1931.
KAUFMANN, F., "Three Meanings of 'Truth' ", *Jl. of Phil.*, 45, 1948.
———, "Verification, Meaning, and Truth", *Phil. and Phen. Res.*, 4, 1944.
———, "Scientific Procedure and Probability", *Phil. and Phen. Res.*, 6, 1947.
LENZEN, V. F., "Philosophical Problems of the Statistical Interpretation of Quantum Mechanics", *Proceedings of the Second Berkeley Symposium on Mathematical Statistics and Probability*, Univ. of California Press, 1951.
———, "The Partition Between Physical Object and Observer", *American Physics Teacher*, 5, 1937.
———, "Physical Causality", *Univ. of Calif. Pub. in Phil.*, 15, 1932.
MARGENAU, H., "The Meaning of 'Elementary Particle' ", *Amer. Scientist*, 39, 1951.
———, "Conceptual Foundations of the Quantum Theory", *Science*, 113, 1951.
———, "Reality in Quantum Mechanics", *Phil. of Sci.*, 16, 1949.
MEHLBERG, H., "The Idealistic Interpretation of Atomic Physics", *Studia Philosophica*, IV, 1949–50; *Posnaniae*, 1950.
MILLER, D. S., "An Event in Philosophy", *Phil. Rev.*, 54, 1945.
MISES, R. VON, and POLLACZEK-GEIRINGER, H., "Probability", *Encyclopedia of Social Sciences*, Macmillan, New York, 1932.
MOORE, A., "The Principle of Induction", *Jl. of Phil.*, 49, 1952.
NAGEL, E., "Probability and the Theory of Knowledge", *Phil. of Sci.*, 6, 1939.
———, "Probability and Non-demonstrative Inference", *Phil. and Phen. Res.*, 5, 1945.
———, "Sovereign Reason", in *Freedom and Experience*, Essays Presented to

H. M. Kallen, ed. by S. Hook and N. R. Konvitz, Cornell Univ. Press, 1948.
———, "The Meaning of Probability", *Jl. of Amer. Statist. Assn.*, 31, 1936.
———, "The Frequency Theory of Probability", *Jl. of Phil.*, 30, 1933.
PAP, A., "Philosophical Analysis, Transl. Schemas, and the Regularity Theory of Causation", *Jl. of Phil.*, 49, 1952.
POPPER, K. R., "Indeterminism in Quantum Physics", *British Jl. of Phil. of Sci.*, 2, 1951.
———, "A Note on Natural Laws and So-Called Contrary-to-Fact Conditionals", *Mind*, 58, 1949.
REICHENBACH, H., "On the Justification of Induction", *Jl. of Phil.*, 37, 1940. Reprinted in Feigl and Sellars, *Readings*.
———, "Philosophical Foundations of Probability", *Proc. of the Berkeley Symposium*, Univ. of California Press, 1943.
———, "Die Kausalbehauptung und die Möglichkeit ihrer empirischen Nachprufung", *Erk.*, 3, 1933.
———, "Kausalität und Wahrscheinlichkeit", *Erk.*, 1, 1930–31.
RYLE, G., "Induction and Hypothesis", *Arist. Suppl.*, 16, 1937.
SCHLICK, M., "Die Kausalität in der gegenwartigen Physik", *Die Naturwissenschaften*, 1931; reprinted in *Gesammelte Aufsätze*, Gerold, Vienna, 1938.
SCHRÖDINGER, E., "Die gegewärtige Situation in der Quantenmechanik", *Naturwissenschaften*, 23, 1935.
SELLARS, W. S., "Concepts as Involving Laws and Inconceivable Without Them", *Phil. of Sci.*, 15, 1948.
———, "Is There a Synthetic A priori?" *Phil. of Sci.*, 20, 1953.
———, "Inference and Meaning", *Mind*, 62, 1953.
SIMON, H. A., "On the Definition of the Causal Relation", *Jl. of Phil.*, 49, 1952.
USHENKO, A. P., HOFSTADTER, A., and GRÜNBAUM, A., "The Conception of Law in Science", a symposium, *Jl. of Phil.*, 50, 1953.
WAISMANN, F., "Logische Analyse des Wahrcheinlichkeitsbegriffs", *Erk.*, 1, 1930.
WILL, F., "Generalization and Evidence," in M. Black, ed., *Philosophical Analysis*, Cornell Univ. Press, 1950.
———, "Will the Future Be Like the Past?" *Mind*, 55, 1946.

VI. PHILOSOPHICAL PROBLEMS OF BIOLOGY AND PSYCHOLOGY

Books

BERTALANFFY, L. VON, *Problems of Life—An Evolution of Modern Biological Thought*, Wiley, New York, 1952; Watts, London, 1952.
Current Trends in Psychological Theory, a symposium, no ed. listed, Univ. of Pittsburgh Press, 1951.
HAYEK, F. A., *The Sensory Order*, Univ. of Chicago Press, 1952.
HULL, C. L., *Principles of Behavior*, Appleton-Century-Crofts, New York, 1943.
———, HOVLAND, C. I., ROSS, R. T., HALL, M., PERKINS, D. T., FITCH, F. B., *Mathematic-Deductive Theory of Rote Learning*, Yale Univ. Press, 1940.
LASLETT, P., ed., *The Physical Basis of Mind*, a symposium, Macmillan, New York, 1950.
MACH, E., *The Analysis of Sensations*, Open Court, Chicago, 1914.
MARX, M., ed., *Psychological Theory: Contemporary Readings*, Macmillan, New York, 1951.
MORRIS, C. E., *Signs, Language and Behavior*, Prentice-Hall, New York, 1946.
PRATT, C. C., *The Logic of Modern Psychology*, Macmillan, New York, 1939.
RUSSELL, B., *The Analysis of Mind*, Macmillan, New York, 1921.
RYLE, G., *The Concept of Mind*, Hutchinson's Univ. Library, London, 1949.

SIMPSON, G. G., *The Meaning of Evolution*, Yale Univ. Press, 1949.
SINGER, E., *Mind as Behavior and Studies in Empirical Idealism*, R. G. Adams & Co., Columbus, 1924.
SOMMERHOFF, G., *Analytical Biology*, Oxford Univ. Press, 1950.
TOLMAN, E. C., *Purposive Behavior in Animals and Men*, Appleton-Century, New York, 1932.
WIENER, N., *Cybernetics*, Wiley, New York, 1948.
WISDOM, J., *Problems of Mind and Matter*, Cambridge Univ. Press, 1934.
———, *Other Minds*, Philosophical Library, New York, 1952.
———, *Philosophy and Psycho-analysis*, Methuen, London, 1952.
WOODGER, J. H., *Axiomatic Method in Biology*, Cambridge Univ. Press, 1937.
———, *Biological Principles*, Harcourt, New York, 1923.
———, *The Technique of Theory Construction*, Vol. II, No. 5 of the *International Encyclopedia of Unified Science*, Univ. of Chicago Press, 1939.

Articles

BERGMANN, G., "An Empiricist Schema of the Psychophysical Problem", *Phil. of Sci.*, 9, 1942.
———, "The Logic of Psychological Concepts", *Phil. of Sci.*, 18, 1951.
———, "The Problem of Relations in Classical Psychology," *Philos. Quarterly*, 2, 1952.
———, "Psychoanalysis and Experimental Psychology", *Mind*, 53, 1944. Reprinted in Marx, M., *Psychological Theory*, Macmillan, New York, 1951.
———, "Theoretical Psychology", in *Annual Review of Psychology*, 1953.
———, and SPENCE, K. W., "Operationism and Theory in Psychology", *Psych. Rev.*, 48, 1941. Reprinted in Marx, M., *Psychological Theory*, Macmillan, New York, 1951.
BLACK, M., "Linguistic Method in Philosophy", in his *Language and Philosophy*, Cornell Univ. Press, 1949.
BORING, E. G., "Gestalt Psychology and the Gestalt Movement," *Amer. Jl. of Psychology*, 1930.
BRAITHWAITE, R. B., "Teleological Explanation", *Arist. Proc.*, 47, 1947.
BROAD, C. D., "Mechanical Explanation and Its Alternatives", *Arist. Proc.*, 19, 1918/19.
BROWN, R., "Dispositional & Teleological Statements", *Philos. Studies*, 3, 1952.
CARNAP, R., "Les concepts psychologiques et les concepts physiques, sonti-ils foncièrement differents?" *Synthese*, 1935.
———, "Psychologie in physikalischer Sprache", *Erk.*, 3, 1933.
DOBZHANSKY, T., "A Critique of the Species Concept in Biology", *Phil. of Sci.*, 2, 1935.
DUCASSE, C. J., "Explanation, Mechanism, and Teleology", *Jl. of Phil.*, 22, 1925. Reprinted in Feigl and Sellars, *Readings*.
FARRELL, B. A., "Experience", *Mind*, 59, 1950.
———, Braithwaite, M., and Mace, C. D., "Causal Laws in Psychology", a symposium, *Arist. Suppl.*, 23, 1949.
FEIGL, H., "Principles and Problems of Theory Construction in Psychology," in *Current Trends in Psychological Theory*, Univ. of Pittsburgh Press, 1951.
FREUD, S., "The Unconscious", Vol. VI, *Collected Papers*, Hogarth Press, London, 1924.
GRELLING, K., and OPPENHEIM, P., "Der Gestaltbegriff im Lichte der neuen Logik", *Erk.*, 7, 1937–38.
HEMPEL, C. G., "General System Theory and the Unity of Science", *Human Biology*, 23, 1951.

HENLE, P., "The Status of Emergence", *Jl. of Phil.*, 39, 1942.
HOFSTADTER, A., "Professor Ryle's Category-Mistake", *Jl. of Phil.*, 48, 1951.
HULL, C. L., "Modern Behaviorism and Psychoanalysis", *Trans. of the N. Y. Acad. of Sci.*, Ser. II, 1, 1939.
———, "The Problem of Intervening Variables in Behavior Theory", *Psych. Rev.*, 50, 1943. Reprinted in Marx, M., *Psychological Theory*, Macmillan, New York, 1951.
JACOBS, N., "Physicalism and Sensation Sentences", *Jl. of Phil.*, 34, 1937.
KOCH, S., "The Logical Character of the Motivation Concept", *Psych. Rev.*, 48, 1941.
LASHLEY, K. S., "Behavioristic Interpretation of Consciousness", *Psych. Rev.*, 30, 1923.
LEWIS, C. I., "Some Logical Considerations Concerning the Mental", *Jl. of Phil.*, 38, 1941. Also reprinted in Feigl and Sellars, *Readings*.
LOVEJOY, A. O., "Meaning of Emergence and Its Modes", *Jl. of Philosophical Studies* (now *Philosophy*), 2, 1927.
MCGREGOR, D., "Scientific Measurement and Psychology", *Psych. Rev.*, 42, 1935.
MEAD, G. H., "Behavioristic Account of the Significant Symbol", *Jl. of Phil.*, 19, 1922.
NAGEL, E., "Mechanistic Explanation and Organismic Biology", *Phil. and Phen. Res.*, Vol. II, No. 3, 1951.
———, "Wholes, Sums, and Organic Unities", *Philos. Studies*, 3, 1952.
ROSENBLUETH, A., WIENER, N., and BIGELOW, J., "Behavior, Purpose and Teleology", *Phil. of Sci.*, 10, 1943.
SCHLICK, M., "De la relation des notions psychologiques et les notions physiques", *Synthese*, 10, 1935. Reprinted in English transl. in Feigl and Sellars, *Readings*.
SELLARS, W. S., "Mind, Meaning, and Behavior", *Philos. Studies*, 3, 1952.
———, "A Semantical Solution of the Mind-Body Problem", *Methodos*, 5, 1953.
SIMPSON, G. G., "Problem of Plan and Purpose in Nature", *Sci. Monthly*, 64, 1941.
SPENCE, K. W., "Theoretical Interpretations of Learning" in S. S. Stevens, ed., *Handbook of Experimental Psychology*, Wiley, New York, 1951.
———, "The Nature of Theory Construction in Contemporary Psychology", *Psych. Rev.*, 51, 1944.
STEVENS, S. S., "Mathematics, Measurement and Psychophysics" in S. S. Stevens, ed., *Handbook of Experimental Psychology*, Wiley, New York, 1951.
STOUT, G. F., "Mechanical and Teleological Causation", *Arist. Suppl.*, 14, 1935.
TAYLOR, R., "Comments on a Mechanistic Conception of Purposefulness", *Phil. of Sci.*, 17, 1950.
TOLMAN, E. C., "Behavior and Purpose", *Jl. of Phil.*, 23, 1925.
TURING, A. M., "Computing Machines and Intelligence", *Mind*, 59, 1950.
WATSON, J., "Psychology as the Behaviorist Views It", *Psych. Rev.*, 1913.
WERTHEIMER, M., "Gestalt Theory", *Social Research*, 11, 1944.
WOODROW, H., "The Problem of General Quantitative Laws in Psychology", *Psychol. Bul.*, 39, 1942.

VII. PHILOSOPHY OF THE SOCIAL SCIENCES

Books

BARNES, H. E., and BECKER, H., *Social Thought From Lore to Science*, 2nd ed., Harren Press, Washington, D. C., 1952.
BECKER, C., *Everyman His Own Historian*, Crofts, New York, 1935.
CASSIRER, E., *The Myth of the State*, Yale Univ. Press, 1946.
COHEN, M. R., *The Meaning of Human History*, Open Court, Chicago, 1947.

COHEN, M. R., *Reason and Law*, Free Press, Glencoe, Ill., 1950.

COBB, J. C., *The Application of Scientific Methods to Sociology*, Chapman & Grimes, Boston, 1934.

EUCKEN, W., *The Foundations of Economics*, Hodge, London, 1950; Univ. of Chicago Press, 1951.

FESTINGER, L., and KATZ, D., *Research Methods in the Behavioral Sciences*, Dryden Press, New York, 1953.

FRASER, L. M., *Economic Thought and Language*, A. & C. Black, London, 1937.

GARDINER, P., *The Nature of Historical Explanation*, Oxford Univ. Press, 1952.

GINSBERG, M., *The Psychology of Society*, Methuen, London, 1921.

GOLDENWEISER, A., *History, Psychology and Culture*, Knopf, New York, 1933.

GURVITCH, G., and MOORE, W. E., eds., *Twentieth Century Sociology*, Philosophical Library, New York, 1945.

HAYEK, F. A., *The Counter-Revolution of Science*, Free Press, Glencoe, Ill., 1952.

HOMANS, G. C., and CURTIS, C. P., *An Introduction to Pareto, His Sociology*, Knopf, New York, 1934.

HOOK, S., *The Hero in History*, John Day, New York, 1943.

———, *Reason, Social Myth and Democracy*, Humanities Press, New York, 1951.

HUTCHINSON, T. W., *The Significance and Basic Postulates of Economic Theory*, Macmillan, London, 1938.

KEYNES, J. N., *The Scope and Method of Political Economy*, 3rd ed. rev., Macmillan, New York, 1904.

LANGLOIS, C. V., and SEIGNOBOS, C., *Introduction to the Study of History*, transl. by G. G. Berry, Holt, New York, 1912.

LASWELL, H., and KAPLAN, A., *Power and Society*, Yale Univ. Press, 1950.

LERNER, D., and LASSWELL, H., eds., *The Policy Sciences*, Stanford Univ. Press, 1951.

LUNDBERG, GEORGE A., *Foundations of Sociology*, Macmillan, New York, 1939.

MCIVER, R., *Social Causation*, Ginn, Boston, 1942.

MANDELBAUM, M., *The Problem of Historical Knowledge; An Answer to Relativism*, Liveright, New York, 1938.

MAYER, J., *Social Science Principles in the Light of Scientific Method*, Duke Univ. Press, 1941.

MENGER, C., *Principles of Economics*, Free Press, Glencoe, Ill.

———, *Untersuchungen uber die Methoden der Socialwissenschaften*, 1883, London School of Economics Reprint, 1933.

MERTON, R. K., *Social Theory and Social Structure*, Free Press, Glencoe, Ill., 1949.

MISES, L. VON, *Human Action*, Yale Univ. Press, 1949.

NEURATH, O., *Foundations of the Social Sciences*, Vol. II, No. 1 of the *International Encyclopedia of Unified Science*, Univ. of Chicago Press, 1944.

PARSONS, T., and SHILS, E. A., eds., *Toward a General Theory of Action*, Harvard Univ. Press, 1951.

POPPER, K. R., *The Open Society*, Routledge, London, 1945; revised edition, Princeton Univ. Press, 1950.

ROBBINS, L., *An Essay on the Nature and Significance of Economic Science*, Macmillan, London, 1935.

ROSE, A. M., *Theory and Method in Sociology*, Univ. of Minnesota Press, 1954.

Theory and Practice in Historical Study, Soc. Sci. Res. Council, 1946.

THOMAS, W. I., and ZNANIECKI, F., *The Polish Peasant in Europe and America*, Intro. to Vols. I and III, Univ. of Chicago Press, 1918–20.

WALSH, W. H., *An Introduction to Philosophy of History*, Hutchinson, London, 1951.

WEBER, M., *The Methodology of the Social Sciences*, Free Press, Glencoe, Ill., 1949.

ZNANIECKI, F., *Social Action*, Farrar & Rinehart, New York, 1935.

Articles

ARROW, K. J., "Mathematical Models in the Social Sciences", in D. Lerner and H. D. Lasswell, eds., *The Policy Sciences*, Stanford Univ. Press, 1951.

BECK, L. W., "The 'Natural Science Ideal' in the Social Sciences", *The Scientific Monthly*, 68, 1949.

BERGMANN, G., "Holism, Historicism and Emergence", *Phil. of Sci.*, 11, 1944.

———, "Ideology", *Ethics*, 61, 1951.

———, and Zerby, L., "The Formalism in Kelsen's Pure Theory of Law", *Ethics*, 55, 1945.

BLUMER, H., "Science Without Concepts", *Amer. Jl. of Soc.*, 36, 1931.

BRODBECK, MAY, "On the Philosophy of the Social Sciences", *Phil. of Sci.*, 21, 1954.

CHAPIN, F. S., "The Experimental Method in the Study of Human Relations", *The Scientific Monthly*, 68, 1949.

———, "The Meaning of Measurement in Sociology", *Pub. of the Amer. Sociol. Soc.*, 24, 1930.

COHEN, M. R., "Causation and Its Application to History", *Jl. of the Hist. of Ideas*, 3, 1942.

DEUTSCH, K. W., "Some Notes on Research on the Role of Models in the Natural and Social Sciences", *Communications of the Institute for the Unity of Science*, Boston, Mass. Reprinted from *Synthese*, 8, 1948–1949.

FEUER, L. S., "Indeterminacy and Economic Development," *Phil. of Sci.*, 15, 1948.

GOMPERZ, H., "Interpretation", *Erk.*, 7, 1938.

FRANK, J., "The Place of the Expert in a Democratic Society", *Phil. of Sci.*, 16, 1949.

HAYEK, F. A., "Economics and Knowledge", *Economica*, 1937. Reprinted in his *Individualism and Economic Order*, Univ. of Chicago Press, 1948.

———, "Facts of Social Science", *Ethics*, October, 1943.

HEMPEL, G. G., "The Function of General Laws in History", *Jl. of Phil.*, 39, 1942. Reprinted in Feigl and Sellars, *Readings*.

KAPLAN, A., "Sociology Learns the Language of Mathematics", *Commentary*, 14, 1952.

KENDALL, P. L., and LAZARSFELD, P. F., "Problems of Survey Analysis", in R. K. Merton and P. F. Lazarsfeld, eds., *Continuities in Social Research*, Free Press, Glencoe, Ill., 1950.

KNIGHT, F. H., "The Limitations of Scientific Method in Economics" in R. Tugwell, ed., *The Trend of Economics*, Knopf, New York, 1924.

LAZARSFELD, P. F., and BARTON, A. H., "Qualitative Measurement in the Social Sciences; Classification, Typologies, and Indices" in D. Lerner and H. D. Lasswell, eds., *The Policy Sciences*, Stanford Univ. Press, 1951.

LITTLE, I. M. D., "Economic Behavior and Welfare", *Mind*, 58, 1949.

LOVEJOY, A. O., "The Meaning of Romanticism for the Historian of Ideas", *Jl. of the Hist. of Ideas*, 2, 1941.

———, "Reply to Professor Spitzer", *ibid.*, 5, 1944.

LUNDBERG, G. A., "Operational Definitions in the Social Sciences", *Amer. Jl. of Sociol.*, 47, 1941–42.

———, "The Concept of Law in the Social Sciences", *Phil. of Sci.*, 5, 1938.

———, "Contemporary Positivism in Sociology", *Amer. Sociol. Rev.*, 4, 1939.

MACDONALD, M., "The Language of Political Theory" in A. Flew, ed., *Essays on Logic and Language*, Philosophical Library, New York, 1951.

MERTON, R. K., "The Role of Applied Social Science in the Formation of Policy: A Research Memorandum", *Phil. of Sci.*, 16, 1949.
MILL, J. S., "On the Logic of the Moral Sciences", Book VI of his *Logic*, Longmans, New York, new printing, 1947.
NAGEL, E., and HEMPEL, C., "Problems of Concepts and Theory in the Social Sciences", a symposium, in *Language, Science, and Human Rights*, Papers of the Amer. Philos. Assn., Eastern Division, I, Univ. of Penn. Press, 1952.
OPPENHEIM, F. E., "Outline of A Logical Analysis of Law", *Phil. of Sci.*, Vol. II, No. 3, 1944.
PAPANDREOU, A. G., "Economics and the Social Sciences", *Econ. Jl.*, 60, 1950.
———, "Types of Empirical Research in Modern Economics," *Economia Internatzionale*, 5, 1952.
PARSONS, T., "The Present Position and Prospects of Systematic Theory in Sociology" in G. Gurvitch and W. E. Moore, eds., *Twentieth Century Sociology*, Philosophical Library, New York, 1945.
POPPER, K. R., "The Poverty of Historicism", *Economica* (N.S.) 11, 1944.
———, "What Is Dialectic?" *Mind*, 49, 1940.
ROSE, A., "The Selection of Problems for Research", *Amer. Jl. of Sociol.*, 54, 1948.
ROTHSCHILD, K. W., "A Note on the Meaning of Rationality", *Rev. of Economic Studies*, 14, 1946–7.
SALOMON, A., "Max Weber's Methodology", *Social Res.*, I, 1934.
SELZNICK, P., "Foundations of the Theory of Organization", *Amer. Sociol. Rev.*, 13, 1948.
SPITZER, L., "Geistesgechichte vs. History of Ideas as Applied to Hitlerism", *Jl. of the Hist. of Ideas*, 5, 1944.
STOUFFER, S. A., "Some Afterthoughts of a Contributor to *The American Soldier*", in R. K. Merton and P. F. Lazarsfeld, eds., *Continuities in Social Research*, Free Press, Glencoe, Ill., 1950.
TINTNER, G., "Foundations of Probability and Statistical Inference", *Jl. of the Royal Statistical Society*, Series A, 112, Part III, 1949.
———, "Scope and Method of Econometrics", *Jl. of the Statistical and Soc. Inquiry Soc. of Ireland*, Univ. of Cambridge Press, 1949.
WALLIS, W. D., "Problems of an Empirical Sociology", *Social Forces*, 1928.
WHITE, M. G., "The Attack on the Historical Method", *Jl. of Phil.*, 42, 1945.
———, "Historical Explanation", *Mind*, 12, 1943.
WILSON, C. B., "Methodology in the Natural and Social Sciences", *Amer. Jl. of Sociol.*, 45, 1940.
ZERBY, L. K., "Some Remarks on the Philosophy of Law", *Jl. of Phil.*, 46, 1949.

VIII. EPILOGUE

Books

ALEXANDER, F., *Our Age of Unreason*, 2nd ed., Harper, New York, 1952.
BARBER, B., *Science and the Social Order*, Free Press, Glencoe, Ill., 1952.
FRANK, P., *Relativity—A Richer Truth*, Beacon Press, Boston, 1950.
HUXLEY, Y., *Heredity, East and West*, Schuman, New York, 1949.
KRIKORIAN, Y. H., ed., *Naturalism and the Human Spirit*, Columbia Univ. Press, 1944.
LUNDBERG, G. A., *Can Science Save Us?* Longmans, New York, 1947.
RUSSELL, B., *Religion and Science*, T. Butterworth, London, 1935.
———, *The Social Impact of Science*, Columbia Univ. Press, 1951.
SANTAYANA, G., *Reason in Religion*, Vol. 3 of *The Life of Reason*, 2nd ed., Scribner, New York, 1922.

SCHLICK, M., *Problems of Ethics*, Prentice-Hall, New York, 1939. (*Fragen der Ethik*, 1930.)
SCHRÖDINGER, E., *Science and Humanism*, Cambridge Univ. Press, 1951.
WHITEHEAD, A. N., *Science and the Modern World*, Macmillan, New York, 1925.

Articles

BROAD, C. D., "Present Relations of Science and Religion", *Phil.*, 14, 1939.
GOMPERZ, H., "Some Simple Thoughts on Freedom and Responsibility", *Phil.* 12, 1937.
HOBART, R. E., "Free Will as Involving Determinism and Inconceivable Without It", *Mind*, 43, 1934.
LUNDBERG, G. A., "Can Science Validate Ethics?" *Bul. of the Amer. Assn. of Univ. Prof.*, 36, 1950
McGILVARY, E. B., "Freedom and Necessity in Human Affairs", *Ethics*, 45, 1935.
PAP, A., "Determinism and Moral Responsibility", *Jl. of Phil.*, 63, No. 12, 1946.
———, "The Verifiability of Value Judgments", *Ethics*, 56, 1946.
STACE, W. T., "Man Against Darkness", *Atlantic Monthly*, 1948.
STOUT, A. K., "Free Will and Responsibility", *Arist. Proc.*, 37, 1936–1937. Reprinted in Sellars and Hospers, *Readings in Ethical Theory*, Appleton-Century-Crofts, New York, 1952.
WIENER, N., *The Human Use of Human Beings*, Houghton Mifflin, Boston, 1950.

Name Index

The following abbreviations are used: *auth.*, for authorship of selections; *ment.*, for mention; *quoted*, for quotation of at least one sentence; *ref.*, for bibliographic reference; *fn*, for footnote (immediately following page number).

Subject Index